THE HOLT SCIENCE PROGRAM

SCIENCE 1 *Observation and Experiment* by Davis, Burnett, and Gross
SCIENCE 2 *Experiment and Discovery* by Davis, Burnett, and Gross
SCIENCE 3 *Discovery and Progress* by Davis, Burnett, and Gross

MODERN BIOLOGY by Moon, Otto, and Towle
MODERN CHEMISTRY by Dull, Metcalfe, and Williams
MODERN PHYSICS by Dull, Metcalfe, and Williams

LIVING THINGS by Fitzpatrick and Bain
MODERN PHYSICAL SCIENCE by Brooks and Tracy
MODERN HEALTH by Otto, Julian, and Tether
HUMAN PHYSIOLOGY by Morrison, Cornett, and Tether

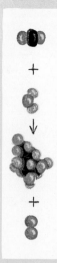

MOD

GREGOR MENDEL EDITION

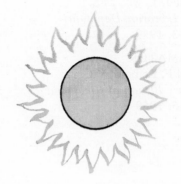

Truman J. Moon
James H. Otto
Albert Towle
Brother Joseph A. Kuntz, S. M.
Brother Edward J. Dury, S. M.

ERN BIOLOGY

HENRY HOLT AND COMPANY · New York

IMPRIMI POTEST
Henry J. Fritz, S.M., M.A.
Censor Deputatus
James M. Darby, S.M., Ph.D.

NIHIL OBSTAT
Vincent J. Lewis, M.S.
Censor Librorum Deputatus
April 13, 1959

IMPRIMATUR
✠ Paul F. Leibold, V.G.
Auxiliary Bishop of Cincinnati
April 15, 1959

JAMES H. OTTO is head of the Science Department of George Washington High School, Indianapolis, Indiana — ALBERT TOWLE is a teacher of biology at James Lick High School, San Jose, California — TRUMAN J. MOON was head of the Science Department of Middletown High School, Middletown, New York — BROTHER JOSEPH A. KUNTZ was Assistant Professor of Biology at the University of Dayton, Dayton, Ohio — BROTHER EDWARD J. DURY is a teacher of biology at Purcell High School, Cincinnati, Ohio.

The cover depicts the process of photosynthesis, or food manufacture, in green plants (represented here only by the leaf), without which life on earth (the circle behind the leaf) would not be possible. The molecular configurations illustrate how green plants, in the presence of the green chemical chlorophyll and radiant energy from the sun, utilize carbon (black atoms), hydrogen (red atoms), and oxygen (blue atoms) in molecules of carbon dioxide and water to manufacture food in the form of glucose (a sugar) and release oxygen.

The title pages repeat the theme of the cover, with animals and man grouped around the leaf in the brown circle (earth) to illustrate that the basic life functions of all animal life are ultimately dependent on photosynthesis in green plants for their food supply, and therefore for their existence.

Preface

IN this day of great emphasis on science in the high school curriculum, the biology course assumes a position of increasing importance. This revision of the Gregor Mendel Edition of MODERN BIOLOGY is designed to aid the teacher in meeting the challenge of present-day science teaching.

MODERN BIOLOGY combines the best features of the type, systematic, and principles courses. In the study of a type organism, the student deals with a complete plant or animal and the interrelation of all its organs and life activities. This approach emphasizes the unity of life. On the other hand, the systematic study of plant and animal groups shows the relationship of all living things, the development of life through various stages of complexity, and the wide variety of organisms which compose our living world. Finally, the study of principles is accomplished largely by the inductive approach. In his study of various organisms, the student discovers those principles which are illustrated by each group of living things. This method of investigation is ideally suited to laboratory study and provides maximum opportunity for research and group or individual project activity.

The organization of MODERN BIOLOGY follows a logical and sequential pattern. Unit 1 introduces biology as a science and relates it to the other sciences. The emphasis on cellular biology in this unit relates the study of biology to many of the most vital areas of research today. Unit 2 broadens the understanding of biological concepts to include the ecological relationships of organisms to their physical and biological environments. The study of classification emphasizes the structural relationship of organisms and introduces the science of taxonomy.

With this general background, the student is prepared to consider specific groups of organisms which illustrate additional principles of structure, function, and adaptation. Unit 3 follows the systematic sequence from simple to more complex organisms in presenting the flowerless plants — algae, bacteria, fungi, mosses, and ferns. Unit 4, the seed plants, is of great biological significance because of the many principles illustrated and because of our close association and dependence upon this group.

Unit 5 presents invertebrate animals, beginning with the protozoans. As each animal group is studied in a systematic sequence from simple to more complex, the student discovers the pattern of animal development. The study of invertebrates provides the background for a consideration of vertebrate life in Unit 6. As the student progresses through the study of the classes of vertebrates, he becomes aware of basic similarities in body structure as well as advances which make each group more efficient than the preceding one.

The study of animal biology leads to the climax study of the human body in Unit 7. Problems relating to radiation and space biology, discussed in two chapters at the close of this unit, are of special significance in this Space Age.

Unit 8 presents the problems of disease and the biological conquest of infection. Genetics, plant and animal breeding, eugenics, and euthenics are presented in the chapters of Unit 9. Although conservation is a constant theme which runs throughout the book, the total conservation program is treated fully in the chapters of Unit 10.

The authors of this Gregor Mendel Edition of MODERN BIOLOGY deeply appreciate the cooperation of Father Henry J. Fritz, S.M., in making this revision one of sound Catholic philosophy, and of Brother Joseph Concannon, S.M.

Foreword

One hundred years ago in Austria a man of medium height, corpulent figure, high forehead and friendly blue eyes, was engaged in teaching physics and natural history at the Brünn Modern School. His garb distinguished him as a Catholic priest and member of the Augustinian order. He was Gregor Mendel, a man interested in all aspects of natural science. As a teacher, his exposition was clear and luminous. He aimed more at stimulating interest than imparting facts. His pupils concurred in praising his method of instruction, his justice and his kindness. These traits won the praise of his contemporaries, but his permanent fame rests on his experiments and discoveries in biology. In his monastery garden he followed carefully for many years the results of the hybridization of plants. His painstaking method and penetrating observation led to the discovery of the basic laws of heredity, known today as the Mendelian laws. Mankind has since benefited immensely from the application of these laws, especially in animal husbandry and farming. In his own lifetime, however, the importance of Mendel's achievement was not recognized. His published report of his discoveries was generally ignored until sixteen years after his death, when three other scientists rescued his work from oblivion. Mendel died as Abbot of his monastery on January 6, 1884, in the sixty-second year of his life.

It is to the memory of Gregor Mendel that the present edition of MODERN BIOLOGY is dedicated. The work is substantially the same as the previous edition that has already been so favorably received by teachers and students in Catholic schools. The modifications that have been made will make the present edition even more acceptable to them. Some of these changes have been made for the sake of scientific precision, others in cases where biological science touches upon the philosophic area. A broad teleological view is maintained, that is, the view that nature operates for definite ends or goals. Countless instances of purpose or design are brought before us in this book. If animals without foresight of ends, and plants with no knowledge whatever, perform manifold and complex activities serving an obvious purpose, we cannot fail to recognize that some ruling Intelligence guides the ways of nature, and we come thus to the knowledge of the existence and providence of the Creator.

As to man's nature in particular, there can be no doubt, for those who grasp the true character of his reasoning processes, of the spirituality of the soul. Although the term *animal intelligence* has become more or less current, the cleverness of animals certainly differs in kind from the conceptual thought which we find in man. Man's intellective capacity, moreover, depends on sense knowledge only extrinsically; that is, sense knowledge is only a preliminary condition for the formation of concept. Some concepts, in fact, rise above all material aspects, as for instance, our concept of truth, virtue, or spirit. Man's mental activities are evidence, not just of a nervous system, but of a spiritual soul.

The word *biology* in its derivation means the science of life. The obvious intent of the biologist is to study the life of bodily things — plants, animals, men — or the life of organisms. But the concept of life pertains to realities beyond the scope of biology. Theology tells us of the life of angels. Reason discloses to us the existence of a living God, and at the same time the fact that He is in no sense material. God's perfections are mirrored in His creatures, as every effect reflects something of the cause that produced it. The life of corporeal beings, marvelous in itself, is but a distant reflection of Infinite Life. Almost 400,000 species of plants and animals are something to amaze and bewilder the mind. How much more sublime must be the Life of Him who gives life to them all!

As an aid toward visualizing the place of biology in its relation to other fields of learning and the objects they pursue, the following schema is presented.

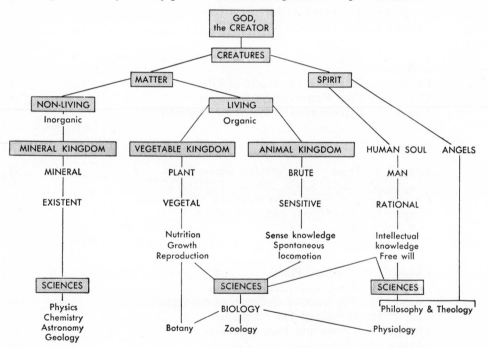

Contents

Preface   v

Foreword   vi

UNIT 1 — BIOLOGY — THE SCIENTIFIC STUDY OF LIVING
        THINGS   x

Chapter 1: The Science of Life   1
Chapter 2: Fundamental Properties of Life   12
Chapter 3: The Physical Basis of Life   21
Chapter 4: The Functional Basis of Life   31
Chapter 5: The Chemical Basis of Life   41

UNIT 2 — THE RELATIONSHIPS OF LIVING THINGS   55

Chapter 6: Balance in the World of Life   56
Chapter 7: Vital Factors of Environment   66
Chapter 8: Classification of Plants and Animals   77

UNIT 3 — FLOWERLESS PLANTS   90

Chapter 9: Algae — The Simplest Green Plants   91
Chapter 10: Bacteria — Beneficial and Harmful Plants   104
Chapter 11: The Fungi — Well-known Thallophytes   113
Chapter 12: The Mosses and the Ferns   126

UNIT 4 — THE HIGHER PLANTS   137

Chapter 13: The Seed Plants   138
Chapter 14: Roots and Their Activities   146
Chapter 15: The Root as an Organ of Absorption   158
Chapter 16: Stems and Their Activities   166
Chapter 17: Leaves and Their Activities   182
Chapter 18: Flowers and Reproduction   200
Chapter 19: Fruits and Seeds   211

UNIT 5 — THE INVERTEBRATES — ANIMALS WITHOUT
        BACKBONES   228

Chapter 20: Protozoa — The Microscopic One-celled Animals   229
Chapter 21: Sponges and Coelenterates — Introduction to the Met-
             azoa   241
Chapter 22: Invertebrates Classified as Worms   252
Chapter 23: The Soft-bodied and the Spiny-skinned Animals   265
Chapter 24: The Arthropods   272

Chapter 25: Insects — A Representative Study   285
Chapter 26: Habits of Some Interesting Insects   294
Chapter 27: The Control of Insect Pests   309

UNIT 6 — ANIMALS WITH BACKBONES   318

Chapter 28: Introduction to the Vertebrates   319
Chapter 29: Fish and Fishlike Vertebrates   326
Chapter 30: Amphibia — Vertebrates with Double Lives   342
Chapter 31: Reptiles — Vertebrates with Scales and Claws   357
Chapter 32: Birds — Vertebrates Adapted for Flight   375
Chapter 33: Mammals — The Highest Forms of Animal Life   396

UNIT 7 — HOW BIOLOGY APPLIES TO OURSELVES   417

Chapter 34: Structure of the Human Body   418
Chapter 35: The Nature of Foods   437
Chapter 36: Digestion of Foods   447
Chapter 37: Respiration and Excretion   459
Chapter 38: The Blood and Circulation   477
Chapter 39: The Nervous System   492
Chapter 40: The Sense Organs   504
Chapter 41: The Body Regulators   515
Chapter 42: Alcohol, Narcotics, and Tobacco   523
Chapter 43: Radiation and Biology   532
Chapter 44: Space Biology   544

UNIT 8 — BIOLOGY AND THE PROBLEMS OF DISEASE   557

Chapter 45: Microbes — Mighty Mites of Infection   558
Chapter 46: Body Defenses and Aids Against Diseases   571
Chapter 47: The Conquest of Disease   581
Chapter 48: The Prevention of Disease   594

UNIT 9 — THE BIOLOGY OF HEREDITY   607

Chapter 49: The Basis of Heredity   608
Chapter 50: The Principles of Heredity   618
Chapter 51: Plant and Animal Breeding   635
Chapter 52: Genetics Applied to Human Inheritance   646
Chapter 53: The Changing World of Life   655

UNIT 10 — SAFEGUARDING OUR NATURAL RESOURCES   670

Chapter 54: Conservation of Soil and Water   671
Chapter 55: Forests and Conservation   684
Chapter 56: Wildlife Conservation   700

Appendix   713

Glossary   721

Index   738

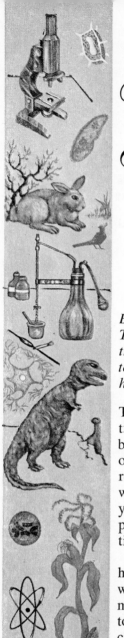

Biology— The Scientific Study of Living Things

Blessed be Thy glorious name, O Lord, . . . Heaven is of Thy fashioning, and the heaven of heavens, and all the hosts that dwell there, earth and sea, and all that earth and sea hold; to all these Thou givest the life they have; none so high in heaven but must pay Thee worship. — Nehemias 9:5, 6

The course in biology will be, for some of you, an introduction to a profession or a career. In the years ahead, the biological sciences will require an ever-increasing number of scientists in our nation's laboratories, experiment stations, research institutes, clinics, and hospitals. For those of you who pursue biology as a science no further than this course, your life will be richer when you are more familiar with the physical and chemical processes involved in the marvelous activity we call life.

The biologist is vital in our scientific world of today. To him we look constantly for increasing knowledge of better ways to use our living resources. It is his job to find better measures for waging our war against the insect hordes, and to gain a more thorough understanding of the laws and principles of heredity and their application to plant and animal industries. The biologist will find more adequate ways to control viruses and bacteria. He will show us how to overcome the biological problems of space travel, and will give us increased knowledge in a vast number of other areas.

CHAPTER 1: **THE SCIENCE OF LIFE**
CHAPTER 2: **FUNDAMENTAL PROPERTIES OF LIFE**
CHAPTER 3: **THE PHYSICAL BASIS OF LIFE**
CHAPTER 4: **THE FUNCTIONAL BASIS OF LIFE**
CHAPTER 5: **THE CHEMICAL BASIS OF LIFE**

The Science of Life

MANY people go through life thinking that toads cause warts, seeds must be planted in a certain phase of the moon, snakes can hypnotize birds, a horsehair can change to a snake, and that blood controls heredity. These are only a few of the myths and superstitions which have been handed down from early times. Biological myths and legends began to disappear when the methods of science were applied to the study of living things.

Today, biology is a highly advanced and specialized branch of science. Biologists are probing the mysteries of life in more than a hundred areas. Each new discovery brings us closer to finding out what life is, how a group of physical and chemical processes interact in a complex combination of substances which form living things, and how plants and animals live in vital relationship to their environments and to each other.

The science of life. The Greeks were the first to give a name to the science of life. They combined the word *bios*, which means *life*, with the word *logos*, meaning *science* or *study*. Together, they form the word **biology,** which means the *science of life*.

The Greeks gave us more than the name biology. The science itself has its roots in ancient Greece. More than 23 centuries ago, Aristotle (*ar*-is-tot-ul), who lived from 384–322 B.C., probably conducted the first extensive biological investigations. He watched the development of a chick in an egg. He also studied the stomach of cud-chewing animals, such as the cow. His dissections included over 50 different kinds of animals. Probably his greatest biological contribution was the grouping and classifying of over 500 different kinds of plants and animals on the basis of their body structure. We still admire Aristotle and honor him as the Father of Biology.

Biology has progressed rapidly in the past fifty years. Had biology progressed steadily from the time of Aristotle, there probably would have been no great

Fig. 1-1. Aristotle lived in Athens during the 4th century B.C. He is famous both for his contributions to philosophy and to science. His classifying of plants and animals has earned him the title of Father of Biology.

The Bettmann Archive

plague and smallpox epidemics during the Middle Ages. We might have had penicillin a hundred years or more ago. By now, we might even have a cure for advanced cancer and heart disease. However, people were hostile to new ideas. Scientists were even cast into dungeons for trying to find out more about the unknown.

Knowledge of biology advanced very little during the Middle Ages. Not until the 17th century could William Harvey, an English doctor, convince the king, and later his fellow doctors, that blood circulated in the body. Only a little more than 160 years ago, Edward Jenner discovered vaccination against smallpox, as we shall discuss in Chapter 47. However, he was ridiculed and condemned for trying to save lives by using it. Even the doctors of France laughed at Pasteur when, less than a hundred years ago, he tried to convince them that disease could be caused by invisible forms of life which could float through the air. And only about 75 years ago did Sir Joseph Lister show doctors how to scrub their hands and sterilize their instruments before performing hospital surgery. These discoveries were great milestones in medicine and biology.

Walk through a modern hospital, visit a biological research laboratory, tour a conservation project, or study a modern farm and you will see how far biology has come in the past 50 years. Then, consider sulfa drugs and antibiotics, X-ray and radium treatment for cancer, hybrid corn and 300-egg hens, blood banks, and the Rh factor. These are discoveries and achievements of recent years. They are some of the reasons you now have the greatest opportunity in the history of the world for a healthy, happy, and long life.

Scientific attitudes and methods. In part, *science* is a vast accumulation of knowledge or facts, added to by each generation and passed on to the next. But science is more than knowledge. It consists of *attitudes* and *methods*. An **attitude** is a pattern of thought, or a feeling, or a way of regarding things. In scientific thinking, the attitude of reason replaces superstition. A mere idea is never accepted until it has become a proved fact. A **method** is an orderly procedure or form of investigation. Scientific methods are universal among scientists of the world and apply to all branches of science.

In the past, scientific attitudes and methods were, for the most part, limited to scientists themselves. Today, through education, radio, television, newspapers, and other channels of information, most of our population lives close to the science laboratories and research centers. Attitudes and methods of science are now part of the thinking of millions of people. This is a scientific age.

Scientific attitudes. As you review the following five scientific attitudes, think of a doctor, a chemist, a horticulturist, a laboratory technician, or an engineer. See if they do not reveal these qualities. How many do you have? Whether you enter the ranks of the professionals and become what we call a **research scientist,** or live in close contact with scientific achievements merely as an interested layman, or **consumer scientist,** your life will have much more meaning if you adopt these scientific attitudes:

1. *Open-mindedness.* The scientist must free his mind of prejudice. The scientist never rejects knowledge because it happens not to agree with an idea of his own.

2. *Careful judgment.* The scientist must never jump to conclusions. He must base his decisions on reliable information and proved facts. Snap judgment could cost a life or bring disaster in some other way.

3. *Desire to learn.* Every scientist has

a healthy curiosity. He wants to know the *why* of things. Every discovery opens new fields of study. The scientist never stops learning.

4. *Belief in cause and effect.* The scientist believes that, as far as the physical world is concerned, things happen for a reason. Nature is orderly, and events are controlled by natural laws. Therefore, there must always be a cause for each occurrence. If this were not true, and if the scientist did not attempt to look for these causes as explanations of the events, we would have made little progress thus far. We would still be living in the age when superstition ruled our thinking.

5. *Active concern for human welfare.* This attitude is a tremendous force behind medical science and many other fields of biology. Much of our scientific effort is directed toward saving lives, lengthening lives, and producing better things for better living.

There are several scientific methods. We often speak of the scientific method as though there were one universal method used by all scientists in investigating a problem. Actually, there are many. The method used depends on the type of investigation. An atomic scientist depends on *mathematical calculations* to predict the outcome of an experiment. Often trial-and-error experimentation would be fatal. The *technical method* is widely used in testing. Much of our new knowledge of science results from use of the *research method.*

The technical method is probably the most widely used in science today. In the *technical method* the scientist is not working toward a new discovery; nor is he trying a new procedure. Instead, he is making an extremely accurate check.

For example, no surgical operation can be performed until a medical technician has determined the kind of blood a patient has, the clotting time, the corpuscle count, and other important facts. The surgeon follows a carefully outlined procedure, tested over and over and described by other surgeons. Before the operation has been completed, it may be necessary to send part of the removed organ to the laboratory for microscopic study.

Similarly, technicians follow outlined procedures in checking the bacteria content of milk and water, the strength of drugs, or the various parts of an organism for the presence of disease. Here are three steps in applying this important method:

1. *Follow an outlined procedure carefully.* The technician must not vary the procedure in any way.

2. *Make accurate observations.* A slip in observation might make the whole test valueless.

3. *Record and report all findings.* Again, the technician must use great care in recording all results of a procedure.

Much of the laboratory phase of your biology course, whether demonstration, group, or individual study, will involve the technical method. If you observe a demonstration, study the procedure carefully, observe the progress of the demonstration, and make an accurate report of the results.

The research method is used to prove or disprove an idea. The *research method* differs from the technical method in that there is no definite outlined procedure. You will have opportunities to use this method in your biology course. It may be an experiment performed by the class, or a project you have planned. Let's look at the steps of the research method as the scientist follows them.

1. *Recognizing and defining a problem.* The more you study biology, the more questions you will want answered. Such questions pose a problem to the scientist.

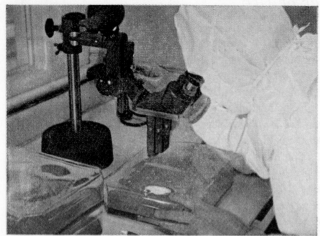

Fig. 1-2. This biologist is a research scientist. He is using special microscopic attachments to observe the growth of monkey kidney cells. These tissue cultures are widely used to grow viruses for vaccines or to develop new vaccines, such as the Salk vaccine shown being administered in Fig. 1-3.

Chas. Pfizer and Co.

He wants to find the answer to it. Why does a plant bend toward the light? How do roots take in water? What causes a heart to beat?

2. *Collecting information related to the problem.* When a research problem leads into the unknown, the scientist uses known facts to take him to the fringe of knowledge. He gathers all available information relating to his problem. For this reason, a scientific library is as important as a laboratory. Your textbook and supplementary readings (found in the lists at the end of each unit in this book) will aid you in solving biological problems included in your course.

3. *Forming an idea or hypothesis.* A **hypothesis** might be called a scientific "hunch." The scientist usually has an idea of what an experiment might prove. However, he must not make up his mind in advance. He must prove or disprove his idea.

4. *Experimenting to prove or disprove the hypothesis.* The scientist thinks up an experiment to prove or disprove the hypothesis. This part of the procedure requires imagination, careful planning, and skill. Frequently, several experiments may be required.

5. *Observing the experiment.* What does the experiment prove? Perhaps something quite unexpected appears in the experiment. The scientist is, of course, a keen observer, and so will notice this. Many of our most important scientific discoveries were not expected until an experiment revealed them.

6. *Organizing and recording data from an experiment.* Every part of the experiment — the way it was set up, what happened during its progress, and the results — must be recorded accurately. These records may be in the form of notes, drawings, tables, or graphs.

7. *Drawing conclusions.* Scientific data are of value only when they are put to use. Drawing a conclusion leads to the discovery of a principle which can be applied to other situations. For example, Dr. Alexander Fleming found in experiments that a mold called *Penicillium* killed certain kinds of bacteria. His conclusion from this observation led to his discovery of penicillin.

How do you set up a scientific experiment? We shall now plan a simple experiment, using two sets of plants, and see how it should be set up. Then we shall see how the same experiment could be made quite worthless with a few slight oversights. The experiment will show the influence of light on the growth of bean seedlings. Our hypothesis is that light is necessary for normal growth and activity of a green plant.

Plant two beans in each of six three-inch pots filled with garden loam. All six pots should be watered regularly and equally. Set three pots on a window shelf in a warm room. The other three should be placed in a dark place at the same temperature as the room. In selecting these locations, be careful to find places where the temperature is the same. The seedlings should be left for four weeks.

Notes must be made of all results during the experiment. At the end of four weeks, the length of all stems can be found by counting the leaves and measuring the distance between them. The color of all plants should also be noted. Data from the three pots in the light, as well as those in the dark, can then be averaged.

The experiment should show that the plants in the light were green, had sturdy stems, and large, healthy leaves. The plants in the dark had longer, spindly stems and small, yellow leaves. We can conclude that light is necessary for growth of a young bean plant. Both sets of plants were grown under the same conditions except for light. Light was the **variable factor;** all other factors were ruled out.

What if the plants in the dark had been growing in clay or sand, while those in the light had been in loam? Or what if we had watered one set more often than the others? Suppose one set had been in a warmer place than the others? The difference in the seedlings could have been due to any one of these variable factors. The experiment would have proved nothing. Similarly, if we had used only one plant in the light and one in the dark, the difference in the rate of growth might have been due to a weak plant. This was the reason for using several plants.

When you plan an experiment, be sure to control conditions so as to test only one *variable factor*. When you are dealing with several factors, plan an experiment to test each factor separately.

The microscope, a basic tool of the biologist. As you proceed through your course in biology, you will become more and more aware of the importance of *magnification* to the biologist. In fact, most of the biological knowledge we accept today has been acquired since the invention and perfection of the microscope. Through the powerful magnifying

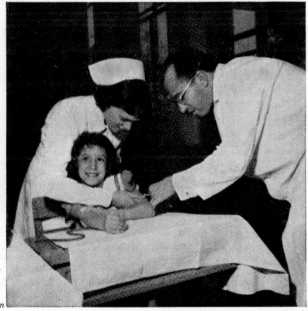

Fig. 1-3. The famous Dr. Jonas Salk is shown inoculating a child against polio with the Salk vaccine. This vaccine was developed and perfected over a period of years by the combined work of many research scientists, such as the one shown in Fig. 1-2.

National Foundation

fections and made the microscope the precision instrument we use now in our laboratories.

A Dutchman, a hobby, and a great contribution to biology. Nearly 300 years ago, in the city of Delft, Holland, Anton Van Leeuwenhoek (*lay*-ven-hook), 1632–1723, made a hobby of grinding lenses. He used small pieces of glass and ground them into magnifying lenses with which he could enlarge objects 40 to 270 times. By mounting his lenses in holding devices, Van Leeuwenhoek made many microscopes. It is said that he made 247 different ones. Each different type of material to be studied required a special microscope.

One of Van Leeuwenhoek's early mi-

The Bettmann Archive

Fig. 1-4. The photograph above is of one of the very early microscopes. Anton Van Leeuwenhoek opened up a whole new world to science when he developed the microscope.

lenses of this remarkable instrument, biologists have peered into the tiny structures which make up plants and animals and which we call *cells*. The cell is the center of all of the life activities of living things. Biologists have made exhaustive studies of countless forms of life which are invisible except under high magnification. Without the microscope, whole areas of biology could never have been developed.

The biologist today owes a great debt to a Dutch lens grinder who made many of the earliest microscopes and to the many scientists who added various per-

Bausch and Lomb

Fig. 1-5. This modern compound microscope, used in research, usually has an eyepiece for each eye and three objectives.

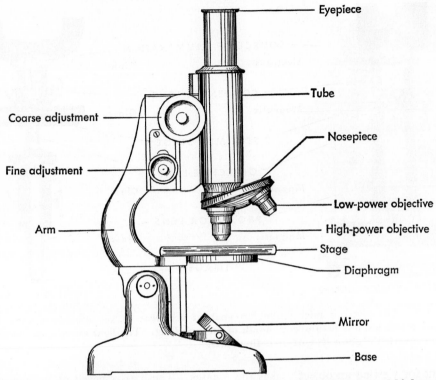

Fig. 1-6. This microscope is typical of those commonly used in high school biology laboratories. It is called a compound microscope because there are lenses in both the eyepiece and the objective.

croscopes was built in order to examine a small fish. It consisted of a tube in which the fish was put. The frame around the tube held a small magnifying lens. By putting his eye close to the lens, Van Leeuwenhoek enlarged the tail of the fish enough to see blood vessels and circulating blood. With other microscopes he saw the fibers in muscles and other minute structures in various plants and animals. To his amazement, he found stagnant water teeming with microscopic animal life, which he described as " cavorting beasties."

While Van Leeuwenhoek did not make the first microscope, his were far more perfect than any of the earlier and even cruder instruments. For this reason, and the fact that he was the first to view plants and animals with a magnifying lens, we usually credit him with the invention of the microscope.

The modern compound microscope. A compound optical microscope of the type widely used in high school biology laboratories today is shown in Fig. 1-6. Lenses are contained in both the *eyepiece* and the *objectives,* which is why it is called a **compound microscope.** Most high school microscopes are equipped with a 10-power eyepiece. This means that the eyepiece lenses alone magnify 10 times. The objectives are cylinders which contain a series of lenses cemented together. The *low-power* objective magnifies 10 times. The usual *high-power* objective magnifies 43 or 44 times. Thus the typical high school microscope can magnify 430 or 440 times (eyepiece magnification times objective magnification).

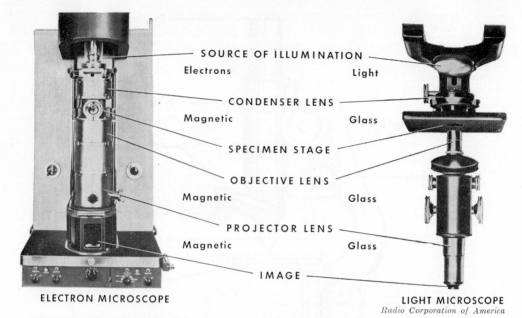

SOURCE OF ILLUMINATION
Electrons   Light

CONDENSER LENS
Magnetic   Glass

SPECIMEN STAGE

OBJECTIVE LENS
Magnetic   Glass

PROJECTOR LENS
Magnetic   Glass

IMAGE

ELECTRON MICROSCOPE   LIGHT MICROSCOPE
Radio Corporation of America

Fig. 1-7. The electron microscope has enabled scientists to see organisms such as viruses, which are less than one-millionth of an inch long. The light microscope on the right is inverted to show its corresponding parts.

Light for viewing an object strikes the *mirror.* The mirror directs the rays through the opening in the *stage,* through the objective, *tube,* and eyepiece to the eye. Objects to be viewed with this type of microscope must be small and sufficiently thin to allow light to pass through.

The electron microscope. Until recent years, the amount of magnification possible with a microscope was limited by the ability of the human eye to see greatly enlarged images. Light has been another problem in high magnification. Both of these limitations are overcome in the **electron microscope.** In this instrument, a beam of electrons in a vacuum chamber replaces ordinary light. The image is received by a photographic plate which is far more sensitive than a human eye. In some cases, the enlarged image is received on a fluorescent screen.

The electron microscope has been of great value in the study of viruses, which cause smallpox, influenza, and other dis-

eases. These extremely small organisms, less than one-millionth of an inch in size, are not visible under the highest power of an optical microscope. Yet they have been photographed and studied with the electron microscope.

What can biology do for you? Some of you may choose a branch of biology as a career. For those who do, your biology course is an introduction to a life-work. For those of you who do not take up biology as a career, your knowledge of living things will be useful in daily life. You will look at a woodland, a field, a bog, or a river with much greater interest when you understand the plants and animals which live there, and the principles which govern their lives.

We can summarize goals and objectives of a biology course as follows:

1. *To answer questions about life and living things.* Can identical twins be of different sexes? Can a child inherit an acquired skill from his parents? How

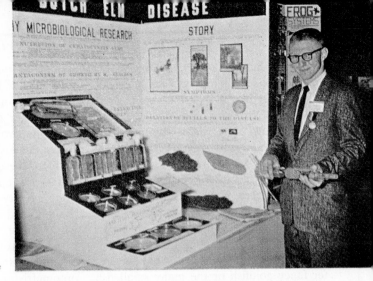

Fig. 1-8. The student science fairs conducted throughout the country are excellent opportunities for you to develop your interests as a consumer scientist. A science fair project often leads a student to choose a career in the sciences.

Science Service

does your body produce immunity to a disease? How is energy stored in food? Is the mother or father responsible for the sex of a child? The answers to these and countless other questions about life are part of the knowledge you acquire when you study biology.

2. *To acquire scientific attitudes and methods.* Biology will help you solve problems. It will increase your powers of observation. It will help you evaluate your observations and draw correct conclusions from what you see.

3. *To understand the basic principles of life.* As you study biology, you will see that all living things fit into an orderly pattern. Basic principles and natural laws influence all of the events in the world of life.

4. *To aid the conservation program.* No organism has been more destructive to living things than man himself. He has slaughtered wildlife, destroyed their homes, poisoned their streams with refuse, leveled forests, and has even destroyed the soil itself. Civilization need not be responsible for such destruction!

5. *To improve our general health standards.* Probably the greatest advances in biology have been in control of disease and improvement of health. At least half of the deaths from diseases

caused by germs could have been avoided. Health education can reduce the number of deaths from heart disease and cancer enormously.

6. *To increase outdoor recreation.* There is no better place to relax and forget the cares and worries of modern complex living than in the out-of-doors. Miles of paved highways lead to forests, lakes, state and national parks, and other places where man can be alone with nature. Biological knowledge will help you to enjoy every hike and trip you make.

7. *To acquaint you with some of the outstanding biologists.* All biology is a

Fig. 1-9. A bird hike gives you a chance to get together with a group as well as to be out-of-doors. Learning about birds is an interesting and worthwhile hobby.

National Audubon Society

record of human achievements. Every phase of modern living has been improved in some way by the contributions of great biologists. We, who enjoy these benefits, should know more about the men and women who gave them to us.

8. *To introduce worthwhile hobbies.* Biology is full of fascinating hobbies. Have you ever watched angelfish glide gracefully through columns of water plants in a tropical aquarium? Many species of tropical fish thrive in the tanks of thousands of amateur aquarists. Others prefer fancy goldfish or the many small fish of our native waters. Bird hikes, nature photography, flower and vegetable growing, insect collecting — biology is full of interesting hobbies.

9. *To improve daily life.* Seeding and fertilizing a lawn, spraying insect pests, protecting food from spoilage, and a great many other contacts you will have with the living world might be classed as biological necessities. Biology will help you perform these tasks more skillfully.

10. *To introduce biological occupations.* Every high school student is giving thought to career opportunities for a lifework. The food industries are always eager to have people who are trained in biology. Nurses, doctors, dentists, and optometrists completed courses in biology. And if you plan to go into the fields of agriculture, bacteriology, or forestry, it is essential that you have a thorough knowledge of biology.

SOME SPECIALIZED BRANCHES OF BIOLOGY

Anatomy	Study of structure of plant and animal organs
Bacteriology	Study of microscopic nongreen plants, some of which cause disease
Cytology	Study of structure and functions of plant and animal cells
Ecology	Study of the environmental relations and distribution of plants and animals
Embryology	Study of the early development of plants and animals
Entomology	Study of insects
Eugenics	Branch of genetics dealing with human heredity
Genetics	Study of heredity
Herpetology	Study of reptiles
Histology	Study of the structure of plant and animal tissues
Ichthyology	Study of fish
Morphology	Study of total structure of plants and animals
Mycology	Study of fungi
Ornithology	Study of birds
Paleontology	Study of the life of past geological periods
Parasitology	Study of organisms which live on or in the bodies of other organisms and derive their nourishment from that organism
Pathology	Study of diseases of plants and animals
Phycology	Study of algae
Physiology	Study of the functions of plants and animals
Protozoology	Study of protozoans (one-celled animals)
Space biology	Study of survival problems of living things in outer space
Taxonomy	Naming, grouping, and classifying of plants and animals
Virology	Study of viruses

What does biology include? Although biology is a single science based on the study of all living things, it includes many special branches.

We usually separate biological science into these broad areas:

1. *General biology* includes the study of living things in general, the principles governing life, and the relationship of living things to their surroundings and to each other.

2. *Botany* is the specialized study of plant life and the relationship of plants to other living things.

3. *Zoology* is the specialized study of animal life and the relationship of animals to other living things.

4. *Human biology* deals with man as a living organism and his relationships to other living things.

These general areas are, in turn, separated into further fields of specialized study. The bacteriologist, for instance, after gaining a general knowledge of biology, usually specializes in one or more of these branches. Some of the more familiar branches of biology are listed in the table on the opposite page.

In Conclusion

You are now ready to explore the living world. We shall use various scientific methods and procedures in our exploration. A page in your text may represent many years of research and study conducted by a biologist of past years. An experiment you conduct in the laboratory might have been an outstanding discovery a few years ago. At times, your study of biology will bring you to the fringe of new knowledge — to a problem which may be under investigation in a research laboratory at this very moment.

What is life? What does it mean to be alive? Let's begin the study of living things with these basic questions. We will not find a complete answer, but we will show you many fascinating things that biologists have discovered about life.

BIOLOGICALLY SPEAKING

attitude	electron microscope	research scientist
biology	hypothesis	science
compound microscope	method	technical method
consumer scientist	research method	variable factor

QUESTIONS FOR REVIEW

1. Aristotle has been called the Father of Biology. What were some of the contributions of this ancient Greek scholar to biology?
2. Why does the study of biology require certain attitudes?
3. List five attitudes associated with modern science.
4. List seven steps of the research method.
5. Explain what is meant by the variable factor in an experiment.

6. What was the single variable factor tested in the experiment with bean seedlings? How were the other factors ruled out of the experiment?
7. Why is the microscope an essential tool of the biologist?
8. How do the electron and compound microscopes differ?
9. List ten goals and objectives of a high school course in biology.
10. List some of the specialized fields in the biological sciences.

APPLYING FACTS AND PRINCIPLES

1. Compare the technical and research methods in terms of purpose and procedure.
2. Why is scientific curiosity an important quality of a research scientist?
3. A person cannot believe the principle of cause and effect and still believe in superstition. Why is this true?
4. In recent tests of the polio vaccine, children of the same age group were given one of two kinds of injections. One group received the Salk vaccine. The other group was given a useless solution made to look exactly like the vaccine in regard to color and consistency. Even the doctors who gave the injections had no idea which substance they were injecting. The vaccine and useless solution were identified by code numbers so that only those who were conducting the experiment knew which children received each of the substances. Why were some of the children given a useless substance, looking exactly like the vaccine? Why was it necessary to use children of about the same age in the experiment?

CHAPTER 2

Fundamental Properties of Life

WHAT is life? How are living things different from nonliving things? Perhaps the answer to these questions seems simple to you — living things grow and reproduce; many of them move about. It may surprise you to learn, however, that biologists do not know everything about the nature of life. Life is a condition which is found in a complex arrangement of chemical substances occurring in all living things. Still, we do not know exactly what life is. We shall be nearer to an understanding if we analyze living things and compare them with nonliving things. This analysis will, at least, throw some light on what life does and on the problems of plants, animals, and man in maintaining and passing on this remarkable condition.

Living and nonliving things. Fig. 2-1 shows a shallow pool at the edge of a wood. A frog is sitting on a rock, while a dragonfly hovers over the pool. A blue-jay is perched on the branch of a shrub, overlooking a squirrel. Mushrooms have sprouted on the ground nearby. The branch of a dead tree lies in the fore-

Fig. 2-1. Examine the drawing carefully and name the living things that are shown in it; likewise, name the nonliving things. Tell why you have classified them as living or nonliving.

ground. It is no problem to separate all the things you see into two groups. The frog, the bird, the squirrel, the mushrooms, the dragonfly, the grass, and the shrub are *living*. We refer to each one as an **organism,** a complete and entire plant or animal. The water, the rocks, and the soil are *nonliving.* How are they different from the organisms? What properties did the tree lose when it died and became a thing which *once lived?* Let us take a closer look.

Life comes only from life. For the bird, life was passed from the parent birds to the egg from which it hatched. Similarly, the life of the grass is the same life which was maintained in the seed as it formed and matured on the parent plant. These organisms will, in turn, pass on life to a new generation of offspring. You might compare this transfer of life to the lighting of new fires from one which is burning. If the fire goes out, the flame is lost. But if new supplies of fuel are lighted from older fires, the flame can be preserved endlessly. Thus, the original life of the earth has been preserved through the ages as one organism gave life to another.

This concept of life is rather recent. At one time, people believed in the theory of **spontaneous generation.** According to this idea, a horsehair could change to a living snake in rain water; a filthy, lifeless substance could change to disease microbes; mud could change to a frog; or decaying meat could become alive with maggots.

In the year 1668, an Italian scientist, Redi (*ray*-dee), conducted a simple but convincing experiment to disprove spontaneous generation of flies. He placed meat in three wide-mouthed flasks. One flask was left open to the air. A second was covered with porous cloth, and a third with paper. The meat decayed in all three flasks. Flies, attracted by the odor, entered the open flask and laid eggs on the decaying meat. These soon hatched into maggots (a stage in the life of the fly between egg and adult). The odor coming from the cloth-covered flask also attracted flies which laid eggs on the cloth. These also hatched into maggots but none appeared in the decaying meat. No maggots appeared in the meat or on the paper covering of the third flask. Thus, nearly 300 years ago, Redi demonstrated one of the first properties of life — *life comes only from life.*

Life is a condition of protoplasm. Let's consider two organisms, a cat and a geranium plant. Both are alive. Is one more alive than the other? Would it surprise you to learn that the cells of both are composed of the same living substance? We call this substance of life **protoplasm** (*proh*-toh-plazm). It is not a definite substance like water, a salt, a

Fig. 2-2. One property of living things is that all members of a given species have the same general form. Notice that the calf of this Hereford cow is basically similar to its mother.

Palmer from Monkmeyer

protein, or a fat. Rather, it is a complex group or system of substances. Life may center in one of the many substances present in protoplasm, but all of its parts are necessary to maintain a living condition.

Biology might be called the study of protoplasm because all life centers in it. It is present in every living thing and thus makes all organisms fundamentally alike, and also makes them different from non-living things. We shall discuss protoplasm more fully in Chapter 3, when we explore the microscopic units of living things.

Living things inherit size and form. While all organisms are similar in protoplasmic content, each grows in form and reaches a size which is characteristic of its kind. You can describe a blue spruce tree, a mule deer, a black bear, or a rainbow trout with reasonable accuracy. With some variation, your description will fit all others of the same kind. Furthermore, you can predict the approximate size each will become when it is mature.

Thus, in producing more of its kind, each organism passes on influences which will control the growth of the offspring and cause it to become like its parents. *Like produces like* — this is another characteristic of living things. We shall explore it more thoroughly in the study of heredity in Unit 9.

Living organisms have a predetermined life span. The *life span* of a plant or an animal is its period of existence — the time between its beginning and its death. No form of organic life can exist indefinitely. There are four stages in the life of every organism: (1) beginning or origin; (2) growth; (3) maturity; and (4) death. Even though living things repair and maintain themselves for long periods of time, the substance composing them finally breaks down. Then they lose their life activity; that is, they die.

The life span of any particular plant or animal, barring disease or accidental death, is about the same as that of all others of its kind. The petunia, marigold, and zinnia plants of your flower garden last scarcely more than a season. The white oak tree may thrive 500 years. A " big tree " of California would still be young at this age. These remarkable trees live several thousand years.

Many members of the insect world have a life span of only a few weeks. Five years is old for some fish. Horses may reach an age of 30 or more. Man's life span averages between 66 and 68 years. Some people live to be much older, while some die younger.

Regardless of what its life span may be, however, eventual death of a living organism is inevitable. This is not true of nonliving things. The substance composing nonliving things is not active in the sense that protoplasm is. A rock you pick up may be millions of years old.

Radium and other radioactive substances do have a definite period of existence. It may be a few seconds or millions of years. The matter composing these substances changes to energy in the form of radiation. And with this release of energy other substances are formed. Scientists speak of the " life " of radioactive materials in terms of the time it takes the matter composing them to change to energy. But this life is quite different from that of the plant or animal, which, when produced by another of its kind, grows, matures, and dies.

Living things maintain constant activity. Living things cannot just exist. Stories you may have heard about an animal entering a lifeless state of **suspended animation** for many years and then coming to life again have no scientific basis. When activity ceases, life also ceases.

Life activity does not refer only to visible signs of life, such as moving around.

Sumner from Monkmeyer

Fig. 2-3. The California redwoods have a life span of several thousand years. The lumber from one of these is enough to build 20 five-room houses.

A tree may look lifeless, but its living parts are in a constant state of activity.

Protoplasm can remain active and alive only as long as energy is released in it. In other words, energy is the force which gives life to living substance. This power must be present throughout life. You use this energy when you read this page, when you think, when you move around. You use it just to stay alive.

The activities of plants and animals are called their **life functions,** or life processes. Like the substance which carries them on, life functions are universal. They are performed by every living thing. This explains why the grasshopper is no more alive than the grass it eats. Life functions make all organisms fundamentally alike and different from nonliving things.

We shall discuss these functions, the substance which performs them, and the

General Biological Supply House

Fig. 2-4. The diet of moose consists principally of sedges and rushes. Also they are good swimmers, so they are usually found living near swamps or lakes.

energy which makes them possible in Chapter 4.

Living things have a critical relationship with their environment. The *environment* of a living thing includes all its surroundings. Factors such as temperature, rainfall, humidity, or water vapor in the air, winds and air currents, soil conditions, and variations in the surface of the earth have a direct influence on life. Environmental conditions differ in various localities. As these conditions vary, plant and animal life in the region varies. Desert plants and animals cannot survive in moist woods. Nor can prairie life survive in swamps. From the arctic wastelands to the tropics and from mountains to valleys, you find certain kinds of plants and animals which find each environment ideal.

The environment must supply plant life with materials with which to produce a food supply. Animals, in turn, eat the plants as food. Thus, plants become part of the necessary environment of animal life. Water is essential to all living things. Some plants and animals require a water environment and thrive in oceans, lakes, or streams. Others require the less abundant water of a bog or a marsh. Still others thrive in the dry surroundings of the desert.

Light is another critical factor of the environment. The dark floor of a forest is an ideal place for young sugar maples and beech trees. The American elm grows better in bright sunshine.

Most living things need oxygen. The earthworm gets sufficient oxygen from air in the soil. The fish depends on oxygen which is dissolved in water. The atmosphere supplies necessary oxygen to the host of plants and animals that live on the surface of the earth.

The food supply, water, light, and air are *requirements for life*. We refer to these requirements as **organic needs** of plants and animals. The environment must supply them, along with other necessary conditions.

Living things respond to conditions around them. Only living protoplasm has the property of reacting to its environment. The **response** may be the growth of a plant root toward a **stimulus** such as water or minerals in the soil. Animals are capable of reacting in more complex ways, or on higher levels. Sight, hearing, touch, taste, and smell are responses to environmental conditions. More complicated responses include flight from an enemy, defense in time of danger, hunting for food, and seeking a favorable environment. Animal responses may even reach the level of intelligent behavior, stimulated by a situation or a condition in the environment. Nonliving substances may be influenced by the environment, as water freezes and becomes ice, but protoplasm is the only substance which is capable of responding to a stimulus.

Living things must reproduce. Since the life span of any plant or animal is limited, **reproduction** is essential if a race of plants or animals is to survive. Reproduction is the ability to produce new living things that are similar to the parents.

Methods of reproduction are strange

and interesting. For instance, fruits may have edible pulp to attract an animal as a means of carrying seeds to a new location. Others are equipped with parachutes and ride the air currents. Animals frequently travel long distances to find conditions suitable for the production and rearing of young. The plant or animal must be able to reproduce at a rate at least equal to the death rate of its kind. Plants usually produce large quantities of seed. The number must be large enough to allow for destruction of seed, failure to lodge in a place suitable for growth, and the high death rate of seedlings. Insects, fish, frogs, and many other animals produce large numbers of young, many of which are destroyed by unfavorable environment or other animals. In cases where fewer young are produced, as in the case of bears, squirrels, deer, and other higher animals, the chances of the young surviving are greatly increased by parental care.

Living things have a survival problem. Plants and animals face a constant struggle for life. Much of this struggle centers around requirements for life. A severe drought, extreme heat or cold, storms, fires, and other catastrophes take a heavy toll of plant and animal life. Seeds often sprout in unsuitable places where they happen to fall. The plants struggle for a time, then die, because the soil is not of the right type, or because there is too much or too little water or light.

Even if the environment is proper, a plant or animal must compete with other living things. Sometimes the struggle is competition for the needs of life. Other times it is a struggle with enemies. A small tree growing from the forest tree floor must compete with many other trees for a place to grow. The robin is a constant threat to the worm and caterpillar. But hawks, crows, bluejays, and cats are a constant threat to robins. The *struggle for existence* is a problem to all living things.

Extinct organisms. Many plants and animals which once thrived on the earth are now gone forever. We classify them as *extinct organisms.* Once parts of the earth supported a large population of dinosaurs. No one knows exactly why these great reptiles disappeared so completely. They had dominated the earth in many regions for millions of years. The saber-toothed tiger, woolly rhinoceros, giant sloth, Irish elk, mastodon, and the

Fig. 2-5. The whooping crane is all but extinct, not only because it has been shot in its flyways, but because its nesting places are vulnerable to predators.

Cruickshank from National Audubon Society

Monkmeyer

Fig. 2-6. The dodo, a relative of the pigeon, was about the size of a turkey. It became extinct because its heavy body and weak wings prevented it from escaping its predators.

mammoth are extinct animals which flourished more recently than the dinosaurs.

At one time the forests of North America were made up of giant ferns and plants called *club mosses,* rather than the trees prevailing today. As the environment changed, they perished. Today, tree ferns are found only in scattered areas where the climate is warm, as in Jamaica and Hawaii.

The curious dodo, shown in Fig. 2-6, was a relative of the pigeon, with a body about the size of a turkey. Sailors found this bird on the island of Mauritius in the Indian Ocean many years ago. They named it the *dodo,* which means " simpleton " in Portuguese. It was well named for it had no fear and could be killed easily with a club. Since the flesh of the dodo was distasteful, few of the birds were killed for food. However, colonists on the island introduced hogs which fed on the dodo and soon exterminated it.

The heath hen, passenger pigeon, and great auk are also numbered among extinct birds. Unless we continue to guard them closely, the whistling swan, ivory-billed woodpecker, whooping crane, California condor, and several other species may be added to the list of extinct birds. Several of these birds lay such a small number of eggs that reproduction cannot keep pace with the rate of mortality.

Variations cause changes in living things. How do plants and animals change and become better suited to an environment? The answer lies in *variations.* This means that no two offspring are exactly alike, nor are they exactly like their parents. Sometimes a slight change is a benefit to an organism. It has a better chance to survive. Often, the change is not an improvement and may hasten its death. By these chance variations which improve the possibility of survival, plants and animals become better suited to their surroundings. This process is called *adaptation.*

Nature is full of examples of adaptation. We shall consider one in the deer family. The whitetail deer ranges over most of North America, Mexico, and Central America. In the north, it is a slender, long-legged animal. It can run at top speed through a dense forest and hurdle logs five feet or more off the ground. In Florida, a tiny deer known as the Key deer lives in the marshes. This " toy " variety of the whitetail deer weighs 50 pounds or less. It can easily hide in a clump of marsh grass. The Key deer could not survive in the northern forest. Wolves and other flesh-eating animals would have exterminated it years ago. But neither could the larger, northern whitetail deer find shelter in the marshes of Florida.

In referring to adaptation, we often speak of an organism as modifying to fit its environment. It is clear that no bird can voluntarily change its color to blend with its surroundings. The ptarmigan (*tar*-mih-gun) of the north does not willingly grow white plumage to blend with the snow in winter. However, it is evident that these adaptations do in fact serve a purpose, and that in the total view of nature, design and purpose have their place. The whole order of nature could not be the result of mere chance.

By taking advantage of variations in organisms in plant and animal breeding we have produced high-yielding crop plants and fruit trees, race horses, saddle horses and draft horses, and cattle suited especially for beef or especially for diary products.

Man is the supreme form of organic life. As a living organism, man faces the same problems of life which confront plants and animals. But one superiority of the human race has placed man far above other living things in the ability to meet these problems. Man is the most intelligent organism. What he lacks in instinct and physical ability, he more than makes up for in intelligence.

He learned long ago that food could be grown in cultivation. This solves the greatest problem facing all other living things. True, a large part of the population in certain places of the earth still faces famine on occasion, but extensive research into other possible food sources will solve this problem in time.

Man has spread his civilization from the tropics to the frigid realms. This does not necessarily indicate great adaptability of man to various environmental problems. If it were not for man's intelligence, human life would probably exist only in the tropics. But he modifies his environment to suit his needs. Clothing, shelter, and heating devices allow people to live in the coldest of climates. Shelter and cooling devices protect them from the summer heat.

Craven from U. S. Fish and Wildlife Service

Fig. 2-7. The northern variety of the whitetail deer shown above is a good example of how an animal is adapted to its surroundings. The long, slender legs enable it to run swiftly through thick forests. The Key deer, on the other hand, illustrates an adaptation of this species which is suited for life in the marshes.

Man controls his natural enemies and, in many cases, puts them to work for him. Even disease microbes, man's greatest enemies in the living world, are coming under his control. Man's intelligence has enabled him to surpass all other forms of animal life.

However, with this ability to control the plant and animal life of the earth comes a tremendous responsibility. Vast numbers of plants and animals have perished as civilization spread in our land, not necessarily because of direct destruction by man, but because of sudden environmental changes he has caused. The leveling of a forest destroys all the plant and animal societies which thrived there. Pollution of a stream or a lake destroys nearly all of its normal plant and animal population. We have made costly mistakes in the past. One of the principal reasons for studying biology is so that we may prevent such tragic mistakes from occurring again in the future.

In Conclusion

To be alive is to be like all other living things and different from nonliving things. Plants, animals, and man are composed of the same life substance and carry on the same life functions.

Remaining alive is a problem because living things cannot just exist. Their body substance responds to conditions around them. The environment must supply the organic needs for life, as well as a suitable place in which to live.

As we continue our study of life and the similarities of living things, we turn to the physical make-up of plants, animals, and man. We shall now return to the study of protoplasm and explore the wonders of a living cell.

BIOLOGICALLY SPEAKING

adaptation	organic need	spontaneous generation
environment	organism	stimulus
extinct organism	protoplasm	struggle for existence
life function	reproduction	suspended animation
life span	response	variation

QUESTIONS FOR REVIEW

1. What does a biologist mean when he speaks of an organism?
2. How is protoplasm different from any other substance?
3. Explain how living things may be distinguished from nonliving things on the basis of definite form.
4. Discuss the term *life span* and indicate the approximate life span of several common plants and animals.
5. How are life functions universal?

6. Describe some of the important varying factors which make up the environment of a plant or animal.
7. What do we mean by the term *organic needs?* List them.
8. Explain the relationship between parental care and number of offspring.
9. By using a plant or animal as an example, illustrate adaptation.
10. Account for the fact that man is superior to all other living things.

APPLYING FACTS AND PRINCIPLES

1. Why were the cloth and paper-covered flasks necessary for Redi to disprove spontaneous generation?
2. Discuss possible reasons for the disappearance of one or more extinct animals.
3. Discuss variation in organic needs and in environmental conditions as they relate to the distribution of living things.
4. Discuss the relationship between variations in organisms, the struggle for

existence, and improvement of plants and animals.
5. The crow, robin, and certain other birds have increased in numbers with civilization. Many other kinds have decreased. Account for this in terms of adaptation.
6. Why do nonliving things lack the possibility of natural improvement?
7. In your opinion, what is the greatest threat to human existence today?

CHAPTER 3

The Physical Basis of Life

WHEN you examine a leaf, you can see the thin, green blade, a network of veins, and the stalk which fastens it to the stem. You may have learned that a leaf is a food factory and that it gives off water vapor. But to understand how this food factory in the leaf works, you will need a microscope. The leaf is far more than a blade, some veins, and a stalk. The microscope reveals a vast number of individual units of many kinds grouped together to form the leaf. Biologists call these units **cells.** Each cell, in turn, consists of a tiny quantity of protoplasm. Here in this leaf, and in millions of other cells in other leaves, is the life of the tree. Here is the center of the tree's life activities.

A real knowledge of cellular biology is essential in any area of biological study. Nearly all the specialized branches of biology relate, in some way, to cells. Physical scientists ushered in the Atomic Age as a result of exhaustive study of molecules, atoms, alpha particles, beta particles, and other invisible forms of matter. Equally important biological discoveries are coming from our nation's laboratories where biologists are finding out more and more about the physical basis of living things — the cell and its marvelous substance, protoplasm.

The discovery of cells and protoplasm. In the year 1665, the English scientist, Robert Hooke (1635–1703), published a description of the microscopic appearance of a piece of cork in a report titled " Micrographia." He had sliced a piece of cork thin enough to let light pass through it for his microscopic examination. To his surprise, he found that the cork was a mass of tiny cavities. Each cavity was enclosed by walls, reminding him of cells in a honeycomb. *Cell* was a logical name for these tiny cavities.

Hooke did not realize, however, that the most important part of these cells was lacking. He saw only the empty shells or walls of cells which had once contained living, active protoplasm.

In 1835, 170 years after Hooke published his report, the French biologist Dujardin (dew-jar-*dan*) discovered that cells have living content. Dujardin referred to the substance that we now call

Fig. 3-1. The photomicrograph on the left is of a very thin longitudinal section of a piece of cork; that on the right is of a cross section. Robert Hooke called these structures cells, although we now know that he saw only the cell wall and no living protoplasm.

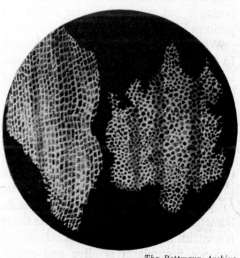

The Bettmann Archive

21

protoplasm as *sarcode*. Three years later, in 1838, Matthias Schleiden (*shly*-den), a German botanist, announced that all plants are composed of cells. A year later, in 1839, Theodor Schwann, a German zoologist, made a similar statement regarding animal structure. The work of these men and other biologists gave us the basis for the **cell theory**, which states that:

1. The cell is the unit of structure of all living things.

2. All cells come from previously existing cells.

3. The cell is the unit of function of all living things.

Protoplasm, a living substance. Can you imagine a chemical mixture being alive? Only protoplasm has this unique and wonderful property. Also, the instant life ceases in protoplasm, its structure changes and it is no longer true protoplasm. New protoplasm is organized only by existing, active protoplasm. Thus, protoplasm is found only in living organisms. It has never been produced synthetically, even though scientists have analyzed its ingredients thoroughly. The problem is not one of bringing together the proper amounts of the substances composing it, but rather of making it live and perform life activities.

What sort of substance is protoplasm? In the first place, it is not a single substance but a complex mixture of many substances. Physically, it is neither entirely solid nor liquid, but gelatinous in texture. Chemists refer to such a substance as a **colloid** (*kol*-loyd). Egg white, face creams, hand lotions, and gelatin desserts are other colloids. The color of protoplasm varies from nearly transparent to grayish, bluish, or even brownish. Sometimes it is almost clear; at other times it contains tiny bubbles or grains.

Since protoplasm is alive and active, its chemical composition is constantly changing. Furthermore, the moment it is removed from an organism for chemical study it ceases to be true protoplasm. This makes it extremely difficult to analyze. However, biologists do have a reasonably accurate idea of the materials of this strange and wonderful substance.

Water forms the liquid portion of protoplasm. While the water content varies greatly, it usually makes up about 70 per cent of the mixture. Associated with water are many solid ingredients. About half of these are *proteins* (*proh*-tee-ins). Recent studies indicate that life in active protoplasm may center in these vital proteins. Other solids found in protoplasm include *starches, sugars, fats,* and *mineral salts.* All these substances are necessary in forming protoplasm and in maintaining its living condition.

The years ahead will undoubtedly yield many new discoveries about the true nature of protoplasm. Scientists in many areas of research are studying its physical and chemical properties and the all-important arrangement of the molecules of the substances composing it. This delicate chemical balance is easily upset by introducing certain foreign chemicals as well as by varying such external physical factors as heat. Much attention is being given to the effects of various kinds of radiation on the physical and chemical aspects of protoplasm. Physical scientists may be near an answer to the question biologists have been asking for many years — how can protoplasm be alive?

The cell, a unit of protoplasm. All the protoplasm composing an organism is contained in its cells. Thus, each cell is a unit mass of protoplasm. The cell is the individual part of which the whole organism is composed. In many-celled organisms, the size of the individual is determined not by the *size* of its cells but by the *number* of cells present.

The protoplasm within a single cell is

specialized. That is, there are distinct and different parts of a cell, all made up of protoplasm. This specialization of cell parts is both structural and functional. We refer to this protoplasmic specialization as cellular **division of labor**. This specialization of protoplasm is carried still further in the great variety of cells in plants and animals for different life activities. When you examine a cell under a microscope, you will see its many specialized protoplasmic structures. When you see a variety of plant, animal, and human cells, you will discover how specialized entire cells can be.

In addition to living protoplasm, cells contain nonliving structures and substances. Some of these are products of the protoplasm. Others were taken into the cell from outside. These nonliving parts are essential for the protoplasm to carry on its functions.

In the study of cells, you will also find that most plant cells differ in several ways from animal and human cells. However, the protoplasm in all cells is fundamentally the same. Fig. 3-2 on the next page shows a plant cell and an animal cell. Notice the ways in which they are alike and those in which they are different.

In classifying the parts of a cell, we can classify the living and nonliving structures into three groups:

1. The *cell wall*. This nonliving structure, formed by living protoplasm, especially in plant cells, forms a case which surrounds and encloses the cell structures inside.

2. The *protoplast*. This includes all the protoplasmic structures or *living content* of the cell.

3. The *inclusions*. These are the *nonliving substances* in the protoplasm.

We shall now discuss each of these three groups in detail.

The cell wall. In most plant cells the protoplast is surrounded with a protective and supporting case, or **cell wall**. At first glance, a cell wall may seem to be only a single layer. However, it is usually composed of several distinct layers. Where two cells lie against each other, the protoplast of each cell has formed a portion of the cell wall separating them. Such a wall has been compared to the plastered walls of a room. The center of the wall is like the layer of lath or plaster board. This portion of a plant cell wall is referred to as the **middle lamella** (luh-*mel*-uh). It is a common boundary between the two cells. Notice that the cells are not tightly packed, but that they have **intercellular spaces** between them. The middle lamella of plant cells contains various **pectin substances** with a jellylike texture. Many fruits, including apples, contain a large amount of pectin, which is released during cooking and forms a jelly as it cools.

The cells on both sides of the middle lamella form layers of **cellulose** (*sel*-you-lohs), which is a carbohydrate related to starch. These layers can be compared to the layers of plaster on both sides of the wall between two rooms. The thickness and strength of the cell wall depend upon the amount of cellulose formed by the protoplast. Many plant cells build still other strengthening materials into their walls.

The walls of cells composing leaf blades, flower petals, pulpy fruits, and other soft plant parts are thin and easily crushed. Cells in wood, plant fibers, and nut shells have thick walls.

Animal cells seldom form a cellulose wall. In this respect, *they are different from plant cells*.

The protoplast. The living cell structures, included in the **protoplast,** compose (1) the *cytoplasm* (*sy*-toh-plazm); and (2) the *nucleus* (*new*-klee-us).

We include in the **cytoplasm,** or cell substance, all the protoplasmic structures lying outside of the nucleus. Various

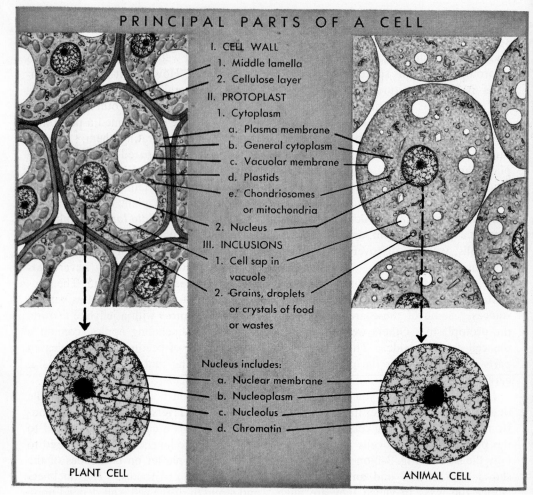

I. CELL WALL
    1. Middle lamella
    2. Cellulose layer
II. PROTOPLAST
    1. Cytoplasm
       a. Plasma membrane
       b. General cytoplasm
       c. Vacuolar membrane
       d. Plastids
       e. Chondriosomes
          or mitochondria
    2. Nucleus
III. INCLUSIONS
    1. Cell sap in
       vacuole
    2. Grains, droplets
       or crystals of food
       or wastes

Nucleus includes:
    a. Nuclear membrane
    b. Nucleoplasm
    c. Nucleolus
    d. Chromatin

PLANT CELL   ANIMAL CELL

Fig. 3-2. The two-dimensional diagram on the left is of a typical plant cell and that on the right of a typical animal cell. How do they differ and how are they alike? Remember that these cells are actually three-dimensional, as shown in Fig. 3-3.

parts of the cytoplasm are highly specialized. We refer to the bulk of the cytoplasm, occupying most of the cell, as *general cytoplasm.*

Where cytoplasm lies against the cell wall, it becomes clear and almost colorless and hardens slightly, forming a thin, living membrane. This is the *plasma membrane.* Pressure inside the cell presses the plasma membrane firmly against the wall in a plant cell, much as air presses the inner tube against the casing in a tire. This makes the plasma membrane hard to see in most plant cells.

In most animal cells, the plasma membrane forms the outer surface of the cell. This membrane is extremely important to the life of a cell since it controls the movement of materials into and out of the general cytoplasm.

Another membrane forms where cytoplasm borders on a central cavity within a cell. We refer to this type of membrane as a *vacuolar* (*vak*-you-oh-ler) *membrane.* It regulates the movement of materials stored in the cavity into and out of the general cytoplasm.

Especially in plant cells, the general

cytoplasm often contains tiny rod-shaped or granular structures visible only when the cell has been stained with special dyes which make the structures stand out. These structures are known as **chondrio-somes** (*kon*-dree-oh-sohms) or, as they are also called, **mitochondria** (my-toh-*kon*-dree-uh). Their exact function is unknown. However, many biologists believe they assist in cell respiration.

The cytoplasm of plant cells often contains structures thought to be living and called **plastids.** These plastids are of several kinds and have special functions.

The most common plastid is the **chloroplast** (*kloh*-roh-plast). These chloroplasts are always present in the cells of leaves and in other green plant parts and contain the important green pigment, **chlorophyll** (*kloh*-roh-fil).

Plastids containing colored pigments other than chlorophyll are referred to as **chromoplasts** (*kroh*-moh-plasts). Some chromoplasts contain a pale-yellow pigment, known as **xanthophyll** (*zan*-thoh-fil). Others contain **carotene** (*kair*-oh-teen), a deep-yellow or orange pigment. These yellow and orange pigments are often present in chloroplasts also. Red and blue pigments may also be present in the chromoplasts of flower petals and the skins of fruits, such as the tomato, cherry, and pepper.

A **leucoplast** (*lew*-koh-plast) is a colorless plastid which often serves as a storage vault for food in a plant cell. Leucoplasts are abundant in the white, or Irish, potato where they serve as places for the storage of starch.

The **nucleus** of a cell appears as a dense, usually spherical, mass of protoplasm, often but not always near the center of the cell. It lies in a mass of general cytoplasm. When you examine a cell under the microscope, the nucleus usually appears slightly darker than the general cytoplasm because of its greater density.

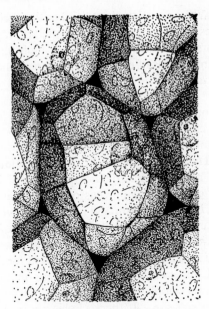

Fig. 3-3. Although a cell may look two-dimensional to you under the microscope, like those in Fig. 3-2, it is important to remember that all cells have thickness.

You can use special stains, such as *iodine* or *methylene* (*meth*-uh-leen) *blue,* to color the nucleus much darker than the cytoplasm and thus make it stand out.

The nucleus is the center of most of the activity of a cell. In addition to regulating cell activities, it is the center of cell reproduction.

Structure of the nucleus. The outer edge of the nucleus is a thin, living membrane, the **nuclear membrane,** as shown in Fig. 3-2. Inside the membrane lies the **nucleoplasm** (*new*-klee-oh-plazm), the bulk of the living content of the nucleus. The dense, gelatinous nucleoplasm usually contains one or more small, round structures. Each of these is a **nucleolus** (new-*klee*-oh-lus), which appears as a tiny nucleus within the nucleus. The function of the nucleolus is not known. It may be a reservoir for storage of materials produced in the nucleus. It is interesting to note that the nucleolus disappears temporarily during cell division.

When a nucleus is stained with special dyes, a network of granular material appears. This is **chromatin** (*kroh*-muh-tin). Chromatin is of extreme importance since it *carries the hereditary characteristics of the individual living thing.* Your hair color, eye color, facial features — all of the characteristics you inherited — are determined by the chromatin of your cells.

The inclusions in cells. The *inclusions* are nonliving materials or parts found in the cytoplasm or nucleus of cells. Cavities in the cytoplasm and nucleus are quite common and are called **vacuoles** (*vak-you-ohls*). They contain a nonliving watery solution consisting of dissolved foods and minerals. If vacuoles occur in the general cytoplasm, this solution is referred to as **cell sap.** If the vacuoles are in the nucleus, the solution is called **nuclear sap.** These solutions found in the vacuoles are essential to normal activity of the cell. Vacuoles of plant cells are often large, especially in older cells. **Food vacuoles,** present in the cells of many lower animals, contain food materials to be digested. Another kind of vacuole you will find in

Fig. 3-4. Cells of onion skin, stained with iodine to show the nuclei, are good examples of typical plant cells for study in the laboratory.

the simplest animal cells, such as the ameba and the paramecium, is the **contractile vacuole,** which functions as a water-regulating mechanism.

Starch grains, oil droplets, crystals of various minerals, and other solid materials may also be present in cells as inclusions.

A glance at several kinds of cells. You could use any part of a plant or animal to examine cells with a microscope. However, certain plant and animal subjects are widely used in high school biology laboratories because they are easy to get and they show cell structures clearly.

The onion skin has always been a favorite subject. If you slice an onion lengthwise and pry the thick scale leaves apart, you can peel a thin, transparent skin from the inner surface of each scale leaf. This skin is only one cell thick. Iodine solution is a good stain for onion cells.

Fig. 3-4 shows onion cells as they appear under the microscope. The cell walls, cytoplasm, vacuoles, and nucleus show very clearly. The outer edge of the cytoplasm is the plasma membrane. Iodine stains the nucleus darker than the cytoplasm. You can see the nucleus and one or more nucleoli. The odor and flavor of onion is onion oil. You can see this as droplets, a form of cell inclusion, in the cytoplasm.

The leaf of *Elodea,* a common little waterweed of ponds and streams, is an ideal subject to show living cells and chloroplasts. In making a slide of an *Elodea* leaf, press the leaf against your hand to warm it a few minutes. Then put it on a glass slide, add a drop of water, and put a thin cover glass on top of it. You will find many rounded or egg-shaped chloroplasts. Some may be moving. You might think the chloroplasts are swimming in the general cytoplasm. But if you look more closely, you can see that all of the chloroplasts in a cell are moving

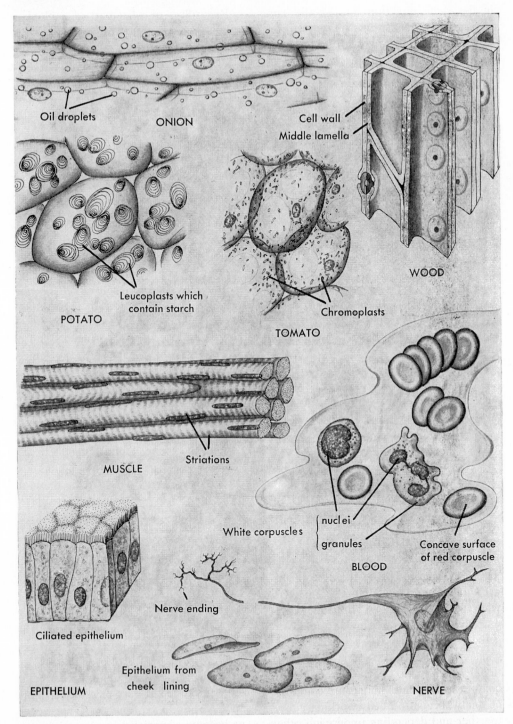

Oil droplets   ONION   Cell wall
Middle lamella

WOOD

Leucoplasts which
contain starch

POTATO   Chromoplasts

TOMATO

Striations

MUSCLE

nuclei
White corpuscles
granules

Concave surface
of red corpuscle

BLOOD

Ciliated epithelium

Nerve ending

Epithelium from
cheek lining

EPITHELIUM   NERVE

Fig. 3-5.   The four groups of cells at the top of this drawing are examples of different types of plant cells; those at the bottom are different types of animal cells.   Notice the great variety of forms that protoplasm can take.

in the same direction and at the same rate. The cytoplasm is moving around and around the cell with chloroplasts floating in it.

The potato is an excellent subject to show starch grains. You can take some of the milklike fluid from the cut surface and put it in a drop of water on a slide. A drop of iodine colors the cells yellowish and the starch grains dark blue.

The skin of a tomato shows cells with chromoplasts, while the pulp is made of a different kind of cell, filled with fluid and stored food. Sources of plant materials are almost unlimited. Directions for preparing slides of plant cells are given in *Research on Your Own* at the end of this unit.

Animal cells are more difficult to prepare for microscopic study than plant cells. They do not have cell walls to make them stand out so clearly. Beef or heart muscles will show the long, narrow cells forming muscle fibers. A drop of methylene blue, a widely used stain, will make the cells stand out more clearly. You can see some of your own cells easily if you scrape the inside of your cheek with a toothpick and mount the slimy material you gather on a slide. Either iodine or methylene blue can be used as a stain.

The cell is the unit of structure of living things. We defined a cell as a unit mass of protoplasm. Since a cell is a unit of life, a single cell could function as a complete organism. This is the case in **unicellular** plants and animals, many of which you will study. In some cases, unicellular organisms are grouped together in colonies. In such **colonial** organisms, the cells have no direct functional relation to each other. More complex plants and animals are composed of many specialized cells working closely together and depending upon each other. Such division of labor among cells is characteristic of a **multicellular** organism.

Regardless of what part of a plant or animal you examine, you will find cells. All the living cells will contain active protoplasm. All the nonliving cells contained protoplasm at some stage in their life, but this living material has either been replaced by nonliving substances or has disappeared. In other words, *the cell is the unit of structure of all living things.*

Is your body, then, a mere mass of millions of cells, all alike and living together in a tremendous colony? Of course it isn't! If it were, you wouldn't be the marvelous organism you are. Your ability would be limited to the activity of a single kind of cell.

Your body and those of complex plants and animals are the result of *cell specialization.* This means that there are many different kinds of cells. Each kind is highly developed for a particular kind of life activity, which leads us to the subject of tissues.

Cells and the organization of tissues. We define a **tissue** as a group of similar cells performing a similar activity. In your body you have muscle tissue, nerve tissue, bone tissue, liquid (blood) tissue, and many others. Plants and animals also have tissues. When you name a tissue of the human body, you think immediately of a certain kind of activity. Your movement is the best movement your muscle cells can provide. Your skeleton is the best framework a bone cell can offer. And your hearing, seeing, tasting, and control of your body are the marvelous work of your nerve cells.

A cell in a tissue is a specialist. The cell must perform all the life activities required to maintain its protoplasm. In this respect it must be like all other cells. But when a cell is part of a tissue, there can be *division of labor.* A nerve cell can become a specialist in one activity because it can depend on other specialists for needs of life. Other cells prepare

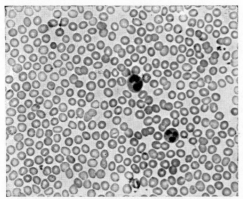

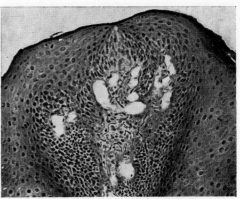

General Biological Supply House

General Biological Supply House

Fig. 3-6. These red and white corpuscles are the cells that form human blood tissue. The red cells are vital in carrying oxygen to the tissues of the body. The white cells work together to fight disease.

Fig. 3-7. Identify the cell membranes and the nuclei of the cells in this photomicrograph. This is a section of the human tongue, showing the tissue that forms the organs called taste buds.

food for it, supply it with oxygen, and carry off its waste materials. The situation is like the doctor who depends on the grocer, carpenter, and machinist. These specialists, in turn, depend on the doctor. If each one was required to do everything for himself, he could never have become a specialist. So it is with cells.

Tissues are grouped to form organs. In plants and animals, even a highly specialized tissue cannot perform a life activity to perfection. This requires a group of tissues, working closely together. We call such a complex part an *organ*. A hand is an organ. It has skin, muscle, bone, tendons, ligaments, blood, and other parts made of different specialized tissues. Your heart, stomach, liver, brain, and kidneys are other organs. The stem or trunk of a tree is an organ. It has bark, wood, pith, and other tissues, all working together. This organ supports the leaves, flowers, and fruit, and moves materials up and down between the roots and leaves.

Organs may be grouped into systems. In the higher forms of life, especially among animals, several organs often perform related functions. Such a group of

organs working together is called a **system.** For example, the digestive system performs functions related to the preparation of food for the body. It is composed of many organs, including the stomach, liver, and intestines. The circulatory system includes such organs as the heart, arteries, and veins. These organs, and the tissues which compose them, are all united in doing the complicated work of circulation.

Complex organisms. The complex plant or animal and man himself are organized in the following way:

1. Protoplasm is contained in all the living cells.

2. Cells are unit masses of protoplasm which make up the organism.

3. Tissues are groups of similar specialized cells.

4. Organs are formed by several tissues, grouped together.

5. Systems are groups of organs performing related functions.

6. The *organism* is the plant, animal, or man as a whole. It may be complex enough to have systems or so simple that it consists of only a single cell.

In Conclusion

We have discussed the physical basis of life, starting with protoplasm and the organization of protoplasm in a cell. Each cell is a unit of life and, in a sense, a tiny living organism. As living things become more complex, cells become specialists. Tissues, organs, and systems allow specialization of protoplasm to the utmost. They make possible the wonderful activities of our own bodies. But the most marvelous activity of the human body is still an activity of a cell, or a group of them.

Just as the cell is the unit of structure of all plants and animals, so it is the unit of their life activities or functions. In the next chapter, we shall examine cells again. This time, we shall approach the cell not from the viewpoint of how it is made, but of what it can do.

BIOLOGICALLY SPEAKING

carotene
cell
cell sap
cell theory
cell wall
cellulose
chlorophyll
chloroplast
chondriosome
chromatin
chromoplast
colloid
colonial

cytoplasm
division of labor
general cytoplasm
inclusion
intercellular spaces
leucoplast
middle lamella
mitochondria
multicellular
nuclear membrane
nuclear sap
nucleolus
nucleoplasm

nucleus
organ
organism
pectin substances
plasma membrane
plastid
protoplast
system
tissue
unicellular
vacuolar membrane
vacuole
xanthophyll

QUESTIONS FOR REVIEW

1. Robert Hooke discovered cells but not protoplasm. Explain why.
2. Name three concepts included in the cell theory.
3. Describe the physical appearance of protoplasm.
4. Protoplasm is a colloid. Distinguish between a colloid and a solution, such as salt water. Name several other colloids.
5. List various substances associated with water in the composition of protoplasm.

6. Discuss the composition of a plant cell wall.
7. List various parts of the cytoplasm of a cell.
8. Describe the living parts of a cell nucleus.
9. Name several cell inclusions.
10. Discuss the make-up of a tissue.
11. Give an example of a plant and an animal organ.
12. Discuss the organization of your body from protoplasm on up to systems.

APPLYING FACTS AND PRINCIPLES

1. Why is it almost impossible to make an accurate chemical analysis of protoplasm?
2. In what sense is a cell a unit of protoplasm?
3. Explain how the various parts of a cell protoplast illustrate specialization and division of labor of protoplasm.
4. Distinguish between unicellular, colonial, and multicellular organisms.
5. Discuss the importance and significance of highly specialized cells in the make-up of your body.
6. The more specialized a cell becomes, the more it must depend on other cells. Explain.

CHAPTER 4

The Functional Basis of Life

W E cannot separate the structure and composition of protoplasm from its activity or functions. If protoplasm ceases activity, it is no longer protoplasm. Life is the combined activities of protoplasm. Thus, protoplasm is both the physical and the functional basis of life.

There are various ways of separating the activities of protoplasm into life processes. We shall discuss ten such processes. Remember, however, that many of these processes are interrelated. All occur simultaneously in a living cell and each one is but a part of the total activity of protoplasm.

Life activities of protoplasm. In order to simplify the study of activities of protoplasm, we shall refer to ten **life functions** performed by living cells as follows:

(1) Supplying of foods; (2) digestion; (3) absorption; (4) respiration; (5) assimilation; (6) excretion; (7) motion; (8) secretion; (9) sensitivity; and (10) reproduction.

Nutritional processes. Several of the life functions are involved in maintaining active protoplasm. These include the supplying of food, digestion, absorption, respiration, assimilation, and excretion. These *nutritional processes* supply energy to support life, they provide the substances used in forming protoplasm, and they accomplish the elimination of waste products from the other activities.

Several vital *chemical processes* are also involved in maintaining active protoplasm. The sum total of these essential processes is called **metabolism** (meh-*tab*-oh-lizm). Some of these processes are chemically destructive — they break down certain body substances, thereby releasing the energy which supports life activity. We refer to this part of metabolism as **catabolism** (kuh-*tab*-oh-lizm). Other chemical processes use foods in building up protoplasm and other substances necessary for life. We call these constructive processes **anabolism** (uh-*nab*-oh-lizm).

Living food factories. All living organisms fall into one of two nutritional groups. Some of them are capable of organizing their own foods during chemical activities of their cells. We refer to these organisms as **nutritionally independent.** Green plants have this property. Other organisms, including nongreen plants as well as animals, lack this food-organizing property and are **nutritionally dependent.** Nutritional dependence introduces an immediate biological problem. Dependent plants and animals can exist only because independent plants produce their foods. Being dependent organisms ourselves, you can see why we are totally dependent on the plants we use as food, directly or indirectly.

The green plant holds the key to the living world because it is the food producer. The soil yields *water* to the green plant. The air supplies *carbon dioxide,* the same gas you exhale from your lungs. These, however, are not foods and protoplasm cannot use them. But inside cer-

U. S. Dept. of Agriculture

Fig. 4-2.   These bracket fungi are parasitic plants, dependent on their host, the tree, for their food supply.

Fig. 4-1.   The green plant is the food producer for the living world.   Here wheat is being harvested for use in making bread, the " staff of life."

International Harvester

tain plant cells are chloroplasts. These chloroplasts contain the green pigment, *chlorophyll.* These cells are the food factories of the green plant. Inside and around these green chloroplasts the substances which compose water and carbon dioxide are rearranged chemically to form *sugar.* This chemical change requires certain protein substances, formed in the protoplasm, known as **enzymes** (*en*-zyms). Enzymes act as **catalysts** (*kat*-uh-lists) in causing many chemical changes to take place in living organisms. During the formation of sugar, chloroplasts absorb energy from the sun and store it in the sugar. This cell activity, the food-making process of green plants, is known as **photosynthesis** (foh-toh-*sin*-theh-sis).

Protoplasm " runs on sunshine " with sugar as fuel. The original sugar produced during photosynthesis may be converted to starch. During still further chemical changes, fats and oils may be formed. While these foods supply the energy requirements, they are only part of the substance necessary to form protoplasm. Remember that proteins constitute nearly half of the solid ingredients of protoplasm. Where does the protein come from? We look to the plant for this, too. In producing protein, the plant adds substances taken from soil minerals to the materials present in sugar. You can see why the living world is dependent on the green plant for its existence. We shall discuss photosynthesis and other chemical processes of the green plant more fully in Chapter 17.

Food-getting among dependent organisms. In some animals, food is taken directly into the cells. In most animals, however, there is an entire digestive system involved not only in the receiving of food but in the chemical preparation of the food for cell use as well.

Many nongreen plants are in the same predicament as animals in that they must take food from a plant or animal source. Most of these dependent plants belong to the group known as **fungi** (*fun*-jy). Among these are such numerous and familiar plants as yeasts, molds, mildews, and mushrooms.

Fungus plants would starve in an environment of soil minerals, water, and air alone. Some fungi live on dead or nonliving materials such as decaying wood and other vegetable matter, dead animals, or food materials like bread, fruits, meat, and cheese. We class these plants as **saprophytes** (*sap*-roh-fyts). **Parasites,** on the other hand, attack a living organism, or **host,** for a food supply. The parasite lives in or on the host over a period of time and causes damage or, in many cases, complete destruction of the host. The tapeworm is a good example of an animal parasite. Other parasites include disease-causing bacteria, mildews, rusts, and smuts.

Strange nutritional relationships. Sometimes two organisms assume a peculiar relationship in securing a food supply. One such relationship is known as **commensalism** (kuh-*men*-suh-lizm). In this case, one organism lives in or on another. Only one benefits, but neither is harmed. A good example is the remora (reh-*mor*-uh) and the shark. The remora is a small fish with suction cups on its upper fin. It attaches to the lower side of a shark and feeds on pieces of the shark's food. The remora thus benefits, although the shark does not. The term commensalism means " common table " or " messmates."

When two organisms live together and both benefit, we refer to the association as **symbiosis** (sim-bee-*oh*-sis). One of the

Fig. 4-3. The sea anemone at the top of this photograph has a commensal relationship with the hermit crab, which, in turn, lives in a whelk shell for protection. What do you think are the advantages to the sea anemone in this relationship?

Ewing Galloway

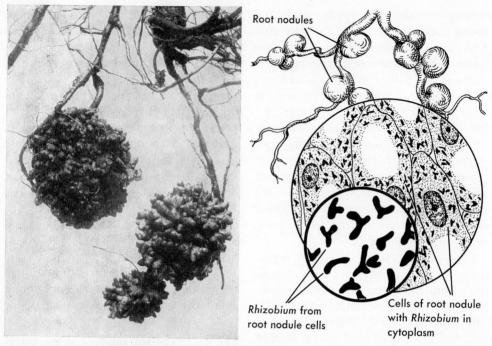

Root nodules

Rhizobium from root nodule cells

Cells of root nodule with *Rhizobium* in cytoplasm

Fig. 4-4. The nodules at the left, containing nitrogen-fixing bacteria, are found on the roots of clover and are similar to those found on other leguminous plants. The diagram at the right is a detail of the bacteria themselves (*Rhizobium*). Of what benefit are the bacteria and the clover to each other?

best examples is the relationship between certain bacteria and the roots of clover. The bacteria live in tiny swellings, or nodules, on the roots of the clover (Fig. 4-4). The root cells of the clover provide moisture and other requirements for the bacteria. The bacteria, in turn, take nitrogen from the air and combine it with oxygen, forming chemical substances called *nitrates* (*ny*-trates), which are essential to the clover and other green plants in the production of proteins.

Digestion, the preparation of food for cell use. Living protoplasm can make use of only a few simple food substances. Carbohydrate foods, which include sugars and starches, enter a cell in the form of **glucose** (*gloo*-kohs). Cells use protein foods in the form of **amino** (uh-*mee*-noh) **acids.** These are the building blocks used in forming protoplasm. Fats are used in

the form of **fatty acids** and **glycerin**. These basic foods which enter cells are quite different from the steak, potatoes, gravy, string beans, and ice cream you eat at the dinner table. Thus, we must make a distinction between the foods *consumed by an organism* and the foods *used by its cells*. We call the changing of food into proper form for cell use **digestion**.

In a plant, digestion may be the simple process of changing starch to sugar. In an animal, the process is often more complicated. In all cases, however, the chemical changes that occur during digestion require digestive enzymes as catalysts.

What is absorption? We may define **absorption** as the movement of foods and other substances into cells and internal fluids, such as blood. In Chapter 3, you learned that a cell protoplast is enclosed by a living plasma membrane. This

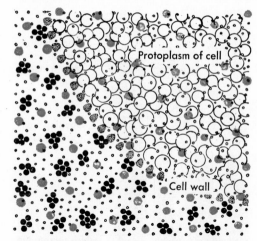

Fig. 4-5. The plasma membrane inside the cell wall is porous, but the particles of the insoluble material (*black*) are joined together in clumps too large to pass through it. The particles of the soluble materials (*green*) and the water (*white*) are small enough to pass through. The particles of protoplasm itself are large and do not leak out.

membrane is important in regulating the movement of substances into the protoplast from outside the cell.

To pass through the plasma membrane, foods, minerals, and other substances must be dissolved in water. That is, their individual particles, or *molecules,* must be spread completely through the molecules of water. A plasma membrane will allow particles of these small sizes to pass through it (Fig. 4-5).

Several forces are involved in cell absorption. Among these are *diffusion* and *osmosis* (os-*moh*-sis), but we shall leave the discussion of these important forces for Chapter 15, which deals with absorption by the root.

Respiration is the breath of life to a cell. When a plant cell produces food, energy is absorbed and is stored in the food. During **respiration,** the food is broken down chemically and the energy is set free. Some of this energy is used to maintain the life processes; some is released as heat.

Most organisms take in oxygen from the environment during respiration. This oxygen combines with food during a destructive chemical process known as **oxidation** (ok-sih-*day*-shun) (Fig. 4-6). Energy, stored in the food, is set free. Water and carbon dioxide are waste products of the process. We refer to organisms which use free oxygen in respiration as **aerobic** (air-*oh*-bik).

Yeasts and certain bacteria release energy from food in the absence of free oxygen. The foods, in this case, are broken down by other chemical processes. We refer to this type of respiration as **anaerobic** (an-air-*oh*-bik).

Assimilation is the organization of protoplasm. Active protoplasm renews itself continually by means of the process called **assimilation** (uh-sim-ih-*lay*-shun). This process is part of the constructive phase of metabolism. During assimilation, amino acids, absorbed into the protoplasm, are organized into more complex protein substances. These, together with water, glucose, fats and fatty acids, minerals, and other ingredients are organized into protoplasm. Assimilation often

Fig. 4-6. During aerobic respiration, the oxygen absorbed by a cell is used in the oxidation of sugar. Some of the energy released during oxidation is used to support the life processes; some is discharged as heat. The carbon dioxide and water formed leave the cell as waste products.

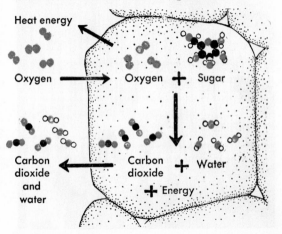

Heat energy

Oxygen → Oxygen + Sugar

Carbon dioxide and water ← Carbon dioxide + Water
                                        + Energy

results in *growth* of the cell and, as additional cells are formed, in growth of the organism.

Excretion is the removal of cell waste materials. The various chemical processes associated with cell metabolism leave waste products which accumulate in the protoplasm. These may be poisonous to the protoplasm and may interfere with normal cell activities. The cell discharges these waste products continually during **excretion** (eks-*kree*-shun).

Unicellular organisms and simple animals, like the sponge, discharge their cell wastes directly into the surrounding water. However, when many millions of cells form a single organism, like your body, the removal of waste becomes a complicated process. Each cell discharges wastes into a fluid which washes the cell. This fluid enters the blood stream. The blood, in turn, delivers

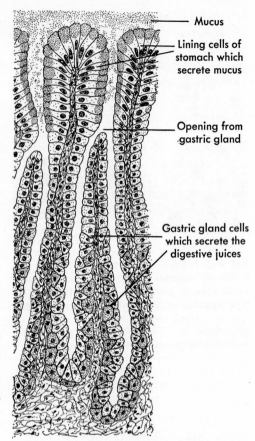

Fig. 4-8. Gastric glands, located in the stomach wall, secrete a digestive fluid that acts on certain foods. These foods are thus made soluble and can later be absorbed into the blood stream for distribution.

Fig. 4-7. The growth of these stalactites occurs as limestone is deposited by dripping water. Living things, on the other hand, grow as new protoplasm forms within the cells.

Luray Caverns

wastes to the kidneys, the lungs, and the skin for elimination from the body.

Secretion is the formation of essential chemical substances by protoplasm. In a sense, every living cell is a tiny chemical factory. It forms chemical substances essential to the life of the cell in the process called **secretion** (see-*kree*-shun).

Among the secretions of cells are the *digestive fluids*. These contain the enzymes necessary for chemical changes in foods. The cells of simple organisms, living independently of other cells, secrete all their own digestive fluids and other necessary chemical substances. In animals having highly specialized organs, certain tissues become specialized in performing this process. These specialized tissues line the digestive system, secreting into the various organs large amounts of digestive fluids and **mucus** (*myou*-kus), a lubricating secretion (Fig. 4-8).

Highly specialized cells in the glands of higher animals secrete powerful chemical substances known as **hormones** (*hor-mohns*). These secretions influence the activity of cells in many parts of the body.

Motion is a basic property of protoplasm. Some of the energy released from food during respiration is used in motion of the cytoplasm in a cell. This movement of cytoplasm is referred to as **streaming.** In a plant cell with a rigid wall, the cytoplasm streams in a circular course around and around the cell. In certain unicellular animals, the streaming cytoplasm pushes against the flexible membrane, causing a bulge in the cell in the direction in which the cytoplasm is moving. As cytoplasm flows into the bulge, the cell moves along, too. The ameba, which we shall study in Chapter 20, exhibits protoplasmic streaming.

Many one-celled organisms have short threadlike projections of cytoplasm called **cilia** (*sil*-ee-uh), which lash back and forth like tiny oars. Still others have long whiplike strands of cytoplasm called **flagella** (fluh-*jel*-uh) [sing. *flagellum* (fluh-*jel*-um)] which propel them through the water (Fig. 4-9). We speak of movement of an organism from one place to another as **locomotion.**

Muscle cells are specialists in motion. Groups of muscle cells accomplish such complicated movements as walking or flying. These cells have the power of shortening, or **contracting.** A single cell contracts only a slight amount (Fig. 4-10). But when many thousands of cells contract in a single muscle, an arm may bend or a leg may move.

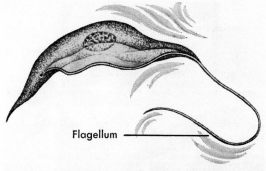

Fig. 4-9. **Some one-celled organisms have a whiplike strand of cytoplasm called a flagellum to propel them through water.**

Contraction of heart muscle cells pumps a flow of blood through the vessels. This contraction accomplishes circulation. Layers of muscle cells in the walls of digestive organs cause a churning action which moves food along. Muscle cells change the diameter of artery walls and raise or lower blood pressure.

Sensitivity is the response of protoplasm to its surroundings. One of the most remarkable properties of protoplasm is its responsive nature, an activity we refer to as **irritability.** This function of protoplasm is easy to observe, but difficult, if not impossible, to explain.

Fig. 4-10. **When muscles contract, movement results. The shortening of the cells is the result of chemical reactions occurring in the cytoplasm of each cell. What are some of the movements that groups of muscles can accomplish?**

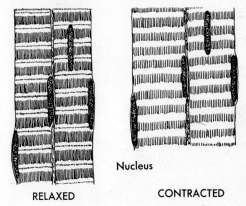

RELAXED   CONTRACTED

Hugh Spencer

Fig. 4-11. This geranium plant is bending toward the sunlight, a reaction which is but one of many tropisms a plant can exhibit.

One of the simplest responses of protoplasm is illustrated in its reaction to certain factors such as light, water, heat, a chemical substance, or an object. Any of these may serve as the *stimulus* in the environment. The *response* in a plant cell may be a change in the rate or direction of growth. Such growth responses may cause a stem to bend toward light or a root to grow toward water. Animal cells capable of locomotion may make a more rapid response by moving *toward* or *away from* the stimulus. Each of the characteristic responses of protoplasm to a stimulus is called a **tropism** (*troh*-pizm).

As organisms increase in complexity, sensitivity is carried to higher and higher levels. Consider your marvelous nervous system — your sense organs, brain, spinal cord, and nerves which extend to and from every part of your body. Consider that you can read and understand this sentence. Then you may realize what protoplasm can accomplish when cells become specialists in sensitivity.

Reproduction and the formation of new cells and organisms. Active protoplasm is constantly assimilating necessary substances. Thus existing protoplasm is repaired and replaced and, in addition, the amount of protoplasm in a cell increases. This increase results in growth of the cell. Is there a limit to this cell growth? Can a cell increase its protoplasm indefinitely? You know, of course, that there must be a limit to the size a cell may become. Yet, active protoplasm always assimilates more protoplasm. This problem is solved by **cell division.** First, we shall consider why it happens; then, how it happens.

As a cell grows, its mass of protoplasm increases. But the volume of protoplasm increases more in proportion than the exposed surface increases, creating a serious problem. The protoplast must receive a continuous supply of oxygen and nourish-

Fig. 4-12. During reproduction, the nucleus divides and each cell forms two new cells.

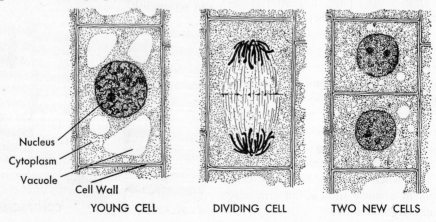

Nucleus
Cytoplasm
Vacuole
Cell Wall

YOUNG CELL   DIVIDING CELL   TWO NEW CELLS

Fig. 4-13. **Some organisms, such as the mold shown above, reproduce asexually by means of spores. These spores leave the parent plant and travel to new locations.**

ment and must pour out its metabolic wastes through the surface membrane. Thus, the volume-surface relationship of a cell is critical.

When a cell is cut into two approximately equal parts, two protoplasts half the size of the original one result. The newly-formed wall adds a surface between them, and allows both protoplasts to continue growth. It is possible to increase the surface area of a cube without adding to its volume, by cutting it into smaller cubes. This principle applies to cell division as well.

Ordinary cell division starts with the division of the nucleus (Fig. 4-12). The chromatin, carrying the hereditary traits of the organism, divides equally so that the two new nuclei will have identical hereditary qualities. Following this, the cell is cut into two approximately equal parts by the formation of a membrane across the cell. In plant cells, this dividing structure is the middle lamella, against which both new cells add layers of a cellulose wall.

Ordinary cell division may be referred to as **mitosis** (my-*toh*-sis), although most biologists limit this process to divi-

sion of the nucleus. In the case of unicellular organisms, division of a cell results in the formation of two complete organisms. In multicellular organisms, cell division results in growth of the tissues.

Many organisms, especially plants, produce special reproductive cells which leave the parent organism and travel through the air or in the water to a new location. Here, if conditions are favorable for growth, they establish a new organism by the process of cell division. We term these reproductive cells **spores**. Since spores are neither male nor female, and do not combine with others, this type of reproduction is called **asexual**.

Plants and animals form another type of reproductive cell known as a **gamete** (*gam*-eet). These cells are either male or female. **Sperm** is a familiar name for a male gamete, and **egg** for a female gamete (Fig. 4-14). Neither a sperm nor an egg is capable of growing into a new organism until the two have combined. The union of the two is termed **fertilization**, and the fertilized egg is the **zygote** (*zy*-goht). The zygote then grows into a new organism by cell division.

Fig. 4-14. **The union of an egg (female gamete) and a sperm (male gamete) is called fertilization.**

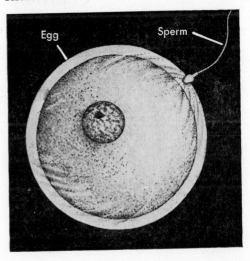

Egg   Sperm

In Conclusion

Organic life is a group of processes carried on by a living substance, protoplasm. These processes are the functional basis of life in every cell, plant or animal, simple or highly specialized. The processes of the most complex animal are really no different from those of the lowest forms of life. They are merely more highly developed.

Protoplasm is the product of a chemical environment. Its substance comes from food, and foods come from soil minerals, water, and air. This brings us to the chemical basis of life, the subject of the next chapter.

BIOLOGICALLY SPEAKING

absorption
aerobic
amino acid
anabolism
anaerobic
asexual
assimilation
catabolism
catalyst
cell division
cilia
commensalism
digestion
egg
enzyme

excretion
fatty acid
fertilization
flagellum
fungi
gamete
glucose
glycerin
hormone
host
irritability
locomotion
metabolism
mitosis
mucus

nutritional dependence
nutritional independence
oxidation
parasite
photosynthesis
respiration
saprophyte
secretion
sperm
spore
streaming
symbiosis
tropism
zygote

QUESTIONS FOR REVIEW

1. What are the nutritional processes?
2. Why are both catabolism and anabolism essential to the life of a cell?
3. In what respect are green plants nutritionally independent?
4. In what way are fungi similar to animals in their food relations?
5. Distinguish between commensalism and symbiosis. Give an example of each.
6. In what form are carbohydrates, fats, and proteins used by cells?
7. Why must all of the substances absorbed by cells be soluble in water?
8. Why is respiration necessary to protoplasm?

9. Distinguish between aerobic and anaerobic respiration.
10. What is the source of the waste products which must be excreted from a cell continuously?
11. In what way is a cell a chemical factory when it performs the process of secretion?
12. Describe streaming in a plant cell. How does it differ in an animal cell?
13. Explain how muscle cells produce movement.
14. Describe a growth response of a plant which illustrates a tropism.
15. How is a plant spore different from a gamete?

APPLYING FACTS AND PRINCIPLES

1. How do the life processes illustrate the basic similarities of living things?
2. Explain why the green plant holds the key to the living world.
3. How is the growth of a cell different from the growth of an icicle, a crystal, or other nonliving things which increase in size?
4. Discuss the relation of cell volume and surface to cell division.
5. Why does the nucleus divide before the cell in ordinary cell division?

CHAPTER 5

The Chemical Basis of Life

THE chemistry of life is a story of elements, the building blocks of matter. Just as bricks can form a walk, a wall, or a house, so do the various chemical elements compose all matter of the earth and atmosphere.

In this chapter, you will study the elements most closely associated with living things. We shall trace them from the atmosphere and the soil to the living cell. We shall follow energy changes from sunlight to the stored energy in food and then to life activity in protoplasm. These are the marvelous changes in matter and energy which transform nonliving materials into plants and animals and give them life.

The properties of matter. We define *matter* as anything which occupies space and has weight. We ordinarily think of *solids* and *liquids* as matter because we can see them and weigh them. But *gases,* such as oxygen and nitrogen, which are present in great quantities in the atmosphere, occupy space and have weight just as solids and liquids do.

Matter may be changed from one form to another. This may be a *physical change,* in which it changes form but not chemical make-up. For example, ice melts and forms water. Or if heat is applied, it can change to steam. Ice, water, vapor, and steam are, of course, the same substance in different physical forms. Similarly, iron is a solid under ordinary conditions, but the high temperature in a blast furnace can change it to a liquid.

The other kind of change is a *chemical change.* A change of this type takes place when wood burns and forms water vapor, carbon dioxide, and ashes. The heat and light given off during the change are energy which was stored in the wood before burning.

What is the Law of Conservation of Matter? If you burn a log in your fireplace, only ashes are left. These ashes are only a small part of the matter of which the log was originally composed. What happened to the rest of it? It would seem that the burning destroyed it. But you did not see the carbon dioxide and water which went up the chimney. This was part of the matter which made up the wood. If you could catch these products and add them to the ash, you would have all of the substances present in the wood. This example illustrates the **Law of Conservation of Matter,** which states that *matter can neither be created nor destroyed during* ordinary *chemical changes.*

Elements are the alphabet of matter. All the words in our language are formed from 26 letters in various combinations. When you look through a large dictionary, you realize what an enormous number of combinations may be formed from so few letters. In somewhat the same way, all matter in the world is composed of 92 basic, natural substances called **elements.** In addition to these natural elements, ten more have been produced as a result of atomic research. You may think of elements as the letters in a chemical alphabet, which spell all substances of the earth and atmosphere. The more common elements that are essential to life are listed in the table which is on pages 44 and 45.

Elements are composed of tiny units of matter called **atoms.** The largest atoms are less than one fifty-millionth of an inch in diameter. Scientists have estimated that the smallest atoms, those of hydrogen, are less than one 250-millionth of an inch in diameter. When we say that atoms are basic units of matter, we mean that *in ordinary chemical reactions,* a substance can be reduced no further than its individual atoms. Similarly, you can re-

Fig. 5-1. The 18 elements essential to life are found in the amounts listed below in a boy weighing 154 pounds.

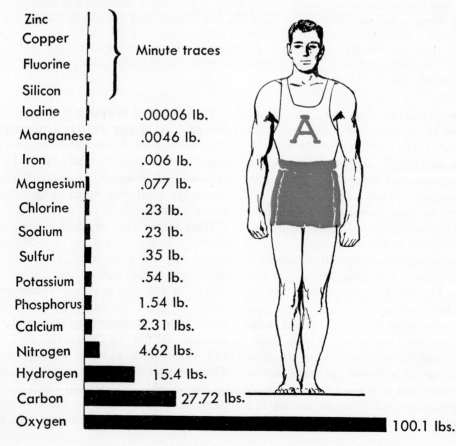

Zinc	Minute traces
Copper	
Fluorine	
Silicon	
Iodine	.00006 lb.
Manganese	.0046 lb.
Iron	.006 lb.
Magnesium	.077 lb.
Chlorine	.23 lb.
Sodium	.23 lb.
Sulfur	.35 lb.
Potassium	.54 lb.
Phosphorus	1.54 lb.
Calcium	2.31 lbs.
Nitrogen	4.62 lbs.
Hydrogen	15.4 lbs.
Carbon	27.72 lbs.
Oxygen	100.1 lbs.

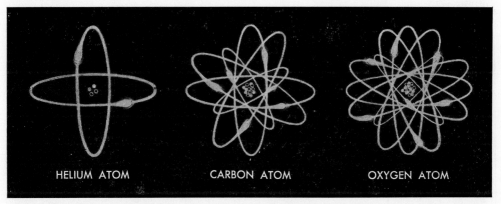

HELIUM ATOM CARBON ATOM OXYGEN ATOM

Fig. 5-2. These diagrammatic representations of atoms show the protons as white circles and the neutrons as black ones. The electrons orbit around the nucleus.

duce a word to its letters, but you can't split up the letters.

The structure of an atom. Atoms were once thought to be indivisible units of matter; that is, there were no smaller particles than atoms. Today, however, scientists know that several kinds of extremely small particles make up the atom. Furthermore, the same fundamental particles compose all atoms. The difference between oxygen, sulfur, gold, and all of the other elements is not in the kind of particles of which the atoms of the elements are composed but in the number and arrangement of these particles.

The center of an atom is a *nucleus* (do not confuse with the nucleus of a cell). The nucleus contains one or more particles with positive electrical charges which we refer to as **protons.** Extremely small particles with negative electrical charges move around the nucleus at a high rate of speed. These are **electrons.** The weight of an atom is determined by the particles in its nucleus. The area occupied by the moving electrons is its volume.

The nuclei of many atoms contain particles other than protons, known as **neutrons.** These particles weigh about the same amount as protons, but have no electrical charges. Thus, they add to the

weight of an atom but do not alter the balance between its positive protons and negative electrons (Fig. 5-2).

Many elements have varying numbers of neutrons. The weights of these atoms vary, although they are the same basic element chemically, as determined by the proton and electron make-up. These atoms with additional neutrons are referred to as **isotopes.** For example, ordinary hydrogen has one proton and one electron and is the simplest of all atoms. An isotope of hydrogen, known as *deuterium,* has a proton and a neutron in its nucleus and thus weighs twice as much as ordinary hydrogen. Another hydrogen isotope, *tritium,* has a proton and two neutrons and weighs three times as much as ordinary hydrogen (Fig. 5-3, page 46). Many atoms, especially isotopes, are unstable and give off particles as they disintegrate. We refer to such substances as being **radioactive.** Flying neutrons, alpha particles (helium nuclei), and beta particles (electrons) are highly destructive to living tissue because of chemical changes they cause in the substances forming protoplasm. We shall discuss these radiation hazards more fully in Chapter 43. Many radioactive elements are valuable in medicine and in biological research, as you will find in later chapters.

THE MORE COMMON ELEMENTS

NAME OF ELEMENT	SYM-BOL	PROPERTIES
Oxygen	O	Colorless, odorless, tasteless gas; heavier than air; will not burn, but things will burn in it
Nitrogen	N	Colorless, odorless, tasteless gas; lighter than air
Hydrogen	H	Colorless, odorless, tasteless gas; lightest element; burns in oxygen and explodes when mixed with oxygen and ignited
Carbon	C	Usually a black solid; usually inactive but burns in oxygen to form carbon dioxide or carbon monoxide
Sulfur	S	Yellow solid; burns in air and forms sulfur dioxide
Phosphorus	P	Yellow, waxy or red solid; yellow (white) phosphorus glows in dark; very active and dangerous; highly poisonous
Iron	Fe	Heavy, gray metal; often magnetic; forms iron oxide (rust)
Calcium	Ca	Gray, brittle metal; reacts with water; never found in pure form in nature
Sodium	Na	Soft, gray metal; very active and dangerous; bursts into yellow flame in water; never found in pure form in nature
Potassium	K	Soft, gray metal; very active and dangerous; bursts into violet flame in water
Iodine	I	Crystalline solid
Magnesium	Mg	Silver-white metal; slightly heavier than water; burns with hot, brilliant flame
Manganese	Mn	Grayish-white metal with slight reddish tinge; similar to iron but not magnetic
Chlorine	Cl	Greenish-yellow gas with choking odor; irritating and poisonous; 2.5 times as heavy as air
Fluorine	F	Greenish-yellow; extremely active gas
Zinc	Zn	Bluish-white, brittle metal; slightly lighter than iron
Silicon	Si	Nonmetallic element; never found in pure form
Copper	Cu	Soft, red, pliable metal; found in many poisonous compounds

ESSENTIAL TO ALL LIVING THINGS

WHERE FOUND IN NATURE	SOURCE TO LIVING THINGS	USE BY LIVING THINGS
About one-fifth of atmosphere; one-half of solid material of the earth; water	Atmosphere; water	In respiration; part of all foods; element in protoplasm
About four-fifths of atmosphere; soil minerals (nitrates)	Soil minerals (nitrates)	Part of all protein; element in protoplasm
Water; all acids; wood; coal; gas	Water	Part of all foods; element in protoplasm
Carbon dioxide in atmosphere; soil minerals; fuels	Carbon dioxide	Part of all foods; element in protoplasm
Deposits in ground; soil minerals (sulfates); as hydrogen sulfide in springs	Soil minerals (sulfates)	Part of many proteins; element in protoplasm
Soil minerals (phosphates)	Soil minerals (phosphates)	Part of many proteins; element in protoplasm, especially in nerve tissue; phosphates present in bone
Ore deposits and soil minerals	Soil minerals	Essential in plants and hemoglobin (red substance) in blood of animals
Soil minerals and rocks, such as limestone and marble	Soil minerals	As a mineral used in forming bone and teeth; essential in blood and other tissues and bone formation
Soil minerals, including table salt	Soil minerals	As a mineral, essential in blood and other tissues and bone formation
Soil minerals	Soil minerals (potash)	Essential for growth
Mineral salts, especially in sea water	Mineral salts	In production of thyroid hormone
Soil minerals and salts in sea water	Soil minerals and sea water	Trace element*
Soil minerals	Soil minerals	Trace element*
Soil minerals (table salt)	Soil minerals	Trace element* In water balance
Soil minerals (fluorides)	Soil minerals (fluorides)	Trace element* Affects tooth enamel
Soil minerals	Soil minerals	Trace element*
Soil minerals	Soil minerals	Trace element*
Soil minerals	Soil minerals	Trace element*

* Biologists are now investigating the role of trace elements in cell metabolism and enzyme action.

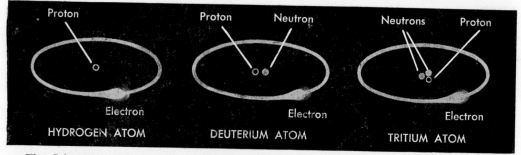

Fig. 5-3. The diagrams above represent the ordinary hydrogen atom, with no neutrons; the "heavy" hydrogen isotope (deuterium), with one neutron; and tritium, with two neutrons.

Elements unite to form compounds. When an element exists by itself, it is called a free element. For example, free oxygen and free nitrogen, along with traces of five other gaseous elements, form the atmosphere. In addition, carbon dioxide is present in varying amounts. This gas contains two elements, *carbon* and *oxygen*. As shown in Fig. 5-5, these elements are combined chemically to form a **compound.**

Fig. 5-4. The medical scientist shown below is pouring a radioactive isotope of chlorine, chlorine-38, to be later administered to a patient. Notice his protective clothing, the small meter, and the shielding bricks.

Brookhaven National Laboratory

Compounds are composed of tiny units called **molecules.** The chemist refers to a molecule of carbon dioxide as CO_2. The expression CO_2 is a chemical **formula.** It shows that a single molecule of carbon dioxide is composed of the atomic particles provided by a carbon atom and two oxygen atoms.

You can produce carbon dioxide by burning pure carbon in the air. The chemist would show the chemical change which takes place by the following equation:

$$C + O_2 \rightarrow CO_2$$

In a chemical equation, the substances on the left of the arrow change form and become the products on the right. No substance is gained during the change; nor is any lost. This is according to the Law of Conservation of Matter.

You have probably seen solid carbon dioxide as dry ice. As a gas, it is colorless, odorless, tasteless, and much heavier than air. It has none of the properties of the carbon which entered into its formation. Aside from being a gas, it has no resemblance to oxygen. Substances burn in oxygen, while carbon dioxide smothers a fire.

Furthermore, a molecule of carbon dioxide is formed only from the substance provided by one atom of carbon and two atoms of oxygen. Suppose an atom of carbon combines with only one atom of oxygen. An entirely different compound, carbon monoxide, is produced. This is the deadly gas which comes from an automobile exhaust pipe, especially when the motor is cold. It has entirely different properties from carbon dioxide.

How could you separate the carbon atom from the oxygen atoms in a molecule of carbon dioxide? This separation would require a chemical change. We can sum up the properties of a compound as follows:

1. The elements producing the compound are combined chemically.

2. A compound has its own physical and chemical properties.

3. The elements forming a compound combine in definite proportions.

4. A chemical change is necessary to split a molecule of a compound and release the elements combined to form it.

Mixtures are different from compounds. In a *mixture,* the elements or compounds forming it are combined physically, but not chemically. No new substance is produced. The mixture has the combined properties of the substances forming it. Furthermore, the substances may be mixed in any proportion. They can be separated from each other by physical means.

Air is a mixture of gases. The following gases compose air at sea level in these approximate percentages by volume: nitrogen, 78%; oxygen, 21%; rare (inert) gases including argon, helium, neon, krypton, and xenon, 1%; carbon dioxide, 0.04%. Water vapor is also present in air and varies from a small amount to 2% or more.

If air were not a mixture of gases, there would be no life on the earth. We breathe air into our lungs, dissolve part of the oxygen into the blood, and exhale the nitrogen and other gases. Aquatic animals absorb oxygen dissolved in water. They cannot make use of the oxygen

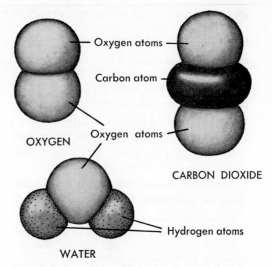

Fig. 5-5. Give the formulas for a molecule of oxygen, carbon dioxide, and water, as shown by this diagram.

combined with hydrogen that forms the water itself.

Compounds can be inorganic and organic. Long before life appeared on the earth, chemical changes were taking place. Elements and compounds were reacting with each other in a continuous change in the substances of the earth. These changes still take place. We speak of such compounds as *inorganic* because they have no relation to life. However, the chemical compounds formed by protoplasm have properties quite different from these inorganic compounds. For one thing, they are built around carbon. We speak of these compounds as *organic* because they relate to the chemical activities of living things.

Organic substances include all living matter, matter which has lived at some time, and nonliving products of plants and animals. Wood, paper, leather, and meat are easily classified as organic. Coal and oil are organic remains of plants of past ages. Other substances such as sugars, starches, fats, oils, proteins, and vitamins, while never alive, are products of living things and are organic.

We can now summarize the complex

chemical relation between inorganic compounds, living organisms, and organic compounds in these brief statements:

1. The elements contained in inorganic compounds provide the substance which is used in forming organic compounds.

2. Organic compounds form living and nonliving parts of a cell and supply the food and energy necessary for life.

Inorganic compounds which supply the elements necessary for life. Turn back

Fig. 5-6. A green plant takes in water and minerals from the soil and carbon dioxide from the air for use in making food.

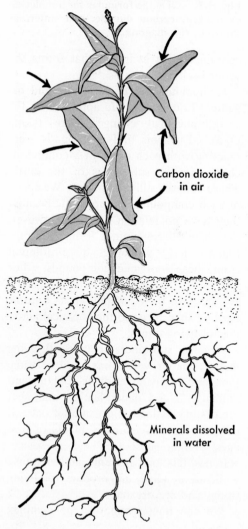

Carbon dioxide
in air

Minerals dissolved
in water

to the table of elements on pages 44–45 and re-read the column, *Source to Living Things.* Two specific inorganic compounds and one group of inorganic compounds supply the elements required by organisms. *Water* supplies both hydrogen and oxygen. Carbon and oxygen come from *carbon dioxide.* The oxygen taken from these two compounds is used in building organic compounds. Do not confuse it with the free oxygen taken from the atmosphere and used in respiration.

All other elements necessary to life come from *mineral compounds.* These may be soil minerals or minerals dissolved in water, as in the case of sea water.

Organic compounds are products of life. As we mentioned in Chapter 4, plants alone are able to produce organic compounds from inorganic substances. Animals, using these plant products, form many organic substances during chemical changes within their bodies. You will recognize many of these organic compounds as foods.

The organic compounds both plants and animals use for food are called **organic nutrients.** We group them into three classes: (1) *carbohydrates;* (2) *fats;* and (3) *proteins.* In addition, living things require vitamins and enzymes, which are complex organic compounds.

What are carbohydrates? A **carbohydrate** is an organic compound containing carbon, hydrogen, and oxygen. The hydrogen and oxygen are present in a ratio of 2:1.

Sugars and starches are examples of carbohydrates. Both are found in the leaves of green plants. The food factories of a green leaf combine the elements in carbon dioxide and water and form sugar. Starch may be formed from the sugar. Sugars may be of various types and may be changed from one form to another by various plants and animals. The more

U. S. Bureau of Home Nutrition

Fig. 5-7. Carbohydrates are energy foods that are necessary for maintaining life activities. The starchy and sweet foods above are all rich in carbohydrates.

common types include: *sucrose,* or cane sugar, from sugar cane, and beet sugar from sugar beets; *lactose,* or milk sugar, from milk; and *glucose,* or grape sugar, from fruits, and blood sugar from carbohydrate digestion.

Similarly, starches are of different types. You are familiar with cornstarch, potato starch, tapioca starch, and others. Did you know that you have a starch factory in your body? Your liver converts excess glucose to animal starch, or *glycogen* (*gly*-koh-jen). As your blood needs more sugar, the liver changes the glyco-

gen right back to glucose, which is delivered to the cells for energy release during respiration.

A third group of carbohydrates, the *celluloses,* forms the walls of plant cells. We use cellulose in everyday life as paper, wood, cotton, linen, hemp, and other plant fibers. Cellulose is highly important commercially as a source of material for plastics.

Carbohydrate foods are important to all living things as a source of the energy necessary to maintain life. Not only in plants which produce them, but also in animals which use them, carbohydrates are vital fuel foods.

What are fats? *Fats,* including oils and waxes, make up a second class of organic compounds. They are composed of carbon, hydrogen, and oxygen, but contain less oxygen than the carbohydrates.

Plant oils are often stored in seeds. Peanut oil, cottonseed oil, corn oil, soy bean oil, castor oil, and linseed oil are important commercially. Animals store food in the form of fat. A diet containing excess sugar and starch results in storage of this excess in fatty deposits. Animal fats, like butter and lard, are important items in our diets. They are highly concentrated energy foods.

What are proteins? Chemically, *proteins* are very complex compounds. They contain carbon, hydrogen, oxygen, nitrogen, and usually sulfur. Some contain phosphorus and iron as well. Carbon, hydrogen, and oxygen come from air and water and are first organized into a carbohydrate. The addition of nitrogen, sulfur, phosphorus, and iron from soil minerals is a very complex chemical process carried on by plants.

In the discussion of assimilation of protoplasm, we referred to proteins as the building blocks of living matter. No other organic compounds can replace proteins in the growth and repair of protoplasm.

Protein molecules are made up of groups of smaller molecules which are called *amino acids.* Of the more than 30 different forms of amino acids, ten are

Fig. 5-8. All the foods shown below are good sources of fat. Of what elements is fat composed?

U. S. Bureau of Home Nutrition

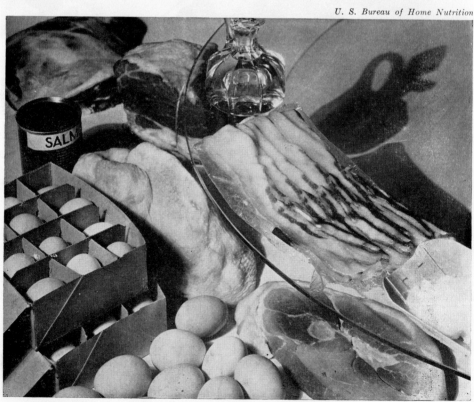

U. S. Bureau of Home Nutrition

Fig. 5-9.   The protein sources shown above are all body-building foods.   They aid in growth and repair of worn-out cells.

known to be necessary for growth and repair of protoplasm.   Proteins which have all ten of these amino acids are referred to as *complete proteins,* among which are lean meat, milk, and eggs.   Beans and wheat are other common sources of protein in our diet.

What are vitamins and enzymes? **Vitamins** and **enzymes** are necessary organic substances, though not actually foods.   Nevertheless, they are essential for normal activity in plants and animals.

Foods vary in the kind and amount of vitamins they contain.   Therefore, we must have a balanced diet to supply the vitamin needs.   Scientists knew little about vitamins until recently.   Today we know that there are many different vitamins and that each kind is essential for some phase of body activity.   We shall discuss them more fully in Chapter 35.

Enzymes are produced in both plants and animals.   They are essential in the chemical process of digestion.   Like vita-

mins, they are complex organic substances.   You will learn more about them in Chapter 36.

Energy exists in various forms.   En-ergy is often defined as *the ability to do work.*   It has no weight, nor does it occupy space.   It is closely related to matter and produces changes in matter.

We classify energy further as *kinetic* or *potential.*   **Kinetic** (kih-*net*-ik) energy is energy of motion.   When it is stored, we call it **potential** (poh-*ten*-shul) energy.

Electricity in a battery is chemical energy until you hook it up.   If it burns a light, or starts a motor, it becomes kinetic energy.   Similarly, the chemical energy stored in the food you eat is potential.   When it is changed to motion of your body and other cell activities, it becomes kinetic.   When you set a mousetrap and spring back the jaw, the trap has potential energy (energy of position) until the trap is sprung.   When it snaps closed, this energy becomes kinetic.

What is the Law of Conservation of Energy? As an illustration of the Law of Conservation of Energy, suppose we start with a steam boiler and a fuel, such as coal, oil, or gas. We ignite the fuel and start a chemical change, oxidation. Chemical energy which was stored in the fuel changes to heat and light. The heat is transferred to water in the boiler, which finally becomes steam under pressure. The steam drives a piston and gives off mechanical energy. A flywheel rotates and, in turn, drives a generator. This converts mechanical energy into electrical energy. Wires carry the electricity to a light bulb, a toaster, or a motor. The original energy in the fuel has been through many changes. Some escaped during the process, but none was lost. This is according to the **Law of Conservation of Energy,** which states that *in ordinary changes, energy is neither created nor destroyed.*

We shall deal with energy constantly in the study of biology because it makes life possible, and it is expressed through matter by the activity of that wonderful substance, protoplasm.

In Conclusion

What does it take to form life substance and to maintain its living condition? It takes the atoms that form about 18 elements, supplied in water, carbon dioxide, and mineral compounds. It takes the marvelous chemical properties that the plant world shows in the production of carbohydrates, fats, proteins, and other organic compounds. In other words, the life of an organism is made possible by the building materials which produce it, by the fuel foods which store energy, and by the other substances which regulate its life activities.

The living world is a series of chemical changes. Some of these changes balance others. Plants produce food for animals, and animals return their substances to plants. Cycles like this go on endlessly in the biological world and each one obeys the Laws of the Conservation of Matter and Energy. We shall explore some of these cycles in the next unit.

BIOLOGICALLY SPEAKING

atom	inorganic	molecule
carbohydrate	isotope	neutron
chemical change	kinetic energy	organic
compound	Law of Conservation	physical change
electron	of Energy	potential energy
element	Law of Conservation	proteins
energy	of Matter	proton
fats	matter	radioactive
formula	mixture	vitamin

QUESTIONS FOR REVIEW

1. How would you explain to a nonscientist what matter is?
2. In what three forms may matter exist?
3. Give two examples of a physical change and two of a chemical change.
4. (a) List ten essential elements. (b) Indicate whether each is obtained by living things from water, carbon dioxide, or minerals.
5. Explain the relation of elements to compounds.
6. How are organic compounds different in origin from inorganic compounds?

7. What three chemical elements are always present in a carbohydrate and a fat?
8. (a) Why do we call carbohydrates fuel foods? (b) What other class of foods yields body fuel?
9. Name three plant oils and three foods which are rich in animal fats.
10. Explain why an organism could not grow on a diet consisting of carbohydrates alone.
11. List the various forms in which energy may exist.
12. Explain the Law of Conservation of Energy.

APPLYING FACTS AND PRINCIPLES

1. Explain why the Law of Conservation of Matter does not apply to radioactive substances such as radium.
2. Farmers sometimes find that cattle don't grow and fill out properly in certain fields, even though the grasses and other plants have abundant water and seem to grow normally. Explain how this is possible in terms of what you have learned about organic foods and growth.

3. Study the properties of oxygen and nitrogen in the table of elements on pages 44 and 45. Then explain why mountain climbers are often easily exhausted at the higher altitudes.
4. Consider that a log burns to ashes in ten hours. Compare the amount of heat given off in such rapid burning with the amount of heat which would be given off over a period of ten years of gradual decomposition.

RESEARCH ON YOUR OWN

1. Prepare a report on the life and work of Aristotle. In discussing his scientific contributions, see if you can discover the attitudes, methods, and achievments which distinguish him as the Father of Biology.
2. In an encyclopedia or reference book, look up Anton Van Leeuwenhoek. Prepare a report on his life and work with early microscopes.
3. Prepare a similar report including the contributions of Hooke, Schleiden, and Schwann to biology through their work with cells.
4. The response of a root to water is greater than to gravity. Using some

bean or corn seeds and boxes of sawdust, plan an experiment to prove or disprove this hypothesis. Be sure to run a control (nonvariable factor) in your experiments.
5. Make a chart showing the life processes in one column and explain briefly in another column how a cell performs each of the processes.
6. Slice an onion lengthwise and separate the thick scale leaves. Peel the skin from the inner surface of a scale leaf and mount a small piece in a drop of water. Stain it with a drop of iodine. Draw a group of cells under low power, showing their walls and nuclei. Then

make a drawing of a single cell under high power, including all the structures you can see.

7. Using an onion cell, show the organization of a complex plant on a chart as follows: start at the bottom of the chart with a drop of protoplasm. Then show a single onion skin cell with its various specialized protoplasmic structures. Next show a group of cells composing a tissue. Above this show a sectioned onion (bulb) as a plant organ. Finally draw an entire onion plant, with its roots, underground stem (the part you sectioned), and the green tubular leaves.

8. Shave some pieces of cork into a drop of water on a microscope slide. Add a cover glass and examine them with the microscope. The following subjects are ideal for showing various cell structures and inclusions:

Elodea (*Anacharis*) *leaf.* Mount a whole leaf in water. Set the slide in bright light for a few minutes before examining it. You will find chloroplasts in the cells and may see them moving in the streaming cytoplasm.

Potato cells. Mount a very thin slice of potato in water and stain it with iodine. Many starch grains, stained blue, will be visible in the cells.

Tomato pulp. Smash a small piece of tomato pulp on a slide and add water. The cells are very large and show nuclei and small, elongated chromoplasts.

MORE ABOUT BIOLOGY

Asimov, Isaac. *Building Blocks of the Universe.* Abelard-Schuman, Ltd., New York. 1957

Asimov, Isaac. *The Chemicals of Life.* Abelard-Schuman, Ltd., New York. 1954

Beeler, Nelson F. and Branley, Franklyn M. *Experiments with a Microscope.* Thomas Y. Crowell Co., New York. 1957

Cook, James Gardon. *We Live by the Sun.* Dial Press, Inc., New York. 1957

Cooper, Elizabeth K. *Science in Your Own Backyard.* Harcourt, Brace and Co., Inc., New York. 1958

Cope, Zachary. *Florence Nightingale and the Doctors.* J. B. Lippincott Co., Philadelphia. 1958

Corrington, Julian. *Exploring with Your Microscope.* McGraw-Hill Book Co., Inc., New York. 1958

Dobell, Clifford. *Anton Van Leeuwenhoek and His Little Animals.* Russell and Russell, Inc., New York. 1958

Hardin, Garrett. *Biology: Its Human Implications.* W. H. Freeman and Co., San Francisco. 1952

Jean, F. C. *Man and His Biologic World.* Ginn and Co., Boston. 1958

Kermak, W. and Eggleston, P. *The Stuff We're Made Of.* Longmans, Green and Co., Inc., New York. 1948

Locy, William A. *Biology and Its Makers.* Henry Holt and Co., Inc., New York. 1935

Meyer, Jerome S. *The Elements: Builders of the Universe.* World Publishing Co., Cleveland. 1957

Milne, Lorus and Milne, Margery. *The Biotic World and Man.* Prentice-Hall, Inc., Englewood Cliffs, N. J. 1958

Moulton, F. *The Cell and Protoplasm.* The Science Press, Lancaster, Pa. 1940

Scientific American. *The Physics and Chemistry of Life.* Simon and Schuster, Inc., New York. 1956

Shippen, Katherine B. *Men, Microscopes, and Living Things.* Viking Press, New York. 1955

Singer, Charles. *A History of Biology.* Rev. ed. Abelard-Schuman, Ltd., New York. 1958

Stevens, Russell B. *Career Opportunities in Biology.* Row, Peterson and Co., Evanston, Ill. 1956

Winchester, A. M. *Biology and Its Relations to Mankind.* D. Van Nostrand Co., Inc., Princeton, N. J. 1958

The Relationships of Living Things

From the divine store-house comes rain to water the hills; it is Thy hand gives earth the plenty she enjoys. . . . What diversity, Lord, in Thy creatures! What wisdom has designed them all. There is nothing on earth but gives proof of Thy sovereignty. — Psalm 103:13, 23, 24

In the forests of our central and eastern states lofty oaks and maples tower above a layer of shade-loving shrubs. Farther west, grasses cover the rolling plains. Evergreen forests cling to the slopes of the Rocky Mountains. And in the far west, dense stands of redwood and Douglas fir send up their magnificent spires 150 feet or more. Sphagnum and leatherleaf thrive in the bog, and water lilies form a marginal zone in lakes. In the desert, the cactus and the yucca survive the scorching sun and parched soil. Each plant society supports its characteristic animal life.

All forms of life are similar in that they are made of protoplasm. All carry on identical processes. All face similar problems of existence. Why, then, do they live in such totally different environments?

You will find the answer in such varying conditions as the composition and texture of the soil, climatic conditions, air movement, light, and other factors. Living things maintain a critical relationship with the physical environment. And they maintain an equally critical relationship with each other.

CHAPTER 6: **BALANCE IN THE WORLD OF LIFE**
CHAPTER 7: **VITAL FACTORS OF ENVIRONMENT**
CHAPTER 8: **CLASSIFICATION OF PLANTS AND ANIMALS**

CHAPTER 6

Balance in the World of Life

WHEN the pioneer first drove his wagon through the eastern hardwood forest, wheels turned over rich, black soil which had grown trees for centuries. Overhead lofty maples, oaks, and ash towered. All about were decaying stumps and fallen trunks of forest giants. As seedlings sprang from the forest floor, they grew in the rich remains of the earlier forest. For some plants, life was just beginning. Nature was engaged in the constructive chemical processes which would yield the forest and support its many animals. For others, life had ended. Nature was reclaiming her chemical stores to build new forests and supply new generations of forest wildlife.

In the destruction of organic substance, nature has recruited other forms of life. Molds, bacteria, and other fungi are indirectly responsible for the forest. Trees cannot grow just from the remains of trees. They require water and carbon dioxide and soil minerals. They need the products of animal decay. Building up and tearing down — food manufacture and food use — growth and decay — this is the balance in the world of life.

Life is a series of processes. The processes of one organism depend on those of another. Plants are benefited by animals. Animals, in turn, are totally dependent on plants.

Life depends on constructive processes; it depends equally on destructive processes. Construction must keep up with destruction. Food is produced by living things and food is used by living things. Living things store energy and use energy. Oxygen is used up, and oxygen is given off. Throughout life, plants and animals grow through constructive processes, only to be destroyed after death by other living things.

Food is a critical need of all organisms. As you read in Chapter 2, food supplies the materials for the formation of protoplasm as well as the energy for maintaining life. To serve as a food, a substance must possess certain properties which make it usable by living protoplasm. Protoplasm alone can give it these properties. In other words, foods are the result of the constructive processes of life.

The food-producing role of the green plant is only half the story of supply and demand in nature. Remember that nature operates in cycles. Food production is a constructive process. It must be balanced by equal processes of destruction. Plants must be replenished with a constant supply of the materials which go into the making of foods. Otherwise food-making would in time exhaust those necessary supplies. At this point, all life enters into the food cycle. Not only the green plants, but all animals and dependent plants as well use up food in maintaining the life processes. The waste products excreted following this food use are, in some cases, the very things green plants need to produce more food, although some require further chemical change before the plant can re-use them.

Foods used for growth undergo further processes of construction in the formation of protoplasm. As long as the organism

56

lives, this substance is temporarily " lost " from the cycle. After death, however, bacteria and other fungus plants reduce the complex substances of the plant or animal body to simple compounds. This is the process of **decay.** Products of decay supply substances to the green plant which can be used in forming more food to supply new generations of living things.

What is a food and energy chain? Fig. 6-1 shows a situation which biologists call a **food chain.** It is repeated over and over on a farm. We start the chain with the sun and its never-ending supply of radiant energy. The corn plant absorbs this energy and locks it into molecules of sugar, which is made from carbon dioxide in the air and from water. Soil minerals, taken in by the roots, supply the elements the corn plant uses in making protein.

The ears, with their many kernels, become the storehouse for the extra foods produced by the corn plant during its growing season. Normally, this food would nourish the young corn seedlings which would sprout from the kernels the next season. But the farmer needs this food supply to fatten his cattle and hogs and to feed his poultry. He picks the ears and stores them in a corncrib. A mouse raids the crib one night and the corn carbohydrates, fats, and proteins become active mouse tissue. But not for very long. A cat sees the mouse and eats it. Now the cat has the substance which the mouse had. It also has the energy which traveled from sun to corn to mouse. We could carry the chain further if something ate the cat. However, we shall assume that the cat dies of old age. Its substance returns to the soil in simple chemical form and enriches it for use by other green plants.

In tracing this food chain, we do not end with the same amount of energy the corn plant absorbed from the sun. The corn plant used some of it in maintaining its own life activities. The mouse used still more. This use of energy by animals explains why people in crowded sections of the earth live directly on rice and other plant foods — feeding corn and other grains to cattle and hogs to produce meat is a luxury. A great deal of the food

Fig. 6-1.   Trace the energy in the body of the cat back to its original source.

substance of the grain is used up in growing the animal and maintaining its life activities.

Chemical cycles in nature. The chemical elements and compounds of the earth have been supplying plants and animals for millions and millions of years. These supplies are used over and over. During constructive processes, elements and compounds are taken from the environment and are used in forming complex organic compounds in plants and animals. Equally important destructive chemical processes break down these compounds and return them to the environment for re-use by other living things. Life would cease if any of these vital chemical supplies were exhausted. However, the cycles in nature continue; chemical substances are used and returned, and life goes on age after age.

The nitrogen cycle. The **nitrogen cycle** involves green plants and several kinds of bacteria. It may or may not involve animals. As you read about the various steps in the nitrogen cycle in the next two paragraphs, follow them in the diagram shown in Fig. 6-2 on page 59.

We shall start our study of the cycle with the green plant and the formation of protein. Its roots absorb *nitrates,* a group of soil minerals. These compounds contain nitrogen in chemical combination with oxygen and, usually, sodium or potassium. In building *proteins,* the plant adds nitrogen from nitrates to carbon, hydrogen, and oxygen which have been organized in an organic compound during photosynthesis. Sulfur and phosphorus may be added from other soil minerals. During *assimilation,* proteins are used in forming plant or animal protoplasm, which happens many times in a food chain. Protein might change from plant to rabbit to fox, or from plant to steer to you in the form of a steak or roast.

When protoplasm dies, **decay** begins. Decay is a bacterial action. Nitrogen is released from the decaying protein in combination with hydrogen as *ammonia.* We refer to this part of the nitrogen cycle as **ammonification.** Other kinds of bacteria, living in the soil, oxidize ammonia and form *nitrites,* which cannot be absorbed by plant roots. Further oxidation by still other bacteria results in nitrates, the mineral compounds from which green plants receive their necessary nitrogen. We refer to nitrate-forming bacteria as *nitrifying organisms* and to the chemical process as **nitrification.** Thus, in starting with nitrates and ending with nitrates, we have completed the nitrogen cycle.

The role of the atmosphere in the nitrogen cycle. As you probably know from your previous science courses, the atmosphere is composed of four-fifths nitrogen. Is this pure nitrogen involved in any way in the nitrogen cycle? It is, but in a roundabout way. Atmospheric nitrogen cannot be used by green plants in their chemical activities. However, two groups of bacteria can oxidize free nitrogen and form nitrites and nitrates in the soil. One of these groups lives in the soil without direct association with a host organism. The other lives on the roots of clover, alfalfa, and other legume plants in a symbiotic relationship with the host. These remarkable bacteria receive sugar from the host and use it in oxidizing free nitrogen to nitrates. The nitrates, formed within the cells of the roots of the host, can be absorbed and used in protein formation. Thus, the bacteria are of great benefit to the host plant. We refer to this most important process as **nitrogen fixation.**

When a farmer plants clover in a field in a crop rotation schedule, he knows he is building up his soil from unlimited supplies of atmospheric nitrogen. What he is actually doing is raising nitrogen-fixing

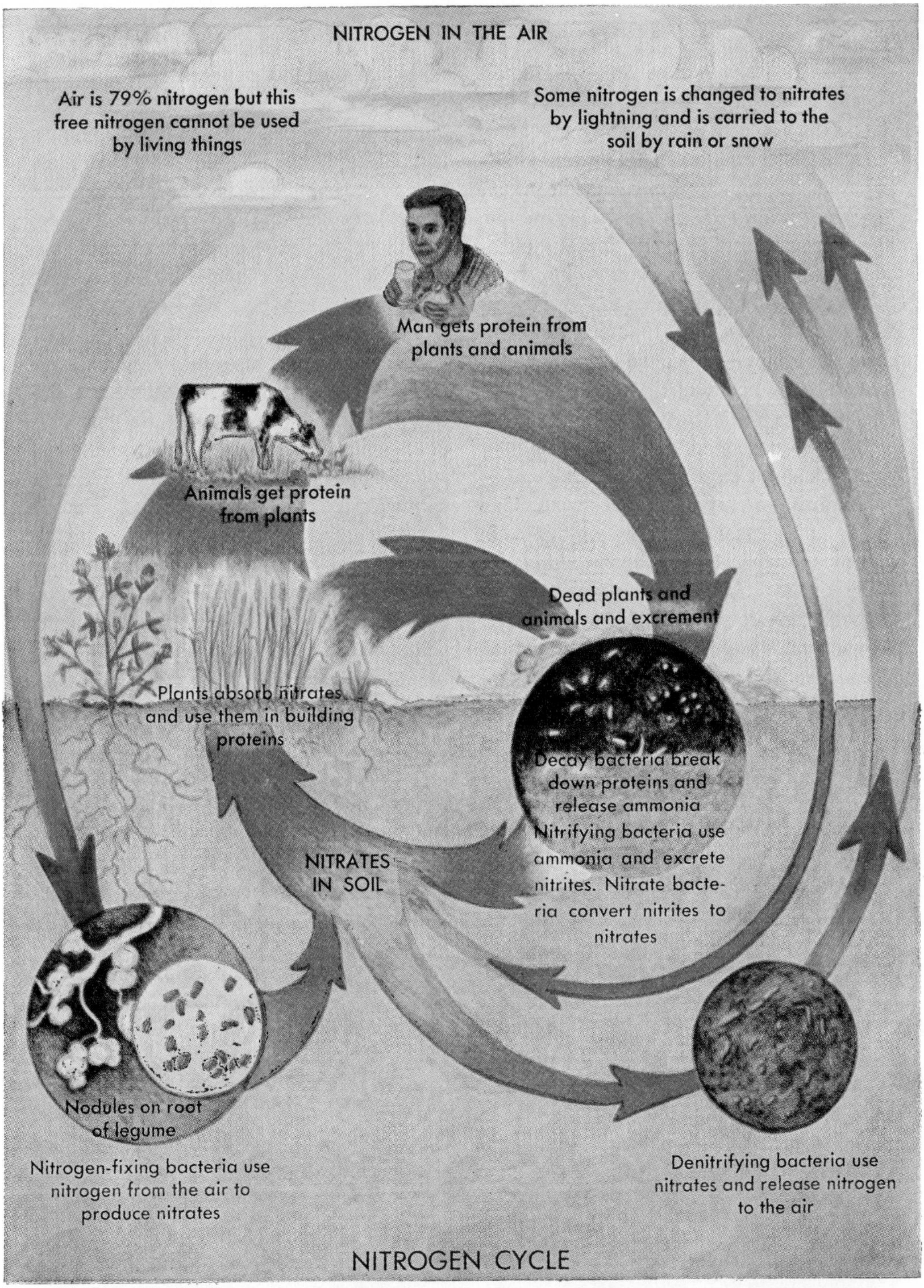

NITROGEN IN THE AIR

Air is 79% nitrogen but this free nitrogen cannot be used by living things

Some nitrogen is changed to nitrates by lightning and is carried to the soil by rain or snow

Man gets protein from plants and animals

Animals get protein from plants

Dead plants and animals and excrement

Plants absorb nitrates and use them in building proteins

Decay bacteria break down proteins and release ammonia Nitrifying bacteria use ammonia and excrete nitrites. Nitrate bacteria convert nitrites to nitrates

NITRATES IN SOIL

Nodules on root of legume

Nitrogen-fixing bacteria use nitrogen from the air to produce nitrates

Denitrifying bacteria use nitrates and release nitrogen to the air

NITROGEN CYCLE

Fig. 6-2. Follow the steps in the drawing from the point at which nitrogen-fixing bacteria use nitrogen from the atmosphere until the cycle is completed. Explain what happens during each stage of the cycle.

bacteria. He will receive the greatest benefit if he plows the clover back into the soil at the end of the growing season.

One phase of the nitrogen cycle is destructive to agriculture. Certain *denitrifying bacteria* break down ammonia, nitrites, and nitrates and liberate nitrogen. In this way, nitrogen is lost from the cycle. Biologists refer to the process as **denitrification.** Fortunately, denitrification does not occur in well-drained, cultivated soil, since denitrifying bacteria are anaerobic. They thrive in soils which are water-logged, or packed so tightly that air cannot easily penetrate.

The oxygen-carbon dioxide cycle. One of the most essential chemical cycles in nature is the **oxygen-carbon dioxide cycle** (Fig. 6-4). Green land plants absorb carbon dioxide from the atmosphere. Aquatic plants use carbon dioxide which is dissolved in water. During photosynthesis, the green plant combines carbon dioxide and water chemically and produces molecules of sugar. Light energy,

absorbed during the process, is stored in the sugar as chemical energy. Further chemical processes of plants and animals form fats, proteins, and other organic compounds, all containing carbon which came, originally, from carbon dioxide. All these chemical changes are included in the *constructive phase* of the oxygen-carbon dioxide cycle.

The *destructive phase* of the cycle involves respiration in both plants and animals, as well as the fermentation and decay processes of yeasts, bacteria, and other fungi. During aerobic respiration, sugar is broken down chemically in a change which requires oxygen. Energy is set free and is used by the living protoplasm. The organic carbon of the sugar returns to the environment as inorganic carbon in carbon dioxide. The rest of the substance remaining from the breakdown of sugar is returned to the environment as water.

The table on page 61 compares photosynthesis and respiration. The numbers

Fig. 6-3. Alfalfa is one of the leguminous plants used to build up the nitrogen content of the soil. Here the tops of the alfalfa are shown being harvested for use as fodder. The rest of the plant is plowed back into the soil.

Allis-Chalmers

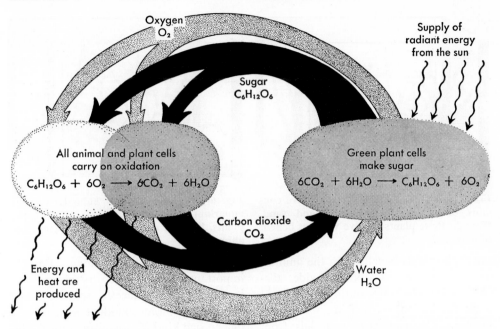

Fig. 6-4. During the oxygen-carbon dioxide cycle shown above, carbon dioxide from the air is taken in by green plants during photosynthesis. Oxygen is a by-product of photosynthesis, but it is used by both plants and animals in respiration.

of molecules involved in both chemical changes are shown. Notice that the processes are opposite chemically. Carbon dioxide and water, the chemical requirements for photosynthesis, are products of respiration. Sugar and oxygen, resulting from photosynthesis, are, in turn, requirements for respiration.

A balanced aquarium involves plants and animals. Did you ever try to keep fish in an aquarium containing nothing but water? They soon use up the dissolved oxygen and come to the surface to gulp air. Goldfish might live under this condition if you change the water frequently and supply them with prepared food.

However, game fish with a greater oxygen need could live in such an aquarium only a short time.

The food and oxygen problem is remedied by adding plants to the aquarium. Fig. 6-5 on page 62 shows an aquarium with plants alone. They can survive without any animals. A snail and fish have been added to the aquarium shown in Fig. 6-6. The plants supply oxygen needed by the animals for respiration. The snail feeds on slime containing microscopic plants and animals. Certain kinds of fish would feed on the plants; others might eat young snails. However, the fish in an aquarium this small require artificial feed-

---

PHOTOSYNTHESIS AND RESPIRATION COMPARED

Photosynthesis	$6\,CO_2 + 6\,H_2O \rightarrow C_6H_{12}O_6 + 6\,O_2$
Respiration	$C_6H_{12}O_6 + 6\,O_2 \rightarrow 6\,CO_2 + 6\,H_2O$

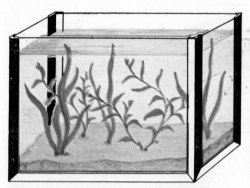

Fig. 6-5. The aquarium shown above contains only water-living plants and sand. How do these plants survive without benefit of animals?

Fig. 6-6. How do the animals in this aquarium benefit from the plants? Do the plants, in turn, derive any benefit from the animals?

ing. The plants benefit from the animals to some extent. Carbon dioxide, discharged into the water during animal and plant respiration, is used in food manufacture. Organic waste materials from the animals decay in the sand and enrich it for the plants.

A completely balanced aquarium should have more plants than animals. Some of the animals should be plant-feeders. These animals in turn are the food supply for flesh-eating animals. Most aquarists overbalance their aquaria with animals. This necessitates feeding the animals and may make an air pump necessary to supply enough oxygen.

Biological balance in nature. The chemical cycles illustrate the interrelation of the processes of plants and animals. Organisms are chemically associated with each other in a living society. Another phase of the *balance of nature* is concerned with the biological relations of living organisms. Any living community is a complex society. It is composed of many kinds of plants and animals, living together in a very close association. If you study any plant and animal society closely, you can discover countless ways in which the plants and animals depend on each other. Some of this dependence involves food supply. Other factors concern environmental conditions. Equally important is the matter of organisms holding one another in check. Some forms of life may be more abundant than others, but no one kind of organism controls the community completely. If you study the day-to-day events in such a living society, you will find out why.

Natural enemies are nature's check on living things. Let's look in on the events in an open-field society. A meadow mouse is running along a pathway through the grasses in search of seeds. By eating seeds, the mouse is reducing the next generation of grasses and other open-field plants. But since plants produce a far greater number of seeds than could possibly grow, the plant population of the community is not actually reduced. Perhaps an owl, such as the one in Fig. 6-7, swoops down and catches the mouse. The owl is one of the *natural enemies* of mice and other small mammals. We speak of it as a *predator* (*pred*-uh-ter) because it preys or feeds on other animals. Suppose there were no owls or other natural enemies of mice. Soon the mice would overrun the field. They might starve by virtue of their own numbers. This has happened many times when animals have become too numerous.

In the forest, the field, the lowland

marsh, and rocky meadows of the mountaintop — wherever life is found — there will also be found a close balance between plant and animal and between prey and predator. Natural enemies are a vital part of the balance of nature.

Civilization has upset the balance of nature. When we clear a forest, plow a field, or landscape a yard, we change what was once a natural, balanced environment. Some plants and animals adjust to the new surroundings; others cannot make the change.

For example, the crow population is probably larger today than at any time when North America was a wilderness. The crow thrives in an agricultural region. There he finds fields of grain and corncribs which he can raid. The English sparrow nests under an eave of a house and finds city life more suitable than life in the country with its competition and natural enemies. A lawn is an ideal place for a robin to find a worm. Coyotes have increased in number in the ranch country of the west. Here they add poultry and livestock to their natural diet of smaller mammals.

Whether a plant or animal benefits or suffers from the changes civilization brings depends on its ability to adapt to new conditions. Often the balance of nature is seriously upset and the more adaptable plants and animals become pests.

Austing from National Audubon Society

Fig. 6-7. The owl is a natural enemy of rodents, such as the mouse shown in this photograph.

Destruction of predatory animals can be unwise. As living things ourselves, we face the survival problem common to all life. Because we are intelligent, we understand the problem and have largely solved it. But we have strong feelings about the survival of more helpless animals.

Before we decide whether an animal is destructive and before we destroy any living thing, we should consider three points.

Fig. 6-8. The English sparrow has adapted itself so well to conditions in cities, where it is removed from such natural enemies as hawks and owls, that it has become a pest.

General Biological Supply House

1. Has the predatory animal increased in number to the point that it is destroying far too many valuable animals? A census study would be necessary to determine this.

2. What is the exact diet of the predator? Does it feed more on overpopulated, destructive animals than on those we consider valuable?

3. If the predator is greatly reduced in number, will other forms of life overpopulate the region? In past years, we have introduced birds and animals we thought were ideal for our conditions. We left their natural enemies in the native land. The animals we introduced then became pests and we had to import some of their original natural enemies. Thus the pest was kept under reasonable control.

Man has interfered with the natural cycles. Under natural conditions, all plants and animals depend on each other. Soil destruction and **erosion** (ih-*roh*-zhun), or loss of the soil by wind or water, is a tragedy of civilization. Normally, soil minerals are used by generations of plants and return to the soil with the death of each generation. Each generation adds organic matter. In this way, rich topsoil accumulates slowly through the ages.

Unfortunately, man has interfered with nature's replenishing process. We cultivate soils to grow crops and then remove the crops from the fields. Much of the phosphorus leaves the farm entirely in the bones of livestock taken to market. Later, crops prove less valuable because of lack of phosphorus and other soil minerals. Finally, we begin to pay the price in vitamin and mineral deficiency. We ultimately suffer economic loss from poor crops grown in worn-out soil. Progressive farmers restore the used minerals in the form of commercial fertilizers, animal manure, and green crops such as clover.

These green crops are plowed back into the soil. Those farmers who do not repay the soil must suffer the consequences.

Our destruction of aquatic environments has been equally disastrous. **Pollution** means that water is poisoned and unfit for most living things. It has created a serious problem in our streams and rivers. As game fish die out, the waters are left to such scavenger fish as carp. Many polluted streams no longer support even these species. Infested with mosquitoes and bacteria, they become foul-smelling open sewers — a health menace and a great discredit to the intelligence of man.

Useless cutting of forests, burning of fields, and draining of swamps and marshes have taken a heavy toll of valuable birds and other animals. Many of these are natural enemies of insects. As a result, insect pests swarm into our gardens and destroy the crops we need for food.

Conservation is our only hope of restoring the balance. Naturally, we cannot restore America to the condition in which our ancestors found it. But it is perfectly possible for us to meet the demands of civilization and still not upset the balance of nature.

We can have forests and fertile fields. We can have clear lakes and streams. We can share our natural heritage with abundant wildlife. Biologists can do this and are doing it in a tremendous program of **conservation,** or saving our natural resources.

Biology has shown us the intricate relationships between living things. It has allowed us to understand the natural cycles and realize the extent to which we have upset them. Conservation will be a constant theme in your biology course. We shall deal with the problem in greater detail in Unit 10, " Safeguarding Our National Resources."

In Conclusion

The living world maintains a natural balance by means of cycles. Plants and animals carry on constructive processes which use simple inorganic compounds supplied by the soil and atmosphere. Equally important are the destructive processes which reduce complex organic matter to simple compounds. In this form, the matter is available to future generations of plants. Thus, cycles continue age after age and living things continue to populate the earth.

Other conditions in nature have a direct and powerful influence on living things. Light, water, and temperature are critical factors in the life of plants. Plants, in turn, control the animal population. In the next chapter, we shall consider the factors of environment which make the desert, the forest, and the bog community.

BIOLOGICALLY SPEAKING

ammonification	erosion	nitrogen fixation
balance of nature	food chain	oxygen-carbon
conservation	natural enemy	dioxide cycle
decay	nitrification	pollution
denitrification	nitrogen cycle	predator

QUESTIONS FOR REVIEW

1. In what way are destructive processes, such as fermentation and decay, essential to food production by green plants?
2. What important gas is released by a green plant as a by-product of sugar formation?
3. Explain the relation between photosynthesis and respiration as chemical processes.
4. (a) For what requirements do animals depend on plants in a balanced aquarium? (b) How do the plants benefit from the animals in such an aquarium?
5. What nitrogen-containing gas is released from decaying protein?
6. What nitrogen-containing minerals are absorbed from the soil by plant roots?
7. Explain why clover or some other leguminous plant is planted to build up soil fertility in a good crop-rotation program.
8. (a) Why would an animal be called a predator? (b) Name several predatory animals.
9. Discuss three points that should be considered before destroying a predator someone thinks has become a pest.
10. Name several ways in which man has interfered with nature's replenishing process.

APPLYING FACTS AND PRINCIPLES

1. Explain why people in many parts of the world cannot afford the luxury of raising animals as a source of supply for food.

2. A farmer has a lowland field which he has fertilized heavily. Crop yield from the field has been good for several seasons. During an unusually rainy spring, the field is flooded for more than a week on several occasions. The corn crop planted later in the season has a low yield. What might have caused this sudden decrease in soil fertility?

3. Give several good arguments for the preservation of predatory animals.

4. As civilization has spread, and more and more natural environments have been destroyed, some native animals have increased while others have decreased. Account for this in terms of adaptability. Give examples of animals which have increased and some which have decreased in your region.

CHAPTER 7

Vital Factors of Environment

O UR study of life thus far has shown that living organisms are chemical products of the surroundings in which they live. These surroundings must provide, also, conditions suitable for maintaining life and carrying on all of the life activities. Living things are products of a set of complicated conditions in nature that we call **environment.**

The environment also provides the protection necessary for the survival of many organisms. It is a shelter from conditions most organisms could not endure. For the many animals which blend with their surroundings, for instance, it is a retreat from a predator in time of danger.

The study of environment as it relates to life is so important that it constitutes a major division of biology. We refer to this branch of biological science as **ecology** (ee-*kol*-uh-jee). Ecologists are at work in every region of the earth — from equatorial forest to polar outpost and from ocean depths to mountaintop — studying the all-important environmental relations of plants and animals. Any forest or field, pond, lake, or ocean tide pool can be an outdoor ecological laboratory.

Environments in nature. When you take a hike, go fishing, or drive through the country, you are undoubtedly aware of the many conditions under which plants and animals live. The conditions in a forest are totally different from those in an open field which borders it. The environment of a ravine or a valley is unlike that of a hillside or mountaintop. Some of these differences are very obvious; others are not so noticeable. Still, all have a critical influence on the plants and animals which live there.

The ecologist refers to the various conditions or influences present in an environment as *factors*. Each environment is made up of many such factors. Some of these are **physical factors** and include such influences as soil conditions, temperature, light, water, atmospheric conditions, and topography of the region. Equally important are the **biotic factors,** or the living surroundings of an organism. Whether or not a plant or animal can survive depends to a great extent on what other forms of life share the environment.

The earth offers a wide variety of conditions for life. Organisms have spread over the surface of the earth until all regions support life in some form. This wide distribution of plants and animals is the result of extreme variation in requirements for life. If all living things required similar environmental conditions, organisms would be crowded into small regions of favorable surroundings and much of the earth would be unpopulated.

Soil, a basic factor of environment. To many of us, soil is just dirt which covers the earth. But to the biologist, soil is one of the most important factors of an environment. Careful examination of soil shows that it varies greatly in different localities. The plant and animal life it supports varies accordingly.

Some soils are heavy and are composed mostly of clay, while others are loose and sandy. Certain soils are classified as *loam* (a mixture of clay, sand, and organic matter); others, as *clay loam* or *sandy loam.* Sandy soils may support a forest of pine in Michigan, New Jersey, Georgia, or east Texas. Heavy loam supports a beech and maple forest in Ohio and Indiana. Water-logged soils of bogs and swamps provide ideal conditions for larch, white cedar, and cypress forests. The rocky, shallow soils of certain mountain slopes produce luxuriant forests of redwood, yellow pine, and spruce in our western states.

Soils vary also in chemical nature. They may be **acid** (sour) or **alkaline** (sweet). Mineral content and decayed organic matter determine the fertility and richness of soil.

The character of a soil is always changing. In one place rocks are breaking down and adding to soil. This breaking-down is due to the action of weather and of chemical disintegration. In other places, the mineral content of the ground is being weakened because of the quantities of salts removed by plants through their roots. Certain soils may be building up through the decay of successive layers of vegetation, while other soils become exhausted because of heavy crop production and failure to replace the exhausted mineral supplies. Much useful farm land is ruined by bad soil care. As soils change, plants and animals must find other suitable environments.

Temperature, a controlling factor of environment. In temperate regions of the earth, including most of North America, temperature changes range from narrow

Fig. 7-1.   Pine forests can flourish in sandy soil.   One reason is because their narrow leaves reduce water loss.

Albert Towle

Fig. 7-2. Elk solve the many problems of survival during the winter months by moving from high-altitude forests to mountain valleys where the temperature is higher.

Goldman from U. S. Fish and Wildlife Service

fluctuations between those of day and night to the much more extreme differences of summer and winter temperatures.

All these temperature conditions affect plants and animals. Any organism must be able to withstand the slight variations between day and night. However, seasonal variations between winter and summer present a much greater problem.

Most trees and shrubs in temperate regions flourish through the warm weather of spring, summer, and fall. They enter a **dormant** or inactive period through the colder months. Leaves may fall and sap may move to parts of the plant which are not injured by freezing. The pine, spruce, and other evergreen trees remain green throughout the winter, even though most activity in the plant has stopped. Plants which are not woody may die to the ground, and then reappear in the spring from dormant roots or from seeds.

Animals meet the problems of seasonal temperature changes. Some animals, like the eastern cottontail rabbit, the white-tail deer, the cardinal, and the bluejay, are permanent residents in their regions. During extremely cold weather, they find protection in woods and thickets; but when snow is on the ground, securing food becomes a serious problem.

Many animals **migrate** or move to warmer regions when winter comes. We usually associate migration with birds, but some other animals also show the tendency to migrate. These seasonal journeys may cover thousands of miles. Many birds of the far north migrate into the northern regions of the United States during the winter months. Meanwhile, summer residents of these same areas have migrated into southern areas, even, in some cases, as far south as the tropics of South America.

The bighorn sheep spends its summers in the treeless meadows near the summit of the Rocky Mountains. As winter approaches, it moves down into the protection of the forests of the mountain slopes. Elk browse in the high-altitude forests of these mountains through the summer months. During the winter, the herds move to the more protected mountain valleys and the nearby plains.

Some animals which remain in a region during unfavorable periods may enter a period of *dormancy*. That is, they reduce their life activities to the minimum necessary for survival. The bear enters a period of **winter sleep.** He finds a hollow log, a cave, or some other protected location, and during the winter sleep he lives on stored fat. His body activities slow down. However, a normal body temperature is maintained and the bear can wake up and even walk around on a mild winter day.

The ground squirrel, chipmunk, woodchuck, and many reptiles and amphibians undergo true **hibernation** during cold weather. The rate of body metabolism drops greatly. Heart action and respiration decrease and the animal loses consciousness. Greatly reduced activity lowers food requirements to the minimum. An animal undergoing true hibernation cannot resume activity until the temperature of the environment increases and the body processes speed up.

During hot weather, many animals enter a period of dormancy sometimes referred to as " summer hibernation." The biological term for this is **estivation** (es-tih-*vay*-shun). A frog may estivate in the cool mud at the bottom of a pond. The box turtle often escapes the heat by burying in a pile of leaves. The period of estivation may be several days or several weeks. The gopher tortoise of the southeastern states finds protection deep in a burrow in the ground. Fish often leave the shallow water and lie in deep regions where the water is cool. The California ground squirrel sleeps in its burrow, thus reducing both its food and water needs.

Water is essential to life. Probably no environmental factor is more important to living things than the water supply. To meet their critical water needs, plants and animals range from organisms living in a complete water environment to those thriving in sun-parched deserts. All living things require water. But the way in which varied plants and animals meet this demand is always interesting to a biologist.

Oceans, lakes, streams, and ponds contain plants and animals which need a constant water environment. Those living in fresh water are called *aquatic.* Those living only in salt water are called *marine.* To the organisms in these environments, water supply is normally no problem. But their body must perform all its functions in water. Removed to land, even in the wettest surroundings, the organisms soon die.

Plants which live on land require less water than aquatic or marine forms. Rainfall is a powerful factor in controlling the lives of these **terrestrial** (ter-*res*-tree-ul), or land-living, plants.

Ecologists classify plants which grow partially submerged in water in very wet surroundings as **hydrophytes** (*hy*-droh-fytes). Among these semiaquatic plants are pond lilies, cattails, bulrushes, and cranberries. Hydrophytes have small

Fig. 7-3. **Earth has been removed to show this woodchuck, or ground hog, in the burrow in which it hibernates during the winter. How can it maintain life during this period?**

Chace from National Audubon Society

Fig. 7-4. Semiaquatic, or hydrophytic, plants need to be partially submerged in water to perform their life functions.

root systems, since water absorption is no problem. Plants which occupy neither extremely wet nor extremely dry surroundings are classified as **mesophytes** (*mez*-oh-fytes). The great variety of mesophytes of North America includes the trees of the hardwood forests of the eastern states as well as the plants of the middle western prairie states. Most of the flowers and vegetables we cultivate in our gardens are mesophytes. For the most part, mesophytes have well-developed roots and extensive leaf areas.

The driest environments are occupied by **xerophytes** (*zer*-oh-fytes). These plants have extensive root systems for absorbing water and greatly reduced leaf area to cut evaporation to the minimum. Xerophytes form the vegetation of dry plains, semideserts, and true deserts. Cacti are examples of xerophytes whose leaves are reduced to spines and which have large, thick stems for water storage.

Major climatic zones of North America. Temperature ranges in the various regions of North America divide it into **climatic zones.** We commonly refer to these as: (1) *polar;* (2) *mid-latitude;* and (3) *tropical.*

Northern Canada, Alaska, Greenland, and other land-masses of the polar regions lie in the area of polar climate. We commonly speak of these areas as the *arctic region.* We find similar climatic conditions above timber line on high mountains. Here, we refer to the region as *alpine.*

Southern Canada and most of the United States lie in the area of mid-latitude climate. This is often referred to as the *temperate region.* The tip of Florida is a *semitropical region.* Through Mexico and Central America, the semitropics gradually become *tropics.*

Within any climatic zone, plants and animals live in broad areas which the

Fig. 7-5. The lush plant growth in this meadow is all mesophytic, because the surroundings are neither extremely wet nor extremely dry.

biologist divides into **formations.** These formations of plant and animal life are based, usually, on precipitation or soil conditions. A desert formation and a forest formation may lie in the same climatic zone. The difference in plant and animal life of the two formations is mostly due to water. Precipitation, in turn, is related to elevation. For instance, high mountain ranges that run north and south usually interrupt air movement in such a way that their western slopes have a rainy climate while their eastern slopes are dry.

Plant formations of the United States. We shall take a quick imaginary trip across the United States, from the Atlantic coast to the Pacific Ocean, and examine the various plant formations.

Let's first enter the southeastern evergreen forest. This stand of pine occupies a broad belt from southern New Jersey to northern Florida and continues westward through the Gulf states to Texas. The climate is suitable for broad-leaved trees, but the sandy soil is ideal for pine. Pines have narrow leaves which reduce water loss. Sandy soil holds little water. Plants must conserve water. Thus, an adaptation to sandy soil is a reduction in leaf surface (Fig. 7-1, page 67).

Farther inland, the soil becomes richer. Here broad-leaved trees form the eastern hardwood forest. This formation was once the most extensive stand of broad-leaved trees in the world before man used them for timber. Rainfall throughout this forest ranges from about 50 inches in the east to 40 inches in the west.

West of this great forest, there was once a tall-grass prairie. Today, it is an area of rich agricultural land in the states of Illinois, Iowa, Missouri, and eastern Oklahoma, Kansas, Nebraska, South Dakota, and North Dakota. Rainfall here varies from about 40 inches in the east to 30 inches in the west. The rainfall is uneven, however. Much of it comes during the

Harvey Miller

Fig. 7-6. The greenery of this alpine meadow flourishes in the shadow of barren mountain peaks. Different types of vegetation are found at different altitudes on the sides of a high mountain.

spring, which is followed by a summer drought, interspersed with occasional showers.

The plains occupy the land west of the prairie. Plains grasses are short and are adapted to an annual rainfall of about 20 to 30 inches. Parts of Montana, Wyoming, and Colorado lie in the Great Plains. This formation has been developed into one of the principal cattle areas of the world because of the luxuriant growth of short grass.

In the Rocky Mountains, forests appear again because of the increased rainfall in the higher altitudes. Western pines, firs, and spruces make up much of the beautiful Rocky Mountain forest. They reach up the slopes to timber line, where rocky soil, high winds, and extreme cold prevent trees from growing.

From the Rocky Mountains, and extending westward to the eastern slopes of the coastal ranges, is an area which receives less than ten inches of rain a year. These lands support sagebrush and other semidesert plants in the north. In the south, they are occupied by true deserts.

Along the coastal ranges of Washington, Oregon, and California are magnificent stands of pine, spruce, redwood, and other cone-bearing trees of the Pacific coastal forest. Here, forest giants reach a height of 200 feet or more. As you may have guessed, rainfall is heavy here. Winds carrying water from the Pacific Ocean bring a rainfall of 80 inches or more. Fogs frequently blanket much of the area. If it were not for the coastal ranges, the land to the east would not be so dry. The air loses most of its water over the coastal ranges and the winds sweeping over the area to the east have lost their moisture.

Light is a critical factor in the environment of living things. Light is essential to all green plants in food-making. But we find many plants and animals living in complete absence of light. Blind fish with undeveloped eyes live in underground streams and rivers in the Mammoth Cave of Kentucky. Likewise, deep-sea fish live at depths to which light cannot penetrate. Many bacteria live without light, and are killed by long exposure to direct sunlight. Careful study of these organisms living in darkness, however, shows that they depend indirectly on light for existence. They all require food and its stored energy for their activities. This food can be traced to the green plant and its food-making processes, which are dependent on light.

Light conditions vary from place to place just as temperatures do. Deep valleys, the floor of a forest, or the north side of a hill are places where plants and animals with low light requirements can thrive. Here we find snails, toads, and salamanders as well as ferns and mosses.

Open fields, southern slopes, and other exposed places offer ideal situations for plants which need full sunlight. With these plants we find rabbits, ground hogs, coyotes, badgers, prairie dogs, ground squirrels, and many other animals living in exposed places.

The atmosphere, a factor of environment. The air about us has an important direct effect on living things. Oxygen composes about 20 per cent of the volume of the air at sea level. With the exception of certain bacteria and a few other organisms, all living things must have free oxygen for life. This oxygen may be taken directly from the atmosphere or as a dissolved gas in water.

Deep-sea life has even a greater oxygen problem. Water receives its supply of oxygen from air. Hence, the oxygen content decreases with depth. The ocean is over 35,000 feet deep in the Mindanao Deep off the Philippine Islands. Yet deep-sea fish thrive there only down to a mile below the surface.

Plants and animals which live in the soil are most abundant near the surface. The depth to which life can penetrate the soil is partly limited by food supply and certainly by oxygen supply.

Air pressure, also, has a direct influence on living things. Storms may destroy plants and drive animals to shelter. Air currents and winds have a much greater effect on life than most of us realize. Winds greatly increase the rate of evaporation of water. Plants and animals of windy plains, prairies, and mountainous regions must survive the wind. They must also survive the accompanying loss of water by evaporation. On mountains, high winds force trees to grow close to the ground and to form their branches only

Ewing Galloway

Fig. 7-7. Why do the branches of this tree grow only in one direction?

on the protected side (Fig. 7-7). The winds also cause a reduction in size of leaves and an increase in root systems.

Land formations provide varied surroundings. Changes in the physical features of the earth, or *topography* (toh-*pog*-ruh-fee), usually occur slowly, but have a great effect on living things. Wind and water carry soils from one area to another. Alternate freezing and thawing during the winter months loosen the soil, and produce cracks in the rocks. These slow processes gradually form new soil.

Such changes of the earth, though slow, are constant. As the earth changes, plants and animals must migrate to new and more favorable areas. They are then replaced by other organisms more suited to the conditions they left behind.

Life is a passing parade. Plants and animals are continually on the move.

That is, the plant population of an area changes gradually. As plants change, animals find new homes. We call this passing parade of living things *succession*.

To see how succession takes place, we shall start with a section of bare soil in an open area. It might be a region devastated by fire or an open field. We shall locate the area in the broad-leaved forest area of eastern United States, where beech and sugar-maple forests once grew over much of the land.

First, the seeds of grasses and other open-field plants alight and sprout and produce a meadow. These plants may dominate and control the region for several years. Next, the seeds of elms, cottonwood, and other sun-loving trees and shrubs find their way into the meadow, and mark the beginning of a forest. The larger plants shade the lower grasses and field plants. Thus environment changes.

It may soon become too shady even for the seedlings of the trees and shrubs. The third stage may be the arrival of seeds of oaks, ashes, and other trees which can stand more shade. These grow among the elms and cottonwoods and gradually assume control. Finally, a dense forest begins to form. The ground becomes moist and fertile, and beech and maple seedlings outdistance all other species in the race for a place in the forest. Eventually, they crowd out most other trees.

We refer to beech and maple trees as **climax plants** because they assume final control of the region. If the succession had been on a ridge, the climax species might have been oak and hickory. Short grasses are climax plants in the Great Plains.

Winds, fires, and other events in nature, as well as man's clearing, may destroy a climax species. Then, if the area is left to nature, succession starts again, but eventually the climax plants will reclaim the region.

The drama in nature goes on endlessly. Conditions in any given area are never permanent or static. Each society of plants that occupies the area alters the environment, and often makes it unsuitable for more of the same plants but favorable for other kinds which then move in. Over a period of time, these changes in plant population prepare the way for the climax vegetation.

Biotic factors of the environment. Plants and animals have an intricate relationship to each other. Much of this relationship concerns the operation of a food chain. Prey and predator occupy the same general environment. Without the prey, the predator could not survive. For example, the woodpecker seeks the forest where insects which live in and on trees are to be found. The forest also supports the squirrel where nut-bearing trees provide ample food and where trees provide

homes and avenues of escape from enemies. Animals, in turn, are a direct benefit to many plants in cross-pollinating flowers and in distributing seeds.

An interesting relationship of one plant to another is illustrated in the American beech, a climax species of the eastern hardwood forest. The beech requires a forest environment for normal growth. Often, when a forest is cleared and several stately beeches are left, perhaps in a yard, they die within a few years. The reason lies in the soil. Beech roots cannot absorb minerals unless they are associated with a particular fungus. This fungus thrives in the soil of a forest. It often dies out when the forest is gone and the land becomes an open area. As the fungus dies, the beech begins to die. Those fungi which live in a symbiotic association with the roots of trees and other higher plants are known as *mycorhiza* (my-koh-*ry*-zuh). Because of their need for these fungi, it is difficult to transplant many forest trees successfully into a yard.

Environmental protection. Many animals survive because they can hide in their surroundings. They lack their own means and methods of defense. Similarly, a predator uses concealment in hunting its prey. Many animals would perish, either as prey or predator, if removed from their usual environment.

Animal camouflage. Did you ever hear a katydid singing on a branch and trace the sound without being able to find the insect? Probably it was sitting right before you, watching you all the time. But its green wing covers blended so perfectly with the leaves around it that you could hardly see it even when you were looking for it. The blending of an animal with its surroundings is a kind of **camouflage.** Many animals owe their existence to this protection.

Animal camouflage involves several principles. Sometimes the animal is colored and marked like its surroundings. When it is, we refer to the camouflage as **protective coloration.** Nature is full of examples of this. The orange background and black stripes of the tiger blend almost perfectly with the grasses and shadows of its environment. A covey of quail crouched in a thicket go unnoticed until they become frightened and fly into the air. The common tree frog has irregular markings of brown and ashy gray which blend with the bark of a tree. The green background and black blotches of the leopard frog and the pickerel frog blend with the grass and water plants of a pond. As you can see, examples of protective coloration are very common in nature and very important to some organisms for survival. Some of the animals blend so perfectly with their surroundings that only the most careful observer is aware of them.

Fish illustrate a slightly different principle, called **countershading.** In this case, darker colors on the upper side fade into light colors on the lower side. The large-mouth black bass is a good example of countershading. The upper region of the body is greenish, and blends with colors on the bottom of a lake or stream. This bass is nearly white on the lower side, so that it blends with the reflection of sky in the water. Thus the fish is pro-

Davidson from National Audubon Society

Fig. 7-8. How does this common yellow perch illustrate the method of protection known as countershading?

tected from enemies above and below it. The effectiveness of countershading is proved when you realize how hard it is to see a fish in the water.

Protective resemblance is still another principle of animal camouflage. In this case, the animal resembles something other than itself. Several kinds of butterflies resemble brown leaves when their wings are folded. The walking stick, a relative of the grasshopper, actually looks like a stick with legs (Fig. 25-7, page 292).

Mimicry (*mim*-ih-kree) is one of the strangest of all protective resemblances. However, in this case the animal looks

Fig. 7-9. Notice the striking resemblance between the monarch (*left*) and viceroy (*right*) butterflies. What advantage do scientists think this likeness is to the viceroy?

General Biological Supply House

like another animal rather than a part of its environment. One example of mimicry is the fact that the robber fly resembles a bumblebee. This gives the fly the protection the bee has earned with its stinger. Another example of mimicry is found in two butterflies, the viceroy and the monarch (Fig. 7-9). The monarch is the common orange and black butterfly you see around milkweed plants. The viceroy looks almost like the monarch, except that it is darker orange and has black bars in its lower wings. It has been said that the monarch has a bitter flavor and, therefore, is avoided by birds. If this is the case, then the more tasty viceroy escapes because it looks so much like the monarch, which birds do not like.

Animal camouflage is one instance of adaptation. It is idle to suppose that no purpose is served by the coloration of some animals blending with that of the environment. However, the fact that animals not so adapted have perished does not account for the appearance of the coloration in those that have survived. Actually, the survival of any living organism requires the continual coordination of so many complex factors in the universe that mere chance cannot be the explanation. Of course, the survivors have not reasoned and planned so as to bring about the beneficial result. However, the fact that the survivors themselves have not planned the result does not mean that design is absent from nature.

In Conclusion

Living things are under the constant influence of both the physical and biotic factors in their environment. Soil, temperature, water, light, atmospheric conditions, and earth changes determine where a plant may grow. The plants, in turn, provide the environment for animals.

As environments change, living things change with them. The plant content of an area changes gradually toward the climax plants in a succession.

Through the ages, variations in animals have resulted in such characteristics as protective coloration, countershading, and mimicry, thus increasing their chances of survival.

In the next chapter we shall deal with similarities and differences in plants and animals which the biologist uses in classifying and naming organisms.

BIOLOGICALLY SPEAKING

acid soil	ecology	mimicry
alkaline soil	environment	physical factor
aquatic	estivation	protective coloration
biotic factor	formation	protective resemblance
camouflage	hibernation	succession
climatic zone	hydrophyte	terrestrial
climax plant	marine	topography
countershading	mesophyte	winter sleep
dormancy	migration	xerophyte

QUESTIONS FOR REVIEW

1. Distinguish between physical factors and biotic factors of an environment.
2. Explain how environmental conditions control the distribution of life.
3. List various types of soil.
4. Discuss ways organisms adjust to seasonal temperature changes. Give an example of each adjustment.
5. Distinguish between winter sleep and true hibernation.
6. Define and give an example of a hy-drophyte, a mesophyte, a xerophyte.
7. Name the climatic zones of North America.
8. What environmental factors are largely responsible for plant formations?
9. What environmental factor limits deep-sea fish to a depth of about one mile below the surface of the ocean?
10. Account for plant succession.
11. Describe several forms of animal camouflage.

APPLYING FACTS AND PRINCIPLES

1. Why is it necessary for an animal to be inactive during hibernation?
2. In hilly parts of the eastern deciduous forest, the trees growing on the south side of a slope are usually different species from those growing on the north side. Discuss reasons for this.
3. Discuss various ways in which plants bring about changes in the soils in which they grow.
4. How do plants alter their environment, thus producing the changes which are partially responsible for succession toward a climax vegetation?

CHAPTER 8

Classification of Plants and Animals

SUPPOSE someone dumped a thousand different postage stamps in a pile and asked you to arrange them in some systematic way. How would you begin? You would probably start by separating them into countries. When you had completed this, you might have 20 or so smaller piles. Then you would continue sorting the piles for each country. The next division might be into issues, or sets of stamps in use at one time. You might have ten or more issues from a single country. Within each issue, there might be stamps ranging from one to 50 cents. You would arrange them in order. Finally, you would be able to find any stamp easily.

Now then, instead of stamps, what if you had a million different living things to group and sort? You would follow the same system — large groups to smaller ones, until you would finally come to a single kind of organism.

Common names of organisms. From earliest times, living things have been given **common names** by the people who lived among them. The early pioneers found plants and animals in the North American wilderness which were quite different from those of the old country. They could not understand the long names the Indians had given many of them, so they chose names of their own. We still use many of these, such as pine, oak, sunflower, cowslip, bluebell, buffalo grass, bluegrass, cattail, rattlesnake, ground hog, and prairie dog. These common names have been handed down from generation to generation. As long as a name means a particular plant or animal to you and you remain in the community where it is used, names of this kind are satisfactory. But as you will see, common names of organisms have created many difficult problems.

Fig. 8-1. Some people call this bird a woodpecker; some call it a flicker; and others, a yellow hammer. Because of so many common names, what are the advantages of using its scientific name?

Cruickshank from National Audubon Society

Common names are confusing. No system was used in choosing common names. In many cases, various regions had their own names for the same plant or animal. Take the flicker for example, a common woodpecker of the eastern United States. Maybe you call it a yellow hammer. Others know it as the goldenwinged woodpecker or the " high-hole." It is said that this bird has over 50 different names. If it migrated to Mexico, it would have another set of names in Spanish. In Brazil, it would have still other names in Portuguese.

In some cases, a single name refers to several different plants or animals. What is a " bluebell "? Dozens of plants with blue, bell-shaped flowers are called bluebells. " Buttercup " is just as confusing. What is a " blackbird "? It is a crow, a raven, a bronzed grackle, a purple grackle, or a rusty blackbird.

Common names are misleading. The duplication of names of plants and animals is not the only problem resulting from common names. In addition, many of the names used in referring to plants and animals are misleading. They have no scientific basis and often give the wrong impression of plant and animal relationships. For example, what is a fish? If you think of a fish as a vertebrate animal with a backbone, scales, fins, and gills, you are using the name correctly and scientifically. The perch, cod, halibut, bass, and salmon are fish. But what about the silverfish? It is an insect. We call clams and oysters shellfish. And we call other animals in no way resembling a true fish crayfish, jellyfish, and starfish. We shall use these names, even in the study of biology, because they have a common meaning. However, when you learn more about these organisms you will understand why the term " fish " is misleading in referring to them.

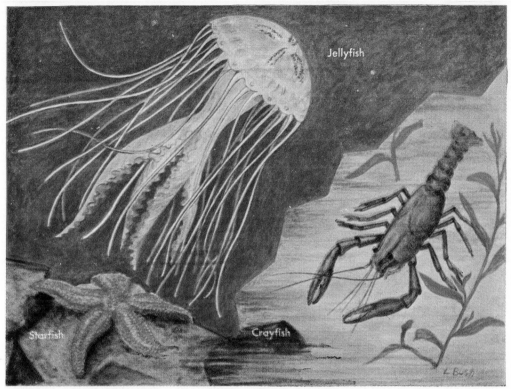

Fig. 8-2. None of the three animals shown in this drawing is actually a fish, nor are they structurally alike or even closely related.

Systems of classification. Since ancient times, various scientists have attempted to devise a system for grouping and naming living things. Aristotle probably devised the first system in ancient Greece. He divided all plants into three groups: (1) the *herbs,* with soft stems; (2) the *shrubs,* with several woody stems; and (3) the *trees,* with a single woody trunk. He divided all animals into three groups on the basis of where they lived: (1) *water-dwellers;* (2) *land-dwellers;* and (3) *air-dwellers.* No doubt, you can see why such a basis for grouping organisms, while it was a beginning, could never have served as a basis for a system of *scientific* classification.

Through the centuries, other men have attempted to devise systems of biological classification. However, it was not until the 18th century that Carolus Linnaeus (lih-*nee*-us), a Swedish botanist, devised a sound and scientifically accurate system. His system, used internationally today, was an outstanding contribution to biology, for which we honor him as the Father of Modern Classification.

Linnaeus discarded the common names of plants and gave each one a scientific name made up of Latin words. None of the names was taken from his own language or from any other modern language.

There are several reasons why Linnaeus chose Latin as the language of scientific classification. First, it is unchanging. Furthermore, many modern languages contain words taken directly from this ancient language. Latin was understood by scientists of all countries. Also, its descriptive powers are ideal in identifying the many characteristics of organisms referred to in scientific names.

Linnaeus published his list of plant names in 1753 and his list of animal names in 1758. The scientific name of each plant had as least two parts. Usually, the name referred either to some characteristic of the organism or to the person who named it. His system spread rapidly and became so popular that he used it later in naming animals. Many of his names are in use today and you can tell them by the *L.* which appears after the scientific name.

How scientific names are written. Linnaeus' system of giving each organism a scientific name of two or more parts is called **binomial nomenclature,** or "two-word naming." The first name refers to the *genus* (*jee*-nus) [pl. *genera* (*jen*-er-uh)] and always begins with a capital letter. The *species* (*spee*-sheez) name follows and usually, but not always, begins with a small letter. The genus name is usually a noun and the species name is an adjective. The placing of the genus name before the species name is regular Latin order. We use a similar system in official lists of names where John Smith appears as Smith, John.

A *genus* is a group of closely related species. A *species* is an individual or distinct kind of living thing like all others of its kind in form, and capable of producing more of the species. For example, *Pinus* is the name of the genus into which all pine trees are grouped. There are many different *species* of pine trees such as *Pinus resinosa,* the red or Norway pine, and *Pinus pungens,* the western yellow pine.

Now, we can straighten out the confusion about the flicker with its 50 or more common names. All scientists call it *Colaptes auratus* (koh-*lap*-teez or-*ay*-tus). This is its scientific name the world over and in any language. This name may seem strange to you, but it has meaning to a biologist. He knows that any other bird with the genus name, *Colaptes,* is a relative of the flicker. *Auratus* refers to yellow, a noticeable characteristic of the flicker.

Scientific names have more meaning when you see how they are used. For example, *Felis domestica* is the scientific name of the common house cat. *Felis onca* is the jaguar, *Felis pardalis* is the ocelot, *Felis concolor* is the cougar or mountain lion, while its African cousin is *Felis leo,* the real lion. You will note that each cat has a different species name. The fact that all belong to the same genus indicates close relationship.

Fig. 8-3. The house cat and the ocelot both belong to the genus *Felis*, indicating that they are very similar structurally (see also Fig. 8-4 on page 81).

American Museum of Natural History

In your biology course, you will study many organisms which have no common names. It is well to know that every kind of living thing has one scientific name known the world over. Man, by the way, is *Homo sapiens*. The species name means *wise*.

The basis of scientific naming and classification. When we say that certain plants and animals are related to each other, how do we know? Why is the cow related to the bison more closely than it is to the fox or wolf? For one thing, both the cow and bison have large molar teeth for grinding plant foods, while the fox and wolf have teeth adapted to flesh eating. Furthermore, both the cow and bison are hoofed mammals, while the fox and wolf have separate toes and claws.

All scientific classification is based on *structural similarity,* the only real basis for grouping living things. Biologists have classified all living things into groups which show structural similarity. They start with very large groups and continue dividing the groups until they arrive at a single kind or species of plant or animal. This is the principle we discussed in connection with classifying the postage stamps of the world in the preview of this chapter.

Scientific classification. If you had a specimen of each of the more than one million kinds of plants and animals known to exist and started grouping them, where would you begin? Wouldn't it be best to first divide them into plants or animals? This is where the biologist begins his classification. He separates living things into two very large **kingdoms,** plant and animal. Next, he divides each kingdom into smaller groups, known as *phyla* (*fy*-luh) [sing. *phylum* (*fy*-lum)].

Phyla are large groups. Some contain several thousand different kinds of plants or animals. Each phylum is, in turn, divided into **classes.** A class contains many **orders.** A division of an order is a *family.* A family contains related genera, and a *genus* is composed of one or more **species.** In some cases, individuals of a single species vary slightly, but not enough to be considered separate species. We refer to them as *varieties.* This adds a third part to the scientific name, in some cases.

Plant and animal phyla. The traditional, time-honored system of classification of the plant kingdom, as used in most botany books, recognizes four phyla. This system was based on general structural similarities of each group. These

Fig. 8-4. The jaguar and the lion also belong to the genus *Felis*. Look up the phylum, class, order, family, genus, and species to which these animals belong.

American Museum of Natural History

PHYLA OF THE PLANT KINGDOM (TRADITIONAL CLASSIFICATION)

PHYLUM	MEMBERS
Thallophyta (thal-*ah*-fih-tuh)	Algae, fungi, lichens
Bryophyta (bry-*ah*-fih-tuh)	Mosses, liverworts
Pteridophyta (ter-id-*ah*-fih-tuh)	Ferns, club mosses, horsetail rushes
Spermatophyta (sper-mat-*ah*-fih-tuh)	Seed plants

PHYLA OF THE PLANT KINGDOM (MODERN CLASSIFICATION)

Subkingdom Thallophyta*	
Euglenophyta (you-glen-*ah*-fih-tuh)	Euglenoid organisms (plant and animal characteristics)
Cyanophyta (sy-an-*ah*-fih-tuh)	Blue-green algae
Chlorophyta (klor-*ah*-fih-tuh)	Green algae
Chrysophyta (kry-*sah*-fih-tuh)	Golden-brown algae (diatoms)
Pyrrophyta (py-*rah*-fih-tuh)	Cryptomonads and dinoflagellates
Phaeophyta (fay-*ah*-fih-tuh)	Brown algae
Rhodophyta (roh-*dah*-fih-tuh)	Red algae
Schizomycophyta (skiz-oh-my-*kah*-fih-tuh)	Bacteria
Myxomycophyta (mik-soh-my-*kah*-fih-tuh)	Slime molds
Eumycophyta (you-my-*kah*-fih-tuh)	True fungi
Subkingdom Embryophyta	
Bryophyta (bry-*ah*-fih-tuh)	Mosses, liverworts
Tracheophyta (tray-kee-*ah*-fih-tuh)	Ferns, club mosses, horsetail rushes, seed plants (vascular plants)

* Since the lichens consist of both an alga and a fungus, they can only be classified as combinations of two of the classes in the Subkingdom Thallophyta.

ELEVEN PHYLA OF THE ANIMAL KINGDOM

Protozoa (proh-toh-*zoh*-uh)	One-celled animals
Porifera (pore-*if*-er-uh)	Sponges
Coelenterata (seh-len-ter-*ay*-tuh)	Jellyfish, sea anemones, corals
Platyhelminthes (plat-ee-hel-*min*-theez)	Flatworms (tapeworm, fluke)
Nemathelminthes (nem-uh-thel-*min*-theez)	Roundworms (hookworm, trichina, vinegar eel, "horsehair snake")
Rotifera (roh-*tif*-er-uh)	Rotifers (wheel animals)
Annelida (an-*nel*-ih-duh)	Segmented worms (earthworm, leech, sandworm)
Mollusca (mol-*us*-kuh)	Clams, oysters, snails, squids, octopuses
Echinodermata (eh-ky-noh-der-*may*-tuh)	Starfish, sea urchins
Arthropoda (ar-*throp*-uh-duh)	Crayfish, lobsters, insects, spiders, centipedes, millepedes
Chordata (kor-*day*-tuh)	Amphioxus and all the vertebrates
Vertebrata (subphylum) (ver-tuh-*bray*-tuh)	Lampreys, sharks and rays, fish, amphibians, reptiles, birds, mammals

phyla are shown in the table on page 82. In recent years, however, botanists have reclassified the plant kingdom into twelve phyla, based on more specific microscopic similarities of each group. The subkingdoms and phyla composing this system of classification are listed below the traditional phyla on page 82. In referring to the plant phyla in later chapters, we have used the traditional classification because it is still in wide use and is generally more familiar than the modern classification.

Eleven major phyla of the animal kingdom, listed in the table above, include most animals comprising this kingdom. We have also included the subphylum of the last and most advanced phylum of animals.

A more complete classification of both plants and animals appears in the Appendix. You should refer to this frequently, as it contains examples and characteristics of each group.

The classification of a grasshopper. Examine closely the grasshopper shown in Fig. 8-5, page 84. It is one of the larger shorthorn grasshoppers. Scientists call it *Schistocerca* (skis-toh-*sir*-kuh) *americana* (uh-mer-ih-*kah*-nuh). We shall follow it through the various groups from kingdom to species as shown in the table at the bottom of page 84. As we follow the grasshopper through its classification, each group we take it into becomes smaller; and with each succeeding group, the individuals making up the group become more closely related.

The kingdom, *Animalia,* includes all animals. The phylum, *Arthropoda* (ar-*throp*-uh-duh), includes only such animals

Bureau of Entomology and Plant Quarantine

Fig. 8-5. Classify this grasshopper from kingdom to species. Name some other animals that belong to the same phylum as the grasshopper.

Hufnagle from Monkmeyer

Fig. 8-6. Although cottonwood trees grow throughout the world, scientists of all nations identify them by the name *Populus deltoides*.

as the insects, spiders, crayfish, centipedes, and millepedes. All have an outer skeleton and jointed appendages such as legs. The class, *Insecta,* rules out all arthropods which are not insects. The order, *Orthoptera* (or-*thop*-ter-uh), includes only a certain group of insects with the peculiar *straight wings* found on crickets, roaches, praying mantes, and grasshoppers. The family, *Acridiidae* (ak-rih-*dy*-ih-dee), separates grasshoppers from the other straight-winged insects. The genus, *Schistocerca,* includes a small

group of closely related grasshoppers, while the species name, *americana,* is given to this one kind of grasshopper. We use only the genus and species in its scientific name.

As is done in the table at the top of page 85, we may compare the classification system to the address on a letter, listed in reverse order. Mail clerks read the address in this order when they sort it in various stations.

Problems in classification. It may surprise you to learn that the distinction be-

CLASSIFICATION OF A GRASSHOPPER

Kingdom: Animalia
Phylum: Arthropoda (jointed-foot animals)
Class: Insecta (all insects)
Order: Orthoptera (straight-winged insects)
Family: Acridiidae (locusts)
Genus: Schistocerca (cleft-tail)
Species: americana (American)

GRASSHOPPER	LETTER
KINGDOM: Animal PHYLUM: Arthropoda CLASS: Insecta ORDER: Orthoptera FAMILY: Acridiidae GENUS: Schistocerca SPECIES: americana	COUNTRY: United States STATE: Illinois CITY: Chicago STREET: Madison NUMBER: 3561 SURNAME: Smith FIRST NAME: John

tween plants and animals is not always definite. Some organisms can actually be placed in both kingdoms.

When Linnaeus devised his classification system, he said that plants have life but lack sensation and the power of locomotion. Animals, according to Linnaeus' idea, have life, sensation, and the power of locomotion.

Had Linnaeus lived today, he would know that the distinction is not that simple. Plants, as well as animals, have sensitivity, and some plants, like the bacteria, have the power of locomotion. Furthermore, some animals, such as the sponge, lack the power of locomotion.

Thus, we cannot think of the plant and animal kingdoms as parallel lines, set apart from each other. Rather, we must think of them as a **V,** as we have shown in Fig. 8-7 on page 86. At the base of the *V* are organisms such as *Euglena* (you-*glee*-nuh), to be discussed in Chapter 20. This and certain other forms of life might be classified only as living — neither distinctly plant nor animal. As we continue up the plant kingdom, the organisms be-

come more and more complex. At the top of the plant kingdom, a seed plant such as the tree is distinctly plant and is far removed from the animal kingdom. The same is true of the animal kingdom. The cow, for instance, is far removed from the tree.

Biologists agree, generally, that a plant differs from an animal in one or all of the following three characteristics:

1. The presence of chlorophyll and capability of photosynthesis.

2. The presence of cellulose in the cell walls.

3. Indeterminate growth. That is, continued growth throughout the life span, with the rate of growth regulated by environmental conditions.

An even greater problem in classification is an exact definition of a species. We defined a species on page 80 as an individual or distinct kind of living thing. But this is only a working definition because the biologist cannot always be sure when to classify two similar plants or animals as separate species and when to classify one as a variety of the other. They

WHY WE USE SCIENTIFIC NAMES

1. They are never duplicated.
2. They are used by people of all countries.
3. They are usually descriptive.
4. They show a systematic relationship to other organisms.

Fig. 8-7. The various forms of life may be thought of as forming a *V*, with the animal kingdom forming one side and the plant kingdom the other. The more complex forms branch out from the simplest form of life at the base of the *V*.

usually agree, however, on the following three general characteristics of a species:

1. A species is structurally different from all other organisms except for sexual differences (male and female), and slight variations resulting from environmental influence.

2. Members of a species can interbreed and produce offspring which are fertile and capable of further reproduction. In other words, all members of a species have the same basic genetic make-up.

3. Members of a species have come from common ancestors and will continue their species characteristics in producing their offspring.

Classification is a highly specialized branch of biology. We refer to it as **taxonomy** (taks-*on*-uh-mee). All biologists deal with classification in some phases of their work. But many work in classification almost exclusively. We call them *taxonomists*. Taxonomists are constantly searching for new forms of life, and report many new species each year. It is the job of the taxonomist to classify these new organisms properly and to give them scientific names. First, he must place each one in its proper genus. Then he must select the species name, which usually refers to a characteristic of the organism or to the person who discovered it.

Taxonomists are at work, also, in re-classifying plants and animals and in correcting errors in classification which have been retained for many years. New discoveries, especially in the field of cell study and heredity, have given the taxonomist a much more accurate basis for classifying the numerous living things of the earth.

In Conclusion

Scientific classification is one of the best examples of the close cooperation of the biologists of the world. Their nationalities, customs, and native tongues may be different, but in the realm of science, they speak the same language. Through international cooperation, most organisms of the earth have been placed in orderly groups which are based on structural characteristics.

We are now ready to start our study of groups of living things. We shall begin with the simplest plants, in which single cells compose an entire organism.

BIOLOGICALLY SPEAKING

binomial nomenclature	genus	species
class	kingdom	structural similaritv
common name	order	taxonomy
family	phylum	variety

QUESTIONS FOR REVIEW

1. Discuss several ways in which common names of organisms are confusing.
2. Give an example of a common name of a plant or animal which is misleading because it indicates an incorrect biological relationship.
3. List several reasons why Latin is an ideal language for scientific classification.
4. On what basis did Aristotle attempt to classify plants and animals?
5. Explain the binomial system of naming plants and animals.
6. List four advantages of scientific names over common names.
7. On what characteristics of an organism is its scientific classification based?
8. Name the classification groups from the largest to the smallest.
9. Why should we represent the plant and animal kingdoms as a *V* rather than as two parallel lines?
10. What do we call the specialized branch of biology which deals with the naming and classification of plants and animals?

APPLYING FACTS AND PRINCIPLES

1. Give examples to show that size, habitat, and diet similarities show no true animal relationships which could be considered in classification.
2. Make a list of plants and animals of your region which have more than one common name.
3. The fox, wolf, and coyote are different species of the dog family. On the other hand, the cocker spaniel, collie, and poodle are breeds of the domestic dog. Distinguish between a species and a breed or variety.
4. How can the principles of scientific classification be made useful in areas outside of biological study?

RESEARCH ON YOUR OWN

1. Set up a balanced aquarium in your classroom or laboratory, using various aquatic plants and animals which live in the ponds and streams of your region. The aquarium should have about an inch of thoroughly washed coarse sand in the bottom in which plants may be rooted. The sand must be coarse to allow sufficient aeration of the roots. Ideal sand for aquaria is available at aquarium supply stores. In addition to the rooted aquatic plants, include some floating varieties. Animals to be included may be small fish, tadpoles, aquatic salamanders, snails, and aquatic insects. After you add the animals, watch them closely for several days to be sure the plants are supplying enough oxygen for them. If you have a balance between plants and animals, the aquarium should need little attention for several months.
2. Make an ecological survey and analysis of life in a meter square of an open field as follows. Set stakes at the corners of a meter square and enclose the area with a string. Using a thermometer, determine the temperature at ground level and at shoulder height. Record the general weather conditions. Determine the soil type as clay, clay loam, sandy loam, etc., and the condition of the soil as wet, moist, or dry. Collect all of the animal life on the surface of the test area. This will require careful searching, especially if the area is grassy. You may need an insect net to capture some of the animals. Place the animals you find in a jar for identification. Identify all of the plants you can and tabulate the result. If the area is grassy, determine the surface area covered with grass.

Select a 25-centimeter square in only one corner of the meter square and remove the soil to a depth of 15 centimeters. Measure the soil temperature at this depth and make a note of moisture conditions. Sort through the soil carefully and remove all animal life.

Tabulate the plant and animal life on the surface of the meter square and in the soil of the 25 centimeter square. Calculate the number of organisms which would be found in the soil of the meter square to a depth of 15 centimeters, based on the result of the analyzed portion. Tabulate the number of plant and animal individuals and species found and all environmental data you can determine. If possible, repeat this investigation in several different kinds of habitats, such as a woods, a hilltop, and a lowland.
3. Prepare one or more habitats for display in the laboratory, using terraria or aquaria with glass covers. Include plants and animals which belong in the habitats you construct. Your habitats might include a desert, a bog, a tropical habitat, or a woodland. Many biological supply houses can supply the plants, animals, and soil, as well as detailed directions for making these habitats.

MORE ABOUT BIOLOGY

Allee, W. C. *Social Life of Animals.* Rev. ed. New American Library of World Literature, Inc., New York. 1958

Andrews, Roy Chapman. *Nature's Ways.* Crown Publishers, New York. 1951

Burton, Maurice. *Animals and Their Behavior.* Longmans, Green and Co., Inc., New York. 1950

Buxton, P. A. *Animal Life in Deserts.* Princeton University Press, Princeton, N. J. 1955

Carpenter, Shirley and Neurath, Marie. *Icebergs and Jungles.* Hanover House, Garden City, N. Y. 1958

Crisler, Lois. *Arctic Wild.* Harper and Brothers, New York. 1958

Dooley, Thomas A. *The Edge of Tomorrow.* Farrar, Straus, and Cudahy, Inc., New York. 1958

Doukan, Dr. Gilbert. *World Beneath the Waves.* John deGraff, Inc., New York. 1958

Editorial Staff of *Life* and Lincoln Barnett. *The World We Live In.* Simon and Schuster, Inc., New York. 1955

Errington, Paul L. *Of Men and Marshes.* The Macmillan Co., New York. 1957

Goetz, Delia. *The Arctic Tundra.* William Morrow and Co., Inc., New York. 1958

Gray, J. *How Animals Move.* Cambridge University Press, New York. 1953

Honour, Alan. *Ten Miles High, Two Deep.* Whittlesey House, Garden City, N. Y. 1957

Jacques, H. E. *Living Things and How to Know Them.* Wm. C. Brown Co., Dubuque, Iowa. 1946

Krutch, J. W. *The Great Chain of Life.* Houghton, Mifflin Co., Boston. 1957

Mason, George, F. *Animal Tails.* William Morrow and Co., Inc., New York. 1948

McClung, Robert. *Animals and Their Young.* Random House, Inc., New York. 1958

Morrow, Betty. *See Up the Mountain.* Harper and Brothers, New York. 1958

Neal, E. G. *Woodland Ecology.* Harvard University Press, Cambridge, Mass. 1958

Parker, Bertha. *Adaptations to Environment.* Row, Peterson and Co., Evanston, Ill. 1946

Rounds, Glen. *Swamp Life — An Almanac.* Prentice-Hall, Inc., Englewood Cliffs, N. J. 1957

Rounds, Glen. *Wildlife at Your Doorstep.* Prentice-Hall, Inc., Englewood Cliffs, N. J. 1958

Ruark, Robert. *The Old Man and the Boy.* Henry Holt and Co., Inc., New York. 1958

Russell, F. S. and Young, C. M. *The Seas.* Frederick Warne and Co., Inc., New York. 1958

Scott, J. *Animal Behavior.* University of Chicago Press, Chicago. 1958

Shippen, Katherine B. *Men, Microscopes, and Living Things.* Viking Press, New York. 1955

Storer, John H. *The Web of Life.* Devin-Adair Co., New York. 1953

Thompson, Stuart L. *Outdoor Rambles.* Longmans, Green and Co., Inc., New York. 1958

Vandivert, Rita. *Common Wild Animals and Their Young.* Dell Books, New York. 1958

Von Buddenbrock, Wolfgang. *The Senses.* University of Michigan Press, Ann Arbor, Mich. 1958

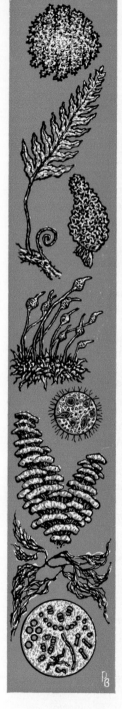

Flowerless Plants

Here are all the herbs, God told them, that seed on earth, and all the trees that carry in them the seeds of their own life, to be your food; food for all the beasts of the earth, all that flies in the air, all that creeps along the ground; here all that lives shall find its nourishment. — Genesis 1:29–31

Would it surprise you to learn that a vast number of plants have no roots, stem, or leaves and that they never bear flowers or produce seeds? In the chapters of this unit, we shall survey the plant kingdom from bacteria to ferns. You will study the oldest forms of vegetation — plants which were flourishing millions of years before the age of seed plants.

Many of the plants you will study here are simple in form. Many are extremely small and require a microscope for examination. But size and complexity are no indicators of importance. Here, among the lowly plants, are organisms which are a constant threat to our survival. Others are of tremendous economic value and even make living possible for us. All are essential, in some way or other, in the organization of our living world.

Flowerless plants have long been subjects of special interest to the biologist. What appears to be greenish pond water becomes a collection of algal cells of intricate design and unusual beauty under the high-power lens of the microscope. A bacteriologist opens a sterile culture and exposes it to the air for a few minutes. Invisible bacteria settle on the surface of a food substance in the culture. Some hours later, single cells give rise to millions of bacteria which now appear as colonies. Thus, the chapters of this unit will introduce you to large segments of the plant kingdom you probably did not know even existed.

CHAPTER 9: **ALGAE — THE SIMPLEST GREEN PLANTS**
CHAPTER 10: **BACTERIA — BENEFICIAL AND HARMFUL PLANTS**
CHAPTER 11: **THE FUNGI — WELL–KNOWN THALLOPHYTES**
CHAPTER 12: **THE MOSSES AND THE FERNS**

CHAPTER 9

Algae—The Simplest Green Plants

ALGAE have been called "the grasses of many waters." This is an appropriate name for them, for several reasons. For one thing, they are as *abundant* as grass. They flourish in rivers and streams, ponds, lakes, and in vast stretches of the oceans of the world. And they are as *important* in these environments as the grasses are on land. Algae are the principal food producers found in water environments. They are basic in the food chain which supports the life of animals that occur in ponds, lakes, rivers, and oceans.

Perhaps you have passed algae by as being merely pond scums, slime, or seaweed. You may even think of them as objectionable. But to the biologist, the algae are a source of never-ending interest.

Many scientists are searching for a more abundant food supply to meet the needs of our growing world population. If we should ever exhaust the harvests of the land, we might have to turn to the water, where algae have been feeding the life of our oceans, lakes, and streams for ages. The "grasses of many waters" await our harvesting as an almost unlimited source of wholesome and nutritious food, if and when they are needed.

What are the algae? Floating or submerged masses of threadlike green, yellowish, or brownish growth are familiar to anyone who has walked along the shore of a pond or stream or rowed across a lake in spring, summer, or early fall. There are algae of many kinds — the simplest green plants and most abundant form of vegetation in aquatic environments. Some algae cling to rocks in a rapids or waterfall or along the seacoast. Tiny one-celled forms may float in the water in such quantity that they give it a pea-soup color. Still others thrive on wet soil and even grow on the moist bark of trees.

Biologists traditionally classify the algae as **thallophytes** (*thal*-oh-fytes), plants which lack the tissues and organs of more complex plants. We relate them to the fungi and lichens by placing them in the great phylum of primitive plants, the *Thallophyta* (thal-*ah*-fih-tuh). More than 30,000 species of algae are known to the biologist and, undoubtedly, many more are yet to be discovered.

The cells of *all* algae contain chlorophyll, and carry on photosynthesis, just as higher plants do. This fact makes them vital in the nutritional relationships of aquatic and marine organisms. Water supplies the dissolved carbon dioxide necessary for photosynthesis. Light penetrates the water and furnishes the energy absorbed in the process. The oxygen released from algal cells during photosynthesis dissolves in water and becomes available for the respiration needs of the many aquatic animals living among the algae. This oxygen is as important as the

CLASSES OF ALGAE

1. CYANOPHYCEAE (sy-an-oh-*fy*-sih-ee). Blue-green algae (fresh-water and salt-water)
Examples: *Nostoc, Oscillatoria, Anabaena, Gloeocapsa*

2. CHLOROPHYCEAE (klor-oh-*fy*-sih-ee). Green algae (fresh-water, salt-water, and land)
Examples: *Protococcus, Chlorella, Spirogyra, Ulothrix, Zygnema, Vaucheria, Hydrodictyon, Oedogonium, Cladophora, Mougeotia,* desmids

3. CHRYSOPHYCEAE (kry-soh-*fy*-sih-ee). Golden-brown algae, yellow-green algae (fresh-water and salt-water)
Example: diatoms

4. PHAEOPHYCEAE (fay-oh-*fy*-sih-ee). Brown algae (salt-water)
Examples: *Fucus* and kelps

5. RHODOPHYCEAE (roh-doh-*fy*-sih-ee). Red algae (mostly salt-water)
Example: *Chondrus*

sugar, starch, oils, and other organic products of the chemical activity of algal cells.

Classification of algae. Although the cells of all algae contain chlorophyll, many of them have additional pigments which hide the chlorophyll, and make the cells appear blue-green, golden-brown, brown, or red. Biologists have used these pigments as a basis for separating the algae into various classes. You will find five classes of algae biologists recognize in their traditional classification listed in the table above. (These classes are given phylum status in the modern classification on page 82.) However, color alone cannot serve as the basis for classifying algae, since the real basis is structure. Certain of the algae classified as brown and red are green in appearance, and some blue-green algae are red in appearance because their pigments are different from typical members of their classes.

Structure and reproduction of algae. Many algae are one-celled organisms. Some float in the water or settle to the bottom, while others swim about like animals. Many algae form **colonies,** con-

sisting of two or more individual cells attached to each other. Even though they are attached to each other, all the cells in a colony of algae live independent lives. They do not depend on each other as do the cells of a leaf of a higher plant.

Many algae form threadlike colonies in which the cells are attached end to end. We refer to these linear groups of cells as **filaments.** Other algae form flat plates of cells or globular or spherical colonies. The cells of many species secrete gelatinous cell coverings which protect the cells from water loss and unfavorable environmental conditions. These gelatinous secretions make many algae slimy in texture and difficult to grasp in the water.

Many forms of reproduction are carried on among the algae. All of them carry on **fission,** or simple splitting of a cell into two parts. When a one-celled alga divides, two new organisms result. Cell division in a colonial form merely increases the size of the colony.

Colonies of algal cells are frequently broken apart by currents of water, passing fish, or animals feeding on them. We refer to this mechanical separation of cells in a colony as **fragmentation.** This breaking up of colonies merely multiplies the number of colonies, since the separated cells continue normal growth and multiplication.

Many algae reproduce asexually by forming **spores.** These spores contain a portion of the protoplast of the mother cell which formed them and each one may swim or float to a new location. There the spore may grow immediately into a new alga or may lie dormant for weeks or months. When environmental conditions are suitable it will then form a new algal cell. By means of spores, many algae spread over wide areas in a single growing season.

Gametes are sexual cells produced in many algae and function only in sexual reproduction. In some cases, both male and female gametes look alike. In others, there are structural differences which make it possible to designate one as an **egg** (female) and the other as a **sperm** (male). Gametes unite during fertilization and produce a **zygote** (*zy*-goht), which, in many algae, undergoes a rest period after which it produces spores which then give rise to new cells.

Because the cells of algae are so small, and because the behavior of the cells during reproduction is so specific, a microscope is almost a necessity in studying them. If you plan to observe living forms of algae, your microscope will reveal fascinating activities in just one drop of pond water.

Blue-green algae. The **blue-green algae** are all one-celled plants which usually form colonies. Some occur in filaments, while others consist of slimy masses of material in which the algal cells are embedded. You can find typical blue-green algae in almost every roadside ditch, in ponds, and in streams. Together with the viruses and bacteria, they are

considered to be the most primitive of plants.

Blue-green algae thrive during the hot summer months, and are a constant problem in drinking water and swimming pools. They give water the familiar " fishy " or " pigsty " odor characteristic of stagnant pools and certain streams. For this reason, biologists check the sources of public water supply regularly for blue-green alga content.

The class name, *Cyanophyceae* (sy-an-oh-*fy*-sih-ee), refers to a blue pigment, **phycocyanin** (fy-koh-*sy*-uh-nin), which, together with chlorophyll, gives these algae their characteristic blue-green color. Colors of various species range from bright blue-green to almost black. However, a few species contain a red pigment. One of these forms appears periodically in the Red Sea and gave it its name in early times.

The cells of blue-green algae are primitive and simple in structure. They lack an organized nucleus, and instead have the nuclear material scattered through the protoplast. The chlorophyll and other pigments present are diffused through the cytoplasm, especially in the region close to the wall. None of the blue-green algae reproduce sexually as do the higher algae. The usual method of reproduction is fission.

Representative blue-green algae. We have selected four common blue-green algae as representatives of this important group. One of the most curious is *Nostoc* (*nos*-tok). You will find it in mud and sand usually just at the point where the ripples from a pond or lake strike the shoreline. A *Nostoc* colony looks like a small, gelatinous ball, ranging in size from a pinhead to a marble, often likened to a peeled grape (Fig. 9-1, page 94). The ball is composed of a gelatinous **matrix.** Embedded in the matrix are many curved and twisted filaments made up of tiny

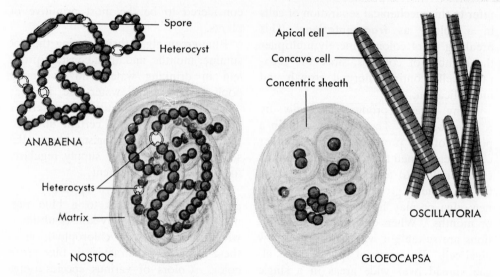

Fig. 9-1. The above diagram illustrates four common blue-green algae. What are the similarities and differences between them?

spherical cells, each of which resembles a pearl bead in a necklace. Distributed along the filaments are curious empty cells with thick walls and pores at either side where they join other cells. These are **heterocysts** (*heh*-ter-oh-sists). They enable the filaments of *Nostoc* to break into shorter pieces. *Nostoc* is, fundamentally, a one-celled plant which forms filamentous colonies surrounded by a gelatinous matrix. Each time a cell divides by fission, it forms two small cells of equal size and thus increases the length of the filament. This is the only method of reproduction in this primitive alga.

Anabaena (an-uh-*bee*-nuh) (Fig. 9-1) is a relative of *Nostoc,* as seen by the similarity in cells and filaments. However, filaments of *Anabaena* are solitary and do not occur together as the filaments of *Nostoc* do. Another difference is the production of spores in *Anabaena,* which can be recognized easily as enlarged, oval cells in the filaments. Each spore is protected by a thickened wall and contains an abundance of stored food. Each spore will, eventually, separate from the parent filament and germinate in a new location.

Gloeocapsa (glee-oh-*kap*-suh) (Fig. 9-1) is one of the most primitive blue-green algae. It can be found on wet rocks and often grows on moist flowerpots in greenhouses, where it forms a slimy, bluish-green mass. The individual cells of this one-celled alga are spherical or oval. The diffused blue and green pigments lie in a zone near the wall. Dark granules may be seen deeper in the cell. Each cell of *Gloeocapsa* secretes a slimy sheath. When a cell divides, each new cell secretes its own sheath within the old one, thus forming characteristic rings or layers of sheaths. A colony of *Gloeocapsa* often contains hundreds of cells, joined by their sheaths in a gelatinous layer.

Oscillatoria (os-il-uh-*tor*-ee-uh) is a filamentous blue-green alga composed of many narrow, disk-shaped cells resembling a stack of coins. The tip, or **apical** (*ap*-ih-kul) **cell,** is round on one side, in many species. Filaments of *Oscillatoria* sway gently back and forth in the water, a characteristic which gave the alga its name. When one cell in the filament dies, the ones on either side bulge into its place and produce a curious **concave cell** (Fig.

9-1). Concave cells are weak places in the filament and cause the plant to break into shorter pieces. *Oscillatoria* becomes abundant in ponds and streams during warm weather.

Green algae. **Green algae** vary from one-celled forms to colonial forms composed of a large number of cells. They are, for the most part, fresh-water algae, although certain members of the group live in strange and interesting environments. Many kinds live in the ocean and a few live in bodies of water even higher in salt concentration than the ocean. Some, to the amazement of scientists, thrive in hot springs. One species grows on the hair of the South American three-toed sloth and gives this animal its peculiar green appearance. Other strange environments include the bodies of one-celled animals, sponges, and jellyfish.

The cells of green algae have a definitely organized nucleus. Pigments — including chlorophyll, as well as yellow *xanthophyll* and orange *carotene* — are contained in the plastids. These pigments combine to give the algae colors ranging from grass green to yellowish-green. Green algae form sugar during photosynthesis and convert it to starch for storage on the chloroplasts. Reproduction is both by fission and by asexual spores, and some of the genera reproduce by sexual gametes.

Protococcus, a common green alga. *Protococcus* (proh-toh-*kok*-us) is one of the most common of green algae, and is an exception among algae in that it does not live in water. Most of you may not have recognized it as an alga, because it grows on the trunks of trees. You may also find it on unpainted wooden buildings and fences. During dry weather you seldom see it, but in wet weather it is very evident. It is most common on the north side of tree trunks because the bark is more moist on the shaded side.

The cells of *Protococcus* are spherical or somewhat oval (Fig. 9-2). Each contains an organized nucleus and a single, large chloroplast. The cells are so small that many thousands cover only a few square inches of bark. They may be carried from tree to tree by birds and insects as well as by the wind during dry weather. Since *Protococcus* is a green plant, it requires no nourishment from the tree on which it grows.

Reproduction in *Protococcus* is by fission only. Following divisions, the cells tend to cling together. This produces the cell groups shown in Fig. 9-2.

Chlorella (klor-*el*-uh) is a single-celled spherical alga somewhat resembling *Protococcus*. It has a large, cup-shaped chloroplast. This alga is especially interesting to the biologist because several of its species live in the cells or tissues of one-celled animals, sponges, and jellyfish. It has also been the subject for much research in the study of photosynthesis as well as in studying alga cultures as a possible source of human food.

Spirogyra, a filamentous green alga. Almost any pond or quiet pool will contain masses of threadlike *Spirogyra* (spy-roh-*jy*-ruh) during the spring and fall

Fig. 9-2. The round cells of the green alga *Protococcus* may occur singly or in colonies of two or more.

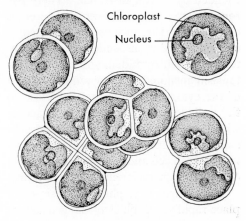

Chloroplast
Nucleus

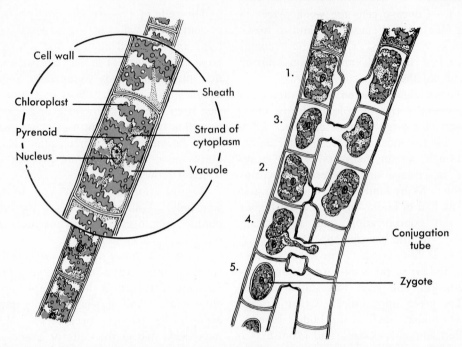

Cell wall

Chloroplast

Pyrenoid

Nucleus

Sheath

Strand of cytoplasm

Vacuole

1.

3.

2.

4.

5.

Conjugation tube

Zygote

Fig. 9-3. Left: one *Spirogyra* cell. Note the ribbonlike chloroplast. Right: conjugation in *Spirogyra*. The sequence is numbered and drawn as seen in nature.

months. The unbranched filaments of this green alga range from a few inches to a foot or more in length. Under a microscope, a thread of *Spirogyra* looks like a series of transparent cells, arranged end to end like tank cars in a train (Fig. 9-3).

Each cell has one or more spiral chloroplasts which wind from one end of the cell to the other. On the ribbonlike chloroplasts are small protein bodies surrounded by a layer of starch. These **pyrenoids** (*py*-reh-noidz) are food reserves of the cell. The nucleus is embedded in cytoplasm and is suspended near the center of the cell by radiating strands of cytoplasm anchored to the pyrenoids. Most of the cytoplasm lies in a layer close to the wall, leaving a large central vacuole which fills with water and dissolved substances. A thin, gelatinous sheath surrounds each cell and gives the filaments of *Spirogyra* a characteristic slippery feeling.

On a bright day, photosynthesis takes place rapidly. Bubbles of oxygen stream from the cells and collect among the filaments, which causes a mass of *Spirogyra* to float to the surface. During the night, the oxygen dissolves in the water and allows the mass to sink. You can see floating colonies of *Spirogyra* and other algae on the surface of a pond, especially in the afternoon of a bright day.

Spirogyra reproduces in two ways. All the cells of a filament undergo fission at certain time intervals. Since the divisions are always crosswise, fission adds to the length of the filaments.

The second method of reproduction is sexual, and occurs when weather conditions are unfavorable for normal growth by fission. We refer to this method of reproduction as **conjugation** (kon-joo-*gay*-shun). You are likely to see it in material collected early in the summer, at the close of the spring growing season, and again in the fall with the approach of cold weather.

Conjugation involves two filaments of

Spirogyra which line up parallel to each other. A small knob grows out from each cell on its inner side, as shown in Fig. 9-3. Then each knob grows until it touches the knob of the cell across from it. Soon the tips of the knobs dissolve and form a passageway between the two cells, which results in a ladderlike arrangement. The content of one cell then flows through the passageway and unites with the content of the other cell. The fused content of the two cells forms a spherical or oval mass which is soon surrounded by a thick protective wall. We refer to this structure as a **zygote.** It is interesting to note that the content of a cell in one filament moves across to the cell of the other, thus producing one filament of empty cells and another containing rows of zygotes. Biologists consider the entire content of a *Spirogyra* cell as a gamete during conjugation, and refer to the union of the two cell contents as **fertilization.**

Soon after conjugation is completed, the zygotes fall from the cells which hold them and undergo a rest period. The thick wall protects the zygote from heat, cold, and dryness. As a zygote, *Spirogyra* can survive a long, cold winter, a summer drought, or may even be transported from one pond to another by a bird or other animal. When conditions are favorable for growth again, the content of a zygote resumes activity. The nucleus divides twice, thus forming four nuclei. Three of these nuclei die. The remaining one becomes the nucleus of the new *Spirogyra* cell which grows from the zygote and establishes a new filament by successive cell divisions.

The life history of Ulothrix. *Ulothrix* (*you*-loh-thriks) is interesting to the biologist because it represents a group of green algae with somewhat different reproductive processes. You can find this alga attached to rocks in swift-flowing, shallow water. The short filaments are anchored by a special cell with fingerlike projections, known as a **holdfast.** The cells above the holdfast each have a chloroplast shaped like an open ring (Fig. 9-4).

Fig. 9-4.   The right drawing shows sexual reproduction in *Ulothrix*.   Why are the gametes called isogametes?   The left drawing illustrates the asexual reproduction that *Ulothrix* undergoes if it has ideal growth conditions.

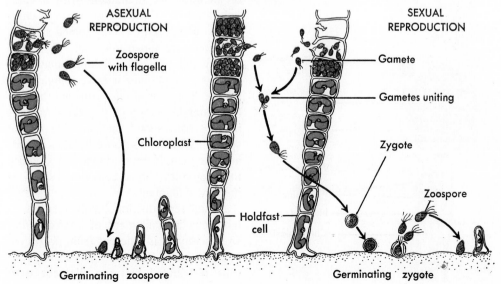

ASEXUAL REPRODUCTION

Zoospore with flagella

Chloroplast

Holdfast cell

Germinating zoospore

SEXUAL REPRODUCTION

Gamete

Gametes uniting

Zygote

Zoospore

Germinating zygote

Under ideal growth conditions, a cell of *Ulothrix* undergoes a series of nuclear divisions followed by a splitting up of the cell content into 2, 4, 8, 16, or 32 oval bodies. Each of these bodies is a new cell because it contains a nucleus and chloroplast. Each one also develops four little hairlike projections called **flagella**. We refer to these tiny cells as **zoospores** (*zoh-oh-spores*) because they resemble one-celled animals. The zoospores burst out of the encasing mother cell and their flagella whip them through the water. When a zoospore reaches a favorable place, it grows into a holdfast cell. This holdfast cell divides into two new cells of which the upper one becomes an ordinary *Ulothrix* cell. This cell then forms a filament by further cell divisions.

Fig. 9-5. This drawing illustrates how the common green alga *Oedogonium* reproduces sexually. Why are its sex cells called heterogametes?

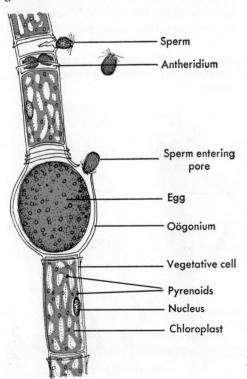

Sperm

Antheridium

Sperm entering pore

Egg

Oögonium

Vegetative cell

Pyrenoids

Nucleus

Chloroplast

At other times, *Ulothrix* cells may undergo similar nuclear divisions and separation of the cell content into 8, 16, 32, or 64 bodies which are very similar to zoospores except that they are smaller and have only two flagella. These are **gametes**, and have definite sex. These gametes leave the parent cell and swim away from the filament. If a gamete meets one of the opposite sex, from another cell, they fuse and produce a zygote. After a rest period, the zygote undergoes nuclear divisions resulting in four nuclei, as in *Spirogyra*. In *Ulothrix*, however, all the nuclei live and, with a portion of the zygote protoplast, become zoospores. Each zoospore may produce a new holdfast cell and, thus, give rise to a new filament. Since the gametes of *Ulothrix* look alike and are alike in structure, the biologist refers to them as **isogametes**. We know that there is a sexual difference in isogametes of *Ulothrix* because fusing gametes come from different filaments.

Life history of Oedogonium. *Oedogonium* (ee-doh-*goh*-nee-um) is a common green alga found in quiet pools, where it grows attached to rocks, sticks, and other objects. Like *Ulothrix*, the plant consists of an unbranched filament with a basal holdfast cell. Each cell has a single chloroplast composed of many joined strands. Pyrenoids are numerous (Fig. 9-5).

Any cell above the holdfast may convert its content into a large, single zoospore. The zoospore is propelled through the water by a ring of flagella surrounding a " bald spot " on one side of the spore. When a zoospore reaches a suitable location, it settles down and modifies to become a holdfast cell, thus establishing a new filament.

Sexual reproduction involves only certain cells in a filament of *Oedogonium*. In this way, it is different from *Spirogyra* and *Ulothrix*. The protoplasts of special cells distributed along a filament each

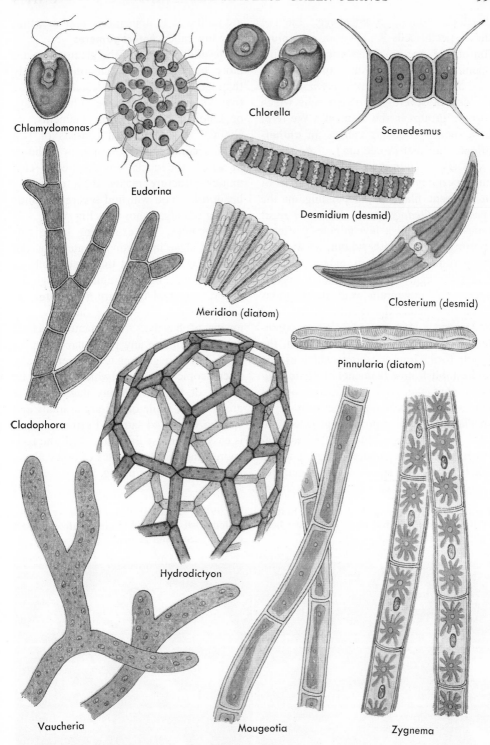

Chlamydomonas

Eudorina

Chlorella

Scenedesmus

Desmidium (desmid)

Meridion (diatom)

Closterium (desmid)

Pinnularia (diatom)

Cladophora

Hydrodictyon

Vaucheria

Mougeotia

Zygnema

Fig. 9-6.   Algae, though among the simplest plants, are represented by a rich variety of interesting forms.

develops into a large, single *egg*. Each of these special cells is called an **oögonium** (oh-oh-*goh*-nee-um) and contains a tiny opening through its wall. In most species of *Oedogonium* two *sperm* develop in each of several shortened cells which form in groups in the filament. We refer to a sperm-producing cell as an **antheridium** (an-ther-*ih*-dee-um). A sperm looks like a miniature zoospore. Eggs and sperm may develop in the same or in different filaments, depending on the species of *Oedogonium*. Within a short time (often only a few minutes) after a sperm leaves an antheridium, it swims to the pore of an oögonium, enters, and fertilizes the egg. This produces a zygote. When the oögonium wall disintegrates some time later, the zygote escapes and undergoes a rest period. When conditions are again favorable for growth, the zygote forms four zoospores which escape and establish new filaments of *Oedogonium*. *Oedogonium* is considered one of the more advanced algae because of its specialized gamete-producing cells and because of the structural difference between the female gamete, or egg, and the male gamete, or sperm. When gametes are unlike as to appearance and structure they are called **heterogametes.**

Desmids. None of the green algae are more beautiful and fascinating to study than the group known as **desmids.** These free-floating algae may be either solitary or colonial. Some form filaments, or chains. A desmid cell consists of two halves, connected by a narrow isthmus in which the nucleus is situated. This unique structure makes them especially beautiful. You will find several desmids among the algae shown in Fig. 9-6.

Flagellates. In examining living cultures of algae in a drop of water, you are almost certain to find tiny green cells or small colonies moving rapidly through the water. Most of these are **flagellates,** so called because they propel themselves by means of flagella. The name *flagellate* does not refer to any particular group of algae but is a general term given to any microscopic organism which moves by means of flagella. Many flagellates are green algae, while others are animals and will be discussed later. Furthermore, it is easy to confuse flagellates with the zoospores and motile gametes of other algae. Find the flagellates in Fig. 9-6.

Fig. 9-7. These kelp live on the bottom of the ocean floor, but close to shore where light can reach them.

Cadbury from National Audubon Society

Fig. 9-8. This red algae, *Chondrus*, is also called Irish moss and is made into a dessert called "sea moss farina."

Hugh Spencer

Diatoms are common in both fresh and salt water. *Diatoms* are one-celled, free-floating algae varying from rectangular, round, triangular, or oval to spindle-shaped or boat-shaped forms. They are sometimes green but more often golden brown. They all contain chlorophyll. The products of their photosynthesis are chiefly oils, instead of carbohydrates. One authority believes that they account for 90 per cent of all the photosynthesis that occurs in salt-water plants. Their walls contain small amounts of *silicon* and *manganese*. The wall is in two sections or valves, one fitting over the other like the top and bottom of a pillbox.

The shells of diatoms are pretty not only because of their shapes, but also because of the many fine lines which form intricate and beautiful designs on their walls (Fig. 9-6). When they die, they fall to the bottom of the pond, stream, or ocean and may form deposits of *diatomaceous* (dy-uh-toh-*may*-shus) *earth.* In California and other parts of the world, these deposits are thick. They are mined and sold as ingredients in various scouring powders, or used in various commercial processes.

The Phaeophyceae and the Rhodophyceae. The *brown* and *red algae* are mostly salt-water forms, better known as "seaweeds." Sizes vary from some small threadlike red algae to the giant brown species of the Pacific Ocean, commonly called *kelp.* They usually live in shallow water near the shore, where light can reach them, but some of the reds live in deeper water. These red algae grow attached to solid objects on the bottom or may grow in mud or sand. Because they vary so much as to structure and reproduction, and are often difficult to get, we cannot study any one type. A brown alga, called *Fucus,* is a favorite for study because it is so common along the seacoast (Fig. 9-9). You may find it as the

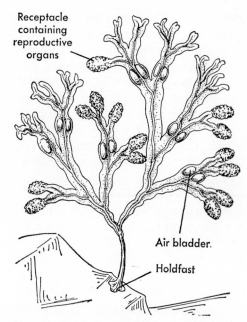

Receptacle containing reproductive organs

Air bladder.

Holdfast

Fig. 9-9. *Fucus* **is a brown alga that grows on rocks at the water line along the Atlantic Coast. Notice the holdfast, which acts as an anchor to the rock.**

packing around oysters, lobsters, and other seafoods which are shipped from the coast to your town.

Economic importance of the algae. The algae are the chief source of food and energy for much of the animal life in environments where they occur. Although many small fish live entirely on algae, one large species of mammals, the whale, also exists primarily on them. Algae are also a good source of the oxygen which is necessary in water for aquatic life.

The use of marine algae as soil fertilizers has long been known. If seaweeds are mixed with the soil, they not only add organic matter to it but also replenish the salts which land-growing plants have removed. Thus algae will return iodine to the soil. Iodine is a chemical element necessary for animal well-being.

While algae are useful in certain parts of the world in the preparation of soups, gelatins, and other foods, we are more likely to find them as a part of our ice cream. A sodium compound, extracted from algae, is added to keep it smooth. This compound may also be used as a stabilizer in chocolate milk, or as a thickener in salad dressings. *Agar-agar* (*ah*-ger-*ah*-ger) is produced from algae in the Indian Ocean and is used in hospitals and laboratories as a base for culture medium for bacteria. The list of other industrial uses of algal preparations ranges from cosmetics to leather-finishing.

An interesting new discovery is that algae can be mass-cultured in plastic tubes or tanks. By continually pumping the algae culture and supplying it with all the best conditions for photosynthesis, such as light, water, and carbon dioxide, the algae multiply rapidly. Periodically, some algae are strained out, dried, and then made ready for use as flour in baking or as a thickening in foods such as soup.

Use of algae in space flights. One of the problems that must be solved before human beings can travel in space is that of disposing of the carbon dioxide that is the waste product of man's respiration. Recent research indicates that certain forms of algae may be useful in accomplishing this purification of the air in a space ship. As you read earlier in this chapter, algae use carbon dioxide and give off oxygen as a waste product in the process of photosynthesis. There are certain hot-climate algae that reproduce faster than cold-climate types. They are, in fact, capable of multiplying a thousand-fold in twenty-four hours. These types, of course, use up carbon dioxide and produce oxygen faster than ordinary types. It is therefore believed that they might be effective both for purifying the air in a space ship and for supplying some of the oxygen needs.

Some algae can do harm. Some algae may become poisonous when they die, and thus pollute the water. This not only makes the water unfit for humans, but also for fish and other water life. Great care is taken in fish hatcheries to prevent this " weediness." A very weak solution of copper sulfate put in the water will kill blue-green algae. This treatment, however, is not recommended for home aquaria because there is considerable danger of overdosing, which would kill the fish.

In Conclusion

Algae compose the great group of independent thallophyte plants. However, while algae are the simplest green plants, they are by no means the least important. They are vital in water environments as food for the animals there.

Algae range from single-celled to many-celled plants and reproduce by simple fission, thus forming new unicellular plants or adding to the size of colonies of cells. Many algae also reproduce asexually by forming zoospores which swim about and form a new plant directly when they germinate. Sexual reproduction also occurs and involves isogametes or heterogametes.

From the algae, we turn to other thallophytes which have no chlorophyll and thus are nutritionally dependent. We shall consider first the bacteria, the lowliest yet, in many ways, the most important thallophytes.

BIOLOGICALLY SPEAKING

antheridium	fission	matrix
apical cell	flagellate	oögonium
colony	flagellum	phycocyanin
concave cell	fragmentation	pyrenoid
conjugation	gamete	sperm
desmid	heterocyst	spore
diatom	heterogamete	thallophyte
egg	holdfast	zoospore
fertilization	isogamete	zygote
filament		

QUESTIONS FOR REVIEW

1. How are the algae fundamentally different from other thallophyte plants?
2. In what respect are thallophytes more simple in structure than higher plants?
3. Explain how colonies of algae increase in size during the growing season.
4. Name five classes of algae and give an example of each.
5. Why are blue-green algae an especially serious problem in a community water supply?
6. Account for the color of blue-green algae.
7. Describe a heterocyst of *Nostoc* or *Anabaena* and explain how it causes filaments to break up.
8. Describe the composition of a ball of *Nostoc.*
9. Account for the slimy texture of *Gloeocapsa.*
10. What characteristic of *Oscillatoria* is referred to in its name?
11. What pigments, other than chlorophyll, are present in the cells of green algae?
12. Describe the habitat of *Protococcus.*
13. Why is *Chlorella* of special interest to biologists?
14. How can you easily distinguish *Spirogyra* from other filamentous green algae under the microscope?
15. Describe conjugation in *Spirogyra.*
16. How can you distinguish a *Ulothrix* spore from a gamete?
17. Some flagellates are plants, while others are animals. What characteristic do they have in common?
18. What characteristics distinguish diatoms from other algae?
19. What are some uses for diatomaceous earth?
20. Describe the typical habitat of red and brown algae.
21. List some of the reasons why algae are economically important.

APPLYING FACTS AND PRINCIPLES

1. What evidence can you give that all algae contain chlorophyll even though many are not green?
2. A colony of 50 algal cells is not a 50-celled plant. Explain why.
3. Both spores and gametes are reproductive cells. How are they different?
4. In what respect are the cells of blue-green algae more primitive than those of green algae?
5. Why is conjugation in *Spirogyra* considered a primitive form of sexual reproduction?
6. In what ways is sexual reproduction in *Oedogonium* more efficient and more advanced than the sexual reproduction in *Ulothrix?*
7. Compare *Spirogyra, Ulothrix,* and *Oedogonium* in regard to specialization of cells in a filament.

CHAPTER 10

Bacteria—Beneficial and Harmful Plants

BIOLOGISTS believe that bacteria were among the first forms of life on the earth. Long before there were any plants capable of carrying on photosynthesis, certain lowly bacteria probably synthesized sugar by obtaining energy from inorganic iron and sulfur compounds instead of the sun. Geologists believe that the extensive deposits of iron ore we are using today are the result of bacterial action during ancient geological times.

Later, when green plants began building up stores of organic compounds, other kinds of bacteria began using them as a food supply. Still other bacteria invaded the tissues of the plants themselves as well as the bodies of animals.

Bacteria have survived through the ages and have increased their numbers until they are today the most abundant form of life. They live, invisibly, almost everywhere. They thrive in the air, in water, in food, in the soil, and in the bodies of host plants and animals. In fact, any environment which can support life in any form will have its population of bacteria.

It is fortunate that most bacteria are harmless, for we have no chance of escaping them. One of our chief biological problems has been learning how to live *with* bacteria — to control the harmful ones and make the best use of those which are beneficial.

What are bacteria? Because they lack chlorophyll, bacteria were at one time thought to be animals. Now we know that they are simple forms of plant life. They are most like the fungi, since the majority of them must take their nourishment from an outside organic food source. They are frequently placed with the fungi in the class **Schizomycetes** (skiz-oh-my-*see*-teez), which means, literally, *fission fungi*. Some biologists place them in a phylum of their own (see page 82) and thus separate them from the other fungi.

The importance of bacteria. We hear so much about disease-causing bacteria that we are inclined to think of all of them as harmful organisms. Fortunately, this is not the case. In fact, many kinds of bacteria are essential in the chemical relations of living things, as you found in your study of the nitrogen cycle. According to their relation to us, we can classify bacteria into three general groups as follows: (1) *harmless bacteria;* (2) *beneficial bacteria;* and (3) *harmful bacteria.*

The harmless bacteria compose by far the largest group. They live in the air, in water, in the soil, and even in our bodies without doing any apparent damage.

Beneficial bacteria include those which live in the soil and are essential to maintaining soil fertility. We make use of many kinds of bacteria in food processing and in industrial processes which require their action. We shall refer to several of these later in the chapter.

Harmful bacteria include those which cause disease as well as organisms which cause food spoilage and destruction of other valuable materials and products. Disease-causing forms are parasites in man or in plants and animals and we designate them as **pathogenic** (path-oh-*jen*-ik) **bacteria.** Those which cause food to spoil and valuable materials to decay are harmful saprophytes.

Structure of bacteria. Bacteria are extremely small organisms, consisting of one simple cell. They range in size from about one ten-thousandth to one fifty-thousandth of an inch in diameter. If these figures mean little to you, consider that several hundred thousand bacteria could be placed on the period at the end of this sentence. Bacteria are barely visible under the high-power lens of a standard laboratory microscope (430X magnification). Special microscopes that provide a magnification of at least one thousand diameters are necessary for the study of most forms.

A bacterial cell is a tiny living protoplast, surrounded by a thin wall. It has no organized nucleus and, of course, no plastids. Structurally, bacteria resemble many of the primitive blue-green algae. The outer edge of the cytoplasm is a plasma membrane, which regulates the movement of various substances between the cell and its environment.

Bacterial cells are surrounded by a **slime layer** which serves for protection of the cell content and allows the cell to stick to the surface of a food supply or to a cell of a host organism.

Certain bacteria are equipped with flagella, which propel the cell through water and other liquids. These flagella are minute threads of cytoplasm which project through the wall and slime layer. They may be situated on one or both ends of a

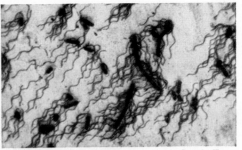

General Biological Supply House

Fig. 10-1. Many bacteria are able to move about in liquids by means of the slender threads of cytoplasm called flagella.

cell and, in some bacteria, are numerous and surround the cell (Fig. 10-1).

Forms of bacteria. While they vary considerably in size, we can classify the thousands of forms of bacteria known to science in three groups. These groups are based solely on the shapes of the cells as follows: (1) **coccus** forms — ball-shaped; (2) **bacillus** forms — oblong or rod-shaped; and (3) **spirillum** forms — spiral-shaped and curved (Fig. 10-2, page 106).

Many coccus and bacillus types form clusters or colonies of cells which are as characteristic as the shape of the individual cells. For example, many coccus bacteria live in pairs. The bacteriologist can look for this characteristic when he is looking for pneumonia organisms in sputum. Other coccus bacteria form clusters or chains that resemble a string of beads. Bacillus, or rod-shaped bacteria, may likewise exist in colonies. The most common bacillus grouping is in chains, resembling a string of sausages. These groups of bacteria are classified as follows:

1. Diplococcus   (dip-loh-*kok*-us) — pairs of round cells, or two-celled filaments.

2. Staphylococcus (staf-ih-loh-*kok*-us) — clusters of round cells.

3. Streptococcus (strep-toh-*kok*-us) — strings or chains of round cells.

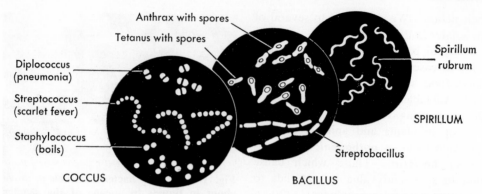

Fig. 10-2. **These are typical examples of the three important groups of bacteria.**

4. Streptobacillus (strep-toh-bas-*il*-us) — strings or chains of rod-shaped cells.

The shape and microscopic arrangement of cells help us to classify bacteria. But you cannot ever identify any bacterium solely by its shape. *Streptococcus,* for example, is a form of ball-shaped bacterium with the cells attached in chains. To many people, the term *streptococcus* is associated with blood poisoning or to a severe throat infection. True, both of these diseases are caused by a streptococcus form. But other organisms of the streptococcus type cause milk to sour and eggs to rot. Similarly, a rod form may cause typhoid, another may produce diphtheria, while others live in the soil and are essential to soil fertility.

Multiplication of bacteria. Bacteria multiply by dividing. They accomplish this apparent mathematical impossibility by the simple method of cell division. When a cell reaches maturity, it merely separates into two cells by forming a wall through the middle. Since a complete organism consists of only one cell, the division of a cell into two parts results in two organisms. Neither cell would be considered the parent cell. Both are young, small, and capable of further enlargement.

One of the most amazing things about bacterial reproduction is the rate at which it may occur. Under ideal conditions, a cell may reach maturity and divide every 20 minutes. This may not seem alarming until you calculate the results. When you consider that a single bacterium under these ideal growth conditions would form a mass weighing 7,000 tons in three days, bacterial multiplication becomes much more significant.

Such rapid increase accounts for the fact that an invisible bacterium growing on a source of food can produce a large, visible colony in a day or two. If you examine a portion of the colony under the microscope, you will see literally millions of bacteria. Fortunately, this rate of division of bacterial cells continues for only a limited time. As the mass of cells becomes larger and larger, the bacteria themselves begin to interfere with each other. Poisonous waste products accumulate, and food supplies often fail to reach many cells in the mass. As a result, cell division ceases and the bacteria become inactive. Over a three-day period, growth is extremely rapid during the first day, much reduced during the second day, and usually ceases during the third.

Spore formation in the bacteria. Many kinds of bacteria, especially the bacillus or rod-shaped types, may modify and protect themselves during unfavorable periods. Each cell may draw its content into a spherical mass which becomes surrounded with a thick protective wall. This special body is called a **spore.** Since a single cell produces only one spore, the total number of bacteria is not increased. Spore formation is not a method of reproduction in the case of bacteria.

Bacterial spores can endure almost unbelievable conditions. They may dry out completely and remain in a dormant condition for years. During the spore stage they may be carried far and wide by various means. Some of these spores even resist boiling water.

When a spore falls on a suitable host, the resting period ends and a new cell develops. By rapid division, the new host may soon support tremendous numbers of bacteria, all having come from the single spore. Spore-forming bacteria are especially dangerous in a hospital. *Tetanus,* more commonly known as *lockjaw,* is caused by a spore-forming bacillus organism.

Conditions for growth. Most bacteria require four conditions for growth: (1) a *suitable temperature;* (2) *moisture;* (3) *darkness;* and (4) a *suitable food supply*.

A *suitable temperature* is essential for bacterial activity, although cold does not kill most of these organisms. It merely stops their activity and causes them to become dormant. Temperature requirements vary among bacteria. The majority of them are most active at temperatures ranging from 80–100° F. However, many kinds of bacteria are active at temperatures above or below this range. Those which cause human diseases grow best at 98.6° F (37° C), or normal body temperature. We use a refrigerator to keep foods at a temperature below that required for activity of most bacteria. Frozen foods keep even longer because the very low temperature stops all bacterial action.

Moisture is a second growth requirement for bacteria. Prolonged dryness will not kill most bacteria but, like low temperature, produces a period of dormancy. In dehydrating foods, we lower the moisture content to a point below the requirement for bacterial action. Foods in this condition can be stored long periods without spoilage.

Darkness is another critical requirement for bacterial activity. Exposure to sunlight retards growth and ultraviolet rays actually kill the cells. Sunlight does not, however, injure the spores of bacteria.

A *suitable food supply* is a fourth requirement for the growth of bacteria. In this respect, bacteria vary greatly. Some are highly specific in their food needs. Most bacteria which cause human diseases require human tissues. Many of these attack only certain tissues, as pneumonia

Fig. 10-3. **The operating rooms of a modern hospital are kept as sterile as possible, unlike those of Lister's time. The sterilamp over the operating table makes use of the bacteria-killing powers of ultraviolet light.**

Ewing Galloway

Fig. 10-4. These tanks provide a germ-free environment for experimental animals. Technicians handle the animals with rubber gloves attached to the inside of an opening at the side of a tank, to prevent introduction of bacteria and other organisms.

organisms live in the lungs, while typhoid organisms live in the intestine. Many bacteria are far more tolerant in their requirements and can live on a wide variety of food materials.

The relation of bacteria to the food supply. The majority of bacteria live in contact with organic matter, either nonliving or living. Saprophytes digest dead organic matter or nonliving substances such as food products. Parasites, on the other hand, invade the bodies of plants and animals and take their nourishment directly from living tissue.

Bacteria secrete powerful **enzymes** which cause external chemical changes in materials from which they obtain their food supplies. When the enzymes have made the matter soluble, it can be absorbed by the bacterial cells and used by the protoplast for energy and growth. Bacterial enzymes are powerful substances. They allow saprophytic organisms to use a variety of organic materials

which are useless to other forms of life. Enzymes secreted by pathogenic bacteria kill the tissues they contact in the host.

In discussing the food relations of bacteria we must not assume, however, that all bacteria require organic compounds. Several small groups of **chemotrophic bacteria,** including those we mentioned earlier in this chapter, make use of inorganic compounds in their chemical activities. Some of these oxidize iron compounds. Others use sulfur compounds. Still others, including the nitrite and nitrate bacteria, oxidize nitrogen compounds.

Bacteria in relation to air. Oxygen is another important factor in controlling the growth and activity of bacteria. Some forms require free oxygen for their respiration and therefore cannot live in the absence of air. These are **aerobic** organisms. Other bacteria are just the opposite and cannot grow in free oxygen. These **anaerobic** bacteria live on the energy released during the chemical changes they bring about. While less numerous than aerobic forms, anaerobic bacteria are abundant in the soil and in water, especially in the mud at the bottom of ponds and streams. Certain anaerobic bacteria cause food to spoil in airtight containers. One of the best-known anaerobes is the tetanus organism, which lives in the soil or on objects as a spore and becomes active in an airtight puncture wound.

Laboratory culture of bacteria. *Bacteriology* is a major branch of biology devoted to the study of bacteria and their many relations to our lives. The bacteriologist must be highly skilled in the techniques of growing bacteria for identification, for study, for determining the bacterial content of water, foods, and other products, and for the many other phases of his work. We shall discuss several of the steps involved in the laboratory culture of bacteria.

Preparation of culture media. While bacteria exist nearly everywhere, they are grown in the laboratory under carefully controlled conditions.

Growth of bacteria in artificially prepared cultures is essential not only to provide organisms for study, but also as a means of identifying them. While useful, the size, shape, and other structural characteristics are not sufficient for classifying a form of bacterium. The bacteriologist must grow the organism in question in various kinds of cultures and observe its effect on a culture medium before he can make a positive identification.

A *culture medium* is a substance on which a bacteriologist grows bacteria. This medium should provide the food substance from which the organisms obtain nourishment. It may be organic materials, such as *agar-agar,* or gelatin to which protein, sugars, and other nutrients have been added. Broths and sugar solutions, or various solid substances, are also

used. Certain disease bacteria require the addition of blood to the medium.

Cultures are frequently prepared in shallow glass dishes called *Petri* (*pee*-tree) *dishes* or in culture tubes plugged with cotton. After the medium has been added to the container, it is *sterilized* to destroy any bacteria which may have entered during preparation. The cultures are then handled carefully to prevent exposure of the sterile media to outside sources of bacteria.

Sterilization procedures. *Sterilization* is the destruction of all life in an area, in a substance, or on an object. It is a highly important phase of the laboratory work in bacteriology.

The bacteriologist makes use of several kinds of *heat* sterilization. An object can be sterilized instantly by passing it through a flame. Hot water is also used extensively. Boiling in an open container (at 212° F) for 10 minutes will kill all bacteria cells and many spores. However, the bacteriologist cannot use this method because it is not complete sterilization.

A steam sterilizer is widely used in bacteriological work. As steam is held in a closed compartment, both the temperature and the pressure continue to increase as long as it is heated. When the pressure has reached 15 pounds per square inch, the temperature is about 250° F. At this pressure and temperature, steam will destroy all bacteria and spores in 15 minutes or less. You have probably seen large steam sterilizers in laboratories or hospitals. An *autoclave,* as such a sterilizer is called, usually has a cylindrical chamber which is closed during sterilization with a heavy lid on one end. A pressure cooker is merely a small autoclave.

A dry-air oven can be used for sterilizing glassware and metal objects. However, hot air is far less effective than steam. In using this method, the oven should be held at 350° F for two hours.

Ewing Galloway

Fig. 10-5. These laboratory technicians are examining colonies of bacteria that have been cultured in Petri dishes and test tubes which were placed in an incubator. The instrument pictured is used to count the number of bacteria colonies per square millimeter of culture.

Other methods of sterilization include *radiation* and the use of *chemicals*. Lamps which give off ultraviolet rays are effective in sterilizing the air in a laboratory or a hospital surgery. Chemicals used in sterilization are referred to as **bactericides,** or germicides. We shall discuss the use of these in the study of disease in Unit 8.

Inoculation of cultures. We refer to the addition of bacteria to a sterile medium as **inoculation** (in-ok-yoo-*lay*-shun). Bacteria may be transferred from an object by pressing it to the medium. Other methods of inoculating a culture medium include the adding of a small quantity of liquid containing bacteria, transferring organisms from another source by means of a sterile inoculating needle, and exposing the opened culture

to the air. When bacteria from a known source are added to a culture medium, great care must be used to avoid introducing other organisms accidentally. This would result in contamination of the culture.

Bacteria grow during incubation. After inoculation, the bacteria which have been added are invisible in the culture. But after two or three days of **incubation,** during which the organisms are provided nourishment, warmth, moisture, and darkness, the individual cells multiply to form several million. The bacteria then become visible in masses, or colonies. The bacteriologist notes carefully the shape, size, and color of these colonies in each kind of culture he uses. Such items are important factors in the identification of bacteria.

Microscopic examination of bacteria. The bacteriologist prepares a *smear* for microscopic examination of bacteria. This is done by transferring a small number of organisms from a culture to a drop of water on a microscope slide. The bacteria are spread into a thin film which is then dried and stained to make the organisms more visible. If an examination of living cells is necessary, the bacteria may be added to a small drop of water on a microscope slide.

Beneficial activities of bacteria. When we consider the beneficial activities of some bacteria, we quickly change our impressions of at least a few of them. The study of the beneficial forms is an extensive one. However, the following are some of the ways in which bacteria are useful: (1) in the food industry; (2) in other industries; and (3) in the soil.

Bacteria in the food industry. We may or may not consider the souring of milk as a beneficial activity. But this process is essential to the dairy industry in making butter and cheese. In the case of cheesemaking, bacteria are necessary in acid formation and in the coagulation of milk protein from which the cheese is made. Certain kinds of aged or ripened cheeses, such as Swiss, Limburger, and Liederkranz, owe their distinctive flavors to bacterial action during the ripening period. Milk sours as a result of the activity of several kinds of organisms which digest the milk sugar (*lactose*) and form *lactic acid*.

Another group of souring or fermenting bacteria lives in fruit juices, where the organisms are associated with *yeasts*. Yeast cells break down the sugar in the fruit juice and form alcohol, after which acetic acid bacteria convert the alcohol into vinegar. Colonies of these beneficial bacteria grow in vinegar jars, and are called " mother of vinegar."

Bacteria in other industries. The finest grade of linen fibers comes from flax plants. The plants are tied in bundles and put in water. Bacteria enter the stems and gradually destroy the stem tissues. This action, called **retting,** loosens supporting fibers from the other tissues. These are then removed and used to make linen threads.

The tobacco industry uses bacterial action in the curing process. Stalks and leaves of the tobacco plant are harvested and hung in special curing barns where sweating occurs at cool temperatures. Bacteria invade the moist leaves and cause fermentation, resulting in special flavors.

The tanning industry, likewise, makes use of bacteria in the processing of leather and animal hides. During tanning, bacteria attack the hides and make them pliable.

In the dairy industry, bacteria help to produce **ensilage** (*en*-sih-lij), a fermented fodder fed to cattle. A special type of structure called a *silo* (*sy*-loh) is filled with shredded corn stalks and leaves which are fermented by souring bacteria. Fermenting not only preserves the ensilage but adds acid, which is of the greatest value in the diet of dairy cattle.

Bacteria in the soil. We have already discussed the importance of decay as well as of nitrite, nitrate, and nitrogen-fixing bacteria in the nitrogen cycle. However, a discussion of beneficial activities of bacteria would not be complete without mention of the importance of soil organisms to agriculture. All the compounds used by plants and animals must, eventually, return to the soil. Soil bacteria cause the chemical changes which convert these complex compounds to forms which can be reused by new generations of plants. The farmer aids this natural process when he spreads manure on his fields and when he plows under a crop as green manure. High agricultural yields require highly productive, fertile soil. Soil bacteria are man's agents in maintaining this fertility.

Harmful bacteria. One of the most harmful activities of bacteria is the spoilage of food. Certain bacteria produce

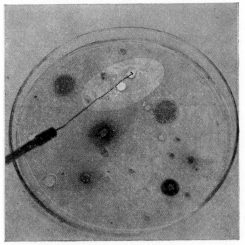

Fig. 10-6. **Here a technician is removing bacteria from a colony by means of a looped needle that has been flamed previously to avoid contamination. He then places a smear of these bacteria under a sufficiently powerful microscope in order to identify them.**

Chas. Pfizer and Co.

poisonous substances, or *toxins,* during the breakdown of foods, which may cause illness or death if eaten. In other cases, the food may simply be made unfit for use.

Milk may be freed of its most dangerous bacteria by **pasteurization** (pas-ter-ih-*zay*-shun), which means heating to a temperature of from 140° to 150° F for a period of 30 minutes, and then cooling quickly.

Most of us have the wrong idea as to what pasteurization really does. It does not completely sterilize the milk. It merely destroys the large majority of bacteria that are present, including those that are capable of causing infectious dis-

eases. Even though pasteurization delays souring milk, the container must still be closed to prevent any of the souring organisms in the air from entering. The milk must be kept cool to keep those bacteria which are already present from multiplying.

We are most concerned with harmful bacteria as they relate to infectious disease. One of our greatest biological triumphs has been the conquest of these diseases, largely in the last century. Unit 8 will continue the study of bacteria as they relate to disease and will introduce two additional groups of pathogenic organisms related to bacteria.

In Conclusion

If numbers of an organism are any indication of success, we must admit that the simplest forms of life are the most successful. Bacteria are not only the most numerous of organisms, but they probably live higher in the air, deeper in the seas, and farther in the ground than any other group of living things.

Their requirements vary widely. Some must live in contact with a living host; others can digest almost any form of organic matter. Still others make use of inorganic compounds and could survive if there were no other forms of life on the earth. Bacteria have still another great survival advantage. If conditions are not favorable for active life, they merely stop activity and enter a dormant condition which can continue for months or even years.

In the next chapter, we shall consider more complex but equally interesting relatives of the bacteria, the fungi.

BIOLOGICALLY SPEAKING

aerobic	coccus	retting
anaerobic	culture medium	Schizomycetes
autoclave	ensilage	slime layer
bacillus	incubation	smear
bactericide	inoculation	spirillum
bacteriology	pasteurization	spore
chemotrophic bacteria	pathogenic bacteria	sterilization

QUESTIONS FOR REVIEW

1. Why are bacteria classified as fungi?
2. Classify bacteria into three groups, based on their importance to man.
3. Of what importance is the slime layer which surrounds a bacterial cell?
4. Classify bacteria into three groups on the basis of the shape of individual cells.
5. Describe several ways in which bacteria are grouped in colonies.
6. By what method and at what rate do bacteria multiply under ideal growing conditions?
7. Describe spore formation in bacteria.
8. Name four requirements for the growth of bacteria.
9. How are chemotrophic bacteria different from other forms?
10. Distinguish between aerobic and anaerobic bacteria.
11. Describe several methods of heat sterilization.
12. Describe several techniques used in inoculating bacteria cultures.
13. Why do bacteria multiply at an unusually rapid rate during incubation under laboratory conditions?
14. Describe several industrial uses of bacteria.

APPLYING FACTS AND PRINCIPLES

1. Discuss the problems a bacteriologist has in identifying a bacterium.
2. On the basis of what you know about growth requirements for bacteria, discuss several methods of preserving foods.
3. What reasons can you give to support the biologists' theory that certain bacteria were among the first forms of life on the earth?
4. The growth of bacteria slows or may cease altogether after two or three days of incubation in a culture. Give several reasons for this.

CHAPTER 11

The Fungi—Well-known Thallophytes

WE cannot escape the fungi. They grow on our food, live in fruit juices, appear on trees, pop up in our yards, and even invade our bodies. Name an organic substance — from paper and leather goods to cheese — and there is probably a fungus which thrives on it.

Fungi are our allies in antibiotic production, in the making of vinegar, and in the cheese and baking industries — to mention only a few of their useful activities. They are our enemies in food warehouses, in the refrigerator, and in wheat fields.

The fungi are so important that a branch of biology is devoted to them. We call the biologist who specializes in work with the fungi a **mycologist.**

What are fungi? When we speak of *fungi,* we refer, in a broad sense, to all plants of the phylum Thallophyta which lack chlorophyll. However, this distinction is one of nutrition rather than structure, and does not indicate a relationship or structural similarity among the various fungi. In fact, certain of the fungi are more like algae than other fungi in form, except for their lack of ability to carry on photosynthesis. Thus, in the study of fungi, you will find great variation in the structure of the plant bodies as well as differences in reproduction.

Biologists divide the fungi into six classes in the traditional classification, as given in the table below.

The Schizomycetes, which include the bacteria already studied, are often separated from the other fungi because of their extremely simple cellular structure. The Myxomycetes, or slime fungi, are also quite different from the other fungi in that they resemble primitive animals in many respects. This leaves four classes of fungi which biologists refer to as *true fungi,* or higher fungi. We shall limit our discussion of fungi in this chapter to members of these four classes. But we must also include the *lichens,* which have curious plant bodies composed of one of the true fungi living in association with an alga.

Characteristics of the true fungi. More than 75,000 different species compose the four classes of true fungi. They vary in size from microscopic organisms to structures as large as mushrooms and puffballs.

Most of the true fungi have plant bodies composed of whitish or grayish filaments, each of which is known as a **hypha** (*hy*-fuh) [plural *hyphae* (*hy*-fee)]. The hyphae vary in length and contain many nuclei. Some hyphae do not have their cells separated by cell walls, while others do have such walls. Therefore, you must think of a hypha as an elongate, continuous structure which is composed of many cells, each with its own nucleus, but with or without cell walls.

The total mass of hyphae is known as a **mycelium** (my-*see*-lee-um). Although chlorophyll is not present in the hyphae of a mycelium, certain fungi contain yellow, orange, red, blue, or green pigments

CLASSES OF FUNGI

1. SCHIZOMYCETES (skiz-oh-my-*see*-teez). Fission fungi
Examples: bacteria, spirochetes, actinomycetes, Rickettsiae

2. MYXOMYCETES (mik-soh-my-*see*-teez). Slime fungi
Examples: slime molds

3. PHYCOMYCETES (fy-koh-my-*see*-teez). Algalike fungi
Examples: water molds, bread mold, black mold, downy mildew

4. ASCOMYCETES (as-koh-my-*see*-teez). Sac fungi
Examples: yeast, cup fungi, morels, blue and green molds, powdery mildews

5. BASIDIOMYCETES (bas-id-ee-oh-my-*see*-teez). Basidium or club fungi
Examples: mushrooms, puffballs, bracket fungi, rust fungi, smut fungi

6. DEUTEROMYCETES (doo-ter-oh-my-*see*-teez). Imperfect fungi
Examples: ringworm fungi, and many other parasites in man, animals, and
        plants

which give them a special color. The complete absence of chlorophyll makes the fungi either parasitic or saprophytic.

All true fungi reproduce asexually by forming spores, which are carried to new environments by wind or water or contact with other agents. Members of all classes but the Deuteromycetes, or imperfect fungi, reproduce sexually as well. However, certain members of the classes which normally reproduce sexually seem to have " lost " this phase of reproduction. Nevertheless, they are placed in their respective classes, rather than with the imperfect fungi, because of similarity in structure.

The fungi are very widespread because of the enormous number of spores they produce. These spores float through the air and lodge on objects. A suitable food supply or host will, almost invariably, be invaded by a fungus if conditions are suitable for growth. Fungi have no light requirements and actually thrive best in darkness. Moisture is, however, a growth requirement, as are warm temperatures, which usually favor the growth of fungi. However, most fungi tolerate a greater temperature variation than do the majority of bacteria. Nearly all true fungi are aerobic, although a few live as anaerobes.

We commonly refer to fungi with such group names as molds, mildews, and mushrooms. For this reason, we shall discuss them in these common groupings. This does not indicate, necessarily, that the groups contain closely related fungi.

Molds are among the most familiar fungi. We use the term *mold* to refer to many kinds of fungus plants. Some of these are Phycomycetes, and resemble algae in structure; others are Ascomycetes, or sac fungi, so named because many of their group produce spores, usually eight in number, in saclike structures, each of which is called an *ascus* (*as*-kus).

Molds thrive in dark, moist places. While warmth stimulates the growth of many of them, others grow well at temperatures near freezing, which makes these molds a serious problem in cold storage plants and in home refrigerators. Molds grow on nearly all foods as well as on wood, paper, leather, and many other organic substances. You may even find mold on the shoes you laid aside in your closet, if the summer months were warm and humid.

It would be incorrect to brand all molds as destructive. Certain of them are used in ripening cheeses. Another mold, which we shall describe later, is directly responsible for the era of antibiotics in medicine.

Bread mold and its relatives. If you moisten a piece of bread, expose it to the air, and set it in a dark place for several days or a week, bread mold is almost certain to appear. *Rhizopus* (*ry*-zuh-pus) is the genus name for this member of the Phycomycetes. The mold starts as a microscopic spore which grows on the surface of the bread, forming a network of silvery, tubular hyphae. Within a few days, the mold grows over the surface of the bread, forming a cottonlike mass of hyphae, the mycelium (Fig. 11-1, page 116).

A portion of bread mold viewed with a hand lens or under the low power of the microscope reveals several distinct kinds of hyphae composing the mycelium. Those hyphae which spread over the surface of the food supply are called **stolons** (*stoh*-lonz). At intervals along the stolons, clusters of tiny rootlike hyphae, or **rhizoids** (*ry*-zoids), penetrate the food supply and absorb nourishment. Rhizoids secrete digestive enzymes which act on the sugar, starch, and any other carbohydrates in the bread. These digested foods are then absorbed into the hyphae of the mold. The flavor, odor, and color

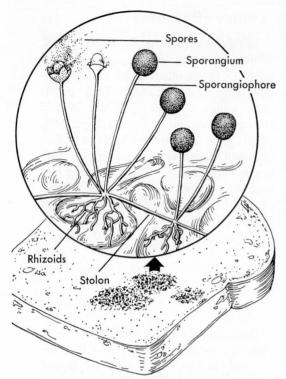

Spores

Sporangium

Sporangiophore

Rhizoids

Stolon

Fig. 11-1. This is what bread mold looks like when greatly magnified. Notice the rootlike rhizoids which extend into the bread and absorb nutrients.

spots which mold produces on bread and other foods are due to chemical changes resulting from the action of these enzymes.

After a few days of growth on the bread surface, black knobs appear among the hyphae of bread mold. Each black knob is a spore case, or **sporangium** (spor-*an*-jee-um) [plural *sporangia*], which is produced at the tip of a special ascending hypha, or **sporangiophore.** Each sporangium is a thin-walled case containing thousands of black spores. When the sporangium matures and dries out, its wall splits and releases the spores, which are blown around by air currents. Each spore may form a new hypha and, in a short time, an entire mold plant.

The water molds, belonging to the genus *Saprolegnia* (sap-roh-*leg*-nee-uh), are relatives of bread mold and also belong

to the Phycomycetes. They are similar to bread mold in having tubular hyphae resembling filaments of algae. Certain of these molds are saprophytes and live on the bodies of dead insects and other animals in the water. Other water molds are highly destructive parasites. They invade the tissues of fish and other aquatic animals where they form patches of cottony tufts. These molds will, in time, kill the host animal. They are a constant problem to the aquarist and, in addition, destroy large numbers of native fish. The spores of water molds are equipped with two *cilia* which propel them to new locations. Cilia are merely short flagella.

Blue and green molds. *Blue* and *green molds* (*Penicillium* and *Aspergillus*) form the familiar powdery growth on oranges, lemons, and other citrus fruits. This powdery substance consists of spores in tremendous numbers which form at the tips of hyphae. The mycelia of these molds are deeply embedded in the tissues of the food source. In addition to citrus fruits, these molds may live on meat and other food products.

In this group of molds we find several of the most valuable of all fungus plants. Several species of one of the blue molds, called *Penicillium,* are used in the processing of fine-flavored cheeses. Cheese manufacturers carefully grow these molds and add them to the cheeses at a certain point in processing. During the aging period, the mycelium of the mold grows through the cheese and, by chemical activity, forms substances which add distinctive flavors. Among the more popular mold cheeses are Roquefort and Camembert. Both are cheeses in which *Penicillium* molds are used.

Today, however, *Penicillium* means much more to us than an organism for the flavoring of cheese. We associate it with one of the most notable medical advances

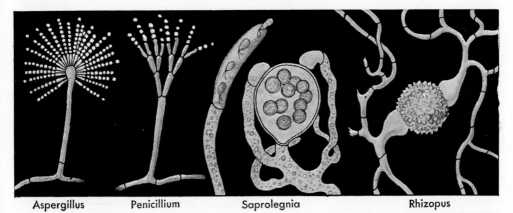

Aspergillus   Penicillium   Saprolegnia   Rhizopus

Fig. 11-2.   These are various types of molds drawn as they would be seen under the microscope.   What characteristic do all molds have in common?

of our time, the discovery of the wonder drug, **penicillin** (pen-ih-*sil*-in).

Penicillin, the drug, is a secretion of some of the *Penicillium* species, formed during normal digestive activity of the mold.   In 1929, Sir Alexander Fleming, an Englishman, discovered the powerful effects of penicillin in checking the growth of certain kinds of bacteria.   But the scientific world did not take notice of his discovery until 1938.   A few years later, industrial concerns perfected methods for large-scale production of penicillin.   Today, entire factories are devoted to producing it.

Mildews are destructive plant parasites. The **downy mildews** belong to the Phycomycetes.   Among the host plants of these dangerous parasites are radishes, mustards, white potatoes, sweet potatoes, cereal grains, sugar cane, tobacco, and lettuce.   One of the downy mildews caused a famine in Ireland in 1845–1846 when it destroyed nearly the entire potato crop.

Many downy mildews form hyphae which grow down among the cells of the host plant.   These hyphae absorb nourishment directly from the tissues of the host and thus are internal parasites.   Other species form downy patches of surface hyphae, usually on leaves of the host, and

send short, branching hyphae, or **haustoria** (haws-*tor*-ee-uh), into the cells.

The **powdery mildews** belong to the class Ascomycetes and are not usually as destructive as downy mildews, since they are external parasites.   They appear as whitish or dark-colored patches, usually on the leaves of the host plant (Fig. 11-3).   Among the host plants of these mildews are lilacs, grapes, roses, clover, apples, gooseberries, and many other flowering plants.

Yeasts are familiar to everyone.   Did you know that a cake of yeast is a culture of tiny plants?   They remain inactive as

Fig. 11-3.   This powdery mildew has as its host the lilac bush.   Why is it called an external parasite?

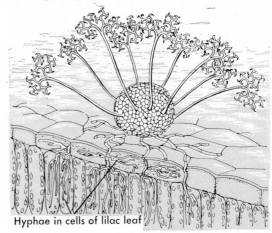

Hyphae in cells of lilac leaf

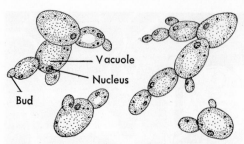

Fig. 11-4. Yeasts are extremely beneficial fungi because of their ability to ferment sugars. What are the two methods of reproduction employed by the yeasts?

long as they are refrigerated. If the temperature rises, the yeast cells become active or start " working " on the sugar and starch which make up the yeast cake.

Yeasts are one-celled fungi belonging to the Ascomycetes. The cells are usually oval (Fig. 11-4). Each cell contains a nucleus and a vacuole. Note that these cells are not hyphae, since each yeast is a unicellular plant. Yeast cells reproduce by *budding*, an unusual form of asexual reproduction. When growth conditions are favorable, a bud starts as a small knob pushing out from the side of a cell. This bud, or daughter cell, grows rapidly and may produce another bud while still attached to the mother cell. Thus a fragile chain of cells, like a string of beads of varying sizes, results. When growth conditions become unfavorable, budding does not occur. Instead, a yeast cell may form spores, usually four in number, and thus becomes a spore-bearing sac, or ascus, characteristic of the Ascomycetes.

The ability of yeast cells to ferment sugar places these tiny fungi among our most valuable plant allies. The cells secrete an enzyme system, known as *zymase*, which acts on sugars during respiration. This is an anaerobic process and may therefore occur in airtight surroundings. During respiration, the sugar is broken down chemically. Energy is released, and *carbon dioxide* and *alcohol*

are formed. You can observe this activity by adding commercial yeast to a 10% solution of molasses (or some simple sugar) in water. Within a few hours, the yeast cells multiply by budding in such numbers that they give the solution a cloudy appearance. Carbon dioxide rises through the solution as tiny bubbles and you can smell the odor of alcohol.

Both products of yeast fermentation are valuable commercially. Yeast " working " in dough forms bubbles of carbon dioxide which swell during baking and make the loaf light. The alcohol is driven off in the baking. Commercial alcohol manufacturers use yeasts to ferment various carbohydrate mashes.

Yeasts are important, also, as producers of vitamin B$_2$, or *riboflavin* (*ry*-boh-flay-vin). This vitamin is essential in normal growth and in the health of the skin, mouth, and eyes. Riboflavin remains in the yeast cells. To obtain it, we must either eat the yeast cells or use a product made of ground yeast.

Wild yeasts are abundant in the air and ferment sugars in natural fruit juices. A few yeasts are pathogenic.

Other Ascomycetes. The *cup fungus* and *morel*, shown in Fig. 11-5, are relatives of the yeast. These Ascomycetes are harmless saprophytes. Cup fungi grow on rotting wood and leaves and on organic matter in rich humus soils. Hyphae penetrate the food supply and absorb nourishment from the host material. The white, orange, or red cups are spore-bearing structures, composed of tightly massed hyphae. Many of these hyphae end in an elongated sac, or ascus, inside of which are eight spores.

The morel, or sponge mushroom, is highly prized for its delicious flavor. This is one of the few mushrooms which you can safely gather and eat. It is easily recognized and is not related to the true mushrooms, many of which are inedible or poisonous. But be sure you identify it before bringing it into the kitchen.

Some of our most serious plant diseases are caused by parasitic Ascomycetes. Among these diseases are Dutch elm disease, chestnut blight, apple scab, peach-leaf curl, and ergot disease of rye.

Basidiomycetes. Basidiomycetes are often called **club fungi**. Both of these names refer to a curious club-shaped structure formed at the end of certain hyphae. This **basidium** (bas-*id*-ee-um), as it is called, usually bears four **basidiospores** externally. Four groups of fungi compose the class *Basidiomycetes*. These include the rust fungi, smut fungi, mushrooms and bracket fungi, and puffballs.

Rust fungi cause many serious plant diseases. There are more than 250 known forms of grain rust which attack wheat, oats, barley, and other cereals. They cause millions of dollars of damage to these crops annually.

Wheat rust is one of the best known of these plant parasites, and is a special problem to farmers. It produces four kinds of spores in a very complicated life cycle which involves not just one, but *two* host plants (Fig. 11-6, page 120).

The rust makes its appearance on wheat during the late spring and early summer months, while the wheat is green and actively growing. The rust forms a mycelium which grows among the cells of the wheat stem and leaves. Tiny blisters appear along the surface of the stem and leaves where clumps of hyphae grow to the surface and discharge their spores. These spores are reddish-orange in color and are all one-celled. Biologists refer to them as red spores, or **uredospores** (you-*ree*-doh-spores). These uredospores can reinfect wheat and spread the disease rapidly by lodging on new plants. Later in the summer, when the wheat is ripening and the plants are turning yellow, a sec-

Hugh Spencer

Fig. 11-5. The morel is a highly prized edible fungus. It belongs to the Ascomycetes group, which also includes the yeasts and powdery mildews, as well as the blue and green molds.

ond spore stage appears. The same hyphae which had produced red spores now produce black spores, or **teliospores** (*tee*-lee-oh-spores). These are two-celled spores with heavy, thick, protective walls.

These black spores *cannot* reinfect wheat. Instead, they remain dormant through the winter on the wheat straw or stubble, or on the ground. Early in the spring, both cells of the teliospores germinate, producing four-celled basidia. One basidiospore forms on each of the four cells of the basidium. These spores are then carried away by the wind. If a spore lodges on a leaf of the common barberry (not the cultivated Japanese barberry), the life cycle continues. After complicated changes have occurred in the tissues of the barberry leaf, tiny cups appear on the leaf surfaces. These contain rows of **aeciospores** (*ee*-see-oh-spores) which drop from the cups and are carried by the wind to young wheat plants as much as 500 miles away. Infection of the wheat and production of red spores follows, thus completing the life cycle.

Both the wheat and barberry are necessary for completion of the cycle. Thus

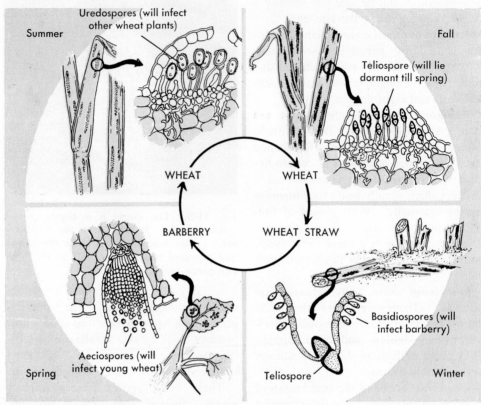

Fig. 11-6. The common barberry and wheat plant are the two hosts necessary for the completion of the life cycle of wheat rust. Trace this cycle from the spring through the following winter in the above diagram.

Fig. 11-7. Trace the life cycle of corn smut from the point at which masses of hyphae develop in the corn plant until the cycle is completed. How does this cycle compare with that of the wheat rust above?

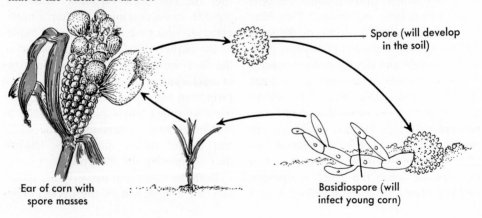

destruction of the common barberry bush is essential in controlling this disease, especially in the northern states where winters are more severe. However, in the southern states during mild winters, red spores may not be killed and can reinfect wheat directly.

Another rust, the *cedar-apple rust,* involves the red cedar tree and the apple and its close relatives. The *white-pine blister rust* causes serious damage to the white pine tree in one stage of its cycle and lives on the wild currant or gooseberry in another.

Smuts are parasites on cereal grains. *Smuts* attack corn, oats, wheat, rye, barley, and other cereal grasses, causing considerable damage.

Corn smut, one of the most familiar of this group, infects corn plants when they are young. Some weeks later, a grayish, slimy swelling appears on the ear, tassel, stem, or leaf (Fig. 11-7). These swellings consist of hyphae. As the corn matures, the hyphae produce large numbers of black, sooty spores which are carried by the wind. These spores may infect nearby corn plants or lie dormant until spring. A germinating spore produces a four-celled, or sometimes three-celled, basidium. Each cell of the basidium produces a single basidiospore, as in the rusts. These basidiospores are carried to corn plants by the wind where they germinate and start a new smut infection. Corn smut may be controlled by burning infected plants, plowing under the stubble after the corn is cut, and destroying the unused stalks and leaves after the corn is picked.

Mushrooms are among the largest and best known of the fungi. We find **mushrooms** in orchards, fields, and woodlands, and popping up suddenly after a warm spring or autumn rain. We seldom see the vegetative mushroom plant. It is a mycelium composed of many silvery hyphae which thread their way through the soil or the wood of a decaying log or stump. A mushroom mycelium may live many years, gradually penetrating more and more area of its host. Digestive enzymes secreted by the hyphae break down organic substances in the host and change them to forms which can be absorbed and used as nourishment by the mushroom plant.

At certain seasons, especially in the spring and fall, small knobs, or *buttons,* develop on the mycelium just below the ground. These consist of masses of tightly-packed hyphae. These buttons develop into the familiar spore-bearing structure we recognize as a mushroom. The mature mushroom consists of a stalk, or **stipe,** which supports an umbrella-shaped **cap.** While pushing up through the soil, the cap is folded downward around the stipe. After forcing its way through the soil, the cap opens out, leaving a ring, or **annulus** (*an*-you-lus), around the stipe at the point where the cap and stipe were joined (Fig. 11-8, page 122).

Most mushrooms contain numerous platelike **gills** on the under surface of the cap, radiating out from the stipe like the spokes of a wheel. On the outside of each gill and extending all around it are hundreds of small basidia, each of which bears four basidiospores. These spores drop from the basidia when mature and are carried by wind and air currents. Each spore forms a new mushroom mycelium if it happens to land in a new environment favorable for growth. If it does not — and not too many do — the spore dies. Some basidiospores are black while others are brown, yellow, white, or pink. If you turn the cap of a fresh ripe mushroom gills downward on a sheet of brown paper, you will usually get a large mass of spores and can identify their color easily.

Basidium

Basidiospore

Cap

Gills

Annulus

Stipe

Hyphae

Fig. 11-8. **This drawing illustrates the development of a mushroom as well as different views of the mature structure. The inset is an enlargement of a gill, showing how the four basidiospores are attached to each basidium.**

Growth characteristics of the fungi. The way in which fungi grow indicates a great deal about their food relations. Many of them tend to grow in circles, as do many molds, ringworm on the skin, which is really a fungus, and the beautiful " fairy ring " mushrooms. In the case of the fairy ring shown in Fig. 11-9, one original mushroom plant developed its mycelium and digested the organic matter available at that spot. As the mycelium expanded into the unused organic matter in the soil around it, new mushrooms were produced periodically at the outer edge of this growing ring of mycelium. As the food supply in the interior of the circle was used, the circle kept growing larger and larger.

You may see the same growth principle if you notice the growth of a mold in a culture dish. The circle will grow larger, which means the newest, most active part of the mold is one the outer edge. The oldest portion is always in the center.

Poisonous and edible mushrooms. The word " toadstool " is frequently used as a popular term for poisonous mushrooms. While many people claim to have methods of distinguishing edible from poisonous varieties, experts tell us there is no certain rule or sign which can be used to distinguish the two types of mushrooms. Frequently, some of the most harmless-looking forms are poisonous and produce severe or, in some cases, even fatal effects if eaten. The only safe advice which can be given is to leave them alone unless you know exactly which forms are edible and which forms are poisonous.

Bracket fungi. *Bracket fungi* are the familiar shelflike growths seen on the stumps or trunks of trees (Fig. 4-2, page

New York Botanical Garden

Fig. 11-9.   What causes these mushrooms to grow in this " fairy ring "?

32). They may be either parasites on living trees, or saprophytes, living on dead wood. They are the most destructive of the wood-rotting fungi. The mycelium of the bracket fungus penetrates the woody tissue of the host and causes it to disintegrate internally. The shelflike reproductive body is telltale evidence of the damage which is occurring within the host. The bracket fungi are woody in texture when old and remain attached to the host year after year. New spore-producing hyphae form on the underside of the shelf, forming layers or rings of growth. Spores are discharged through tiny pores located on the underside of the shelflike growth.

Puffballs. *Puffballs* resemble mushrooms except that the reproductive structure never opens to discharge the spores.

It merely dries and splits open, thus releasing the spores into the air. Puffballs are round or pear-shaped growths, usually white in color. Nearly all species are edible if collected when young and before the spores mature. No poisonous puffballs are known to exist.

Imperfect fungi. The biologist places all the fungi which do not belong in the other classes in the Deuteromycetes, or *imperfect fungi.* The majority of imperfect fungi are most like the Ascomycetes.

Many of the imperfect fungi are of great importance as parasites in man, animals, and plants. Among the plant diseases associated with this group are those of corn, oats, wheat, citrus fruits, tomatoes, cabbage, lettuce, beans, and apples.

The ringworm fungi produce several

Fig. 11-10. The " death angel " is a poisonous mushroom which can be fatal if eaten in enough quantity.

Hugh Spencer

Fig. 11-11. The puffball is an edible fungus that bears its spores in clublike cases. Some puffballs are two feet in diameter.

Hugh Spencer

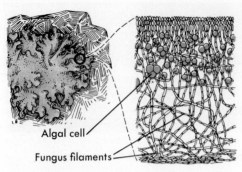

Fig. 11-12. A lichen is actually two kinds of plants living together with mutual benefit — an alga and a fungus. What does the fungus obtain from the alga?

skin infections in man, including ringworm, barber's itch (ringworm of the scalp), and the all too familiar " athlete's foot." Thrush is a serious infection of the mucous membranes of the mouth and throat caused by an imperfect fungus resembling the yeasts.

Lichens reveal a curious plant relationship. While *lichens* are usually grouped with the fungi, they could probably also be placed with the algae, because an alga and a fungus make up the plant body of a lichen. While various lichens differ in structure, the alga is usually one of the green or blue-green forms while the fungus is one of the Ascomycetes.

The plant body of a lichen consists of a mass of fungus hyphae among which the algal cells are scattered (Fig. 11-12). Lichens are of three general types. Some form a hard, granular crust (*crustose lichens*). Others resemble flattened, leathery leaves (*foliose lichens*). Still others form a network of slender branches (*fruticose lichens*) (Fig. 11-13).

A lichen is a perfect example of **symbiosis,** because both the alga and the fungus benefit from the association. In fact, neither could survive alone in the environments where lichens live. The fungus depends on the alga for food, produced by photosynthesis. Although the alga is, in a sense, a " slave," it is protected and kept moist by the fungus hyphae.

The biological " teamwork " illustrated

Fig. 11-13. The foliose lichen on the left has flattened leaves, while the branching stems of the fruticose lichen on the right are its most distinguishing characteristic.

Hugh Spencer   *Carolina Biological Supply House*

in a lichen allows it to live in places where few other plants can survive. Many lichens grow on tree trunks. Others cling to rock surfaces far above timber line in the alpine zone of high mountains. These lichens are important pioneer plants. Gradually, they cause rock surfaces to crumble and, as they add their own remains season after season, produce organic matter which is the basis for soil. This soil can then support other plants.

Lichens are among the most abundant plants of the wind-swept tundra of the far north. One of these lichens, *Cladonia,* is so valuable as food for reindeer that it is commonly called *reindeer moss.*

Symbiosis in higher plants. Biologists have been investigating an interesting symbiotic relationship between certain fungi and the roots of higher plants. Many Ascomycetes and Basidiomycetes which live in the soil are parasites on the roots of trees and shrubs. Some form a mass of hyphae around a young root. Others enter the root and live as internal parasites. It is believed that the fungi aid the root in absorbing minerals, especially nitrogen compounds. The fungi, of course, take nourishment from the root tissues. We refer to such a root fungus as a **mycorhiza,** as you will recall from the discussion of symbiotic relationships in Chapter 4.

In Conclusion

The fungi are a group of thallophytes lacking chlorophyll. Fungi must grow on organic materials because they have no chlorophyll and thus cannot make their own food. If the food source is living material, the fungus is a parasite. If the source is nonliving, the fungus is a saprophyte.

Among the most important groups of fungi are mushrooms, bracket fungi, molds, mildews, rusts, smuts, blights, yeasts, and bacteria.

Fungi may be beneficial or harmful, depending on their source of food. Among the valuable fungi are certain of the mushrooms, some of the molds, and yeasts. Certain molds, mildews, rusts, and smuts are blight-causing organisms and among the most destructive plants in the entire plant kingdom.

In the next group of plants, we shall examine some members which are more like the familiar land plants of the field, woods, and garden. These, the mosses and ferns, show many advances over the simple algae and fungi.

BIOLOGICALLY SPEAKING

aeciospore	haustoria	sporangium
annulus	hypha	sporangiophore
ascus	mycelium	stipe
basidiospore	mycologist	stolon
basidium	mycorhiza	teliospore
budding	penicillin	true fungi
cap	rhizoid	uredospore
gill	riboflavin	zymase

QUESTIONS FOR REVIEW

1. What one characteristic do all fungi have in common?
2. (a) Name six classes of fungi. (b) Which of these classes are included in the true fungi?
3. Describe the mycelium of a true fungus.
4. Describe the different kinds of hyphae which make up a bread mold plant.
5. How can bread become inoculated with bread mold even though there are no molds close by?
6. Discuss several ways in which *Penicillium* molds are valuable.
7. Why are downy mildews more destructive to higher plants than the powdery mildews?
8. Describe budding in yeast.
9. How are the products of yeast fermentation used commercially?
10. Describe the production of four kinds of spores by wheat rust.
11. What stage in the life cycle of corn smut relates it to the rusts?
12. Describe the structure of a mushroom reproductive body.
13. How are puffballs different structurally from mushrooms?
14. Name several human infections caused by imperfect fungi.
15. How does a lichen show symbiosis?

APPLYING FACTS AND PRINCIPLES

1. Why are the fungi of greater direct economic importance than the algae?
2. (a) How is bread mold similar to certain of the algae? (b) How is it different?
3. Mildew diseases of higher plants are more prevalent some summers than others. Account for this.
4. Sweet cider will ferment rapidly in a warm place even when it is in a tightly closed container. Explain why.
5. Why are yeast preparations valuable in treating acne and other skin disorders?
6. Explain why certain kinds of mushrooms and molds often grow in a circular ring.
7. Why is a severe epidemic of wheat rust likely to follow a mild winter?
8. Explain why lichens can grow on barren soil and rocks without contact with organic matter.

CHAPTER 12

The Mosses and the Ferns

AT one time the mosses and ferns were probably the most common form of plant life on the earth. Their importance now is due not so much to their presence today as to the remains of their ancient relatives. Ancient green plants stored up the energy from the sun which shone on the earth millions of years ago. Now this energy is released when we burn the remains of these plants as coal or oil.

Still another reason for our attention to these plants is the fact that their reproductive cycle is somewhat more complicated than that of the majority of the thallophytes. A study of the mosses and ferns also helps us understand the process of seed formation in the modern seed plants.

The Bryophyta. The *bryophytes* (*bry*-oh-fytes) consist of two main groups of plants, the *mosses* and the *liverworts*. They are found in every section of the world, and at great extremes in temperature and altitude. They probably were the first plants to live exclusively on the land. However, some members of the group still live in water. Together with lichens they serve as soil builders. Gradually they wear away large rocks by acid secretions.

No bryophyte plant body is very large. Although they live on land, these plants have no structures which can carry water to their leaves very efficiently. Nor do they have true roots, so they cannot absorb much water from the soil. Thus, the bryophytes, while showing a more complicated reproductive cycle, do not have cell specialization for water movement on a large scale. Such a specialization is necessary for a large plant to live successfully on land.

Mosses. You have seen *mosses* growing in cracks in shaded sidewalks, on moist ground under trees, or in clumps in deep woods. What looks like a tuft or carpet is, actually, a compact clump of moss plants. Each plant has its tiny " stem " with a cluster of " leaves " encircling it. If you pull one of these tiny plants from the soil, you will find a group of hairlike rhizoids growing from the base of the stem. Mosses do not have true roots containing conducting tissues, as do higher plants, but the rhizoids serve a purpose by anchoring the plant and by absorbing some water and dissolved minerals from the soil. Mosses do, however, have structures which resemble the leaves and stems found in higher plants.

Life cycle of the moss. The moss plant which we commonly see is only one phase of the life cycle. If you examine the diagram in Fig. 12-1, page 128, you see that each moss plant goes through a reproductive cycle in which an asexual spore-producing stage forms a sexual gamete-producing stage. This, then, in turn, forms the spore stage again. A type of reproductive cycle like this illustrates *alternation of generations*. To put it another way, the **sporophyte** (spore-producing plant) alternates with a **gametophyte** (gamete-producing plant).

At the tips of the leafy stems of the mosses, and entirely hidden by the leaves, are many *reproductive organs*. Some species bear both male and female organs on the same plant. Other species have the male organs on one plant and the female organs on another. Inside the male organs we find sperm, which are the male sex cells, or gametes. A **gamete** is any sex cell. Sperm are discharged from the male organs and swim to the female organs. Dew provides enough moisture for this transfer. Inside each female organ is an egg. This is the female sex cell, or gamete. One sperm enters the neck of the female organ and unites with an egg. The union of sperm and egg is called *fertilization* and results in the formation of a *zygote*. This process is part of the gametophyte, or sexual stage, of the life cycle.

Fertilization starts the sporophyte, or asexual phase, of the cycle. The zygote always remains in the female organ. Soon it begins to grow and produces a slender stalk which grows up and out of the leafy shoot of the plant. The top of the stalk swells and becomes a large mass of tissue called a **capsule**, which is covered with a

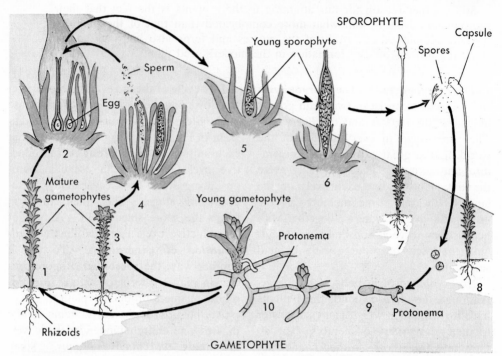

Fig. 12-1. Life cycle of the moss. Stages 1–4 show the female (1, 2) and male (3, 4) gametophyte plants. After fertilization, the sporophyte generation (5, 6, 7) grows out of the top of the female plant. Spores form in the capsule (sporangium) at the top of the sporophyte (8) and, when mature, fall to the ground and give rise to a new generation of gametophyte plants (9, 10).

thin hood. Inside the capsule are many microscopic *spores*. These are asexual. That is, they are neither definitely male nor female. When the spores are ripe, the hood falls off, the capsule opens, and the spores escape. They are carried off by the wind, and when they fall on the ground they begin to grow, provided environmental conditions are right. The sporophyte stage has ended and the gametophyte stage begins.

Each spore produces a small threadlike structure called a **protonema** (proh-toh-*nee*-muh). All the cells that make up the protonema have chlorophyll and can make their own food. Their resemblance to algae is startling and once caused many scientists to class them as close relatives of the algae. Some threads of the protonema produce short buds

which grow into a new moss plant. Other threads enter the ground and become the rhizoids. Thus, a new moss plant is formed and this gametophyte will soon form sex cells.

Economic importance of the mosses. The *sphagnum* (*sfag*-num), or peat-forming mosses, are the most widely used. Sphagnum grows in small lakes and bogs, where it forms floating mats. These mats increase in size and thickness each year as generation after generation occupies the surface of the mat. Plants of previous years decompose slowly, settle to the bottom, and form *peat*. In time, the growth of sphagnum mats in a lake may close the water entirely, causing the lake to enter the bog stage. Eventually, what was once a thriving, open lake may become a deep deposit of brownish-black

Fig. 12-2. Although the leafy gametophyte stage of the moss plant is more familiar, it is often possible to see the slender stalks and sporangia of the sporophyte plant, such as are shown in this enlarged photograph.

Hugh Spencer

peat. Large sphagnum mats are often invaded by larger plants — rushes, grasses, shrubs, and even trees.

Dried sphagnum is valuable to nurserymen because of its absorbent qualities. It holds water like cotton, and is used for packing the roots of garden plants like roses, iris, and chrysanthemums to prevent their drying out during shipment. This same absorbent quality of sphagnum

Fig. 12-3. Sphagnum, or peat moss, is valuable commercially as a mulch in gardens and for packing nursery stock for transplanting.

Hugh Spencer

makes it valuable to the gardener as a *mulch*. It can be worked into the soil or placed on the surface to make the soil loose and to hold water during the usually dry summer months.

Other mosses are important to us as pioneer plants in rocky areas. The small amount of soil which collects in cracks on the bare surfaces of cliffs and ledges is sufficient to support moss plants. The rhizoids secrete substances which break down rocks gradually and thus form more soil. As mosses die and decompose season after season, they form enough soil to anchor the roots of larger plants.

The liverworts. Much less familiar than mosses are their relatives, the *liverworts.* These curious small plants grow in wet places, often along the banks of streams, around the outlet of a spring, or on rocky ledges. The moist soil and flowerpots in greenhouses are other good places to find liverworts. They look like thin, leathery leaves laid flat against the ground. One of the common liverworts resembles a thin tongue with Y-shaped branches at the tip. Under ideal conditions, a clump of liverworts may cover a considerable area. Male and female sex organs are formed in curious structures

General Biological Supply House

Fig. 12-4. The common liverwort *Marchantia* has reproductive structures that resemble small umbrellas.

like umbrellas which rise about an inch above the flat plant body. A liverwort in such a condition is interesting to find and will reward your careful search in moist habitats. A common liverwort, *Marchantia* (mar-*kan*-shih-uh), appears in Fig. 12-4.

The Pteridophyta — ferns and their relatives. To appreciate the ***pteridophytes*** (ter-*id*-oh-fytes) fully, we should have lived millions of years ago during the age in which they were in their glory. Then they were not limited to a few places in the woods, or swamp, or hillside, or flowerpot. They formed large forests which covered the wet, marshy land common at that time. Ferns much like those of today flourished during this past age, but tree ferns 30 to 40 feet high were also abundant.

Although no man ever saw these great forests of ferns, today we are reaping the benefits of their existence. During this age, referred to as the *Carboniferous Pe-*

riod, great layers of fern remains accumulated in the swampy areas where they grew. Later, the movements of the earth compressed these layers into layers of coal. It has been estimated that it took 300 feet of compressed vegetation to form 20 feet of coal. When we consider what coal has meant to industry, we might almost conclude that the high civilization of modern America has sprung from the pteridophyte vegetation of millions of years ago.

Most of us are familiar with ferns as clumps of plants with graceful, deeply-cut leaves. In all but the few remaining tree ferns of the tropics, the stems are underground, creeping horizontally just below the surface. These underground stems, called ***rhizomes*** (*ry*-zomes), bear clusters of true roots which spread through the ground, anchoring the plant and absorbing water and dissolved minerals.

Life cycle of the fern. The fern you find in the shaded woods or growing as a potted plant is the sporophyte stage of the life cycle (Fig. 12-5).

When the familiar fern leaves are mature, small dots called **sori** (*sor*-eye) [sing. *sorus*] appear on the lower side. The sori differ in shape and location in different kinds of ferns. Some people become alarmed when sori appear and remove them carefully, thinking the fern is diseased.

Each sorus consists of a cluster of helmet-shaped **sporangia,** each of which contains numerous *spores.* The sporangium is attached to the sorus by a short stalk. Since the fern plant bears sporangia and spores, it corresponds to the stalk and capsule of the moss.

When the spores are mature, the sporangium bursts open and releases them. The tiny spores are easily picked up by the wind and carried to new locations. If a spore falls in a moist place, it begins to grow.

The spore grows into a short filament of cells with rhizoids. The second, or the gametophyte stage, of the fern life cycle has begun. This stage at first resembles the protonema of a moss. However, unlike the moss, the filament broadens at the tip and becomes a flat, heart-shaped structure called a **prothallus** (proh-*thal*-us). When fully grown, the prothallus is one-quarter to one-half inch in diameter. The flat prothallus is green and clings close to the ground, held by a cluster of rhizoids which form on the underside at the rounded or lower end of the " heart." It would be an interesting project for you to try to raise some fern prothalli.

Fig. 12-5. The fern life cycle. Stages 1 and 2 represent the sporophyte generation, which is familiarly seen above the ground. Stages 3–7 represent the gametophyte, which develops on the ground and is seldom seen because it is so small. The young sporophyte (8, 9) develops from the fertilized egg.

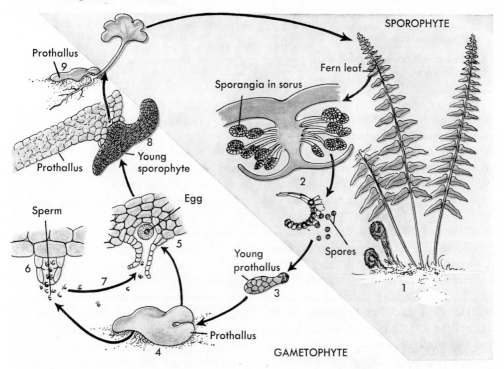

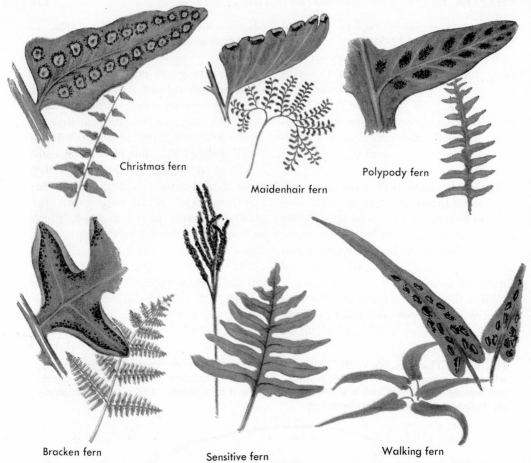

Christmas fern

Maidenhair fern

Polypody fern

Bracken fern

Sensitive fern

Walking fern

Fig. 12-6. **Note how the location of the sori with their sporangia differs with various kinds of ferns.**

The male sex organs containing sperm develop among the rhizoids. Several female sex organs form near the notch at the upper end of the prothallus. Each one contains an egg. In most ferns, the eggs and sperm mature at different times. Thus, when sperm escape, they swim in the film of dew to another prothallus. It is interesting that both bryophytes and pteridophytes, while largely land plants, still require water for fertilization. When a sperm fertilizes an egg, a zygote is produced. This marks the end of the gametophyte stage and the beginning of the sporophyte stage. It is interesting to note that this prothallus stage of a fern corresponds to the leafy-shoot stage of the moss.

Immediately after fertilization, the zygote grows into a young fern plant. Soon, the young fern becomes established with a root, a leaf or *frond,* and a stem. The stem bears additional leaves and the familiar fern clump results. Thus the sporophyte is the most conspicuous part of the life cycle of the fern.

Relatives of the fern. Closely related to the ferns are two groups of plants, fairly common in some localities. The *Equisetums* (ek-weh-*see*-tums), or *horsetail rushes,* are often seen in wet places or around the margins of lakes. They appear as slender, dark green, rodlike stems bearing light-colored cones at their tips. The leaves are reduced to small scalelike

Fig. 12-7. The horsetail rush (*Equisetum*) is a relative of the fern. Notice the greatly reduced leaves growing in a circle on the stem.

Hugh Spencer

structures growing in circles around the stem at regular intervals (Fig. 12-7).

Club mosses resemble true mosses only in general appearance and constitute another group of the fern relatives. These plants bear curious club-shaped reproductive structures at the tops of certain of their branches (Fig. 12-8). They are found in rich, damp woods, or creeping along the rocky slopes of mountains. Like the ferns, both horsetails and club mosses are now merely remnants of the once flourishing age of pteridophytes. At that time they were the size of present-day trees. You can still see their remains in the form of leaf or stem imprints in coal.

Fig. 12-8. Club mosses are also related to the ferns. They are rapidly becoming extinct in some areas because of their widespread use in decoration at Christmas time.

Brooklyn Botanic Garden

In Conclusion

The two intermediate plant phyla between the thallophytes and the spermatophytes (seed plants) are the bryophytes and pteridophytes. They both show a complicated life cycle in which one spore-producing stage, the sporophyte, produces a gamete-producing stage, the gametophyte, in an alternation of generations.

The bryophytes have the mosses as their chief representatives and the pteridophytes, the ferns. The fact that these plants once covered the earth is important to man today because of the coal they formed millions of years ago.

Our survey of the plant kingdom thus far has shown us the simpler, flowerless, less-noticed forms of plant life. In the next unit we shall discuss the great group of seed-bearing plants (spermatophytes) with which you are already familiar from your previous general science courses. They too will prove to be an important and interesting collection of living organisms.

BIOLOGICALLY SPEAKING

alternation of generations
bryophyte
capsule
gamete

gametophyte
prothallus
protonema
pteridophyte

rhizomes
sorus
sporangia
sporophyte

QUESTIONS FOR REVIEW

1. In what way does the water-conducting structure of the bryophytes prevent them from growing into large plants?
2. Describe briefly the two phases in the life history of the moss.
3. Explain what is meant by alternation of generations.
4. What process separates the gametophyte from the sporophyte?
5. Describe briefly the formation of a peat bog.

6. In what ways are the mosses important to man?
7. Describe coal formation.
8. List the various structures in the order of their appearance in the life cycle of the fern.
9. Describe the way in which the fern produces its spores.
10. In what ways are the gametophyte generation and the sporophyte generation of the fern connected with each other?

APPLYING FACTS AND PRINCIPLES

1. Why do you suppose that we seldom find more than one sporophyte growing from a single leafy stalk of moss, although that stalk usually bears more than one female sex organ?
2. What reasons can you give for the pteridophytes dying out as the common plants in the world? Refer to the *Carboniferous Period*.
3. Compare the sporophyte plant of a moss and a fern and explain in what ways the fern is more advanced.
4. List ways in which the fern is better suited to life on land than the moss.

RESEARCH ON YOUR OWN

1. Make a collection of algae from the ponds, streams, or seashore in your vicinity. Try to identify them. Most algae can be cultured in an aquarium or in large glass jars. Frequent inspection may show some of the specimens in different reproductive stages.

2. In an aquarium which has chiefly one-celled algae, try to strain the water through a fine-mesh cloth. Dry the resulting material in an oven. Then add it, using sterile techniques, to a sterile jar of water and add a dropper of water containing one-celled animals. Test the water periodically to determine the growth of the one-celled animals. Keep a control jar which has not had the algae material added.

3. Scrape some of the white " tartar " from your teeth and smear the material on the slide. Pass the slide through a flame many times, and then place several drops of stain (methylene blue will do) on it. Let the slide stand for a few minutes, then wash it by allowing water to run over it, and let it stand to dry. Examine under the microscope. Make a careful and complete record of what you have done and observed.

4. Prepare some culture dishes and inoculate them with bacteria or expose them to some source of bacteria, such as air. However, when inoculating some of the dishes, have an ultraviolet or a " sun " lamp shining on the dish. What type of growth do you find in the dishes after incubation?

5. Moisten a piece of bread and expose it to the air for about 30 minutes. Put it in a covered dish and keep it in a warm, dark place. After a few days, a growth of mold should appear. Observe it closely. Inspect a part of it under the microscope.

6. Sow some moss or fern spores on a layer of damp, moist soil to produce gametophyte plants. Keep the soil covered. The spores from several fern species may be obtained from a local greenhouse.

7. Using a special agar medium, molds can be cultivated in Petri dishes and test tubes if the same procedures are used as shown in the chapter on bacteria. Various places for obtaining specimens are soil, air, mold-covered objects, and molded food materials.

8. Add various quantities of an antibiotic to the food supply of animals, being sure to keep some other animals of the same kind as controls. Observe any change in weight, appearance, and general vitality of the test animals.

9. Fern spores can be planted on agar media in Petri dishes. Prothallia should then develop. The surface of the agar should be kept moist.

MORE ABOUT BIOLOGY

Christensen, Clyde M. *The Molds and Man*. The University of Minnesota Press, Minneapolis, Minn. 1951

Cobb, Boughton. *A Field Guide to the Ferns*. Houghton, Mifflin Co., Boston. 1956

Conrad, Henry S. *How to Know the Mosses and Liverworts*. William C. Brown Co., Dubuque, Iowa. 1956

Duggington, C. L. *The Friendly Fungi*. The Macmillan Company, New York. 1957

Hausman, Leon. *Beginner's Guide to Fresh-Water Life*. G. P. Putnam's Sons, New York. 1949

Hausman, Leon. *Beginner's Guide to Seashore Life*. G. P. Putnam's Sons, New York. 1950

Hylander, Clarence. *Sea and Shore*. The Macmillan Company, New York. 1950

Hylander, Clarence. *The World of Plant Life*. The Macmillan Company, New York. 1958

Jaques, H. E. *Plant Families and How to Know Them*. William C. Brown Co., Dubuque, Iowa. 1948

Miner, R. W. *Fieldbook of Seashore Life.* G. P. Putnam's Sons, New York. 1950

Morgan, Ann Haven. *Fieldbook of Ponds and Streams.* G. P. Putnam's Sons, New York. 1930

Needham, James and Needham, Paul R. *A Guide to the Study of Fresh-Water Biology.* Comstock Publishing Assoc., Ithaca, New York. 1938

Needham, James and Needham, J. Lloyd. *Life in the Inland Waters.* Comstock Publishing Assoc., Ithaca, New York. 1937

Neurath, Marie. *The Wonder World of Strange Plants.* Lothrop, Lee, and Shepard Co., Inc., New York. 1957

Pelezar, Michael J., Jr. *Microbiology.* McGraw-Hill Book Co., Inc., New York. 1958

Prescott, G. W. *How to Know the Fresh-Water Algae.* William C. Brown Co., Dubuque, Iowa. 1954

Rahn, Otto. *Microbes of Merit.* Ronald Press Co., New York. 1945

Russell, Norman H. *An Introduction to the Plant Kingdom.* The C. V. Mosby Co., St. Louis, Mo. 1958

Sterling, Dorothy. *The Story of Mosses, Ferns, and Mushrooms.* Doubleday and Co., Inc., New York. 1958

Tressler, Donald. *The Wealth of the Sea.* The Century Co., New York. 1937

U. S. Dept. of Agriculture. *Grasses.* Supt. of Documents, Govt. Printing Office, Washington, D.C. 1948

The Higher Plants

The Lord thy God means to settle thee in a fair land, a land that has water coursing down in streams . . . a land of wheat and barley, of vine and fig-tree and pomegranate and olive; a land where oil flows, and honey. Here without fear of want thou mayest win thy livelihood. — Deuteronomy 8:7–10

When we speak of higher plants, we refer generally to the seed plants. These are the plants with which you are most familiar. Some of the seed plants are aquatic; others live in the wet surroundings of bogs, marshes, and streams. By far the largest number of seed plants, however, live on land, where they are the most important and conspicuous forms of vegetation.

The chapters of this unit will describe the tissues and organs of the seed plants. You will discover how these plants are suited to the many environments they occupy. Roots, stems, and leaves perform activities of a seed plant far more efficiently than the simple plant body of the thallophyte. Flowers, fruits, and seeds are specialized parts that have removed these plants from dependence on water for reproduction.

We live in the age of seed plants. This unit will tell you why these plants have become the supreme form of plant life.

CHAPTER 13: **THE SEED PLANTS**
CHAPTER 14: **ROOTS AND THEIR ACTIVITIES**
CHAPTER 15: **THE ROOT AS AN ORGAN OF ABSORPTION**
CHAPTER 16: **STEMS AND THEIR ACTIVITIES**
CHAPTER 17: **LEAVES AND THEIR ACTIVITIES**
CHAPTER 18: **FLOWERS AND REPRODUCTION**
CHAPTER 19: **FRUITS AND SEEDS**

The Seed Plants

L ONG years ago, when giant dinosaurs roamed the earth, a new kind of plant was slowly invading the forests of ferns and fernlike plants. The age of the seed plants had dawned. Since that time, more than 200 million years ago, other forms of vegetation have been forced to yield more and more of the land to seed plants, the most advanced of all plants.

Today, seed plants dominate the land masses of the earth. Mosses and ferns, which once grew in great numbers, are now reduced for the most part to scattered clumps and patches. Seed plants form our forests and spread over fields and plains. They have invaded dry lands and deserts. Their frontiers lie in the windswept, treeless plains of the far north and the rocky slopes of high mountains. Beyond here, the mosses in their last retreat hold the shallow, barren ground.

On land, seed plants reign supreme. Their specialized tissues and highly developed organs are the most perfect of the plant kingdom.

Spermatophytes — the seed plants. The fourth phylum of the plant kingdom, the **Spermatophyta** (sper-mat-*ah*-fih-tuh), includes all plants which produce seeds. A **seed** is an embryo plant covered by one or more protective seed coats (Fig. 13-1). Food stored in a seed nourishes the young plant until it is established in its new location. In a sense, a seed is a packaged plant, ready for delivery.

A seed may travel through the air, float in the water, be carried on the fur of an animal, or lie dormant for many months. When conditions are favorable, the seed coats soften and the young plant pushes out its root and its shoot. By means of seeds, plants spread to new locations. Reproduction by seeds is highly efficient. It is one of the reasons the seed plants have gained domination of the earth.

Fig. 13-1. A seed consists of an embryo plant, stored food, and one or more protective coats. The bean seed is enclosed in a fruit while that of the pine is not.

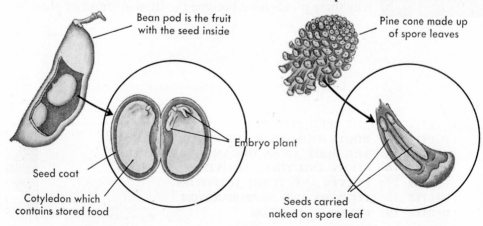

Bean pod is the fruit with the seed inside

Pine cone made up of spore leaves

Embryo plant

Seed coat

Cotyledon which contains stored food

Seeds carried naked on spore leaf

Fig. 13-2. The cycads are gymnosperms that flourished in early geological eras, but are now quite rare. They are halfway between tree ferns and palms in appearance.

Two great classes of seed plants. We divide the phylum Spermatophyta into two large classes: (1) the **Gymnospermae** (*jim*-noh-sperm-ee); and (2) the **Angiospermae** (*an*-jee-oh-sperm-ee). The gymnosperms are the more primitive and older seed plants. The name means, literally, *naked seeds* (Fig. 13-1). It refers to the fact that their seeds are not enclosed in a fruit. Gymnosperms flourished in earlier stages of the conquest of the land by seed plants. Some of their members lived as far back as the Carboniferous, or coal-forming, Period. Today, large numbers of gymnosperms are extinct. We know them only in the form of fossils. *Fossils* are imprints of living things of long ago preserved in rocks, or are plant and animal parts which have been displaced by minerals in the earth's crust. However, many gymnosperms, including the pine, spruce, fir, and several other forest trees, are of great value in our civilization.

The class Angiospermae includes all of the flowering plants. The flower produces the fruit, which, in turn, encloses the seeds.

A living fossil. Many years ago, priests of China found a curious tree in the forests of the interior. They planted it in the temple gardens. Later it was introduced into gardens in Japan. Little did these ancient priests know that they had found and preserved the last species of an order of gymnosperms, the *Ginkgoales* (ging-koh-*ay*-leez). You may know the ginkgo tree (*Ginkgo biloba*), for it is now cultivated in yards and parks of the United States and other countries.

The leaves of the ginkgo are wedge-shaped and two-lobed, unlike those of any other tree. Most of the leaves grow in clusters at the tips of curious spurs spaced along the branches. Some of the branches lack these spurs. The ginkgo is often called the maidenhair tree because its leaves closely resemble those of the maidenhair fern. Its fruits look like

Fig. 13-3. The ginkgo tree was once found only in China and Japan, but is now a familiar sight in the United States. The insert is a close-up of the unusual fruit and leaf.

American Forest Products Industries

Fig. 13-4. The Douglas fir, a conifer, is the most important source of lumber in the western part of the United States.

large berries and are extremely foul-smelling.

The ginkgo is a fine tree for planting in the yard. In time it will grow as high as 100 feet with a diameter of nearly four feet. If you do plant a ginkgo, you will have one of the rarest of all living plants — a single species of a single genus — the last survivor of an entire order.

Cone-bearing gymnosperms — the conifers. The word *conifer* refers to the fact that trees of that name bear woody *cones*. These consist of scalelike struc-

tures, called **spore leaves,** which bear winged seeds on their upper surface. Conifer seeds are scattered by the wind.

Conifer leaves are either in the form of needles or flat scales. Most coniferous trees keep their needles all winter. The new ones which are formed in the spring take the place of the old ones which fall to the ground. Exceptions to this are the bald cypress and the larch. These two conifers lose their needles each autumn.

Of all the kinds of gymnosperms which ever lived, the conifers are best suited to present world environments. Many coniferous species have disappeared, but the conifers remain today in many parts of the world. They still flourish and are dominant in many parts of North America. The table below lists the genera of some modern North American conifers.

We have included the scientific names of these genera because you will see them if you look at nursery catalogs. Conifers are widely used in yard plantings. Cultivated varieties of the red cedar, white cedar, hemlock, and yew are ideal for planting along the foundations of houses. Large conifers are widely planted as windbreaks around farm houses and as trees in city yards. Pines, spruces, and hemlocks are ideal for these purposes. The Colorado blue spruce is unsurpassed as a single tree in a yard planting.

Conifers are ideal as timber trees. Many species thrive in sand and rocky soils, which are unsuitable for the broad-leaved forest trees.

CONIFERS TODAY

Pine (*Pinus*)	White cedar, arborvitae (*Thuja*)
Spruce (*Picea*)	Bald cypress (*Taxodium*)
Fir (*Abies*)	Redwood (*Sequoia*)
Hemlock (*Tsuga*)	Douglas fir (*Pseudotsuga*)
Red cedar (*Juniperus*)	Yew (*Taxus*)
Larch, tamarack (*Larix*)	

SOME FAMILIES OF MONOCOTS

FAMILY	FAMILIAR MEMBERS
Cattail	Common cattail
Grass	Cereal grains, bluegrass, sugar cane, bamboo, timothy
Sedge	Sedges
Arum	Indian turnip (Jack-in-the-pulpit), skunk cabbage, calla lily
Pineapple	Pineapple, Spanish moss
Lily	Lily, onion, tulip, hyacinth
Amaryllis	Amaryllis
Iris	Flag, iris
Orchis	Lady's slipper, orchis, orchid
Palm	Coconut palm, date palm, palmetto

SOME FAMILIES OF DICOTS

Willow	Willow, poplar (cottonwood), aspen
Walnut	Walnut, hickory
Birch	Birch, alder, hazel
Beech	Beech, chestnut, oak
Pink	Pink, carnation, chickweed
Water lily	Water lily, pond lily
Crowfoot	Buttercup, hepatica, columbine, delphinium, larkspur
Poppy	Poppy, bloodroot
Mustard	Mustard, radish, turnip, cress
Rose	Rose, apple, hawthorn, strawberry, pear, peach, plum, cherry
Pulse (legume)	Bean, pea, clover, alfalfa, locust, redbud
Flax	Flax
Maple	Maple
Mallow	Marshmallow, hollyhock, hibiscus
Parsley	Parsley, parsnip, carrot, sweet cicely
Heath	Laurel, rhododendron, azalea, heather, blueberry, cranberry, huckleberry
Mint	Catnip, spearmint, peppermint, nettle, sage
Nightshade	Tomato, potato, tobacco
Figwort	Mullein, snapdragon, digitalis (foxglove)
Composite	Dandelion, daisy, sunflower, zinnia, aster, marigold, thistle, dahlia

Before leaving the conifers, we might mention that they hold the record for height, trunk diameter, and age among trees. A *Sequoia,* or giant redwood, in the Calaveras Grove in California towers 300 feet above the ground. This tree is over 30 feet in diameter and is estimated to be 4,000 years old. However, this trunk diameter and age are surpassed by a cypress tree, the Big Tree of Tule, growing about 200 miles south of Mexico City. It is 50 feet in diameter and is estimated to be over 5,000 years old.

Flowering plants. The angiosperms, or flowering plants, are divided into two large subclasses: (1) the *Monocotyledonae*

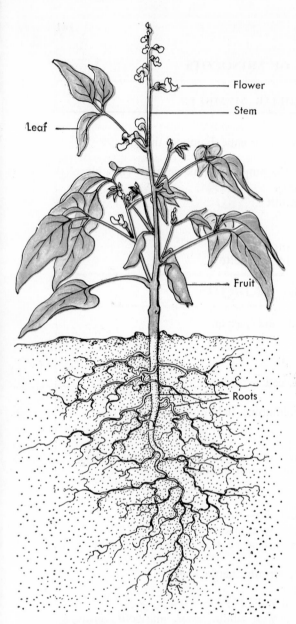

Fig. 13-5. As you look at this drawing of a flowering bean plant, name the activity each organ performs.

(*mon*-oh-kot-ih-*lee*-duh-nee), or *monocots;* and (2) the *Dicotyledonae* (*dy*-kot-ih-*lee*-duh-nee), or *dicots*. A **cotyledon** is a special kind of leaf which develops in the seed. It absorbs, stores, and digests food and nourishes the young plant after the seed has sprouted and until it is well

established. **Monocots** produce a single seed leaf, while **dicots** have two. As we study the various parts of flowering plants, we shall point out other differences between monocots and dicots. These will include differences in the arrangement of root and stem tissues, the form of leaf veins, and the number of flower parts.

Flowering plants are represented by over 40 orders, including more than 140 families. Species of flowering plants number approximately 250,000.

You are probably familiar with many of the families of flowering plants listed in the table on page 141.

The plant body of a flowering plant. Each organ of a flowering plant is highly developed for performing certain activities (Fig. 13-5). The root, stem, and leaf are *vegetative organs*. They perform all the processes necessary for life *except* the formation of seeds. This does not mean, however, that plants cannot multiply directly from their roots, stems, or leaves. If you have sprouted roots on a pussy willow stem in a jar of water, you know you can plant the stem and grow a new plant. Root, stem, and leaf cuttings, as well as budding and grafting, are methods of vegetative reproduction.

The **root** anchors the plant in the ground. It spreads through the soil and *absorbs* water and soil minerals. It *conducts* these to the stem for delivery to the leaves. Many roots *store* food reserves and return them to the plant as needed.

The **stem** produces the leaves and *displays* them to the light. It is a busy thoroughfare, for it *conducts* water and minerals upward and carries foods that have been manufactured in the leaves downward. Like the root, the stem often serves as a place of food *storage*. In many plants, green stems aid the leaves in *food manufacture*.

The **leaf** is the center of much of the plant's activity. It is the chief center of *food manufacture*. It exchanges gases with the atmosphere during *respiration*. Much of the water absorbed by the root has a one-way trip through the plant. It escapes from the leaf as water vapor during *transpiration* (trans-pih-*ray*-shun).

After a period of growth, a plant usually starts reproduction. **Flowers** are specialized *reproductive organs*. They are followed by **fruits** and **seeds**. As the flower withers, the fruit develops from certain of its parts. Within the fruit are the seeds, each containing an embryo plant, which are ready to be carried to a new environment. There they sprout and establish a new generation of the same kind of plant.

Tissues of flowering plants. The various organs of higher plants perform their activities with great efficiency because of the specialized tissues which form them. We shall study these tissues more thoroughly when we discuss each of the plant organs in greater detail in the chapters to follow. However, before dealing with any individual organ, you should be familiar with the names of various tissues and the general functions of each. These are summarized as follows:

Epidermis (ep-ih-*der*-mis) — an outer protective layer which prevents loss of water, injury, and the entry of disease-causing organisms.

Cork — a waterproof covering of dead cells, especially in woody plants. It serves the same general purpose as an epidermis, but is more efficient.

Parenchyma (puh-*ren*-kih-muh) — a thin-walled, soft tissue of the type forming flower petals, leaf blades, and the *cortex* and *pith* regions of stems and roots. Food manufacture and storage of food and water are functions of parenchyma tissues.

Xylem (*zy*-lem) — a supporting and conducting tissue. Large cells called *vessels* and small cells called *tracheids*

(*tray*-kee-ids) are thick-walled conducting tubes. Xylem *fibers* give strength, especially to stems and roots. This is the tissue which makes up the large area of a stem called *wood*.

Phloem (*flow*-em) — a tissue including long, slender cells, or *sieve tubes,* for conduction and phloem *fibers* for support. Phloem occupies the inner bark of trees.

Embryonic tissue — composed of small, actively dividing cells. During the growing season, embryonic tissues divide continuously and give rise to cells which mature into other plant tissues. Embryonic tissue at the tips of roots and in the buds of stems forms the tissues which result in growth in length. The *cambium* layer between the bark and the wood causes growth in diameter.

Herbaceous and woody plants. To a biologist, an *herb* is any plant with a soft stem which lasts for only one growing season. Garden vegetables and flowers, cereal grains, and many of our common weeds are herbaceous. In short, any plant with a stem which is not woody and which dies to the ground at the end of the growing season is **herbaceous** (her-*bay*-shus).

Woody plants include trees, shrubs,

Fig. 13-6. **This photomicrograph of a cross section of a woody stem shows xylem tissue. The large cells in the center develop in the spring, when water is needed most.**

Dr. Oswald Tippo

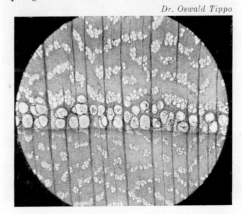

Fig. 13-7. This profusion of blooms is composed entirely of annuals. There are phlox in the foreground, zinnias in the middle, and marigolds at the back.

W. Atlee Burpee Co.

and certain vines such as the wild grape, Virginia creeper, and poison ivy. In a woody stem, the conducting and supporting tissues form layers which are added to year after year. Growth of the stem continues each year from embryonic tissues in various growing points.

The life span of a seed plant varies from one season to many centuries. Plants which live for only one season are called *annuals*. These plants, including the zinnia, marigold, bean, and pea, grow from a seed, mature, reproduce, and die in a single growing season.

Biennials live two seasons. The first year they produce vegetative parts only. At the close of the first season, the stem dies down. Food reserves are stored in the root. The plant then grows during its second season and bears the flowers. When seeds are produced, it dies. Beets, carrots, and parsnips are biennial vege-

Fig. 13-8. The rosette on the left is the vegetative growth produced by a biennial, the foxglove, in its first year. The flowering growth of the second year is shown on the right.

Albert Towle   *New York Botanical Garden*

tables. Among the biennial garden flowers are the sweet William, digitalis (foxglove), and Canterbury bells.

Perennials live more than two seasons. In most cases, they form their vegetative organs the first year, but do not produce flowers until a season or more later. Herbaceous perennials die to the ground each year. The roots remain alive and new stems and leaves grow each season. Delphiniums, lilies, columbines, and daisies are herbaceous perennials. Woody perennials include the trees, shrubs, and many vines. Once perennials have started to flower, they usually continue season after season, if conditions for growth are good.

Edward S. Thomas

Fig. 13-9. The beautiful iris is a common garden perennial.

In Conclusion

What if the seed plants had not replaced most of the more primitive plants during the past ages? There would have been no cereal grains for breakfast foods and flour, no potatoes, tomatoes, lettuce, onions, radishes, and other vegetables in our stores. Could our civilization ever have developed in such plant surroundings?

You might debate this point, but one thing is certain. Our plant and animal industries, in fact, our very survival, is geared to the seed plants.

In the next chapter, we shall start with the first root which grows from a seed. In other chapters, we shall study the vegetative organs, then the reproductive organs of flowering plants. We shall come to the seed again as the climax of reproduction.

BIOLOGICALLY SPEAKING

Angiospermae	flower	phloem
annual	fossil	seed
biennial	fruit	Spermatophyta
conifer	Gymnospermae	woody
cork	herbaceous	xylem
cotyledon	leaf	root
dicots	monocots	spore leaves
embryonic tissue	parenchyma	stem
epidermis	perennial	

QUESTIONS FOR REVIEW

1. On what basis are the seed plants divided into two great classes, gymnosperms and angiosperms?
2. Explain why we speak of the ginkgo tree as a " living fossil."
3. Describe several uses made of conifers in yard plantings.
4. Name five well-known families of monocots and five well-known dicot families.
5. Name the three vegetative organs of a seed plant and describe briefly the functions of each organ.
6. List six specialized tissues of a seed plant.
7. (a) Distinguish between herbaceous and woody plants. (b) Give several examples of each type.
8. Discuss the life cycle of annual, biennial, and perennial seed plants.

APPLYING FACTS AND PRINCIPLES

1. Discuss possible reasons for the disappearance of most gymnosperms and the rise of angiosperms through past ages.
2. Discuss various ways in which high development of the organs of angiosperm plants has given them an advantage over other kinds of plants in the struggle for existence.
3. Many of our most beautiful garden flowers are annuals. Why are they ideally suited to garden needs?

CHAPTER 14

Roots and Their Activities

WE shall start our study of seed plants from the ground up. You will find how much real activity takes place under the ground and how important this activity is to supply the needs of the plant. A great deal of activity also takes place above ground, but the basis for this above-ground activity occurs under the ground. You will learn why the root is such an efficient anchor and why you have to tug so hard to pull up a mere dandelion or other weeds.

There are many different kinds of roots, each adapted to the needs of its plant. To get a real understanding of the work of the root, we shall start by exploring its various regions and its tissues. We shall begin this study with the first root of a young seedling as it enters the soil.

The origin of the root system. When a seed first begins to grow, two parts push out of the seed coats. The young shoot grows upward and soon it unfolds its first leaves. The first, or **primary root,** lengthens rapidly and quickly pushes its way down into the soil. After a short period of growth, *branches,* or **secondary roots,** begin to appear, first near the top of the primary root, and later farther

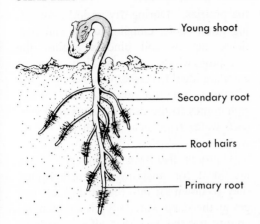

- Young shoot
- Secondary root
- Root hairs
- Primary root

Fig. 14-1. Secondary roots branch out from the primary root and grow until the complete root system has formed.

down. As roots branch and rebranch, they develop the complete root system (Fig. 14-1).

You have probably wondered how a root system compares in size with the stem and branches. There is no definite rule, since different kinds of plants vary in this respect. The size of the root system differs also in various soil conditions. But you can estimate that the average land plant has about as much or more below ground as above ground.

Root systems. If the primary root continues to grow, it will remain the largest root of the root system. We refer to such a root as a *taproot*. This main root, with its branching secondary roots, forms a *taproot system* (Fig. 14-2). If the taproot is large, as in the case of the carrot, beet, radish, and parsnip, we term it *fleshy*. Fleshy taproots serve as underground storehouses for the food supply of the plant. For this reason, many of them are used for food by man.

Some taproots are very long and slender. The alfalfa root grows 15 feet or more into the soil. The root system of corn or bluegrass is quite different. In these plants, the primary root lives only a short time. Secondary roots may grow

as a cluster at the base of the stem. We call these slender roots *fibrous roots*. They form a *diffuse root system* because of their characteristic spreading. While most diffuse root systems are composed of fibrous roots, a few plants have fleshy diffuse root systems. Among these are the dahlia and the sweet potato.

Often, you can determine the kind of root system a plant will produce even in the seedling stage. Put some radish and oat seeds between moist blotters in a covered dish. Examine the root systems after a few days or a week. The radish will have a distinct taproot, with small secondary roots. This taproot continues to grow and will become the radish you eat. You may have difficulty in distinguishing the primary root and the large secondary roots of the oat seedlings. This primary root lives only a short time. Secondary roots form a diffuse root system.

The corn seedling is similar to the oat, except that its diffuse roots live only a

Fig. 14-2. Compare the fibrous root system of the plant on the left with the taproot system of the plant on the right. Which acts as the better soil binder?

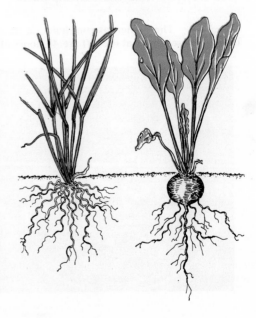

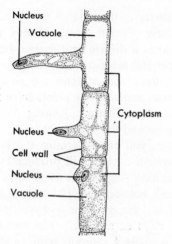

Nucleus
Vacuole
Cytoplasm
Nucleus
Cell wall
Nucleus
Vacuole

Fig. 14-3. Note that each root hair is an extension of a single epidermal cell near the tip of a root. Root hairs develop best in well-aired, moist soil.

week or so before they are replaced by roots which grow out from the base of the stem.

Taproots and diffuse roots — advantages of each. Variation in the form of root systems accounts partially for the fact that plants live in so many different environments. The shallow roots of grasses are ideal for absorption of water and dissolved minerals from the rich topsoil of the prairies. During dry periods, spreading grass roots, clinging to the soil particles, act as soil binders against the sweeping winds. The shallow roots of cacti are ideal for desert conditions, where rainfall is low and very seasonal. When rain comes to the desert, cactus roots absorb water from near the surface over a wide area.

Taproots also have advantages. They are ideal for anchorage. Furthermore, they go down far into the ground and can get at the deep water supplies, which accounts for the fact that alfalfa, with its long taproot, absorbs water after the grasses growing with it may have turned yellow and brown. It explains, also, why oak and hickory forests, with their deep roots, thrive on dry hillsides and why the date palm survives in dry, arid regions.

Young roots and root hairs. Roots of seedlings show another important characteristic of young roots. A short distance back of the tip, you can see white, fuzzy growths extending from the surface of the roots. These tiny **root hairs** are important in absorption. Root hairs are delicate projections of the outer cells or **epidermis** of the root. They should not

Fig. 14-4. The numerous root hairs on these radish seedlings give the roots their fuzzy look. The seedlings at the left are 48 hours old, while those on the right are 96 hours old.

Dr. Oswald Tippo

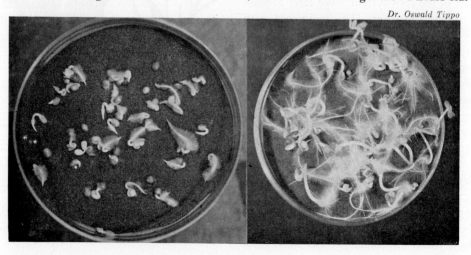

be confused with secondary roots, which, like primary roots, are composed of many cells. Root hairs are produced in a zone about one to two inches long. As the root moves downward, new root hairs form close to the tip and older ones wither away near the top. Thus, they are constantly extending into new areas of soil as the young root pushes on (Fig. 14-3).

Detailed structure of a root tip. Cut off a root half an inch or so back of the tip, slice it thinly lengthwise, and examine it with a microscope. You will see the cells composing it and also several important regions. These regions are: (1) the *root cap;* (2) the *embryonic region* (region of cell division); (3) the *elongation region;* and (4) the *maturation region* (Fig. 14-5).

Regions of the young root. At the tip is the **root cap,** which protects the delicate end. As the cap is pushed through the soil by the growing root behind it, its outer surface is torn away. The addition of new cells to the inner surface, however, keeps it in constant repair.

You may wonder at the fact that the delicate root tip can force its way through soil without damage. The root tip partly *pushes* its way and partly *dissolves* its way through soil. The gas, carbon dioxide, combines with water to form a weak acid called *carbonic acid.* Carbonic acid is familiar to you as the soda or " fizz " water used at the soda fountain. Root caps give off carbon dioxide into the soil water and so form carbonic acid. This in turn aids the progress of the young root by dissolving minerals in its path. As roots grow over smooth rocks, their pattern is often etched into the surface by the carbonic acid they form.

Immediately behind the cap, at the tip of the root proper, is the **embryonic region,** or growing point of the root. Cells of this region are small and contain large nuclei. They are constantly dividing, thus giving rise to new root cells.

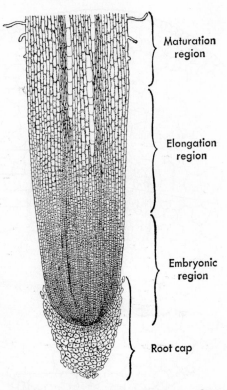

Fig. 14-5. This drawing shows an enlarged root tip, much as it would appear when seen under a microscope. Notice the blunt, thimble-shaped root cap. It protects the delicate embryonic region from injury by soil particles.

Back of the embryonic region, cells gradually lengthen until they reach full length a considerable distance from the tip of the root. This lengthening of cells marks the **elongation region,** which causes the forward movement in the growth of the root tip.

After the cells have grown to full length, they change further. Cells on the surface give rise to root hairs, while those inside the root change somewhat as they become special tissues of the mature root. Modification of cells to form these special tissues marks the **maturation region** of the root.

Regions and tissues of a mature root. The tissues of a root are distinct under

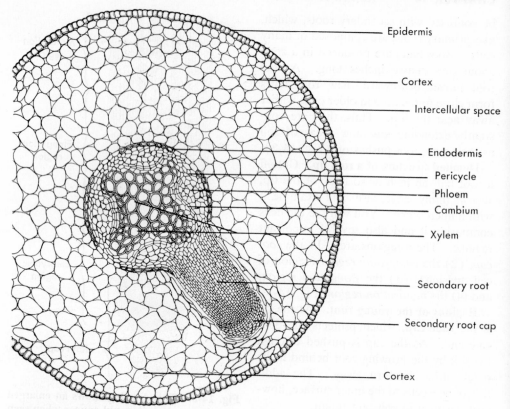

Epidermis

Cortex

Intercellular space

Endodermis

Pericycle

Phloem

Cambium

Xylem

Secondary root

Secondary root cap

Cortex

Fig. 14-6. This cross section of a buttercup root shows its various tissues and the spaces between them. Summarize the functions of each of the tissues.

the microscope (Fig. 14-6). If available, use a cross section especially prepared for microscopic examination. The **epidermis** shows as a single layer of brick-shaped cells. Under the epidermis are layers of rounded, loosely-packed cells, the **cortex**. This is the principal storage area of the root, and is several cells thick. The **endodermis** is a single layer of cells, often with thick walls, located at the inside edge of the cortex.

The **pericycle** is a layer of thin-walled cells lying at the outer edge of the central cylinder and just inside the endodermis.

The **central cylinder** is the principal conducting and strengthening region of the root. It is composed of *xylem* and *phloem* tissues, and may contain *cambium* and *pith* tissues.

The **xylem** is the *water-conducting tissue* because it is the path through which water and soil minerals travel *upward* to the stem and leaves. The conducting portion of the xylem is composed of large, rounded, thick-walled cells. They are long, empty cells which resemble pipes. These cells live only a short time, but continue to serve as channels of conduction long after death. In addition, the xylem contains numerous smaller cells which give great strength to the root. We commonly speak of the xylem tissues as *wood*.

The **phloem,** or *food-conducting tissue,* lies outside the xylem. If the xylem is arranged in the form of a cross as in some roots, like the buttercup shown in Fig. 14-6, you can find the phloem between the arms of the cross in rounded groups. Foods, produced in the stem and leaves, travel *downward* through the phloem cells.

Secondary thickening in the root. The primary tissues we have described do not increase as the root continues its growth. However, the **cambium** adds secondary xylem cells on its inner side and secondary phloem cells on its outer side by continuous cell division during the growing season. This produces a root like the carrot, shown in Fig. 14-7.

The outer edge is a corky layer, the **periderm,** which develops from the pericycle. Inside the periderm is a thick layer of phloem, most of which has been formed by the cambium. This is a food-conducting and storage region. The cambium appears as a line at the inner edge of the phloem. The center of the carrot is xylem, much of which has been formed by the cambium during secondary thickening. This is the water-conducting region of the carrot. Notice that the secondary roots extend from the xylem. This permits the flow of water and minerals into the main conducting vessels leading upward to the stem and leaves.

These same regions are shown in the cross section of the carrot in Fig. 14-7.

An old root, such as the root of a tree, contains many layers of xylem and phloem, formed by the cambium season after season. The outside of the root is covered with a thick layer of bark. Such a root is an efficient organ of conduction and anchorage, but no longer absorbs water.

Responses of roots to their surroundings. If you happen to plant a seed upside down, will the roots grow out of the soil? Is it mere chance that willow or poplar roots enter cracks in a sewer and clog it with a ball of roots? If a root growing downward strikes a rock, will the rock stop its progress indefinitely?

The various parts of a plant respond,

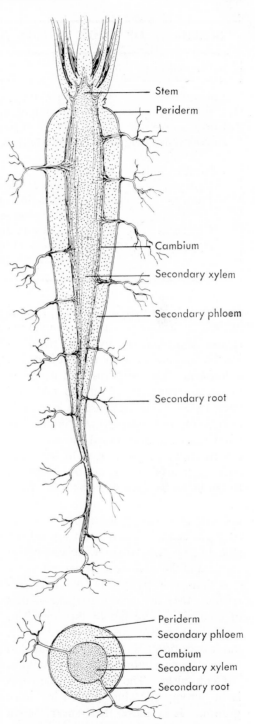

Stem
Periderm

Cambium

Secondary xylem

Secondary phloem

Secondary root

Periderm
Secondary phloem
Cambium
Secondary xylem
Secondary root

Fig. 14-7. The same root regions can be seen in both longitudinal and cross sections of a carrot.

SUMMARY OF ROOT TISSUES AND THEIR SPECIAL FUNCTIONS

TISSUE	FUNCTION
Epidermis	Absorption and protection
Root hairs	Increase of absorption area
Cortex	Storage of food and water
Endodermis (boundary layer)	Separation of cortex from central cylinder
Central cylinder	
Pericycle	Origin of secondary roots and formation of periderm
Phloem	Conduction of manufactured food downward from the stem and leaves
Cambium	Increase in diameter of central cylinder
Xylem	Conduction of water and dissolved minerals upward to the stem and leaves

rather slowly, to certain factors or *stimuli* in their environment. The automatic response of a plant or any of its parts toward a stimulus or away from it is called a **tropism**. The tropisms that occur in plants are summarized in the table on page 153. If the response is in the direction of, or *toward,* the stimulus, as when a root grows toward the earth, we call the response *positive*. On the other hand, a stem shows a *negative* response to the earth because it grows *away* from it. If a stimulus causes more growth on one side of a root than on the other, the root will bend. It may bend toward the stimulus, or away from it, depending on the area of the root most influenced.

Although tropisms are automatic responses, they do serve a purpose — that of maintaining the life of the organism. The root is not aware of soil and water, but it does profit by them. Tropisms are another manifestation of design in nature.

Geotropism. The gravity of the earth is a strong stimulus influencing root growth. It is more than sheer weight which causes the root to grow toward the stimulus of gravity. The stem is equally heavy and yet it grows away from the

Fig. 14-8. In *A* of this experiment to illustrate geotropism, the test tube has just been inverted. In *B*, after some time, the roots have begun to grow downward and the stem upward. What is acting as the stimulus to cause the roots to react in this manner?

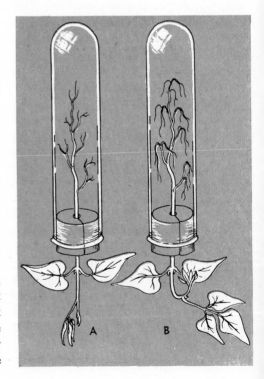

earth. **Geotropism** (jee-*ot*-roh-pizm) directs the growth of the root toward the earth and its supplies of soil water and dissolved minerals. Without this important stimulus, roots would probably not grow deep enough to reach these necessary substances.

To test geotropism, split a test tube cork to the middle and enlarge the center sufficiently to receive the stem of a well-started seedling. Slip the seedling through the split to the center opening with the roots turned toward the bottom of the tube. Fill the tube with water and insert the cork and seedling securely, as in Fig. 14-8. It is best to seal the cork with warm paraffin. Invert the tube so that the roots point upward. Make a record of the experiment at the beginning and note the time required for downward growth of the roots.

Hydrotropism. Water is a very strong stimulus, and may cause a root to grow toward it from a considerable distance. This response is **hydrotropism** (hy-*drot*-roh-pizm) (Fig. 14-9). It is shown in the vast number of fine roots which force their way into water pipes or spread through the moist topsoil. They grow in these directions in spite of the force of gravity, which attracts them downward. The great response of the shallow roots of willows, cottonwoods, and elm trees makes them undesirable for planting near drains, sewers, or septic tanks.

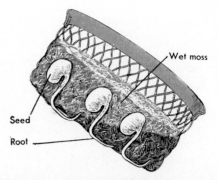

Fig. 14-9. This experiment shows that water is an even stronger stimulus to plants than gravity. As you can see, the root is growing toward the wet moss. What is this type of response called?

You can show hydrotropism and the comparative strength of water and gravity as stimuli in the following experiment. Make a basket of hardware cloth, or other large meshed wire similar to the one in Fig. 14-9. Fill the basket with moist peat moss or sawdust and plant seeds (lima beans are good) near the bottom. Tilt the basket at an angle of about 45 degrees in a dark place or in a light-proof box. Why should the seeds be in a dark place? The roots will start downward at first as they respond to gravity. When they have penetrated through the sieve, however, they will turn back toward it in response to the water stimulus. The experiment shows that the water in the moss, in this case, is a more powerful stimulus than gravity.

SUMMARY OF TROPISMS

NAME OF TROPISM	TYPE OF REACTION
Chemotropism	Response to chemicals, such as soil minerals
Geotropism	Response to gravity
Hydrotropism	Response to water
Phototropism	Response to light
Thermotropism	Response to heat
Thigmotropism	Response to touch

U. S. Dept. of Agriculture

Fig. 14-10. The soil profile taken in this cornfield reveals a thick layer of topsoil. In some parts of the country the topsoil layer is only one or two inches thick.

Root environments. In a discussion of **soil roots,** we need to consider the soil itself as a root environment. We need to know how it is formed, how it varies from place to place, and the critical relationship of the root to the soil.

Soil is a mass of rock particles of various sizes, formed through weathering, freezing, and thawing, together with humus, composed of decayed plant and animal remains. The mineral portion of soil may be coarse sand, fine sand, or clay, depending on the size of the particles.

Through the ages, plants have enriched this mineral matter with the organic remains of their roots, stems, and leaves. These have become part of the soil through the process of decay. This organic matter, together with mineral matter, forms **topsoil.** The many bacteria, molds, and other soil microorganisms

Fig. 14-11.   Plants are adapted to different conditions in many ways.   The bald cypress of the South, which grows in swamps, requires great quantities of water.

U. S. Forest Service

which live in topsoil are essential to its fertility.

The *texture* of soil refers to the size of the particles and the amount of space between them. The average loam soil is said to contain spaces amounting to from one-third to one-half of its total volume. Spaces between soil particles are very important to the root, since they contain air and fill with water after rains. This allows the water to seep gradually to those areas in which roots are absorbing. As water seeps down through the soil, it dissolves soil minerals and carries them to the root.

Organic matter in soil holds water. It swells and keeps the soil loose. This explains why rich woods dirt is usually moist. Manure, leaf mold, and peat moss are excellent soil conditioners. We speak of them as **mulches.**

Loam soils have an ideal balance between mineral and organic matter for the majority of garden and crop plants. However, we cannot say that most plants live best in loam. Some plants thrive in heavy clay. Others require the almost pure organic soil of bogs, or loose, dry sand.

Aquatic roots are found on such plants as the duckweed and the water hyacinth. They are usually small and few in number and lack root hairs. They do not need extra surface on the epidermis for absorption because they live in a water environment.

The bald cypresses of the southern United States require great quantities of water. They grow in swamps and are rooted in water-covered soil. These roots also extend above the water and serve to buttress the tree (Fig. 14-11). It is also believed that these buttress roots supply air to the submerged roots.

Many plants in the tropics produce **aerial roots.** Tropical orchids live on trees and absorb water from the falling rain and from the very humid atmosphere (see Fig. 14-12). The debris which collects around the roots is enough to supply the mineral needs. Aerial roots have a thick, spongy cortex, making possible absorption from the atmosphere.

Adventitious roots. The roots we have discussed thus far have developed from the primary root or from one of its branches. However, in some plants roots develop from the stem or even from the leaves. Such roots are **adventitious** (ad-ven-*tih*-shus) (Fig. 14-13, page 156).

You have probably noticed the circle of roots which grows from the joint of the corn plant just above the ground (Fig. 14-13). These are a kind of adventitious root called *prop* or **brace roots.** These roots grow into the ground, and help the underground roots support the stem. If soil is piled around the stem, additional brace roots develop from the next joint above the soil line. In fact, all the roots of the corn plant are really

Fig. 14-12. Although many roots grow downward into the ground, some plants, like the orchid shown below, have roots that grow in the air. How do these aerial roots receive water?

Ewing Galloway

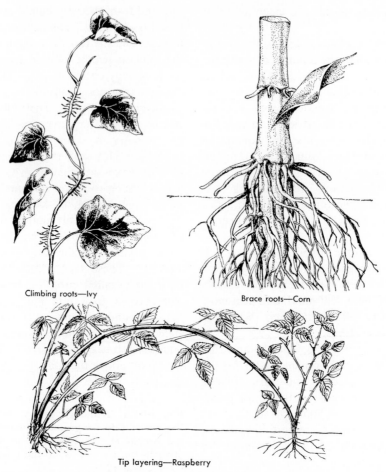

Climbing roots—Ivy

Brace roots—Corn

Tip layering—Raspberry

Fig. 14-13.   Notice that none of these adventitious roots grows from the primary root.

adventitious, since they come from the stem and not the short-lived primary root.

Roots for propagation.   In certain plants, if the stem lies in contact with the soil long enough, roots will grow from the joints and produce new plants.   Climbing roses can be started by burying a portion of a stem until it has taken root.   Raspberry bushes root from the stem in a similar way, except that the roots usually form at the tip of the stem.   This process is called *tip layering* (Fig. 14-13).

Some plants, like the begonia and sedums, can be propagated from leaf cuttings placed in moist sand.   Other examples of adventitious roots for propagation include the roots which form on pussy willow stems when cut and put in a container of water, and the roots which form on strawberry runners as they reach into new areas of the patch.

Climbing roots.   Poison ivy, English ivy, and other vines produce clusters of roots along the stem.   These roots cling to a wall or to some other support and hold the stem securely.   Such plants also have ordinary soil roots which absorb water and dissolved minerals.

Direct uses we make of roots.   We use roots indirectly when we use any part of a plant.   However, there are many direct uses we can make of roots.   In many plants, the root is the principal reservoir for stored foods. The root is greatly thickened to receive the food reserves. We grow many of these plants as **root crops** for eating. Among them are the carrot, beet, parsnip, radish, turnip, rutabaga, and sweet potato.

The roots of some plants contain valuable drugs used in making medicines. These medicinal plants include licorice, ginseng, rhubarb, marsh mallow, and sassafras. Other roots, such as the horseradish, are used for seasoning. The madder and yellowwood trees produce dyes in their roots. At one time these dyes were widely used.

In Conclusion

The next time you look at a plant, try to visualize its root system. Think of the underground activity which is necessary to support the part of the plant you see above the ground. And the next time you see a plant bending in a strong wind, think of the root system as its anchor. How marvelous are these highly efficient plant organs — the roots!

In order to maintain a continuous flow of water from root tip to leaf, the root must absorb soil water, which contains dissolved minerals which are so necessary for life processes to go on in the cells. How does the root get this soil water? We shall study this in Chapter 15.

BIOLOGICALLY SPEAKING

adventitious root	endodermis	root cap
aerial root	fibrous root	root crops
aquatic root	fleshy root	root hair
brace root	geotropism	secondary root
cambium	hydrotropism	soil
central cylinder	maturation region	soil root
cortex	mulches	taproot
diffuse root	pericycle	tip layering
elongation region	periderm	topsoil
embryonic region	primary root	tropism

QUESTIONS FOR REVIEW

1. From the standpoint of origin, distinguish a primary root from a secondary root.
2. Generally speaking, how does the root area of the average land plant compare with that of the stem?
3. Describe the general form of taproot and diffuse root systems.
4. Root hairs are sometimes incorrectly called branch roots. From the standpoint of origin and structure, why is it incorrect to speak of a root hair as a branch or secondary root?
5. (a) Name four regions of the root tip. (b) Discuss the activity in each of these regions.
6. Why is carbonic acid important to the growth of a root?

7. (a) Name seven tissues of a mature root, from outside to inside. (b) State the function of each tissue.
8. Distinguish between adventitious roots and normal roots.
9. Describe several special functions that are performed by adventitious roots.
10. Make a list of several common root crops.

APPLYING FACTS AND PRINCIPLES

1. Oak and hickory trees thrive on dry ridges and hillsides. What kind of root system would you expect these trees to have?
2. A plant dug up with a large ball of dirt has a far better chance of living than one taken out with the roots exposed, even though these roots are not torn off. Why is this true?
3. Roots thicken by adding secondary tissues. How are these tissues formed?
4. Branch roots grow from the pericycle at the outer edge of the central cylinder. Why is the attachment of the branch root to the central cylinder extremely important?
5. Explain the importance of hydrotropism to the life of a plant.

CHAPTER 15

The Root as an Organ of Absorption

YOU know that a plant has a far better chance of living after transplanting if you move it with a large ball of soil. Do you know why? Some people think the large roots are very important. They do anchor the plant but they do not absorb water and dissolved soil minerals. Absorption takes place near the tip of a root where it is no larger than a piece of string. Absorption also takes place in the ends of tiny branch roots. In these root tip areas the epidermis is young and active. Root hairs project into the soil and increase its absorbing surface greatly. These tiny feeding structures are torn off if you disturb the soil with which they are in contact. Thus you should not shake the earth off a plant when you dig it up.

The cell membrane and absorption. All the substances which a cell's protoplast receives, and the waste materials it discharges, must pass through the plasma membrane of that cell. Therefore, it is not hard to see why the study of membranes and the passage of various substances is extremely important in biology. Keep in mind that the absorption we discuss in connection with roots also applies to all living cells.

Biologists believe that cell membranes

contain tiny pores through which substances pass. They have also found that cell membranes are *selective* in the passage of these substances. Some substances can enter; others cannot because the membrane seems to reject them. Furthermore, chemical changes in the protoplast often determine what substances will pass through the membrane and in what quantity they will enter. A cell may absorb a certain substance for a time. Then, because of a change in the protoplast, the cell may reduce or stop further absorption of that substance.

Absorption is an extremely complicated process. Scientists still do not understand all of the factors involved. But we can study certain physical principles involved in absorption — principles which are in no sense limited to cells.

Diffusion, the spreading out of molecules through space. Let's visualize a substance as a mass of quivering molecules. These molecules bump into each other like a crowd of people at a bargain counter. Just as we want to escape from such a crowd and find space to move around in freely, so molecules tend to spread apart from each other. This spreading out of molecules in space is known as **diffusion.**

To illustrate diffusion, let's imagine that you open a bottle of peppermint oil in the corner of a closed room (Fig. 15-1). Peppermint oil molecules are *concentrated* inside the bottle. This means that there are many of them packed close together. As soon as you open the bottle they start diffusing into the air. Soon you begin to smell peppermint across the room. As the process continues, the peppermint odor becomes stronger. More and more peppermint oil molecules are mingling with the molecules of gases that are in the air. Finally, when all the peppermint oil molecules are mixed equally with the air, diffusion stops. A state of

Fig. 15-1. When a bottle of peppermint oil is opened in a room, the molecules of oil diffuse into the air until they are scattered evenly throughout the room.

equilibrium has been reached. If you could see the molecules, you would discover that the entire room, as well as the bottle of peppermint oil, contained a uniform mixture of peppermint oil and air.

According to the laws of diffusion, *two things happened.* Peppermint oil diffused from the bottle into the air, and air diffused into the peppermint oil bottle. Both movements were from a region of *greater* concentration to a region of *lesser* concentration. Diffusion continued until the concentration of air and peppermint oil was equal in all parts of the room.

Other familiar examples of diffusion. Solids and liquids, or liquids and other liquids, may diffuse as readily as gases *if they normally mix and do not repel each other.* Drop a cube of sugar into a glass of water. As the sugar dissolves, taste

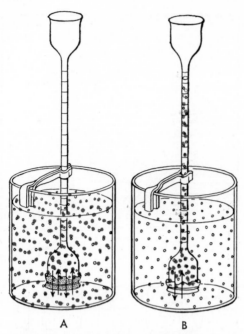

Fig. 15-2. The left-hand experiment illustrates the passage of both water and molasses through a muslin membrane that is equally permeable to both. The right-hand experiment shows the diffusion of water only through a semipermeable membrane, in the process called osmosis.

mee-uh-bul) to the substance which passes through it.

Examine the apparatus shown in Fig. 15-2. You can set this up easily in the laboratory. A thistle tube (a funnel can be used) is fastened to a ring-stand clamp. The lower end of the thistle tube is submerged in water. The bulb of the thistle tube is filled with molasses. A piece of muslin is tied tightly over the open end of the bulb.

Two things happen in this experiment. Water molecules diffuse from the jar, through the muslin, into the molasses in the thistle tube. At the same time, molasses molecules diffuse through the muslin into the water. You can see this happen over a period of a few hours. Finally, molasses and water molecules are equally distributed both inside and outside of the thistle tube. This is an **equilibrium**. Diffusion stops. Muslin is permeable to both water and molasses molecules.

Now we shall repeat the experiment exactly except for one item. Instead of muslin, we shall use a piece of parchment or a piece of animal bladder to cover the thistle tube. Something quite different happens. This membrane is *permeable* to water. Water molecules pass back and forth through it. Most of the flow is into the molasses because water molecules are less concentrated there. Molasses molecules should diffuse into the water, but the membrane stops them, or at least interferes with their movement. We say that this membrane is **semipermeable** (differentially permeable) because it is permeable to different substances in different degrees. As the experiment progresses, water and molasses rise in the thistle tube. Why? Molasses molecules cannot come out, and water continues to come in. You can see that this builds up a pressure. If the water and molasses could not rise in the tube, the pressure would probably burst the membrane.

the water from time to time. You will be able to taste the increase in the number of sugar molecules. Finally, the sugar will dissolve completely without any stirring. Sugar molecules diffused from a region of greater concentration (the lump) into a region of lesser concentration (the water). Meanwhile, water molecules diffused into the sugar. When equilibrium was reached, all parts of the water tasted equally sweet.

Diffusion through membranes. The study of diffusion becomes more complicated and more interesting when a membrane is involved. **Membranes** are thin materials such as cellophane, a portion of an animal bladder, a piece of parchment, or a piece of muslin. Membranes allow certain substances to pass through. A membrane is said to be **permeable** (*per-*

Water continues to diffuse into the molasses until the weight of the liquid in the tube causes enough pressure against the membrane to stop the flow.

Osmosis, a special type of diffusion. The experiment we just described illustrates **osmosis** (os-*moh*-sis), a special kind of diffusion. Scientists do not agree on an exact definition of osmosis. They do agree that it is a form of diffusion and that the diffusion is through a semipermeable membrane. But they do *not* agree on the substances which pass through the membrane during osmosis. Chemists and physicists refer to osmosis as the passage of a liquid, a gas, or a dissolved solid through a semipermeable membrane. According to this definition, everything which passes into or out of a cell does so by osmosis.

Other scientists limit osmosis *to the passage of water alone.* They say that substances dissolved in water enter by diffusion and independently of water. Water is the medium in which molecules of dissolved substances reach the cell membrane. But at that point, the dissolved substances may be rejected by the membrane while the water passes through. In line with the majority of biologists, we shall define *osmosis as the diffusion of water through a semipermeable membrane.* The flow of water is from a region of *greater* concentration of water molecules to a region of *lesser* concentration of water molecules, according to the law of diffusion.

The root hair and the soil — an osmotic system. Think back to the osmosis experiment with the thistle tube. Now let's substitute a root hair for the thistle tube; the cell content for the molasses; a living plasma membrane for the membrane fastened over the mouth of the thistle tube; and for the jar of water, the water in the soil (Fig. 15-3). Inside the cell, there are solutions of various substances dissolved in water. One of these is protoplasm, containing about 70 per cent water. Cell vacuoles contain solutions of minerals, food materials, and other dissolved substances. The soil water also contains

Fig. 15-3. Water enters the root hairs from the soil by osmosis. It moves through the root by successive osmosis, as osmotic pressure is built up in each succeeding cell.

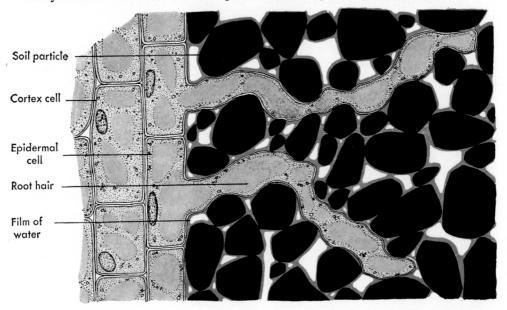

Soil particle

Cortex cell

Epidermal cell

Root hair

Film of water

Fig. 15-4. Turgor enables a plant to push through surfaces as resistant as cement sidewalks.

dissolved minerals, but *normally*, not as much as the cell content. In other words, the concentration of water molecules outside the cell is greater than inside. The soil water is separated from the cell content only by a thin, porous cell wall and the semipermeable plasma membrane. Can you predict what will happen? Water will diffuse from the soil into the root hair.

Successive osmosis. Now let's think of the whole root. The root hair is an outgrowth of an epidermal cell. Inside are many layers of cortex cells. When the epidermal cell takes in water, the concentration of water molecules becomes greater than that of the cortex cell lying against it, so that water passes from the epidermal cell to the cortex cell. As the water content in this cell increases, the next cortex cell receives water from it. As the second cortex cell receives water from the first, the first one receives water from the epidermal cell. The epidermal cell, in turn, takes in more water from the soil through its root hair.

This diffusion of water from cell to cell continues to the xylem vessels in the central cylinder of the root. Here, water and dissolved minerals move upward to the stem. We call this cell-to-cell diffusion of water *successive osmosis.*

Turgor, the result of water pressure in cells. As water diffuses into a cell during osmosis, it builds up a pressure inside the cell which we call *osmotic pressure.* It makes the cell firm, just as you can make a paper sack rigid by filling it with water. The cells, in turn, make the whole plant stiff and firm. We call this stiffness of plants due to osmotic pressure in their cells, *turgor.* It is very important in supporting tender plants whose stems are not stiffened by woody fibers. Leaves and flowers are stiffened by cell turgor. When turgor is lost, they wilt.

When a plant is fully turgid, the pressure in its cells may be as great as 60 to 150 pounds per square inch. Fruits and vegetables often burst when their cells can no longer withstand the pressure. Turgor permits the mushroom and delicate seedling to push through the hard ground. There are even cases where concrete has been cracked by the push of a growing plant, as in the case of the seedling maple tree in Fig. 15-4.

Turgor in roots cells creates root pressure. Pressure in root cells is maintained, or even increased, from outside to inside. Thus, when water reaches the xylem vessels of the central cylinder, it enters the pores of their thick walls with considerable force.

We can show the force of such *root pressure* by cutting off a plant near the ground. Water runs out of the severed vessels. In plants such as grass, tomato, strawberry, and clematis, root pressure may be great enough to force water through the stem and out through the ends of leaf veins, where it appears as drops. We call this loss of excessive wa-

Dr. Oswald Tippo

Fig. 15-5. The guttation occurring in these strawberry leaves is the result of root pressure forcing water through the stem and out through the tips of the leaf veins.

ter **guttation** (guh-*tay*-shun). It occurs especially in the evening, through the night, and early in the morning when the water content of the atmosphere is high and little or no water is evaporated from the leaf surfaces. Loss of water through a cut stem is called **bleeding.**

However, root pressure alone cannot supply all the force necessary to raise water through the stem. It could never push water to the top of a tree. In Chapter 16, you will study other forces which add pull to the push of root pressure.

Plasmolysis and loss of turgor in cells. So far we have discussed only the entry of water into a cell during osmosis. Is water ever taken out of the cell? Yes, it is, and that occurs when the greater water-attracting solution is outside the cell.

To demonstrate " reverse osmosis " and loss of turgor, slice two pieces of potato. Put one in strong salt water and the other in fresh water. The slice in salt water soon becomes limp, while the slice

in fresh water, which is the control, remains stiff and turgid. The control shows that slicing alone did not cause the limpness. Water must have passed from cells into the salt solution, because in this case the water concentration was greater inside the cells than outside.

The collapse of cell protoplasm and loss of turgor due to the loss of water is called **plasmolysis** (plaz-*mol*-ih-sis). You can see this in Fig. 15-6, page 164. Temporary plasmolysis may be corrected by intake of water. If the condition continues very long, the cell will die.

Now you can understand why salt kills grass. You can understand too why shipwrecked men die from drinking salt water. The cells of your mouth, throat, and stomach are just as subject to plasmolysis as are the cells of roots and leaves. Plasmolysis explains, also, why too heavy an application of strong fertilizers to the soil may kill the roots they contact. Most fertilizers contain large

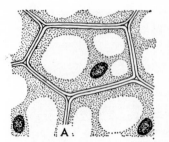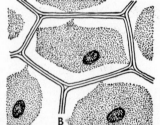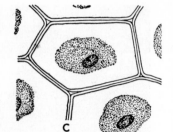

Fig. 15-6. The diagram above shows the result of plasmolysis, or loss of turgor. A. Turgid cell of a potato. B. Partially plasmolyzed cell. C. Completely plasmolyzed cell.

quantities of chemical salts, forming solutions which attract soil water strongly.

Osmosis is a purely physical process. Whether a cell takes in water by osmosis, or loses it to its environment by the same process, depends on two critical physical factors: (1) concentration of water inside the cell; and (2) concentration of water outside the cell.

If water enters a cell, it is because the water concentration is less inside than outside. Concentration of water inside is related directly to the amount of dissolved minerals and soluble food materials contained in solution in the vacuoles. The greater the amount of these dissolved substances, the less the concentration of water and, therefore, the greater the water-attracting power of the cell solutions. Similarly, the lower the water content of protoplasm, the greater its water attraction.

Absorption through the forces of imbibition. Many organic substances, such as starch, gelatin, wood, and seed coats absorb large quantities of water, which causes them to swell. The absorption of water by a solid, resulting in swelling, is called *imbibition* (im-bih-*bih*-shun). Imbibition is different from osmosis in that water enters the substance which absorbs it rather than entering a solution. When wood imbibes water, it swells because water molecules enter the wood substance.

When you first put a wooden boat in the water, it may leak for a time. Then as the wood imbibes water and swells, the cracks close and it stops leaking. A wooden shingle roof may be full of cracks during dry weather, but when a rain comes, the shingles swell and close the cracks. Another example of imbibition is the swelling of dry beans when soaked overnight before baking (Fig. 15-7).

Absorption of minerals. Absorption by the root concerns not only the intake of water, but the entry of dissolved mineral substances as well. They pass through the membranes of root hairs in solution with water. Together with water, they move through the cortex to the inner tissues of the central cylinder where they are conducted to other parts of the plant.

The relation of dissolved minerals to water in the soil solution is very close. We might assume that they enter the root with water during osmosis and imbibition. But biologists have found evidence that mineral absorption may be independent of water intake. This phenomenon of mineral intake has been called *selective absorption*. It takes into account the variation of mineral content found in different plants even when they are grown under similar conditions of soil environment.

Broccoli has a high calcium content. But peas, growing under the same conditions in the same soil, will not have the same high calcium content because selective absorption is different in peas than in broccoli.

How rapidly do plants absorb soil minerals? A very graphic answer was given to this question by a representative of the Oak Ridge Operations, United States Atomic Energy Commission. During an address on the use of radioisotopes in biology, the speaker produced two potted tomato plants. One was watered with distilled water, and the other with water containing a radioactive phosphate (a soil mineral). In less than 45 minutes, the water containing the radioactive phosphate was absorbed through the root hairs of the tomato plant and moved up into the leaves. This was proved by removing a leaf and testing it for the presence of radioactivity with a Geiger counter. The plant had shown no radioactivity at the beginning of the experiment. The control plant showed no radioactivity either before or after the experiment.

Mineral salts containing radioactive

Fig. 15-7. Compare the size of the dry beans (*left*) with those which have been soaked overnight in water (*right*). To what is the swelling of the beans attributed?

elements will enable biologists to learn more about absorption. The technique will show what minerals are absorbed by certain plants and what ones are rejected. It will also show the rate at which soil minerals enter roots.

In Conclusion

Now perhaps you can see why the transplanting process can be so hazardous for a plant. Unless great care is taken to keep a large ball of earth around roots, wilting will probably take place. The plant may even have the young areas of its root system so severely damaged by transplanting that it will never recover. Osmosis and absorption will therefore cease because they can occur only in these younger areas at the tips of roots.

The entire contact of the plant with its soil environment depends on a healthy, functioning root system. If this is upset drastically, the plant cannot survive.

The root, important though it is, is only one of several different plant organs. True, the average seed plant could not exist without its root system. But it would have just as much trouble living without its stem. Let's take a look at the stem in Chapter 16 and see what part it plays in the life of a seed plant. We shall see why the stem is just as important to the plant as the root is.

BIOLOGICALLY SPEAKING

bleeding	membrane	root pressure
diffusion	osmosis	selective absorption
equilibrium	osmotic pressure	semipermeable
guttation	permeable	successive osmosis
imbibition	plasmolysis	turgor

QUESTIONS FOR REVIEW

1. Give an illustration of diffusion of gases and explain what takes place.
2. Distinguish between a permeable and a semipermeable membrane.
3. Define osmosis so as to distinguish it from other types of diffusion.
4. Explain how successive osmosis takes place in the cells of a root.
5. Discuss cell turgor — what it is, what causes it, and why it is important to cells.
6. How do turgor and root pressure assist in the upward movement of water?
7. Describe the cause and result of loss of turgor in plant cells.
8. How do we know that mineral absorption is independent of water absorption in a root?

APPLYING FACTS AND PRINCIPLES

1. A man spread a heavy application of fertilizer on his lawn and watered it well. A few days later, his grass turned brown. There were no chemical compounds in the fertilizer which could poison the grass tops. What do you think probably killed this man's grass?
2. In what respect is imbibition different from osmosis?
3. Discuss the use of radioactive substances in the study of mineral absorption by roots.
4. Explain how manure, peat moss, and compost (decayed vegetable matter) keep the soil moist.

CHAPTER 16

Stems and Their Activities

YOU might think of a root as the plant's receiving department for soil water and minerals. The leaf is a factory where these raw materials are used in the production of foods. The stem is the supply line — a vital link between these organs. Through long conducting tubes of the stem tissues, a constant stream of water and dissolved minerals moves up to the leaves. Foods travel down through other tubes. *Conduction* is one of the chief activities of stems.

Equally important to the plant is the *production* and *display* of leaves and flowers, both important functions of stems. In most plants, the leaves are so arranged on the stem that they receive sufficient light for the needs of the particular plant.

Food manufacture, usually associated with leaves, is an activity of the stem in many plants. Green tissues in the outer region of many stems greatly increase the food-producing area of the plant.

Some stems serve as vaults for the *storage* of water and food reserves. The white potato plant sends most of its food reserves into the thick underground stems we dig as potatoes.

Herbaceous and woody stems. Those stems which are usually soft and green are classified as **herbaceous stems.** Some examples of them are the stems of tomatoes, beans, peas, corn, grasses, and lilies. Herbaceous stems lack the woody tissues which give strength to trees and shrubs. However, the stiffness of many herbaceous stems is due to cell turgor. If the stem loses water, it wilts. Most herbaceous stems grow very little in diameter and last only one season. In plants like the hollyhock, columbine, delphinium, and shasta daisy, the stem is herbaceous and annual, while the root is more woody and perennial. Both the root and the stem are annual in the marigold, zinnia, nasturtium, morning glory, tomato, bean, and pea.

Woody stems, on the other hand, are perennial. They grow in length, increase in diameter, and form branches season after season. The woody tissues of these stems give them great strength and allow them to reach much greater size than an herbaceous stem.

The external structure of a woody stem. The twig of a tree is an ideal subject for study of the external structure of a woody stem (Fig. 16-1). In regions where trees shed their leaves during autumn, a dormant winter twig is especially suitable.

Buds are perhaps the most noticeable structures on the dormant stem. Each bud contains a growing point of the stem — a place from which a new stem, leaves, and flowers may develop. In cold climates, *winter buds* are protected by overlapping **bud scales** which completely enclose the tender growing point. These bud scales serve to protect the delicate tissues inside from drying out.

Fig. 16-1. **This diagram illustrates the external structure of a woody stem. How do woody and herbaceous stems differ?**

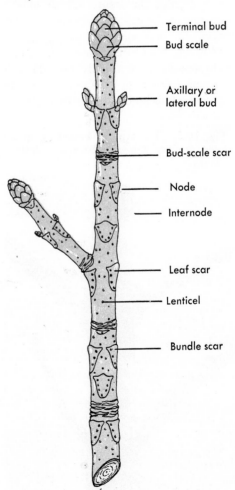

- Terminal bud
- Bud scale
- Axillary or lateral bud
- Bud-scale scar
- Node
- Internode
- Leaf scar
- Lenticel
- Bundle scar

We classify buds further according to their position on the twig. The **terminal bud,** not present on all twigs, is located at the tip and contains the terminal growing point of the stem. Along the sides are **lateral buds,** from which branches may develop. They are usually smaller than terminal buds and usually different in shape.

At intervals along the twig, circular, oval, or shield-shaped **leaf scars** mark the point of attachment of leaf stalks from previous seasons. On the leaf scars, minute dots called **bundle scars** show the location of the conducting vessels which carried water and dissolved minerals into the leaf from the stem. These bundle scars are of a definite number and arrangement, depending on the species.

You will note in examining the lateral buds that they are usually just above a leaf scar. When the leaf was attached to the twig, these buds were in an angle between the leaf stalk and the twig. We call this angle the **axil.** Lateral buds produced in the leaf axils are given the special name of **axillary buds.**

A **node** is the point at which leaves or branches are produced from a stem. The space between two nodes is called an **internode.** In examining several twigs, note that a single leaf, two leaves, or three or more leaves may develop from a node. If a winter twig has one leaf scar at each node, the leaves are **alternate.** If there are two leaf scars, the leaves are **opposite.** If three or more leaf scars are present at each node, the leaves are **whorled.**

Along the internodes, especially on young twigs, you can see tiny pores called **lenticels** (*len*-tih-suls) opening through the bark. These let air enter and water escape from the twig, especially while it is young and active. In an old twig, they cease to function.

Fig. 16-2. The type of branching in a tree depends on bud arrangement. Opposite buds produce opposite branches (*left*). Alternate buds produce alternate branches (*right*).

Hugh Spencer   *Albert Towle*

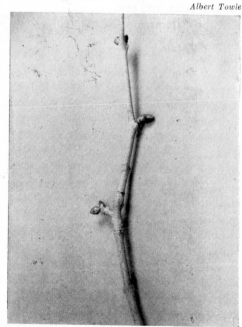

Fig. 16-3. All the branches of these evergreen trees arise from the main stem or trunk. What causes such excurrent branching, and what are the advantages of this type of branching?

You can find other interesting structures on certain twigs. When terminal buds swell and drop their scales at the beginning of the growing season, a series of rings encircling the twig marks the place where the bud scales were fastened. These **bud-scale scars**, at intervals along a twig, show the exact location of the terminal bud during previous seasons. Thus, by starting at the present terminal bud and counting the sets of bud-scale scars along the twig, you can find the exact age of a twig.

Some twigs bear characteristic thorns which make them very easy to identify. These thorns may be either short and broad, long and pointed, or branching. In some cases, thorns are outgrowths of the epidermis. They may also be modified branches. The thorns of hawthorn trees and the branching thorns of the honey locust are examples of stems modified into protective thorns. The thorns on a rose, however, are outgrowths of the epidermis.

Branching is due to bud arrangement. If a young tree has a strong terminal bud, and terminal buds of other years escape injury, the main stem will continue upward, forming a central shaft. Branches will grow from this as a result of the development of lateral buds. We class such trees, characterized by forming branches from a central shaft, as **excurrent** (Fig. 16-3).

Excurrent branching is shown in the pine, fir, spruce, hemlock, redwood, and cypress. These trees, unless injured or diseased, have a perfect cone-shaped outline. A strong central shaft rises to a point at the tip of the tree. Branches grow horizontally at regular intervals along the stem, decreasing in length from bottom to top. This difference in length is due to a difference in age, the oldest branches being located at the base, while

Fig. 16-4.   The elm tree is an example of deliquescent branching, in which the branches arise from older branches as well as from the trunk.

the youngest are at the top. By counting the number of circles or whorls of branches along the trunk, you can tell the age of the tree fairly accurately.

Among the advantages of the excurrent type of branching are:

1. Small resistance to storms due to slender tops.

2. Branches which may bend downward and shed snow easily.

3. Pyramid shape allowing light to reach all branches to the base of the tree.

The willow, cottonwood, and elm have quite a different form of branching. These trees produce a single trunk which divides, usually rather low, to form several large branches. The effect is a spreading pattern of growth called **deliquescent** (del-ih-*queh*-sunt) (Fig. 16-4). This growth results when twigs lack a terminal bud, or when lateral buds form branches which equal or exceed growth

from the terminal bud. In trees like the buckeye, horse chestnut, and magnolia, terminal buds develop flower clusters. Lateral buds form branches, resulting in a spreading, deliquescent pattern.

Branching form often determines the timber value of trees. Quite obviously, trees forming large, central shafts far exceed the spreading type in timber value. This characteristic growth of pine makes it ideal for lumber, while spruce and fir are suitable for telephone poles.

In the case of the oak, walnut, hickory, maple, and other forest trees, long trunks develop under forest conditions, although the same trees branch more freely in open places. Foresters have found that the best timber trees are these types which are found growing in dense stands.

How do stems grow?   To show the way in which stems grow, let's assume that a tree is 30 feet high, one foot in diameter, and that the first branch is exactly six feet above the ground. After ten years, we return to the tree and find that the trunk is now 16 inches in diameter and 40 feet high. After this period of growth, how far is the first limb from the ground? The answer is *still six feet*. Growth in length has occurred at the tips of all the branches. The stem regions below the tips have not lengthened at all!

In plants, certain areas called **growing regions** are the only places where growth occurs. Only in these special areas can new tissues form as a result of cell division. Furthermore, the growing regions of the stem are of two distinct types: (1) those causing increase in length; and (2) those causing increase in diameter.

Stems grow in length by forming new tissues at their tips, or, in some cases, at the nodes. You will remember that such growing points are also found at the tips of roots. The growing area, or embryonic region, of the stem is much like the root, except that it is longer and not protected by a cap. The embryonic region of a stem is often several inches long, while the corresponding region of the root is only a small fraction of an inch long. As new tissues are produced at the stem tip, they continue to grow until they reach maximum size. Once they have matured, they can never lengthen again. Growth in length is limited to the actively-dividing cells of the growing point.

Growth in diameter results from the activity of an entirely different region, located deep in the tissues of the stem. To discover this region, we must study in detail the regions and tissues which make up the stem.

The internal structure of woody stems. If you cut a young branch of a tree, you can see three distinct regions, as shown in Fig. 16-6, page 172. The outer region, or *bark*, is distinct from the area of *wood* within. Usually, a core of *pith* occupies the center of the stem, although the

Fig. 16-5. The wood of hardwood trees is heavy, close-grained, and resistant. Note the tall, straight trunks that have resulted from growth in reduced light.

U. S. Forest Service

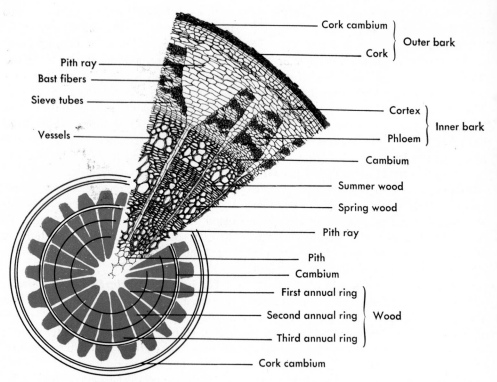

Fig. 16-6. This diagrammatic cross section of a three-year-old woody stem shows the arrangement of its internal tissues.

pith of a large tree is often difficult to find because it is so very small in comparison with the large amount of wood. A fourth region, the *cambium,* lies between the bark and the wood and consists of a very thin, slimy layer of delicate tissue.

The wood in an old stem often appears to be of two types. The outer area is usually light in color and consists of active, functioning wood, or **sapwood.** Sapwood is absolutely necessary for the tree to live. Next to the sapwood is a cylinder of darker wood called **heartwood.** This occupies the center of the stem and surrounds the cavity where the pith originally was. The tissues composing the heartwood are dead and often filled with gums or resins which give it a characteristic dark color. Heartwood is of no use to the tree except for support. However,

it is useful to man because it makes beautiful furniture.

Annual rings form circles through the wood, one outside the other, and mark each season's growth of wood. You can determine the approximate age of a stem by counting them. Besides the rings you can see additional markings by examining a cross section of a woody stem as, for example, the end of a log. The **pith rays** appear as lines radiating to the outside of the wood like the spokes of a wheel. Some types of wood, such as oak, show especially prominent rays.

Bark — its structure and activity. The term **bark** includes much more than just the outer covering of a tree. It is a region of the stem, composed of several kinds of tissues.

A young twig is covered, for a time, by a thin epidermis which protects the young stem from injury and disease. Soon, however, the epidermis is replaced by a tissue called **cork**, which forms the outer covering we see on a branch or tree trunk. Cork is composed of dead cells arranged in layers and containing special substances which give it a characteristic waterproofing. The corky layer protects the stem from mechanical injury, from disease, and from loss of water.

As stems grow in diameter, the outer corky layer splits. Consequently, it is constantly renewed. New cork is produced by a special layer of cells called the **cork cambium.** The cells which compose the cork cambium divide frequently and add new cork on the inside as it is destroyed on the outside. The structure of the cork cells and the continual splitting of the cork layer due to the growth of the stems result in the characteristic appearance of tree trunks — scaly, peeling, grooved, fissured, or, in some cases, smooth. The cork tissue of a tree is often called the *outer bark* to distinguish it from other bark tissues within.

Inside the cork and cork cambium lie two other important bark tissues composing the *inner bark.* The outer one of these, the **cortex,** is composed of large thin-walled cells arranged like stones in a wall. In young stems, the cortex cells contain green chloroplasts and carry on food manufacture. As the stem matures and cork begins to form, this function ceases, and the cortex becomes an area of *food storage.*

Inside the cortex lies the innermost layer of the bark, the **phloem.** The phloem consist principally of large, thin-walled **sieve tubes** which conduct *food materials* dissolved in water. Since food materials usually come from the leaves, the phloem carries then *downward* toward the roots. In plants like wheat and rye, however, foods are conducted *upward* through the phloem to the heads of

grain at the tip of the stem. Tough, thick-walled fibers, the **bast fibers,** may often be seen associated with the phloem tubes. These fibers give toughness to the bark.

Activities of the cambium. The small ring of active tissue between the bark and the wood, called the **cambium,** is responsible for all increase in thickness of the stem.

During the spring and summer, the cambium is active in producing new cells by division. It forms new phloem tissues on its outside surface and new wood tissues on its inside surface. During one season of cambium activity, many more wood cells than phloem cells are formed. That is why the wood area of a tree is always much greater than its bark thickness.

The tissues composing wood. *Wood,* or **xylem,** tissues extend from the cambium to the pith in the center of the stem. Wood consists of several kinds of cells. The largest of these are the **vessels** which appear in the stem as large, thick-walled tubes. Viewed from the ends in a cross section of wood, they are nearly round. If you cut a stem lengthwise, the vessels appear as long tubes arranged end to end forming continuous channels through the stem. Other wood cells called **tracheids** are often grouped among the vessels. Tracheids are smaller than vessels and are longer and more angular. The smallest wood cells are the **fibers,** which have thick walls and very little cell activity.

Cells of the **pith rays** are quite different from the vessels, tracheids, and fibers. They are thin-walled, and form rows of two or three cells in width, and contain protoplasm and a large nucleus.

As woody stems increase in thickness, year after year, the wood formed by the cambium is arranged in layers. Frequently, the cambium produces two kinds of wood during the season: (1) **spring wood**, containing many large vessels

U. S. Forest Service

Fig. 16-7. The approximate age of this tree can be determined by counting the annual rings of the trunk. What tissue forms the rings?

mingled with tracheids and fibers; and (2) ***summer wood,*** containing few vessels and large numbers of fibers. (Refer to Fig. 13-6, page 143, for a photograph of these two types.) This difference in texture between spring and summer wood results in layers which appear as the annual rings.

The pith region of the stem. The central core of ***pith*** is scarcely noticeable in an old woody stem. In the young stem, however, the pith occupies a proportionally large area and serves as an important place of storage. Since pith is not produced by the cambium, it never increases in size. Regardless of the size to which a tree may grow, its pith never increases beyond the amount present during the first year of growth.

Girdling. We refer to the destruction of the entire bark region around a tree as ***girdling.*** This may be done by such bark-chewing animals as rabbits, beavers, porcupines, deer, or horses. In some cases, girdling is done deliberately, as in Fig. 16-8. Girdling will usually kill a tree in a single season.

Why does girdling kill a tree? When the bark is completely destroyed on a portion of the trunk of a tree, the downward movement of dissolved foods through the phloem tubes is interrupted at the point of the injury. The stem tissues and the roots normally supplied with food through the phloem channels of the destroyed bark are deprived of food and gradually die of starvation. Evidence of the death of the roots below the wound is found in gradual loss of leaves and death of the branches in the region above the wound.

Movement of materials through the stem. We can understand how water and minerals can rise from the roots to the leaves of a small plant. But did you ever wonder how columns of water can move upward a hundred feet or more through the trunk of a towering tree? Biologists have investigated several forces which seem to be involved in this remarkable occurrence. However, many aspects of this phenomenon remain a biological mys-

Fig. 16-8. Why does girdling, or removing a circular section of bark on a tree, eventually result in the death of the tree?

U. S. Forest Service

SUMMARY OF STRUCTURE AND ACTIVITIES OF A STEM

REGION	TISSUE	ACTIVITY
Bark	Epidermis (only on young stems)	Protection
	Cork	Protection
	Cork cambium	Production of cork
	Cortex (only in young stems)	Storage and food manufacture
	Phloem tubes	Conduction of food usually downward
	Bast fibers	Strengthening of bark
Cambium	Cambium cells only	Formation of phloem, xylem (wood), and rays
Wood	Xylem vessels	Conduction of water and minerals upward
	Tracheids	Conduction and strengthening of wood
	Xylem fibers	Support
	Pith rays	Conduction laterally
Pith	Pith	Storage

tery. Biologists agree, generally, that at least four forces are involved. These are: (1) root pressure; (2) capillarity; (3) transpiration pull; and (4) cohesion.

Root pressure and capillarity. You found, in the study of water absorption by the root, that root cells normally have a high osmotic pressure. As water passes from the cells to the xylem vessels extending through the root and stem, it is forced upward with considerable force. This force is great enough to *push* water to the leaves of a small plant. It can be observed in many plants when the stem is cut off and water *bleeds* from the severed xylem vessels of the stump. However, *root pressure* alone could force water but a short distance through the stem of a tall plant. We must search for other forces which operate with root pressure for a possible explanation.

Fig. 16-9 illustrates a second force, known as **capillarity**. When the end of a small tube is placed in a liquid, the liquid rises in the tube to a level *above* that at which it stands in the larger container. The smaller the diameter of the tube, the

higher the liquid will rise. This rise is due to the attraction of the liquid by the surface of the tube. If you substitute the many tiny xylem vessels in a stem for the capillary tubes, you can see why water rises in a stem, even when it is cut off and placed in a container of water, as in a bouquet of flowers.

Fig. 16-9. Notice in this demonstration of capillarity that the water rises highest in the tube with the smallest bore. What is the explanation for this observation?

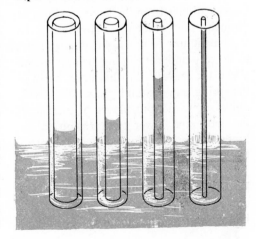

Transpiration pull and cohesion. Biologists believe that the greatest force involved in the rise of water through a stem is a *pull* rather than a *push*. This force is called the **transpiration pull.** During transpiration, leaves lose water to the atmosphere by evaporation. As the cells closest to the atmosphere lose water, they in turn, take water from the cells adjacent to them. Thus a flow of water passes through the leaf tissues to the atmosphere. As water is lost from the leaves, a continuous column, extending from the leaf through the branches and trunk, is lifted upward.

The lifting of a column of water involves still another force, **cohesion.** You are demonstrating cohesion when you draw a liquid up through a soda straw. As you remove liquid at the top of the straw, you lift an entire column through the straw. The particles of the liquid cling together by cohesion. Cohesion results in the lifting of columns of water and dissolved substances through the xylem vessels of roots and stems, as water is drawn upward by transpiration pull.

The movement of foods in stems. We refer to the movement of dissolved foods in plants, chiefly through the phloem sieve tubes, as **translocation.** The forces involved in this movement are not fully understood. The usual direction of food translocation is from the leaves *downward* through the phloem. However, the movement may be upward from the leaves to flowers and developing fruits situated above the leaves. Furthermore, early in the spring, sap containing dissolved foods moves upward from places of storage in the roots and lower stem region to the branches and developing buds of many trees and woody shrubs and vines.

The movement of foods is too rapid to be explained by diffusion from one phloem cell to another. Other forces must be involved. Some biologists believe that

the pressure in the phloem cells decreases from the leaves through the stem, thus causing a flow toward the cells of lower pressure.

It is interesting that most of the conduction of water and minerals as well as foods is vertical through a stem — either upward or downward. There seems to be but little horizontal conduction across a stem.

Plant propagation by means of stems. While conduction, support, and storage are the most outstanding functions of a stem, **propagation,** or multiplication of plants by stems, is another function. Propagation may occur either naturally or artificially.

Grafting consists of bringing into close contact the cambium layer of a live, dormant twig and the cambium layer of the tree on which it is to grow. This can be accomplished by tapering the end of the twig, or **scion** (*sy*-un), to be used and inserting it into a slit prepared in the rooted branch, or **stock,** which is to receive the graft. Such a graft can be successful *only if the cambiums of scion and stock are brought into contact with each other.* Also, grafting is successful only when stems of the same species or closely related species are united. We cannot graft an apple twig to an oak tree, but we can graft several varieties of apple trees onto a single apple stock.

Budding is similar to grafting except that a *bud* rather than a twig is united with the stock (Fig. 16-10). In budding, a vigorous bud is selected and removed with a piece of bark surrounding it. The bud is united with the stock by slipping the piece of bark under the bark of the stock, which has been loosened by a T-shaped cut. In this way, the cambiums of scion and stock are united. In both budding and grafting, the wound resulting from the operation should be covered with wax to prevent the entrance of bacteria and the different kinds of rotting fungi.

Pruning woody plants. We call the cutting of surplus branches of trees and shrubs *pruning*. We do this for several reasons: (1) We may wish the plant to conform to a certain shape. (2) We may want the plant to produce more fruit rather than so many leaves. (3) We want a transplanted tree or shrub to recover quickly. Thus, we reduce the number of branches and the resulting leaves so there will be only a small loss of water. (4) We want our plant to be healthy so we cut off all dead or decaying branches.

As a rule, it is better to prune in the winter when the sap is not rising. Then the cut ends will not bleed and lose the food-bearing sap.

The structure of an herbaceous stem. Herbaceous stems differ from woody stems chiefly in having much less xylem (woody) and phloem tissue. These two occur in most herbaceous stems in the form of long strands called **fibrovascular** (fy-broh-*vas*-kyoo-lur) **bundles** which run lengthwise through the stem.

The stems of dicots and monocots. We can classify herbaceous stems, according to structure, in two types: (1) the *dicot,* represented by the tomato, buttercup, bean, and other plants with broad leaves and soft stems; and (2) the *monocot,* including iris, orchids, lilies, grasses, sedges, and corn (Fig. 16-11, page 178).

The herbaceous dicot stem. If you section the stem of an herbaceous dicot plant (your teacher will tell you a good one to use in your community), you will see several distinct regions. The outer layer of the stem is a thin *epidermis* which serves for protection. Inside the epidermis is a layer of *cortex,* composed of loosely-packed cells containing chlorophyll. These manufacture food as well as store it. Within the cortex, the *fibrovascular*

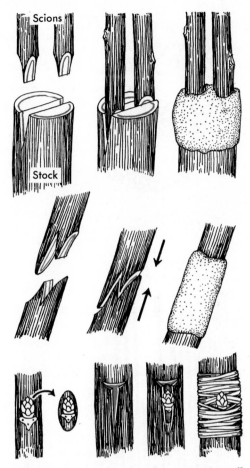

Fig. 16-10. The top row of drawings illustrates cleft grafting; the center row, whip grafting; and the bottom row, budding.

bundles occupy a ring-shaped zone. These bundles contain xylem and phloem tissues. In some species, the bundles form a continuous ring. In others, the ring is separated by broad *pith rays*.

Many herbaceous dicot stems develop a cambium in the form of a thin layer which runs through the ring of the bundle cylinder. The cambium separates the phloem in the outer portion of the bundle from the xylem tissues within. The activity of the cambium in producing new phloem and xylem cells results in an increase in the diameter of the stem. However, the herbaceous dicot stem does not

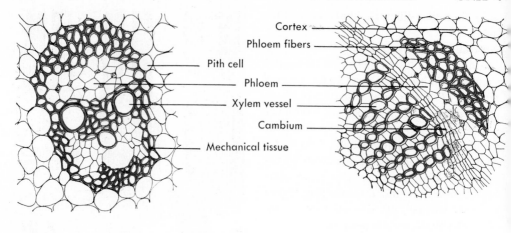

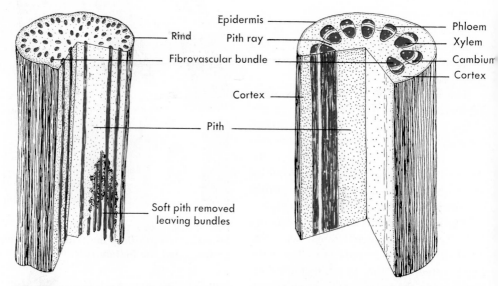

MONOCOT STEM AND BUNDLE   HERBACEOUS DICOT STEM AND BUNDLE

Fig. 16-11. **Compare the longitudinal and cross sections of a typical monocot stem (corn) and herbaceous dicot stem (bean). Note that monocots lack cambium.**

live through the winter, so the growth in diameter of the stem is only for one season.

The structure of a monocot stem. If you cut a section across a corn stem, you will find the tissues very differently arranged from those in the dicot stem.

The outer covering is a **rind** composed of thick-walled, hard cells. Its functions are to support the plant and to protect the other stem tissues. The bulk of the stem consists of a pith whose cells have

thin walls. Through the pith you will see numerous fibrovascular bundles which are *scattered* at random, rather than being arranged in a ring. In other words, monocot stems have *scattered bundles* while dicots have their *bundles in a ring.*

Monocots lack a cambium, so that they usually grow in diameter only until their cells have reached a maximum size. This is why they are generally long and slender as in the iris, orchids, lilies, grasses, and sedges. Their leaves have sheathed bases which wrap around the stems from one node to the next lower one.

Aerial stems. We classify a stem which grows above the ground as *aerial.* Such stems range in length from a fraction of an inch to the towering trunk of a forest tree. In general, we group aerial stems as: (1) shortened; (2) creeping; (3) climbing; and (4) erect.

1. *Shortened stems.* **Shortened stems** are aerial but they are so reduced in size that they frequently seem to be lacking entirely. For this reason, the dandelion, primrose, and carrot are often called *stemless,* although anyone referring to them as such has failed to notice the short, disk-shaped stem growing just above the root.

2. *Creeping stems.* The **creeping stem,** like the shortened stem, remains close to the ground, but its leaves spread much more widely as a result of its length. Plants with creeping stems often form patches or communities of plants all connected by *runners,* which is the name their stems are often given. The creeping stem is weak and slender. Lacking woody tissues for support, it must grow along the surface of the ground. Like plants with shortened stems, creeping plants need open places where they do not have to compete for light with taller plants.

3. *Climbing stems.* As a rule, **climbing stems** are slender and very long. Like creepers, they lack enough woody tissue to stand erect, and so are curiously modified in raising their leaves to light by clinging to supports.

The pole bean, sweet potato, and morning glory lift themselves into the air by *twining* around an object with encircling growth of the stem. On the other hand, the grape and the cucumber produce **tendrils,** which are really modified stems. These tendrils serve as a means of grasp-

Pakeltis from National Audubon Society

Fig. 16-12. The climbing stem of this grape vine produces tendrils, which are really modified stems. The plant grasps its support with these tendrils.

ing a support and holding the stem securely. The pea plant climbs by tendrils which develop from the tips of leaves. The tip of the tendril grows unequally on different sides, causing it to swing through the air in circles as it grows. Thus it can reach anything within the radius of its swing, which is often several inches.

4. *Erect stems.* We call a stem **erect** which stands above the ground with no attachments to an object. Such stems may range from a few inches to several hundred feet high. They may be herbaceous or woody.

Underground stems. Would you think to look for a stem in the ground? Probably you wouldn't, but you are familiar with several kinds of **underground stems** (Fig. 6-13, page 180). You may not think of them as stems because of their unusual location.

You cannot dig up a clump of iris or

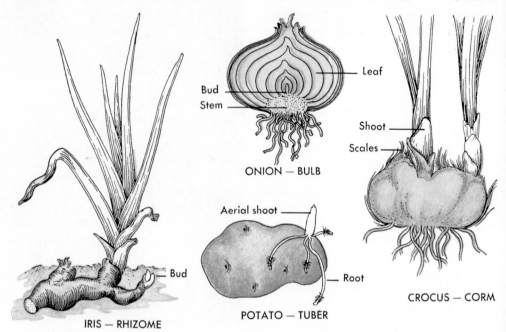

Bud
Stem
Leaf
ONION — BULB

Shoot
Scales

Aerial shoot
Root
POTATO — TUBER

CROCUS — CORM

Bud
IRIS — RHIZOME

Fig. 16-13. Although one does not ordinarily think of stems as growing under the ground, the four types shown above are all underground stems. Explain why they are classified as stems and not as roots.

lily-of-the-valley without noticing the fleshy underground stem which creeps horizontally close to the surface. This rootlike stem is a *rhizome* (*ry*-zome). If you examine a rhizome closely, you will see buds which develop at the nodes and produce leaves and flowers. The nodes are separated by internodes. On the lower side, nodes give rise to clusters of roots. Rhizomes may be thick and fleshy and filled with food, or they may be slender as in the case of quack grass and other grasses.

Tubers are enlarged tips of rhizomes which are swollen with stored food. The white potato is an example of one. A tuber, like other stems, has nodes at which buds or " eyes " develop. Internodes separate the eyes. Each bud may form an aerial shoot and reproduce the plant. You plant potatoes by cutting " seed " potatoes into pieces, each with several eyes, and putting them into the ground.

A *bulb* is a large underground bud. It has thick leaves and a stem which is reduced to a small disk. Cut an onion lengthwise and notice the small stem at the base. The leaves grow in compact layers. Roots grow from the lower side. Tucked away in the center is a flower bud. This will grow through the leaves at the top of the aerial stem when the bulb is planted the next season. The daffodil and tulip are examples of plants having a bulb.

A *corm* is different from a bulb in that most of it is stem covered with thin scales. One or more shoots develop from buds on the top. Roots grow from the lower side. The gladiolus and crocus are examples of corms.

Gardeners often speak of any underground stem as a " bulb." Lilies, daffodils, and tulips produce true bulbs. Crocuses, gladioli, and elephant ears form corms.

In Conclusion

Had you ever thought of the forces necessary to raise columns of water a hundred feet or more through the vessels and tracheids of a tree? Had you wondered how a tree trunk could support tons of branches and leaves in a wind? Did you know that stems do not grow all over but only at growing points?

A stem is a remarkable organ — a jack of many trades. In the next chapter, we shall study the leaf. Here, marvelous chemical processes lay the foundation for the entire living world. If a chemist were to duplicate these processes in the laboratory, he would achieve one of the greatest scientific triumphs of our age.

BIOLOGICALLY SPEAKING

aerial stem	deliquescent	rhizome
annual ring	excurrent	rind
axil	fibers	root pressure
axillary bud	fibrovascular bundle	sapwood
bark	girdling	scion
bast fibers	grafting	sieve tube
bud	growing region	spring wood
bud scale	heartwood	stock
bud-scale scar	herbaceous stems	summer wood
budding	internode	tendril
bulb	lateral bud	terminal bud
bundle scar	leaf scar	tracheid
cambium	lenticel	translocation
capillarity	node	transpiration pull
cohesion	phloem	tuber
cork	pith	vessel
cork cambium	pith rays	whorled
corm	propagation	woody stems
cortex	pruning	xylem

QUESTIONS FOR REVIEW

1. Name five specialized activities of stems.
2. (a) Distinguish between herbaceous and woody stems. (b) Give examples.
3. From what danger does a bud protect the growing point of a twig during the winter season?
4. Explain how the branching pattern of a tree is determined by the arrangement of buds.
5. Distinguish between sapwood and heartwood in regard to appearance and use to the tree.
6. Name four tissues found in the bark regions of a woody stem and list the functions of each tissue.
7. In what direction are water, minerals,

and dissolved foods moved through the rays of a stem?

8. In many stems, spring wood is easily distinguished from summer wood. Describe the difference in structure in these types of wood.

9. Explain how the cambium causes increase in the diameter of a woody stem.

10. What two tissues of a stem must be united if a graft is successful?

11. List several reasons for pruning a woody plant.

12. What three tissues form the fibrovascular bundles of herbaceous stems?

13. How can an herbaceous dicot stem be distinguished from a monocot stem by the arrangement of its fibrovascular bundles?

14. Name four underground stems and give an example of a plant producing each type.

APPLYING FACTS AND PRINCIPLES

1. Why are forest-grown timber trees more valuable than the same species grown in open places?

2. Compare the way in which a tree grows with the growth of your body.

3. Rabbits, beavers, horses, and deer often chew the bark of young trees. If they girdle the tree, it usually dies within a few weeks or months. Explain.

4. When the leaves of a tree drop off in the fall, much of the upward movement of water and soil minerals through the stem ceases. Explain why.

5. Most plants with shortened stems grow in open fields or prairies. Why?

6. Pruning is usually done in winter but some plants react better when pruned in the spring. Why?

CHAPTER 17

Leaves and Their Activities

EARLY one morning, a transcontinental bus was passing through a southwestern Indian village. One of the passengers happened to notice an old Indian sitting quietly on the roof of his house facing the east, awaiting the first rays of the morning sun. For centuries, his ancestors had observed this primitive sun worship.

To the Indian the rising sun meant another day of growth for his crops and more food for himself and his animals. Without the sun, he would have nothing. So in his own way, he gave thanks each morning.

We owe our life to the energy of the sun. We owe it to leaves, too, for the leaf is the plant organ where the energy from sunlight is locked into organic compounds. In this chapter, you will explore the food factories of a leaf. You will follow water and minerals into the leaf and trace the stream of foods out of the leaf to places of storage.

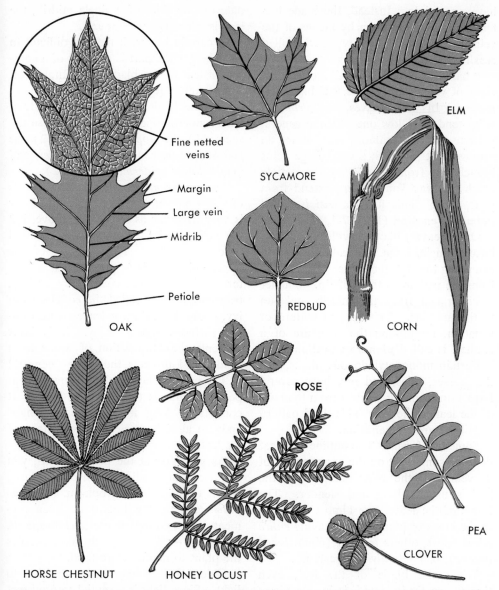

Fine netted veins

Margin

Large vein

Midrib

Petiole

OAK

SYCAMORE

ELM

REDBUD

CORN

ROSE

HORSE CHESTNUT

HONEY LOCUST

PEA

CLOVER

Fig. 17-1. Numerous veins act as pipelines to carry water to every part of a leaf. Identify the various types of venation and compounding shown in this drawing.

External features of a leaf. A typical leaf consists of a thin green portion, the **blade,** which is strengthened by a network of veins (Fig. 17-1). **Veins** are really fibrovascular bundles which enter the blade, much as blood vessels branch and rebranch in reaching all the tissues of our bodies. In addition to strengthening the blade, the veins carry water, dissolved minerals, and food materials between the leaf and the stem.

Usually the blade is attached to the stem by a stalk or **petiole** (*pet*-ee-ohl). At its base, the petiole joins the stem at a node. Veins, in turn, connect with the petiole at its upper end. Some leaves have no petiole. Instead, the blade fastens directly to the stem by means of the veins. Leaves of this type are called **sessile** (*ses*-il).

What is venation? We call the arrangement of veins through the leaf blade **venation**. In most leaves, the *principal veins* tend to follow one of three general patterns. The sycamore leaf shows an arrangement in which several large veins branch out from the tip of the petiole much the way your fingers extend from your hand. This first pattern is called **palmate venation** (Fig. 17-1, page 183).

Other leaves, like the willow and elm, have a single, large vein called a **midrib** extending through the center of the blade from the petiole to the leaf tip. Smaller veins branch from the midrib and run to the margins. This second pattern of venation, resembling the structure of a feather, is called **pinnate venation.**

Certain monocotyledonous plants, like the grasses, lilies, and iris, have several large veins running *parallel* from the base of the leaf to the tip. This third pattern is called **parallel venation.**

Some leaf forms. The outline of a leaf depends somewhat on the arrangement of its veins. If the veins are parallel, the leaf is usually long and slender. The forms of the leaves are almost as varied as the kinds of plants; some having *entire edges* (lily), others *toothed* (elm), *lobed* (maple), or *finely divided* (carrot).

When the blade of the leaf, even though greatly indented, is in one piece, it is called a **simple** leaf. There are many leaves, however, where the blade is divided into three or more parts. In such a case, we say the leaf is **compound** and each separate part of the blade is called a **leaflet.** When the leaflets radiate from a common point as in the clover and horse chestnut, the leaf is **palmately compound.** When the leaflets are arranged opposite each other, as in the pea, or alternate on the sides of a single midrib, the leaf is **pinnately compound.**

In certain leaves, it may be difficult to tell whether the part is a leaflet of a compound leaf or the blade of a simple leaf.

Internal structure of leaves. If you cut across the blade of a leaf and study it with a microscope, you will see these tissues: (1) the *upper epidermis;* (2) the *palisade layer;* (3) the *spongy layer;* and (4) the *lower epidermis* (Fig. 17-2).

The **upper epidermis** usually consists of a single layer of cells. Often this layer is very irregular as seen from above, but the cells are brick-shaped when viewed in cross section. The function of the upper epidermis is to prevent loss of water. It is sometimes covered by a waxy, transparent layer called the **cuticle,** as in ivy, cabbage, and most leaves whose upper surfaces appear shiny. This layer prevents the evaporation of water from inside, and protects the tissues beneath.

The palisade layer. Just below the upper epidermis is the **palisade layer.** It consists of long narrow cells arranged endwise at right angles to the surface of the leaf.

As you look at the palisade cells, you will see many bodies called chloroplasts, which occur in the cytoplasm. **Chloroplasts** contain the important green pigment or coloring matter, **chlorophyll.** This remarkable green substance enables the plant to manufacture food.

Chlorophyll is extremely sensitive to light. Since light is essential to food formation, chloroplasts must be exposed to it. But too much light destroys chlorophyll. The shape of the palisade cells meets this critical light situation by allowing the chloroplasts to receive intense light in the upper regions, and to escape from light somewhat in the lower portion.

The spongy layer of the leaf. Under the palisade layer is a **spongy layer,** which consists of thin-walled cells and air

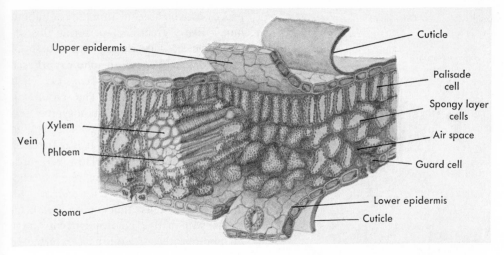

Fig. 17-2. The leaf is an extremely well-organized food factory. What is the function of each tissue shown in this cross section of a small portion of a leaf?

spaces. It is penetrated in all directions by large and small veins. The spongy cells are rounded, irregular, loosely-packed, thin-walled, and full of protoplasm. They also contain chlorophyll. However, their chloroplasts are fewer and lighter in color than those of the palisade cells. In the cells of the spongy layer, as in the palisade layer, food-making and other leaf functions are carried on. These cells also give off water to the air spaces.

The *air spaces* are usually large, irregular cavities among the spongy cells. They are connected with each other and to the outside by way of the *stomata* (*stoh*-muh-tuh) [sing. *stoma* (*stoh*-muh)]. The air spaces receive water vapor from the spongy cells and pass it out through the stomata. They also let oxygen and carbon dioxide pass to and from all the cells of the spongy layer.

The *veins*, containing xylem and phloem tubes and fibers, are scattered through the spongy layer. They transport water and foodstuffs and support the blade of the leaf.

The lower epidermis of the leaf. The *lower epidermis* usually has only one layer of cells. It contains many stomata. These regulate the passage of air and water vapor to and from the inside of the leaf (Fig. 17-3, page 186).

The stomata. *Stomata* are small slit-like pores, about one-twentieth as wide as the thickness of this paper. On each side of the pore is an oval *guard cell* containing chloroplasts. The guard cells regulate the opening and closing of the stomata. Influenced by warmth and sunlight, as well as by other factors, the stomata open when there is an excess of water to be passed off. They close in a drought. The function of the stomata is threefold: (1) regulating the giving off of water vapor; (2) admitting carbon dioxide used in making sugar and setting free oxygen, the leftover product of food manufacture; and (3) admitting oxygen when needed for respiration, and giving off carbon dioxide formed by respiration.

However, stomata would not be of much use if it were not for the many air spaces in the spongy tissues into which they open. By means of these air spaces, all parts have access to air for sugar making, respiration, and other functions. The number of stomata varies from 60,000 to

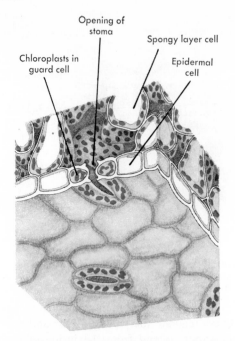

Opening of
stoma

Spongy layer cell

Chloroplasts in
guard cell

Epidermal
cell

Fig. 17-3. Countless stomata are found in the lower epidermis of most leaves. Their function is to control intake of air and outgo of water vapor and gaseous wastes.

450,000 per square inch. There are usually more stomata on the lower surface than on the upper. Floating leaves have all their stomata on the upper surface. In vertical leaves, they are about evenly distributed.

Chlorophyll, the green coloring matter of plants. Chlorophyll is the most important part of the leaf. Practically the whole function of the other parts is to expose the chlorophyll to light and to provide it with materials on which to work. Chlorophyll is a complex substance composed of carbon, hydrogen, oxygen, nitrogen, and magnesium. For its formation small amounts of iron compounds are necessary.

A marvel of plant life. Nature has gradually unfolded her truths to the ever-searching scientist. But with all his knowledge and skill, he has yet to discover the workings of a series of chemical processes which occur in nature all about him. Every green leaf performs this remarkable activity during the course of every day. We call it **photosynthesis.** We understand what happens, but can't explain how it goes on. The reason scientists cannot duplicate photosynthesis is because it is so closely associated with the process of life itself. It is a function of a *living green cell.* However, only certain cells are capable of photosynthesis, because it requires *chlorophyll.* All living plant cells that contain chloroplasts with active chlorophyll can carry on photosynthesis. We have referred to this process in earlier chapters, now we shall explore it more fully here.

Chlorophyll, the agent of photosynthesis. Often chemists find that two substances put together react only when a third substance is added. But the third substance does not enter into the reaction — its presence merely causes the reaction. Such a substance is called a **catalyst.** Chlorophyll bears this kind of relation to photosynthesis. It serves as a catalyst or agent without being consumed or changed chemically as the chemical reaction occurs.

You can remove chlorophyll from a leaf easily by merely heating it in alcohol or some other solvent. You might even assume that you can use this catalyst in the laboratory and carry on photosynthesis artificially. But you cannot, because photosynthesis seems to operate successfully only in a living cell.

Besides chlorophyll, chloroplasts contain substances called **enzymes** which are important to photosynthesis. Enzymes also serve as catalysts and, together with chlorophyll, cause the chemical reaction of photosynthesis without being used up in the process.

Raw materials for photosynthesis. From what substances are paper, wood, coal, oil, sugar, starch, and thousands of

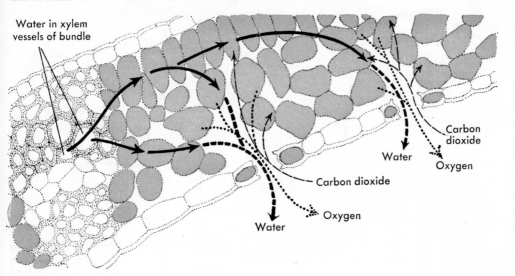

Fig. 17-4. In the leaf cross section above, trace the movement of liquid water and carbon dioxide during photosynthesis. What happens to the excess water vapor and to the oxygen given off as a waste product of photosynthesis?

other organic compounds formed? The answer is very simple — carbon dioxide and water. These two abundant inorganic compounds are the only materials necessary for photosynthesis (Fig. 17-4).

Plant roots absorb *water* from the soil and carry it through the stem to the leaves. *Carbon dioxide* enters with air through the stomata and is removed in the leaf tissues. In living chloroplasts, these two substances are combined chemically, by means of chlorophyll, to form a compound quite different from either.

The energy factor in photosynthesis. Carbon dioxide, water, and chlorophyll alone cannot result in photosynthesis. The product which these three form must also contain *energy*. This energy must be absorbed by living cells as *light*. The sun is the source of light in nature and is, therefore, the source of energy for photosynthesis. Direct sunlight is not necessary, however. Plants may use artificial light in the process. Plants can be grown indoors with nothing but artificial light, if it is adequate.

Photosynthesis involves two kinds of changes. One is a **chemical change** during which carbon dioxide and water unite to form a new product. The other is an **energy change**. Radiant energy (light rays), which is quite useless in supporting life, is converted into *chemical energy*. It is locked into the product and is released in the body of a plant or animal as energy for life.

The product of photosynthesis. We have now discussed four requirements for photosynthesis: (1) a living cell with chlorophyll and various enzymes; (2) carbon dioxide; (3) water; and (4) light energy. As a result of a series of complex chemical changes, **glucose**, the product of photosynthesis, is formed. Glucose is simple sugar. Chemists refer to it as a *hexose* because it contains six atoms of oxygen.

The exact nature of the chemical reactions involved in photosynthesis have long been a mystery. However, with **carbon-14**, a radioactive form of carbon used as a tracer in radioactive carbon dioxide, scientists have made amazing new discoveries (Fig. 17-5, page 188).

Argonne National Laboratory

Fig. 17-5. This research scientist is growing plants in an environment containing radioactive carbon dioxide. He traces the path of the gas through the plant in an attempt to see how and where it is used.

We now know that the carbon dioxide molecule is the structure used in the formation of glucose. Light energy provides the power necessary to take hydrogen from the water molecule and combine it chemically with carbon dioxide. As this occurs, some of the light energy is stored in the glucose as chemical energy.

There is evidence, also, that several intermediate compounds are produced as steps in glucose formation during photosynthesis. One of these products is *glyceric acid* ($C_3H_6O_4$). This product exists only a short time before further chemical changes convert it to glucose.

The addition of hydrogen to carbon dioxide during photosynthesis transforms inorganic substances into an organic compound. This vital chemical bridge provides the basis for a series of chemical changes which occur in both plant and animal cells. Many plants convert glucose to *starch* as it forms during photosynthesis. Others change it to *oil,* as in the onion and peppermint plant. The sugar cane, sugar beet, and sugar maple form a more complex kind of sugar known as *sucrose.* This is often referred to as a *double sugar* (disaccharide) because it is formed from two molecules of glucose. Some of the glucose formed in cells is converted to *cellulose,* which is a component of the cell wall.

The waste product. Carbon dioxide containing radioactive carbon-14 has provided the scientist with a tool for solving still another riddle about photosynthesis. What is the source of the oxygen released as a waste product during the process? Until recently, this oxygen was thought to come from carbon dioxide. Now, we know that this is not true. It is released from water molecules when light energy causes the chemical separation of hydrogen and oxygen.

However, while we speak of oxygen as a waste product of photosynthesis, it is in no sense wasted. In fact, it is as important biologically as the glucose which results. Some of the oxygen is used by the plant itself in respiration. Much of the oxygen passes out of the leaves through the stomata into the air. Here it is taken in by all living things for use in supporting respiration.

Photosynthesis — a definition. We can condense this discussion of photosynthesis into one brief definition as follows:

Photosynthesis is the process by which certain living plant cells combine carbon dioxide, water, and light energy, in the presence of chlorophyll, to form glucose and release oxygen as a waste product.

We may state it even more simply in a chemical equation, showing the amount of each substance involved and the proportions of the elements included in each as follows:

$$6CO_2 + 6H_2O + energy \longrightarrow$$
(carbon   (water)   (light)
dioxide)

$$C_6H_{12}O_6 + 6O_2$$
(glucose)   (oxygen)

This equation means that six molecules of carbon dioxide and six molecules of water combine, with energy included, to form one molecule of glucose with six molecules of oxygen left over. The glucose contains stored energy which is later released in the body of a plant or animal.

Experiments to show that green plants produce starch (photosynthesis). You can take leaves from active green plants, scald them to kill the protoplasm and to release the chlorophyll, and then boil them in alcohol to remove the green color. (CAUTION: *Do not use a flame near alcohol. Use a tube or vessel set in a pan of water and heat on an electric hot plate.*) If you test these leaves with iodine, a dark blue color appears, proving that starch is present. The chlorophyll had to be removed so that this blue could be seen. (The glucose is formed before the starch, but its presence is not so easy to prove.)

To show that chlorophyll is necessary for photosynthesis, you can treat a leaf from a green-and-white-leaved geranium

Fig. 17-6. The geranium leaf on the left is to be boiled in alcohol to remove the chlorophyll. On the right, it has been treated with iodine to indicate the areas where starch is present.

Before   After

1. Heated in alcohol   2. Treated with iodine

as shown in Fig. 17-6, page 189. You will find little starch in the white portions.

To show that light is necessary for photosynthesis, areas of an active leaf can be covered with corks pinned through both sides. After a few days the covered portions will not yield to the starch test, while the exposed parts will still do so. Another proof of the need for light is to keep a plant entirely in the dark, as a check experiment, and when it has become pale, to test for starch, which will be lacking. Of course, in both experiments you should use the same kind of plant, under the same conditions (except the light) as a control.

An experiment to show that green plants produce oxygen. Oxygen is the waste product of photosynthesis, given off when glucose is made. Since it is easier to collect a gas over water, a water plant is good for this experiment, but all green plants carry on the same process.

Fig. 17-7. Notice the oxygen bubbles that are being given off by the *Elodea* plant in the funnel. How could you prove that the gas is oxygen?

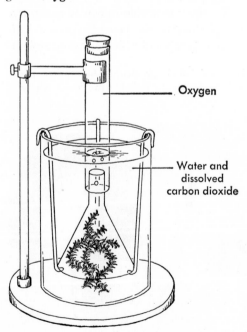

Oxygen

Water and dissolved carbon dioxide

A water plant (such as *Vallisneria, Sagittaria, Elodea,* or *Myriophyllum*) is submerged under a glass funnel whose stem is covered with a glass tube. The tube is corked at one end, filled with water, and inverted (Fig. 17-7). If you set the apparatus in the sun, bubbles of gas will rise in the funnel and collect in the tube. Before removing the cork to make a test for the gas which is collecting in the funnel, lower the tube so that the water in it is on the same level as that in the jar. This will prevent a downward rush of water in the tube when the cork is removed. Otherwise, air would rush in from the top and thus dilute the gas. Test the gas by lowering a glowing splint in the tube. It will burst into flame and show the presence of oxygen. If carbon dioxide is dissolved in the water, the production of oxygen will go on much faster because carbon dioxide is one of the materials used in photosynthesis, and that in the jar is soon exhausted.

Another experiment similar to the one above ought to be set up in the dark to prove again that light is the source of energy for photosynthesis.

To prove that the oxygen did not come from the water, another check can be made, using the same apparatus but without a plant, in which case no oxygen is produced. What does this experiment prove?

Conditions for photosynthesis. The rate of photosynthesis depends on several important factors, both inside the plant and in its surroundings. Probably the most critical internal factor is the condition of the food-making cells. The chlorophyll content of their chloroplasts is related directly to the general condition of the plant as well as to the environment which supplies water, light, and the proper minerals for chlorophyll.

Water is necessary both as a material for the process and to maintain healthy cells capable of food manufacture. The *carbon dioxide* content of the atmosphere is another critical factor since the gas serves likewise as an essential material. *Light* serves a double role as the energy source for the process and as a requirement for chlorophyll formation.

Temperature is an extremely critical factor since it affects cell activity. Summer temperatures, ranging from 80° to 90° F, are ideal for photosynthesis. As the temperature drops, the process slows down. It stops altogether near the freezing point. Likewise, a rise in temperature above 100° F slows down the enzymes involved. This rise lowers the rate of photosynthesis accordingly.

Photosynthesis supplies the basic needs for all life, both plant and animal. The most direct importance of photosynthesis is food production. Sugar, the direct product, is an essential food. From this basic substance, plants and animals build other food substances including starches, fats, oils, proteins, and vitamins. These all contain the energy from photosynthesis and are related directly to the activity of green-plant tissues. Thus, the green plant is the primary agent of energy storage for use by the living world.

Energy from fuels. Our modern civilization runs on power — power obtained largely from natural fuels. One of man's earliest achievements was the use of fire from wood. Wood contains stored energy taken originally from the sun during photosynthesis. We start a chemical breakdown of wood by igniting it and thus releasing this stored sunshine as heat and light energy. Wood has served for ages as a simple source of energy for heating, cooking, and fueling machines.

As civilization advanced, other fuels were discovered to supply more complicated machines. Plant remains of past ages were unearthed in the form of coal and oil deposits. The sunshine of millions of years ago, still locked inside the molecules of these fossil fuels, serves as most of the energy supply for civilization.

Storage and translocation of foods. During a bright warm day, photosynthesis forms glucose in leaf cells much more rapidly than the plant can remove it to other parts. As a result, most leaves convert the sugar to starch either immediately or soon after it is formed. As the day's food manufacture progresses, starch grains become more and more abundant. About the middle of the afternoon, the starch content reaches its peak.

In the evening, light is reduced and photosynthesis slows down. It stops almost entirely at night but may continue slightly on a clear, bright, moonlit night. Through the night, the stored starch in the cells of the leaf is digested to sugar, which dissolves in water. The **translocation**, or movement of the sugar solution through the veins into the stem, continues all night. At daybreak, when photosynthesis begins again, the food-making cells are cleared of stored food and are ready for the product of a new day's activity.

Formation of fats. Glucose production during photosynthesis is the beginning of a series of food-making processes which occur in both plants and animals. One such group of processes results in the formation of *fats* and *oils*. The process is by no means limited to leaf tissues, since light and chlorophyll are not necessary. All living cells, both plant and animal, possess the "machinery" necessary for fat and oil formation.

Fats are formed largely as storage products and are used later as energy foods. Many plants like soybeans, castor beans, cotton, flax, wheat, and others store in their seeds oils which serve as important articles of commerce. Animals also change carbohydrates to fats and store them under the skin and in other regions of the body.

Formation of proteins. Nitrogen, sulfur, and phosphorus are three elements present in *proteins* along with carbon, hydrogen, and oxygen. The former three enter the plant from the soil as dissolved mineral salts. During complicated chemical reactions, these mineral salts are broken down in the cells of the plant and together with carbohydrates are recombined to form proteins.

Accordingly, plants require not only carbon dioxide and water, but fertile soil as well, in order to form proteins. Photosynthesis may produce abundant carbohydrates, but unless the soil can supply the necessary mineral salts, proteins cannot be formed.

The green leaf has often been compared to a factory because of its ability to produce food substances. The table below shows how the two are similar in functions.

Respiration goes on in all living tissues. During *respiration,* oxygen enters the leaf through stomata. This gas combines with foods, especially sugar, during the chemical process called *oxidation.*

Oxidation breaks down the sugar and forms water and carbon dioxide as waste products, releasing energy stored in the sugar molecules. The carbon dioxide and water which originally composed the sugar are released as waste products. The energy is used by the cells to perform their life activities. We can summarize respiration as follows:

Sugar + oxygen $\longrightarrow$
   water + carbon dioxide + energy

Chemically, respiration may be shown as follows:

$C_6H_{12}O_6$ + $6O_2$ $\longrightarrow$
(sugar)   (oxygen)

   $6H_2O$ + $6CO_2$ + energy
   (water)   (carbon
            dioxide)

You will note that, from the standpoint of chemical change, respiration is the *exact opposite* of photosynthesis, a fact which is pointed out in detail in the table on page 193.

Photosynthesis and respiration are by no means balanced in the plant. Since photosynthesis is limited to the daylight hours, it occurs more rapidly than respiration. Respiration, on the other hand, takes place during both day and night. Furthermore, a plant normally builds up a much greater supply of carbohydrates than it needs. Biologists estimate that a corn plant uses only about one-fourth of

THE LEAF AS A FACTORY

The factory	Green leaves (or other green tissues)
The workrooms	The cells of palisade and spongy layers
The machines	Chloroplasts with chlorophyll
The power	Sunlight
Raw materials	Carbon dioxide and soil water
Supply department	Root hairs, ducts, air spaces, stomata
Transportation department	Ducts, sieve tubes, pith rays
Product	Glucose
Waste product	Oxygen
Hours of work	Manufacturing department, daylight; transportation and supply departments, day and night

COMPARISON OF PHOTOSYNTHESIS AND RESPIRATION

PHOTOSYNTHESIS	RESPIRATION
Constructive process Food accumulated Energy from sun stored in glucose Carbon dioxide taken in Oxygen given off Complex compounds formed Produces glucose Goes on only in light Only in presence of chlorophyll	Destructive process Food broken down (oxidized) Energy released Carbon dioxide given off Oxygen taken in Simple compounds formed Produces CO_2 and H_2O Goes on day and night In all cells

its total food supply during a growing season.

During daylight, the water and carbon dioxide released in respiration, as a result of oxidation, supply only a fraction of the needs of photosynthesis. Conversely, the oxygen released during photosynthesis is a much greater quantity than is needed for respiration. During the day, then, leaves take in carbon dioxide and release oxygen through their stomata. At night, when respiration alone takes place, oxygen enters the leaf and carbon dioxide is given off.

Plant and animal respiration are essentially the same. Both plants and animals exchange gases between the body and the atmosphere. Respiration uses oxygen for oxidation and releases carbon dioxide as a waste product. Animals and man need more energy for body activity than plants, so their *rate* of respiration is greater than that of plants. Animals and man *breathe* by means of muscular processes. But breathing is *not* respiration and you should not confuse the two. Breathing is merely the means by which animals and man take in oxygen and give off carbon dioxide. Plants have no lungs or other organs for breathing. Gases diffuse into and out of the plant through the leaf stomata and the lenticels of young stems.

Transpiration in plants. During the growing season, a plant conducts a continuous stream of water up through its roots and stem into the leaves. This flow of water carries dissolved minerals which are used in the manufacture of proteins, chlorophyll, and other products. Some water is used for maintaining cell turgor, and some for photosynthesis. With all of its uses, however, much more water is absorbed than the plant can use. Accordingly, the excess escapes from the plant through the leaves.

During the process known as *transpiration* water passes from the spaces of the spongy areas through the stomata and into the air as a vapor. While leaves are primarily concerned with transpiration, other plant parts may likewise pass water vapor into the atmosphere.

The control of transpiration. Transpiration is more than evaporation. We see this when we note the difference in the *rate* at which it occurs under different conditions. The rate of transpiration is controlled *to a limited extent* by the opening of the stomata. This opening is, in turn, controlled by the shape of the guard cells. When the guard cells change shape, the size of the opening between them also changes. When the guard cells are full of water, they swell and enlarge

Fig. 17-8. Although transpiration is controlled somewhat by the stomata, too much water is frequently lost on a hot day. The plant on the right is wilted because of excess transpiration and resulting loss of turgor in the cells.

Brooklyn Botanic Garden

the opening. Then water escapes rapidly. But when the guard cells contain little water, they collapse and reduce further water loss. A closed stoma slows up but does not entirely stop transpiration.

The opening and closing of leaf stomata are influenced to a great extent by external factors. Light, humidity of the air, and temperature affect the guard cells and, hence, the escape of water vapor.

That leaves cannot entirely stop transpiration, even with their stomata closed, is clearly shown in the wilting which frequently occurs on hot days. Such wilting ceases in the evening when the atmosphere cools and absorption makes up the water deficiency. Transpiration is especially dangerous to plants after transplanting. The removal of some of their leaves reduces the evaporation of water vapor from the leaves. Fig. 17-9 illustrates the fact that plants give off water vapor.

Fig. 17-9. *A.* **Water vapor from the plant is condensing on the sides of the bell jar.** *B.* **The water vapor turns the indicator (cobalt paper) pink in 15 minutes.** *C.* **The blue color of the cobalt paper in this control jar does not change.**

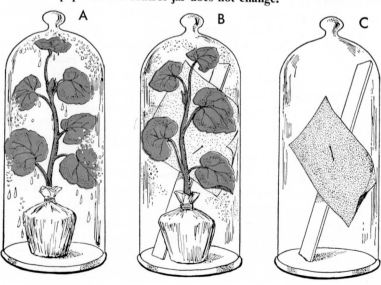

Leaves in relation to light. No factor of the physical environment has so great an influence on the leaf as light. As a source of energy necessary for food manufacture, light has a direct bearing on the nutrition of the entire plant. The supply of food depends on the extent to which a plant displays its leaves to light.

The critical relationship between a leaf and light is shown in the influence of light on leaf area. In places of reduced light, as for example the inside or lower branches of a tree, leaves tend to be larger than those at the tips of branches or at the top where abundant light strikes them.

Light influences leaf growth further in the make-up of the internal tissues. Leaves exposed to bright light usually develop one or more layers of compact palisade cells on the upper side. They also have many cells in the spongy layer. Shaded leaves have loosely arranged palisade cells, or none at all, and they have fewer spongy cells than leaves growing in bright light (Fig. 17-10, page 196).

The arrangement of leaves in respect to light. Leaves are arranged on the stem in a way which will expose each to the most light. Each leaf is produced at a different angle on the stem. For example,

SUMMARY OF LEAF ACTIVITIES

PROCESS	CENTER OF ACTIVITY	APPARATUS	MATERIALS REQUIRED	PRODUCT	BY-PRODUCT
Photosynthesis	Palisade and spongy cells (cortex of green stems)	Chlorophyll, enzymes	Water, carbon dioxide	Glucose (may be changed to starch)	Oxygen
Digestion	All living cells	Protoplasm, enzymes	Starch, oils, fats, proteins	Simple sugars, fatty acids, glycerin, amino acids	
Fat formation	All living cells	Protoplasm, enzymes	C, H, and O from carbohydrates	Fats and oils	
Protein formation	All living cells	Protoplasm, enzymes	C, H, and O from carbohydrates; N, S, and P from minerals	Proteins	
Respiration	All living cells	Protoplasm, enzymes	Foods (especially carbohydrates) and oxygen	Energy	Carbon dioxide and water
Translocation	Leaf cells and veins	Water as a conducting medium	Sugar (dissolved in water)		
Transpiration	Leaf epidermis	Stomata	Water	Water vapor	

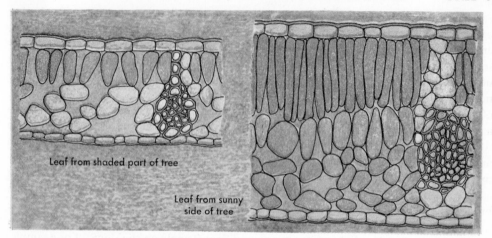

Leaf from shaded part of tree

Leaf from sunny
side of tree

Fig. 17-10. Compare this cross-section drawing of a leaf grown in the shade and that of a leaf grown in sunlight. Notice the difference in the amount of palisade tissue.

two leaves arranged in a north-south direction will alternate with leaves arranged in an east-west direction. Thus, one leaf does not shade another growing from the node under it.

The general arrangement of leaves on the stem tends to put each in the best position to get light. Any rigid placing of leaves would not be very effective among plants which must compete with one another for light. Individual leaves can adjust the position of their blades by a bending of the petiole. The bending is due to the fact that the cells away from the light are stimulated to grow faster than those facing the light. This response is called **phototropism** (foh-*tot*-troh-pizm).

Effects of moisture on leaves. Like light, moisture affects the size and growth of leaves. In regions of heavy rainfall and moist atmospheric conditions, leaves are usually large. As rainfall decreases and air becomes drier, leaves tend to become smaller. In extremely dry places, plants may have hardly any leaves at all, as in the cactus where leaves are reduced to mere spines.

Leaf coloration. The change in the color of leaves in the fall is explained on

the basis of light, temperature, and moisture.

During the late spring and summer, leaves are green because chlorophyll is present in the chloroplasts. During the growing season, chlorophyll is constantly destroyed by light, but is replaced just as quickly by the activity of the leaf cells.

In addition to chlorophyll, the chloroplasts also contain the yellow pigment **xanthophyll,** and the orange pigment **carotene.** Chlorophyll masks these two other pigments so we hardly know they exist.

With the coming of fall, the temperature is apt to drop below the point necessary for chlorophyll formation. Light destroys the remaining chlorophyll, then the previously hidden yellow and orange pigments begin to appear.

The cool weather and increase in air moisture also produce the red pigment **anthocyanin** in many leaves. This red pigment does not form in the chloroplasts, but in the cell sap in vacuoles of the leaf cells. It is formed from food materials. This pigment accounts for the red appearance of leaves of many woody plants during the cool spring and fall season.

Brown coloration results from the

Groffman from Franklin

Fig. 17-11.   What causes xanthophyll, carotene, and anthocyanin pigments to appear in leaves in the autumn?

death of leaf tissues and the production of *tannic acid* within the leaf.

The falling of leaves from their branches. The natural fall of leaves is caused by an **abscission** (ab-*sih*-shun) **layer** consisting of a row of cells across the base of the petiole (Fig. 17-12). Soon after the layer forms, its walls separate from the stem and leave the petiole attached only by its fibrovascular bundles. The slightest jarring or gust of wind will cause the leaf to drop. A thin layer of cork cells seals the scar where the leaf was attached to the stem.

While evergreen trees do not shed all their leaves at any one time, new leaves usually appear during the spring and replace those of the previous season.

Special leaf modifications. Leaves frequently may be reduced to mere **tendrils,** or the skeleton of veins, or they may develop as thorns. Some plants like *Sedum*

have leaves thickened with stored food and water. These may even reproduce the plant. Perhaps the most curious adaptation of leaves is found in the tubular, vaselike leaves of the *pitcher plants,*

Fig. 17-12.   During the cool weather of autumn, the cell walls of the abscission layer separate from the stem so that the slightest jarring will cause the leaf to drop.

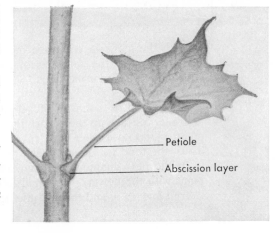

Petiole

Abscission layer

which form living flytraps. *Venus's-fly-trap* has leaves which form strange " double-jawed " traps for catching small insects (Fig. 17-13). These insectivorous plants secrete special enzymes that digest the small insects which their leaves trap. They are the only plants able to do this.

Fig. 17-13. The leaf of the *Venus's-flytrap* is modified in such a way that it can capture insects. The unsuspecting victim in this case is a bee, which in the top photograph is approaching the leaf. In the middle photograph, the insect has been trapped; and in the bottom photograph, completely engulfed. The plant then secretes special enzymes which digest the insect.

International News Bureau

In Conclusion

With the leaf, we complete our study of the vegetative organs of a seed plant. Most of the activities of the root and stem serve to supply the leaf with materials and conditions for the many vital processes which are carried on by the leaves.

At the end of a season of activity, many plants shed their leaves. New, active leaves take up their work the following growing season. Even the evergreen plants lose their old leaves and grow new ones at regular intervals. Thus, the food factories of seed plants remain young and active.

In the next chapter, we begin the study of the reproductive parts of the plant with the flower. We shall follow the reproductive process from flower to fruit and seed, and through the development of the new plant.

BIOLOGICALLY SPEAKING

abscission layer
blade
carbon-14
compound leaf
cuticle
glucose
guard cell
leaflet

lower epidermis
midrib
palisade layer
palmate venation
parallel venation
petiole
phototropism
pinnate venation

sessile
simple leaf
spongy layer
stomata
upper epidermis
vein
venation

QUESTIONS FOR REVIEW

1. Why is it important that leaf blades in most cases be thin and broad?
2. Name two important functions of leaf veins.
3. Distinguish between dicot and monocot leaves on the basis of their vein structure.
4. Name the tissues of a leaf from top to bottom.
5. Why are the numerous spaces in the spongy layer necessary for leaf activity?
6. Discuss the location, structure, and function of the stomata of a leaf.
7. Explain the role of chlorophyll in photosynthesis.
8. Why is light necessary for photosynthesis?
9. Name several fuels which can be traced back to photosynthesis.
10. Explain why soil minerals are necessary for protein formation in green plants.
11. Compare photosynthesis and respiration in regard to substances necessary for the processes, waste products formed, and energy changes that occur.
12. Explain how the rate of transpiration varies with the water content of a plant and conditions of the atmosphere.
13. Discuss the relation of leaf area and size to atmospheric moisture.
14. Why do various pigments appear in leaves during the fall season?

APPLYING FACTS AND PRINCIPLES

1. Most of the cells of a leaf have thin walls. Why is this important to the activities of a leaf?
2. The duplication of photosynthesis in the laboratory, independent of a green plant, would be one of the greatest scientific advances of all time. Do you think it will ever be done? Why, or why not?
3. If photosynthesis did not occur at a much greater rate than does respiration in green plants, there would be no animal life on earth. Explain why this is true.
4. Do you agree or disagree with the belief that plants should be removed from a sick room at night? Explain your opinion.
5. A nurseryman planted a tree in full leaf during the month of June. After planting, he pruned back the branches and removed many of the leaves. Why did this give the tree a far better chance to survive?

CHAPTER 18

Flowers and Reproduction

FLOWERS are among the most beautiful creations of nature. But to the plants producing them, flowers are more than beautiful creations. A flower is a specialized organ which reproduces the species. It exists only a short time and then parts of it develop into the fruit. The fruit contains the seeds which, in turn, produce a new generation of plants.

In this chapter you will learn the parts of a flower and the role that each part plays in reproduction. You will discover that bright petals are not always a necessary part of the flower and that in fact many plants around you bear small, inconspicuous flowers.

The structure of a flower. A **flower** is really a modified branch in which the leaves are extremely altered to form the parts of the flower. A typical flower, such as the geranium, apple blossom, snapdragon, sweet pea, or petunia, has four sets of parts (Fig. 18-1). These parts grow from a special flower stalk or **pedicel** (*ped*-ih-sel), the end or tip of which is the **receptacle**. The outer ring of floral parts consists of several green leaflike structures called **sepals** (*see*-puls). Together, the sepals form the **calyx** (*kay*-liks). The sepals cover and protect the rest of the flower in the bud stage. They also help to support the other parts when the bud opens.

Inside the calyx is the **corolla** (kor-*oh*-luh), which consists usually of one or more rows of **petals**. These are often, but not always, brightly-colored. The calyx and corolla frequently attract insects, as we shall see later. They may also help to protect the inner parts.

In certain flowers, both the calyx and corolla are the same color. It is possible to miss the fact that both parts are present.

Two kinds of **essential parts** are concerned directly with reproduction: (1) the **stamens** (*stay*-mens); and (2) the *pistil,* located in the center of the flower. Each **stamen** consists of a slender stalk, or **filament**, supporting a knoblike sac called an **anther**. The anther produces yellow or reddish powdery grains called **pollen** (*pol*-en), which play an important part in reproduction.

The **pistil** is in the center of the flower (Fig. 18-2, page 202). It consists of a sticky top, called a **stigma**, a slender stalk, or **style**, which supports the stigma, and a swollen base, or **ovary**, which is joined to the receptacle of the flower stalk. Inside the ovary are the **ovules**, which will later become seeds. The ovules are attached to the ovary either at its base, or along the side walls, or to a special stalk running lengthwise from the base of the ovary to the base of the style. Ovules may number from one to several hundred, depending on the kind of flower.

Types of flowers. A flower which contains all four main parts: (1) *calyx;* (2) *corolla;* (3) *stamens;* and (4) *pistil* is **complete** (cherry, rose, lily). If one or more of these parts is missing, the flower is **incomplete**. Where the stamens and pistil are both present in the same flower, even though the sepals and petals are missing, the flower is **perfect** (wild

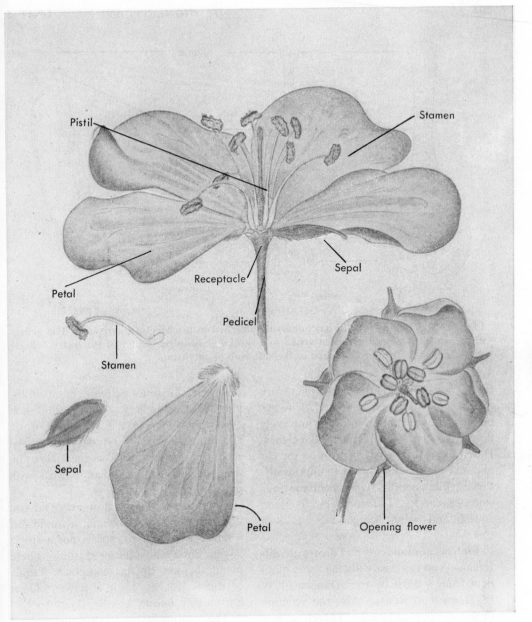

Fig. 18-1. The wild geranium is a complete flower, having all four main parts on one flower.

ginger and some maples). If either the stamens or pistil is missing, the flower is **imperfect,** although other parts may be present (pussy willow, cottonwood, corn).

Many of our common trees, like the willow, cottonwood, birch, and alder, produce imperfect flowers. Therefore, there are two kinds of flowers present. One kind contains only stamens and is therefore called a **staminate flower.** The yellow pussy willows in early spring are usually staminate flowers of the willow.

Some plants bear imperfect flowers on separate plants — that is, staminate flowers on one plant and **pistillate** on another, as in the willow and cottonwood

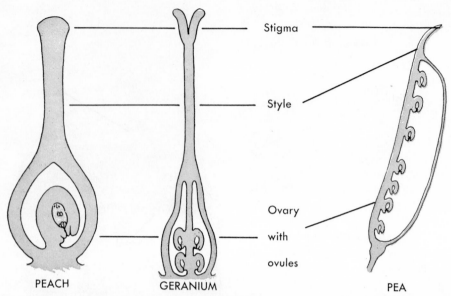

Fig. 18-2. The peach pistil has one ovule attached to the base of the ovary. The geranium pistil has several ovules attached to a special stalk in the center of the ovary, while the ovules in the pea are attached to the side wall of the ovary.

(Fig. 18-5, page 204). These plants are called **dioecious** (dy-*ee*-shus). Other plants produce both kinds of imperfect flowers on the same plant, as does corn. Here the pistillate flowers form on the ear and the staminate flowers compose the tassel. Plants of this type are **monoecious** (mon-*ee*-shus). The corn, birch, alder, squash, and walnut are good examples of this type.

Flowers of monocots and dicots are different. You can easily distinguish a monocot from a dicot by the arrangement of tissues in their stems. Also the venation of the leaves is different. Therefore, it is not surprising that the flowers of these two great groups differ. A **monocot flower,** such as a lily, a tulip, or an iris, has flower parts in threes or in multiples of three, such as six (Fig. 18-6, page 205). A lily has three sepals, three petals inside the sepals and usually the same color, six stamens, and a pistil with a three-part stigma and three chambers in the ovary.

Flowers of **dicot plants** usually have

their parts in fours or fives, or in multiples of these numbers. You will find such an arrangement in the buttercup, rose, and columbine (Fig. 18-7, page 205). An exception to this rule is the magnolia, which is one of few dicot flowers with parts in threes or sixes.

What are composite flowers? Did you know that a daisy, a zinnia, a sunflower, a dandelion, or a cosmos is not a single flower, but a whole flower cluster? These plants belong to the composite family of dicots. They form a flower cluster known as a **head.**

The sunflower, and other composites, has two kinds of flowers forming the head (Fig. 18-3). The so-called petals around the outside are actually individual **ray flowers,** which serve to attract insects but do not usually produce seeds. Smaller **disk flowers** fill the center of the head. Each disk flower develops a small, dry fruit.

The entire head of the dandelion is made up of ray flowers. Each will produce a tiny one-seeded fruit which will leave the head on a parachute.

The anther and pollen formation. Pollen grains develop in four **pollen sacs** in each anther. If you cut an anther from a large stamen such as that of the lily or tulip, you will see the sac quite clearly with a hand lens.

When the pollen is ripe, the sacs open as the anther splits. The grains are then exposed to wind, water, or insects.

Pollen grains vary in size, shape, and texture. Some are rough, while others are smooth (Fig. 18-4). Each grain consists of cytoplasm and two nuclei, one the **tube nucleus** and the other the **generative nucleus**.

Pollination. Seed development occurs after flowering only if pollen is transferred from the anther of a stamen to the

Hugh Spencer

Fig. 18-3. The sunflower is a composite flower, having numerous disk flowers at its center and ray flowers around the outside. What is the function of the ray flower?

Fig. 18-4. The pollen grain of each plant species, when viewed microscopically, has a characteristic form. Certain proteins in pollen grains are responsible for hay fever and rose fever.

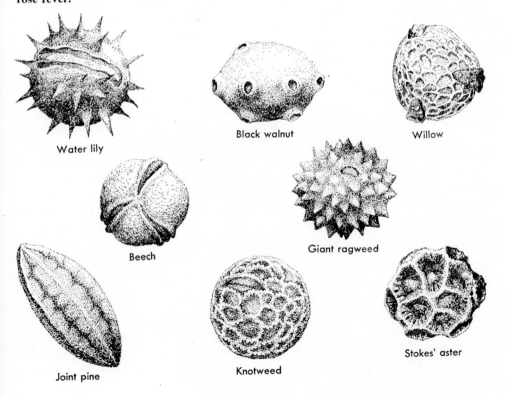

Water lily

Black walnut

Willow

Beech

Giant ragweed

Joint pine

Knotweed

Stokes' aster

Fig. 18-5. The flowers of the pussy willow are imperfect. The pistillate flowers are shown on the right, and the staminate flowers on the left.

stigma of a pistil of the same kind of plant. This transfer of pollen from anther to stigma is **pollination** (*pol*-in-ay-shun), one of the most vital phases of reproduction.

Self-pollination is the transfer of pollen from anther to stigma in the same flower or to the stigma of another flower on the same plant. If flowers on two separate plants are involved, the process is called **cross-pollination.**

The transfer of pollen from one plant to another in cross-pollination requires an outside agent. The chief ones are: *insects, wind,* or *water*. Curious adaptations of different kinds of flowers are frequently necessary to accomplish pollination by the outside sources.

Adaptations for pollination. Chief among the *insect pollinators* are bees. But moths, butterflies, and certain kinds of flies visit flowers regularly and in so doing carry on cross-pollination.

Insects come to the flower to obtain the sweet nectar which is secreted deep in the flower from special glands at the base of the petals. Bees swallow nectar into a special honey stomach where it is mixed with saliva and converted into honey. When they return to the hive, the bees deposit the honey in six-sided cells of the comb and use it later as food.

The plump hairy body of the bee makes it an ideal pollinator (Fig. 18-8). To reach the nectar glands at the base of the flower, the bee must rub its hairy body against the anthers. These are usually located near the opening of the flower. When the insect visits the next flower, some of the pollen is sure to rub against the sticky stigma of the pistil as a new supply is brushed off the stamen.

Brightly-colored petals and sweet odors aid insects in locating flowers. Nectar guides in some flowers may be brightly-colored stripes located on the petals.

We must include at least one bird in discussing agents of pollination. Tiny hummingbirds feed on nectar of certain flowers. Their long bills and equally long tongues reach down to the nectar glands while the bird hovers over the flower.

The flowers of wind-pollinated plants are much less striking than are those pollinated by insects. They are usually borne in dense clusters near the ends of branches. As a rule, petals are lacking and the flowers seldom have any nectar. Frequently, the stamens are long and produce enormous quantities of pollen. The pistils are also long and the stigmas are large and often sticky to catch pollen grains that are blown about by the wind. Pines, cottonwood, willow, walnut, corn, oats, and other wind-pollinated plants literally fill the air with pollen when their stamens are ripe.

Natural prevention of self-pollination. While not always the case, a great many plants form better seed as a result of

Fig. 18-6. The tulip, a monocot, has flower parts in multiples of three.

Fig. 18-7. A dicot usually has flower parts in fives, as columbine, or multiples of five.

cross-pollination than self-pollination. Accordingly, nature has provided various means of avoiding self-pollination in certain plants. Imperfect flowers on separate plants are a guarantee of cross-pollination. Likewise, imperfect flowers on the same plant, as in the corn, usually result in cross-pollination, because pollen

is carried from the tassel by the wind to the ear of another plant.

The shape of many perfect flowers such as the sweet pea and iris is irregular. The pollen can hardly get to the pistil of the same flower except by accident, but is almost certain to be crossed when the flowers are visited by insects. Frequently, the

Fig. 18-8. The bee is an ideal pollinator because of its plump hairy body. What are the other agents by which plants are pollinated?

stamens and pistil mature at different times in the same flower, so that when the pollen is ripe the pistil has not matured sufficiently to receive it, or the reverse.

Artificial pollination. By controlling pollination, a plant breeder can make scientific crosses and produce new and improved varieties of plants. There are several ways of preventing natural self-pollination from occurring before artificial pollination can be carried out. One method is the removal of the stamens of a flower before the pollen is mature. Another is to cover the flower with a sack. To prevent pollen from other plants reaching the pistil, that is, to prevent cross-pollination, the flower may be covered with a sack after the stamens have been removed. The breeder then selects the plants he wants to use as parents and transfers pollen from the stamens of one to the pistil of the other (Fig. 18-9).

Pollen allergy. To many, pollen isn't a pleasant subject to discuss because it is associated with an **allergy** we commonly refer to as *hay fever* or *rose fever*. The content of certain pollen grains causes swelling, irritation, and itching of the membranes of the eyes, nose, and throat, in some people. The *spring type* of pollen allergy is usually due to tree pollens. Grasses and plantain are usually responsible for the *summer type*. The *fall type,* most common of pollen allergies, is usually due to ragweed. The fall type usually starts about mid-August and lasts until the first frost.

Pollen allergies are nearly always caused by wind-carried pollen. Many people associate goldenrod with hay fever. However, doctors have found that the usual cause is ragweed growing with the goldenrod. The pollen grains of goldenrod are waxy and are not easily carried by wind.

An attack of seasonal hay fever usually begins and ends on about the same day each year, which shows that weather vari-

Fig. 18-9. These men are artificially cross-pollinating onion plants. The man at the left is covering the flowers with sacks to prevent them from pollinating naturally, while the man at the right is using a blower to insert pollen under one of the sacks.

U. S. Dept. of Agriculture

ations from year to year have little effect on the time plants bear their pollen. In many cities, pollen counts of the air are reported in the daily newspapers.

In treating hay fever the doctor first finds out which pollen or pollens are involved by giving a series of skin tests. Extracts from various pollens present in the air during the patient's allergy are put in scratches in the skin, or they may be injected under the skin with a hypodermic needle. If the patient is sensitive to a particular pollen, a raised area which itches violently appears. When the doctor has found out the kind of pollen involved, he can give a series of hypodermic injections or " shots " containing the pollen substance in increasing strength. Usually these bring at least partial relief. Various drugs, including *antihistamines* (an-tih-*his*-tuh-meens), which shrink swollen membranes, may bring temporary relief. However, these should be used *only under a doctor's care.*

Structure of an ovule. The formation of pollen in the flower is only half the story of reproduction. The other half concerns the **ovules,** which develop in the ovary at the base of the pistil early in the formation of the flower.

A pistil sectioned lengthwise shows the **stigma** at the tip, the slender **style** and a swollen **ovary** at the base, in which are one or more ovules. For the sake of simplicity in studying the detailed structure of an ovule, we shall use an ovary containing a single ovule, like the peach (Fig. 18-11, page 208). Many flowers produce ovaries with numerous ovules, as do the bean, pea, orange, and apple.

The ovule is attached to the ovary wall by a slender stalk through which nourishment reaches the ovule during its development. The walls of an ovule are composed of two layers, or **integuments.** A tiny pore, or **micropyle** (*my*-kroh-pile), leads through the integuments to the in-

terior of an ovule at its attached end. An oval **embryo sac** occupies most of the interior of the ovule. Eight nuclei lie within the embryo sac at the time of fertilization. Three of these nuclei lie in a group at the end of the embryo sac farthest from the micropyle. These are the **antipodals.** Near the center are two **polar nuclei.** The largest nucleus at the end of the embryo sac nearest the micropyle is the **egg,** or female nucleus. On either side of the egg is a **synergid** (sih-*ner*-jid).

Growth of the pollen tube and fertilization. As a result of pollination, the pollen grains reach the stigma of the pistil. Once a grain lands there, it begins to form a long **pollen tube,** which grows through the surface of the stigma and the soft tissue of the style and reaches the micropyle of the ovule. Then it enters through the tissue around the embryo sac, and the tip end dissolves (Fig. 18-11, page 208).

Now let's go back to the pollen grain at the time it was released from the anther. At that time it has two nuclei: one, the *generative nucleus;* the other, the *tube nucleus* (Fig. 18-10). While the pollen tube pushes down into the style, the tube nucleus stays down near the tip of the tube. The generative nucleus divides and forms two **sperm nuclei.** These are the male

Fig. 18-10. The pollen grain, when ripe and ready to leave the anther, contains one generative nucleus and one tube nucleus. As the pollen tube grows, the generative nucleus divides and forms two sperm nuclei.

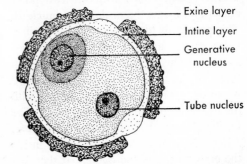

Exine layer

Intine layer

Generative nucleus

Tube nucleus

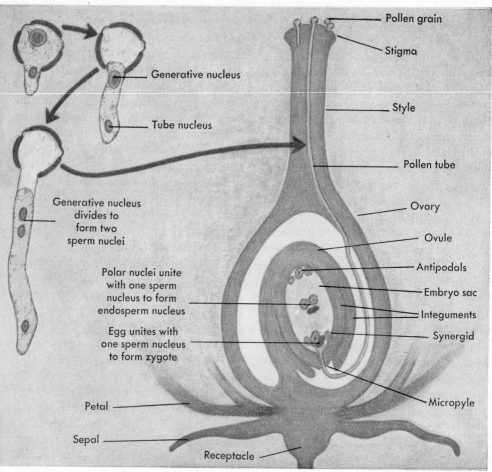

Fig. 18-11. The drawings on the left illustrate how the pollen tube and sperm nuclei develop from a pollen grain. The right-hand drawing shows the ovule of a peach in detail at the time of fertilization.

reproductive nuclei. When the tube reaches the embryo sac in the ovule, these nuclei are discharged from the tip end.

One sperm unites with the two polar nuclei and forms the **endosperm nucleus.** This process is termed *triple fusion,* since three nuclei are involved. The endosperm nucleus grows into the endosperm tissue of the seed, an area in which food is stored. The other sperm unites with the egg, a union called **fertilization.** The fertilized egg then becomes a **zygote.** After it is formed, it begins to grow inside the embryo sac of the ovule. It then be-

comes a young embryo plant enclosed in the seed.

After fertilization, the flower has served its purpose. The sepals and petals fall away (sometimes, though, the sepals remain as part of the fruit), the stamens wither, and only the ovary in the pistil remains. The ovary contains the seed or seeds inside. It develops into the fruit, which ripens, and at its maturity the seeds escape and begin to grow into new plants.

Our native flowers. All around you, native plants of the roadside, field, forest,

Fig. 18-12. The trillium (*left*) and the lady's-slipper (*right*) are both common North American wildflowers. The trillium is so named because its leaves are in groups of three. The lip of the lady's-slipper flower somewhat resembles a slipper.

and pond bear their flowers in an almost continuous succession from early spring until fall. In many sections of the country, the spring flowers of a woodland transform the forest floor into a flower garden for several weeks. Violets, buttercups, trilliums, anemones, spring beauty, hepaticas, crowfoot, and squirrel corn are among these early spring flowers. Later, plants of the field and roadside add their color to the landscape.

Among the most beautiful of all flower gardens is the Alpine meadow in summer. High above timber line in the great mountain ranges, the rocky slopes lose their snow in early summer and are transformed into a garden of unsurpassed beauty.

Many think of a desert as being colorless. But during the period when cacti and other desert plants bloom, the reds and pinks and yellows of desert flowers make it a place of great beauty.

The beauty of our wild flowers has led to the extermination of many. In every region there are plants which need protection. If you happen to find one, admire it in its native haunt, but don't pick it or dig it up. Perhaps future generations will enjoy more of these interesting and unusual plants if you put forth an effort to spare them.

In Conclusion

When fertilization is completed, the flower has served its purpose. The petals fall and the stamens wither. The ovary of the pistil grows rapidly and matures into the fruit. Inside the ovary, each ovule grows into a seed, containing an embryo plant and a food supply.

In the next chapter, you will follow the development of the fruit and seed. You will probably have to change your idea of what a fruit really is.

Within the protective covering of seed coats, tiny embryonic plants may float through the air or ride long distances on the fur of an animal. This is nature's method of spreading plants to new locations.

BIOLOGICALLY SPEAKING

allergy	generative nucleus	pollen sac
anther	imperfect flower	pollen tube
antipodals	incomplete flower	pollination
calyx	integument	ray flower
complete flower	micropyle	receptacle
corolla	monoecious	self-pollination
cross-pollination	ovary	sepal
dioecious	ovule	sperm nuclei
disk flower	peduncle	stamen
egg	perfect flower	staminate flower
embryo sac	petal	stigma
endosperm nucleus	pistil	style
essential parts	pistillate flower	synergid
fertilization	polar nuclei	tube nucleus
filament	pollen grain	zygote

QUESTIONS FOR REVIEW

1. The sepals and petals of a flower are often spoken of as " accessory parts " because they do not function directly in reproduction. What purpose do they serve?

2. Name the essential parts of a flower which function directly in reproduction.

3. Both dioecious and monoecious plants bear imperfect flowers. Distinguish between these two kinds of plants and give an example of each.

4. Explain how you can distinguish a monocot flower from a flower of a dicot plant on the basis of number of floral parts.

5. The head of a composite flower, such as the sunflower or dandelion, is not a single flower but a flower cluster. Explain the structure of a composite flower.

6. (a) Describe the structure of an ovule at the time of fertilization, and locate the eight nuclei of the embryo sac. (b) Explain triple fusion involving one sperm and fertilization of the egg by the other.

7. Name three agents of pollination.

8. Discuss some characteristics of insect-pollinated flowers which serve as devices for attraction.

9. Describe various ways in which certain plants avoid self-pollination.

10. Distinguish the various types of hay fever and name a plant responsible for each type.

APPLYING FACTS AND PRINCIPLES

1. Most seed plants produce huge quantities of pollen grains. In proportion to the amount of pollen produced the number of ovules is very small. Why?

2. If the weather is rainy and cold during the apple blossom season, the apple crop will probably be greatly reduced even though the weather isn't cold

enough to injure the flower parts. Give possible reasons for this.

3. Most wind-pollinated trees flower in the early spring. What reason can you give for this?

4. Explain why the flowers grown in gardens and those bought from a florist are much less apt to cause pollen allergy than those growing wild.

5. Explain why you might find an unusual plant along a highway or a railroad track.

CHAPTER 19

Fruits and Seeds

A FOREST of mighty trees is a beautiful sight, but when you consider that at one time nearly a whole forest could have been carried in your pocket, the processes involved in its growth seem even more wonderful. Yes, " great oaks from little acorns grow," and a seed no larger than a pea produces the pine.

This chapter begins with the withering flower and ends with a new plant established in new surroundings and leading its own life. Before the seed pushes its root into the soil or sends up its shoot, it may have traveled many miles from the parent plant. Vegetation moves by scattering seeds. Once a seed has sprouted, the plant must live or die where it happens to grow because it no longer has the ability to move; it is securely rooted in its new surroundings. While many seeds lodge in unfavorable surroundings, a few sprout in ideal places and although the mortality of seeds and seedlings is high, enough survive to carry on the species year after year.

From flower to fruit and seed. Fertilization brings a sudden end to the work of the flower. As the sepals, petals, and stamens wither, a group of special hormones force the plant to pour its full energies into the development of the ovary and the ovules inside. After a few weeks, the ovary and its contents ripen. In many plants, other nearby parts, such as the receptacle or the calyx, enlarge and become part of the fruit, so that we can define a *fruit* as a *ripened ovary, with or without associated parts.* A **seed,** on the other hand, is a matured ovule which is enclosed in the fruit.

A fruit need not be fleshy, like an apple, a peach, or an orange. A kernel of corn, a hickory nut, a bean pod with its beans, a sticky burr of burdock, and a cucumber or pumpkin are just as much fruits as the fleshy, juicy type. Thus the biological meaning of the word *fruit* is quite different from the meaning used in a grocery store.

The relation of fruits and seeds. Let's remember one important fact about seeds: the new plant grows from a seed, not from a fruit. But the fruit is highly important because it encloses the seed and protects it from water-loss, disease, insect attack, and other dangers while it is developing. Later, the fruit serves as a

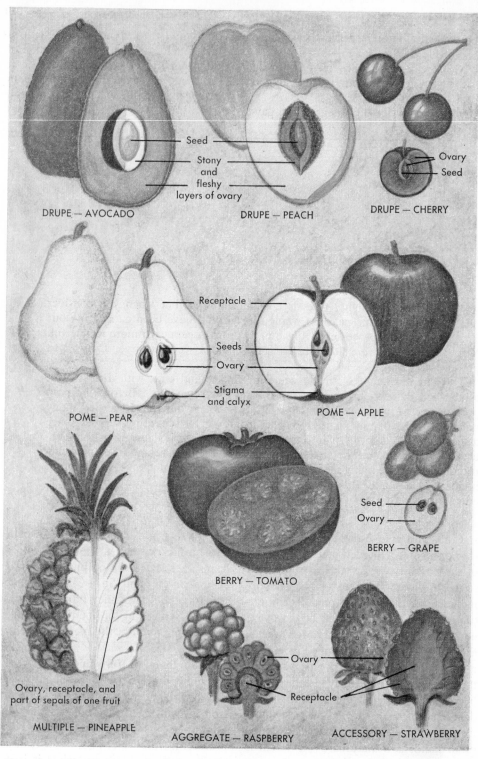

Fig. 19-1. In what way does the fleshy covering of the fruits shown in this diagram aid in seed dispersal?

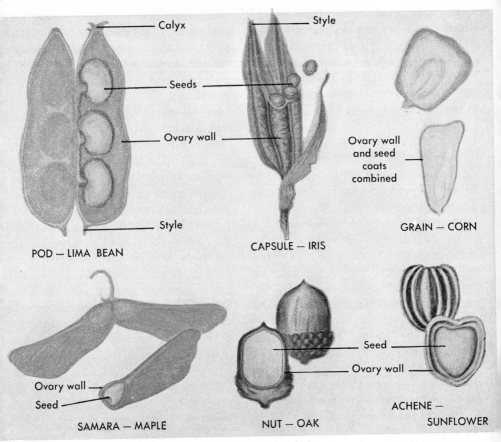

Calyx

Style

Seeds

Ovary wall
and seed
coats
combined

Ovary wall

Style

GRAIN — CORN

POD — LIMA BEAN

CAPSULE — IRIS

Seed

Ovary wall

Ovary wall

Seed

ACHENE —
SUNFLOWER

SAMARA — MAPLE

NUT — OAK

Fig. 19-2.   The fruits shown above become dry when they are ripe.   Which fruits are dehiscent and which are indehiscent?

device for distributing the seeds. The fruit may be a tempting meal for a bird or another animal or it may serve as a parachute or a wing for dispersal through the air. In some cases, a fruit bursts open and throws the seeds out when it ripens, or it may develop specialized devices for clinging to the fur of animals or the feathers of birds in order to leave its original home. Later in this chapter we shall discuss more fully the ways in which fruits and seeds are dispersed.

Structure of typical fruits. Fruits, like the flowers from which they develop, vary greatly in structure. The apple is especially interesting because it involves more than the ovary and ovules in its develop-

ment. Have you ever noticed a swollen region in the stem of an apple blossom or a rose just below the sepals? This is the *receptacle.* The ovary is located in this swollen region, below the petals and sepals, and as the apple develops, the receptacle enlarges and becomes part of the fruit. The ovary wall is the edge of the papery core and the ovules develop into the seeds which lie in the chambers of the core. Examine the sectioned apple in Fig. 19-1 and find the various parts we have described. At the end opposite the stem, you can see the calyx of the apple blossom, the dried stamens, and the stigma of the pistil. We refer to a fruit of this type as a *pome.*

The peach is another type of fruit which we classify as a **drupe**. The ovary wall of this type ripens in two layers — an outer fleshy layer and a hard inner layer. The outer layer is the part you eat while the inner layer forms the stone, or pit. One or two seeds lie in a chamber inside the hard wall of the pit (Fig. 19-1). Other kinds of drupes include the cherry, plum, apricot, and olive. In the case of the almond, for example, we discard the worthless fleshy portion, open the pit, and eat the seed.

The bean is a type of many-seeded fruit known as a **legume** (*leg*-yoom). Most of a bean pod is a greatly enlarged ovary wall. The pointed end is the style and sometimes the stigma remains as a tiny knob on the end of the style. At the stem end, you can see the calyx of the bean blossom. The " string " is a fibrovascular bundle which brings food and water to the attached seeds. The small undeveloped beans you sometimes find in a pod are shriveled ovules which were not fertilized. As the bean ripens, the pod dries out and splits open. The seeds loosen from their stalks and fall out. This type of fruit is produced only by one large family called *Leguminoseae* (leg-yoo-mih-*noh*-see-ee). Included in this family, along with the beans and peas, are the clovers, alfalfas, soybeans, locusts, Kentucky coffee-trees, and many others.

Classification of fruits. In classifying various kinds of fruits, we divide them first into *fleshy* and *dry* fruits. You are familiar with such fleshy fruits as the apple, pear, cherry, banana, tomato, and gooseberry. Fruits which become dry when they are ripe include the various legumes, iris and poppy capsules, hickory nuts, acorns, and the winged fruits of the maple, ash, and elm (Fig. 19-2, page 213).

We classify dry fruits further as: (1) **dehiscent** (dee-*hih*-sunt) — those which split along definite seams when ripe; and (2) **indehiscent** (in-dee-*hih*-sunt) — those which do not open along definite seams when ripe. The bean, milkweed pod, lily, and iris capsules are dehiscent fruits. The acorn and winged fruits of maple, ash, and elm are typical indehiscent fruits.

The table on page 215 gives the classification of some of the more common types of fruits.

How seeds are dispersed. When seeds mature, they must be carried from the parent plant by some means or other. If they fall to the ground close by, the parent plant will be surrounded by struggling seedlings and few of these will have much chance of survival. Nature avoids this waste by attempting to scatter seeds as far as possible from the parent plant, a process we refer to as **seed dispersal** (Fig. 19-3, page 216).

Sometimes only the seed is transported, but often the entire fruit is carried to a new location. In some cases, seed dispersal is a mechanical process, while in other cases an outside agent, such as the wind, water, a bird, or some other animal, is involved. We shall consider some of the methods by which fruits and seeds travel from the parent plant.

Pod fruits, like the bean and pea, often twist as they ripen as a result of changes in the amount of moisture in the air. This causes a strain on the pod so that it bursts open suddenly and with enough force to throw the seeds some distance from the parent plant. Another interesting example of *mechanical dispersal* of seeds is the fruit of the garden balsam, or touch-me-not. When the fruits of this plant are ripe, they open upon the slightest touch and curl upward violently with the result that the seeds may be thrown several feet. Capsules, like the poppy, do not split open along the sides, but holes form around the top as the ovaries ripen.

CLASSIFICATION OF FRUITS

TYPE	STRUCTURE	EXAMPLES
	Fleshy Fruits	
Pome	Outer fleshy layer developed from calyx and receptacle; ovary forms a papery core containing seeds	Apple, quince, pear
Drupe	Ripened ovary becomes two-layered — outer layer fleshy; inner layer hard, forming stone or pit, enclosing one or more seeds	Plum, cherry, peach, olive
Berry	Entire ovary fleshy and often juicy; thin-skinned and containing numerous seeds	Tomato, grape, gooseberry
Modified berry	Like berry, but with tough covering	Orange, lemon, cucumber
Aggregate fruit	Compound fruit composed of many tiny drupes clustered on single receptacle	Raspberry, blackberry
Accessory fruit	Small and hard; scattered over surface of receptacle; edible portion formed from enlarged receptacle	Strawberry
Multiple fruit	Compound fruit formed from several flowers in a cluster	Mulberry, pineapple
	Dry Fruits (Dehiscent)	
Pod	Ovary wall thin, fruit single-chambered, containing many seeds; splits along one or two lines when ripe	Bean, pea, milkweed
Capsule	Ovary containing several chambers and many seeds; splits open when mature	Poppy, iris, cotton, lily
	Dry Fruits (Indehiscent)	
Nut	Hard ovary wall enclosing a single seed	Hickory nut, acorn, pecan
Grain	Thin ovary wall fastened firmly to single seed	Corn, wheat, oats
Achene	Similar to grain, but with ovary wall separating from seed	Sunflower, dandelion
Winged fruit or samara	Similar to achene but with prominent wing attached to ovary wall	Maple, ash, elm

They resemble salt shakers and as the fruit sways back and forth on a long and flexible stem in the breeze, seeds sift out.

The delicious flesh of the apple, grape, or cherry is a sort of biological bribe. Birds and other animals feed on the fruits and scatter the seeds. Often the seeds pass through the digestive tract of an animal unharmed because their cellulose covers cannot be digested, and then they are deposited far from the parent plant. Did you know that many walnut and hickory trees are planted by squirrels?

Animals aid in fruit and seed dispersal

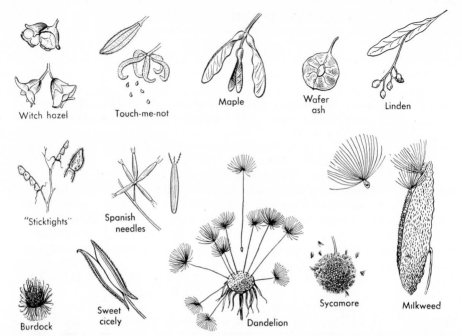

Witch hazel   Touch-me-not   Maple   Wafer ash   Linden

"Sticktights"   Spanish needles   Sycamore   Milkweed

Burdock   Sweet cicely   Dandelion

Fig. 19-3.   Describe the various ways in which these fruits and seeds are adapted for dispersal.

in another way. Many plants produce fruits with stickers or spines which cling to the fur of animals. You might have aided plants in seed dispersal if you ever sat down after a hike in the fall to pick off the "beggar's lice," "stick-tights," and burdocks that were stuck to your clothes.

Water is the agent of dispersal for many seeds. The coconut palm, for instance, often lives close to the shore and drops its fruit into the water. The thick, stringy husk of the coconut is waterproof. When the seed germinates, a sprout pushes through one of the three "eyes" on the end of the hard covering. Grass-like plants, known as sedges, are among some other plants which may drop their fruits into the water. They, like the coconut, are generally found along the shores of oceans or the banks of rivers and streams where their seeds may have found a foothold on the land.

The *wind* is the agent of dispersal for many fruits and seeds. When the milkweed pod splits open, the wind empties the pod of its seeds and each, equipped with a miniature parachute, is carried to a new location (Fig. 19-4). You have probably blown the fluff off a dandelion or thistle head. The fruits of these plants often travel long distances on their tiny tufts. In the spring, the cottonwood tree fills the air as spring breezes empty its catkins of cottony tufted seeds. The winged seeds of maple, ash, elm, and pine whirl in the air like tiny propellers and are scattered to a considerable distance from the place where they develop.

What is a seed? We defined a *seed* as a matured ovule and as the final product of plant reproduction. Actually, a seed contains a tiny living plant, the **embryo** (*em*-bree-oh), **stored food,** and the **seed coats.** The stored food nourishes the young plant from the time it starts to grow until it can produce its own food by photosynthesis. The regions in which food is stored may vary with different seeds. In some seeds, food is stored in thick " seed leaves," the **cotyledons,** which are not true leaves because they develop as a part of the seed.

You may have seen thick cotyledons on the stems of such young plants as the green bean or lima bean shortly after they have pushed through the garden soil. They are located below the true leaves and last for only a few days before they wither and fall off. The number of cotyledons in the seed serves as the basis for the classification of the angiosperms. Monocot plants have only one cotyledon in their seeds, while dicot plants have two.

Not all seeds have the same kind of food stored in the cotyledons. A grain of corn, for example, has its starchy food stored in a tissue known as **endosperm,** while the cotyledon contains oils and proteins. This tissue, filling much of the corn seed, develops from the endosperm nucleus after it unites with one of the two sperms during fertilization. On the other hand, the major part of the bean seed is made up of the two cotyledons which store a large amount of starch as well as proteins and oil. Some seeds have a large endosperm, while others have a very small endosperm or none at all. One of the latter is the bean.

Seed coats cover the seed and protect it from drying out and from other dangers before it germinates. Usually, there are two seed coats, but some seeds have only one. The outer coat is usually tough and thick. The inner coat is much thinner.

Structure of a bean. The bean seed is usually kidney-shaped (Fig. 19-5, page 218). The outer seed coat, the **testa,** is smooth and may be white, brown, red, or other colors, depending on the species. An oval scar on the concave side, the **hilum** (*hy*-lum), marks the place where the bean was attached to the wall of the pod. Near one end of the point of at-

tachment is the tiny pore, the **micropyle.** The pollen tube grew through this tiny opening in the wall of the ovule just before fertilization. The inner seed coat of a bean is a thin, white tissue which is difficult to separate from the testa. Both of these coats have developed from the wall of the ovule.

If you soak a dried bean and remove the seed coats, the cotyledons will separate easily, the water having entered through the micropyle. Note that the cotyledons fill the space within the seed coats and that they are thick and fleshy and not at all leaflike. Abundant food is stored in them in the form of starch, protein, and oil.

Lying between the cotyledons are the other parts of the embryo plant. A fingerlike projection, the **hypocotyl** (hypoh-*kot*-ul), fits into a protective pocket

Fig. 19-4. The pod of the milkweed plant opens when ripe, and the wind carries the tufted seeds great distances.

Black St

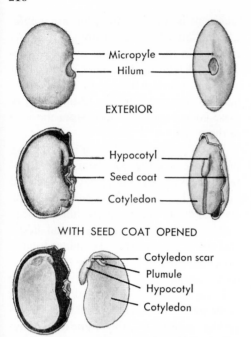

Fig. 19-5. **This diagram is of the external and internal structures of a bean seed.**

of the seed coats. It eventually grows into the lower part of the stem and roots of the plant, where the cotyledons can be seen attached to its upper end.

The **plumule** (*ploom*-yool) joins the upper end of the hypocotyl. It consists of two tiny leaves, folded over each other, and between them lies the minute bud that will later form the plant's terminal bud as the plumule develops into the shoot. The location of the cotyledons is important to the seedling. Both the hypocotyl and the plumule will grow rapidly when the seed germinates and the cotyledons, located around them, supply nourishment to both.

Structure of the corn kernel. Each corn grain is really a complete fruit, and therefore it corresponds to the bean pod and its contents rather than to the individual bean seed. However, there is only one seed in each grain and it completely

fills the fruit, the outer coat of the kernel having been formed from the flower's ovary wall. A very thin inner seed coat is fastened tightly to the outer one and is only one cell layer thick. It developed from the wall of the ovule.

The *micropyle* is covered by the fruit coat, but there is an obvious *point of attachment* of the corn fruit to the cob. This structure corresponds to the stalk of the bean's flower and is the pathway through which the developing fruit received its nourishment.

On one side of a grain of corn you can see a light-colored, oval area which marks the location of the embryo. This is faintly visible through the fruit coat. Near the top of the kernel, on the same side as the embryo, you will find a tiny point, the **silk scar**, where the corn silk was attached.

If you cut a grain of corn lengthwise through the region of the embryo, you can

Fig. 19-6. **This diagram shows the relation between surface features and internal structures of the corn seed.**

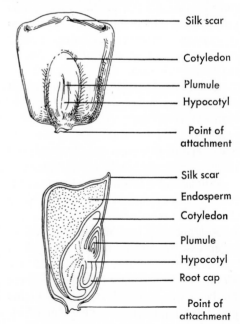

see the internal parts clearly, especially if you put a drop of an iodine solution on the cut surface. The *endosperm* fills much of the seed (Fig. 19-6). This part of the seed developed from the endosperm nucleus after fertilization. The endosperm contains sugar and starch, and will turn blue when treated with iodine. This reaction indicates that there is a large quantity of starch present. The embryo, however, does not contain starch, but it does contain considerable protein. Sweet corn stores sugar in the endosperm, but field corn stores starch, which accounts for the fact that we eat the garden variety and not the other.

The embryo, consisting of the hypocotyl, plumule, and cotyledon, lies on one side of the corn grain. The hypocotyl points downward, toward the point of attachment, and is surrounded by a protective cap. The plumule is also protected by a sheath or cap. The leaves of the plumule are rolled, not folded as they are in the bean, into a compact " spear," which pushes easily through the soil when the seed germinates.

The corn has only one cotyledon which partly surrounds both the hypocotyl and the plumule and lies against the endosperm. During germination, the cotyledon absorbs and digests food from the endosperm, besides furnishing some of its own, and supplies it to the growing seedling. Notice that in the corn grain most of the energy-producing food is stored outside the embryo rather than in the cotyledon, as we found in the case of the bean.

Dormancy in seeds. Many seeds go through a rest period before they germinate. This rest period, or **dormant state,** may be a few weeks, an entire season, or several years. Many plants bear seeds in the fall and their seeds are normally dormant throughout the winter, but germinate during the following spring or summer.

Drought, cold, and heat are all enemies of the tiny plant, although it is enclosed in protective seed and fruit coats. When conditions are favorable for growth of a particular seed, however, the period of dormancy ends and **germination,** or sprouting, begins.

While some seeds may lie dormant for several years and still remain alive, there is a limit to the length of this period. Some seeds may live for almost 100 years in a dormant state and then germinate

COMPARISON OF TYPICAL DICOTYLEDONOUS AND MONOCOTYLEDONOUS SEEDS

BEAN	CORN
Testa with hilum and micropyle plainly visible	Hilum and micropyle covered by a three-layered fruit coat. The true seed coat lies inside of it
Two cotyledons	One cotyledon
Large embryo	Small embryo
No endosperm	Large endosperm
Plumule fairly large	Plumule rather small
Plumule leaves folded	Plumule leaves rolled
The fruit is a pod, with several seeds	The fruit is a single grain, with one seed

when conditions become satisfactory. On the other hand, some seeds, like the maple, germinate almost immediately after falling from the tree, with the result that you frequently see a large number of young maples starting to grow under the parent tree in the late spring.

In the case of annuals that grow in colder climates, seeds are the only form in which the plants can survive the winter months. Their period of dormancy normally extends from one growing season to the next. The seeds of many perennials likewise lie dormant through the winter months and germinate the following spring or summer. In many cases, cold weather increases the percentage of seeds that germinate the following spring. Foresters have found this to be true in the case of the seeds of the tulip tree, or yellow poplar, as it is sometimes called.

The ability of seeds to germinate after dormancy is called **viability** (vy-uh-*bil*-ih-tee). Seed viability depends on the conditions during dormancy and on the amount of food stored in the cotyledons and endosperm. Cool, dry places are ideal for storing seeds, while warmth and moisture lower viability.

Commercial seed growers run viability tests and mark the results on various lots of seeds they sell. If you check the reported viability test, you can find out the percentage of germination to expect. If a lot of seeds has a viability of 92 percent, you can expect 92 seedlings from each 100 seeds you plant. Remember, however, that viability may vary since only relatively few representative samples are used in each test.

Conditions for germination. For germination, most seeds require at least three conditions. These are: (1) *moisture;* (2) the *correct temperature;* and (3) *oxygen.* The amount of each of these required varies greatly with different kinds of plants.

Seeds of many water plants germinate under water where there is plenty of moisture, a quite even temperature, and oxygen dissolved in the water. The seeds of most land plants, while they need moisture, cannot germinate under water. They require less moisture, an extreme example being the desert plants where the dew supplies sufficient water for the process of germination.

Before a seed germinates, it usually absorbs considerable water, causing the seed to swell and soften its seed coats. But too much warm moisture during the growing season encourages the growth of fungi which may cause the seeds to decay.

The temperature at which seeds germinate best is also variable. A maple seed can germinate on a cake of ice, but growth will be slow and survival very uncertain under these conditions. Others, like corn, require much higher temperatures, with a range of between 60° and 80° F. being the most suitable for the majority of seeds.

During germination, the cells of a seedling are dividing very actively. This increased activity requires a much higher rate of respiration than that of an older plant and you can see, therefore, why the oxygen supply to a seedling is critical. That is the reason the soil in a garden should be loose and the seeds planted sufficiently near the surface to give them an ample supply of oxygen.

Food changes during germination. Much of the food stored in the cotyledons or endosperm of a seed is starch. The plant changes this to sugar by the action of an enzyme known as **diastase** (*dy*-uh-stase), and the cells of the embryo absorb it. This change accounts for the sweetish flavor of sprouting seeds and explains why sugar is extracted from sprouting grain (malt) or why soybean sprouts are sometimes used in cooking.

Germination of the seed and growth of the seedling. The manner in which the

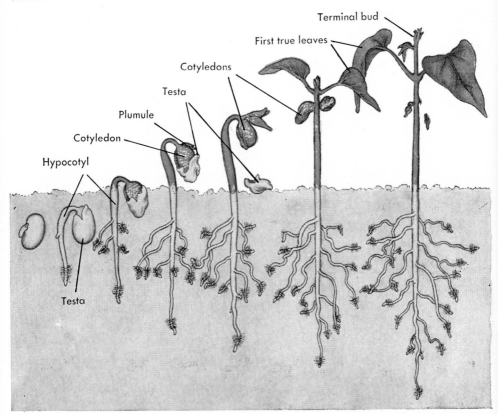

Fig. 19-7. This is a drawing of the various stages in the germination of the bean seed. The cotyledons, which are a source of food for the growing seedling, finally fall off when the plant can produce its own food.

seed germinates and the *seedling* establishes itself varies in different kinds of plants and in the location of the seed during germination. If the seed is lying on the surface, the hypocotyl must penetrate the soil from above, and the plumule will grow freely upward. If, on the other hand, the seed is completely buried, the plumule must grow through the soil and unfold its leaves above the surface while the hypocotyl grows downward. We shall follow the stages in the germination of a bean seed and a grain of corn and see how this is accomplished.

Fig. 19-7 shows the stages in the germination of a bean. After the bean has absorbed water and softened its seed coats, the hypocotyl grows out through the

seed coat. The *lower part* of the hypocotyl grows downward and forms the *primary root* of the seedling, while the *upper part* is growing upward and forming an arch which pushes its way to the surface. After the hypocotyl arch appears above the ground, it straightens out and lifts the cotyledons upward. The cotyledons turn outward and release the plumule, which grows upward to form the **shoot**. Then the minute leaves unfold, forming the first true leaves of the plant.

The stem lengthens rapidly, developing more leaves, and the small bud which was between the plumule leaves of the seed becomes the terminal bud of the plant. The cotyledons remain attached to the stem for a time, below the true leaves.

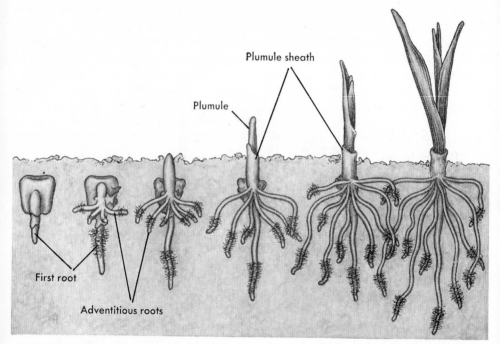

Fig. 19-8. Note that in the germination of the corn seed, neither the hypocotyl nor the cotyledon grows above ground.

But as the plant becomes better able to supply its own food by photosynthesis, the cotyledons wither, and finally fall off.

The corn embryo also takes in water after it has been planted and pushes its hypocotyl through the softened fruit and seed coats. This forms a temporary primary root which is soon replaced by branch roots that develop from the bottom of the stem. The leaves of the plumule, which are tightly rolled and are encased in a sheath, penetrate the surface of the soil. After reaching the surface, the leaves unroll and the stem continues its growth upward to form the cornstalk. Neither the hypocotyl nor the cotyledon of a corn grain grows above the surface of the soil, as was the case in the germination of the bean (Fig. 19-8).

You need not worry about a root growing upward and a shoot entering the soil if you happen to plant a seed upside down. The lower part of the hypocotyl has a strong *positive* response to gravity, and the plumule an equally strong *negative* response.

Seeds as food — cereal grains. Of all the plant parts used for food by man, seeds are the most important, and among them the cereal grains easily take first place.

These cereals are the fruits of various cultivated grasses and include wheat, corn, rice, rye, barley, and oats. They are the most important group of foodstuffs used by man and other animals. Cereal grains contain very little water, hence farmers can store them in cribs, bins, and elevators for considerable periods without spoilage. All are rich in starch. Some, like wheat, contain much protein, and others, like corn, are rich in oil.

The protein of wheat, *gluten*, makes a flour that is good for baking and yields a light loaf which no other grain will form.

All cereals, especially if the whole grain is used, supply such essential elements as phosphorus, sulfur, potassium, calcium, magnesium, and sodium. They are easily cultivated, ripen quickly, and yield plentifully if grown in proper soil. The history of cereals is as old as that of the human race. Wheat was used by the early Egyptians and corn by the North American Indians. Rice has been cultivated by the Chinese for over four thousand years.

Cultivation of cereal grains. *Wheat* is the most important cereal food both in Europe and in America. The United States leads other nations in its production. Our wheat-producing lands are the " bread basket " of the nation, extending through much of the Middle West. Several kinds of wheat, requiring quite different conditions for growth, are grown in different regions.

North Dakota, South Dakota, and parts of Minnesota are the centers of *spring wheat* production and have made cities such as Minneapolis the milling centers of the nation. The rich soils and bright sunshine of these northern prairie states are ideal for varieties of spring wheat which are planted in the spring and harvested in the autumn. Wheat of this type produces a hard seed with abundant gluten, making it ideal for flour.

The *winter wheat* area occupies a belt farther south and more extensive. Here the grain is planted in the fall and harvested in late summer of the next year. Although grown in many other states, the principal winter wheat belt includes Ohio, Indiana, Illinois, Iowa, Missouri, Nebraska, Kansas, and Oklahoma. A third important type of wheat called *durum,* or hard wheat, is grown still farther west.

Corn is another important crop of the Middle West. Although corn is grown in two-thirds of the states, the area of heaviest production (the Corn Belt) runs

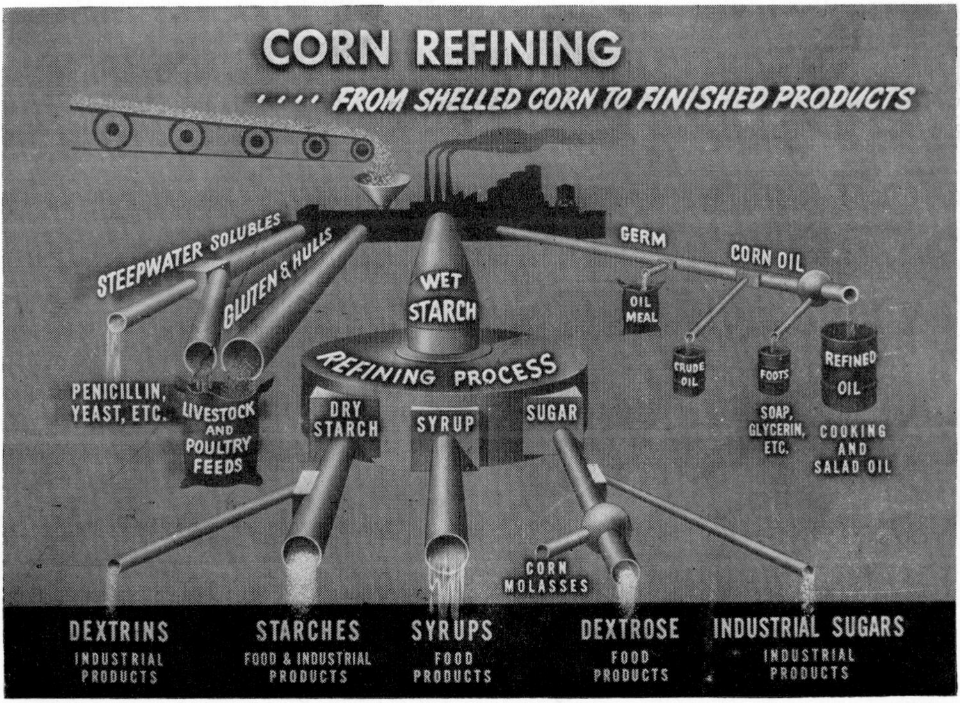

Fig. 19-9. Some think only of a delicious summertime vegetable when they think of corn. Notice the many other products of corn refining.

Corn Industries Research Foundation

in an area from western Ohio through Indiana, Illinois, Iowa, Missouri, and Nebraska. Almost all of the corn now planted is hybrid corn. The hybrid field varieties are used for flour and animal food. The hybrid garden varieties give a larger yield and are better for home freezing and canning than the older varieties.

Rice probably feeds more people in the world than any other grain. It is the chief cereal of India and China. In this country it is grown in some parts of Louisiana, Texas, Arkansas, and California. Rice requires warm semiaquatic conditions and so must be grown in low-lying regions or areas which can be flooded readily.

Oats are important items in the diet of livestock, both as a grain and as fodder. The ripened stalks and leaves of oats, together with wheat stalks, are used as straw. By various mechanical processes, such as rolling, oats are prepared for human use as an important cereal food.

Barley and *rye* also are grown as crops in many sections of the nation. Barley is widely used in preparing various food products as well as for fodder and malt, while the use of rye in the baking industry is well known.

Legume fruits. Next in importance to the cereal grains are the legumes, which include the bean, pea, soybean, and peanut. Legumes are rich in protein, starch, and oil, and, like the cereals, may be stored in the dry form. *Bush beans, pole beans,* and *lima beans* are important crops in gardens of all sizes. *Peas,* too, are an important crop in the spring garden. Both as fresh vegetables and as material for the cannery, peas are indeed an important food.

Soybeans are rapidly becoming a major crop, due to the development of many new uses for their seeds. Aside from the use of soybeans as food for man and animals, various commerical uses have been developed. As a source of material for plastics, soybeans have found their way into the manufacture of automobile parts, radios, and other products of industry.

In the sandy soils of the southeastern coastal states, the *peanut* is grown extensively. Its greatest use is for food after the nuts have been roasted and crushed into peanut butter. Peanut oil is also extracted for food and industrial uses. In the region where peanuts are grown extensively, the leaves and stems of the plant are used for animal food much as clover is used.

Nuts. While larger and richer in protein and oil than cereals, *nuts* are used less for food because the crop takes so long to mature, requires so much space to grow, and is too bulky to store.

For the most part, the walnuts, chestnuts, and hickory nuts of commerce are gathered from native places. In many places, however, English walnut and pecan (species of hickory) trees are cultivated as crops.

In Conclusion

When you consider what a seed contains, it is really quite a remarkable thing. It is a tiny plant, packaged for shipment, and provided with the food it needs to get started. It is the stage in which plants can be moved to claim new places. Whether the new environment will be good or poor and whether the embryo plant will ever grow out of its covering is all a matter of chance.

Far more seeds are lost than germinate. But nature allows for the loss in the great abundance of seeds produced.

Had you ever thought how over-production of seeds affects your life? How much of your daily diet comes from seeds? Think of the flour we make from cereal grains and of the beans, peas, and corn you eat. Think of the breakfast food most of us eat. Seeds receive the richest food stores of the plant. It is no wonder that they are basic foods of the animal world. And since plants produce so many more than are needed, we can supply our food needs and still have enough left to establish other generations of plants.

BIOLOGICALLY SPEAKING

cotyledon	germination	receptacle
dehiscent	hilum	seed
diastase	hypocotyl	seed coat
dormancy	indehiscent	seed dispersal
drupe	legume	silk scar
embryo	micropyle	testa
endosperm	plumule	viability
fruit	pome	

QUESTIONS FOR REVIEW

1. Explain the relation between the flower and the fruit.
2. Name several ways in which the fruit serves the seeds which it encloses.
3. Explain how the apple flower, as well as the stem, is involved in the formation of the apple fruit.
4. Using the peach or plum as an example, describe the structure of a stone fruit.
5. Dry fruits may be either dehiscent or indehiscent. On what basis do we divide them into these two groups?
6. What method of seed dispersal is shown in pod fruits which twist and open suddenly?
7. (a) Give several examples of fruits which are dispersed by the wind. (b) Explain how they are modified for this type of dispersal.
8. Describe modifications of fruits for dispersal by animals.
9. What purpose do cotyledons serve?
10. Describe the parts of a bean embryo.
11. Name three conditions required for seed germination.
12. How does the young shoot of the corn plant force its way through the soil in which it grows?

APPLYING FACTS AND PRINCIPLES

1. A seed will not germinate until it has enough water to soften the seed coats. How is this an automatic safeguard against germination during unfavorable conditions?
2. Explain why seeds planted in heavy clay soil or set too deep may germinate very slowly, if at all.
3. Food is stored in many seeds as starch. During germination, the starch is changed to sugar by the action of the enzyme, diastase. Why is this change necessary?
4. Certain weeds are often more common in some areas than in others. Why is this true?

RESEARCH ON YOUR OWN

1. Examine the staminate cones of a pine or other conifer. These are the pollen-producing cones which appear for a short time in the spring. At other seasons, you can buy them from biological supply companies. Dust some pollen on a microscope slide and examine it under high power. If you can get pollen from several genera, study the variations in the kinds of conifer pollen.

2. Make a list of common garden flowers and classify them as annuals, biennials, or perennials.

3. Cut a blotter or a piece of paper towel to fit the bottom of a covered dish (a **Petri** dish is good). Wet the blotter and drain off the excess water. Lay three radish seeds on the blotter, spacing them well apart. Cover the dish and set it in the dark. Repeat, using corn, peas, or beans. Examine the dishes daily for a week. Study the growth of the primary root and the formation of secondary roots and root hairs. Your observations might include measurements or drawings.

4. Cut a carrot lengthwise and crosswise and find the periderm, phloem, cambium, xylem, and secondary roots. Record your observations in a drawing. Additional fleshy roots, such as a radish, parsnip, turnip, and beet, might be used for comparison with the carrot. Notice especially the origin of the secondary roots. You can pry the central cylinder out of the carrot cut lengthwise and see the secondary roots which have grown through the phloem.

5. Cut several slices of potato or cucumber. Put some of them into a dish of water. Put others into a dish containing salt water (strong solution). After five or ten minutes, examine the slices in both dishes. Explain your results.

6. Count out ten prunes. Select an average prune and measure its length and width. Weigh the ten prunes and record the weight. Put them into a dish of water and allow them to soak overnight. On the following day, measure the length and width of an average-sized prune. Drain all the water from them and weigh them. Record the increase in size and weight of water imbibed.

7. Collect twigs from 20 different trees of your region. Classify them to genus (maple, ash, oak, etc.), using a tree book giving twig characteristics. Mount your twigs on a piece of cardboard and label each.

8. Extract some chlorophyll from a leaf by grinding it up and placing it in warm alcohol. Put one tube of extracted chlorophyll in bright light and another in a dark place. Examine the tubes after two or three days and explain your results.

9. Pick a vigorous leaf from a plant as you come to school in the morning (plantain, which grows in most lawns, is good). Extract the chlorophyll with alcohol and test the leaf for the presence of starch with iodine. In the late afternoon, take another leaf from the same plant. Repeat the test and explain the results. This experiment must be done on a sunny day.

10. Wet two pieces of muslin, burlap, or other cloth about one foot wide and three feet long. Select 100 seeds of the same kind. Lay them out in rows, spaced well apart, on one piece of cloth. When the seeds are arranged, lay the other piece of cloth over them. Then, roll the two pieces loosely. This is a " rag doll tester " used in viability tests. Keep the cloth roll moistened for several days. When the seeds have germinated, unroll the cloths and count the number of seeds which have sprouted. Since you used 100 seeds, the number which sprout will be the percentage of viability.

MORE ABOUT BIOLOGY

Asch, John. *The Story of Plants.* G. P. Putnam's Sons, New York. 1949

Collingwood, G. H. *Knowing Your Trees.* The American Forestry Assoc., Washington. 1947

Fenton, Carroll Lane. *Plants That Feed Us.* John Day Co., Inc., New York. 1958

Fernald, Merritt and Kinsey, A. C. *Edible Wild Plants of Eastern North America.* Harper and Brothers, New York. 1958

Grabe, Andrée V. *Complete Book of House Plants.* Random House, Inc., New York. 1958

Grimm, William C. *Pocket Guide to the Trees.* Stackpole Co., Harrisburg, Pa. 1958

Harlow, William M. and Harrar, Ellwood S. *Textbook of Dendrology: Covering the Important Forest Trees of the United States and Canada.* 4th ed. McGraw-Hill Book Co., Inc., New York. 1958

Huxley, A. J. *Exotic Plants of the World.* Garden City Books, New York. 1957

Hylander, C. J. *Plants and Man.* The Blakiston Co., Philadelphia. 1941

Jacques, H. E. *Plant Families and How to Know Them.* Wm. C. Brown Co., Dubuque, Iowa. 1948

Kumlien, L. L. *The Friendly Evergreens.* Rev. ed. Rinehart and Co., Inc., New York. 1954

Lane, Ferdinand C. *The Story of Trees.* Doubleday and Co., Inc., Garden City, N.Y. 1952

Miller, Edwin D. *Plant Physiology.* McGraw-Hill Book Co., Inc., New York. 1938

Peattie, Donald Culross. *A Natural History of Trees of Eastern and Central North America.* Houghton, Mifflin Co., Boston. 1950

Peattie, Donald Culross. *A Natural History of Western Trees.* Houghton, Mifflin Co., Boston. 1953

Petrides, George A. *A Field Guide to Trees and Shrubs.* Houghton, Mifflin Co., Boston. 1958

Platt, Rutherford. *1001 Questions Answered About Trees.* Dodd, Mead and Co., Inc., New York. 1958

Quinn, Vernon. *Leaves — Their Place in Life and Legend.* Frederick A. Stokes Co., New York. 1957

Quinn, Vernon. *Seeds — Their Place in Life and Legend.* Frederick A. Stokes Co., New York. 1938

Schery, Robert W. *Plants for Man.* Prentice-Hall, Inc., Englewood Cliffs, N.J. 1952

Selsam, Millicent. *Play with Seeds.* William Morrow and Co., New York. 1957

Symonds, George W. *The Tree Identification Book.* M. Barrows and Co., New York. 1958

Zim, Herbert S. *Flowers: A Guide to the Familiar American Wildflowers.* Simon and Schuster, Inc., New York. 1950

UNIT 5

The Invertebrates— Animals Without Backbones

Here lies the vast ocean, stretching wide on every hand; this, too, is peopled with living things past number, great creatures and small . . . and all look to Thee to send them their food at the appointed time; it is through Thy gift they find it, Thy hand opens, and all are filled with content. — Psalm 103:25, 28

It is amazing how much biology you can study in a single drop of water, which is where we shall begin the study of animal life. A pond or stream or roadside ditch teems with tiny organisms strangely different from the animals of the larger world of life. Some of these spring from a stalk and some dart about with thousands of tiny hairlike oars.

After studying these tiny creatures, we shall explore the animal life of shallow ocean stretches, with their jellyfish and corals, sponges and starfish. These creatures, together with the various kinds of worms, clams, snails, lobsters, spiders, insects, and a host of others are classified as invertebrates.

CHAPTER 20: **PROTOZOA — THE MICROSCOPIC ONE–CELLED ANIMALS**

CHAPTER 21: **SPONGES AND COELENTERATES — INTRODUCTION TO THE METAZOA**

CHAPTER 22: **INVERTEBRATES CLASSIFIED AS WORMS**

CHAPTER 23: **THE SOFT–BODIED AND THE SPINY–SKINNED ANIMALS**

CHAPTER 24: **THE ARTHROPODS**

CHAPTER 25: **INSECTS — A REPRESENTATIVE STUDY**

CHAPTER 26: **HABITS OF SOME INTERESTING INSECTS**

CHAPTER 27: **THE CONTROL OF INSECT PESTS**

CHAPTER 20

Protozoa—The Microscopic One-celled Animals

NOW that we have become acquainted with some of the Thallophyta which compose the vegetation of the microscopic world of life, we shall turn our attention to the animals in this society of tiny living things.

While these organisms are the simplest animals, if you examine their life activities, you may conclude that they are not so simple. Their bodies consist of a single animal cell living a solitary existence, yet these bodies are capable of performing all the processes of life. We realize that protoplasm is remarkable indeed when we see one of these tiny-celled creatures, without any specialized organs, moving about, taking in food, excreting waste products, and reproducing at regular intervals. Biologists call these one-celled animals **Protozoa** (proh-toh-*zoh*-uh), which means, literally, " first animals." They are well named, for they were probably the beginning of all animal life — animal life in its most primitive form.

Plants, animals, and basic forms of life. You know that plant life and animal life are basically similar because plants and animals are composed of a universal substance, protoplasm. But there are of course some differences between the two types. Plant cells usually have cell walls and chlorophyll, which animal cells seldom have. Plants are usually anchored, while animals usually move around a great deal. A plant commonly grows at certain growing tips — the buds on its stem, and the tips of its roots. Animal growth is not, on the other hand, usually confined to these areas. Animal protoplasm usually shows more sensitivity to stimuli than plant cells do. But notice that all these differences between plants and animals are *not* hard and fast divisions.

The Protozoa are considered to be at the extreme bottom of the animal kingdom because they are **unicellular** (one-celled) and relatively simple.

Fig. 20-1. A drop of water taken from a stagnant pond reveals a rich variety of protozoans when viewed under a microscope.

Bausch and L

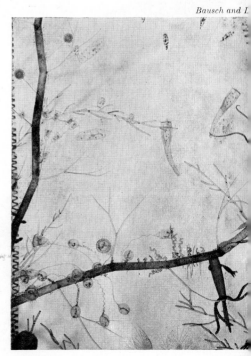

229

CLASSES OF PROTOZOA

1. SARCODINA (sar-koh-*dy*-nuh). Move by pseudopodia.
Examples: *Ameba, Arcella, Endameba,* foraminifers, radiolarians

2. MASTIGOPHORA (mas-tih-*gof*-er-uh). Move by flagella.
Examples: *Euglena, Volvox, Trypanosoma, Leishmania*

3. SPOROZOA (spor-oh-*zoh*-uh). No structures for locomotion; form
spores.
Example: *Plasmodium*

4. CILIATA (sil-ee-*ay*-tuh). Move by cilia.
Examples: *Paramecium, Vorticella, Stentor, Stylonychia*

Classification of Protozoa.   Before studying the Protozoa, review Fig. 8-7 on page 86, which shows examples of animals and plants arranged in order of increasing complexity. The division of Protozoa into four classes is based on the means of locomotion (see table above).

A mass of living jelly. *Ameba* (uh-*mee*-buh), the most primitive of true animals, can best be described as " animated jelly." On first seeing it, you might mistake an ameba for a particle of nonliving matter, for it bears little resemblance to other members of the animal kingdom.

Fig. 20-2. Many of these interesting ciliated protozoans may be found in a pond near your school.

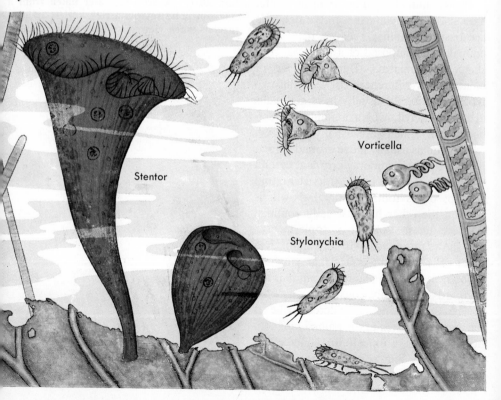

Stentor

Vorticella

Stylonychia

But the fact that this tiny blob of grayish jelly moves of its own accord, ingests food, and grows in size puts it immediately in the realm of animal life.

Amebae may be collected by taking slime from the bottom of streams and ponds and from the surface of the leaves of aquatic plants. The experience of collecting samples and searching through the microscopic " jungle " for an ameba is a rewarding one. Under the microscope, the ameba appears as an irregular mass of jellylike protoplasm surrounded by a thin membrane (Fig. 20-3). If you find an active animal, you will notice that the cytoplasm has a constant flowing motion. This moving cytoplasm presses against the thin cell membrane and produces numerous projections called *false feet,* or **pseudopodia** (soo-doh-*poh*-dee-uh). This type of locomotion is called **ameboid movement.** A closer look at the ameba will show that the cytoplasm is of two different types: (1) a clear, watery **ectoplasm** (*ek*-toh-plazm) is found next to the cell membrane; (2) the **endoplasm** (*en*-doh-plazm), found inside the ectoplasm, is an area that is more dense and resembles gray jelly with pepper sprinkled through it. The nucleus can be seen as a bronze-colored mass that continually changes its position with the flowing cytoplasm.

How the ameba gets food. When the ameba comes in contact with a one-celled green alga, a small diatom, or another tiny animal, it extends pseudopodia which entirely surround the food. Part of the membrane of the ameba now becomes the lining of a **food vacuole** (Fig. 20-4), which is inside the cytoplasm. Digestion is accomplished by enzymes formed by the cytoplasm, which pass into the vacuole and act on the food substances. Digested food is absorbed by the cytoplasm, and may then be oxidized to release energy, or assimilated to form additional

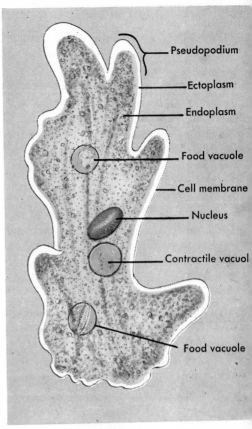

Fig. 20-3. This drawing shows some of the structures of the ameba. Give the function of each structure.

Fig. 20-4. The ameba reacts to a particle of food by surrounding it. The particle plus water becomes a food vacuole.

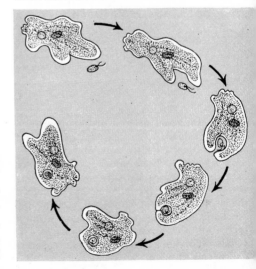

protoplasm. Undigested particles remain in the vacuole and pass out of the cell at any point in the membrane. Thus the ameba carries on all its functions without the help of other cells — a thing the cells of higher animals and man cannot do.

The oxygen necessary to maintain the life of these animals diffuses through the cell membrane. Most of the carbon dioxide and soluble wastes pass out through the cell membrane. However, with the intake of food, and by the process of osmosis, much useless water comes into the body of the ameba. If the ameba didn't have a method of ridding itself of this excess water, it would swell up like a balloon and burst. As the excess water accumulates, it forms a **contractile vacuole.** When this vacuole reaches maximum size, it discharges the water through a temporary break or pore in the cell membrane.

Sensitivity in the ameba. The response of an ameba to conditions around it is a good example of the sensitivity of protoplasm. It has no eyes, yet it is sensitive to light and seeks areas of darkness or dim light. It has no nerve endings such as we associate with the sense of touch, yet it reacts to jarring. It moves away from the objects with which it comes in contact in the water.

You can see how the ameba responds to food by placing small amounts of it in a culture. Watch how the ameba cells flock to the place where the food is located. This does not happen by mere chance. The food, perhaps by means of chemical attraction, acts as a stimulus to the cells. Unfavorable conditions, such as dryness or cold, cause some species of ameba to become inactive and to withdraw into a rounded mass. When favorable conditions return, the organisms resume activity.

Reproduction in the ameba. In the presence of abundant food and ideal conditions for growth, the ameba rapidly reaches maximum size. At this size, the mass or volume of protoplasm has become so great that the membrane surface is not large enough to supply adequate food and oxygen, or to remove waste. Reproduction now occurs by division of the mature cell into two smaller organisms. The nucleus divides first, and its two portions move to opposite ends of the cell. The rest of the protoplasm then separates gradually, forming two distinct masses. Each new mass has a nucleus and is capable of independent life and growth (Fig. 20-5).

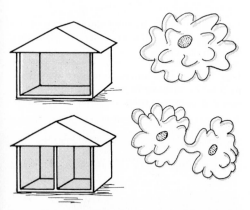

Fig. 20-5. **The diagrams at the left show a room before and after a dividing partition has been added. The diagrams at the right show an ameba before and after a dividing membrane has been added. The surface area in both cases has increased by adding a new wall, but the volume has remained the same. Thus, a large cell such as the ameba is able to increase its surface without increasing the volume of protoplasm. It builds a dividing partition in the process called cell division.**

Biologists have found that, at a temperature of 86° F, an ameba cell requires approximately 20 minutes in order to make a complete division. When conditions for growth are ideal, each cell matures and divides again after about three days.

Euglena, plant or animal? *Euglena* (yoo-*glee*-nuh) lives in fresh-water ponds and streams where it is often so abundant that the water is a brilliant green.

Under the microscope, the euglena appears as a spindle or pear-shaped cell which swims about freely. The front, or *anterior end,* is rounded, while the rear, or *posterior end,* is usually pointed (Fig. 20-6).

Since the euglena possesses some characteristics of plants and some characteristics of animals, it has been claimed by both botanists and zoologists. Because of one of its methods of locomotion, it is often placed in the second class of Protozoa, the Mastigophora. The organism swims by means of a *flagellum* which is attached to the anterior end and is nearly as long as the one-celled body. The flagellum is held straight in front, and the tip is rotated, thus pulling the organism rapidly through the water.

Unlike other members of the class Mastigophora, the euglena has a second method of locomotion. This type of movement is so characteristic of the euglena that we call it *euglenoid movement.* It is accomplished by a gradual change in the shape of the entire cell. The posterior portion of the body is drawn forward, causing the cell to assume a rounded form, after which the anterior portion is extended, thus pushing the cell forward.

The internal features of the euglena show an interesting combination of plant and animal characteristics. The outer covering is a thin, flexible membrane like the membranes of typical animal cells. At the anterior end of the cell is a *gullet* opening which leads to an enlarged *reservoir.* The gullet and the reservoir closely resemble similar structures in relatives of the euglena that are distinctly animal. Near the gullet is a very noticeable red *eyespot.* This tiny bit of specialized protoplasm is especially sensitive to light and serves to direct the organisms to bright areas in its habitat. Near the cen-

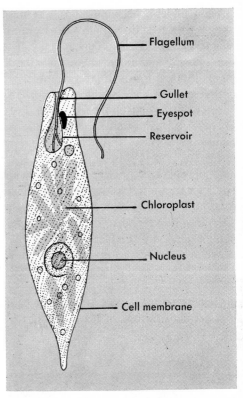

Fig. 20-6.   Is the euglena a plant or an animal?

ter of the mass of cytoplasm is a large *nucleus.*

Perhaps the most striking plant characteristic of the euglena is the presence of numerous oval *chloroplasts* which are scattered through the cytoplasm. These bodies contain *chlorophyll.* Most species of the organism carry on photosynthesis and live independently of any outside source of food. Some species eat bacteria. When euglenae are kept in the dark, they lose their chlorophyll and begin to absorb dissolved organic matter from the water in which they live. Food materials pass through the cell membrane in a way characteristic of animal cells. Thus, these organisms live as green plants in the presence of light but assume a form of animal nutrition when light is not available.

The euglena multiplies rapidly by cell

division under ideal conditions. A mature organism splits lengthwise, forming two new cells. Thus, a euglena may give rise to teeming millions within a few days, if conditions for growth are favorable.

Paramecium, a complex protozoan. *Paramecium* (pair-uh-*mee*-see-um) lives in quiet or stagnant ponds where a scum often forms. In order to culture it in the laboratory, submerged pond weeds may be collected, placed in a jar with pond water, and set aside in a warm place for a few days. As the weeds decay, a scum forms on the surface, and large numbers of paramecia may be found.

When a drop of water containing paramecia is placed on a slide under the micro-

Fig. 20-7. Compare the structure of this paramecium with that of the ameba in Fig. 20-3.

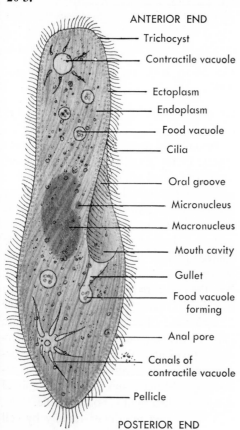

ANTERIOR END

— Trichocyst
— Contractile vacuole
— Ectoplasm
— Endoplasm
— Food vacuole
— Cilia
— Oral groove
— Micronucleus
— Macronucleus
— Mouth cavity
— Gullet
— Food vacuole forming
— Anal pore
— Canals of contractile vacuole
— Pellicle

POSTERIOR END

scope, the most striking characteristic of this unicellular animal is its rapid movement. It appears to swim rapidly through the thin film of water between the slide and cover glass. Actually, its rate of movement is quite slow — about three inches per minute; but the microscope magnifies the speed to the same extent as it does the object. A few strands of cotton or filaments of algae serve as effective barricades in preparing a slide for examination of these moving organisms. Methyl cellulose (which is now used as a wallpaper paste) may also be used to increase the density of the solution. This slows down the animals, and allows an opportunity for the detailed study of structure.

The paramecium is shaped like the sole of a shoe (Fig. 20-7). Although it doesn't change its shape as an ameba does, it is by no means rigid. It often bends around an object it happens to meet when swimming. The definite shape or form of the cell is maintained by a thickened cell membrane called a **pellicle** (*pel*-ih-kul) surrounding the protoplasm.

Paramecia move by tiny, hairlike **cilia**, which project through minute openings in the cell membrane. These cilia are arranged in rows and are lashed through the water like tiny oars. Although they cover the entire cell, they are most easily seen along the edges of the organism.

Another striking feature of the paramecium is a deep **oral groove** along one side of the cell. This depressed area is lined with long cilia which cause the animal to rotate around its long axis as it swims through the water. The paramecium has a definite *anterior end* which is rounded, and a more pointed *posterior end* — a perfect design in streamlining. The oral groove runs from the anterior end toward the posterior end. The action of the cilia, which line the oral groove, and the movement of the animal forward, force food particles into the **mouth cavity**. The mouth cavity resembles the opening of a funnel, and it leads to a narrow tube, the **gullet**. Bacteria and other food particles forced into the gullet enter the cell protoplasm and form a **food vacuole**. When the food vacuole reaches a certain size, it breaks away from the gullet, and a new one begins to form.

When the food vacuole breaks away from the gullet, the movement of the protoplasm carries the vacuole in a circular course around the cell. During this circulation, digestion and absorption occur as in the ameba. Undigested food passes through a special opening in the pellicle called the **anal** (*ay*-nul) **pore**. This tiny opening is located near the posterior end of the cell but is completely closed except when in use and is quite difficult to see.

The **contractile vacuoles** are two in number and have a definite location, one near either end of the cell. Surrounding each vacuole are numerous **canals** which radiate from the central cavity into the cytoplasm. The canals enlarge as they fill with water, after which their content is passed to the central cavity and emptied out at the surface through an opening.

As in the ameba, the contractile vacuoles of the paramecium serve primarily to remove excess water that has entered with food and by osmosis. Some soluble waste may be eliminated by these contractile vacuoles, although most of the waste products appear to diffuse through the pellicle. Respiration in the paramecium is accomplished by diffusion of oxygen and carbon dioxide through the pellicle.

Sensitivity in the paramecium. The reactions of paramecium cells to conditions around them are remarkable, considering that this animal, like the ameba, has no specialized sense organs. Except when feeding, the cells swim constantly, bumping into objects, reversing, and moving around them in a trial-and-error fashion. This response to the stimulation caused by bumping into objects is called the **avoiding reaction** (Fig. 20-8). The reaction also occurs from such stimuli as excessive heat and cold, chemicals, and lack of oxygen. Paramecia tend to move into regions of low acidity, a response which is of value to the animal for the following reason. Bacteria form an important source of food for paramecia. Bacteria accumulate on decaying organic matter and cause the water to be slightly acid, so that paramecia are drawn to it.

The **trichocysts** (*trih*-koh-sists), which normally appear as minute lines just inside the pellicle, are used as a means of defense. When a larger protozoan approaches, the trichocysts of the paramecium explode special protoplasmic threads into the water through tiny pores. These threads are quite long and give the organism a bristly appearance. A bit of acetic acid or iodine added to some water which

Fig. 20-8. This diagram shows the avoiding reaction of the paramecium. Notice how the animal meets an obstacle, backs up, changes direction, and tries again.

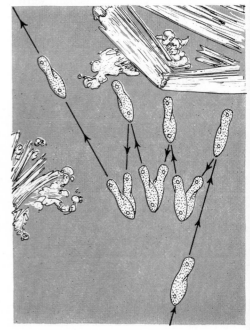

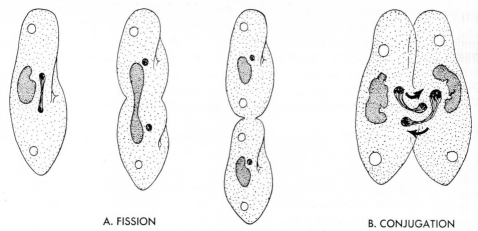

A. FISSION   B. CONJUGATION

Fig. 20-9. *A.* **Reproduction in the paramecium. Trace the steps involved in fission.** *B.* **Conjugation of paramecia. Trace the steps involved. Why is conjugation not considered reproduction?**

contains paramecia will often cause the trichocysts to discharge.

Reproduction in the paramecium. The organism has two different kinds of nuclei, which are located near the center of the cell. A large nucleus, or **macronucleus,** regulates the normal activity of the cell. Near the large nucleus is a small nucleus, or **micronucleus,** which functions during reproduction. Some species of paramecia have more than one micronucleus.

Reproduction may involve two distinct processes: (1) *fission,* and (2) *conjugation.* **Fission** involves the separation of a cell in two parts in a way similar to the reproduction of amebae. The micronucleus first begins to divide, and each half begins to move towards either end of the animal. Following this, the macronucleus divides in the same manner. Then the entire cell constricts and soon two animals form (Fig. 20-9). The cells formed in this manner are called **daughter cells.** Under ideal conditions, fission may occur twice a day. This would produce over 700 generations per year. If all the daughter cells were to live and ideal conditions could be maintained, the total mass of paramecia at the end of five years would be millions of times greater than that of the earth!

Apparently paramecia undergo **conjugation** before fission during periods of adverse conditions. During conjugation, two paramecia unite by joining together in the region of the oral groove. Their cell membranes become quite thin at the point where the two cells join. The macronuclei of both cells break up and finally disappear. The micronuclei divide several times and some of the resulting micronuclei disappear, until finally two micronuclei are left in each paramecium. One of these micronuclei from each animal then migrates across into the other partner. The partners separate and the two micronuclei now present in each animal unite, resulting in a nucleus which is a mixture of material from the two paramecia. These nuclei divide and eventually reorganize a new macronucleus and a new micronucleus in each cell.

You have probably realized that conjugation is not actually reproduction because no new individuals are formed. Rather, for some species, the cells are revitalized, thereby increasing their vitality to continue reproduction by fission.

COMPARISON OF AMEBA AND PARAMECIUM

	AMEBA	PARAMECIUM
Form	Variable	Constant
Locomotion	Pseudopodia	Cilia
Speed	Slow	Rapid
Food-getting	Pseudopodia surrounding food	Cilia; oral groove
Food taken in	At any point on membrane	Through gullet
Digestion	In food vacuole	Same
Respiration	Diffusion of oxygen and carbon dioxide through cell membrane	Same
Excretion	Through cell membrane	Same, plus anal pore
Sensation	Responds to light, heat, contact, etc.	Same
Reproduction	Fission	Fission; conjugation

Specialization of protoplasm in the Protozoa. The euglena, ameba, and paramecium were selected as typical examples of Protozoa. Biologists have found about 20,000 different species of this group. They are all one-celled animals ranging from simple creatures like the ameba to complex organisms like the paramecium. The progression through these organisms from simple to complex forms shows the increasing specialization of protoplasm. Different degrees of specialization are especially well illustrated in a comparison of the structure and activity of the ameba and paramecium, as in the table above.

Economic importance of the Protozoa. Many of the Protozoa lead a rather unimportant existence in fresh-water ponds and streams. Certain of their number, however, are of great economic importance. They are a source of food for larger animals and form part of the food chain of a pond.

Some Protozoa, notably the ones living in salt water, secrete a hard wall made of *calcium* (*kal*-see-um) or *silicon* (*sil*-ih-kon). These substances may form elaborately beautiful patterns (Fig. 20-10). Members of this group, the **foraminifers** (for-uh-*min*-ih-fers) and the **radiolarians**

(ray-dee-oh-*lair*-ee-uns), are responsible for the formation of many of the limestone and chalk deposits throughout the world. As they die, their miniature skeletons fall to the bottom of the sea, and there, with billions of others, form a muddy deposit. If, as the earth's surface changes, this deposit is dried out, it will become hard.

The fact that Protozoa help to digest food in the intestines of some animals is an excellent illustration of a symbiotic

Fig. 20-10.   This highly magnified radiolarian, though elaborate and beautiful, is composed of but one cell.

American Museum of Natural History

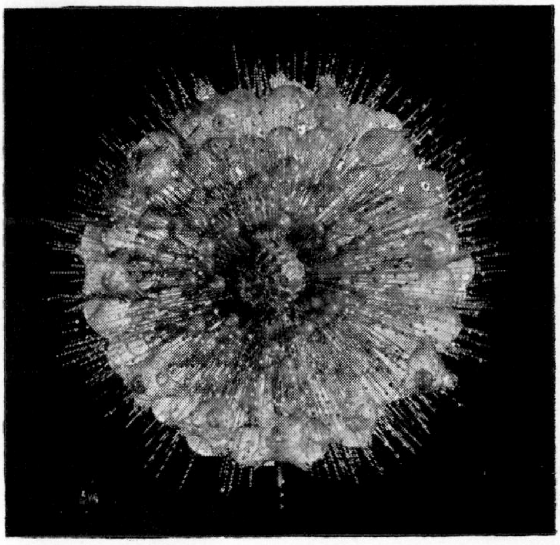

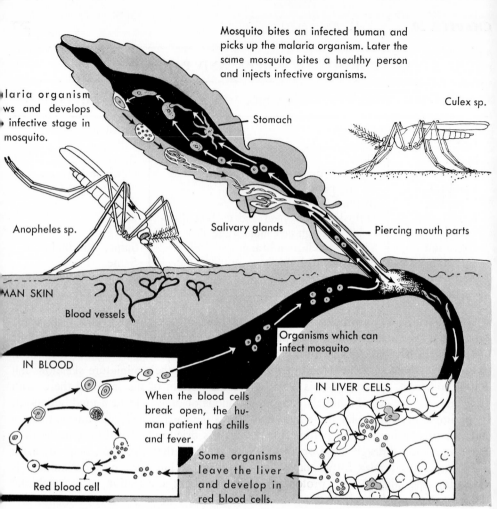

Mosquito bites an infected human and picks up the malaria organism. Later the same mosquito bites a healthy person and injects infective organisms.

Culex sp.

[M]alaria organism ...ws and develops ... infective stage in mosquito.

Stomach

Anopheles sp.

Salivary glands

Piercing mouth parts

[HU]MAN SKIN

Blood vessels

Organisms which can infect mosquito

IN BLOOD

When the blood cells break open, the human patient has chills and fever.

Red blood cell

Some organisms leave the liver and develop in red blood cells.

IN LIVER CELLS

Fig. 20-11. Trace the life cycle of *Plasmodium* as shown here. The *Culex* mosquito shown at the upper right is the common species that does *not* carry *Plasmodium*.

relationship. In cattle they play such a role; and in the intestines of termites, Protozoa are chiefly responsible for digesting the woody material the insects eat.

The spore-forming Protozoa. All *spore-forming Protozoa* are parasites and have no method of locomotion. In these animals, reproduction by spores is accomplished in the following manner: (1) first the nucleus divides into many small nuclei; (2) then a small amount of cytoplasm surrounds each nucleus to form a *spore;* (3) finally the protozoan breaks apart, and releases these little spores. The spores may be enclosed in a resistant

wall or they may be surrounded only by a cell membrane.

The parasite which causes malarial fever in man and other warm-blooded animals is a good example of a spore-forming protozoan. When a female *Anopheles* (uh-*nof*-eh-leez) *mosquito* bites a person suffering from malaria, some of these protozoan parasites pass into the insect's stomach. These parasites grow, reproduce, and work their way into the mosquito's blood stream where they travel to the glands of the mouth. When this infected mosquito bites a human being, the malarial parasite, *Plasmodium* (plaz-

moh-dee-um), is introduced into the human blood stream. From the blood stream, it first invades the liver and then, about two weeks later, a red blood cell (Fig. 20-11). Here it forms so many spores that the membrane of the red blood cell breaks and liberates the young spores, as well as waste products from the parasite. Each spore finds a new red blood cell and the cycle is repeated. In about two weeks (after the infectious mosquito bite) there are about a billion parasites in the body. The chills and high, sweating fevers are caused by the release of large amounts of wastes into the blood stream when the red blood cell bursts.

There are three major species of *Plasmodium* that cause malaria in humans. One species forms spores and bursts the red blood cells every day. A person infected with this parasite would have chills and fever every 24 hours. Another species forms spores every other day, thus causing chills and fever every other day. The third species repeats its cycle every three days, thus causing attacks of chills and fever at intervals of 72 hours.

Other pathogenic types of Protozoa. When the disease-producing Protozoa are studied, many people are surprised to find that the great majority of humans and most animals are infected with some type of protozoan. In man and most animals, the favorite place for these infections is the intestine, where a flourishing collection of these animals may be found. Therefore, if you examine the intestinal contents of a freshly-killed animal under the microscope, you will probably see a great many Protozoa. Some of them are harmless and may even be helpful, but many are pathogenic. The latter live on material in the intestine, robbing the host of its food. Some may invade the intestinal wall, show up later in the blood stream, and finally lodge in some other part of the body.

Contaminated water or food can be the source of infection by an ameba which causes *amebic dysentery* (*dis*-en-tair-ee). This ameba causes diarrhea, which results in poor nutrition and loss of water from the tissues of its human host. Although this disease more commonly occurs in the tropics, it is fairly common in the temperate zones. *African sleeping sickness* is caused by one of the parasites which move by flagella, the *Trypanosoma* (try-pan-oh-*soh*-muh). It is carried to a human host by the *tsetse* (*tset*-see) fly. Many local and international health organizations are waging a determined battle to reduce the occurrence of these two diseases in the world.

In Conclusion

Protozoa, the simplest forms of animal life, are one-celled animals which function as complete organisms. The euglena is considered to be a connecting link between the plant and animal kingdoms, since it has certain characteristics of both groups.

The ameba represents a simple form of animal life. This shapeless mass of living protoplasm lacks the specialization of other protozoan cells, yet in its primitive way, performs all of the processes of life. Paramecia, on the other hand, illustrate a high degree of specialization.

Of great importance are the disease-producing forms of parasitic protozoans that live in the bodies of animals and man. Many of the protozoans that cause disease, such as the malaria parasite, require two hosts in order to complete the life cycle.

The next chapter will introduce us to some other very interesting animals, but they are made up of many cells rather than one cell. They are more complex than the Protozoa.

BIOLOGICALLY SPEAKING

ameboid movement
anal pore
anterior end
avoiding reaction
cilia
conjugation
contractile vacuole
daughter cells
ectoplasm
endoplasm

euglenoid movement
eyespot
fission
food vacuole
foraminifers
gullet
macronucleus
micronucleus
mouth cavity
oral groove

pellicle
posterior end
Protozoa
pseudopodia
radiolarians
reservoir
trichocysts
unicellular

QUESTIONS FOR REVIEW

1. (a) What are the chief classes of Protozoa? (b) What characteristic divides them into classes? (c) Give an example of each.
2. List the characteristics of the euglena which tend to make it an animal, and those which tend to make it a plant.
3. Describe the way in which the ameba obtains its food.
4. Describe the way in which the paramecium obtains its food.
5. Compare the motion of the ameba, paramecium, and euglena.

6. Why is the ameba even more simple than the euglena and other Protozoa?
7. (a) Explain how paramecium cells multiply. (b) How are they rejuvenated?
8. In what ways does the paramecium show sensitivity?
9. Describe the life cycle of *Plasmodium*.
10. Mention several ways in which Protozoa are important to man.
11. Name some of the pathogenic Protozoa and the diseases they cause.

APPLYING FACTS AND PRINCIPLES

1. In what ways are the Protozoa important parts of the plant and animal population of a pond?
2. Biologists frequently say that understanding the life processes of a single protozoan will enable them to understand the life processes of complicated organisms like man. Explain why this is probably true.
3. What useful functions could certain

Protozoa perform in the human intestine?
4. What reasons can you give for the fact that the paramecium has two contractile vacuoles rather than one, as does the ameba?
5. What stage in development would you consider best for treatment, once a person has become infected with the malarial parasite? Why?

CHAPTER 21

Sponges and Coelenterates— Introduction to the Metazoa

I N studying the Protozoa you learned how a single cell performed all the activities by which we recognize life. In contrast to these one-celled organisms are the animals whose bodies are composed of many cells. We call this second large division of the animal kingdom the **Metazoa**. After learning about the metazoan phyla you will see what a relatively simple life the protozoans lead.

Although the adult metazoans may be complicated in structure, you should remember that their life also began as a single cell. This cell was no larger than a protozoan. While the fertilized egg of a metazoan develops into an efficient group of cells, the protozoan is destined to remain in the unicellular condition. Many factors are involved when cells are grouped together as a *multicellular* (many-celled) organism. Before we look at some of the metazoan phyla, we must see what some of these factors are.

Division of labor. Is any advantage gained by cells living in close association with other cells, as they do in the body of a metazoan? Perhaps we can answer this question by reviewing the story of Robinson Crusoe.

After Crusoe's ship was wrecked, he found himself alone on an island. He had to catch and prepare his food. He had to make his clothes and shoes. He had to build his house and protect himself from any enemies. Even though he learned how to do all these things, he could not devote enough time to any one job to excel in it. He was like a protozoan, in which one cell must perform all life activities without the aid of any other cells.

On the other hand, if there had been ten men shipwrecked with Crusoe, each could have specialized in a job. One man could have hunted food, while another was building a house or making clothes for the group. They could have formed a small society with much greater efficiency than that of Crusoe's simple, solitary existence.

An increase in numbers allows for *division of labor*, which takes place in the many-celled organisms like the metazoan animals. Different cells become specialists in performing certain functions for the benefit of all the cells.

The modification of a cell to perform a specialized activity is *adaptation*. The more perfectly a plant or animal is adapted to its environment, the better is its chance to survive; the same principle applies to a cell. As we study metazoan animals, from the more simple ones to those which are more complex, we shall find increasing cell specialization. As a result of this specialization, the animal is better able to adjust to its environment. Cell specialization is carried to the highest degree in the vertebrates, the subphylum to which man belongs (see Appendix in back of book). **Vertebrates** are metazoan animals which have a backbone. The **invertebrates**, except for the

241

protozoans, are metazoan animals which do not have a backbone.

Interdependence of cells. Division of labor and cell adaptation result in the dependence of cells on each other, or the situation called *interdependence.* The man who devotes his life solely to one task is liable to lose the ability to do other necessary things. He depends on other specialists for help in these phases of his life. When cells are specialized for one activity, they become dependent on other cells for other activities. The ameba can live independently in a pond. But a muscle, nerve, or bone cell when removed from your body cannot live independently.

Some metazoan phyla. We shall study nine large phyla of the metazoans. The table on page 243 gives a summary of the most important characteristics of these phyla. When you are studying an animal that represents a certain phylum, keep in mind the characteristics of that phylum. By *characteristics* we mean the features (degree of specialization) which all members of that phylum have in common.

When studying any animal, ask yourself this question: What degree of specialization does this animal have which places it in this particular phylum? If you can answer this question, you will be on your way to knowing the metazoa.

The sponges. The phylum **Porifera** (pore-*if*-er-uh) includes the simplest of the metazoans in which the cells show considerable *independence,* yet sufficient interdependence to classify them as real metazoans. They have often been referred to as " loose aggregations of cells."

Most of these animals are marine, although there are a few fresh-water species. Living sponges may vary in color from white, gray, brown, red, orange, and yellow to purple and black. They may live singly, or in colonies so massed that they make an encrusting layer over the surface of a rock.

Because of the fact that sponges are pierced with tiny holes through which water flows, they have been given the name *Porifera* which means " pore-bearers." These pores are called **incurrent pores** because they carry water into the central

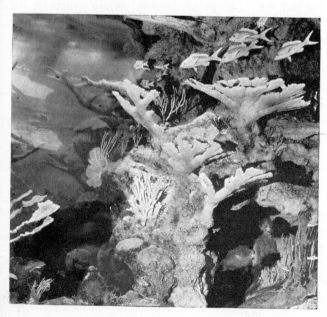

Fig. 21-1. This underwater view shows several forms of animal life, especially corals. Why do we speak of these animals as simple metazoans?

SUMMARY OF IMPORTANT METAZOAN PHYLA

PHYLUM	DEGREE OF SPECIALIZATION	REPRESENTATIVES
PORIFERA (pore-*if*-er-uh) (sponges)	Cells in two layers, penetrated by numerous canals. Slight specialization for food-getting, digestion, and reproduction	Salt-water and fresh-water sponges
COELENTERATA (seh-len-ter-*ay*-tuh)	Cells in two layers around a central cavity. More specialized than sponges. Capable of movement and defense	Jellyfish, hydra, coral polyps, sea anemone
PLATYHELMINTHES (plat-ee-hel-*min*-theez) (flatworms)	Cells in three layers; various organ systems; many parasitic. Bodies flattened and unsegmented	Planaria, flukes, tapeworms
NEMATHELMINTHES (nem-uh-thel-*min*-theez) (roundworms)	Round, unsegmented bodies; various organ systems; many parasitic	*Ascaris,* pinworms, *Trichinella,* hookworm, vinegar eel, " horsehair snake "
ROTIFERA (roh-*tif*-er-uh)	" Wheels animals " with rows of cilia around mouth; well-developed digestive system	Rotifers
ANNELIDA (an-*nel*-ih-duh) (segmented worms)	Body divided into segments; organ systems well developed	Earthworm, leech, sea worm, *Tubifex*
MOLLUSCA (mol-*us*-kuh)	Mantle and muscular foot present; soft bodies with or without a protective shell; well-developed organ systems	Clam, oyster, scallop, snail, slug, squid, octopus
ECHINODERMATA (eh-ky-noh-der-*may*-tuh)	Radially symmetrical, spiny skinned, highly complex organs; true nerves	Starfish, brittle star, sea urchin, sand dollar, sea cucumber, crinoids
ARTHROPODA (ar-*throp*-uh-duh)	Segmented bodies, jointed appendages; external skeleton, well-developed ventral nervous system; all senses present	Lobster, crayfish, crab, insects, spiders, ticks, centipedes, millepedes
CHORDATA (kor-*day*-tuh) [Subphylum Vertebrata (ver-tuh-*bray*-tuh)]	Animals having a backbone; internal and external specialization; brain; varied locomotion, never more than two pairs of limbs	Fish, amphibia, reptiles, birds, mammals (including man)

<>
</>

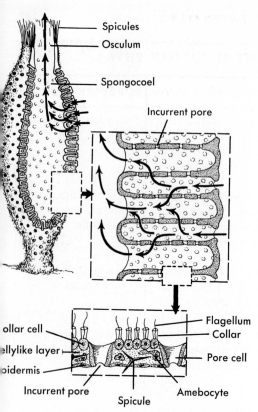

Fig. 21-2. **Water is continually drawn into the sponge by the flagella of the collar cells. It passes through the minute pores into the spongocoel and out through the osculum.**

cavity, or **spongocoel** (*sponge*-oh-seel). Somewhere, usually near the top, the sponge has a large hole called the **osculum** (*os*-kyoo-lum), or **excurrent pore**, which lets the water out of the spongocoel.

If we examine a single, simple sponge, we see that it consists of a hollow body, the walls of which contain many tiny tubes. The body of the sponge consists of two layers of cells separated by a layer of jellylike substance, loose cells, and **spicules** (*spik*-yools). The spicules form the body support (skeleton) of the sponge. The outside layer or **epidermis** can be compared to the skin of higher animals because it is protective. Many of the cells of the inside layer have curi-

ous collars with flagella projecting through them. The flagella of these **collar cells** set up currents which draw water into the sponge's body through the incurrent pores and force it out the osculum (Fig. 21-2).

How sponges get food. The existence of a sponge is dependent upon a water environment. A single sponge may filter nearly a quart of water every hour. Diatoms, small protozoans, bacteria, and other small particles of organic matter are brought into the sponge with the water. These particles of food are caught by the collars and ingested by the collar cells. Some of the loose cells in the jellylike layer resemble amebae and wander throughout this layer, taking the ingested food from the collar cells to distribute it to other parts of the organism. These wandering **amebocytes**, as they are named, also carry waste and carbon dioxide for disposal. How does this method of feeding show that the division of labor also causes the interdependence of cells?

The sponge would be a shapeless mass of animal matter if it did not have a skeleton. The *spicules* of the jellylike layer comprise the skeleton. Their variation in form and composition is an important characteristic which is used in dividing the phylum Porifera into its classes. Some of these spicules are composed of hard lime, some of silicon, and others are of a tough but flexible substance called **spongin**. The material used in the formation of the spicules is extracted from the water by the sponge cells and formed by the amebocytes.

The bath sponge produces the pliable and leathered skeleton composed of spongin fibers. Spongin is a secretion of the cells. When we use a sponge to clean a car, we are using this spongin skeleton of the animal.

Sponges reproduce in several ways. During periods of freezing temperatures

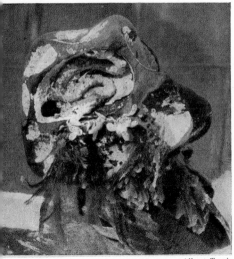

Albert Towle

Fig. 21-3. Simple sponges, such as those in the center of the photograph above, are often found in colonies encrusted on a rock. The more complex type of sponge shown at the right is sold for use as a bath sponge.

Black Star

or drought, little groups of amebocytes and a few spicules break off the parent sponge. These cell masses are surrounded by a heavy coat of organic material and are called **gemmules** (*jem*-yooles). Each one is capable of growing into another sponge when favorable environmental conditions return. Although this mode of *asexual reproduction* is characteristic of fresh-water species, some marine sponges also produce gemmules. Another method of asexual reproduction is by **buds** which develop near the base of the sponge. These buds are groups of cells which enlarge on the parent sponge for a time, then break off and live independently.

Sponge growers make sponges multiply by cutting them in pieces and sowing the pieces in special sponge beds. Each piece then *regenerates* a new sponge. To **regenerate** means to form a complete organism by rebuilding the missing parts. This is not a method of reproduction as it is not normally used by the sponge, but

is utilized by commercial sponge fishermen because it is much faster than budding.

Sexual reproduction occurs as a result of the formation of eggs and sperm. It is an interesting fact that the sperm cells enter the sponge by way of the incurrent pores, are taken into the cytoplasm of the collar cells, and are then transferred by the amebocytes to the ova or eggs.

Fresh-water sponges are small and of no commercial importance. Some marine sponges, especially in warmer oceans, grow to be very large and are collected by divers or drag hooks. These animals are then piled on shore or hung in the rigging of the boat until the flesh has decayed. The remaining spongin skeletons are then washed, dried, sorted, and sometimes bleached. They are then ready for marketing.

Famous sponge fishing grounds include the Mediterranean and Red Seas, the waters around the West Indies, and Tarpon Springs, Florida.

Ewing Galloway

Fig. 21-4. This coelenterate is called a sea anemone because it resembles a flower of that name. It lives in tide pools on rocky shores.

The coelenterates. Strange indeed are the pulsating jellyfish which bob around in the ocean currents, dangling long, stringy tentacles under a floating, inflated sac. Also in the phylum **Coelenterata** (seh-len-ter-*ay*-tuh) are the hydroids, corals, sea fans, sea anemones, and Por-

tuguese man-of-war (see table below) Some are very beautiful to see and other are so tiny as to be almost invisible. Animals of this group are of a somewhat more complex structure than the Porifera but are still simple. The body is two layered, with a jellylike material separating the two layers of cells. A coelenterate has a baglike body cavity which has a single opening, or mouth, surrounded by **tentacles** bearing stinging cells. Coelenterates live either as individuals or united to form colonies. All these animals are aquatic — a few live in fresh water, but most are marine.

The hydra. The characteristics of this phylum can be seen in one of the most common fresh-water coelenterates, the **hydra**. There are white, green, and brown species which live in quiet ponds, lakes, and streams. The body of a hydra consists of two layers of cells. We call the outer layer the **ectoderm** and the inner layer the **endoderm**. These animals are attached to rocks or water plants by a sticky secretion of their **basal discs**. Because of their small size, transparency, and habit of contracting into little knobs when disturbed, these hydra are often overlooked. Yet they are abundant and are the only really successful organisms among the few members of their phylum

CLASSES OF COELENTERATA

1. HYDROZOA (hy-droh-*zoh*-uh). Solitary or colonial; fresh water and marine; reproduction by asexual buds and gametes; alternation of generations in many forms.
Examples: hydra, *Obelia,* Portuguese man-of-war

2. SCYPHOZOA (sy-foh-*zoh*-uh). Only marine forms; polyp stage usually absent.
Examples: *Cyanea, Aurelia*

3. ANTHOZOA (an-thoh-*zoh*-uh). Only marine forms; solitary or colonial; body cavity with partitions; many tentacles.
Examples: sea anemone, coral

Fig. 21-5. The hydra moves by a kind of somersaulting. It bends over, attaches the tentacles to the bottom, loosens the base, swings the base over the mouth, and attaches itself to the bottom. After loosening the tentacles, it repeats the process.

that have invaded fresh water. A hydra may leave one place of attachment and float or move to another, or secrete a bubble at the base and float to the surface upside down. The hydra also moves in an odd somersaulting fashion (Fig. 21-5).

How the hydra gets food. When a small animal comes in contact with one of the tentacles of a hydra, many stinging cells, or **nematocysts** (*nem*-uh-toh-sists), explode and pierce the victim's body with tiny hollow barbs. Since each barb is attached to the tentacle by a thin thread, the combined effort of many threads prevents the escape of the hapless victim. At the base of each barb is a small poison sac which discharges its contents through the hollow barb and into the prey, thus paralyzing it.

Once the prey has been stilled, the tentacles bend inward and push it through a circular mouth and into a large, internal *gastrovascular cavity* (Fig. 21-6). The cells lining this cavity secrete fluids which digest the food. Absorption takes place in these same cells and also in the cells lining the hollow tentacles. Undigested particles and wastes pass out through the mouth. Biologists consider this arrangement to be the beginning of a digestive system.

The behavior of the hydra. We have now observed one reaction of a coelenterate which shows a definite advance over the more primitive sponge. The tentacles have coordinated their efforts in order to catch and push food into the

mouth. Also, if you touch a tentacle of an extended hydra with a needle, all the tentacles and the body contract suddenly. The stimulus to one tentacle travels to cells of the other tentacles and the body. This is done by a series of nerve cells, called the **nerve net,** which lie in the middle layer of the body. The contraction itself is accomplished by slender fibers

Fig. 21-6. This drawing of a hydra shows the external and internal structures. The hydra has two layers of cells with a jellylike material between them.

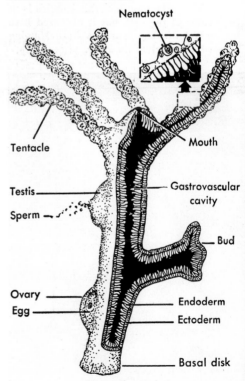

Nematocyst

Tentacle

Mouth

Testis

Sperm

Gastrovascular cavity

Bud

Ovary

Egg

Endoderm

Ectoderm

Basal disk

lying in the ectoderm, and these can be compared to the muscle cells of higher animals. The hydra has no real nervous system such as is found in higher animals, and it has no brain.

Reproduction in the hydra. The hydra accomplishes *asexual reproduction* by forming **buds.** A bud appears first as a knob growing out from the side of the adult. Later this knob develops tentacles, and after a period of growth it separates from the parent and lives independently. In this method of reproduction, the bud is a small outgrowth of endoderm and ectoderm and is capable of growing into a new organism (Fig. 21-6). In the case of a plant, the bud is an undeveloped shoot which will elongate the stem or develop leaves or a flower; but it will not become a whole new organism.

Also, like the sponge, the hydra has remarkable powers of regeneration. If an animal is cut into pieces, each piece will regenerate the missing parts and become a whole animal again.

Sexual reproduction usually occurs in autumn. The eggs are produced along the body wall in little swellings called **ovaries;** the sperm cells are formed in similar structures called **testes.**

The egg is fertilized in the ovary, and the zygote grows into a spherical, many-celled structure with a hard protective cover. In this stage it leaves the parent and goes through a rest period before forming a new hydra.

Jellyfish. Marine free-swimming coelenterates are commonly called *jellyfish.* These vary in size from forms which are barely visible, to those with a diameter of seven feet and with a tentacle spread of 100 feet. Because of their stinging cells, these creatures have earned the respect of swimmers who have come in contact with them.

In studying the mosses and ferns, you learned that these plants show an *alternation of generations.* One example in the animal kingdom of this same alternation between a sexual and an asexual phase may be found in the *Aurelia* (or-*ee*-lee-uh), a common jellyfish. These animals float and swim near the surface of the ocean, and can sometimes be seen in harbors or cast upon the beaches.

The adult animal, called a *medusa,* resembles a bell with scalloped margin from which protective *tentacles* hang (Fig. 21-8). Located at each of the eight indentations of the margin is a *marginal sense organ.* Each sense organ consists of a pigmented spot which is sensitive to light, an organ of balance, and a third portion which is thought to be sensitive to chemicals in the water.

In the center of the bell is a square-shaped *mouth* surrounded by four *oral lobes,* or *lips,* that hang down like tentacles. The mouth leads to a short *gullet*

Fig. 21-7. The mouth of this jellyfish is in the center of the bell, but is obscured here by tentacles. The tentacles bear stinging cells which paralyze the prey.

Hermes from National Audubon Society

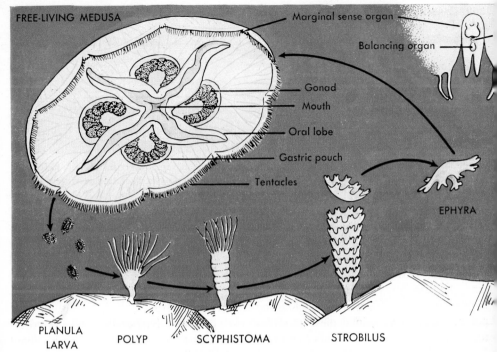

FREE-LIVING MEDUSA

Marginal sense organ

Balancing organ

Gonad

Mouth

Oral lobe

Gastric pouch

Tentacles

EPHYRA

PLANULA
LARVA   POLYP   SCYPHISTOMA   STROBILUS

Fig. 21-8. Trace the life cycle of *Aurelia* as shown in this diagram. Why does *Aurelia* illustrate alternation of generations?

which opens into a *gastrovascular cavity*. Four *gastric pouches* radiate from the gastrovascular cavity.

The **gonads** (*goh*-nadz) (testes in the male and ovaries in the female) underlie the gastric pouches. In a male medusa, the sperm are shed through the mouth and into the water. When the sperm are taken in through the mouth of the female, they fertilize eggs which have been shed into the gastrovascular cavity. These fertilized eggs (*zygotes*) pass out to the folds of the oral lobes where they are protected for a short time.

As the zygote develops, it forms a small, oval-shaped, ciliated larva called a *planula* (*plan*-you-luh) (Fig. 21-8). In this form the young swim away from the protective folds of the female parent. The planula is the beginning of the *asexual* phase in the life cycle of *Aurelia*. It swims around for a while but soon attaches to a rock or on seaweed, where it develops tentacles, begins feeding, and is

called a *polyp*. As the polyp continues to feed and grow, it buds off more polyps. This budding may continue for many months, but in fall and winter, the polyp elongates, forming horizontal divisions. This stage is called a *scyphistoma* (sy-fis-*toh*-muh). Soon this part of the asexual stage resembles a pile of saucers and is known as a *strobilus* (*stroh*-bih-lus). One by one, the uppermost "saucer" develops marginal tentacles and a mouth, then breaks loose and swims away to become an adult *Aurelia*. The very young medusa is called an *ephyra* (eh-*fy*-ruh), and it marks the beginning of the *sexual* phase in the cycle.

Other coelenterates. The *Portuguese man-of-war* is really a floating colony of animals that has the ability to deliver a severe and poisonous sting. It is found in the Gulf Stream and occasionally drifts to the British coast.

The **coral** is the only coelenterate of economic importance. The **polyp** is a

Fig. 21-9. The drawings above show the three different kinds of coral reefs. Left: the marginal type that grows around an island. Center: the barrier reef that is widely separated from the land. Right: an atoll with an open lagoon.

small, flowerlike animal only a fraction of an inch in length. Most polyps live in colonies and build skeletons of lime which they extract from the sea. This lime skeleton, or " house," is firmly cemented to the skeleton of a neighboring polyp. When one animal dies, its skeleton remains for the attachment of another. Lime from coral increases in size so that a single mass may support many thousands of animals living on the surface of the skeletons of their ancestors. In some species these masses are solid, while other corals build delicate and intricate fan-shaped structures (Fig. 21-1, page 242).

Over a period of time large coral reefs are built up. These are most common in the warm shallow oceans and may be of three types: (1) the *marginal type,* close to the beach; (2) the *barrier type,* forming a ring around an island with a wide stretch of water between the beach and the reef; or (3) a ring with an open lagoon in the center, called an *atoll* (*at-ohl*) (Fig. 21-9).

The Great Barrier Reef off the northern coast of Australia extends about 1,100 miles parallel to the coast. It is about 50 miles wide. The extent of the coral formations became apparent during World War II when coral was found to be useful in the construction of airstrips and roads. Coral, fashioned into jewelry, may be found in stores and shops all over the world. Some corals are also bleached and dyed various colors to be used in flower arrangements or for decorations in homes.

In Conclusion

When cells are joined together, as in the body of a metazoan, it is possible to have division of labor so that cells become more efficient at special tasks. However, by becoming specialists, the cells must give up the ability to perform some of the tasks; they then become dependent on others.

The sponges have this characteristic of interdependence of cells. They represent a step above the protozoans in complexity, as their bodies are composed of loose groups of cells held into shapes by skeletons of spicules. These animals pump water through their bodies to obtain food and oxygen.

The coelenterates are slightly more complex in structure. They have tubular bodies formed by two layers of cells separated by a jellylike layer. The coelenterates are able to catch food actively and defend themselves by tentacles bearing nematocysts. These simple creatures might be regarded as nature's first effort to produce an animal with tissues.

As we continue through the invertebrate phyla in the next chapter, we shall consider three groups of animals classed as worms. However, their elongated bodies are about the only thing the various worms have in common. You may be surprised at the complex internal structure of the members of these invertebrate phyla.

BIOLOGICALLY SPEAKING

amebocyte	gemmule	ovaries
basal disc	gonads	polyp
buds	incurrent pore	Porifera
Coelenterata	interdependence	regeneration
collar cell	invertebrate	spicules
ectoderm	Metazoa	spongin
endoderm	multicellular	spongocoel
epidermis	nematocyst	tentacles
excurrent pore	nerve net	testes
gastrovascular cavity	osculum	vertebrate

QUESTIONS FOR REVIEW

1. What principal characteristic distinguishes the protozoans from the metazoans?
2. How does an increase in the number of cells in a metazoan permit division of labor?
3. What is the chief difference between the invertebrate and the vertebrate animals?
4. Describe the usual habitat of the sponges and coelenterates.
5. Compare the method of feeding in a sponge and a hydra.
6. Give examples of regeneration in the sponges and coelenterates.
7. In what ways are the jellyfish and hydra alike? In what ways are they not alike?
8. What is the function of nematocysts?
9. (a) Describe the formation of a coral reef. (b) What are three types of coral reefs?

APPLYING FACTS AND PRINCIPLES

1. Compare the ways in which division of labor is shown in modern civilization with the ways it is shown in a metazoan.
2. Why is it essential that a jellyfish be hollow?
3. How is a knowledge of the regeneration capabilities of sponges used commercially?
4. Upon what is the classification of sponges based?
5. How do you account for the fact that some sponges die when exposed briefly to air and promptly returned to water?
6. Why do biologists consider the sponge the most primitive form of metazoan life?

CHAPTER 22

Invertebrates Classified

as Worms

W HEN you think of a worm, you probably visualize a lowly, crawling animal — possibly the " night crawler " you put on your hook
if you go fishing. This night crawler is a true worm. However,
it is only one kind of worm and totally different from the members of two
other invertebrate phyla which contain worms. Some worms have hardly
any internal systems. Others, like the earthworm, have " hearts " and blood
vessels, brain and nerve cords, and many other well-developed organs.

Before we begin our study of the worms, let's review the general forms of
the organisms which we have already studied. Animals which have no definite shape (such as the ameba and many sponges) are said to be **asymmetrical.** All the other organisms have a definite form and are **symmetrical.**

Three types of symmetry. (1) *spherical symmetry,* (2) *radial symmetry,* and
(3) *bilateral symmetry* are the three types
of symmetry. The radiolarians or *Volvox*
are animals with **spherical symmetry.**
They may be divided into two equal parts
by any plane passing through the diameter of the body. A baseball is a good
example of a spherically symmetrical object. Animals with spherical symmetry
have no efficient mode of locomotion and
usually float on or near the surface of
water.

Radial symmetry is best demonstrated
by the sea anemone. This coelenterate
has a central disc from which the tentacles radiate out like the spokes of a wheel.
The central axis is formed by the mouth
and passes through the center of the body.
The animal may be divided into two equal
parts by any plane which passes through
the diameter of the " disc " and through
the central axis. Some simple sponges,
most coelenterates, and most adult
echinoderms (which we shall study in
the next chapter) are radially symmetri-

cal. This type of symmetry allows the
stationary animals to encounter food and
enemies from all sides.

Bilateral symmetry is exhibited by the
higher animals. It means, literally, " two-
sided shape." Only one plane can separate animals with this kind of symmetry
into two similar parts. This plane must
pass through the longitudinal axis,
through the center of the back, and
through the center of the front. This
would not divide the animal into identical
parts, but the pieces would be mirror
images. Animals with bilateral symmetry
have a definite right and left side; they
have an upper, or **dorsal**, surface and a
lower, or **ventral**, surface; they have a
definite *anterior* and *posterior* end. All of
the vertebrates and most of the invertebrates have this type of shape. The anterior end usually contains a concentration of nervous tissue and the sense
organs for testing the environment.

The flatworms. The worms are divided into three phyla (see table on page
243). The least complex of these phyla

252

is the **Platyhelminthes** (plat-ee-hel-*min*-theez), or flatworms. These flat-bodied animals have the usual two layers of cells, *endoderm* and *ectoderm,* which you saw in the coelenterate group. In addition, the flatworms have a middle layer called the **mesoderm.** All the organs and tissues of the body develop from these three layers of cells, which will also be true in all the other animals we shall study. It is true, too, of man. The flatworms consist of three classes: (1) *fresh-water forms;* (2) *flukes;* and (3) *tapeworms.*

Aquatic flatworms. Planaria (plan-*air*-ee-uh) are common fresh-water flatworms which are found under stones in streams or ponds (Fig. 22-1). They may be attracted to a piece of raw meat tied to a string and left in a pond or stream for a few hours. Planaria are one-quarter to one-half an inch long and may be black, brown, or white. They are bilaterally symmetrical, blunt at the anterior end and pointed at the posterior end. The two **eyes,** or **eyespots,** on the anterior end of the planaria are responsible for its nickname, " the cross-eyed worm." The mouth of a planaria is located on the ventral surface near the center of the body. When the animal feeds, the **pharynx** (*fair*-inks) may be thrust out.

Planaria are scavengers because they clean up dead organic matter in the water. They also feed on small water animals. Food enters through the mouth and passes into the **intestine,** where it is digested.

Fig. 22-1.   *A.* The planaria, a fresh-water flatworm, has a definite head with eyes that can distinguish light and dark.   *B.* Notice in this drawing of the nervous and digestive systems that the intestine has only one opening.   *C.* This cross-sectional view shows the cellular layers and the cilia on the ventral surface.

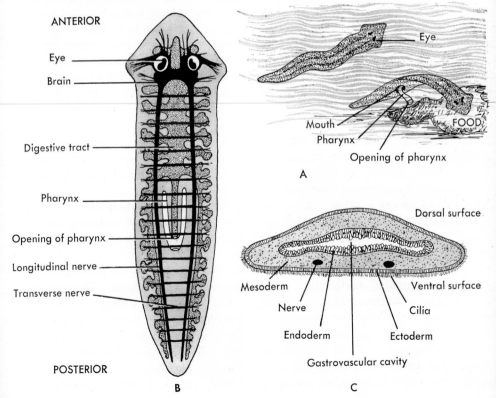

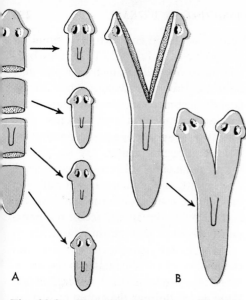

Fig. 22-2. The diagrams above illustrate the planaria's remarkable powers of regeneration. Note that in *A*, even the most posterior portion of the animal will regenerate a head to produce a new planaria. In *B*, a two-headed planaria results.

Since the intestine is a branched tube with only one opening, undigested matter is given off through the mouth. Absorption takes place through the many branches of the intestine, and the digested food passes to all parts of the body in the fluid-filled spaces.

The nervous system is well developed in the planaria. Just beneath the eyes there is a mass of nervous tissue, the brain. Many nerves, leading from the brain, supply the anterior region, and two **longitudinal nerves** also run along either side of the body near the ventral surface. These nerve cords are connected to one another by **transverse nerves,** giving the nervous system a ladderlike appearance. From the longitudinal nerve cords, many branches go out to the surface area. The nervous system allows the planaria to have coordinated movement, as well as to respond to stimuli on all parts of the body. The nervous system tells this multicellular organism what is happening to

all the cells in its body. For instance, the eyes perceive light and the animal reacts by turning away from the light source. Other nerves cause the planaria to react to water currents by turning toward the direction from which the water is coming.

When watching a planaria in a glass dish or an aquarium, you will see that they have two distinct motions. One is a muscular movement whereby the anterior end of the body moves from side to side. The other is a forward gliding motion. The gliding motion is accomplished by almost imperceptible muscular contractions aided by cilia on the ventral surface (Fig. 22-1, page 253).

Reproduction in the planaria is accomplished either asexually by fission, or sexually. Each animal is **hermaphroditic** (her-maf-roh-*dih*-tik), which means that it possesses both male and female organs. Cross-fertilization occurs, and then the eggs are shed in capsules. Often these capsules, usually containing less than ten eggs, are attached to rocks or twigs in the water. In two or three weeks the eggs hatch and minute planaria emerge.

Like the sponges and many coelenterates, some planaria have remarkable powers of regeneration. Some will regenerate complete worms from almost any piece (Fig. 22-2). The parasitic flatworms, however, have no ability to replace lost parts. This is true of parasitic animals in general.

Flukes. The **flukes,** members of another class of Platyhelminthes, are dangerous parasites in many animals, including man. The flukes have complicated life histories, usually involving a snail and one or more other hosts. The sheep liver fluke, for instance, lives as an adult in the gall bladder of the sheep. Eggs pass from the gall bladder to the intestine and, if they fall into water after they are eliminated by the sheep, they hatch into young worms called **larvae** (*lar*-vee) [sing.

larva (*lar*-vuh)], which enter the body of a particular kind of snail. In the snail, the larvae pass through several stages during which they increase in number by asexual reproduction. They then leave the snail, crawl upon blades of grass along water, and form a **cyst** (*sist*), or resting stage. If a sheep eats this cyst within ten days after it has been formed, the fluke enters the sheep's liver and the cycle starts again (Fig. 22-3).

The widespread condition of human fluke infections in the world is not confined to the Orient, where they are most common. In almost all cases the best control of flukes is to eliminate one of the hosts in their life cycle. Usually this is a snail of some particular species.

Tapeworms. The **tapeworm**, a member of still a third class of Platyhelminthes, is the best known of the parasitic flatworms. An adult tapeworm has a flat, ribbonlike body and is grayish white in color (Fig. 22-4, page 256). The knob-shaped head is equipped with **suckers** and, in certain species, with a ring of **hooks**. Below the slender neck there is an indefinite number of nearly square sections, extending to a length of as much

as 30 feet. Since new **body segments**, or **proglottids**, are formed at the head end, the oldest sections are on the posterior end. The proglottids are essentially masses of reproductive organs. The worms are hermaphroditic, and eggs formed in a proglottid are fertilized there. When the eggs mature, the proglottids break off and are eliminated with body wastes. They may be eaten by some animal such as a pig, cow, or fish.

Tapeworms enter the human body in a cyst stage when the flesh of infected hogs, cattle, or fish is eaten. Each cyst contains a fully developed tapeworm head. In the human intestine, the head is released from the cyst and attaches itself to the intestinal wall. The worm grows by adding new segments. As segments containing eggs pass from the intestine with body waste, they may be eaten by hogs or cattle. In the body of the pig, cow, or fish, the eggs form young larvae which burrow into the muscles and form cysts. The cycle is repeated when man eats improperly cooked flesh containing these cysts.

The tapeworm has no digestive system. It has no need for one because it absorbs,

Fig. 22-3. Flukes are parasitic flatworms. Here you see the life cycle of the sheep liver fluke as it passes from the body of the sheep to the snail, and then to the grass which the sheep eats.

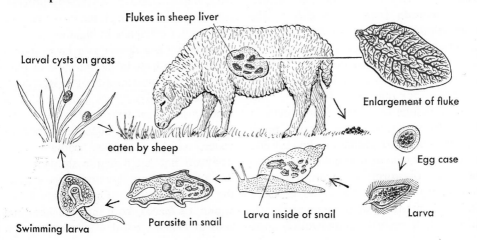

Flukes in sheep liver

Larval cysts on grass

Enlargement of fluke

eaten by sheep

Egg case

Swimming larva

Parasite in snail

Larva inside of snail

Larva

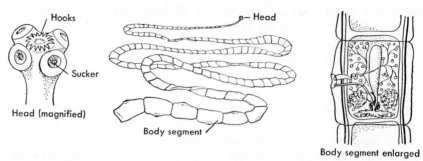

Fig. 22-4. Inspection of meat has greatly reduced the number of tapeworm victims. However, it is best to avoid eating meat that is not cooked thoroughly.

into each segment, the food which has been digested by the host. By doing this, the tapeworm robs the host of needed nourishment. Such loss of a system or structure by an animal which is a parasite is called **degeneration.**

You will notice that in each case of the disease-producing worms, infection is spread and picked up as a result of poor sanitary conditions. The fertilized eggs of the worms are given off with the intestinal wastes, the **feces** (*fee*-seez). If these feces are not properly disposed of, the eggs are eaten by animals, and the infection is spread.

Roundworms. The next phylum of worms, the roundworms or **Nemathelminthes** (nem-uh-thel-*min*-theez), is famous for certain of its parasitic members. There is only one class in this phylum, the **Nematoda** (nem-uh-*toh*-duh). The roundworms are long, slender, smooth worms which are tapered on both ends. These worms have no body divisions or segments and thus differ from the earthworms. They may be as short as 1/125 inch or as long as 4 feet. They occur in soil, fresh water, salt water, and as parasites in plants and animals. The parasitic roundworms include the hookworm, trichina worm, pinworm, whipworm, *Ascaris,* and guinea worm. When you consider that over one-third of the human race is infected with parasitic roundworms, their

importance can hardly be overestimated. Harmless roundworms include the vinegar eel, " horsehair snake," and the very numerous beneficial soil nematodes.

The nematodes are more complex than the flatworms. Their digestive system is a distinct tube or cylinder with an opening at each end, housed in a long, worm-like body which is also a tube. This enables the animal to take in food through an anterior opening, the **mouth,** to digest it and remove the usable parts as it passes along the canal. Finally the undigested material is eliminated through a posterior opening, the **anus** (*ay*-nus). In the case of the hydra, one opening was used for both food entrance and elimination of undigested substances. The arrangement of a tube within a tube, however, makes possible the orderly progression of material through the digestive tract and greater efficiency in handling it.

Ascaris (*as*-kuh-ris) is a large roundworm which lives in the intestine of pigs, horses, and sometimes man (Fig. 22-5). Females are larger than males, and may reach a length of nearly 12 inches. *Ascaris* eggs enter the human by food or water which has been contaminated. They do not hatch in the stomach, but begin to hatch in a few hours when inside the small intestine. Once hatched, the young, or *larvae,* bore into the intestinal wall to begin a ten-day journey through the body. This journey carries them into the blood stream and to the lungs. When they reach the lungs, these worms pass into the air passages, through the throat, and are swallowed so as to pass into the digestive tube once again where they grow to maturity in about two and one-half months. After fertilization, the eggs are surrounded by a thick, rough shell and passed out through the genital pore of the female worm. A mature female lays about 200,000 eggs each day. These eggs pass out of the body of the host with the feces, and the cycle continues.

The **hookworm** of the southern states and all semitropical and tropical regions is a serious health menace. Larvae develop in the soil and enter the body by boring through the skin of the feet. Next they enter the blood vessels and travel through the heart to the vessels of the lungs. In the lungs, they enter the air passages and travel through the windpipe to the throat. They are swallowed and pass through the stomach to the intestine, where they attach themselves to the wall by means of jaws. In the intestine the larvae grow to adult worms. The worms suck blood from the vessels in the intestine wall.

Loss of blood lowers the victim's vitality by producing anemia. Excretions produced by the worms poison the victim and produce characteristic laziness. Thus a typical hookworm victim may be quite shiftless and his growth may be retarded, although the latter is not always true. In the intestine, the worms reproduce, and the fertilized eggs leave in the fecal wastes. If these happen to lodge in warm, moist soil, they develop into minute larvae which can enter through cracks in the feet and eventually return to the intestine. Thus, three factors are responsible for the spread of this disease: (1) improper disposal of sewage; (2) warm soil; and (3) going barefoot. Public health agencies have done a re-

markable job in reducing the number of cases in the southern United States.

The *Trichina worm* or **Trichinella** (trih-kih-*nel*-uh) is one of the most dangerous of the parasitic roundworms. It is estimated that over one-fifth the population of the United States suffers from this infection. This roundworm passes its first stage in the pig, dog, rat, or cat as a cyst in the muscles. If raw or uncooked scrap meat is fed to pigs, it may contain some of these cysts. In the intestine of a pig that eats infected scrap meat, these worms multiply, pass into the blood stream and into muscles where they again form cysts. When a human eats undercooked, infected pork, these cysts are released and

Fig. 22-5. Side views of a female and male *Ascaris* are shown on the left. The top and right are views of a dissected female.

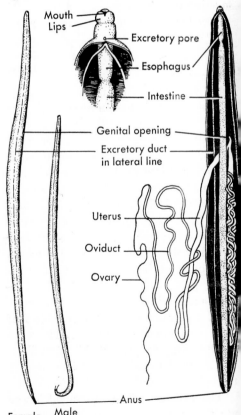

Mouth
Lips
Excretory pore
Esophagus
Intestine
Genital opening
Excretory duct in lateral line
Uterus
Oviduct
Ovary
Anus

Female   Male

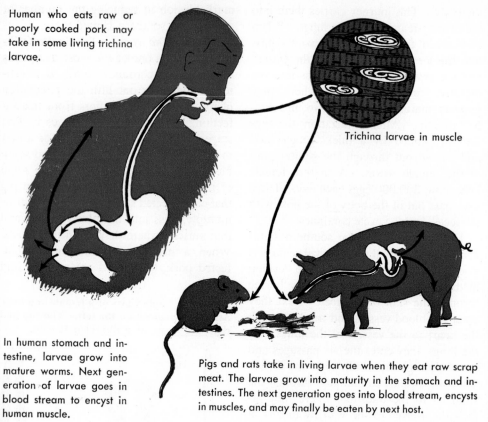

Human who eats raw or poorly cooked pork may take in some living trichina larvae.

Trichina larvae in muscle

In human stomach and intestine, larvae grow into mature worms. Next generation of larvae goes in blood stream to encyst in human muscle.

Pigs and rats take in living larvae when they eat raw scrap meat. The larvae grow into maturity in the stomach and intestines. The next generation goes into blood stream, encysts in muscles, and may finally be eaten by next host.

Fig. 22-6. Trace the life cycle of the *Trichina* worm from the time it infects a pig to its encystment in human muscle.

the larvae mature in the intestine (Fig. 22-6). Each mature worm emits about 2000 young into the blood stream, which eventually form cysts in the muscles of the human. Since as many as 15,000 cysts have been found in one gram of muscle tissue, you can well understand how they would interfere with the proper functioning of the muscle as well as cause much pain. This disease is known as **trichinosis** (trih-kih-*noh*-sis). One method of prevention of this disease is to feed hogs only cooked scrap meat. However, the best way to prevent this disease, as well as other parasitic worm infections, is to cook all meat thoroughly.

The annelids. The segmented worms are the most advanced of the worms in body structure. They belong to the phylum **Annelida** (an-*nel*-ih-duh), which is commonly divided into four classes (see Appendix). Most of the segmented worms live in salt water, some live in fresh water and others, including the common earthworm, live in the soil. The annelids seem to be in a half-way spot between the very simple Protozoa and the highly complicated vertebrates. For this reason, and the fact that they are rather common, many biologists study them closely. They are considered to be typical invertebrates, in a limited sense (see Figs. 22-7 and 22-8).

If you examine a common earthworm, you will notice immediately that its body consists of many rings or segments. Furthermore, you will see that the front, or *anterior end,* is more pointed and darker than the *posterior end.* There is no separate head, nor are there any visible sense organs. The **mouth** is on the anterior end and is crescent-shaped, lying below a **prostomium** (proh-*stoh*-mee-um), which is a kind of upper lip. The vertical slit at the posterior end is the opening of the intestine, or **anus.** The segments are often numbered by biologists, starting with the segment containing the mouth as number one, in order to locate definitely any special structure. On segments 32–37 there is a conspicuous swelling called the **clitellum** (klih-*tel*-um), which is involved in the animal's reproduction (Fig. 22-9, page 260).

Four pairs of bristles, or **setae** (*see*-tee), project from the under surface and sides of each segment, except the first and the last. The setae assist the earthworm in movement and in clinging to the walls

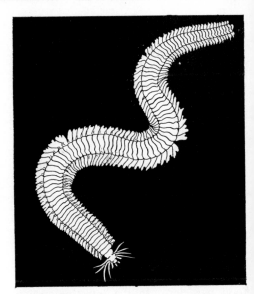

Fig. 22-8. *Nereis,* or the sandworm, is one of the primitive annelids. You can see one protruding from the whelk shell in Fig. 4-3, page 33.

of its burrow, as those who hunt night crawlers can testify.

The earthworm moves by burying its anterior setae into the soil, then shortening its body by a powerful series of **longitudinal muscles** which stretch from anterior to posterior ends. The worm then sinks its posterior setae into the soil, withdraws its anterior setae, and pushes forward by making itself longer. It does this by constricting the **circular muscles** which are found around the body at each segment, so that the worm becomes thin and long.

As you study this animal, you will notice that it not only consists of many cells, but many kinds of specialized cells. These specialized cells are grouped together and each group performs the same function, so they are said to make up a *tissue.* The tissues that are grouped together to form larger structures which perform a definite function are called *organs.* The earthworm is so arranged that a whole series of organs takes care of

Fig. 22-7. The leech is a member of one of the four classes of annelids. Notice the suckers at each end of the animal.

Hugh Spencer

some fundamental body process. These are called *systems*. Thus we can study, in the earthworm, the *digestive, circulatory, nervous,* and *reproductive* systems.

Digestive system of the earthworm. Below the prostomium is the **mouth** of the earthworm. There are no jaws or teeth, but it sucks in food (soil) by its muscular **pharynx**. The food particles then pass through a long **esophagus** (ee-*sof*-uh-gus) into a round organ called the **crop**. This acts as a temporary storage place for food. From the crop the food is forced into a very muscular organ called the **gizzard**. There, by rhythmical contractions, the food is ground up by grains of sand rubbing the food particles. In the **intestine**, which stretches from segment 19 to the end of the worm, complete digestion takes place.

Enzymes break down the food chemically, and the blood which circulates through the intestine walls absorbs it.

The complex organs of the digestive system of the earthworm take up most of the room in the interior of the animal. The earthworm consumes large quantities of soil which contains organic matter. The useless inorganic matter passes through the system largely unchanged and is deposited on the surface of the ground in the form of *casts*. This method of feeding loosens and enriches the soil and is of great importance to soil fertility.

Circulatory system of the earthworm. As food is digested, the blood in the circulatory system picks it up for distribution to all cells of the body. In the simpler animals we have studied so far, the digested food had only to diffuse a short

Fig. 22-9. In this diagram of an earthworm the anterior portion is dissected to illustrate the well-developed nervous and circulatory systems.

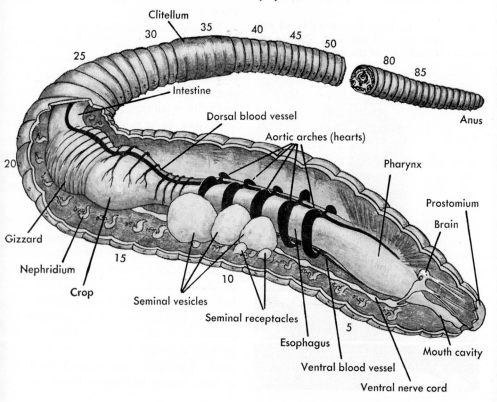

distance to reach all the cells of the body. But in higher forms the distances are greater and more food material is needed by the many specialized and very active cells of the body. Therefore in these animals we find a special transportation or distribution material, the circulating fluid called **blood.**

The blood of the earthworm then moves through a series of closed tubes, or vessels. It flows forward to the *anterior* (front) end in a **dorsal** (top) **blood vessel** and moves toward the *posterior* (back) end in a **ventral** (bottom) **blood vessel.** Small tubes connect the dorsal and ventral vessels throughout the animal except in segments 7–11. There, the five connecting tubes are large and muscular. By alternate contraction and relaxation, they keep the blood flowing. They are not true hearts, but are called **aortic** (ay-*or*-tik) **arches.**

The earthworm has no respiratory system. The earthworm absorbs oxygen and gives off carbon dioxide through a thin skin. This skin is protected by a thin **cuticle** which is secreted by the epidermis and which is kept moist by a slimy mucus also produced by epidermal cells. A moist surface is necessary for oxygen to be absorbed and carbon dioxide to be given off. If the worm is dried by the sun it will die because the exchange of these gases can no longer take place.

Excretion in the earthworm. Nitrogen-containing waste materials from the cell activities are removed to the outside of the body by little tubes. There are two such structures, called **nephridia** (neh-*frih*-dee-uh), in nearly every segment. Each one corresponds to one of the tiny tubes in the kidneys of higher animals.

Nervous system. The nervous system coordinates the movements of the animal and sends impulses received from sense organs to certain parts of the body. There is a very small brain, or nerve cen-

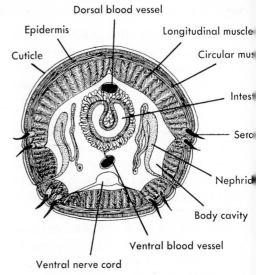

Fig. 22-10. This is a cross-sectional drawing of one of the abdominal segments of the earthworm. How would a similar view of an anterior segment differ?

ter, in segment 3. From it run two nerves which form a connecting collar around the pharynx and join to become a long **ventral nerve cord.** There are enlargements called **ganglia** (*gang*-glee-uh), or nerve centers, in each segment. Three pairs of nerves in turn branch from each ganglion. The earthworm has no eyes or ears, but is nevertheless sensitive to light and sound. Certain cells in the skin are sensitive to these stimuli, and the impulse is carried rapidly to the muscles of the earthworm. How quickly they can react to a flash of light at night when you hunt them for the next day's fishing!

Reproduction in the earthworm is complex. Each earthworm forms both eggs and sperm. However, the eggs of one worm can be fertilized only by sperm from another worm. In Fig. 22-11 on the next page you will see **seminal vesicles** (*ves*-ih-kuls) which store the sperm formed in each earthworm, and **seminal receptacles** which hold sperm received from another worm.

Sperm from one worm travel from the seminal vesicles, through openings in segment 15, to the seminal receptacles of another worm, through openings in segments 9 and 10. Here they are stored until eggs are laid. When the eggs mature later, they pass from the ovaries through openings in segment 14 and are deposited in a slime ring secreted by the clitellum. As this ring is pushed forward, sperm are released from the seminal receptacles and fertilization occurs. The slime ring slips from the body and becomes the cocoon in which the young worms develop.

The study of the earthworm can be rewarding if you think carefully about its organization and structures. Find out how each performs its functions and how they all depend on one another. You will see then how a common invertebrate animal has an organization and activities which are quite similar to yours.

The leech is another segmented worm. The *leech* (Fig. 22-7), also called a " bloodsucker," is found in streams and ponds. It is an external parasite on fish and other aquatic animals, but may attach itself to your skin while you are swimming.

In sucking blood, a leech attaches itself to some vertebrate by the posterior sucker, applies the anterior sucker to the skin, and makes a wound with the aid of little jaws inside the mouth. The salivary glands of the leech secrete a substance which prevents the clotting of blood while the worm is taking a meal. Leeches were used frequently for medicinal purposes in the Middle Ages, when it was thought beneficial to draw blood. Now the salivary substance is extracted and used to slow clotting after surgery.

Fig. 22-11. Although an earthworm has the reproductive organs of both sexes, it exchanges sperm with another animal in the manner shown below. Sperm travel from the seminal vesicles of one worm to the seminal receptacles of the other.

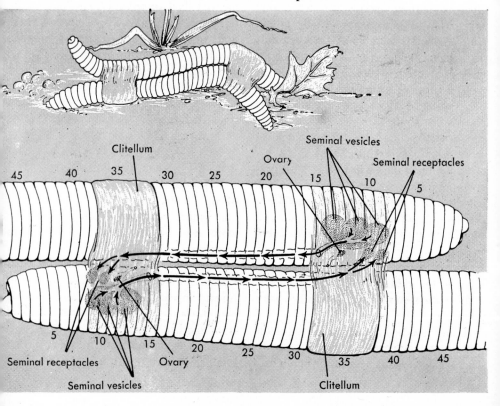

SUMMARY OF CHARACTERISTICS OF THE WORMS

	PLATYHELMINTHES (plat-ee-hel-*min*-theez)	NEMATHELMINTHES (nem-uh-thel-*min*-theez)	ANNELIDA (an-*nel*-ih-duh)
BODY TYPES	Flat, unsegmented bodies	Round, unsegmented bodies	Body divided into segments
TYPE OF LIFE	Many parasitic	Many parasitic	Majority *not* parasitic
ORGAN–IZATION	3 layers, many organ systems	3 layers, many organ systems	3 layers, organs well developed
DIGESTIVE SYSTEM	Open at one end only	Mouth and anus	Mouth and anus
REPRO–DUCTION	Asexually by fission; sexually — hermaphroditic, cross-fertilization	Sexual, definite male and female	Sexually hermaphroditic, cross-fertilization
CIRCU–LATION	None present	None present	5 aortic arches, large dorsal vessel, small ventral vessel
NERVOUS SYSTEM	2 longitudinal nerve cords	2 nerve cords, one dorsal, one ventral	One large ventral nerve cord

 *In Conclusion*

This chapter has taken you through an interesting part of the animal kingdom. You have seen animals which are not limited to the tissue level as are the coelenterates, but whose bodies are instead composed on the organ level of development. The animals we have discussed in this unit are composed of three cell layers. You have discovered how an animal can degenerate and live as a parasite that depends on the body activities of the host organism. Perhaps it was surprising to find that a close relative of a dangerous parasite like the fluke can live harmlessly in a stream.

In the following chapter, we shall continue the study of the invertebrate groups with two interesting and still more specialized phyla. Included in these will be the clam, oyster, octopus, starfish, and sea urchin.

BIOLOGICALLY SPEAKING

Annelida	eyespot	Platyhelminthes
anus	feces	proglottids
aortic arch	ganglia	prostomium
asymmetrical	gizzard	radial symmetry
bilateral symmetry	hermaphroditic	seminal receptacle
blood	intestine	seminal vesicle
clitellum	larva	setae
crop	longitudinal nerve	spherical symmetry
cuticle	mesoderm	symmetrical
cyst	Nemathelminthes	transverse nerve
degeneration	Nematoda	trichinosis
dorsal	nephridia	ventral
esophagus	pharynx	

QUESTIONS FOR REVIEW

1. (a) Name and define the types of symmetry. (b) Give an example of each.
2. What advantage does bilateral symmetry have over spherical symmetry? What advantage does it have over radial symmetry?
3. Why do we classify the various worms into three separate phyla?
4. What is the significance of the three layers of cells found in flatworms?
5. In what ways does the planaria " sample " its environment?
6. In what ways are the flatworms more complex than the sponges and coelenterates?
7. In what way does the tapeworm show degeneration?
8. In what ways do the nematodes show an advance over the flatworms?
9. Describe the life cycle of *Ascaris*.
10. How does the trichina worm reach the human body?
11. How does an earthworm move?
12. Trace a particle of food through the digestive system of the earthworm, naming the organs through which it passes.

APPLYING FACTS AND PRINCIPLES

1. Discuss regeneration in the planaria.
2. Trace the path followed by *Ascaris* through the body by naming all the structures through which it passes. At what stages during its development are symptoms of disease most likely to be present?
3. Compare the advantages of the annelids' nervous system over that of the planaria.
4. What measures are important to take in an effort to control parasitic worms?
5. Symptoms of tapeworm infestation usually include loss of weight and general tiredness. Account for these conditions.
6. Trichinosis can become a hopeless disease. Why is it almost impossible to treat?

CHAPTER 23

The Soft-bodied and the Spiny-skinned Animals

THE **mollusks** (*mol*-usks) are soft-bodied animals. When you think of a mollusk, you probably picture a clam or an oyster, but there are others. The octopus, the squid, and the garden snail are mollusks. Although this may surprise some of you, this chapter will show many characteristics which are alike in these apparently very different forms.

The starfish and its relatives are in still another phylum and are more complex organisms than one would think. They are the spiny-skinned animals commonly seen in tidepools of the wave-splashed coasts. We shall also examine some of their structures in this chapter. Biologists do not always agree on how to place these two phyla of invertebrates properly in the animal kingdom.

Mollusks. The Mollusca are often called *shellfish*. This, however, is not a good name because they are not fish; many of them live on land, and many lack shells entirely. Some mollusks live in fresh water; many of them are marine. The mollusks have been used for food, money, eating utensils, jewelry, buttons, dyes, tools, and weapons since earliest times. Great deposits of mollusk shells on mountain tops indicate to the geologist the locations of prehistoric seas. The

five classes into which we divide the mollusk phylum are listed in the Appendix at the back of the book.

The general body plan of a mollusk consists of a *head, foot,* and *visceral hump* (Fig. 23-1). The **visceral hump** contains the digestive organs, excretory organs, and the heart. It is covered by a **mantle,** or thin membrane, which often secretes a shell by taking lime from the water. Where the mantle hangs down over the sides and rear of the animal, the **mantle**

Fig. 23-1. Although no living mollusk looks exactly like this, all the major characteristics of the phylum are shown in this generalized diagram. The arrows indicate direction of water flow in the mantle cavity.

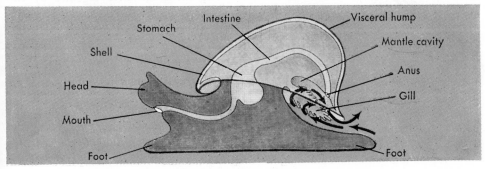

cavity is formed. In this cavity are the **gills,** which are the respiratory organs. Undigested matter passes into this cavity before it is carried outside through the anus.

Since a current of water must pass through the mantle cavity to bring in fresh oxygen and food, and to carry away carbon dioxide and waste, the mollusks that build shells have a problem. The solution seems to have been in the growth of tubes or *siphons*. The **incurrent siphon,** or *ventral siphon,* takes water into the mantle cavity while the **excurrent siphon,** or *dorsal siphon,* takes water out of the mantle cavity.

The major characteristic which divides this phylum into its classes is the type of shell, if present.

Bivalve mollusks. Common **bivalves** include the clams, oysters, scallops, and mussels. These animals have two shells, or valves, connected by a hinge. If you look at a clam shell closely you will see that it consists of three distinct layers (Fig. 23-2). The inside layer, which is next to the mantle in the living animal, is smooth and glistening. It is called the

Fig. 23-3. **How does its hatchet-shaped foot aid the clam in digging?**

pearly layer. If a grain of sand becomes lodged in the mantle, this layer builds up around the sand and forms a pearl. The next layer is composed of crystals of calcium carbonate and is named the **prismatic layer.** The outermost layer is thin, and may be peeled off when the shell dries. It resembles dried shellac or varnish. This is called the **horny outer layer.** It forms part of the hinge, and protects the middle layer from being dissolved by small amounts of acid which may be in the water.

The shells are held together by two muscles called the **anterior** and **posterior adductor muscles.** If you have ever pried apart the valves of an oyster or clam, you know the strength of these muscles.

The name " hatchet-footed " is given to the bivalves because of the shape of the foot (Fig. 23-3). When digging, the muscular foot extends out and is long and narrow. The end of the foot then spreads out to form a hatchet-shaped anchor.

Fig. 23-2. **Notice the three distinct layers of a clam shell, all of which are manufactured by the mantle.**

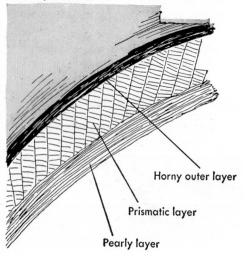

Horny outer layer

Prismatic layer

Pearly layer

When this muscular foot shortens, the anchor holds, and the animal is pulled down into the sand. The clam is a rapid digger as some of you, no doubt, know!

How does a bivalve feed? The bivalve has two siphons: a *ventral siphon* to bring in water, and a *dorsal siphon* to expel water (Fig. 23-4). As a clam lies partially buried in the mud or sand, the shells remain partly open and the two siphons extend into the water. When water enters the mantle cavity, it passes up through the gills. Then the water passes the anus, where undigested matter is excreted, and out the dorsal siphon. As water passes over the gills, two processes occur: (1) oxygen diffuses in and carbon dioxide diffuses out; and (2) small particles of organic matter stick to a thin mucous layer on the gills. The surface of the gills has cilia which are continually beating, thus carrying the mucus up to the dorsal surface. At the dorsal surface of the gills, the cilia beat forward to carry the mucous strands and trapped organic matter to the mouth. Animals which feed in this manner are said to be *mucus feeders*. From the mouth, food passes through a short esophagus to the stomach and then to a digestive gland, the cells of which take in and digest the food. Absorption takes place and a circulatory system, pumped by a heart, carries the colorless blood to all parts of the body. Undigested matter passes through the intestine and out the anus.

Bivalves have a well-developed nervous system with several large ganglia. Also the edges of the mantle contain sensory cells which are sensitive to contact and light.

Univalve mollusks. Common univalves or **gastropods** (*gas*-troh-pods) include land and water snails, conches, and abalones (ab-uh-*loh*-nees). If you were to take the generalized mollusk in the diagram in Fig. 23-1, page 265, turn the visceral hump around halfway, remove the gills, and put some spirals in the shell, the

Fig. 23-4. The arrows in this diagram of a dissected clam indicate the direction of water flow. How does food get from the mantle cavity to the mouth?

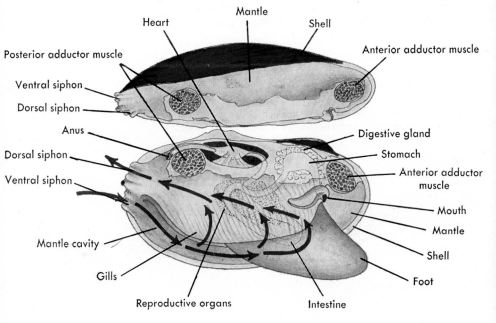

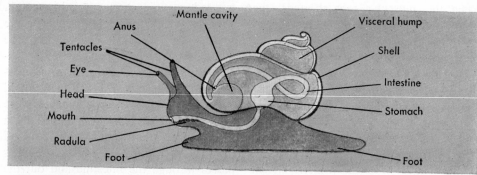

Fig. 23-5. Compare the structure of this land snail with that of the generalized mollusk shown in Fig. 23-1 and with that of the bivalve mollusk shown in Fig. 23-4. In what ways is the snail similar to these and in what ways is it different?

animal would look much like a snail. The land snail is a good mollusk to study as it is easily obtained and will move around freely while being observed. See if you can find the prominent structures on a land snail, as in Fig. 23-5.

The terrestrial snail moves at a " snail's pace " of about ten feet per hour. The flat, muscular foot secretes slime on which it travels in rhythmic waves. The eyes of land snails are on the tips of two tentacles. When touched, the snail draws in these tentacles, somewhat as the toe of a stocking vanishes when you turn it inside out.

The slug looks like a snail which has lost its shell. It comes out at night, leaving trails of slime wherever it goes. Slugs eat plant leaves and cause considerable damage, as do snails.

Method of feeding. The fresh-water snails in a school aquarium are excellent for observing the feeding mechanism of a gastropod. Here you will see the mouth of the animal open, a tonguelike structure scrape the glass of the aquarium, and the mouth close again. This is repeated at very frequent intervals, so that you can take a closer look. With a magnifying glass you can see that this " tongue " is very rough. This structure is named the *radula* (*rad*-yoo-luh), which literally means " scraper." It is like a file, and actually files or scrapes algae from the glass side of the aquarium. Now you can see how garden snails and slugs can cause such damage to your plants, as they are also equipped with radulas.

" **Head-foot** " **mollusks.** The *cephalopods* (*sef*-uh-luh-pods) include the octo-

Fig. 23-6. The squid is one of the most highly-developed invertebrates. The shell of the animal is internal and consists of a thin, horny plate.

Marine Studios, Marineland, Florida

pus, squid, cuttlefish, and chambered nautilus. The octopus has no shell, the nautilus has an external shell, and the squid and the cuttlefish have an internal shell. The giant squid is probably the largest of all the invertebrates, sometimes weighing as much as two tons. Accounts of battles between whales and giant squids have enlivened tales of the sea for many years. However, the octopus has the worst reputation of the cephalopods, which is probably undeserved. One species may possibly be dangerous to man, but there are not enough proven accounts of loss of life to be definite on this point. Some of the squid have luminescent organs, but their function is still uncertain.

Echinoderms. The starfish, brittle star, sea urchin, and sand dollar are common examples of the phylum *Echinodermata* (eh-ky-noh-der-*may*-tuh). They have a hard, shell-like, radially symmetrical body covered with spines. The spines may be long as in the sea urchin, or very short, as in the sand dollar. All the echinoderms are marine.

The starfish is not a fish, in spite of its name. When alive, the five, or rarely six, *rays* which radiate from a central disk are movable. In a groove on the lower side of each ray, there are two rows of *tube*

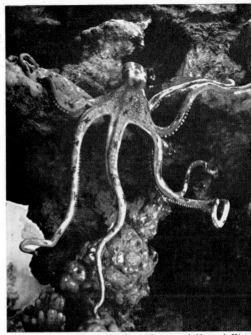

American Museum of Natural Histc

Fig. 23-7. The octopus is a cephalopod without a shell, and with very well-developed eyes. It moves by pulling itself over the rocks with its tentacles.

feet (Fig. 23-9, page 270). They are part of a *water-vascular system*. The tube feet are connected to canals which lead through each ray to a circular canal in the central disk. This *ring canal* has an opening to the surface, the *sieve plate*, on the dorsal side. When the starfish

Fig. 23-8. The teeth of the sea urchin (*left*) can be seen in the center of its shell in the ventral view. The movable spines have been removed. On the right is a photograph of a sea cucumber. In what ways are the two animals alike?

American Museum of Natural History

American Museum of Natural History

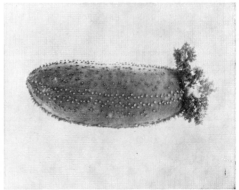

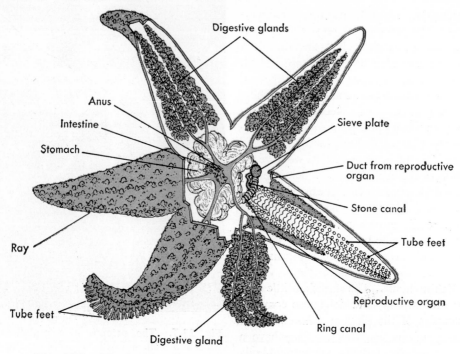

Digestive glands

Anus

Intestine

Stomach

Sieve plate

Duct from reproductive organ

Stone canal

Ray

Tube feet

Tube feet

Reproductive organ

Digestive gland

Ring canal

Fig. 23-9.   The drawing above is of the dorsal view of a dissected starfish.

presses its tube feet against an object and forces water out of the canals, the feet grip firmly by means of suction.   Return of water to the canals releases the grip.

The starfish uses its water-vascular system in opening the shells of clams and oysters, its principal food.   The body

arches over the prey with the rays bent downward.   The shells of the clam or oyster are gripped firmly by the tube feet, and a steady pull is exerted at the same time.   The starfish secretes a substance which paralyzes the clam or oyster. After a while the shell muscles of the prey

Fig. 23-10.   The dorsal view of the starfish on the left shows its spiny covering and the sieve plate, which is the external opening of the water-vascular system.   Tube feet lie in the grooves shown in the ventral view on the right.

tire, and the halves of the shell separate. At this point, the starfish pushes out its stomach from a small opening in the center of the lower side. The stomach, turned inside out, enters the shell and digests the body of the clam or oyster, leaving only the shell. Although starfish have extensive skeletons, they are quite flexible and can bend very easily around an oyster.

Oystermen are on constant lookout for starfish in clam or oyster beds. An active, adult starfish can destroy eight to twelve oysters a day. Formerly, men tore starfish to pieces thinking that they were destroying these pests. Actually, they were multiplying their troubles, for a starfish ray, with a portion of the central disk, can *regenerate* and become an entire new starfish.

Food passing from the stomach of the starfish goes into digestive glands in which digestion is completed. Some undigested matter passes out through the mouth. Above the stomach is a short intestine which ends in the anus on the dorsal surface.

The starfish are either male or female, and the reproductive organs lead to the outside by small ducts. During the re-

American Museum of Natural History

Fig. 23-11. When eating, the starfish turns the lower part of its stomach inside out and extends it through the mouth.

productive season, eggs and sperm are shed to the outside where fertilization takes place in the water. The female starfish may produce as many as 200 million eggs in a season.

In Conclusion

In the study of the mollusks and echinoderms, you have investigated some of the most prominent members of the animal society of the shallow seas and tidepools. You have studied the mollusks which live in the sea, in fresh water, and on the land. The food habits and radula of the terrestrial gastropod enable it to eat our plants, so that they are considered pests.

In the chapters to follow, we shall continue the study of invertebrates with a phylum which, if numbers indicate importance, is the most important of all invertebrate groups. Here we find such well-known animals as the insects, the crayfish and lobster, the spider, and scores of others.

BIOLOGICALLY SPEAKING

adductor muscle	horny outer layer	radula
bivalves	incurrent siphon	ray
cephalopod	mantle	ring canal
Echinodermata	mantle cavity	sieve plate
excurrent siphon	mollusks	tube foot
gastropod	pearly layer	visceral hump
gill	prismatic layer	water-vascular system

QUESTIONS FOR REVIEW

1. Trace a particle of food from the outside to the digestive gland of the clam, naming the organs through which it passes.
2. What characteristics of the mollusks divide the phylum into classes?
3. What are the three common characteristics of all mollusks?
4. In what ways do the cephalopods differ from the gastropods?
5. What layers are formed in the making of the shell by the mantle?
6. What characteristics of the echinoderms distinguish them from other invertebrate animals?
7. Describe the movement of the starfish.
8. How does the water-vascular system assist the starfish in eating?
9. How does the oyster form a pearl in its shell?

APPLYING FACTS AND PRINCIPLES

1. What property of mollusks makes them of help to the geologist?
2. In what ways have the mollusks been of value to man? In what ways have they been a pest?
3. Why do people usually put snails in aquaria?
4. Shells of mollusks are frequently ground up and used as fertilizer. What are some of the substances these shells add to the soil?
5. How are chitons able to live above the water line on rocky surfaces and still resist drying out and dying?

CHAPTER 24

The Arthropods

THE large phylum **Arthropoda** (ar-*throp*-uh-duh), commonly called the arthropods, outnumbers all other kinds of animal life. Like knights of old, these invertebrates wear a suit of protective armor, completely covering the softer internal body parts. The hard outer covering, or **exoskeleton,** is one of their most striking characteristics. But their name refers to their jointed feet (*arthros* = joint; *poda* = feet).

Arthropods thrive in nearly all environments in widely varied forms. Few living creatures are more widely distributed than the insects, one of the classes of animals included in this phylum. We also find in this group such familiar animals as spiders, centipedes, millepedes, crayfish, crabs, and lobsters.

CLASSES OF ARTHROPODS

CLASS	BODY DIVISIONS	APPENDAGES	BREATHING	EXAMPLES
CRUSTACEA (kruh-*stay*-shuh)	2 — cephalo-thorax, abdomen	5 pairs or more	Gills	Lobster, crab, water-flea, sow-bug, crayfish
CHILOPODA (ky-*lop*-oh-duh)	Head and numerous body segments	1 pair on each segment except first one behind head and last 2	Tracheae	Centipede
DIPLOPODA (dip-*lop*-oh-duh)	Head and numerous body segments	2 pairs of legs on each body segment	Tracheae	Millepede
ARACHNIDA (uh-*rak*-nih-duh)	2 — cephalo-thorax, abdomen	4 pairs of legs	Tracheae and book lungs	Spider, mite, tick, scorpion
INSECTA (in-*sek*-tuh)	3 — head, thorax, abdomen	3 pairs of legs; usually 1 or 2 pairs of wings	Tracheae	Grasshopper, butterfly, bee, dragon fly, moth, beetle

Some characteristics of arthropods. To the casual observer, the graceful butterfly has little in common with the crayfish lurking under a rock in a stream. But careful study of these quite different animals will show that they have much in common. The characteristics which make the butterfly similar in structure to the crayfish also relate these creatures to spiders, scorpions, and centipedes. These points of similarity are:

1. Jointed **appendages,** which include legs and other body outgrowths.

2. An exoskeleton of **chitin** (*ky*-tin), which is as an external skeleton instead of the internal bony support we have.

3. A segmented body, which refers to the distinct divisions of the exoskeleton.

4. A dorsal heart; that is, one that is located above the digestive system.

5. A ventral nervous system, with the main nerves below the digestive system.

There are five classes of arthropods. In the classification of the arthropods, such widely varied forms as butterflies and crayfish, spiders and centipedes are segregated into classes. This large phylum is commonly divided into five classes, as shown in the table above.

Each of these classes has all the fundamental characteristics of arthropods, and, in addition, certain characteristics of the class to which it belongs. For example, the **Crustacea** (kruh-*stay*-shuh) have two pairs of antennae, or "feelers," on the front of the body, two distinct body regions, two or more pairs of legs, a chitinous exoskeleton which contains lime, and often structures called **gills** for respiration. The **Insecta,** on the other hand, have one pair of antennae, a body composed of three parts, three pairs of legs, often two pairs of wings, and an exoskeleton composed of chitin lacking lime.

They respire by means of air tubes called *tracheae* (*tray*-kee-ee).

The arthropods show a great advance over other animals already studied. Worms, especially the earthworm, show a high degree of specialization of body parts and the presence of specialized internal organs. In our study of the Crustacea as typical arthropods, we shall deal with animals such as the crayfish, lobster, and crab, which are adapted for aquatic life. Division of labor among their various organs is carried to an even higher point than we found in the earthworm. All of this specialization has resulted in an efficient animal, very well-adapted to our present world. The segmented body is, of course, common to both the arthropods and the annelids. The ventral nervous system first appeared in the worms.

The crayfish — a common crustacean. The *crayfish* is large, easy to observe, characteristic of arthropods in its struc-

ture, and easily obtained in nearly all rivers, lakes, and streams containing lime.

The body is covered with a dark gray limy exoskeleton which is divided into two regions. The first of these regions, called the **cephalothorax** (sef-uh-loh-*thor*-aks), includes the head and a second region, the **thorax** (Fig. 24-1). These are separate in many arthropods. The cephalothorax is covered by a hard plate or shell known as the **carapace** (*kair*-uh-pace). Attached to the rear of the cephalothorax is a second distinct body region, the **abdomen,** which is composed of several movable segments.

It may seem strange to find the skeleton on the outside of the body of an animal. Whether internal or external, however, skeletons serve the same purpose. They give the body form, protect delicate internal organs and aid in motion by serving as attachments for muscles.

The Crustacea, with their armor-plated

Fig. 24-1. The crayfish, shown from a dorsal view (*left*) and a ventral view with head enlarged (*right*), is a common crustacean.

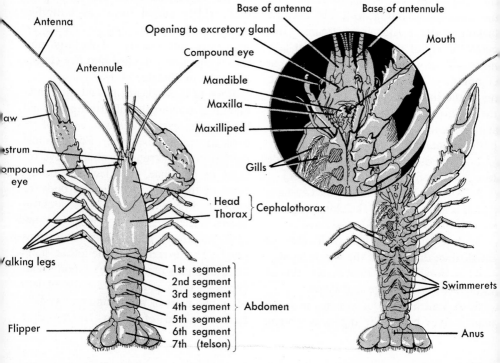

bodies, are among the best-protected arthropods. This protective cover extends even over the legs, which may be bent only at special joints. The heavy carapace, covering the head and thorax, gives special protection to these vital regions of the body. It is like a plate of armor, but is even more efficient, for it is a shield far lighter than a warrior ever carried. The color of the strong, light, and flexible exoskeleton blends with the surroundings so that the crayfish escapes the notice of its enemies (*protective coloration.*)

The front of the carapace extends forward in a protective beak, the **rostrum** (*ros*-trum). On either side of the rostrum are the eyes. These are set on short movable stalks and are composed of numerous lenses. For this reason, we speak of them as **compound eyes.**

The head appendages of the crayfish. Beginning at the *anterior* (head) *end,* we see first the **antennules,** in the basal segment of which are sacs that contain the equilibrium and hearing apparatus. The large " feelers," or **antennae,** attach just posterior to the antennules. Then come the **mandibles** (*man*-dih-buls), or true jaws, and two pairs of **maxillae** (max-*il*-ee), or little jaws, which aid in chewing the food. The jaws work from side to side and not up and down, because they are merely leglike appendages adapted for chewing and so continue to have a horizontal motion, as do the legs.

The appendages on the thorax of the crayfish. The first appendages of the thorax are three pairs of **maxillipeds** (max-*il*-ih-peds), or " jaw feet." Their function is to hold food during chewing. Next come the large claws, obviously for protection and food-getting, then two pairs of legs with tiny pincers at the tip, and two more pairs with claws. These four pairs of legs are concerned mainly with walking. Attached to the maxillipeds, to the eight legs, and to the large

claws are feathery *gills* which extend up under the carapace into the gill chambers.

The abdominal appendages of the crayfish. The appendages of the abdomen are called **swimmerets** and are small on the first five segments. They are used by the female as an attachment for her eggs in the process of reproduction. The sixth swimmeret is enormously developed into a flipper, or **uropod,** located at the extreme posterior part of the body. The appendage of the seventh segment is lacking, and the segment itself is reduced to a flat, triangular part called the **telson.** The sixth and seventh segments together form a powerful organ for backward locomotion, for they can be whipped forward by the strong muscles of the abdomen, making the animal shoot backward at high speed. Some biologists consider that the crayfish has only six abdominal segments, and that the telson is an extension of the abdomen and not a segment.

What are homologous organs? When organs (either in the same or different animals) were developed from the same part — that is, whose origin and structure are similar, allowing for certain modifications — they are called **homologous** (hoh-*mol*-uh-gus) **organs.** The antennae and claws of the crayfish are homologous to the swimmerets. Likewise the arm of man is homologous to the foreleg of the horse, even though the functions of the arm and foreleg are so different.

Analogous (an-*al*-uh-gus) means similar in function. We might say that the gills of the crayfish and the lungs of man are analogous because both perform the function of respiration, but we cannot say they are homologous. The gills are developed from the legs, while the lungs are outgrowths of the throat. Their structure is quite different.

Food-getting by the crayfish. The crayfish eats many different kinds of food. Although it prefers animal food, it will

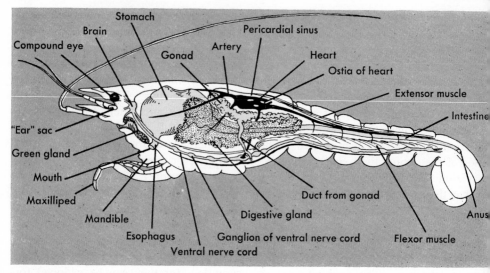

Fig. 24-2. In this longitudinal section of the crayfish, the term *gonad* refers to the ovary in a female and the testis in a male.

eat available plants. It is a scavenger and doesn't seem to object if the animal, which it is to eat, has been dead a long time! The food enters the stomach through the esophagus. There are tooth-like structures in the stomach which grind the food into smaller particles. When the particles of food are finely ground, they pass through folds of tissue, which act as a strainer, into another portion of the stomach where a mixing with digestive juices occurs. From here, the digested food passes into the digestive glands where absorption takes place. Undigested particles pass on through the intestine, instead of entering the digestive glands, and are excreted through the anus (Fig. 24-2). There are also special excretory organs in the crayfish called **green glands,** which lie anterior to the stomach and open close to the base of the antennae.

Circulatory and nervous systems. The colorless blood of the crayfish is pumped by the heart into seven large arteries which pour the blood over the major organs of the body. Blood is collected in a number of spaces called *sinuses.* One large sinus surrounds the heart and is termed the **pericardial** (pair-ih-*kar*-dee-ul) *sinus.* From here, blood enters the heart through three pairs of holes called **ostia** (*os*-tee-uh). This method of circulation is called an **open system.**

The nervous system, though similar to that in worms, is much more specialized. The senses of touch and smell, located in the antennae, maxillae, and maxillipeds, are acute. The eyes are on movable stalks and are compound, each consisting of numerous lenses, but the sight is probably not keen. " Ear " sacs are located at the base of the antennules and probably aid in balancing. Hearing is poorly developed, but the sense of taste is well developed.

While these sense organs do not seem very efficient, enormous advance can be seen when we compare the crayfish with the earthworm. The worm probably feels only touch and vibrations carried by the land or water through the body wall, with a possibility that chemical and heat or light sensations are registered in the region of the head. Since the degree in which an animal can get in touch with its environment marks the stage of its advancement, the Crustacea far excel the worms in development.

How the crayfish moves. The function of locomotion is taken care of by the legs and by the tail flipper which drives the crayfish swiftly backward. Also, by means of the four pairs of walking legs, the crayfish can travel forward and sideways. All movements are operated by powerful muscles, assisted by the exoskeleton.

The large muscle in the dorsal part of the abdomen is called the **extensor muscle** as it *extends,* or *straightens,* the abdomen. The muscle in the ventral part of the abdomen is the **flexor muscle.** It *flexes,* or *bends,* the abdomen.

How the crayfish respires. Respiration in Protozoa is accomplished by contact of the cell with dissolved oxygen in the water; in the worm through the body wall with oxygen in the air. In the crayfish we find **gills.** These are especially developed organs for the exchange of oxygen and carbon dioxide between the animal and its environment. These gills are thin-walled to allow for the passage of gases. They are provided with many blood vessels to receive oxygen and to carry it to all cells, and also to liberate carbon dioxide.

The gills are arranged to insure a constant flow of fresh water over them. They move in the water with every motion of the legs or maxillipeds. The gills are protected by the carapace, which extends over them and forms a chamber. This chamber can hold moisture for some time, thus keeping the animal alive when it is removed from the water.

Life history of the crayfish. Frequently, crayfish can be found during the spring months with curious berrylike structures attached to the swimmerets on the lower side of the abdomen. These are the fe-

males, and the curious berrylike structures are *eggs.* The eggs number about 100. At the time they are laid they are fertilized by *sperm* which have been stored in small sacs on the lower side of the female's body since the mating which occurred the previous fall. The eggs generally hatch in about six to eight weeks, depending on the temperature and other conditions of the water. During the interval between laying and hatching, they remain securely fastened to the swimmerets. When first hatched, the young are quite different in appearance from the adult. During a series of changes called **molts,** they become more like their parents in form.

How molting takes place. From the time of hatching until adult size, molting occurs at increasingly long intervals. Most crayfish molt seven times the first year. After that, the animals usually molt about once or twice a year (Fig. 24-3). The average life span of the crayfish is three or four years.

This molting, which consists of shedding the exoskeleton, is a direct result of

Fig. 24-3. The pattern of growth in the arthropods is drawn in black; that in the vertebrates is drawn in color. Why can anthropod growth, or molting, be compared to a flight of steps?

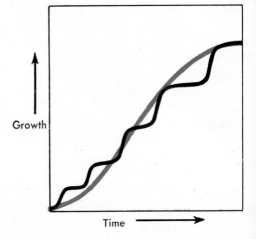

Growth

Time

having the hard parts of the body on the outside. Animals which have an exoskeleton cannot grow larger unless they shed their armor. When the crayfish is ready to molt, the lime is partly absorbed from the skeleton, the carapace splits across the back, water is withdrawn from the tissues, which causes them to shrink, and the animal literally humps itself out of its former skeleton. It also leaves behind the lining of its stomach and its teeth. Immediately following this process, water is absorbed and growth proceeds very rapidly. The lime is replaced in the new and larger armor. Usually the later molts take place quickly and in hidden locations. The animal is totally help-

less and a prey to all sorts of enemies while growing its new suit.

The regeneration of lost parts. During molting or in battle with enemies, appendages are often lost or injured. In the latter case, the limb is voluntarily shed. A double membrane prevents much loss of blood, and a whole new appendage is gradually developed to replace the injured member. This process is another example of *regeneration*.

Crustacea at home. Many of you have doubtless more than once pulled up a crayfish firmly attached to the bait on your fishline. It is one of the most common inhabitants of streams and ponds where lime is dissolved in the water. You

Fig. 24-4. These forms of small crustaceans are usually found in ponds and streams or moist places on land. What characteristics do they have in common?

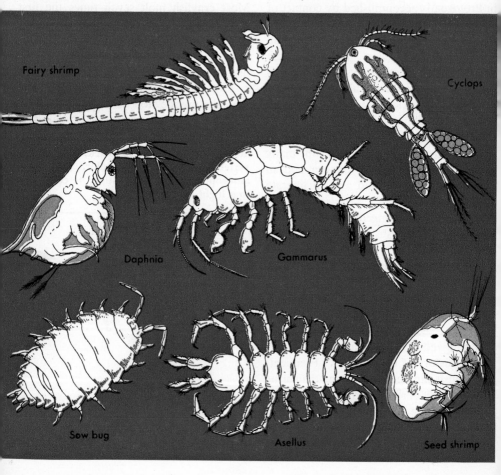

Fig. 24-5. This lobster is capturing a crab in its pincers. In what ways are these two animals alike?

can see it at any time of the day or night, although it feeds primarily at night, and is most active at dusk and daybreak.

Since the crayfish readily consumes dead organisms in any condition, it is considered of benefit as a scavenger. In certain parts of the country, especially in the Mississippi River basin, crayfish cause extensive damage by making holes in earthen dams and levees and by burrowing in fields, thus destroying cotton and corn crops.

Other crustaceans. Some of you may not live near a stream where crayfish can be found, or near the ocean where other Crustacea (lobster, crab, prawn, shrimp, barnacle) can be studied. You can still study a crustacean by using the terrestrial *pill bug* or *sow bug*. These are always found under stones and logs in moist places. Although they show some differences (which allow them to live on land), the crustacean characteristics are present and may be observed (Fig. 24-4). They

may be kept for weeks by feeding them slices of potato or carrot and keeping them in a cool place.

Economic importance of Crustacea. Many Crustacea are of great economic importance to man. The lobster, the big brother of the crayfish, inhabits the cool waters of the Atlantic Coast from the Carolinas to Labrador. Lobster fishing is an important industry in many of the New England states, especially along the coast of Maine. In summer, the lobsters come into the shallow water close to the shore, where they live among submerged rocks.

Another kind of lobster, the *spiny lobster,* lives in warmer regions of the ocean along the coasts of Florida, California, and the West Indies. This species lacks the large pincers of its northern cousin. The extremely long antennae are as characteristic of the spiny lobster as are the prominent spines which cover the front part of the body.

The *blue crab* ranks next to the lobster as a table delicacy. These animals live in the shallow grassy ocean bays where they move about in search of decaying matter or any kind of animal they can catch. The body of the crab differs from the lobster in that it is short and broad rather than elongated. The abdomen is much reduced in size and folds under the broad cephalothorax. Large pincers serve as organs of defense and food-getting. " Soft-shelled " crabs are merely edible crabs which are captured immediately following a molt. In a few days, these table delicacies form a hard shell again. The name *blue crab* comes from the fact that the feet are blue in color.

A discussion of Crustacea as items of food would be incomplete without mention of the *shrimp*. These creatures resemble other Crustacea in general form, but are distinct in that they have five pairs of walking legs and a much enlarged and highly muscular abdomen. They are fast swimmers, moving backward in true crustacean fashion. When alarmed, they bury themselves in the sand along the bottom and thrust out their eyes and antennae to keep in touch with their surroundings.

The shrimp industry is very important in the Gulf Coast states, as well as in California. Louisiana, Texas, and California supply much of the shrimp for inland markets.

Many forms of minute Crustacea thrive in the waters of inland ponds and lakes. The small size of many of these forms brings them into contact with the microscopic Protozoa of the community. The strange-appearing *Cyclops,* with its large, single eye, the *Daphnia* or water flea, with its jerky movement, and the peculiar " back-swimming " fairy shrimp appear in swarms in certain bodies of fresh water during rather unpredictable periods. They serve as food for small fish and are a much sought item by aquarists.

The barnacles which attach themselves to the hulls of ships and other structures in salt water cause great damage. A great number on a ship's hull may reduce its speed by as much as 20 per cent.

Fig. 24-6. What are the differences between the centipede (*left*) and the millepede (*right*)?

U. S. Dept. of Agriculture

Arthropods with many legs. The *Chilopoda* (ky-*lop*-oh-duh) and *Diplopoda* (dip-*lop*-oh-duh) are often grouped together as one class — *Myriapoda* (meer-ee-*ap*-oh-duh), which means "many feet." Perhaps you have wondered how a centipede or millepede can operate so many legs and not get them tangled in each other. Their movement is certainly an excellent example of coordination. These curious wormlike arthropods are often seen racing away with a rippling sort of motion when their hiding place under a log, stone, or piece of rubbish has suddenly been disturbed.

Centipedes belong to the class Chilopoda and have bodies composed of many segments. The head bears the antennae and mouth parts; the first body segment bears a pair of poison claws; each following segment (except the last two) bears one pair of walking legs (Fig. 24-6).

Millepedes or "thousand-leggers" belong to the class Diplopoda and also have bodies composed of many segments. Like the centipede, the head bears antennae and mouth parts; all the body segments (except the last two) bear two pairs of legs each. Hence, the name Diplopoda, which means "double feet." Millepedes are frequently slow-moving and are likely to roll into a ball when disturbed. Centipedes, on the other hand, are fast-moving and difficult to capture. In tropical countries, centipedes may measure 12 inches long and their bite may be quite poisonous. Some have as many as 173 pairs of legs, but 35 is average.

Spiders — familiar arachnids. Unfortunately, *spiders* are one of several groups of valuable animals whose reputations have been spoiled by a few undesirable members. With a few exceptions, spiders are extremely valuable because of their destruction of harmful insects. They belong to the class **Arachnida** (uh-*rak*-nih-duh).

Some kinds of spiders, called *orb weavers,* spin elaborate webs of tiny silken threads which are remarkable engineering feats. The web serves as a trap to capture flying insects. When a victim becomes entangled in the sticky threads of the web, the spider races out of its hiding place along the margin. Its bite poisons the prey. When the insect has become somewhat quieter, the spider binds it securely in a case of threads spun around the victim as the spider turns it over and over. Other spiders do not spin webs, but live as solitary individuals stalking their prey as they roam about.

The spider resembles an insect but differs in several respects (Fig. 24-8, page 282). It has eight legs instead of six, and the head and thorax are joined to form a cephalothorax as in the Crustacea. The first pair of appendages, the **chelicera** (keh-*lis*-er-uh), are enlarged and

Fig. 24-7.   The orb weavers spin beautiful symmetrical silken traps for the unwary.

Hugh Spencer

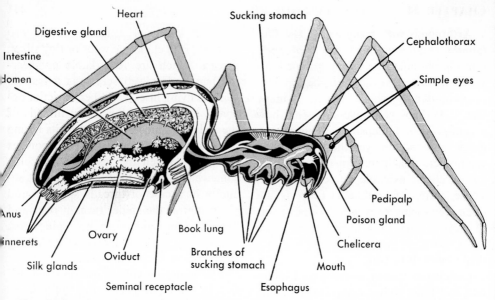

Fig. 24-8. A longitudinal section through a female spider would show these structures. Give the function of each structure.

serve as poison fangs. They are hollow and have small openings in the tip through which poison may be injected into the prey. They then suck the juices from the victim's body. The second pair of head appendages in the spider are called **pedipalps.** They are sensory and are used especially in reproduction by the male spider. On the tip of the abdomen of many spiders are three pairs of **spinnerets.** Each spinneret consists of hundreds of microscopic tubes through which the fluid silk, from the silk glands, flows. When the silk passes into the air, it hardens into a thread. This silk is used in making the spider's web, to build cocoons for eggs, to build nests, and as a guide so the spider can find its way back home. Young spiders of many species spin long silken threads which catch in the wind and carry them to distant places. This procedure is known as *ballooning.*

The respiratory organs of spiders are called **book lungs** because the folds of membrane resemble the pages of a book.

Among the most famous spiders are the *tarantula,* or banana spider, the *black widow,* famous for its very poisonous bite, and the *trap-door spider* of the western desert regions.

Reproduction in spiders. The mature male can be distinguished from the female usually by size alone — the male is usually the smaller. However, in species where there is no size difference, the pedipalps of the male are much larger near the tips. At maturity, the male transfers sperm to special receptacles at the tips of the pedipalps. These sperm are then placed in the *seminal receptacle* of the female, who sometimes devours the unfortunate smaller male afterward. At the time of egg-laying, the eggs are fertilized as they pass out the genital pore and into a nest or cocoon which the female has prepared.

Other arachnids. Spiders are related to many other forms of animal life. *Scorpions,* found in southern and southwestern United States and in all tropical countries, are provided with a long segmented abdomen terminating in a venomous "stinger." The sting of a scorpion, while painful, is seldom fatal to man. Campers

Gerard from Monkmeyer

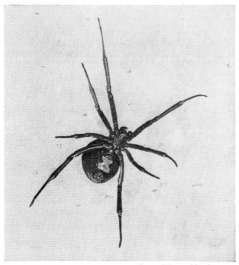

Fig. 24-9. The black widow is recognized by its round, black abdomen and the red spot resembling an hourglass on its ventral surface. Its bite, although seldom fatal, can cause severe pain.

have found them annoying in that they like to crawl in empty shoes during the day to escape bright light. Scorpions live solitary lives except when mating, after which the female often turns upon her mate and devours him. The young are brought forth alive and spend the early part of their existence riding on the mother's back.

The *harvestman,* or *daddy longlegs,* is one of the most useful of the arachnids, since it feeds almost entirely on plant lice. It leads a strictly solitary life, traveling through the fields in search of its prey.

Mites and *ticks* are among the more notorious arachnids, causing considerable damage to man and other animals. They live mostly as parasites on the surface of the bodies of chickens, dogs, cattle, man, and other animals. Some forms, like the Rocky Mountain tick, carry disease. The Texas-fever tick causes an annual loss of more than $50,000,000 to cattle raisers.

Harvest mites, or *chiggers,* are immature stages of mites which attach themselves to the surface of the skin and insert a beak through which they withdraw blood (Fig. 24-11). They are almost microscopic in size and give no warning of their presence until a swollen area causes great itching and discomfort. After a few days, the sore becomes covered with a scab and disappears.

Albert Towle

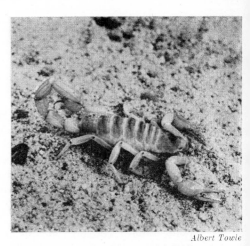

Fig. 24-10. The sting of a scorpion, which is inflicted from the end of the tail, is intended for small prey, but it can be very painful to man.

Fig. 24-11. This photograph shows a chigger magnified over 50 times. The animal has eight legs, as do all arachnids, and its bite can cause great discomfort to man.

American Museum of Natural History

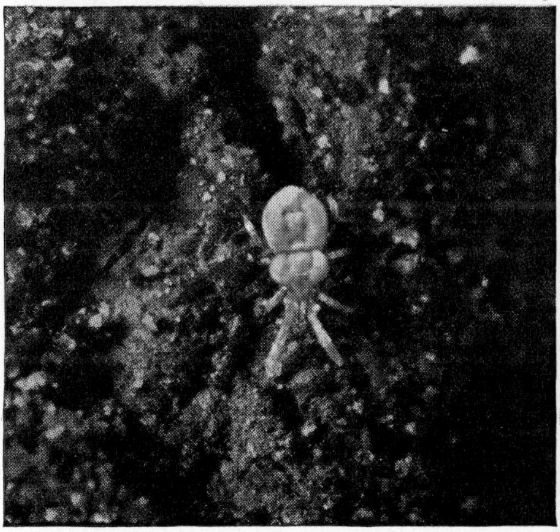

In Conclusion

The arthropods comprise the largest phylum of animals, containing more different forms than all other animal phyla combined. The insects comprise by far the largest class of arthropods, which include, in addition to insects, the crustaceans, arachnids, chilopods, and diplopods.

All of these classes are similar in possessing, among other characteristics, exoskeletons containing chitin, jointed appendages, and segmented bodies.

Among the most economically important arthropods are the crustaceans, which include the lobster, crab, shrimp, and numerous minute inhabitants of pond water. The most famous arachnids are spiders; other arachnids are the harvestman, scorpions, chiggers, ticks, and mites.

In the next three chapters, we shall consider the insects, the most abundant class of arthropods.

BIOLOGICALLY SPEAKING

abdomen	compound eyes	molting
analogous organs	Crustacea	open system
antennae	Diplopoda	ostia
antennules	exoskeleton	pedipalps
appendage	extensor muscle	pericardial sinus
Arachnida	flexor muscle	rostrum
Arthropoda	gills	spinnerets
book lungs	green glands	swimmerets
carapace	homologous organs	telson
cephalothorax	Insecta	thorax
chelicera	mandibles	tracheae
Chilopoda	maxillae	uropod
chitin	maxillipeds	

QUESTIONS FOR REVIEW

1. What are three external characteristics of an arthropod which distinguish it from other animals?
2. (a) What are the five principal classes of arthropods? (b) Give examples.
3. In what ways are the arthropods similar to the earthworm?
4. What are some advantages and disadvantages of an exoskeleton?
5. What are the main parts of the crayfish skeleton?
6. How do the gills in the crayfish carry on the process of respiration?
7. How does the crayfish reproduce?
8. To what stimuli is the crayfish sensitive and what structures assist in the sensitivity?
9. What three crustaceans are important to man because of their food value?
10. (a) Why are most spiders extremely beneficial animals? (b) What reasons can you give for the fact that many people are genuinely afraid of arachnids?
11. What other animals besides the spiders are classified as arachnids?
12. How does a centipede differ from a millepede?

APPLYING FACTS AND PRINCIPLES

1. Why is it especially important for an armored animal like the crayfish to have long antennae?

2. In which of the following localities do you think the crayfish would be likely to produce weaker exoskeletons — in waters flowing through limestone rock or in waters flowing through granite? Explain.

3. What advantage is it for the young crayfish to cling to the adult's swimmerets until after the second molting?

4. In terms of molting of the crayfish, explain each of the following common fisherman's terms: " soft craw," " peeler," and " hard craw."

5. How do barnacles do damage in other ways than to reduce a ship's speed?

CHAPTER 25

Insects—A Representative Study

M OST of us want to get out the spray gun when we think of insects. And it is true that many of them are our enemies. The flies, mosquitoes, and hundreds more do great harm to man and his activities. However, the praying mantis, ladybug, bee, silk moth, and many other insects are helpful. Certainly the class Insecta is the most numerous, both as to genera and individuals, of the great phylum Arthropoda.

The life cycle of some insects, such as the butterfly, is still a marvel which scientists study intensively. Some insects can remain alive in a vacuum, and then surprisingly stay alive when the vacuum is suddenly filled. One species lays its eggs in hot water springs which are ordinarily at a temperature of 120° F. There is even one kind of beetle which can bore through a lead cable!

Countless species. There are about twice as many kinds of insects as all the other living animals combined. More than 675,000 species of insects have already been recorded. Experts regard this as not more than half of all insects in existence! Not only are there many kinds of insects, but each kind produces thousands of offspring. Consider, for example, the locusts and May flies, whose swarms can darken the skies. Insects have been extremely successful in their struggle for existence, mainly because of their special adaptations.

How to recognize an insect. Some people speak of any small flying or crawling animal as a " bug." They are wrong on two counts! First, a true bug is a member of only one order of insects. Second, what some people call a bug may be a spider or a centipede. These, of course, are not insects at all.

Insects include that division of the arthropods which have three separate body regions: (1) *head;* (2) *thorax;* and (3) *abdomen.* The head bears one pair of antennae and three pairs of mouth parts. The thorax of an insect bears

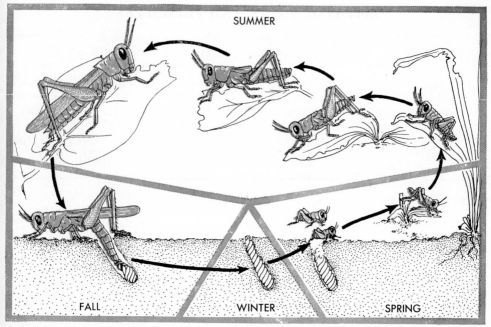

Fig. 25-1. The life history of the grasshopper shows incomplete metamorphosis. Identify the different stages in this history.

three pairs of legs and, in many, the wings. The abdomen has as many as 11 segments and never bears legs. The reproductive structures are usually found on the eighth, ninth, and tenth segments. Insects breathe by many branched tubes called *tracheae*.

A high degree of specialization. The mouth parts of insects are adapted for different kinds of food. Some insects have chewing mouth parts with strong jaws to grind up leaves. Some have piercing and sucking mouth parts with which they are able to suck up plant juices or blood from animals, as do the mosquitoes. Some insects have a siphoning-tube type of mouth with which they can probe flowers for the nectar. On warm, sunny days we have all seen butterflies going from flower to flower gathering the sweet juices.

The wings and legs of insects are wonderfully developed for swift locomotion. Some are adapted for aquatic life, some take refuge by burrowing, some live in colonies like the bees and ants, while others fight their battles alone. Some have become swift in running, leaping, or flying, while others have become so used to staying in one place that they have lost their legs entirely, as for example the scale insects.

Metamorphosis in insects. In many animals, the development from egg to adult includes several more or less distinct stages, instead of being a gradual increase in size. Such a series of stages in a life history is called *metamorphosis* (met-uh-*mor*-foh-sis). Many insects, such as the mosquito, caddis fly, and dragonfly, spend part of their lives in an aquatic environment, breathing by gills. These insects undergo a complete change during their last molt and become terrestrial organisms with a tracheal breathing system. The butterflies and moths, in their immature stages, are called caterpillars. Insects with life cycles in which

THE LARVA OF THE	beetle fly mosquito IS CALLED butterfly moth	grub maggot wiggler caterpillar or " worm " caterpillar or " worm "

the young are not at all like the adults are said to have **complete metamorphosis.** The stages in their lives are four: (1) the **egg;** (2) the **larva;** (3) the **pupa** (*pyoo-*puh); and (4) the **adult.**

A great many insects lay their eggs in the ground. Some place them in water, others protect them with a varnish (lac insect and tent caterpillar), or with a frothy mass (tussock moth), while other insects lay their eggs on leaves or stems of plants. The larvae of many insects have separate names, which confuse the relationship. Refer to the table above for the popular names of a few larvae.

When we speak of silkworms, or apple worms, etc., we are really referring to larval forms of moths. Cabbage worms are larvae of butterflies; the " carpet bug " is the larva of a beetle.

The *pupal* stage is a resting stage. You are all familiar with the cocoon of the moth or the chrysalis of the butterfly. They are the pupae of these insects.

In other insects, the differences between the immature and the adult forms are slight. **Incomplete metamorphosis** is the term applied to their life cycle. There are three stages: (1) the **egg;** (2) the **nymph;** and (3) the **adult.** In insects with this type of growth, the nymph usually looks like the adult except for some minor features such as: smaller size, absence of wings, and absence of reproductive structures (Fig. 25-1). Since the grasshopper is an insect with incomplete metamorphosis, and since it is so widely distributed, we shall study it as a representative of the class Insecta.

The grasshopper. Of the many orders of insects, eight are commonly seen throughout the United States. The grasshopper is a member of the order **Orthoptera** (or-*thop*-ter-uh). This name means " straight-winged " and refers to the narrowly folded wings, held straight along the body when not actually used in flight. As in all arthropods, the skeleton is external, but it differs from the crayfish in that it contains no lime. It consists entirely of the light, tough substance *chitin.*

The mouth parts of the grasshopper. The mouth parts are adapted for biting

Fig. 25-2. **The mouth parts of the grasshopper are especially adapted for chewing plant materials. The mandibles, for instance, are notched and move sideways.**

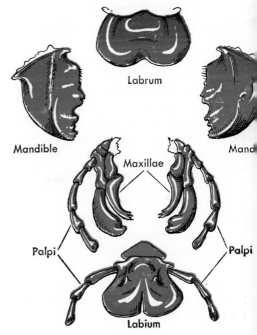

Labrum

Mandible   Mand

Maxillae

Palpi   Palpi

Labium

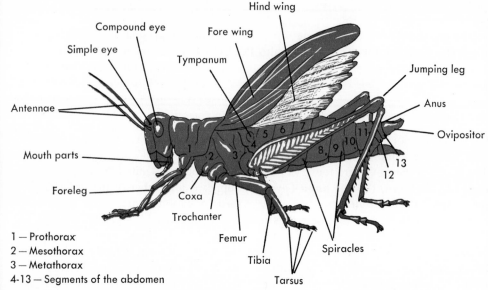

Fig. 25-3.   Note the structures found on the head, on each of the three divisions of the thorax, and on the abdomen in this external side view of the grasshopper.

1 — Prothorax
2 — Mesothorax
3 — Metathorax
4-13 — Segments of the abdomen

and chewing plant material, such as leaves and stems. Named in order from the anterior end, they consist of (1) *labrum* (*lay*-brum); (2) *mandibles;* (3) *maxillae;* and (4) *labium* (*lay*-bee-um). Though the mouth parts of insects are greatly modified to suit different kinds of food, these four sets of organs are still usually present.

The **labrum** (Fig. 25-2, page 287) is the two-lobed upper lip which fits over the toothed, horizontal jaws, or **mandibles.** A pair of **maxillae,** or accessory jaws, are next behind the mandibles. These aid in cutting and holding food, and also have a sense organ, like a short antenna. This is called a **palpus** (*pal*-pus). Posterior to the maxillae comes the **labium,** or lower lip, a deeply two-lobed organ, also provided with palpi, which aid in holding food between the jaws.

In insects like the butterflies and moths, the maxillae join to make a hollow sucking tube. In the case of mosquitoes, the mouth parts are tiny lances placed around a sucking tube.

The thorax consists of three segments. The segments of the thorax are: (1) the *prothorax;* (2) the *mesothorax;* and (3) the *metathorax* (Fig. 25-3). The **prothorax** is a large saddle-shaped segment to which the head and first pair of legs are attached. The middle segment, or **mesothorax** (mes-oh-*thor*-aks), bears a pair of legs and the first pair of wings. The last segment, the **metathorax,** bears the jumping legs and the last pair of wings.

Legs of the grasshopper. The typical insect has six legs. Each of these consists of five parts or segments connected by strong joints and adapted for locomotion (Fig. 25-3). In some insects, like the grasshopper, the posterior pair is also enormously developed for jumping. The foot, or **tarsus,** is provided with spines, hooks, or pads to give a firm grip when jumping or crawling. The long joint next to the tarsus is called the **tibia** (*tib*-ee-uh). The other long joint, the **femur** (*fee*-mer), is equipped with enlarged muscles for jumping. The **trochanter** (troh-*kan*-ter) joins the **coxa** near the body, and they act almost like a ball and socket, permitting freedom of motion.

The grasshopper's wings. The *anterior* wings are long, narrow, and rather stiff. They protect the more delicate underwings and act as planes in aiding flight and leaping. The *posterior* wings are thin and membranous. They are supported by many veins and, when not in use, are folded lengthwise like a fan under the narrower anterior wings.

The abdomen consists of ten segments. Each segment of the abdomen is composed of an upper and lower part, united by a membrane which allows the segment to expand and contract in the process of breathing. A pair of tiny openings called **spiracles** (*spy*-ruh-kuls) lead into the abdomen through eight of the segments. These are the external openings of the respiratory system and connect with the tracheae. The segment next to the thorax bears the ears, which are large, membrane-covered cavities. Each is called a **tympanum** (*tim*-puh-num).

The extreme posterior segments in the female grasshopper bear two pairs of hard and sharp-pointed organs called **ovipositors** (oh-vih-*poz*-ih-ters). The in-

sect uses them to dig a hole in the ground in which to lay eggs. Males lack such organs. The tip end of their abdomen is enlarged and rounded upward.

Some insects, like the sawfly and certain *ichneumon* (ik-*new*-mun) flies, have long hairlike ovipositors with which they pierce wood and lay eggs so that they are deeply hidden. The sting of the bee and wasp is an example of an ovipositor modified for defensive purposes.

The skeletal and muscular systems. The skeletal system of the grasshopper has been described before as an exoskeleton and its various parts have been mentioned. Inside the skeleton are arranged many sets of muscles, each attached to various parts of the skeleton. All are involved in producing the complex movements of the animal. In fact, there are more different separate muscles in the grasshopper than there are in man.

The digestive system. The horizontal action of the mandibles enables the grasshopper to bite off pieces of leaves or other materials which it uses for food. The labrum and labium are notched (Fig. 25-2). This allows for a blade of grass, for example, to be held edgewise

Fig. 25-4.   Refer to this internal view of the grasshopper as you are reading about the structures.

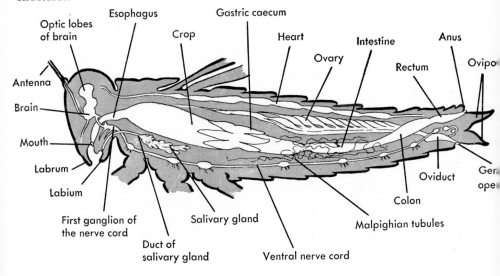

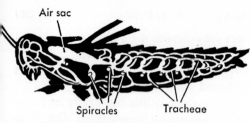

Air sac

Spiracles   Tracheae

Fig. 25-5. This diagrammatic view of the dissected abdomen of the grasshopper indicates the arrangement of the tracheal sytem.

to the mouth, while the mandibles pinch off a piece. The grass is then sucked into the mouth, where it passes into the **esophagus**. On either side of the esophagus is a **salivary** (*sal*-ih-very) **gland**, which secretes juices that moisten the food as it is eaten (Fig. 25-4, page 289).

The food next enters the **crop**, where it may be stored for a time. Sometimes, when the grasshopper is disturbed or injured, it regurgitates food from the crop. From the crop the food passes into the region known as the **gizzard**, which is lined with thin plates of chitin-bearing teeth. Here the food is shredded. At the end of the gizzard are thin plates through which the partly digested food is strained into a much larger region, the **stomach**. On the outside of the stomach are six double pouches, the **gastric caeca** (*see-kuh*), which produce enzymes that pour into the stomach to complete digestion. Through the stomach walls, the digested food is absorbed by the blood stream. The remainder passes into the **intestine**, which is composed of the **colon** (*koh*-lon) and **rectum**, emptying through the **anus**.

The excretory system. Waste material from the cells is picked up by the blood. A series of tubes called the **Malpighian** (mal-*pig*-ee-un) **tubules** collect the wastes from the blood in the body cavity. They are then passed into the last part of the intestine and out through the anus.

The circulatory system. Blood in the grasshopper is in an *open system*. This means that the blood flows throughout the body cavity of the insect instead of

through tubes (arteries and veins). However, there is a definite circulation. Blood is forced out of the anterior end of the tubular, muscular **heart** through the **aorta**. It then flows from the aorta through its open anterior end and enters the body cavity near the head. As blood flows through the body toward the posterior end, it bathes all of the body organs. Blood is drawn into the heart from a cavity, or *sinus*, which surrounds it. Paired openings in the row of heart chambers admit blood for recirculation.

The respiratory system in the grasshopper. The **tracheae**, or air tubes, form an amazingly complex network inside the animal. Here and there the tracheae widen into larger **air sacs** (Fig. 25-5). Every tissue in the body is supplied with air which is used in respiration. Eight pairs of *spiracles* on the abdomen and two pairs on the thorax, each protected by hairlike structures, are the intake and outgo openings of the tracheae. The movement of the abdomen and wings is sufficient to pump air in and out of the tracheae. By diffusion, oxygen and carbon dioxide are exchanged in the tissues.

The grasshopper receives messages from the outside through its sense organs. The antennae, the most anterior appendages, are many-jointed and serve as the receptors of the senses of touch and smell. There are two kinds of eyes (Fig. 25-6). Three **simple eyes** are located respectively above the base of each antenna and in the groove between them. The large **compound eyes** project from a part of the front and sides of the head and are composed of hundreds of six-sided lenses. The shape, location, and number of lenses seem to adapt the insect for sight in several directions at one time, but the image formed is probably not very sharp.

Most insects are considered to be nearsighted, yet they may be able to distinguish colors. We know that night-flying moths seek white flowers, while flies and some other insects are attracted by red and blue.

The stimuli received through the sense organs are then relayed by nerves to certain parts of the body, such as a muscle. The muscle will contract on being thus stimulated, and action in the insects will occur. Nerve centers, called **ganglia**, act as switches for the message to go to the proper structures for coordinated action. The brain itself is an enlarged ganglion composed largely of **optic lobes**. The sight of your approaching hand is enough to cause the grasshopper to start moving away, and fast. This complicated activity is begun, controlled, and coordinated by the nervous system.

The reproductive system. In insects the sexes are separate. This means that sperm cells are produced in **testes**, found in the male. Egg cells are produced in **ovaries**, found in female animals. Biologists use symbols to refer to the separate sexes. ♀ denotes a female organism or part, and ♂ refers to the male. The male deposits the sperm cells in a special storage pouch, the **seminal receptacle**, of the female. The sperm remain here until the eggs are ready for fertilization.

The female grasshopper digs a hole in the ground with her *ovipositor*. Here she deposits her fertilized eggs which are protected by a gummy substance. About 100 or more eggs are laid in the fall and hatch in the next spring. When they hatch, the young grasshoppers are called *nymphs* (Fig. 25-1). They are small and wingless, but they look like the adult in many ways. However, the head is large in proportion to the body.

Like all arthropods, the nymphs grow by molting, usually about five times. Molting takes 30 to 40 minutes and during the process the insect is weak and sometimes dies. The old exoskeleton splits along the thorax and the nymph

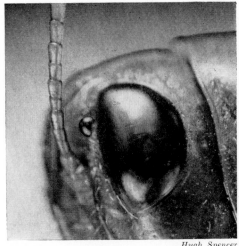

Hugh Spencer

Fig. 25-6.   The upper photograph is of the simple and compound eyes of the grasshopper, while the lower is a close-up of the compound eye.

Hugh Spencer

comes out head first. Then it grows rapidly and a new exoskeleton quickly forms.

Relatives of the grasshopper. It is easy to see that the meadow grasshopper and the katydid are related. The wings of the katydid look so much like leaves — even to the veining — that we cite this as a good case of *protective resemblance*. Other Orthoptera are the cricket, roach, walking stick, and praying mantis.

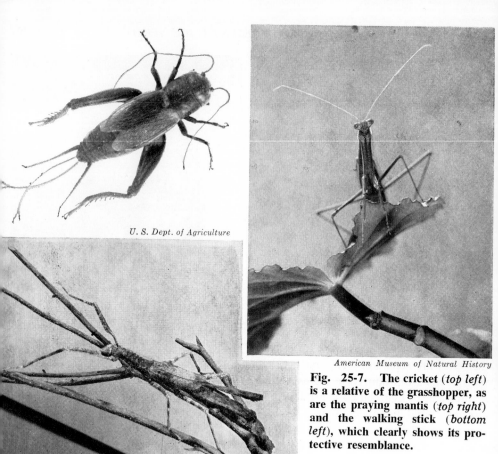

U. S. Dept. of Agriculture

American Museum of Natural History

Fig. 25-7. The cricket (*top left*) is a relative of the grasshopper, as are the praying mantis (*top right*) and the walking stick (*bottom left*), which clearly shows its protective resemblance.

American Museum of Natural History

The grasshopper and its relatives are mostly harmful to man. Swarms of grasshoppers (" locusts ") have plagued both the Old and New World throughout history. Every few years farmers in the Middle West have to fight these pests to save their crops.

The only useful relative of the grasshopper is the *praying mantis,* which eats other insects, many of them harmful. You can buy mantis egg cases at some seed stores. The eggs hatch in the spring and the adults remain in the garden where they eat other insects. Thus the mantis is extremely helpful, and is quite harmless despite its ferocious look.

In Conclusion

The grasshopper, an insect belonging to the order Orthoptera, shows the characteristics of all arthropods in having an exoskeleton of chitin, a segmented body, and jointed appendages. Other characteristics of its body structure include three body regions, three pairs of legs, two pairs of wings, one pair of antennae, and spiracles and tracheae. The grasshopper is a member of the largest class of arthropods, the insects.

The eight body systems of the grasshopper show what a high degree of specialization it has. The digestive, excretory, and respiratory systems are important groups of organs for the general functioning of the animal. Skeletal and muscular systems are involved in motion. Coordination and internal communication are taken care of by the circulatory and nervous systems. The reproductive system shows separation of the sexes. The life history of the grasshopper shows an incomplete type of metamorphosis.

We shall turn to other orders of insects to see what other variations this class of arthropods can show.

BIOLOGICALLY SPEAKING

adult	labium	palpus
air sacs	labrum	prothorax
colon	larva	pupa
compound eye	Malpighian tubules	salivary glands
complete metamorphosis	mesothorax	simple eye
coxa	metathorax	spiracles
egg	nymph	tarsus
femur	optic lobes	tibia
gastric caeca	Orthoptera	trochanter
incomplete metamorphosis	ovipositor	tympanum

QUESTIONS FOR REVIEW

1. What characteristics of the grasshopper make it similar to the crayfish?
2. List the characteristics of the grasshopper which relate it to other insects as a group.
3. Most animals have important organs located on the head. In what respects is the grasshopper an exception to this rule?
4. How do the grasshopper's legs illustrate adaptation?
5. What are the eight body systems of the grasshopper and the function of each?
6. What is the chief difference between the blood system of the grasshopper and that of man?
7. What is the chief difference between the respiratory system of the grasshopper and that of man?
8. (a) What kind of metamorphosis does the grasshopper undergo? (b) What happens during this metamorphosis?
9. What protection is given the eggs of the grasshopper during the winter?
10. Which relative of the grasshopper is considered to be a useful animal? Why?

APPLYING FACTS AND PRINCIPLES

1. What reasons can you give for the insects' being able to withstand unusual temperatures, pressures, and other environmental conditions?
2. Give reasons to support the statement, " Insects are the most successful creatures in the world."
3. What advantages are there to an insect in having the complete metamorphosis type of life cycle?

CHAPTER 26

Habits of Some Interesting Insects

INSECTS are all around us. They are so numerous and there are so many kinds that only very wintry weather could prevent an enthusiast from observing the ways of these six-footed creatures. A person who studies insects is an **entomologist** (en-toh-*mol*-uh-jist), and the professional entomologist is always in demand. His services are needed by medicine, agriculture, and industry. Even the ordinary citizen occasionally seeks his advice.

But the amateur can also find entomology a useful hobby as well as an enjoyable pastime. The ants, bees, and wasps, with their complex social orders, are fascinating. Even the true bugs and the hard-shelled insects called beetles are worth a fleeting glimpse. The kinds of eggs, where laid, and how protected, the adaptations of larvae for food-getting and concealment, the methods of pupating and emergence of the adults make a round of absorbing events. If you actually see all the stages in the final three- or four-day transition from the green-jeweled pupa to the adult of the monarch butterfly, you will be amazed at the miracle.

Common orders of insects. We cannot study all the insects, but we can take a look at a few of them. There are 22 different orders of insects. The table on page 307 lists the eight orders which are probably the most common in temperate regions, and gives characteristics and examples of each.

Insects can be found in your home, your school, outside in fields and ponds, on trees, under stones, and hiding on plants with almost perfect camouflage. The collector who looks only casually for insects will find quite a few. However, the observer who is willing to watch quietly and examine his surroundings will find a great many of these animals.

Making an insect collection can be fun — it is a way to get to know insects first hand. There is no better way to remember how many wings are on a bee than to examine a bee. If you should decide to make a collection, a net may be helpful in catching some of them. A covered jar, in which you have put a poison such as carbon tetrachloride (cleaning fluid), is a necessary part of the equipment. Pinning them after they are dead, and putting them in a box are the next steps. Then you are ready to classify them into orders. Let's examine some of the characteristics of these orders.

The order Lepidoptera. *Butterflies* and *moths* belong to the order *Lepidoptera* (leh-pih-*dop*-ter-uh), which means " scale-winged." Their brilliant colors are due to microscopic scales on their wings, which make a mosaic pattern. If you handle living moths and butterflies, be sure to hold them by the thorax and with only light pressure of the fingers. Just a light touch on the wings with your hands will remove some scales and injure the insect for flight.

Most people confuse butterflies and moths. If you look at the table on page 298, you will see that it is usually not difficult to distinguish between them.

Head of a butterfly or moth. Unlike the grasshopper, the head of a butterfly or moth is hairy, often even shaggy, because of the presence of scales. The eyes

294

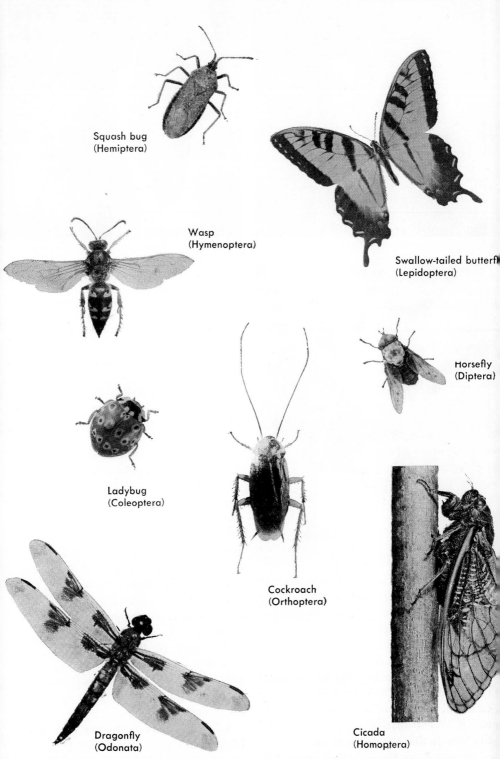

Squash bug
(Hemiptera)

Wasp
(Hymenoptera)

Swallow-tailed butterfly
(Lepidoptera)

Horsefly
(Diptera)

Ladybug
(Coleoptera)

Cockroach
(Orthoptera)

Dragonfly
(Odonata)

Cicada
(Homoptera)

Fig. 26-1. The common insects shown above are representative of eight of the insect orders.

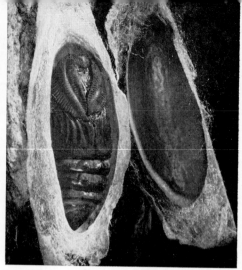

Fig. 26-2. The Cecropia moth is a familiar example of the order Lepidoptera. In the bottom left photograph, the caterpillar is starting to spin its cocoon. At the top left, the cocoon is shown securely attached to a twig; and at the top right, it has been opened to show the pupa inside.

are compound and large and rounded, and the neck is flexible. The mouth parts are different from those of the Orthoptera because they are adapted for sucking nectar from flowers. The maxillae are enormously lengthened and locked together to form the coiled feeding tube or **proboscis** (proh-*bos*-is). When extended, it may equal all the rest of the body in length, and is able to reach the nectar glands of the flowers that these insects visit.

In most cases the labium is reduced in size to two feathery palpi. This set of mouth parts represents structures which are *homologous* to those of the grasshopper, but they are adapted for different functions.

Thorax region of butterflies and moths. The legs of the Lepidoptera are small and weak, but have the same general structure as do all insects. Obviously the butterfly spends much of its time in the air and uses its legs only for clinging to some surface. The wings are large; the colored scales help the few veins in giving strength to the wing, and in some cases aid in protective coloration. The butterfly, though easily supported by its large wingspread, is not a swift flier.

Abdomen of the Lepidoptera. The abdomen resembles that of the grasshopper, but has fewer visible segments and, as in all insects, is the least specialized body region.

Life history of butterflies and moths. Most Lepidoptera deposit the eggs on or near the material which is to be the food of the young. Some pass the winter in

296

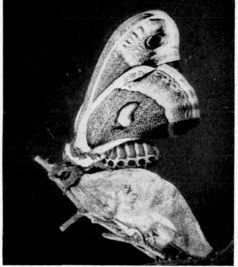

Fig. 26-3.   At the top left, the moth is seen emerging from its cocoon.   At the top right, the moth is seen pumping its wings; and finally, in the bottom right photograph, it is seen in its full adult splendor.   What is the stage between adult and caterpillar that is not shown?

this stage, but usually eggs are deposited in the spring and develop into caterpillars the following summer.

The egg does not hatch into a form anything like the adult.   Instead, it produces a wormlike *caterpillar,* or **larva,** with biting mouth parts.   But it has three pairs of legs and some extra pairs of fleshy legs at the end of the abdomen called **prolegs.** The caterpillar eats ravenously, grows big and fat, and molts several times.   It needs tremendous amounts of food to keep up this rapid growth, so it is during this stage that the insect does extensive damage.

When full grown, the caterpillar usually seeks a sheltered spot, hangs with its head down, and becomes very quiet. The body shortens and thickens, the exoskeleton splits down the back and is shed, and the animal now forms the resting stage or **pupa.**   The butterfly pupa rests in a hardened case, often brown in color, which is called a **chrysalis** (*krih*-suh-lis). The moth larva usually spins also a strong case of silk, the **cocoon** (kuh-*koon*).

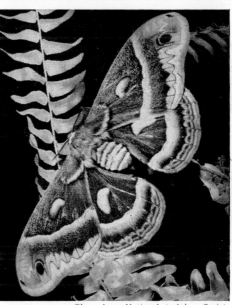

The pupal stage, in which the Lepidoptera usually pass the winter, is not actually a period of entire rest because at the end of the encasement, the insect emerges, totally changed, as the **adult** butterfly or moth.

While the function of the larva is simply to eat and grow, the adult eats only the nectar of flowers, and its lifework consists of producing or fertilizing the eggs for the next generation.   Since the life development of these insects consists of distinct stages, it is an example of

STAGES OF COMPLETE METAMORPHOSIS

EGG	{ Deposited near source of food { Period of increase in number
LARVA	{ Period of eating and growth (often harmful to man) { Worm, grub, caterpillar, or maggot stage
PUPA	{ Period of quiet; transformation { Usually passes winter in this stage { May have cocoon or chrysalis surrounding the pupa
ADULT	{ Reproductive stage

complete metamorphosis. Bees, beetles, and flies pass through a similar series of changes, as given in the above table.

Protective coloration. Color protection is evident among both adult insects and their larvae. Many are green like the grass and leaves among which they live and on which they feed. The green color is often due to chlorophyll in their food showing through their delicate tissues. Others are colored like dead leaves, flowers, or bark — whichever may be their usual background. The brown grasshopper resembles the ground on which it alights.

As we mentioned in Chapter 7, some insects resemble other objects, rather than just their background. This form of camouflage is called *protective resemblance* and is found in the walking stick, which looks very much like the small twigs among which it lives (Fig. 25-7, page 292). *Mimicry* is a form of protective resemblance in which the animal looks like another species, as the viceroy looks like the monarch (Fig. 7-9, page 75).

Economic importance of Lepidoptera. Many butterflies and moths visit flowers to obtain nectar, which they drink through their long tubelike proboscis. In doing so, they aid in cross-pollination.

The beautiful wings of many butterflies are used in jewelry, in trays, and in plastic lampshades and screens.

The greatest economic value of the Lepidoptera, however, is in the production of silk. The silkworm is the larva of a small moth which has been domesticated by man nearly 4,000 years.

Among the Lepidoptera are numerous forms which are notorious for the damage their larvae cause. The apple worm alone

COMPARISON OF BUTTERFLY AND MOTH

BUTTERFLY	MOTH
Flies during the day	Generally flies in the dark
Pupa in chrysalis	Pupa in cocoon
Wings vertical when at rest	Wings held horizontally
Antennae knobbed	Antennae feathery
Abdomen slender	Abdomen stout

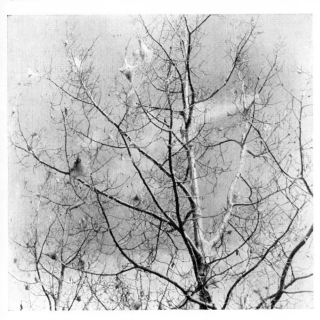

Fig. 26-4. The larval stage of a butterfly or moth can be destructive, as is evident from this photograph of a quaking aspen which has been defoliated by tent caterpillars.

U. S. Forest Service

can destroy over $12,000,000 worth of fruit annually. Millions of dollars are spent every year by the New England states in an apparently losing fight against the gypsy and brown-tail moths. Cabbage worms, tomato worms, and corn ear worms, are all Lepidoptera larvae which cause damage.

Migrations of Lepidoptera. When we think of migration, the birds and the locusts come to mind first. However, one of the strangest habits of some butterflies and moths is that they migrate. It is startling to realize that these slow flitting creatures are capable of traveling thousands of miles across land and water.

The monarch, also called the milkweed butterfly, is one of the strongest fliers of the Lepidoptera. In late summer these butterflies gather by the thousands in northern Canada and begin a long flight southward. Some of them travel to the Gulf states to spend the winter, but their habits there have not been studied. Others travel a southern route along the Pacific Coast. At some time between the middle of October and the first of No-

vember, a flight of tens of thousands arrive on the Monterey Peninsula in the small town of Pacific Grove, California. Here they seek shelter in a specific grove of pines. These butterflies hang by their legs from the branches and needles in such large numbers that the trees appear to be solid brown (Fig. 26-5). These

Fig. 26-5. These monarch butterflies spend the winter in a pine grove in California after migrating from Canada.

Shropshire Camera Exchan

monarchs stay there in a state of semihibernation, until the winter is over. On warm sunny days throughout the fall and winter, many will be seen flying about the gardens gathering nectar.

In March, the monarchs fly out over Monterey Bay to begin their northward flight. As they fly north, they lay eggs on milkweed plants. It is very unlikely that any of the travelers ever reach their northern home, as many die after the eggs are laid. However, after the eggs hatch, the larvae pupate, the young butterflies emerge, and the trip northward is continued. These new butterflies also lay eggs on milkweed as they progress.

By late summer, the monarchs begin amassing for their southward journey to the same locality and the same trees where their ancestors of two generations past spent the winter. Although we attribute the monarch's behavior to instinct, the factors causing the migrations and the ability of these butterflies to find their way is not well understood.

Social insects. It is fascinating to watch the activities around a beehive or an ant hill. We call these animals *social insects* because various members of the colony perform special tasks. They are members of the order **Hymenoptera** (hy-men-*op*-ter-uh), which means "membrane-winged," and which also includes bees, wasps, and related insects. One group in the colony gets food, another reproduces, and still another group protects the colony from enemies. The tasks differ, of course, depending on the kind of insect.

Instinct alone accounts for the high degree of division of labor in the beehive, the wasp nest, and the colony of ants. Contrary to common opinion, these insects probably are no more intelligent than any other insect forms. Yet the marvelous efficiency with which they carry on their routine tasks could well be imagined to illustrate high intelligence.

The order Hymenoptera includes not only those forms which live in colonies and show a high degree of division of labor, but numerous solitary forms as well. Members of this order are characterized by two pairs of membranous wings (if wings are present), biting or sucking mouth parts, complete metamorphosis, and a definite constriction between the thorax and the abdomen.

The structure of the body of the honeybee. A typical member of this order is

Fig. 26-6. The worker bee (*left*), the queen (*middle*), and the drone (*right*) each play a special role in the hive. Their social habits illustrate a communal way of life.

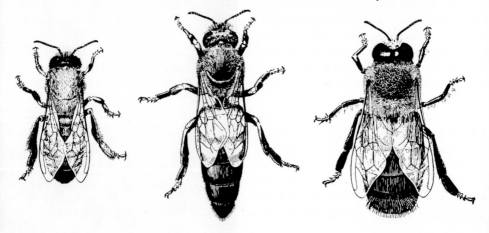

the **honeybee,** which we shall study in some detail as a remarkable example of adaptations of structure and function. The body regions are distinct, the head is attached to the thorax by a flexible neck, and the thorax to the abdomen by a slender waist. Each region is highly developed.

The sensitive elbowed antennae, the enormous compound eyes, and three simple eyes can easily be seen. But the mouth parts are complicated and are a set of tools by themselves. The labrum is small, and the labium is developed into an efficient lapping tongue. The mouth parts are used in making the cells of honeycomb from beeswax as well as collecting nectar from flowers.

The thorax is large, strong, and provided with powerful muscles which operate the legs and wings.

Bees are swift and enduring fliers. Their wings, small but well proportioned, operate at high speed, producing the familiar hum. The *anterior* wings are much the larger, and the *posterior* wings may be attached to them by tiny hooks for aid in flying.

The abdomen consists of six segments, with an ovipositor or sting at the posterior end. Only in the queen is the ovipositor developed as a true egg-laying organ. The worker bees, which are undeveloped females, produce no eggs and have the ovipositor modified into the well-known "sting." This is a complicated organ consisting of two barbed darts operated by strong muscles and enclosed in a sheath. The darts are connected with a gland which secretes the poison and makes a bee sting so painful. On the four last abdominal segments of the workers are glands which secrete the wax used in comb-making.

Life history of the honeybee. The life history of the honeybee is a fine example of communal life and mutual help. Each

member of the colony works for the good of all. This habit has resulted in great success as a whole, as well as remarkable development for each individual. There are three forms of bees in any colony: (1) the *queen;* (2) the *drones;* and (3) the *workers* (Fig. 26-6).

The queen is nearly twice as large as a worker. The queen has a long pointed abdomen, and her particular function is the production of eggs to continue the colony. In one day she may produce as many as 3,000 eggs — the equivalent of twice her own weight. The development of a queen instead of a worker is due to special treatment of a fertile egg. The workers enlarge the wax cell in which the egg is to grow, and when the grublike larva hatches, feed it with extra portions of food called " royal jelly." After being thus fed for five days, the larva spins a silken cocoon, changes to a pupa, and is sealed into her large waxen chamber by the workers. When the mature queen emerges from her cell, she seeks out other queen larvae in the colony and kills them, or if she finds another adult queen, they fight until one is killed. She never uses her sting except against another queen.

If the workers prevent her from destroying the other queens, she leaves the hive, taking with her from 2,000 to 20,000 bees to seek a new home. By " swarming " in this manner, new colonies are formed and overcrowding is prevented.

After a few days the queen takes a wedding flight up into the air where she mates with a drone, or male bee, receiving several million sperm cells. Then she returns to the hive and begins her lifework of laying eggs. This is no small task as one queen may produce as many as one million eggs per year and often lives from five to ten years. Although we call her a queen, she is in no sense the ruler of the hive but rather its common mother.

The drones. The *drones*, while larger than the workers, are smaller than the queen and have a thick, broad body, enormous eyes, and very powerful wings. They develop from unfertilized eggs. Their tongues are not long enough to get nectar, so they have to be fed by the workers. During the summer a few hundred drones are tolerated in the colony, because one of them must function as a mate for the new queen. The rest are of no use in the hive. This easy life has its troubles, however. With the coming of the autumn, when honey runs low, the workers will no longer support the drones, and sting them to death. Their bodies may often be found around the hives in the early autumn.

The worker bees. The *workers* are by far the most numerous inhabitants of the hive. They are undeveloped females, smaller than drones, and with the ovipositor modified into the sting. Workers may number from 10,000 to 100,000 in a hive. With the exception of reproduction, all the varied industries and products of the hive are their business. They perform, at different times, many different kinds of work, as well as provide the three hive products — *wax, honey,* and *propolis* (*prop*-oh-lis), a type of bee glue used to cover holes in the hive. In summer they literally work themselves to death in three or four weeks, but bees hatched in the fall may live six months.

One recent discovery has been that bees communicate with each other by a complicated set of dances. By this novel method they inform the workers in the hive as to the kind, the distance, the direction, and the amount of nectar to be found. The bees are good navigators and find their way to the source of nectar and back to the hive by the angle of the sun's rays.

Products of the beehive. *Wax* is a secretion from the abdominal segments of workers. It develops after they have gorged themselves with honey, and have then suspended themselves by their feet in a sort of curtain. As the wax is produced, it is removed by other workers, chewed to make it soft, and then carried to still another group who build it into a comb.

The *comb* is a wonderful structure, composed of six-sided cells in two layers. It is arranged so as to leave no waste space, and to afford the greatest storage capacity using the least material. Not only is it used for storage of honey and "beebread" (a food substance made from pollen and saliva), but also for the rearing of young bees. The eggs are put, one in a cell, by the queen, making what is called a **brood comb.**

Honey is made from the nectar of flowers that is taken into the crop of the bee. Here the sugars are changed to a more easily digested form and are then emptied into the comb cells. There the honey is left to ripen and thicken by evaporation before being sealed.

The removal of honey by man does not harm the bees if enough is left for their winter use. About 30 pounds are enough to feed an average colony of 40,000 bees for an ordinary winter.

Propolis is another product of the hive. It is a brown substance gathered from the sticky leaf buds of some plants. Propolis is used to make the interior of the hive smooth, to help attach the comb, to close up holes and cracks, and even to varnish the comb if it is left unused for a time.

Industries of the colony. Not only do the workers prepare the wax, honey, and propolis as needed, but some attend and feed the queen or drones. Some act as nurses to the hungry larvae, feeding them with partly digested food from their own stomachs. Other bees clean the hive of dead bees or foreign matter,

Philip Gendrea

Fig. 26-7. This exposed split log shows the interior of a nest of carpenter ants, which belong to the order Hymenoptera and, like the bees, are social insects. Note the runways cut by the workers, and several cocoons containing the pupating larvae.

while still others fan with their wings to ventilate the hive. All the time thousands of workers are bringing in nectar, pollen, and propolis as needed for the use of the colony.

Such a *communal,* or colony, life illustrates the highest development of division of labor found among any animals lower than man. It occurs among some ants and wasps as well as bees, though nowhere is it carried to a higher point than in the honeybee.

Other Hymenoptera. Like the bees, ants are social insects and the colony requires a queen. Unlike the bees, most ants can't sting, but they bite with jaws more powerful in proportion to their size than those of any other insects. It is an interesting and generally unknown fact that during the early autumn males and females develop which have wings

and so are able to fly out to start new colonies.

Wasps and ichneumon flies. Wasps, both solitary and social, and hornets, are interesting, not only because of personal experiences we may have had with their stings, but because some of them are probably the original papermakers of the world. Their nests are made from a sort of pulp obtained from strips of wood chewed vigorously and mixed with secretions from the mouth.

It is quite probable that no members of the Hymenoptera are more valuable to us than the tiny ichneumon flies which manage to lay their eggs under the skin of living caterpillars and thus kill them.

The insect order Odonata. The word *Odonata* (oh-doh-*nay*-tuh) comes from a Greek word meaning " tooth." It is probable that the larval stage of these insects is responsible for their name. The larval form lives in streams where it preys on the larvae of many other insects. It catches them by rapidly extending its elongated labium. To some, perhaps this lower lip resembled a big tooth that shot out to catch prey. The wings of the Odonata are membranous and do not overlap. At rest they are held at right angles to the body. The abdomen is long, but there is no stalk connecting it to the thorax. These insects, exemplified by the dragonfly and damsel fly, are very beneficial. Not only are they predators when in the larval stage, but even as adults they fly over water, catching mosquitoes, gnats, and other small insects.

The order Coleoptera. About 250,000 species of beetles have been recorded, and most of them can be recognized as beetles by anyone because of their hard forewings that fit closely over the body and that resemble a shell. They all have strong jaws and complete metamorphosis, and belong to the order **Coleoptera** (koh-lee-*op*-ter-uh), which means " sheath-winged."

Wood-boring beetles cause extensive losses; buffalo " bugs " are destructive to carpets and furs; potato beetles ravage gardens; weevils damage grain and cotton. Texas alone has paid more than $150,000,000 in the attempt to control the boll weevil. The Japanese beetle, first discovered in this country in New Jersey in 1916, has already become a great menace to fruit trees and other crops. On the other hand, carrion beetles are scavengers, ladybugs eat scale insects and thus aid the citrus fruit industry, and Calosoma beetles have been introduced into New England and elsewhere to help control the gypsy moth.

Hemiptera include many pests. The " half-winged " insects have sucking mouth parts and incomplete metamorphosis. The edges of their wings overlap, and only half of the wing is thickened. One or two forms are wingless. The insects belonging to **Hemiptera** (heh-*mip*-ter-uh) are the only insects constituting the *true bugs.* Among them are many of our worst pests, such as the chinch bug, bedbug, squash bug, and stinkbug. Others, less harmful to us, include aquatic insects like water striders, back swimmers, and water boatmen.

In the Homoptera we find sucking insects. The word *homoptera* (hoh-*mop*-ter-uh) means " similar wings," though some of the members of the order **Homoptera** are wingless. When wings are present, they are held over the body in an inverted V, like the roof of a house. All have sucking mouth parts and incomplete metamorphosis. Plant lice, scale insects, mealy bugs, leaf hoppers, and others take a huge toll of our wild and cultivated plants. We are indebted, however, to the lac insect, which alone of the Homoptera is of economic benefit. We get *shellac* from it, which is used throughout the world as a base for lacquer, wood finishes, and in the manufacture of phonograph records.

The cicada (sih-*kay*-duh) is a common representative which lives underground from two years in the case of one species to 17 years in the case of another species. They then tunnel to the surface and spend a week or two as adults. Their high-pitched and strident notes, coming from the treetops, are familiar on hot summer evenings.

The Diptera are the two-winged insects. The **Diptera** (*dip*-ter-uh) have mouth parts which are fitted for piercing, rasping, and sucking. Their metamorphosis is complete.

One of our most notorious enemies in the insect world is the housefly. Because of the fact that it breeds in filth, people are often infected with typhoid, dysentery, and other filth-borne diseases.

U. S. Dept. of Agriculture

Fig. 26-8. The housefly carries disease-causing organisms on the many hairs covering its body. What characteristic places the housefly in the order Diptera?

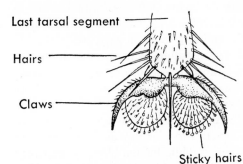

Last tarsal segment

Hairs

Claws

Sticky hairs

Fig. 26-9. This enlarged drawing of the foot of the housefly shows the projections and sticky hairs which adapt the animal to carrying filth. Why is the housefly considered one of our most notorious enemies?

Other Diptera include the mosquitoes, which are known for the annoying habits as well as their disease-carrying characteristics. The tsetse fly of Africa, responsible for the transmission of the protozoan-caused disease, sleeping sickness, also belongs in this order.

The housefly. The common *housefly* (*typhoid fly*) has large eyes, short, fleshy antennae, and a club-shaped sucking tube. It never bites, but the related stable fly or horsefly bites cattle and man. Its wings are well developed and operate at high speed because of the powerful muscles of the thorax. The six legs are also well developed, and the feet have claws and sticky hairs which aid in clinging (Fig. 26-9). Unless these hair tips are free from dust, they do not stick well and the fly cannot walk easily on smooth surfaces. You have probably noticed the care with which it cleans its feet by constantly rubbing them against each other.

About 200 *eggs* are deposited in horse manure or in similar matter by the female. They hatch in one day into the larval form called **maggots,** and in this stage do some good as scavengers. After eating and growing for five or six days, the larvae pass into the pupal condition, inside the last larval skin, which thus takes the place of a cocoon. From this stage, adults emerge in about a week. The whole development from egg to adult takes about two weeks. Breeding begins early in spring and continues until the cold weather starts. Flies multiply at a tremendous rate. If reproduction were unchecked and all offspring survived (which fortunately is not the case), then

REPRODUCTION OF FLIES

1st generation (eggs that hatch from first female)	200	(100 females)
2nd " (100 females x 200 eggs each)	20,000	(10,000 females)
3rd " (10,000 x 200)	2,000,000	
4th "	200,000,000	
5th "	20,000,000,000	
6th "	2,000,000,000,000	
	2,020,202,020,200	in 12 weeks

one fly laying 200 eggs would result in 2,020,202,020,200 flies in 12 weeks, as shown in the table on page 305.

The mosquito. In the **mosquito,** the mouth parts — labrum, tongue, mandibles, and maxillae — are reduced to sharp lancelike bristles. They are enclosed in the labium as a sheath, and are adapted for piercing and sucking. In order to dilute human blood so that they can withdraw it and prevent it from clotting in the proboscis, they inject a little saliva. This causes the usual irritation and swelling we call a *mosquito bite.*

The female usually lays her eggs in water. Ponds, rain barrels, and even tin cans furnish ideal breeding places. The eggs are deposited as single eggs or in tiny rafts, consisting of many eggs covered with a waterproof coating. When they hatch, the larvae emerge downward into the water, and become the familiar **wigglers.** The mosquito larva breathes air, which it obtains through a tube projecting from the posterior of its abdomen. Often it can be seen with this tube at the surface and the body hanging head downward in the water (Fig. 26-10).

The pupa stage is also passed in the water and differs from most insect pupae in that it is active like the larva. It differs from the larva in having a large head provided with two air tubes for breathing. The adult emerges from the pupa, whose shed skin acts as a raft. At this critical time the mosquito must not fall overboard or get its wings wet before they are expanded, or it will die. There are exceptions to the above description, but it pertains to most mosquitoes.

Our most common northern mosquito, *Culex* (*kyoo*-lex), occasionally carries encephalitis, or sleeping sickness. *Anopheles* carries the protozoan *Plasmo-*

Fig. 26-10. These larvae of the *Culex* mosquito obtain oxygen by means of a breathing tube which penetrates the surface of the water.

Philip Gendreau

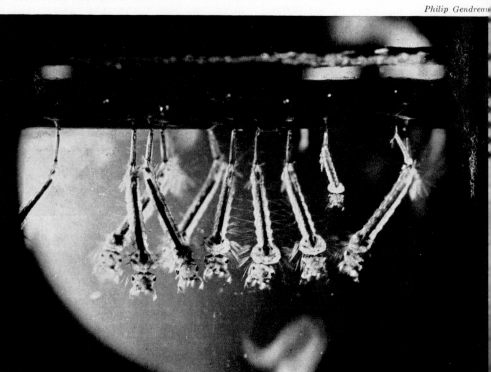

SUMMARY OF CHARACTERISTICS OF INSECT ORDERS

ORDER	META-MOR-PHOSIS	MOUTH PARTS IN ADULT	ECONOMIC IMPORTANCE OF SOME	EXAMPLES
ORTHOPTERA (or-*thop*-ter-uh) ("straight-winged")	Incomplete	Chewing	Damage to crops Pests	Grasshoppers, crickets, katydids, locusts, cockroaches
LEPIDOPTERA (leh-pih-*dop*-ter-uh) ("scale-winged")	Complete	Siphoning	Damage crops Damage foods and grains Damage clothing	Butterflies, moths
HYMENOPTERA (hy-men-*op*-ter-uh) ("membrane-winged")	Complete	Biting or sucking	Pollinate flowers Pests Parasitize other pests Make honey	Bees, wasps, ants
ODONATA (oh-doh-*nay*-tuh) ("toothed")	Incomplete	Biting	Destroy harmful insects	Dragonflies, damsel flies
COLEOPTERA (koh-lee-*op*-ter-uh) ("sheath-winged")	Complete	Sucking or chewing	Destroy crops Pests Prey on other insects	Weevils, ladybirds, ground beetles
HEMIPTERA (heh-*mip*-ter-uh) ("half-winged")	Incomplete	Sucking	Damage plants Pests Disease	Squash bugs, all true bugs
HOMOPTERA (hoh-*mop*-ter-uh) ("like-winged")	Incomplete	Sucking	Damage crops and gardens	Aphids, mealy bugs, cicada, scale insects
DIPTERA (*dip*-ter-uh) ("two-winged")	Complete	Sucking or chewing	Carry disease Pests	Flies, mosquitoes

dium, which causes malaria (Fig. 20-11). *Culex* may be distinguished from *Anopheles* by the fact that the latter stands almost on its head when at rest, while *Culex* holds its body more nearly horizontal. *Aëdes* (ay-*ee*-deez), the mosquito that carries the virus of yellow fever, is a tropical species and does not usually invade our temperate regions.

The economic importance of insects. Probably only a minority of insects are distinctly detrimental to man. Yet these obnoxious forms are so prominent and well known that popular opinion is apt to condemn all insects. Coping with animals so numerous and active as insects calls for accurate knowledge of their habits and life histories.

Their harmful activities are to:

1. Destroy grain, vegetables, and fruit (numerous species).

2. Injure shade trees (tussock, gypsy, and leopard moths).

3. Carry disease germs to animals and man (fleas, lice, flies, mosquitoes).

4. Act as agents in the spread of plant diseases (hoppers and aphids).

5. Destroy buidings and wood (beetles, ants, termites).

6. Annoy and injure by bites and stings (wasps, mosquitoes, gnats).

7. Affect food (beetles, cockroaches).

8. Destroy clothing and fabrics (clothes moths, carpet beetles).

9. Act as parasites on domestic animals and man (botflies, fleas, lice).

On the other hand, we owe to insects useful processes and products such as:

1. Pollinating of flowers (bees, butterflies, moths, certain types of flies).

2. Furnishing of silk (silk moth cocoon).

3. Furnishing of honey and wax (bees).

4. Furnishing of shellac (lac insect).

5. Supplying dye (cochineal insect).

6. Furnishing of material for ink (gall insects).

7. Acting as scavengers (maggots, beetles).

8. Killing of injurious insects (ladybugs, ichneumon flies).

In Conclusion

Eight orders include most of the insects you know best. The characteristics which group the class Insecta into orders are: type of metamorphosis, type of wings, and type of mouth parts.

The order Hymenoptera includes bees, ants, and wasps, which are remarkable for the highly specialized societies in which they live. Three kinds of individuals — workers, queens, and drones — divide the labors of the beehive. Most of the duties fall to the workers. The high degree of specialization of activities in the colony of social insects is attributed to instinct rather than to intelligence.

In the next chapter we shall see how we can apply our knowledge of the life cycles and food habits of insect pests, crop destroyers, and the carriers of disease in order to control them.

BIOLOGICALLY SPEAKING

brood comb
chrysalis
cocoon
Coleoptera
comb
Diptera
drone
entomologist

Hemiptera
Homoptera
honey
Hymenoptera
Lepidoptera
maggots
Odonata
proboscis

prolegs
propolis
queen
social insects
wax
wigglers
worker

QUESTIONS FOR REVIEW

1. What are some of the places where insects can be found?
2. Why are the mouth parts of the butterfly considered homologous to the mouth of the grasshopper?
3. Describe the four stages in the complete metamorphosis of the butterflies and moths.
4. How are mimicry and protective coloration useful to insects?
5. In what stage may the Lepidoptera be harmful?

6. Many of the Hymenoptera may be considered well disciplined. Why is this trait often confused with intelligence?

7. Do bees communicate with each other in the hive? Explain.

8. (a) What are the different types of bees? (b) Describe the functions of each in the hive.

9. Give the life history of the housefly.

10. In trying to eliminate mosquitoes, why is prevention better than cure?

APPLYING FACTS AND PRINCIPLES

1. Suggest a plan for checking on bee habits in order to discover how they communicate with each other.

2. Biologists state that the army ant of the tropics is entirely blind. Name some other animals which lead successful lives in spite of the fact they are missing one or more of the senses of higher animals.

3. (a) Can a little fly grow to be a large fly? (b) Why?

4. What is really meant by an " order " of insects?

5. The bee's sting is a modified part of the reproductive system. To what part of the grasshopper would you say that it is homologous?

6. How do you think an insect can find its way with only the sun's rays to guide it?

7. Which stage in the development of the housefly is easiest to control? Why?

CHAPTER 27

The Control of Insect Pests

BIOLOGISTS have established an international rogue's gallery for the chief criminals among the insects. Methods of control have been discovered as a result of many hours of research in the laboratories of colleges and universities, the Department of Agriculture, and state agricultural institutes. Through these and other important agencies, the war against insects will continue. In fact, this has become a major activity, as it has been estimated that insects cause over 750 million dollars worth of damage each year to plants alone in this country. As new pests make their appearance from abroad, it is necessary to develop measures to stop their destructive activities.

It remains for us as citizens to take full advantage of the weapons now available and to take an active part in the war against our numerous insect pests.

Fig. 27-1.   The louse, a small, wingless insect, is parasitic on warm-blooded animals.

Why are insects apt to become dangerous pests?   While most other forms of life have struggled to maintain their numbers with the spread of human civilization, insects have increased rapidly and have become a dominant form of animal life.   There are three good reasons for this dominance:

1. *Small size* is a distinct advantage to the insect.   Insects escape attention until the damage they have done has become noticeable.   Shelter is no problem as hiding places need be no larger than a crack in the bark of a tree, the lower side of a leaf, or a tiny hole in the ground.   Small size removes these organisms from the danger of starvation — a frequent problem faced by larger animals.   Small amounts of food will maintain an insect and, if food becomes scarce in one locality, the insect can easily travel to another.

2. *Adaptability* gives the insect another advantage over most other forms of life.   Many organisms are so definite as to their requirements that they cannot leave a specific environment, which is not so with the insects.   They range far and wide over the land and many seem equally at home in a great variety of conditions.   Temperature changes, moisture variations, and other variable factors of environment seem to have little effect on most of them.

3. *Rapid rate of reproduction* is still another advantage.   A single individual may lay from 100 to several thousand eggs, although not all of them will hatch.   Thus the population increases to almost

INSECTS AS VECTORS OF DISEASE

INSECT	METHOD OF TRANSMISSION	DISEASE
MOSQUITOES	Female *Anopheles* transmits a protozoan	Malaria
	Aëdes transmits an organism, probably a virus	Yellow fever
	Several species transmit roundworms	Filariasis
FLIES	Housefly transmits bacteria; contaminates food and water	Typhoid fever
	Tsetse fly transmits protozoan	African sleeping sickness
LICE	The human louse transmits Rickettsiae	Typhus fever
FLEAS	Many species of fleas transmit bacteria to man, rats, and ground squirrels	Bubonic plague ("Black Death")
BUGS	The kissing bugs (Hemiptera) transmit trypanosomes to humans	Chagas disease

staggering figures during a single season, as we saw in the case of the housefly on page 305.

Insects are often related to disease. World War II brought problems in the control of insect-borne diseases. Epidemics of deadly typhus fever broke out in Italy near the close of the war, causing high mortality among the troops and the civilian population. Medical science has proved definitely that this disease is carried by the human body louse. Therefore, the control of typhus depended on destruction of the carriers. Utilizing the powerful insecticide, DDT, the United States Army Medical Corps began the systematic " delousing " of all the communities in which typhus had appeared, and the epidemic was stopped. Insects such as the body louse that carry disease and are able to transmit disease are called *insect vectors* (see table on page 310).

Although bedbugs are not directly associated with any particular disease, they may carry certain infections which invade the human blood stream. A few other diseases, especially one known as *relapsing fever,* have been traced to this insect pest. The best way to rid a house of bedbugs is to enforce cleanliness in all daily activities. A spray containing DDT has been found to be effective against them.

Of course, the role of flies and the several species of mosquitoes in the spreading of disease remains the most pressing problem confronting us in insect control.

We have four good weapons against the insect world. The war against insects is fought with four principal methods as weapons used in the attack. The struggle against them is effective only when all four of these methods are employed: (1) *quarantine;* (2) *conservation of natural enemies of insects;* (3) *environmental control;* and (4) *chemical control.*

Quarantine as a control measure. Colonists and importers have brought unknowingly at least 75 species of our harmful insects into the country in the form of eggs or larvae concealed on plants or in fresh fruits. The Bureau of Entomology and Plant Quarantine operates under the U. S. Department of Agriculture. It has inspectors in every port of entry in the country. Their duty is to confiscate and destroy any plants or fruits coming into the country that are suspected of carrying harmful insects or fungus pests.

The Bureau is always alert to discover local areas where insect pests exist inside

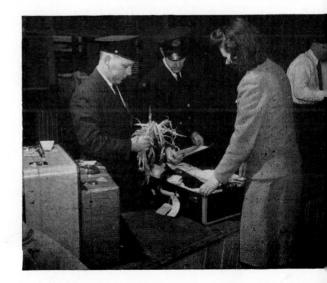

Fig. 27-2. Plant quarantine inspectors carefully examine all materials arriving from foreign countries for signs of insects and disease.

U. S. Dept. of Agriculture

Fig. 27-3. The boll weevil is about a quarter of an inch long. It infests the cotton plant and does serious damage throughout the Cotton Belt.

struggling today with the European corn borer, the Mexican bean beetle, the Japanese beetle, the Oriental peach moth, the gypsy moth, the cotton boll weevil, and many other foreign insect pests.

The conservation of natural enemies. Perhaps you have wondered how, if Japanese beetles are so terribly destructive, the Japanese are able to raise any plants at all. The answer concerns **natural enemies** of insects. Insects were present in America before our ancestors arrived from other lands. Yet, even without any control measures, these insects were held in check by natural enemies. The fact that our worst pests are imported species is explained also in terms of natural enemies. Introduced insects are free from those animals which held them in check in their native land. Consequently, they have multiplied here at a tremendous rate. Attempts have been made to import the natural enemies. Frequently, however, they also become pests, thus creating a still greater problem. This situation should impress on us how ex-

our own country in order that unaffected areas may be kept free. Many state governments have special officials to help prevent widespread insect destruction. All roads and transportation lines leading out of an infected area are watched in the same way as are ports of entry.

If **quarantines** had been in operation earlier in our history, we might not be

Fig. 27-4. Here a member of a sanitation squad is shown spraying oil on pools in a swampy region as a method of mosquito control. From what you know about mosquito larvae, why is this method effective?

tremely important it is to preserve the balance of nature.

Birds are the most important natural enemies of insects. Much of our success in combating insects depends on conservation of our bird life. We still have not learned this lesson completely, for we needlessly destroy necessary nesting places and feeding grounds for our most important allies in the war on insects.

Snakes, frogs, spiders, and toads are other valuable natural enemies of the insect world. But our attitude toward these creatures is far from enlightened. How many of you have felt that you have rendered a valuable service by killing a harmless garter snake which lives largely on small rodents and insects?

Nature controls insect population by means of environment. Temperature changes and varying amounts of moisture are good examples of nature's controls. In some cases, man can control insects by changing their *environment*. For instance, we can control certain insects by rotating crops in one area. This method is good for such localized pests as beetle grubs and others, but it is ineffective against those insects which migrate.

Another way is to drain those places where they breed. Ditches, ponds, and various shallow bodies of water must be drained regularly so as to make it impossible for certain insects to complete their life cycle. This is especially true in the case of the mosquito.

Still another effective method of environmental control is to correct faulty methods of sewage disposal. Many insects breed in sewage. And if modern disposal is practiced, the breeding places are destroyed.

Equally important is proper garbage disposal. Again, some insects breed in this type of filth, and the best way to prevent such breeding is to burn or treat it to be sure that none of it is dumped in places where insects can get at it. We should not forget man's mechanical methods of insect control, however. The fly swatter, traps, fly paper, and electric screens are still common ways of insect destruction.

Chemical control. Where other methods fail, man resorts to chemistry to get rid of insect pests. Although **chemical control** is expensive, it is the most effective in the majority of cases. Chemicals for use in insect control may be divided into four groups: (1) *stomach poisons;* (2) *contact insecticides;* (3) *fumigants;* and (4) *repellents.* The first three are called **insecticides**, which means, literally, "insect-killers." You can see by the names of the insecticides that the most efficient use for killing a certain pest will depend upon the feeding habits of that insect.

Fig. 27-5.   This elm tree is dying of Dutch elm disease, which is a fungus infection spread from one elm tree to another by a beetle.

Fig. 27-6. Elaborate rigs such as the one shown above are used in orchards to spray insecticides and fungicides on all the trees.

Stomach poisons are used against chewing insects such as beetles, grasshoppers, and various caterpillars. These insects eat the leaves of the plants they attack. If the leaves are coated with a poison, the insects usually die as a result. The stomach poisons may be sprayed on plants in a liquid form, which causes a fine film to be deposited on the leaves and stems, or they may be dusted as a fine powder.

Some insects, such as the true bugs, aphids, lice, and scale insects, get their food by sucking plant juices. A thin coat of a stomach poison doesn't bother them because they push their beaks through the poison, and in doing so do not take it into their stomachs. **Contact poisons,** therefore, are used against these sucking insects. These insecticides kill as they come in contact with the insect's body. Your state's agricultural experiment sta-

tion will gladly give you directions for making and using these poisons. They are either sprayed or dusted on plants where the insects will come into contact with them, or they are sprayed on the insects themselves. Many of these sprays act as respiratory poisons by clogging or poisoning the tracheae of insects, thus causing them to suffocate. Oil sprays are well known for this ability.

The third type of chemical control employs *gases* like carbon disulfide or the very poisonous hydrocyanic acid. Peach borers, the pink bollworm, and the common clothes moth may be controlled by using such **fumigants.** But they are effective only in a confined area and should be used only by someone who is an expert in handling them.

Repellents actually do not kill adult insects, although they may injure the larvae. They are either sprayed or dusted or merely allowed to evaporate in closed areas like closets. Camphor and creosote are two of the oldest repellents. The more modern types include *paradichlorobenzene* (pair-uh-dy-klor-oh-*ben*-zeen) and *naphthalene* (*naf*-thuh-leen). Certain insects, like the clothes moth, will

Fig. 27-7. In what stage of its life cycle does the clothes moth damage woolens?

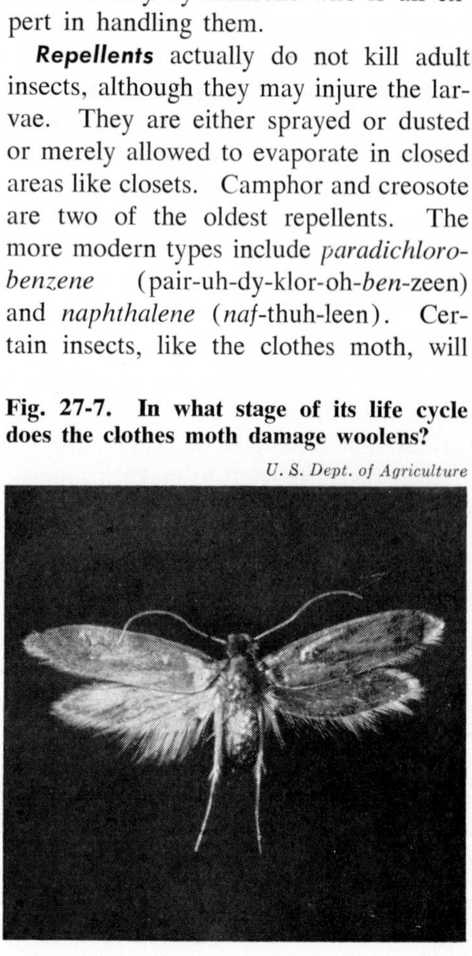

not lay their eggs where these chemicals are present.

The newer synthetic chemical insecticides. The new field of synthetic insecticides is best represented by DDT (which is short for *dichloro-diphenyltrichloroethane*). It is not a recent discovery, although we have only used it during the past ten or twelve years. It was first used effectively in World War II to control body lice and mosquitoes. Now we use it for fly and mosquito control as well as for general garden and farm insect control.

DDT is available in the form of powders, sprays, and convenient "bombs." It is extremely potent against many kinds of insects, which it kills because of its effect on the nervous system. The chitin in the skeleton seems to attract and hold the DDT. Roaches, mosquitoes, and bedbugs succumb quickly in air containing DDT mist. It is effective in the dairy barn to control annoying flies. Important agricultural uses of DDT include spraying of orchards and garden crops. Unfortunately, DDT is as effective against bees as it is other insects. Hence, care must be used in its application to avoid the destruction of valuable insects and birds.

DDT is a poisonous chemical. It is almost insoluble in water and so is usually available either in the form of a powder or as an oil-solvent spray. The powder can be absorbed through the skin as can the spray. Persons using it must use the greatest care and must see that none gets on any part of the body. Children and pets should never be allowed where it is being used.

Several new insecticides have recently appeared, but no one insecticide is perfect. Man still must know his old enemy, the insect, thoroughly before he can choose a successful weapon for its control. The war against the insects is a never-ending and expensive struggle.

In Conclusion

Insects, because of their small size, adaptability, and rapid rate of reproduction are among man's worst pests. Certain forms may suddenly appear in epidemic proportions, causing serious damage to shade trees, fruit trees, and crops. Perhaps the most annoying of all insects are those which invade our homes.

Several control measures are employed in the fight against insect pests. In order to use the most effective measure, however, the life history and habit of each pest must be well known. Quarantines, conservation of natural enemies of insects, environmental control, and chemical control are all methods that are used to control insects. The most rapid results are obtained by using various types of chemical poisons.

Our next unit will discuss the familiar animals with backbones (the vertebrates), and perhaps some that are not quite so familiar. As you read about the various vertebrates, compare them with the invertebrates which you have just studied.

BIOLOGICALLY SPEAKING

chemical control
contact poison
environmental control
fumigant

insect vector
insecticide
natural enemies

quarantine
repellent
stomach poison

QUESTIONS FOR REVIEW

1. Why is a knowledge of the life history of insects necessary in order to cope with them?
2. Why are insects likely to become dangerous pests?
3. In what ways are insects related to the spread of disease?
4. List as many natural enemies of insects as you can.
5. How does nature control insects?
6. What specific measures can man take to control insect pests as far as their environment is concerned?
7. Why is there no really perfect insecticide?
8. What are five most destructive insect pests in your neighborhood?
9. What effect may DDT have on man?
10. What action of DDT makes it an effective insecticide?

APPLYING FACTS AND PRINCIPLES

1. In what ways are screens, netting, refrigeration, building codes, and flood control related to insect control?
2. Why is insect control considered an international problem?
3. What do you think are the chief reasons why malaria did not get a start in this country after World War II, even though many men returned from service with the disease?
4. Make a list of the common insect pests in your community. Then list the insecticide you would use for each, and tell why you would use it.
5. Why is rat control closely bound up with insect control?

RESEARCH ON YOUR OWN

1. Collect samples of water from several sources, including a stagnant pool, back waters of a stream, or a fish pond. How many different kinds of protozoans can you find?
2. Make a chart of protozoan diseases, including the names of each disease, the organism afflicted, the nature of the disease, and the protozoan which causes it.
3. In a large gallon jar prepare a protozoan culture. Check the most common forms found each day. Keep records to show how the population of the culture and the appearance of the water change daily.
4. The ability of hydra to regenerate can be easily shown if a single specimen is isolated in a watch-glass and cut into three or more pieces with a finely-drawn glass rod or sharp razor.
5. Garden slugs and large snails are quite abundant in most areas. Kill them with chloroform and dissect them to show their intricate structure.
6. The culture of snails in an aquarium is an interesting hobby. Notice their movement and reproductive cycle. Classify as many as you can.
7. Daphnia may be cultured in the laboratory by providing them with a culture which has an abundance of bacteria. Partially decayed material in the water will foster their growth. The Daphnia should be removed with a cloth net when their numbers seem

to diminish, and then be transferred to another aquarium.

8. Establish a demonstration ant colony in your classroom. The colony may be in a glass jar or in a special demonstration container. If a jar is used, wrap it in black paper until the ants have established runways along the glass. The ants may be obtained from nature or from a supply house.

9. Cut through a gall on a twig to expose the insects living inside. What stage are the insects in?

10. Count the number of chirps of a cricket per ten seconds. Find the exact temperature. Plot a curve to see if there is any relationship between the temperature and the number of chirps. Do other sound-making insects have any such relationship?

MORE ABOUT BIOLOGY

Arnov, Boris, Jr. and Mindlin, Helen M. S. *Wonders of the Ocean Zoo.* Dodd, Mead and Co., Inc., New York. 1958

Berrill, N. F. and Berrill, Jacquelyn. *1001 Questions Answered About the Seashore.* Dodd, Mead and Co., Inc., New York. 1957

Bushsbaum, Ralph. *Animals Without Backbones.* The University of Chicago Press, Chicago. 1948

Chu, H. F. *How to Know the Immature Insects.* Wm. C. Brown, Dubuque, Iowa. 1949

Daniel, Hawthorne and Minot, Francis. *The Inexhaustible Sea.* Dodd, Mead and Co., Inc., New York. 1958

Gertsch, Willis J. *American Spiders.* D. Van Nostrand Co., Inc., Princeton, N.J. 1949

Halstead, Bruce. *Dangerous Marine Animals.* Cornell Maritime Press, Cambridge, Md. 1958

Hausman, L. S. *Beginner's Guide to Fresh-Water Life.* G. P. Putnam's Sons, New York. 1959

Hausman, L. S. *Beginner's Guide to Seashore Life.* G. P. Putnam's Sons, New York. 1949

Hegner, Robert and Hegner, V. Z. *Parade of the Animal Kingdom.* The Macmillan Co., New York. 1942

Jahn, T. L. *How to Know the Protozoa.* Wm. C. Brown, Dubuque, Iowa. 1949

Jaques, H. E. *How to Know the Insects.* Wm. C. Brown, Dubuque, Iowa. 1947

Klots, Alexander. *The World of Butterflies and Moths.* McGraw-Hill Book Co., Inc., New York. 1958

Lapage, G. *Animals Parasitic in Man.* Penguin Books, Baltimore, Md. 1957

Little, V. A. *General and Applied Entomology.* Harper and Brothers, New York. 1957

Lutz, Frank I. *Field Book of Insects.* Rev. ed. G. P. Putnam's Sons, New York. 1935

Morgan, Ann Haven. *Fieldbook of Ponds and Streams.* G. P. Putnam's Sons, New York. 1930

Needham, James and Needham, Paul R. *A Guide to the Study of Fresh-Water Biology.* Comstock Publishing Co., Ithaca, N.Y. 1938

Pennak, R. W. *Fresh-Water Invertebrates of the United States.* The Ronald Press Co., New York. 1953

Russell, F. S. and Yonge, C. M. *The Seas.* Frederick Warne and Co., Inc., New York. 1958

Swaim, Ralph B. *The Insect Guide.* Doubleday and Co., Inc., Garden City, N.Y. 1948

U. S. Dept. of Agriculture. *Insects.* Supt. of Documents, Govt. Printing Office, Washington, D.C. 1952

Walford, Lionel A. *Living Resources of the Sea.* The Ronald Press Co., New York. 1958

Zim, Herbert S. and Cottam, Clarence. *Insects: A Guide to Familiar American Insects.* Simon and Schuster, Inc., New York. 1951

Zim, Herbert S. *Seashores: A Guide to Shells, Sea Plants, Shore Birds, and Other Natural Features of American Coasts.* Simon and Schuster, Inc., New York. 1955

Animals with Backbones

The very beasts will tell thee, the birds in air will be thy coun-sellors; the secret is known in every cranny of the earth, the fish in the sea will make it known to thee, none doubts, I tell thee, that all this is the Lord's doing: all living things that breathe . . . lie in the hollow of His hand. — Job 12:8–10

This unit introduces the most perfect group of animals in ex-istence — a group which excels all others in body structure and efficiency in performing the life functions. Biologists call this group the *vertebrates* because its members have a spinal column composed of bones, called *vertebrae,* which runs down the back. But the spinal column, while responsi-ble for the name of the group, is not nature's greatest achieve-ment in this group of super-animals. More important is the nerve cord it encases and the highly developed brain the nerve cord joins. A highly developed nervous system is the key to biological supremacy of the vertebrates.

On the land, in the air, and in the sea, vertebrates are the most important animals. When you study the various verte-brates, you will be preparing for the study of your own body in the next unit. And by learning about the sharks and rays, fish, amphibians, reptiles, birds, and mammals, you will be-come familiar with the animals which are most important to us as sources of food, beasts of burden, sources of pleasure, and as pets.

CHAPTER 28: INTRODUCTION TO THE VERTEBRATES
CHAPTER 29: FISH AND FISHLIKE VERTEBRATES
CHAPTER 30: AMPHIBIA — VERTEBRATES WITH DOUBLE LIVES
CHAPTER 31: REPTILES — VERTEBRATES WITH SCALES AND CLAWS
CHAPTER 32: BIRDS — VERTEBRATES ADAPTED FOR FLIGHT
CHAPTER 33: MAMMALS — THE HIGHEST FORMS OF ANIMAL LIFE

CHAPTER 28

Introduction to the Vertebrates

TODAY we live in an age of vertebrates. Across the wide stretches of ocean depths, sharks and rays and salt-water fish reign supreme. They are the most important marine animals. Fresh-water fish dominate the inland lakes and ponds, rivers, and streams. Birds are nature's most highly developed flying organisms. And on land, mammals surpass all other organisms in importance. Man, the most perfect living thing, dominates the entire living world. Intelligence, ingenuity, and inventive genius have made him master of the land, the sea, and the air.

In the study of invertebrates, you followed a gradual development of body structure from a single cell to a complex organism, such as an arthropod or a mollusk. In the vertebrate group, you will find life in its most highly developed form.

A quick review of invertebrate development. Nature seems to have tried several plans of body development in various invertebrate animals. In the protozoan phylum, the specialization of a single cell is carried to the limit. Consider the paramecium with its cilia and trichocysts, its gullet, and contractile vacuoles. The " slipper animalcule " is a truly marvelous cell, but it takes many cells to make a complex animal.

You were introduced to a large colony of cells in the sponges and coelenterates. The beginning of tissues is found in the

Fig. 28-1. What outstanding characteristic does this vertebrate skeleton show that is common to all members of the group?

American Museum of Natural History

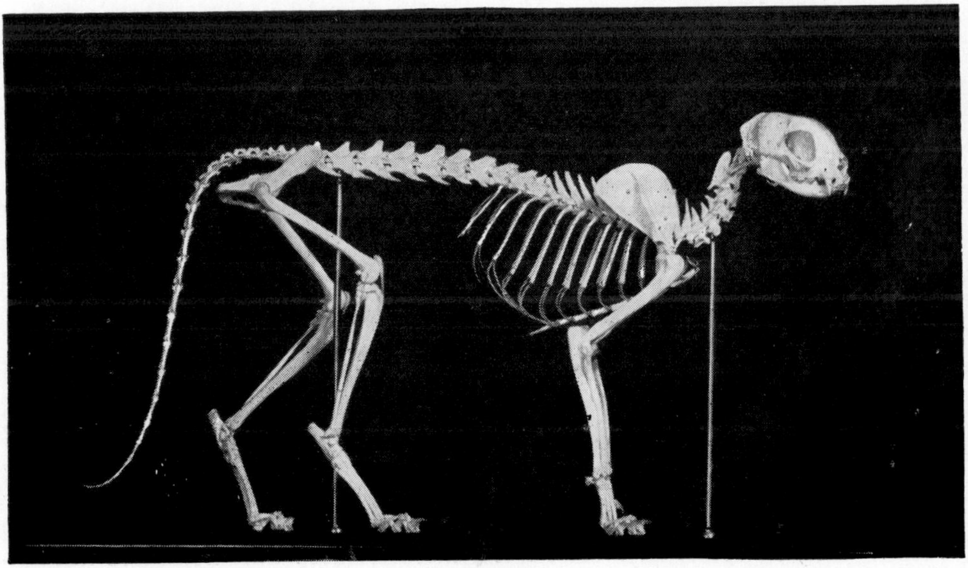

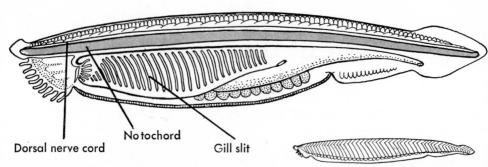

Dorsal nerve cord   Notochord   Gill slit

Fig. 28-2.   All chordates have a notochord in the early stages of their life.   *Amphioxus*, shown above, is a primitive chordate that retains the notochord throughout its life. The lower right-hand drawing is approximately life-size and shows the segmental arrangement of muscles.

ectoderm and endoderm of these animals. In the flat and round worms, there are organs which perform such functions as digestion, reproduction, excretion, and irritability with much greater efficiency. The segmented worms reveal a more advanced and efficient tubular digestive tract and an elongated body divided into a series of segments; a well-developed circulatory system transports blood through closed vessels in this group of worms.

The clam and other mollusks have the greatest possible protection for a highly developed, soft-bodied animal. Their shells are both a fort and a prison. Mollusks have not advanced much in many millions of years.

The arthropods combine protection with freedom of movement. However, their suit of armor is heavy, so that the size of an arthropod is limited by chitin. In most cases, arthropods have remained reasonably small. Numbers alone maintain their place of importance in the living world.

Why have the vertebrate animals become so important?   The vertebrates have neither shell nor hard exoskeleton (except certain reptiles and mammals). A strong internal framework, or endoskeleton, supports a body which is able to move freely and gracefully. This fact

prevents protection of the soft body parts, except in certain vertebrates, such as the turtle and armadillo, which develop a hard outer covering. However, the highly developed vertebrate brain and nervous system more than make up for the lack of outer protection. In escaping from enemies, the vertebrate animals depend on their keen sense organs and efficient movement, as well as on their instinct and intelligence.

What are vertebrates?   The **Vertebrata** (ver-tuh-*bray*-tuh) is one of four subphyla of the phylum **Chordata** (kor-*day*-tuh).   This phylum is the most advanced in the animal kingdom. Three subphyla of chordates are known by biologists but are not particularly important to man. One includes two classes of wormlike animals which live in the sea.   The strange sea squirt represents another subphylum.   The fishlike lancelet, probably the best known of the primitive chordates, represents a third subphylum. However, the vertebrates alone make the phylum Chordata important today.

How are chordates different from other animals?   Early in their life all chordate animals have a gristlelike rod running lengthwise along the top side of the body. We call this rod a **notochord** (*noh*-toh-kord) (Fig. 28-2).   The more primitive chordates keep their notochord throughout life. Some of the lower vertebrates, such as the sea lamprey, retain the notochord, but it becomes surrounded by cartilage structures of the spinal column. The notochord disappears early in the development of other vertebrates and is replaced by the vertebrae (*ver*-tuh-bree) of the spine.

The phylum name *Chordata* refers to the notochord. *Vertebrata* refers to the **vertebrae,** or bones of the spinal column. Thus we usually speak of vertebrates as animals that have backbones.

Other characteristics of chordates include a nerve cord which runs down the dorsal side of the body. In vertebrates, the bones of the spinal column enclose a dorsal nerve cord, or spinal cord. In invertebrates, such as the earthworm, the main nerve trunk lies on the ventral side of the body.

Paired gill slits form openings in the throat of chordates. However, like the notochord, these disappear early in the development of such higher vertebrates as the reptile, bird, and mammal.

Classes of vertebrates. The many kinds of living vertebrates are usually divided into seven classes, as the table on page 322 and Fig. 28-3 on page 323 show. The classes are listed in order of their complexity. In the chapters to follow, we shall consider each class as we make a brief survey of vertebrate animal life.

The outstanding characteristics of vertebrates. Although fish, frogs, reptiles, birds, and mammals may seem very different to you, they are actually similar in many ways. Their similarities include:

1. A body with a head and trunk and, in many cases, a neck and a tail.

2. Never more than two pairs of locomotive appendages present. These may be fins, flippers, wings, arms, or legs.

3. Eyes, ears, and nostrils in the head.

4. Eyelids and separate teeth present in most forms.

5. An internal skeleton (**endoskeleton**) of bone and/or **cartilage** (a gristlelike tissue).

6. A spinal column or backbone composed of vertebrae.

7. Two body cavities: (a) a dorsal cavity for the nervous system; and (b) a larger ventral cavity for the other internal organs.

8. A heart on the ventral side of the body; red blood corpuscles.

The vertebrate body is composed of many specialized systems. The vertebrate systems contain many highly developed organs. These systems include:

1. *Integumentary system* — the outer body covering and special outgrowths such as scales, feathers, or hair for protection.

2. *Muscular system* — muscles which are attached to bones and produce body movement; muscles which form the walls of the heart and of the digestive organs and blood vessels.

3. *Skeletal system* — the bones and cartilage structures which make up the body framework.

4. *Digestive system* — the many specialized organs concerned with the preparation of food for use by the body tissues.

5. *Respiratory system* — gills or lungs and related structures which are used in the exchange of gases between the organism and its external environment.

6. *Circulatory system* — the heart and blood vessels which function as the transportation system of the body. Vertebrates have a " closed " circulatory system, as you have already learned.

7. *Excretory system* — the organs which remove wastes from the body.

8. *Endocrine system* — glands which produce secretions necessary for the normal functioning of the other systems.

9. *Nervous system* — the brain, the spinal cord, nerves, and special sense

organs — the most highly developed system of a vertebrate.

10. *Reproductive system* — the male or female organs of reproduction.

Lines of development in the vertebrates. The skeleton shows an interesting development in the vertebrate classes. The sea lamprey, sharks, and rays have a cartilage skeleton throughout life. Fish, amphibians, reptiles, birds, and mammals develop a bony skeleton. These animals start life with a cartilaginous (kar-tih-*laj*-ih-nus) framework. However, early in life, bone cells replace most of the cartilage. Minerals deposited in the bones make them hard and strong.

The classes of vertebrates show also an interesting change from a water existence to life on land. The lampreys, sharks, rays, and bony fish are adapted only for life in water. Their limbs are in the form of fins. Their gills absorb dissolved oxygen from the water during respiration. Water flows over the gills through gill slits in the throat. After you have studied the frog as a representative amphibian, you will realize that it represents a transition from water to land. During the tadpole stage, a frog is a fish-like animal with gills and a fin.

The vertebrate heart and brain show great development over those of the invertebrates. The fish heart has only two chambers. One chamber receives blood from the body, while the other pumps blood to the gills. The frog has a three-chambered heart and a more complex circulation. Birds and mammals have a still more complex heart consisting of four chambers. One side of the heart receives blood from the body and pumps it to the lungs. The other side receives blood from the lungs and pumps it to the body. This heart is really a double pump. Man's heart also consists of four chambers.

Similar advances can be seen in the brain of the vertebrates. One brain region known as the **cerebrum** (*sair*-eh-brum) is the center of instinct, emotion, memory, and intelligence. This brain area increases in relative size through the classes of vertebrates. The brain of the mammal has the largest cerebrum in relation to the size of the body.

Vertebrate behavior is highly developed. Highly developed sense organs keep the vertebrate in close contact with its environment. The well-developed brain, spinal cord, and nerves extending to and from all regions of the body provide the basis for complex **behavior**.

There is a reason for every nervous **response** an animal makes. The condition or situation which brings about the response is referred to as a **stimulus**.

SEVEN CLASSES OF VERTEBRATES

NAME OF CLASS	EXAMPLES
1. CYCLOSTOMATA (sy-kloh-stoh-*may*-tuh)	Sea lamprey, brook lamprey, hagfish
2. CHONDRICTHYES (kon-*drik*-thih-eez)	Shark, ray, and skate
3. OSTEICHTHYES (os-tee-*ik*-thih-eez)	All bony fish
4. AMPHIBIA (am-*fib*-ee-uh)	Frog, toad, salamander
5. REPTILIA (rep-*til*-ee-uh)	Snake, lizard, turtle, crocodile
6. AVES (*ay*-veez)	All birds
7. MAMMALIA (mam-*ay*-lee-uh)	All mammals

Fig. 28-3. The above are representatives of the seven classes of vertebrates. What characteristics do they all have in common?

Often, the response is purely automatic, or *involuntary*. The animal reacts to the stimulus without any control on its part. However, an animal can control many of its responses. We call such controlled responses *voluntary*.

Much of the activity of a higher animal is controlled by *instincts*. These are forms of involuntary behavior, since the animal performs them without a deliberate decision. We do not know the actual cause of instincts. However, we do know that they involve the brain and have a powerful influence on behavior.

Self-preservation is a basic instinct in all vertebrates as well as many invertebrates. In times of danger, an animal will respond to the " flight or fight " instinct of self-preservation. Have you ever cornered an animal which would normally flee? A seemingly harmless animal like a squirrel will bite and claw viciously if it cannot escape from an enemy.

Animals are born with instincts. The sucking instinct directs the nursing mammal early in life. Instinct causes the tiny

Fig. 28-4. Species preservation is one of the strongest instincts in animals. These opossum babies ride safely on their mother's back until they can take care of themselves.

Encyclopaedia Britannica Films

bird to pick its way through the shell at the time of hatching.

A second and even stronger instinct directs animal reproduction and care of the young. This is *species preservation.* This is the instinct which, for instance, drives the Pacific salmon up the streams of the Northwest to spawning beds. The adult salmon lose their lives so that a new generation may come downstream to the ocean. This instinct also causes the sunfish to defend its nest against an intruder from which it would normally flee.

A higher form of behavior, known as a *conditioned reaction,* or *conditioned reflex,* is common among vertebrates. We say that a reaction becomes conditioned when a particular behavior response continually follows a specific stimulus, resulting in habit formation. We develop this level of behavior when we teach a dog to " heel " at a command or " shake hands " at a given signal. Even fish in an aquarium can be trained to go to one special corner of the tank when you approach, if you always feed them in this particular place.

Intelligent behavior is still more complicated. It involves memory of past experiences. It also requires judgment in controlling responses. An intelligent response is a deliberate act which has been considered in the light of past experiences. Memory, association, and judgment are all involved in learning.

Instinct can be observed in all vertebrates. To a lesser degree, most of the vertebrates are capable of conditioned reactions. Birds and mammals exhibit intelligent behavior to some degree. However, man is supreme among vertebrates in high development of intelligence due to his great capacity for memory, association, judgment, and self-control. He is unique among living things in his ability to profit by experience and apply learning to the solution of his problems.

In Conclusion

As you study the vertebrates, you will see some characteristics developed to the highest degree. The fish excels in swimming — its streamlined body cuts through the water like a torpedo. The frog is at home both on land and in the water. The bird has long been the model for life in the air. We have even borrowed its wing design in the aircraft industry.

The antelope and gazelle hold speed records among land animals. The elephant is a symbol of strength. What about man? Man is no match for other vertebrates in physical abilities. But brain is superior to brawn. Man rules the living world.

In the next chapter, we shall begin our study of vertebrates of the ocean depths, lakes, rivers, and streams. Here the primitive fishlike vertebrates and the many bony fish, the most important of aquatic animals, are found.

BIOLOGICALLY SPEAKING

behavior	instinct	species preservation
cartilage	intelligent behavior	stimulus
cerebrum	involuntary response	vertebrae
Chordata	notochord	Vertebrata
conditioned reaction	response	voluntary response
endoskeleton	self-preservation	

QUESTIONS FOR REVIEW

1. What characteristics distinguish the vertebrate skeleton from that of lower animals?
2. How would you distinguish between the chordates and the vertebrates?
3. Describe and locate the notochord.
4. Name seven classes of vertebrates and give an example of each class.
5. What are eight vertebrate characteristics?
6. Name ten vertebrate systems.

7. Which of the various brain regions is concerned with instinct, emotions, and intelligence?
8. What is the relation between a stimulus and a response?
9. Which do you regard as more efficient, the endoskeleton or the exoskeleton?
10. Why are conditioned reactions and intelligent behavior limited to vertebrate animals?

APPLYING FACTS AND PRINCIPLES

1. Why are instinct and intelligence more vital to survival of a vertebrate than to an invertebrate, such as a clam, a starfish, an insect, or a crayfish?
2. Discuss the improvement of vertebrates through the various classes, using the skeleton, organs of respiration, heart, and brain as illustrations.

3. Self-preservation and species preservation are instincts. Which is stronger? Give one or more illustrations to prove your answer.
4. How can you distinguish instinctive behavior from intelligent behavior in observing the activity of various vertebrate animals?

CHAPTER 29

Fish and Fishlike Vertebrates

IT isn't hard to interest most people in a discussion of fish. Fishing is a favorite sport for millions of Americans from childhood on. The fly rod, spinning rod, casting rod, and tackle box often replace the more simple cane pole and a can of worms. But the thrill of the tug of a fish on a line remains the same.

The biologist classifies most of the fish you know as *bony fish*. In the oceans, these fish mingle with the more primitive sharks and rays. The shark and ray represent another class of vertebrates. The most primitive of the vertebrates are represented by several species of eel-like creatures which live in our fresh-water lakes and streams.

Fish are the most important animals in water environments. When you study the adaptations of the fish for life in water, you will discover why for millions of years they have controlled the oceans, lakes, and waterways as rulers of the deep.

Blood-sucking "vampires" of the Great Lakes. About 30 years ago, a deadly vertebrate menace made its way from the waters of Lake Ontario through the Welland Canal at Niagara Falls, into Lake Erie. The sea lampreys were invading new waters. During a much earlier migration these lampreys had left their native waters of the Atlantic coastal region to move up the St. Lawrence River into Lake Ontario. Here their movement was stopped by Niagara Falls. But the Welland Canal, built to carry shipping around the Falls, gave them passage into Lake Erie. Ten years later, the lamprey hordes had spread through Lake Huron. They traveled through the Straits of Mackinac into Lake Michigan and through the locks at Sault St. Marie into Lake Superior.

What sort of creature is this death-dealing sea lamprey? Biologists place it in the class **Cyclostomata** (sy-kloh-stoh-may-tuh), or *Agnatha,* a small group of primitive vertebrates. The sea lamprey has a slender eel-like body. The mature lamprey reaches a length of two to three feet and a weight of two to five pounds. Its skin is soft and slimy, brownish-green and blotched or mottled. Paired fins are lacking in the lamprey. Two single fins along the back and a tail fin aid in swimming in the weaving or rippling manner characteristic of the lamprey.

The head of a lamprey is curious and quite different from that of a fish. Instead of jaws, the lamprey has a funnel-like mouth lined with sharp, horny teeth (Fig. 29-1). A rasping tongue, also bearing teeth, lies in the center of the mouth. Small eyes are situated on either side of the head. Between the eyes, on the top of the head, is a **nasal opening** which leads to a sac containing nerve endings associated with the sense of smell. Seven oval gill slits, resembling portholes of a ship, lie in a row on each side of the head behind the eyes.

During its adult life, the sea lamprey lives as a very destructive predator. It attaches its sucking mouth to the side of

326

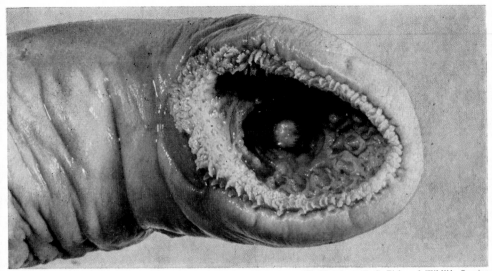

Haddon from U. S. Fish and Wildlife Service

Fig. 29-1.   This is a close-up of the menacing sucking mouth of the sea lamprey.   The class name *Cyclostomata* means, literally, " round-mouthed."

a fish and chisels a hole through the scales with its rasping teeth (Fig. 29-2). It feeds on the blood of its victim and may even suck out internal organs.   Its favorite host is the lake trout, one of the finest game fish of the Great Lakes. When trout are not available, the sea lamprey attacks whitefish, pike, and other species.

The sea lamprey has nearly exterminated the lake trout in Lake Huron and is rapidly destroying other species.   At present, the lake trout are disappearing rapidly in Lake Michigan and Lake Superior.

Our hope of eliminating the lamprey menace.   The spawning habits of the lamprey may provide the chance to destroy this deadly menace.   Sea lampreys reach sexual maturity in the Great Lakes during the months of May or June.   At this time, they enter fast-flowing streams which feed the lakes.   They lay their eggs in circular depressions in the gravel bottom of cold streams.   An average female lays from 50,000 to 100,000 eggs. After about 20 days of development, the eggs hatch into tiny, blind larvae.   The larvae leave the nest and float downstream until they reach quiet water with a mud

Fig. 29-2.   The sea lamprey is a threat to many game fish.   The trout in this picture has been scarred by one.

U. S. Fish and Wildlife Service

bottom. Here they burrow into the mud and start a period of inactive life which lasts three to four years. During this period, the larva lies in a U-shaped burrow and feeds on plant and animal matter that is drawn into the mouth in a current produced by moving cilia. During the winter of the third or fourth year, the larva changes to an adult and starts its journey downstream to the lake. It lives about one year as an adult, feeding constantly on fish.

Two methods of lamprey control are in use today. One is the lamprey trap, designed to capture the adults as they migrate upstream to spawn. Electrodes charged with 100 volts of electricity are put in a row across the stream, which charges the water and stops the movement of all aquatic animals (Fig. 29-3). The migrating lamprey and fish swim along the edge of the charged area into traps. Here the lamprey are destroyed. The fish are caught and put back into the stream above the traps.

A more recent method of lamprey control makes use of a poison which kills the larvae buried in the streams. Recent tests of a larvicide in certain rivers flowing into the Great Lakes indicate nearly 100 per cent larva deaths. But biologists do not know that all sea lamprey migrate to spawn. If some of them remain in the shallow waters of the lakes, neither traps nor larvicides will be effective.

Sharks and rays. To the class **Chondrichthyes** (kon-*drik*-thih-eez), or *Elasmobranchii* (ee-las-moh-*brank*-ee-ee), belong the few remaining fish of those which controlled the ancient seas. Sharks and rays make up this class of primitive fish. The shark resembles the true fish in many ways. However, certain of its characteristics put it in a separate class.

Fig. 29-3.   Traps charged with electricity are effective in bringing about the destruction of the blood-sucking lamprey.

Field and Stream Magazine

American Museum of Natural History

Fig. 29-4.   The white shark, a man-eating species, is found in the warm waters of tropical regions.

The body of a shark is torpedo-shaped. Its fins resemble those of true fish.   The upper portion of the tail fin is longer than the lower portion — a characteristic of ancient fish.   The shark's mouth is a horizontal slitlike opening on the lower (ventral) side of the head.   The jaws are lined with sharp razor-edged teeth.   Water enters the mouth, passes over the gills on each side of the head, and is forced out through pairs of gill slits.   Gills, as you probably know, are the special respiratory organs of fish and their relatives. The skeleton of sharks and rays is composed of cartilage rather than bone.

Sharks include the largest living fish. The whale shark, the giant of sharks, reaches a length of 50 feet or more and a weight of over 20 tons.   The great white shark, or man-eating shark, may exceed 40 feet in length (Fig. 29-4).

The rays are often called devilfish, blanket fish, or sting rays.   They swim gracefully through ocean waters, moving their great flat bodies like wings.   Often they lie half-buried in the sand of the ocean bottom.   The whiplike tail of a ray has a sharp barbed stinger on the tip.   It causes a painful wound when driven into a victim.   Sting rays often come close to shore.

The true fish.   Biologists put all true fish in the class **Osteichthyes** (os-tee-*ik*-thih-eez).   These have a bony skeleton

with *gills* as respiratory organs.   Limbs are in the form of **fins**.   Most fish have an outer covering of overlapping *scales*, or plates.   Fish are ideally suited to aquatic life.   In a wide variety of forms, they live in practically every water environment of the earth.

The body of a fish is divided into three regions: (1) head;   (2) trunk;   and (3) tail.   In most cases, the body is perfectly streamlined — tapered at both ends, or spindle-shaped.   The lack of a

Fig. 29-5.   The tail of the sting ray has a sharp barbed stinger which is capable of inflicting a severe wound.

American Museum of Natural History

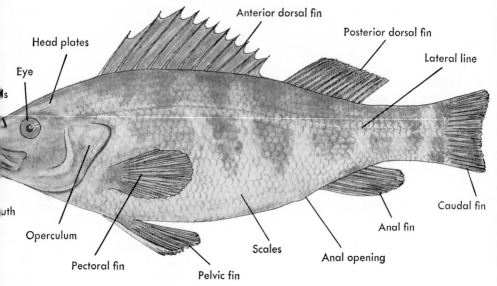

Fig. 29-6.   This drawing shows the external structure of a bony fish, the yellow perch.

neck is no disadvantage to a fish. It can turn its body as easily in the water as most other animals can move their heads.

Many people confuse the tail of a fish with the tail fin. The tail is the solid muscular region posterior to the trunk. The tail fin is an outgrowth of this region. **Scales cover the body of most fish.** Carp and goldfish have large, loose scales. Those of the trout are extremely small. Catfish have no scales at all.

Scales grow from pockets in the skin and overlap like shingles on a roof. Scales increase in size as a fish grows. In other words, a young fish has the same number of scales it will have at maturity. As scales grow in size, concentric rings are formed. These rings are closer together in regions of winter growth than in summer growth, thus making it possible to distinguish seasons of scale growth and determine the age of the fish.

A slimy secretion of the skin seeps between the scales and forms a covering which lubricates the body. This body slime is important in locomotion and in escape from enemies. The body slime is important, too, in protecting the fish from attack by parasitic molds and other or-ganisms. If you handle a fish with dry hands, you remove some of the slime and expose the body to parasites. You can avoid this by wetting your hands before you pick up a fish.

Many fish have bright colors, often arranged in lines, bars, or spots. Furthermore, the brightness of these colors changes with environmental conditions. Much of the coloration of fish is due to pigments present in special cells of the skin, known as **chromatophores** (kroh-*mat*-oh-fores). Light reflected from rocks, water plants, and other surfaces in the water acts on nerves which control the chromatophores. When chromatophores disperse their pigments, bright colors appear. Contraction of the pigments causes the colors to fade. Colors produced by pigments in the chromatophores show through the transparent scales. Other colors of fish are due to the reflection of light from the scale surfaces.

Many fish illustrate **countershading**, as we mentioned on page 75 of Chapter 7. Darker pigments on the dorsal side of the body tone down the bright light which strikes the fish from above. As a result, the upper side blends with the lighter side, giving the body a uniform appearance when viewed from the side. Furthermore, the darker colors on the dorsal side blend with the bottom or with deep water when the fish is seen from above. The light colors on the ventral side blend with the bright light on the surface when the fish is viewed from below.

Head structures of the fish. The many species of fish vary greatly in body form. However, many fish are similar to the yellow perch, shown in Fig. 29-6.

The head tapers toward the mouth, offering the least possible resistance as the fish moves through the water. The protective covering of the head is in the form of plates instead of scales. The mouth is large and is situated at the extreme anterior end. Carnivorous fish, such as the yellow perch, have numerous sharp teeth extending from the jawbones and from the roof of the mouth. These teeth slant toward the throat, making it easy to swallow a prey, but hard for the prey to escape. The tongue is fastened to the floor of the mouth and is not movable. It functions as an organ of touch rather than one of taste.

Two nasal cavities lie on the top of the head, anterior to the eyes. Paired nostrils lead to each nasal cavity. The nostrils function in smell only. They do not connect with the throat and are not involved in respiration. The fish has no external openings to the ears. The ears are embedded in the bones of the skull and probably function as balance organs in addition to receiving vibrations carried by the bones of the skull.

The eyes of most fish are large and somewhat movable. Eyelids are lacking. The pupils are large compared with those of other vertebrates, and admit the maximum amount of light.

At each side of the head is a crescent-shaped slit which marks the posterior edge of the gill cover, or **operculum** (oh-per-kyoo-lum). This hard plate serves as a protective cover for the gills beneath it. By raising the unattached rear edge of the operculum, you can see the gills lying in a large gill chamber. The edges of the opercula nearly meet on the lower side of the fish, where the head fastens to the trunk at a narrow **isthmus.**

Structures of the trunk and tail. Various kinds of fins develop from the trunk and tail. Each fin consists of a double membrane, supported by cartilaginous or spiny rays. Fins serve a variety of purposes in the fish and differ in form in various species.

Two kinds of fins are paired. These are considered homologous with the limbs of other vertebrates. The **pectoral fins** are nearest the head, and correspond to the front legs of other vertebrates. Posterior to these are the **pelvic fins**, which correspond to hind legs. The paired fins serve as oars when the fish is swimming slowly. In addition, they aid in steering and in maintaining balance when the fish is resting. They are used, also, in moving backward. The **caudal fin** grows from the tail and aids in propelling the fish. **Dorsal fins** are situated along the top middle line of the trunk. Many fish have a single dorsal fin. Others, like the yellow perch shown in Fig. 29-6, have two dorsal fins.

The anterior or spiny dorsal fin contains sharp projections which aid in defense. The spines of this fin raise upward toward the head, thus making swallowing of the perch tailfirst difficult. The posterior or soft dorsal fin lacks these spines. Both dorsal fins serve as a keel to keep the fish upright while swimming. Another single fin, the **anal fin,** grows along the middle line on the lower side. This fin, like the dorsal fin, serves as a keel and helps to maintain balance.

Powerful muscles, arranged in zigzag plates, occupy the region of the trunk

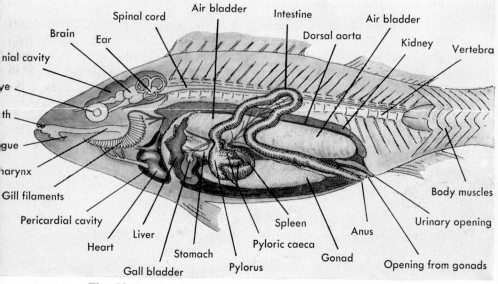

Fig. 29-7.   This is a lateral view of a dissected yellow perch.

Labels (clockwise):
Brain · Spinal cord · Air bladder · Intestine · Dorsal aorta · Air bladder · Kidney · Vertebra · Body muscles · Urinary opening · Opening from gonads · Gonad · Anus · Pyloric caeca · Spleen · Pylorus · Stomach · Gall bladder · Heart · Liver · Pericardial cavity · Gill filaments · pharynx · gue · th · ye · nial cavity · Ear

above the spinal column. A thinner muscle layer lies along the body wall on the sides of the trunk. The tail region is solid bone and muscle. The weight of these muscles makes the body top-heavy and causes a dead fish to float upside down. Slow movement of the pectoral and pelvic fins while a fish is at rest prevents it from turning over in the water.

If you examine the sides of a fish closely, you will notice a row of pitted scales extending from the head to the tail fin. This is the *lateral line*. Nerve endings lie under the pitted scales. The nerves of the lateral line probably aid the ears in feeling vibrations. The lateral line is also a pressure organ, indicating the depth at which the fish is swimming.

The digestive system of the fish. Many fish are vegetarians and feed on algae and other water plants. Carnivorous species eat other animals such as frogs, other fish, and a wide variety of invertebrates, including crayfish, worms, and insects. Some fish, like the bass and pike, swallow fish almost as large as themselves. Especially in carnivorous fish, the mouth is a large trap for capturing prey. The throat cavity, or *pharynx,*

leads to the opening of the short *esophagus* (Fig. 29-7). The esophagus, in turn, joins the upper end of the stomach. The *stomach* is in line with the esophagus, thus allowing a large prey to extend from the stomach through the mouth and even protrude for a time as digestion occurs. A rather short *intestine* leads from the lower end of the stomach. A muscular valve, the *pylorus,* is situated at the junction of the stomach and intestine. Just below the pylorus, several short tubes or pouches extend from the intestine. These are the *pyloric caeca.* Pyloric caeca may secrete digestive fluids. Digestion continues as food moves through the short loops of intestine. A well-developed *liver* lies close to the stomach. The *gall bladder,* attached to the liver, passes bile to the intestine through a tube, or duct. Digested food is absorbed by the blood through the intestine wall. Indigestible matter leaves the intestine through the *anal opening* on the lower side.

Circulatory system of a fish. The blood of a fish is similar to that of other vertebrates. It contains both red and white corpuscles. The *heart* (Fig. 29-8) pumps blood through a system of vessels of three types. **Arteries** carry blood from the heart to the gills, then to all other regions of the body. The arteries lead to thin-walled **capillaries** which penetrate all of the body tissues. The capillaries, in turn, lead to **veins**, which return blood to the heart.

The heart lies in the **pericardial cavity** on the lower side of the body just behind the gills. A large vein, the **cardinal vein**, receives blood from its various branches coming from the head, trunk and tail, and the liver (Fig. 29-9). Just above the heart, the cardinal vein enlarges into a thin-walled sac, the **sinus venosus**. This sac joins the first heart chamber, or **auricle** (*or*-ih-kul), often referred to as the *atrium*. From the auricle, blood passes into the **ventricle** (*ven*-trih-kul), the thick-walled, muscular pumping chamber of the heart. Blood is pumped from the ventricle with great force through the **ventral aorta**, leading to the gills. This artery begins with a muscular bulblike structure, the **bulbus arteriosus** which is attached to the ventricle. This structure is very noticeable in the fish heart. The ventral aorta branches to the two sets of gills, then rebranches to form arteries which lead to the four gills on each side of the head. Another large artery, the

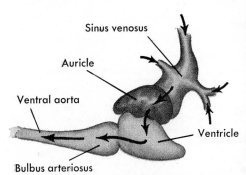

Fig. 29-8. The fish heart has one auricle and one ventricle. What is the function of each of these chambers?

dorsal aorta, receives blood from the gills and, through its branches, supplies the head, trunk, and tail. Blood returns to the heart through the cardinal veins, thus completing the circulation. Some of the blood returns through veins from the digestive organs and the liver. Various cell wastes are removed as blood circulates through the kidneys.

The blood of a fish passes through the heart only once during a complete circulation. The heart receives impure (deoxygenated) blood from the cardinal vein and pumps this same blood through the ventral aorta to the gills. In circulating through the gills, the blood discharges carbon dioxide and receives oxygen.

Fig. 29-9. In this diagram showing circulation in the fish, note that the blood flows in a single circuit: from body to heart to gills and to body again.

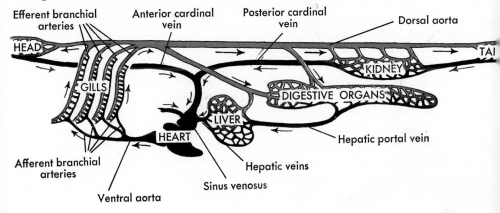

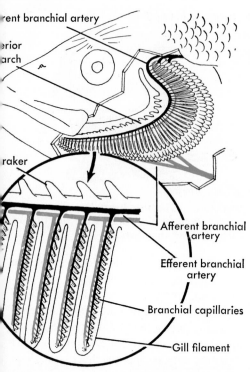

rent branchial artery

erior
arch

raker

Afferent branchial
artery

Efferent branchial
artery

Branchial capillaries

Gill filament

Fig. 29-10. This drawing shows an entire gill, much enlarged, as seen from the side. What are the functions of each part?

each gill filament, where the blood enters a network of capillaries. Here carbon dioxide is discharged from the blood and oxygen is absorbed through the thin walls of the capillaries and filaments. Oxygenated blood returns to the gill arch and flows out the top of the gill through the **efferent branchial artery** to the dorsal aorta.

The fish requires a continuous flow of water over its gills. Water is drawn into the open mouth as the gill arches expand and enlarge the cavity of the pharynx. The edge of the operculum is pressed against the body as water is drawn in. The mouth is then closed, the gill arches contract, and the rear edge of the operculum is raised, thus forcing the water over the gill filaments and out of the gill chamber around the raised edge of the operculum. The forward motion of the fish aids this process when the fish is swimming.

An essential internal organ of the fish is the air bladder. A thin-walled sac, the *air bladder*, lies in the upper part of the body cavity of a fish. In some fish it connects with the pharynx by a tube. The air bladder is inflated with gases (oxygen, nitrogen, and carbon dioxide) which pass into it from the blood. The bladder acts as a float and adjusts the weight of the fish so that it equals the weight of the water it displaces. This balance allows the fish to float without rising or sinking.

Fish live at various water levels at different seasons of the year. The air bladder adjusts to these variations by losing air to the blood or receiving additional air. When a fish is adjusted to deep water and is caught and brought to the surface suddenly, the air bladder expands and may push the esophagus into the mouth. One group of fish known as *darters* has no air bladder. They sink to the bottom after each of their jerky swimming motions.

This pure (oxygenated) blood is received from the gills by the dorsal aorta for circulation to the body tissues.

The gills are organs of respiration. In a bony fish such as the yellow perch, four gills lie in a gill chamber on each side of the head. A gill consists of a cartilaginous **arch** to which are attached a double row of thin-walled threadlike projections called **gill filaments** (Fig. 29-10). These filaments are richly provided with capillaries, so that the blood is brought into close contact with the water over a large surface. The gill arches have hard, fingerlike projections called **gill rakers** on the side toward the throat. These prevent food and other particles from reaching the filaments and keep the arches apart to allow free circulation of water.

Blood enters a gill at the base of the arch through the **afferent branchial artery**. Branches of this artery enter

The nervous system is quite complex.
The nervous system of the fish includes the brain, spinal cord, and the many nerves which lead to all parts of the body.

The brain lies in a small bony cavity, the *cranial cavity*. It consists of five distinct parts (Fig. 29-11). At the anterior end are the **olfactory lobes** from which the nerves, sensitive to odors, extend to the nostrils. Behind these lobes are the two lobes of the **cerebrum** which control the voluntary muscles. In these lobes instincts are centered. Back of the cerebrum are the **optic lobes,** the largest of the fish's brain. Optic nerves lead from these lobes to the eyes. Behind them lies the **cerebellum** (sair-eh-*bel*-um), which coordinates muscular activity, and, finally, the **medulla** (meh-*dul*-uh) **oblongata,** which controls the activities of the internal organs. The **spinal cord** passes down the back from the medulla and is encased in the vertebral column. Nerves connect the spinal cord with all parts of the body.

The fish's brain is not highly developed when compared to those of higher vertebrates. It shows, however, a great advance over the so-called " brains " of invertebrates. As you study the brains of other vertebrates, compare them with the fish brain. The same regions are present. There is, however, a gradual increase in the size of the cerebrum in proportion to the other brain regions as vertebrates become more advanced. As the cerebrum increases in size, there is a corresponding increase in nervous activity on higher levels, such as emotional responses, memory, and intelligence.

Sensations of the fish. The relatively large optic lobes of the brain indicate that fish have a well-developed sense of sight. However, vision at even moderate water depths is greatly reduced because of insufficient light. Fish are known to be nearsighted and probably do not see ob-

jects clearly at distances greater than a few feet. The fish eye focuses on objects by moving the nearly spherical lens forward or backward rather than changing the shape of the lens, as in our eyes. Scientists are not sure whether the fish sees colors or lives in a world of black, white, and shades of gray.

The range of vibrations to which the ears are sensitive is very great in the fish. However, they are most sensitive to vibrations of the same frequency as those to which the human ear is sensitive. The bones of the skull in which the ears are embedded function efficiently in transmitting vibrations from water to the sensitive ear structures.

Probably the most acute sense of a fish is that of smell. Scientists have conducted extensive experiments to demonstrate the reaction of fish to odors in the water. It has been found that fish can distinguish the odors of many water

Fig. 29-11.   This is a dorsal view of the fish brain.   Compare its development with that of some of the higher invertebrates.

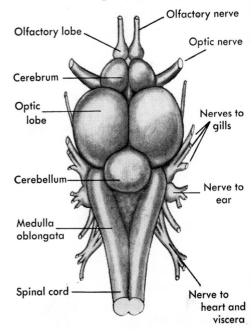

Olfactory nerve
Olfactory lobe
Optic nerve
Cerebrum
Optic lobe
Nerves to gills
Cerebellum
Nerve to ear
Medulla oblongata
Spinal cord
Nerve to heart and viscera

Fig. 29-12. Some fish build nests. Compare the stickleback nest (*left*), consisting of strands of algae, with that of the sunfish (*right*).

plants, even when these plants are dipped for only a short time in pure water. Similarly, they can detect the odor of hands washed in a stream as well as the odors of many animals, especially mammals. Scientists now believe that odors direct fish to feeding areas among water plants. It is possible, too, that salmon find the mouths of rivers and streams during the spawning season by the odors of plants living in these fresh-water bodies.

Reproduction in the fish. The reproductive organs, or **gonads**, lie in the posterior region of the body cavity. The opening from the gonads is just behind the anal opening.

Eggs develop in the single **ovary** of the female over a period of several months. As the eggs enlarge, the ovary swells, and may bulge the sides of the fish. Sperm develop in the paired **testes** of the male. Soon after the female lays her eggs, or **spawns**, the male swims over

them and discharges a sperm-containing fluid, or **milt**. Sperm swim to the eggs and fertilize them, and the development of the young fish begins. This development may require from two to six weeks or more, depending on the temperature of the water. The developing fish is nourished by a large quantity of nonliving material, the yolk, which is present in the egg. A part of the yolk known as the *yolk sac* remains attached to the young fish a short while after hatching.

Many fish, like the sunfish, deposit their eggs in a depression made in the bottom of a stream. After spawning, the male guards the nest, fighting off any intruder. Another fish, the stickleback, makes a curious nest of algae (Fig. 29-12). The male builds the nest and drives the female into it for spawning. Then he chases her away and takes entire charge of the nest and eggs. Channel catfish spawn in holes in a bank or in a discarded can or other receptacle which they find on the bottom.

Guppies, mollies, moons, and swordtails are fresh-water tropical species commonly reared in home aquaria. These curious fish bear their young alive. The female retains the eggs within her body and receives sperm from the male during mating. The young fish develop internally and are brought forth alive.

Many eggs never receive sperm. Large numbers are eaten by fish and other aquatic animals before they have had a chance to hatch. After hatching, the young fish are in constant danger of being eaten by cannibalistic fish and other animals. Regardless of the high mortality rate, the species survives because of the tremendous number of eggs laid. This number varies from about 500 in the case of the trout to six or seven million in the codfish.

Spawning habits of various fish. The spawning habits and life history of fish vary with different species. As a rule, fresh-water fish spawn in the waters where they normally live, although they often travel to shallower water for this purpose. However, many fish travel long distances to spawning areas — from lakes and rivers into small streams, from fresh-water streams to the ocean, and from the ocean into fresh-water streams.

Among the most interesting fish migrations is that of the eel. This long, slender fish lives in rivers and streams of the coastal regions and may be found in smaller numbers much farther inland. As the spawning time approaches, adult eels that live in streams flowing into the Atlantic Ocean and Gulf of Mexico begin a long journey to the sea. They swim to spawning grounds far out in the Atlantic Ocean between the West Indies and Bermuda. Each female eel lays nearly 10 million eggs. After spawning, both male and female adult eels die.

The eel larvae which hatch from the fertilized eggs are transparent at first. Soon they change into yellowish " elvers " which remain in the ocean until they have reached a length of about two inches. The young eels enter the mouths of rivers and streams in droves. The males travel upstream only a short distance. However, the females continue on a distance of 1,000 miles or more.

The eel matures in three to eight years, then starts its long return trip to the spawning grounds in which it began life. It is interesting that both North American and European eels spawn in the same ocean waters. However, the young eels always find their way to the rivers and streams of their respective continents.

Life history of salmon. The adult Pacific salmon lives in the ocean all along the northern coast. In spring or early summer, both sexes migrate in enormous numbers up the Columbia and other rivers, often for hundreds of miles. During these " runs," the canners make their annual catches by means of barriers or machines which scoop up the passing fish.

The adults begin to make their last journey during the month of March. Slowly at first, and later at the rate of many miles per day, they work their way against the current of the river to the spawning beds where they themselves hatched from eggs three or four years earlier. Here, in water not warmer than 54 degrees, each female deposits about 3,500 eggs. The male spreads milt over them, but many eggs are not fertilized, and hence do not develop.

The eggs are deposited on fine gravel, a process which extends over several days. Soon after spawning the adults die. After 30 to 40 days, the eggs hatch. However, as is usual with fish, the yolk remains attached until it is absorbed and the *fry,* as young fish are frequently called, can shift for themselves.

Fig. 29-13. Salmon travel upstream against the current to spawning beds.

The economic importance of fish. Of the 13,000 known species of fish, at least 5,000 have food value. Among the most important salt-water food fish are the cod, haddock, mackerel, herring, and halibut, sole, tuna, and sea perch. Fresh-water species, taken from the Great Lakes and other lakes and the larger rivers, include the yellow perch, whitefish, lake trout, wall-eyed pike, northern pike, buffalo, carp, catfish, and others. It is hard to estimate the annual revenue from *commercial fishing* and the number of people who depend on the fishing industries. The value of the Pacific salmon catch each year amounts to about $15,000,000, while the Atlantic cod returns about $20,000,000. The value of *sport fishing* cannot be measured in financial terms.

Fish supply many products in addition to food. *Cod liver oil* is one of the best sources of vitamins D and A. Similar oils are extracted from the livers of halibut and sharks. *Fish oil* is used in the manufacture of certain paints. Many dog, cat, poultry, and other livestock feeds contain *fish meal,* made from fish not generally used as human food. *Glue* is made from the waste parts and bones of fish. The scales of certain fish are used in making artificial pearls.

Commercial fishing. Ocean fishing usually involves a fleet of small boats which tow nets between them or set nets in the form of a large trap. The ocean, or marine, fisherman generally concentrates on a few varieties of edible fish which are abundant in the waters of his region. In the case of the tuna, the fish are caught individually with hook and line from the sides of special boats.

Fresh-water commercial fishing is most frequent in the Great Lakes and in the larger rivers. Gill nets, which catch the fish just below the gill covers, are widely used in the Great Lakes for catching whitefish, lake trout, wall-eyed pike, and yellow perch. Catfish, buffalo fish, carp, sheepshead, and suckers are caught abundantly in the larger rivers.

Sport fishing. *Game fish* are the delight of the angler because of the sport in catching them. To save the fresh-water game fish for anglers, most states have imposed rigid regulations on the methods used in catching them.

The yellow perch is called " the fish for the beginner " because so little skill is required in catching it. It is found in the Great Lakes and in many of the smaller inland lakes and ponds. The bass family is well represented in inland

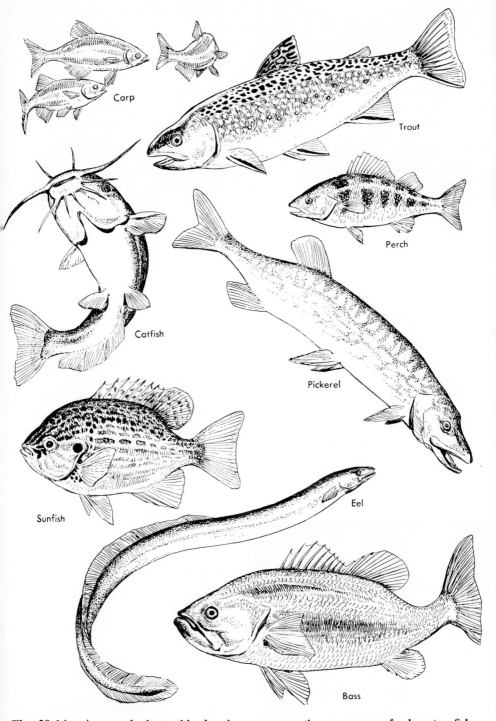

Fig. 29-14. As you look at this drawing, compare these common fresh-water fish. The trout, pickerel, and bass are considered game fish. They put up a considerable fight when caught on a hook.

lakes and streams in the form of the large-mouthed black bass, the silver bass, the rock bass, the crappie, and others.

The members of the pike family are fighters. Among them are the great northern pike, which weighs 25 pounds or more; the pickerel, which is smaller; and the giant of them all, the muskellunge, found in the larger lakes of northern United States and Canada.

Trout are the prize of the more advanced angler who has mastered the use of the fly rod. This fresh-water member of the salmon family is found in cold mountain streams and, in the case of certain species, in lakes.

The amateur aquarist. Many collectors specialize in small varieties of native fish, such as darters and minnows. The collection of native fish may be housed in any standard aquarium, although an air pump is usually necessary to maintain a sufficient supply of oxygen in the water. In collecting native fish, one should be careful not to include small specimens of game fish which are under the legal size limit. The number of small varieties upon which there is no restriction is great enough to provide the collector with abundant collecting possibilities.

Goldfish are a specialty among many collectors. As a result of years of specialized breeding, a large selection of beautiful forms is available. Comets, fantails, veil-tails, telescopes, moors, and shubunkins are among the many forms available.

Brightly-colored tropical fish in a wide variety of forms are ideal subjects for the more advanced collector. The supply of these varieties has become an important industry in America and many other countries. Species from southern United States, Central America, South America, Africa, China, and far-off Borneo are available in tropical fish stores. They must be maintained in water ranging from 70 to 80° F, thus necessitating heaters in most sections of the country. Along with the brightly-colored fish, the tropical aquarium provides opportunity to grow numerous aquatic plants.

Fish conservation is a complex problem. Fish conservation involves reconditioning the lakes and streams, a hatchery program, law enforcement, and public cooperation. Fish conservation is tied in closely with water, soil, forest, and wildlife conservation. We shall discuss all of these topics in detail in Chapter 56.

In Conclusion

No vertebrate has challenged the fish for control of the oceans and bodies of fresh water. A streamlined body with scales and fins, gills, and a two-chambered heart seem to be perfectly adapted to an aquatic environment. Alligators and water-dwelling snakes, swimming and diving birds, whales and seals share the water with fish. But none of these higher vertebrates compares with fish in importance in the water.

In your study of the next group of vertebrates, the amphibians, you will find many fishlike animals. Others, such as the toad, are land dwellers. In studying these animals you will find the basic structures of fish carried to a higher degree of perfection in the development of a land animal.

BIOLOGICALLY SPEAKING

air bladder
anal fin
auricle
branchial artery
bulbus arteriosus
cardinal vein
caudal fin
cerebellum
Chondrichthyes
chromatophores
cranial cavity
Cyclostomata
dorsal aorta

dorsal fin
fry
gall bladder
gill arch
gill filament
gill raker
isthmus
lateral line
medulla oblongata
milt
olfactory lobe
operculum
optic lobe

Osteichthyes
pectoral fin
pelvic fin
pericardial cavity
pyloric caecum
pylorus
scales
sinus venosus
spawn
spinal cord
ventral aorta
ventricle

QUESTIONS FOR REVIEW

1. Describe the manner in which the sea lamprey attacks its prey.
2. What methods are being used to control sea lampreys?
3. What characteristics distinguish the shark from bony fish?
4. How does the body slime protect a fish?
5. Describe countershading in the fish.
6. Name the fins of the yellow perch, and discuss the use of each.
7. Describe the organs of the alimentary canal of a fish in the order in which food passes through them.
8. Describe the structure of the fish heart.
9. Trace a drop of blood from the ventral aorta through a gill to the dorsal aorta, and describe changes in the blood during its circulation through a gill.
10. (a) Locate and describe the air bladder. (b) What is its function?
11. Name the various regions of the fish brain and the kind of nervous activity centered in each part.
12. Discuss the efficiency of the various sense organs of a fish.
13. Describe the life history of the salmon and the eel.
14. Name several commercial products which come from fish.

APPLYING FACTS AND PRINCIPLES

1. Explain how the body covering, limbs, and sense organs of a fish are ideally suited to life in the water.
2. Give possible reasons why a fish dies in the air even though the air contains more oxygen than the water in which it lives.
3. Tropical aquarium fishes sometimes develop a strange disorder as a result of chilling. The fish float to the surface or sink to the bottom when they are not actively swimming. They may even turn over while they are swimming. What internal organ would you believe is affected by this disorder?
4. Fish lay enormous numbers of eggs, yet seldom overpopulate the waters in which they live. Give several reasons to account for this.
5. What conclusions might you draw regarding the ancestry of the salmon and eel, on a basis of the spawning habits of these fish?

CHAPTER 30

Amphibia—Vertebrates with Double Lives

NATURE has revealed a very important secret in the class that includes salamanders, frogs, and toads, which are grouped together under the name of **Amphibia** (am-*fib*-ee-uh). The members of this class show how vertebrates left the water to live on land. The term " double life " refers to the two distinct phases of the life of most of these curious animals. Certain kinds remain aquatic throughout life, others live in marshes and alternate between sun baths and dips in the pool. Still others leave the water entirely early in life and never return except to establish new generations of their kind in the water where they began their own lives.

Characteristics of the Amphibia. The name *Amphibia* means, literally, " having two lives." It refers to the fact that the frog and its relatives are, for the most part, aquatic, fishlike animals when young, but land-dwellers when they become adults. This series of changes is a *metamorphosis* just as is the life history of certain insects. In this transition from water to land forms, many strange combinations of gills and lungs, fins and legs occur. Gills are found on animals with legs, and fins occur, too, sometimes accompanied by lungs.

In general, the Amphibia are distinct from other vertebrate animals in the following ways: (1) body covered by a thin, flexible, and usually moist skin, without scales, fur, or feathers; (2) feet, if present, often webbed; (3) toes soft and lacking claws; (4) immature or larval forms, vegetarian; adults usually carnivorous; (5) heart two-chambered in larvae, but three-chambered in adults; circulation well developed; (6) eggs fertilized externally as soon as laid; and (7) metamorphosis occurring.

Orders of Amphibia. Amphibians flourished in an era of the geological past called the *Carboniferous Period*. During this period many of the plants which formed our coal deposits were living, which explains the name *carboniferous*. The amphibians we have today are but a small segment of the numbers which flourished during this ancient period. At least ten orders of amphibians are known to be extinct. Just three remaining orders include all of the living amphibians.

The order **Apoda** contains a few surviving legless amphibia of the tropics. These strange, wormlike creatures are often called *caecilians* (see-*sil*-ee-uns). A second order, **Caudata,** includes amphibians which have tails throughout life. Here we place the familiar *salamanders* and *newts*. The most familiar amphibians are the frogs and toads, members of the order **Salientia**. Frogs and toads are different from other amphibians in that they lack tails in the adult stage. These animals, along with certain of the salamanders, undergo an interesting transition.
(*Text continued on page 344.*)

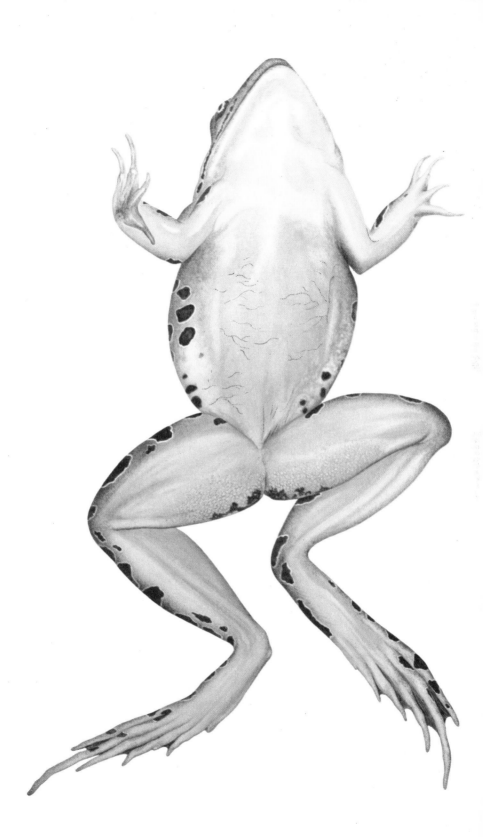

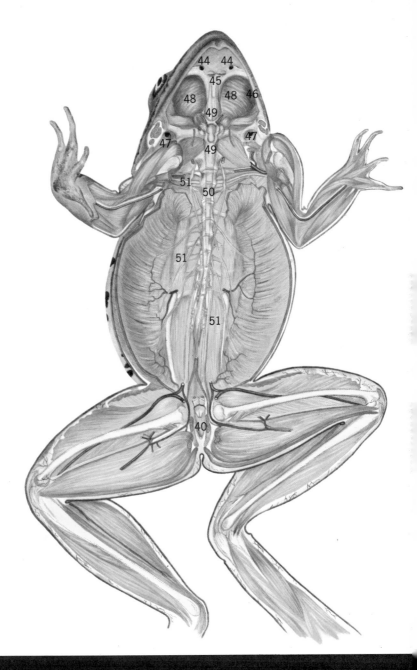

Key to the Structures of the Frog

1. Transverse abdominal muscles
2. Vertical abdominal muscles
3. Muscles to floor of mouth
4. Sockets for attachment of arms
5. Shoulder muscles
6. Right auricle of heart
7. Left auricle of heart
8. Ventricle of heart
9. Great veins to right auricle
10. Great artery from heart (conus arteriosus)
11. Liver
12. Stomach
13. Pancreas
14. Small intestine
15. Large intestine (rectum)
16. Spleen
17. Mesentery
18. Abdominal vein
19. Leg muscles
20. Tongue
21. Glottis opening
22. Trachea
23. Lungs
24. Sinus venosus
25. Pulmonary veins
26. Gall bladder
27. Bile duct
28. Hepatic portal vein
29. Sockets for attachment of legs
30. Gullet
31. Vein from kidneys (posterior vena cava)
32. Kidneys
33. Dorsal aorta
34. Fat bodies
35. Ovaries
36. Oviducts
37. Openings of oviducts
38. Egg sac (uterus)
39. Urinary bladder
40. Cloaca
41. Lining of mouth
42. Veins from legs to kidneys (renal portal vein)
43. Ureters
44. Internal nostril openings
45. Vomerine teeth
46. Teeth of the upper jaw
47. Openings of Eustachian tubes
48. Eye sockets
49. Brain
50. Spinal cord
51. Spinal nerves

Fig. 30-1. The mud puppy is an aquatic salamander familiar to many fishermen.

(*Text continued from page 342.*)
They change from an aquatic life as a larva to a semiaquatic or terrestrial life as an adult.

Salamanders and newts have tails throughout life. You are probably familiar with several of the *salamanders,* although you may have called them lizards. Many salamanders resemble lizards in general form. Both have elongated bodies, long tails, and short legs. However, a salamander has soft, moist skin and lacks claws on its toes. The lizard has a scale-covered body and claws on its toes, characteristics of reptiles almost never found among the amphibians. Some salamanders have no legs at all.

Fig. 30-2. The tiger salamander is widely distributed in North America.

American Museum of Natural History

Salamanders range in size from a few inches to species several feet in length. The giant salamanders are represented in the United States by the *American hellbender* which reaches a length of two feet or more. This large salamander with loose grayish or reddish-brown skin, lives in the streams of the eastern United States. One of its relatives, the giant salamander of Japan, grows to five feet long and is the largest living amphibian.

Another large salamander of the Middle West is the *mud puppy* or *water dog* (*Necturus*). Many an unsuspecting fisherman has been startled when he pulled one of these slimy salamanders from a mud bottom stream in the late evening or night. The mud puppy may reach a length of two feet. It has a flattened, rectangular head, small eyes, a flattened tail and two pairs of short legs. The most striking feature of the body is the pair of dark red, bushy gills which are attached at the base of the head just above the front legs (Fig. 30-1). When the animal is in the water, these gills wave slowly back and forth. They are retained throughout life.

The mud puppy spends the day hiding under rocks or buried in the mud at the bottom of a stream. It comes out at night in search of crayfish, insect larvae, and worms. When caught, it usually bites vigorously. However, the bite is not dangerous and is definitely not poisonous. The poisonous secretion of the mud puppy's skin is not harmful to man.

The *tiger salamander,* shown in Fig. 30-2, is found in most of the United States. It is one of the larger salamanders, reaching a length of six to ten inches. The bright yellow bars and blotches on a background color of dark brown give it its name. This salamander lives as an aquatic, gill-breathing larva for about three months, after which it leaves the water and lives on land. Both lungs and the thin, moist skin function in respiration during the land-dwelling stage. Certain of these salamanders remain aquatic throughout life and reproduce while still in the larval, or *axolotl,* stage. This curious characteristic once led biologists to believe that the axolotl and tiger salamander were different species of salamanders. The axolotl, which produces eggs or sperm, is one of the rare instances in which a larval stage reaches sexual maturity.

The *spotted salamander* might easily be confused with the tiger salamander, since the two species are similar in size and color. However, the spotted salamander is shiny black with yellow spots. Its tail is round, while that of the tiger salamander is flattened laterally.

We often speak of the land-dwelling stage of small salamanders as **newts.** The *crimson-spotted newt* is especially interesting to the biologist because of its " triple life." This small salamander hatches, usually in May, into a gill-breathing aquatic larva. After about two months, it changes to a land-dwelling stage with lungs. The coral-red color of this stage gives it the name *red eft.* One or two years later, the skin color changes to greenish-olive with crimson spots along the sides. The newt returns to the water and resumes aquatic life, breathing through its skin while under water and using its lungs at the surface.

The salamanders we have discussed are but a few of the many kinds you can find under piles of wet leaves, under rocks in stream beds, in abandoned wells, and in other moist places. Aquatic and land-dwelling stages of salamanders make ideal specimens for aquaria and moist terraria. With a little coaxing, they will eat meal worms or small insects from your hand.

Toads are the most valuable members of the Amphibia. Toads are important from the standpoint of insect destruction.

While some people are careful to avoid toads in the woods or destroy them when they see them, better-informed gardeners protect them for the service they render in destroying insects.

The toad is the most terrestrial of all amphibians, and after leaving the water early in life, never returns except to lay eggs. The toad starts life as a tiny black tadpole which soon grows legs, absorbs its tail, and hops onto land as a small, black froglike creature. It soon develops the warty skin characteristic of its kind. Adults of the common toad, *Bufo,* are usually greenish- or reddish-brown above and grayish-yellow beneath.

Toads sleep most of the day under rocks or boards, but are active at night, snatching insects with their quick, sticky tongue. When disturbed, they have no choice but to lie close to the ground. The toad has lost the swimming ability of other amphibians and on land moves with clumsy motion. In its " in-between " existence, this unfortunate creature lacks efficient locomotion in any environment, and is able to survive only because of its protective coloration.

Tree frogs are often heard but seldom seen. Another member of the Amphibia is the tree frog, *Hyla,* which, though common, is seldom seen because of its almost perfect protective coloration. Its song is familiar enough when the " peepers' " cheerful chorus ushers in the early spring. It seems hardly possible that so loud a song can come from so tiny a frog, little more than an inch long. But if we are patient and successful enough to hunt one out with a flashlight at night, the reason for their loud voice is clear. The little *Hyla* can expand its throat into a vocal sac twice the size of its head, and with this enormous drum can produce its remarkable music.

On each toe these true tree climbers have a sticky disk by which they can climb

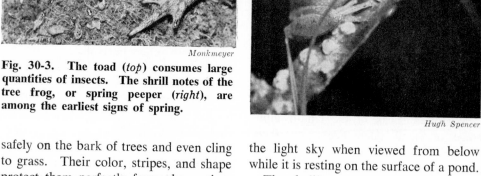

Monkmeyer

Fig. 30-3. The toad (*top*) consumes large quantities of insects. The shrill notes of the tree frog, or spring peeper (*right*), are among the earliest signs of spring.

Hugh Spencer

safely on the bark of trees and even cling to grass. Their color, stripes, and shape protect them perfectly from observation.

The eggs are laid in early spring and the tiny reddish **tadpoles** feed on mosquito larvae. The adults eat ants and gnats, which ought to give these frogs a place in our affection. A curious fact about their tadpole stage is that they often leave the water before the tail is entirely resorbed. Apparently they are able to breathe air earlier in their metamorphosis than the majority of other frogs.

Frogs are the best known of the Amphibia. The most common frog in the United States is the *leopard frog,* which inhabits nearly every pond, marsh, and roadside ditch. It frequently travels considerable distances from the water and may be seen hopping through the grass in meadows. Its name comes from the large dark spots, or blotches, surrounded by yellow or white rings which cover the grayish-green background color of the skin. The under surface of the leopard frog is creamy white, thus blending with

the light sky when viewed from below while it is resting on the surface of a pond.

The *bullfrog,* so named because its sound resembles the distant bellowing of a bull, is the most aquatic of all frogs. It never leaves the water except to sit on the bank of a lake or pond at night. The color of the bullfrog varies from green to nearly yellow, although the majority of them are greenish-brown. The under surface of the body is grayish-white mingled with numerous dark splotches.

The large fully-webbed hind feet of the bullfrog make it an excellent swimmer. These legs are well developed and ten inches long in large specimens. The bullfrog's diet is quite varied and includes insects, worms, crayfish, and small fish.

The economic importance of frogs. Much of the diet of frogs consists of insects. If they had no other value at all, this service alone would justify their protection. Many states have recognized their value and have passed laws regulating the hunting of frogs and prohibiting their capture during the breeding season.

The large hind legs of the bullfrog are a table delicacy. Frog farms, occupying large marshy areas, supply much of the demand for legs. The smaller species of frogs are widely used by fishermen for bait. As a biological specimen for dissection in the laboratory, the frog has long been a favorite. Since its internal organs are arranged similarly to those of the human body, the frog dissection is an excellent introduction to human anatomy.

In recent years, male frogs have been used for pregnancy tests. Hospitals and clinics have become one of the best customers of frog collectors. With all of these uses, you can see that we must guard our frog population and conserve the lakes, marshes, and other watery habitats in which they thrive.

Anatomy of the frog. Facing page 342 you will find a leopard frog as seen by the " Trans-Vision " process. The first page (Plate I) shows the lower side of the frog. The upper side is shown on the last page (Plate VIII). As you turn the pages between these, you will see the internal organs at various depths of the body. Pages on the right show the front (ventral) side of the organs. The left transparencies show the organs of the back (dorsal) side.

As we discuss the structure of the frog — its form and body covering, legs, head structure, and internal organs — find the various organs in the plates of the " Trans-Vision."

External structure of the frog. The frog's body is short, broad, and angular. It lacks the perfect streamlined form we found in the fish. For this reason, the frog is not the graceful swimmer the fish is, nor does its awkward hopping on land compare with the graceful movement of most other land animals. This is the price the frog must pay for living in two environments.

The skin is thin, moist, and loose. It is richly supplied with blood vessels. Glands in the skin secrete *mucus* which reaches the surface through tiny tubes. This slimy substance makes the frog difficult to hold. The skin lacks any protective outgrowths such as the scales and plates of fish and reptiles.

Adaptations of the frog's legs. The front legs of the frog are short and weak. Each has four inturned toes with soft rounded tips (Fig. 30-5, page 348). The front feet lack a web and are not used for swimming. The inner toe of a male frog is enlarged, especially during the breeding season. The front legs are used to prop

Fig. 30-4. The leopard frog (*top*) is the most familiar frog found in North America. The bullfrog (*bottom*), named for its low bellowing call, is the largest of all North American frogs.

Gluck from National Audubon Society

Austing from National Audubon Society

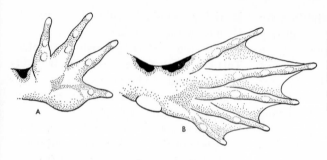

Fig. 30-5. The drawing at the left shows the front (*A*) and hind foot (*B*) of a frog. The fully-webbed hind foot enables the animal to be an excellent swimmer.

up the body on land and to break the fall after a leap.

The hind legs are enormously developed and adapted in several ways for swimming and leaping. The thigh and calf muscles are very powerful. The ankle region and toes are greatly lengthened, forming a foot which is longer than the lower leg. A broad flexible **web membrane** lies between the five long toes, and makes the foot an extremely efficient swimming organ. The hind legs fold together along the body when the frog is resting on land. In this position, the animal is ready for a sudden leap.

The head and its structures. Probably the most noticeable structures of the head are the eyes. The eyes of frogs and toads are among the most beautiful of the animal kingdom. The bronze-colored iris

Fig. 30-6. The tongue of the frog is especially well adapted for catching insects because of its flexibility and stickiness. Note how it is attached at the front of the mouth.

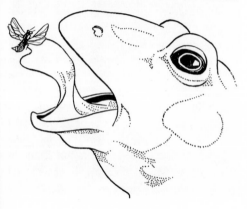

surrounds the large black pupil opening. Muscles attached to the eyeball rotate the eye in its socket. The frog's eyes bulge above the head, but can be pulled into their sockets and pressed against the roof of the mouth. In this position, they help to hold food in the mouth.

When the eyes are pulled down, the upper and lower eyelids fold over them. The bulging eyes serve as periscopes when the frog is under water. It can float just below the surface with its eyes above water. A third eyelid, the **nictitating** (*nik*-tih-tay-ting) **membrane,** joins the lower lid. This thin covering keeps the eyeball moist on land and serves as a protective covering when the frog is under water.

The nostrils are located far forward on top of the head, allowing the frog to breathe air with all but the top of the head submerged.

The frog has no external ears. The eardrum, or **tympanic** (tim-*pan*-ik) **membrane,** lies on the surface of the body just behind the eyes. The cavity of the middle ear lies just below the tympanic membrane. A canal, or **Eustachian** (you-*stay*-kee-un) **tube,** connects each middle ear with the mouth cavity. The inner ears are embedded in the skull.

The frog's mouth is enormous. The frog's mouth extends literally from ear to ear. If you watch a frog catch a fly, you will discover why the mouth must be so large. It serves as an insect trap. Its thick sticky tongue is a food-getting device. The tongue is attached at the front in the floor of the mouth and has two projections on the free end (Fig. 30-6).

When a frog catches an insect, the mouth opens wide and the tongue flips over and out. The insect is caught on the sticky tongue surface and is thrown against the roof of the mouth. The mouth snaps shut and the insect is swallowed. This happens so quickly you can hardly see it. Two **vomerine teeth,** projecting from bones of the roof of the mouth, aid in holding the prey. The frog has no teeth on the lower jaw. Those on the upper jaw are small. In toads, both sets are lacking.

Inside the frog's mouth, as shown in Fig. 30-7, you can see various openings. The internal nostril openings lie in the roof near the front, on either side of the vomerine teeth. Far back on the sides of the roof of the mouth are the openings of the Eustachian tubes. In a corresponding position in the floor of the mouth of a male frog are openings to the **vocal sacs.** When a frog croaks, air is forced through these openings into bladderlike sacs which expand between the ears and the shoulders. This action adds resonance and volume to the sound. When the frog croaks under water, air is forced from the lungs, over the vocal cords, into the mouth and back to the lungs. The throat contains two single openings — a large **gullet opening** leads to the stomach; below the gullet opening is the slitlike **glottis,** the opening to the lungs.

Digestive system of the frog. While the diet of the adult leopard frog consists largely of insects and worms, it can swallow even larger prey because of its large, elastic **gullet.** The short gullet leads to the **stomach,** an oval enlargement of the food tube. The stomach is large at the gullet and tapers at the lower end. Here the stomach joins the small intestine at a point referred to as the **pylorus.** The

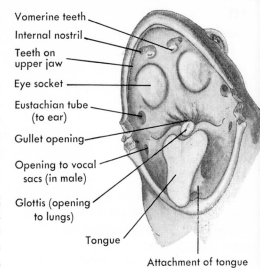

Vomerine teeth
Internal nostril
Teeth on upper jaw
Eye socket
Eustachian tube (to ear)
Gullet opening
Opening to vocal sacs (in male)
Glottis (opening to lungs)
Tongue
Attachment of tongue

Fig. 30-7. The drawing above shows the internal structure of the frog's mouth. Its proportionately large size is an adaptation for food-getting.

stomach content passes into the small intestine through a muscular **pyloric valve.**

The **small intestine** lies in several loops supported by a fanlike membrane, the **mesentery** (*mes*-en-tair-ee). The small intestine of the frog is proportionally longer than that of the fish. At its lower end, the small intestine leads to a short, broad **colon,** or *large intestine.* The lower end of the large intestine, leading to the anal opening, is termed the **cloaca** (kloh-*ay*-kuh). The walls of the cloaca contain openings of the ureters from the kidneys, the urinary bladder, and the oviducts in the female.

The large three-lobed **liver** partially covers the stomach. It is a large storehouse for digested food and a digestive gland which secretes bile. The bile collects in the **gall bladder** on the dorsal side of the liver and passes into the upper small intestine through the **bile duct.** The **pancreas,** a second digestive gland, lies inside of the curve of the stomach. Pancreatic fluid passes into the small intestine with bile through the bile duct. Both of these fluids are necessary for intestinal digestion. **Mucous glands** in the walls of the stomach and intestine secrete mucus, a lubricating fluid. Tiny **gastric glands** in the walls of the stomach secrete gastric fluid, another vital digestive fluid.

We find in the frog a digestive system like that of other vertebrates. A long food tube, or *alimentary canal,* is composed of specialized regions where digestion and absorption of digested food take place. The length of the alimentary canal increases the efficiency of both these processes.

The respiratory system of the frog. Have you ever wondered how the frog, an air breather, can stay under water for long periods and lie buried in the mud at the bottom of a pond through a winter hibernation? The answer lies in *skin respiration.* The skin of the frog and other amphibians is thin and richly supplied with blood vessels. While the frog is in the water, dissolved oxygen passes through the skin to the blood. Carbon dioxide is given off. Respiration through the skin supplies the frog's needs as long as it is quiet. During hibernation, the body processes continue at a very slow rate. The oxygen need is very low. However, body activity, such as swimming, greatly increases the need for oxygen and the skin cannot supply enough. The frog therefore comes to the surface and breathes air.

We inhale and exhale air by increasing and decreasing the size of our chest cavities. This is accomplished by movement of the **ribs** and **diaphragm** (*dy*-uh-fram), a muscular partition at the bottom of the chest cavity. The frog has no diaphragm and therefore has no chest cavity; nor does the frog have ribs, which explains why it must force air into the mouth and out of it by up-and-down movement of the floor of the mouth. When the frog lowers the floor of its mouth with the

mouth closed, air rushes into the mouth through the open nostrils. When the floor of the mouth springs up, air passes out through the nostrils.

The lining of the mouth is well adapted for respiration because it is thin, moist, and richly supplied with blood vessels. At this point we need to distinguish mouth breathing from lung breathing. The frog may pump air in and out of its mouth for some time without using its lungs at all. When the lungs are used, the nostrils are closed by flaps of skin, as the floor of the mouth rises. The glottis opens and admits air to the trachea and lungs. Then, with the nostrils still closed, muscles along the sides contract with a twitching action and the floor of the mouth is thrust down, thus creating a partial vacuum in the mouth. Thus air is partially forced and partially drawn out of the lungs. The upthrust of the mouth immediately following this seems to be higher than usual, and forces air back into the lungs. After exchanging air once or twice from mouth to lungs and lungs to mouth, the frog resumes mouth breathing through the open nostrils.

Thus the frog depends on its lungs only to supplement mouth breathing of air. As you might expect, the lungs are small when compared with higher animals which depend entirely on lung breathing. The lungs are thin-walled sacks that lack the spongy tissue ours have.

The circulatory system. The circulatory system of the frog shows an advance over that of the fish and a step toward the complex system of the higher vertebrates. One of these advances is a three-chambered heart, consisting of **two auricles** and a muscular **ventricle** (Fig. 30-8). **Deoxygenated** blood which has supplied its oxygen to the tissues enters the right auricle from various parts of the body. Blood from the lungs, which is

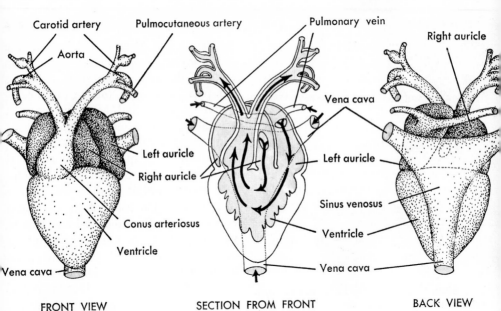

| Carotid artery | Pulmocutaneous artery | Pulmonary vein | Right auricle |

FRONT VIEW   SECTION FROM FRONT   BACK VIEW

Fig. 30-8. In the frog heart, three branches of the vena cava lead to the right auricle. Pulmonary veins lead from the lungs to the left auricle. Blood from both of these chambers passes through valves to the ventricle, then out of the heart through the conus arteriosus. This large vessel divides above the heart and gives rise to the right and left carotid, aorta, and pulmocutaneous arteries. The right figure shows the heart viewed from the back side, where the venae cavae enter the sinus venosus and the pulmonary veins enter the left auricle.

oxygenated when the lungs are in use, enters the left auricle. The auricles contract simultaneously and fill the ventricle. Contraction of the ventricle forces blood out a large vessel, the **conus arteriosus**, which lies against the front side of the heart. This large vessel divides at once into two branches like a letter Y. Each of these branches divides again into three arteries. The anterior pair are the **carotids** (kuh-*rot*-ids). They carry blood to the head. The middle pair, or **aortic arches**, bend to the right and left around the heart and join just below the liver to form the **dorsal aorta**. This great artery supplies the muscles, digestive organs, and other body tissues. The posterior, or **pulmocutaneous** (pul-moh-kyoo-*tay*-nee-us), arteries form branches which supply the lungs, mouth, and skin.

Blood returning from the body is laden with carbon dioxide and other cell wastes and has been relieved of much of its oxy-

gen. Three large veins, the **venae cavae**, join a triangular, thin-walled sac, the **sinus venosus**, on the back side of the heart, which, in turn, empties into the right auricle. Part of the blood returning to the heart from the lower parts of the body flows through vessels of the digestive organs and absorbs digested food. Then this blood flows into the **portal vein** and passes through the liver on its way to the right auricle. During each complete circulation of the blood, some of the blood passes through the kidneys where nitrogen-containing wastes from cell activity and water are removed.

The frog's circulatory system shows several advances over that of the fish. Blood passes through the two-chambered heart of the fish only once in making a round trip through the body. The three-chambered frog heart receives blood both from the body and from the lungs and pumps blood to the head and body as

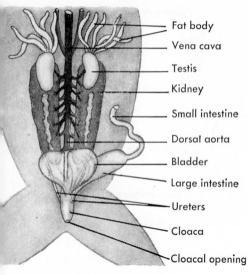

- Fat body
- Vena cava
- Testis
- Kidney
- Small intestine
- Dorsal aorta
- Bladder
- Large intestine
- Ureters
- Cloaca
- Cloacal opening

Fig. 30-9. This drawing illustrates the uro-genital organs of a male frog.

well as to the various centers where respiration takes place.

The excretory system of the frog. The frog's skin is a vital organ of excretion since it is here rather than in the mouth or lungs that most of the carbon dioxide is discharged from the blood. The liver removes certain wastes and eliminates them with bile or converts them into urea for removal by the kidneys. The large intestine eliminates undigested food and other wastes. However, the kidneys are the principal organs of excretion. They receive wastes from the blood which flows into them through the renal arteries and out through the renal veins. The kidneys are large, dark red organs lying on either side of the spine against the back body wall. *Urine* collects in the kidneys and flows to the cloaca through tiny tubes, the **ureters** (you-*ree*-ters), that you can see in Fig. 30-9. The urine may be excreted immediately, or it may be stored after being forced into the bladder through an opening in the cloaca.

The frog's nervous system. The frog's brain shows a considerable advance over that of the fish. **Olfactory lobes** lie at the anterior end of the brain (Fig.

30-10). The elongated lobes of the **cerebrum** are proportionally larger than those of the fish. Posterior to these are the prominent **optic lobes**. The **cerebellum** is just behind the optic lobes. It is small in the frog and is a band of tissue lying at right angles to the long axis of the brain. The spinal cord enlarges at its anterior end to form the **medulla**. The spinal cord is shorter and thicker than that of the fish. Pairs of **spinal nerves** branch from the cord and pass to various parts of the body through openings between the vertebrae. Leaving the brain are ten pairs of **cranial nerves**.

Reproductive system. Since the reproductive organs of the frog are internal, it is difficult to distinguish the sexes except during the breeding season, when the thumb of the male is enlarged. The male reproductive organs are two oval, creamy white or yellowish **testes**. They lie in the back, one on each side of the spine, above the anterior region of the kidneys. Sperm develop in the testes and pass through tubes, the **vasa efferentia**, into the kidneys. When the sperm are dis-

Fig. 30-10. Compare the dorsal view of the brain of the frog with that of the fish in Fig. 29-11.

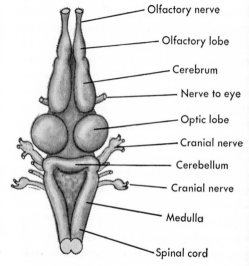

- Olfactory nerve
- Olfactory lobe
- Cerebrum
- Nerve to eye
- Optic lobe
- Cranial nerve
- Cerebellum
- Cranial nerve
- Medulla
- Spinal cord

charged, they pass through the ureters and on into the cloaca. Some species of frogs have an enlargement, the **seminal vesicle,** at the base of each ureter.

Eggs develop in a pair of large, lobed **ovaries** in the female, which attach along the back above the kidneys. During the breeding season, the eggs enlarge, burst the thin ovary walls and are freed into the body cavity. Movement of the abdominal muscles works the eggs toward the anterior end of the body cavity. Here are funnel-like openings of the long coiled **oviducts.** The eggs are fanned into the oviduct openings by cilia. Near their opening into the cloaca, the walls of the oviducts secrete a gelatinous substance which surrounds each egg. At the base of each oviduct is a saclike **uterus** in which the eggs are stored until they are laid through openings into the cloaca.

Most frogs have a mass of yellow **fat bodies** attached above the kidneys. These contain much of the food used during hibernation.

Fertilization and development of the eggs. The female leopard frog usually lays her eggs sometime between the first of April and the middle of May. The male is present with the female at the time the eggs are laid. As the eggs pass from the cloaca of the female, the male spreads sperm over them. As a result of this *direct fertilization,* most of the eggs receive sperm.

The jellylike coat which surrounds each egg swells in the water and joins the eggs in a rounded, gelatinous mass. In this clump, the eggs look like small beads, each surrounded by a transparent covering (Fig. 30-11). Not only does the jelly protect the eggs from injury, but it makes them more difficult for a hungry fish to eat. Also it serves as the first food of the young tadpole.

The frog egg is partly black and partly white. The white portion is the yolk or stored food material which will nourish the tadpole during development. The dark portion contains the living protoplasm of the egg and a dark pigment. The yolk is heavier than the rest of the egg, causing the eggs to float in the water dark side up. The black pigment on the upper side absorbs heat from the sun while the lighter lower half blends in with the light from the sky and makes the eggs hard to see from below. The gelatinous covering holds much of the heat in the mass. After eight to twenty days, depending on the weather conditions and water temperature, the tadpole hatches and wiggles away from the egg mass.

From tadpole to adult — the metamorphosis of the frog. Just after hatching, the tadpole is a tiny, short-bodied creature with a disklike mouth. It clings to the egg mass or to a plant (Fig. 30-12, page 354). Yolk stored in the body nourishes the young tadpole until it starts

Fig. 30-11. **This mass of frog's eggs is lodged in the leaves of a plant in a pond. What purpose does the gelatinous covering serve?**

Edward S. Thoï

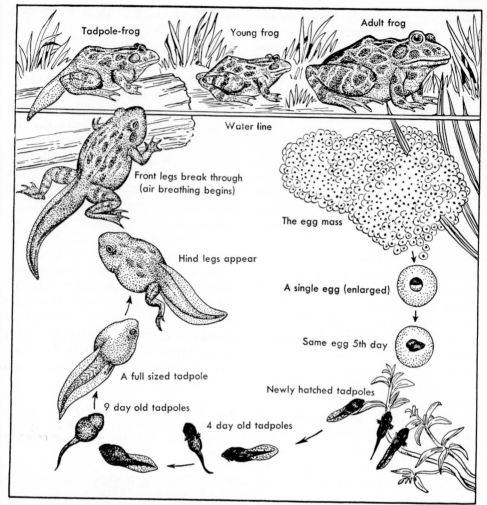

Tadpole-frog

Young frog

Adult frog

Water line

Front legs break through
(air breathing begins)

The egg mass

A single egg (enlarged)

Hind legs appear

Same egg 5th day

A full sized tadpole

Newly hatched tadpoles

9 day old tadpoles

4 day old tadpoles

Fig. 30-12. **Trace the life history of the frog in the diagram above. The length of time for metamorphosis varies in different species of frogs.**

to feed. Soon after hatching, the body lengthens and two pairs of external gills appear at the sides of the head. The tail lengthens and develops a caudal fin. The mouth opens and the tadpole begins scraping the leaves of water plants with horny lips.

Soon after the tadpoles become free swimmers, the horny lip disappears. A long, coiled digestive tract develops and the tadpole starts living on vegetable scums. Gradually a fold of skin grows backward over the gills like a flap and

leaves a small opening on the left side through which water passes out of the gill chambers. At this stage the tadpole is a fishlike animal with a lateral line, fin, two-chambered heart, and a one-circuit circulation. The animal also has a relatively long, spirally-coiled intestine.

The change to an adult frog is remarkable. The hind legs appear first. The front legs begin to form at about the same time but do not appear for some time. They remain hidden under the operculum. Soon after the appearance of the front legs, the tadpole then starts resorbing (not shedding or eating) its tail. Late in the metamorphosis, the tadpole's mouth broadens and teeth develop. While these external changes have been taking place, equally important internal changes have been occurring. A saclike chamber, resembling the air bladder of the fish, forms back of the throat. This divides into two sacs which become the lungs. The heart becomes three-chambered and the gill arteries change to the carotids, aortic arches, and the pulmocutaneous arteries. The gills stop functioning and the tadpole comes to the surface frequently to gulp air. The thin skin and broad, flat tail still play an important role in respiration during this critical time.

Even before the tail is entirely resorbed, the tadpole leaves the water and comes to land as a young frog. From this stage to the full-grown adult frog requires usually about a month. The metamorphosis of the leopard frog varies from 60 to 90 days. Full-grown adults usually appear about the first of July. The bullfrog usually spends two winters as a tadpole and its entire metamorphosis may last as long as three years.

Regeneration in Amphibia. Many amphibians, especially salamanders, have a remarkable ability to regenerate lost or injured body parts. A foot, a portion of a limb, or part of the tail may be lost in escaping from an enemy. Such amputated organs may be regenerated rapidly. The power of regeneration is present, also, in the tadpole stage of frogs and toads, especially in the early phases. However, this ability to regenerate disappears as the tadpole matures and is lacking entirely in the adult frog and toad.

Hibernation and estivation in the frog. The frog, as well as the fish and reptile, are " cold-blooded " vertebrates. This does not mean that their blood is always cold. It means that the body temperature of these animals varies with the temperature of the surroundings. Man maintains a constant average body temperature of about 98.6° F by regulating the rate of food oxidation and resulting heat release in the tissues as well as heat loss from the body surface. The cold-blooded vertebrates carry on much slower oxidation and do not maintain a constant body temperature.

With the coming of fall and the seasonal lowering of temperature, the body temperature of the frog drops to the point where it can no longer be very active. It buries itself in the mud at the bottom of a pond or finds shelter in some other protected place in the water. Heart action slows down to the point that blood hardly circulates in the vessels. The moist skin supplies the greatly reduced oxygen necessary for keeping alive. The tissues are kept alive by the slow oxidation of food stored in the fat bodies and liver. Nervous activity almost ceases and the frog lies in a stupor. This is the condition of the frog during **hibernation,** or winter rest. With the coming of spring, the warm days speed up body activity and the frog gradually resumes active life.

The hot summer months bring other problems. Lacking a device for cooling the body, the frog must escape from the extreme heat. It may lie quietly in deep cool water or bury itself in the mud at the bottom of a pond, in the condition of summer inactivity referred to as *estivation.* In many cases, smaller ponds dry up during midsummer and the frogs and other cold-blooded animals survive only by burying themselves in the mud and estivating. With the coming of cooler weather and the return of water to the pond, they come out of estivation and continue normal activity until hibernation.

In Conclusion

Having studied the frog, you can see why it has long been a favorite subject for biological study. Each individual frog passes through various stages of development from a fishlike larva to an adult terrestrial amphibian. In the adult stage, the organs and systems of the frog are complex and efficient. Biologists still marvel at its three-chambered heart with the complicated valves and arteries. The respiratory system is fascinating, too. Lungs alone cannot supply the frog's breathing needs. But lungs, mouth, and skin together compose an efficient respiratory team. Of course, if the skin is to be used in respiration, it must be thin and moist. Thus the frog may not leave the water or a moist environment entirely.

In the next class of vertebrates, you will find animals which, while similar to the frog in many ways, are much better suited to life on land. Scales furnish a more efficient protective covering for the reptile. Claws on the toes, if the animal has toes, make climbing and running possible. Lungs take over the role of respiration. You will find many well-known and interesting vertebrates in this next class.

BIOLOGICALLY SPEAKING

Amphibia	fat body	Salientia
aortic arch	glottis	seminal vesicle
Apoda	mesentery	tadpole
bile duct	newt	tympanic membrane
carotid artery	nictitating membrane	ureters
Caudata	oviduct	uterus
cloaca	oxygenated blood	vasa efferentia
conus arteriosus	pancreas	vena cava
deoxygenated blood	portal vein	vocal sacs
diaphragm	pulmocutaneous artery	vomerine teeth
Eustachian tube	salamander	web membrane

QUESTIONS FOR REVIEW

1. What several characteristics of amphibians distinguish them from other vertebrates?
2. How many orders of amphibians are represented by living members today?
3. (a) In what ways do salamanders resemble lizards? (b) Name several characteristics which make them different from lizards.
4. In which stage is the tiger salamander known as an axolotl?
5. Describe the "triple life" of the crimson-spotted newt.
6. Of what economic value are toads?
7. What are several economic uses of frogs?
8. How does a frog go about catching a flying insect?
9. How can a frog croak under water?
10. Name the organs forming the alimentary canal of a frog, in the order in which they receive food.

11. What three arterial branches carry blood from the great artery leading from the frog's heart?

12. What are the chambers of a frog's heart?

13. How is urine conducted from the frog's kidneys to the cloaca and bladder?

14. What various changes occur during the development of a tadpole? Name these changes in the order in which they occur.

APPLYING FACTS AND PRINCIPLES

1. Discuss problems in the life of a toad resulting from its " in-between " existence.

2. Frogs breathe air, yet they lie buried in the mud at the bottom of a pond during the winter months. Explain how this is possible.

3. In what respect is the direct fertilization of the frog's eggs more efficient than spawning in fish?

4. Explain how the frog illustrates relationship to the fish in its early development.

5. In what ways are the heart and circulatory system more highly developed in the frog than in the fish?

CHAPTER *31*

Reptiles—Vertebrates with Scales and Claws

SOME 200 million years ago, a new era in geological history was dawning. The earth was entering an age referred to by the geologist today as the *Mesozoic Era.* Amphibians were declining after a long period of supremacy among the animals of the earth. Reptiles were gradually replacing them. During the Mesozoic era, often referred to as the *Age of Reptiles,* giant dinosaurs fed on the leaves of the upper branches of trees while others tore flesh from their victims with savage teeth. Sea serpents churned the waters of ancient seas and giant batlike reptiles glided from cliffs and tree tops.

For nearly 100 million years, reptiles were unchallenged, especially on the land. Then their numbers began to decline and have continued to do so to the present time. Today only a small segment of this once flourishing group remains. Reptiles are most abundant in the tropics. Their numbers reduce in the mid-latitude climates and disappear entirely in the polar regions of the Arctic and Antarctic. A few small islands have offered a haven for several rare reptiles which would have perished ages ago if they had been within reach of the predators which destroyed them on the larger land masses.

Reptiles are fascinating animals to study, if you learn to avoid the relatively few harmful ones. As you study the reptiles, you may have to overcome some of the fear and prejudice long associated with these valuable vertebrates.

Fig. 31-1. The herbivorous *Stegosaurus*, though formidable looking, had a very small brain in proportion to its body size, and could not protect itself with its teeth. Here a *Stegosaurus* is being attacked by a small, carnivorous *Allosaurus*.

Ewing Galloway

The Age of Dinosaurs. Fossilized bones and eggs and footprints preserved in rock are all that remain of the age in the distant past when dinosaurs roamed the earth. Yet, with this evidence, gathered in many parts of the world, and considerable imagination, the biologist has been able to piece together a vivid picture of the earth when dinosaurs dominated animal life.

Dinosaur is an appropriate name for these ancient reptiles, for it means " terrible lizards." Many of the dinosaurs were no larger than our larger lizards today. However, some of them were giant beasts which would dwarf an elephant. These are the best-known dinosaurs.

The largest of the dinosaurs was the thunder lizard, or *Brontosaurus* (bron-toh-*sor*-us). This giant measured 75 feet in length, about 15 feet in height, and weighed 30 tons or more. It lived in shallow lakes and marshes and fed on water plants. Its enormously long neck was balanced by an equally long and heavy tail. The plated lizard, while smaller than the thunder lizard, was one of the heaviest-armored of the dinosaurs. *Stegosaurus* (steg-oh-*sor*-us), as this 30-foot monster has been named, had a double

row of plates projecting two feet from its back. Pairs of spines near the end of the tail served as deadly weapons with which to lash out at an enemy. *Stegosaurus* had a ridiculously small head with a cranial cavity no larger than that of a small dog. An auxiliary " brain " 20 times larger than the true brain consisted of a mass of nerve tissue formed by the spinal cord in the hip region. This second " brain " is thought to have controlled the seven-foot hind legs and ponderous tail of the animal.

The king of dinosaurs was the ferocious tyrant lizard, or *Tyrannosaurus* (ty-ran-oh-*sor*-us), which is probably the most terrible creature ever to roam the earth. It walked erect on its powerful hind legs and balanced its heavy body with its long tail, much in the manner of a kangaroo. Its front legs were short but powerful and its long claws could tear most prey into shreds. This giant flesh-eating reptile was nearly 50 feet in length and towered 20 feet in height. Its powerful jaws were rimmed with double-edged teeth three to six inches long and could rip the hide of even an armored victim.

You may wonder how creatures such as these ever became extinct. Had they possessed a brain in proportion to their brawn, they might exist today. But many fell victims to more intelligent animals which invaded their haunts, while others wandered into asphalt pits and bogs and sank to their doom. Other forms could not survive the gradually changing conditions of their environments. Many must have starved to death because, as their own numbers increased, they were competing for the same limited food supply. The last of these giant reptiles probably perished during the Cretaceous Period, near the close of the Mesozoic Era. This was approximately 60 to 100 million years ago. Never again did reptiles dominate the animal life of the earth.

Classification of living reptiles. Some 6,000 species of reptiles exist in the world today as remnants of the once flourishing Age of Reptiles. About 275 species are found in the United States. Some are much like their ancestors; others have become greatly modified.

Of the 16 orders of reptiles which once existed, only four orders are represented today. One of these remaining orders is nearly extinct, and is represented today by a single species. The table below lists the remaining orders of reptiles.

Characteristics of reptiles. Biologists consider the reptiles one step above the amphibians in structural development. On the other hand, they are below the birds and mammals in development of the

vertebrates. As you compare reptiles with amphibians such as the frog, you will discover ways in which they are similar and characteristics which make them different. Reptiles show the following characteristics: (1) body usually covered with scales; (2) skin dry, not moist and slimy; (3) feet, if present, have claws on the toes; (4) eggs internally fertilized and, if laid, have a protective shell. Certain species retain the eggs within the body and bring forth the young alive; (5) no metamorphosis; (6) gills never present, as both young and adults breathe with lungs; and, (7) body temperature changes with environment (cold-blooded).

Sphenodon, a reptile relic of a bygone age. One of the rarest animals on the earth today is the sole surviving species of the reptile order Rhynchocephalia. This ancient reptile, even older than the dinosaurs, is the tuatara, or *Sphenodon punctatus* (*sfee*-noh-don punk-*tay*-tus), as the biologist calls it. This strange survivor of the Age of Reptiles miraculously escaped extinction through the ages in far-off New Zealand and certain offshore islands. The first English settlers who came to New Zealand, together with the hogs and other domestic animals they brought, destroyed the few remaining tuataras on the mainland. Today, the last surviving tuataras are found on a few small islands in the Bay of Plenty and in

ORDERS OF REPTILES

NAME OF ORDER	REPRESENTATIVES
Testudinata (tes-too-dih-*nay*-tuh) or Chelonia	Turtles and tortoises
Rhynchocephalia (ring-koh-seh-*fay*-lee-uh)	*Sphenodon* or tuatara
Squamata (squah-*may*-tuh)	Lizards and snakes
Crocodilia (krok-oh-*dil*-ee-uh)	Alligators, crocodiles, gavials, and caymans

Fig. 31-2. *Sphenodon punctatus* is an interesting reptile because it is the only surviving species of a once-flourishing order.

American Museum of Natural History

Cook Strait off the coast of New Zealand. It is a challenge to biologists to preserve the few remaining tuataras.

The tuatara reaches a length of about two feet and resembles a large lizard (Fig. 31-2). Its skin is dark olive, marked with numerous light colored dots. Its eyes resemble those of a cat. The most unusual characteristic of the tuatara is a **parietal** (puh-*ry*-ih-tul) **eye** in the top of its head. While not a functioning sense organ, this strange eye has the remains of a retina and other eye structures. The tuatara hides in a burrow during the day, coming out at night to feed on insects, worms, and other small animals. The eggs are buried in a shallow depression in the ground, where they remain almost a year before hatching. The female tuatara usually lays 12 to 14 eggs. The fact that the tuatara lives well in captivity may make it possible to preserve this rare species in the reptile collections of the world.

Snakes, the most widespread reptiles. Snakes are not only the most numerous reptiles but are also the most widely distributed. They are most abundant in the tropical regions. Their numbers reduce in cooler climates to 126 species in the United States and only 22 species in Canada. No snakes are found in Alaska.

Of the more than 2,000 species of snakes in the world, a relatively small number are poisonous. The harm caused by these dangerous snakes is far outweighed by the valuable service rendered by others in destroying large numbers of insects and destructive rodents.

Snake myths and superstitions. Probably no other animal has been surrounded with as many false ideas and ridiculous superstitions as the snake. This is unfortunate, since it has resulted in the destruction of countless valuable snakes by people who thought they were performing a service. The following list clarifies some common misconceptions about snakes:

1. Snakes are not slimy. The scales covering their bodies are dry and slick. The body often feels cold because its internal temperature is no warmer than that of the surroundings.

2. They cannot jump from the ground, nor do they have to strike from a coil.

3. The forked tongue is not a fang and cannot inflict a wound. The tongue aids in smelling, as you will find later.

4. No snake was ever known to take the tip of its tail in its mouth and roll down a hill like a hoop.

5. Snakes do not have hypnotic powers. They cannot charm victims nor cast spells.

6. No snakes have poisonous breath. Several species hiss loudly when aroused,

but this is only part of a defensive " act " they perform instinctively.

7. Snakes do not steal milk from cows. The milk snake and other species live around barns and feed on rats, mice, and other rodents. They would not drink milk if offered it.

8. Rattlesnakes do not add one rattle each year, but usually two or three, depending on the number of times they shed their skins.

9. The removal of fangs from a poisonous snake does not make it harmless. New fangs will soon develop.

10. The setting of the sun has nothing to do with the death of a wounded snake. Reflex action may cause continued muscular contractions several hours after apparent death of a snake. However, these contractions are influenced by the reduced temperature in the evening rather than the setting of the sun.

11. Snakes do not swallow their young to protect them in times of danger. They have no interest in their young. Furthermore, the young would be digested in the stomach, as is the case with snakes which feed on other snakes.

Snakes developed from lizards in early times. Biologists believe that, at some ancient time, certain lizards developed a burrowing habit and, through variation of offspring, with the best-adapted surviving, gradually lost their limbs. This change, of course, required countless generations and resulted in the snakes of the present.

The snake became ideally suited for conditions in the world today, and the most widespread reptile. All snakes have lost evidence of a pectoral girdle and front limbs. A few, including the boa constrictor and python, still have the remains of a pelvic girdle and hind limbs which are reduced to short spurs. We may assume, however, that legs are " going out of style " among snakes and even these vestiges will disappear in time.

Body structure of a snake. If you examine the elongated body of a snake closely, you can distinguish the head, the trunk which contains the body cavity, and a tail which extends beyond the anal opening. As in all reptiles, the snake's body is covered with scales. Those on the back and sides of the body are small and oval, thus allowing great flexibility. The head of many snakes, including our nonpoisonous species, is covered with plates. The North American pit vipers, including the rattlesnake, have scale-covered heads. The scales on the lower side of the body form broad plates, known as **scutes.**

Snakes shed the outer layer of scales several times each season during a process known as **molting.** As this thin layer loosens all over the body, the snake usually hooks a loose portion to a sharp object such as a twig and works its way out of it. After molting, the newly exposed scale surfaces are bright and shiny.

Structures of the head. The snake's mouth is large and is provided with a double row of teeth on each side of the upper jaws and a single row in the lower jaw. The numerous conical teeth slant backward toward the throat. None of the teeth serve for chewing but are necessary to hold the prey as it is swallowed whole.

The sense of smell is very acute in snakes. Olfactory nerve endings lie in the nasal cavities which open as paired nostrils near the front of the head. The sense of smell is made more acute with the aid of the curious forked tongue which is thrust from a sheath in the floor of the mouth close to the front, through a small opening which is left when the jaws are closed. The tongue receives dust and other odor-bearing particles from the air and transfers them to tiny pits close to the front of the roof of the mouth. These **Jacobson's organs,** as they are called, contain nerve endings which are highly sensitive to odors.

Lilo Hess

Fig. 31-3. Pythons obtain their food by crushing their prey in powerful coils.

The snake's eyes have no lids and, in this respect, are different from those of other reptiles. A transparent scale covers the eye. This scale becomes cloudy just before molting and causes temporary vision difficulty. The eyeball can be turned in its orbit. Movement of the lens focuses the eye sharply on objects, especially at close range. Many snakes have round pupils. Biologists have discovered

Fig. 31-4. The rattlesnake poisons its prey with venom before swallowing it whole. Notice the modified head structures for poisoning and swallowing.

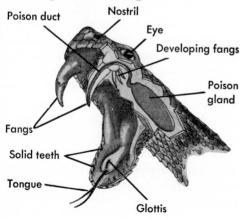

Poison duct
Nostril
Eye
Developing fangs
Poison gland
Fangs
Solid teeth
Tongue
Glottis

that these snakes are most active in daylight. On the other hand, vipers, pit vipers, boas, and pythons have elliptical pupils, similar to those of a cat. These snakes are most active at night.

The ears are embedded in the skull and have no external openings. Thus, the snake cannot hear vibrations that are transmitted by the air. However, the skull bones transmit vibrations resulting from jarring to highly sensitive ear mechanisms.

Feeding habits of snakes. All snakes feed on living animal prey. No vegetarian snakes are known to exist. We classify snakes into three groups, based on feeding habits.

Many snakes, including most of our nonpoisonous species, merely seize a prey in the mouth and *swallow it alive.* Most of these snakes feed on insects, frogs, toads, lizards, and other small animals.

The python, boa, king snake, bull snake, and other large-bodied snakes make use of a more specialized method of food-getting. These snakes seize the prey, usually by the head, wrap coils around it with lightning speed, and kill it quickly by *constriction* (Fig. 31-3). The powerful coils squeeze the victim with such force that its chest is compressed and breathing is stopped. In addition, the pressure cuts off the victim's circulation and stops the heart. The shock kills the prey, often without breaking a bone. If, after the first constriction, the snake feels a pulse in its victim, it will squeeze again. Swallowing starts immediately after the prey is killed. Biologists have found that warm-blooded animals are killed much more quickly by constriction than cold-blooded prey.

A relatively small number of snakes *poison the prey* before swallowing it. Poisonous snakes secrete **venom** in modified salivary glands at the sides of the head. When a poisonous snake strikes, paired fangs are thrust into the victim.

American Museum of Natural History

Fig. 31-5. **What adaptations for swallowing large prey are shown in this view of a snake skull?**

Venom flows from the poison glands through ducts which enter the fangs (Fig. 31-4). The hollow fangs, through which venom flows into the victim, are like hypodermic needles. The amount of venom injected varies with the size and species of snake. However, smaller species, as well as the young of larger species, have more concentrated venom. Thus, their bites may be just as dangerous as those of larger poisonous snakes.

The venom of pit vipers acts in the blood stream of the victim, where it destroys red corpuscles and smaller blood vessels, causing hemorrhage. The venom of the cobra and its relatives, including the North American coral snake, acts on the nervous system, causing paralysis.

Adaptations for swallowing. It is amazing to watch a snake swallow a prey four or five times larger than its own body. This feat is possible because of several modifications of the jaws. The lower jaws are not joined directly to the skull, but fasten to a separate **quadrate bone** which acts as a hinge and allows the jaw to drop downward and forward (Fig. 31-5). The two halves of the lower jaw are fastened at the front by an **elastic ligament,** which permits each half to operate independently of the other. The numerous slanting teeth hold the prey firmly during the swallowing process.

During swallowing, one side of the lower jaw may pull the prey into the mouth while the other side is thrust forward for a new grip. By this see-saw action, the prey is pulled down the throat much as you might pull in a rope hand over hand. The snake literally crawls forward around its prey.

The process of swallowing is so long that special adaptations are necessary to permit the snake to breathe while a large prey is in its mouth and throat. The **trachea** extends along the floor to a **glottis opening** near the front rim of the lower jaw (Fig. 31-4).

Locomotion in snakes. Several methods of locomotion are found among snakes. The most common method is **lateral undulatory movement.** The body winds from side to side, forming broad curves. The snake pushes against irregularities which give it a grip in moving forward. The entire body follows along the same track in this type of movement, used when the snake is crawling rapidly. This type of movement is also used by water snakes in swimming.

A snake may crawl slowly in a straight line by **caterpillar movement.** Several scutes are pushed forward in several sections of the body. The posterior edge of each scute grips the ground while the body is pulled forward by waves of muscular contraction.

A third method of movement, known as **side winding,** is used by snakes of the sandy desert regions. Here, the body is twisted into S-shaped loops and is raised from the ground except for two or three points of contact. The sidewinder " walks " across the sand on these loops.

You may be relieved to learn that most snakes travel at a speed of less than one mile per hour. The fastest ones cannot exceed three miles per hour. You can walk at this speed with ease and you can run a short distance at a speed of from 10 to 20 miles per hour. Thus you need have no fear of being run down by a snake!

Internal organs of a snake. Over 300 pairs of ribs attach to the vertebrae of the spine in a snake. These ribs are set in muscle and are flexible to permit movement and to allow large prey to pass through the body. The gullet and stomach are highly elastic and the digestive secretions are powerful, in order to accommodate whole prey.

The well-developed lungs lie in the anterior region of the body. The flexible ribs allow expansion of the body wall in breathing. The heart is large and has a wall or **septum** partially dividing the ventricle into the two chambers. This is an advance over the amphibian heart. Since the snake is cold-blooded, the rate of food oxidation is much lower than that of a warm-blooded animal. For this reason, snakes feed at intervals of several weeks and may go a year or more without feeding. The reptile is at a disadvantage in being cold-blooded and living on land however. In cold regions, it cannot be active during the winter. During hot weather, it must seek shelter through the day since it has no method of cooling the body below the outside temperature.

Reproduction in snakes. The majority of snakes lay eggs which resemble those of the other reptiles. Each egg contains stored food to nourish the young snake during its development, and is enclosed in a tough white shell. The eggs receive no care from the female after being laid and no incubation except the warmth of the sun. Egg-laying snakes are called **oviparous** (oh-*vip*-uh-rus), and include the black snake and blue racer.

A smaller group of snakes, including the garter snake and the copperhead, bring forth their young alive, usually in the late summer (Fig. 31-6). The eggs are retained in the reproductive organs, where they develop into young snakes. During development, there is no nourishment provided from the mother's body as in the highest group of animals, the mammals. Snakes which bring forth the young alive are classed as **ovoviviparous** (oh-voh-vy-*vip*-uh-rus), as distinguished from the higher animals which are called **viviparous** (vy-*vip*-uh-rus) and which nourish their young during development.

Some nonpoisonous snakes of North America. *Garter snakes* are the most common snakes in North America, having about 20 species included in their wide range. They live in fields and along stream banks where they feed on insects, worms, frogs, and toads. Garter snakes are harmless and do considerable good in holding smaller animals in check.

American Museum of Natural History

Fig. 31-6.   The garter snake is ovoviviparous, bringing forth its young alive.

Probably the most terrifying snake to approach is the *hog-nosed snake,* also called the *spreading viper* or *puff adder.* When surprised along the path, this plump-bodied little snake puts on an act which terrifies all but the most informed student of snakes. Amid loud hisses it suddenly raises its head and spreads its neck widely in true cobra fashion. If this act fails, it twists its head, opens its mouth and falls limp on its back as though dead. However, a person familiar with the ways of this little creature knows that the hog-nosed snake is one of few species which will not bite even when picked up.

The *black snake,* and its western variety, the *blue racer,* inhabit the central eastern United States. They are large snakes, usually four to six feet long and are covered with smooth satiny scales. When disturbed, they may fight viciously, though their bite is not poisonous. They are exceedingly valuable, since their diet includes large numbers of small rodents. The intelligent farmer never destroys a black snake near his barn, because one snake destroys more small rats and mice than several cats.

The *bull snake* of the Middle West is one of the largest snakes in the United States, and may reach nearly seven feet in length. It is a powerful constrictor and feeds on rats, mice, gophers, squirrels, and rabbits. It is exceedingly valuable in the wheat fields where it lives, and certainly warrants protection.

Anyone who does not appreciate snakes should be especially interested in conserving the *king snake,* for this individual is among the worst enemies of other snakes. It attacks them viciously and does not hesitate to seize the deadly copperhead or rattlesnake in its strong coils. King snakes vary in color from nearly black with narrow white lines to the brilliantly colored *milk snake* falsely accused of milking cows.

Fig. 31-7. The milk snake (*below*) is a common harmless snake also called the spotted adder. It ranges from Virginia to Iowa and northward. Its diet consists not of milk, as its name would indicate, but of mice that sometimes frequent dairy barns. The ring-necked snake (*right*) is another nonpoisonous snake of North America. The ring around its neck is yellow, while its back is ash-colored or sage green, and its belly orange-red.

Poisonous snakes of North America. About 20 kinds of poisonous snakes live in the various parts of the United States. We can group them as follows: (1) rattlesnakes (about 15 kinds); (2) copperhead and water moccasin; (3) coral snakes (2 kinds); and (4) yellow-bellied sea snake.

The *rattlesnakes* are the most widely distributed poisonous snakes. They belong to the family of *pit vipers,* so named because of a deep pit between the eye and the nostril which is believed to contain nerve endings sensitive to heat. Of the 15 or more kinds of rattlesnakes found in the United States, at least 12 species occur in the southwest. These include the prairie rattlesnake, western diamond rattlesnake, and horned rattlesnake, or " sidewinder " of the desert regions. The range of the timber rattlesnake includes most of eastern United States. The largest of North American rattlesnakes, the diamondback, lives in marshy areas of the southeast. Six- to eight-foot specimens have been taken in the swamps of the southern states.

Fig. 31-8. The garter snake (*above*) has a characteristic longitudinal yellow stripe down its back. It is a harmless ovoviviparous snake that feeds on worms, frogs, salamanders, and small birds' eggs. The hognosed snake (*right*) is also called the puffing adder, blowing adder, viper, spreading adder, flat-headed adder, or sand viper. Most of these names are descriptive of this snake's formidable protective behavior, although it is, in fact, quite harmless.

Fig. 31-9. The poisonous coral snake (*left*) has beautiful bands of red, yellow, and black scales, and a small, blunt head. Since it bites rather than strikes, it does no harm unless actually stepped on or handled. The diamondback rattlesnake (*below*) is so named because of the markings on its back. It is a rather thick-bodied, large-headed snake of sluggish disposition. It is not inclined to strike except when disturbed or when in pursuit of its prey.

Rattlesnakes have a series of dry segments, or **rattles,** on the end of the tail. When the snake is disturbed, it vibrates these rapidly, causing a whirring sound, which explains why, even though rattlesnakes are widely distributed, few people are bitten by them. Usually you can step away from danger when you hear and recognize a rattlesnake's warning.

The head of a rattlesnake is large and triangular. The jaws are puffy, because of the presence of poison glands (Fig. 31-4). Near the front of the upper jaw is a pair of large, hollow teeth, or **fangs.** The fangs are fastened to a bone which is hinged on the upper jaw so that when the snake's mouth is closed, the fangs fold upward against the roof of the mouth. They are pulled down by muscles when the snake opens its mouth to strike. The rattlesnake can strike fiercely a distance of one-third the length of its body or more. The fangs are driven deep into the flesh of its victim and poison flows from the glands, through the fangs, and into the wound. Both the length of the fangs and the large amount of poison

Photos from American Museum of Natural H

Fig. 31-10. The copperhead (*above*) is a poisonous pit viper, as is the rattlesnake, but it is more dangerous as it has no warning rattles and is quicker than the rattlesnake. It is found in most parts of the eastern United States. Notice the hourglass patterns formed by its scales. The cotton-mouth moccasin, or water moccasin (*left*), is a water-dwelling snake. It gets its name from the white interior of its mouth, which is displayed when the snake is aroused.

injected make the rattlesnake bite extremely dangerous, especially when the fangs happen to go into a vein.

Rattlesnakes, especially the diamondback, have several economic uses. The skin is used for purses, belts, and other articles. The flesh is eaten in many regions. The venom is " milked " from captive specimens and is used for making **antivenin,** a biological product used in treating bites of all the pit vipers.

The *copperhead,* another of the pit vipers, is highly dangerous because it strikes without warning. Copperheads usually live in dry woods of hilly country, which accounts for another of its names, *highland moccasin.* The plump body seldom reaches over three feet in length. The head is a bright copper shade. The body is marked with alternate irregular bands of light brown and dark reddish-brown arranged in an hourglass pattern.

The *water moccasin,* or *cotton-mouth moccasin,* is a close relative of the copperhead, both being members of the same genus. It lives in the warm, sluggish rivers, streams, and backwaters of the lower Mississippi region and east through the Carolinas, Georgia, and Florida.

One species of *coral snake* lives in eastern United States and is most abundant in Florida. This snake does not strike in the manner of a pit viper but bites viciously when handled. The venom of the coral snake is, ounce for ounce, more deadly than that of any other North American poisonous snake. Another species, the *Sonora coral snake,* inhabits the Southwest.

The *yellow-bellied sea snake,* while essentially a tropical species, has been reported in the coastal waters of the Pacific Ocean off the coast of California below San Diego. This single representative of the sea snakes in the waters of the New World is frequently seen off the west coast of tropical South America, Central America, and Mexico. Its eel-like body, long head, and flattened, paddlelike tail are different from other snakes. The body is dark brown above and bright yellow below. The yellow-bellied sea snake is the smallest of the sea snakes, rarely exceeding 30 inches in length. Its bite is highly poisonous. Since it is strictly a marine species, few people are endangered by it. However, fishermen dread this snake and with good reason, for a specimen is often hauled aboard a fishing vessel accidentally.

Treatment of snakebites. We now have efficient methods of treating the bites of pit vipers. Treatment must be started immediately since much of its success depends on preventing the spread of venom through the blood stream. The following steps should be taken at once:

1. Keep the victim quiet and reassured, to prevent speeding up of heart action.

2. Put a constricting band, made from a piece of cloth, a cord, or a necktie, between the wound and the heart. Tighten it firmly, but not enough to cut off the circulation completely. The tourniquet should be loosened by a doctor.

3. With a clean knife or razor blade, cut a gash about one-quarter of an inch deep between the fang marks. The blade should be sterilized before use.

4. Suck out as much blood and venom as possible, using a suction bulb if you have a snake-bite kit.

5. If a snake-bite kit is available, give an injection of antivenin serum according to the directions given. If not, rush the victim to the nearest doctor's office or hospital, where antivenin shots and other treatments can be started.

Lizards. Of the more than 2,500 species of lizards, only a small number are native to the United States. They are chiefly tropical animals. Many lizards are strange and beautiful. Their resemblance to legendary dragons and monsters of the Age of Reptiles has given many people the idea that they are dangerous. Yet, among all of the fierce-looking creatures included in this large suborder of reptiles, only two types are poisonous.

Lizards vary in size from the tiny swifts or skinks and tropical geckos to the " dragon lizard " which may be 15 feet or more in length. Many lizards have four legs and climb and run rapidly. Others have lost their legs and might be mistaken for snakes, except for their jaw structure, ear openings (but no ears), and movable eyelids. The wormlike lizards have no legs and have nearly lost their scales. Their pinkish bodies and blunt rounded tails resemble worms. These curious lizards live in rich soil, especially in the tropics.

The American *chameleon* (kuh-*meel*-yun) is probably the best known of lizards. This graceful lizard, with two inches of body and three inches of tail, has the ability to change its color. This protective adaptation results from a change in the size of pigment glands in the skin. Its colors range from bright green to grayish and brown, depending on such factors as temperature, surroundings, and other environmental stimuli.

The *horned toad,* which has plenty of horns but is not a toad, lives in the dry plains of western United States. It is a relative of the dragonlike *iguana* (ih-*gwah*-nuh) of the tropics. Its spiny skin not only protects it from enemies but prevents evaporation of water. Horned toads often spend many hours basking in the sun without moving. They appear

Fig. 31-11.   The Komodo dragon lizard, found in the Dutch East Indies, is the largest of all known lizards.   This 15-foot reptile may weigh as much as 250 pounds.

American Museum of Natural Histo

Fig. 31-12. **The horned toad** (*left*) **is actually a true lizard. It has several hornlike spines on the head, and its broad, flat body is covered with spiny scales. The poisonous Gila monster** (*right*) **has a sluggish but ugly disposition. It may reach a length of two feet.**

dead except for occasional blinking of the eyes. This small lizard survives because its color blends closely with the sand and spiny cacti of its environment.

The common *swift,* or fence lizard, may be seen darting swiftly along wooden fences and fallen tree trunks. The *skinks* include several kinds of lizards, some with legs and some without. They have large, rounded, shiny scales which give them a glassy appearance. The *collared lizard* is one of the most beautiful animals of the southwestern desert region. These lizards, especially the males, have a bright green body covered with yellow spots. The collar is sooty black and the throat a deep orange.

The *Gila* (*hee*-luh) *monster* of the Southwest and its close relative, the *beaded lizard* of Mexico and Central America, are the *only poisonous lizards.* The skin of the Gila monster is covered with rounded, raised scales arranged in beautiful designs of orange or pink, and black or brown that resemble Indian beadwork. The name " monster " is misleading, for a large Gila monster is less than two feet long. Poison glands and grooved teeth are situated in the rear of the lower jaw. When the Gila monster bites, it closes its jaws with great force

and turns its head from side to side, thus digging its teeth into the victim. The poison affects the heart of the victim and can be fatal to man. While not as dangerous as poisonous snakes, this lizard should be avoided.

Crocodilians. Twenty-five species of alligators, caymans, crocodiles and gavials belong to the order Crocodilia. These great reptiles live in tropical and subtropical waters. Stories about crocodilians hunting and devouring human beings have been exaggerated. However, one species, the man-eating crocodile of the Nile River, will attack a man if molested or if hungry enough. One species of *alligator* is found throughout the coastal area of South Carolina, Florida, and the Gulf States as far west as the Rio Grande. Alligators spend much of their time lying half-submerged in the water or basking in the sun on the edge of a stream or on an island. Projecting eyes and snouts permit them to float almost completely under water and still breathe freely and look about. Their scaly backs look like a rough log as they wait for the approach of some aquatic animal.

Alligator hide is in great demand for the manufacture of fine shoes, purses, and luggage. Newly hatched alligators are shipped to pet stores all over the nation. If they are kept in an aquarium or tank of warm water and fed regularly, they may live in captivity for many years. Many of the alligators used or sold commercially come from alligator farms in the southern states.

Crocodiles are the most widely distributed of the crocodilians, especially in the Old World. The largest of the crocodiles is the salt-water crocodile which lives in the ocean and comes up the rivers of the Far East. The Nile crocodile is most famous. This large reptile, from 15 to 20 feet long, can dash out of the water, seize a victim, including a man, knock it down with a blow of the powerful tail, and then drag it under water to drown. The American crocodile is found in the marshes of southern Florida, the West Indies, Mexico, and Central America. The crocodile is more aquatic than the alligator. It is easily distinguished from the alligator by its grayish-green color, triangular head, pointed snout, and a fourth tooth on either side of the lower jaw which fits into notches on the outside of the upper jaw. The American crocodile is active and treacherous and will attack without warning if disturbed.

Caymans are relatives of the alligator, found in Central and South America. Two species of crocodilians are known as *gavials*. One of these is found in northern India; the other in the Malayan Islands of Borneo and Sumatra. The gavial has a narrow snout with characteristic lumps around the nostrils at the tip. It is a very shy reptile, seeking seclusion in muddy streams. Its diet consists mostly of fish.

Turtles are familiar reptiles. If you want to know what the earliest reptiles were like, examine a turtle. It has changed but little in the past 200 million years. This ancient reptile form outdates even the lizards and the dinosaurs.

The turtle seems to have been nature's experiment with armored vertebrates. The curious body structure of the turtle was highly successful in one sense, since the turtle has survived for such a long time. However, of the more than 7,000 species of reptiles, only 300 are turtles. It seems that the turtles have neither increased nor decreased in number since very ancient times. The turtle also seems to have reversed the trend of vertebrates to leave the water and live on land. The majority of turtles live in water at least part of the time. However,

Fig. 31-13. The alligator (*left*) and the crocodile (*right*) are most easily distinguished by the shape of their jaws.

Hugh Spencer   *Hugh Spencer*

Fig. 31-14. The box turtle (*left*), unlike most turtles, is primarily a land-dwelling species. The painted turtle (*right*) is the most widely distributed turtle.

all species come to the land to lay their eggs and bury them in shallow depressions.

Turtles are interesting to many people. Thousands of small turtles pass through pet stores on their way to home aquaria and fish bowls. And it is not uncommon to find a pet box turtle or painted turtle thriving in a backyard enclosure or fish pond.

Many people are confused by the names *tortoise, terrapin,* and *turtle.* Biologists speak of turtles which live on land as **tortoises.** These hard-shelled, slow-moving turtles have strong feet and claws for walking on land and digging. Most tortoises are vegetarians, living on a variety of plant foods. Several of the hard-shelled, fresh-water, edible turtles are known as **terrapins.** These turtles are found in markets in many sections of the country. The large ocean-dwelling forms with limbs in the form of flippers are **true turtles.** However, for convenience, we shall refer to all of them as turtles.

Structure of the turtle. The turtle is an excellent example of animal protection. The armor plating in the form of an upper and lower shell probably accounts for its survival since very ancient times. Most turtles can withdraw all their body parts to the safety of the shell in time of

danger. Some turtles can even close their shells.

The upper shell, or **carapace,** of a turtle is covered with epidermal plates, or **shields,** arranged in a symmetrical pattern. While these shields vary in number and arrangement in various kinds of turtles, they are the same in all members of a species. The shields vary in color and in markings. Beneath the shields are bony plates which are fused together to form a protective case. The shape and arrangement of these bony plates does not match the epidermal shields above them. The lower shell, or **plastron,** has similar epidermal shields covering bony plates. The carapace and plastron join on the sides in a bony **bridge.**

The head of a turtle is generally pointed or triangular. The mouth lacks teeth. The margins of the jaws form a sharp beak with which the turtle bites off chunks of food. There is a pair of nostrils at the tip of the head, making it possible for a turtle to submerge in the water, leaving only the tip of the head above the surface for air breathing. The eyes are well developed and are protected by three eyelids. In addition to fleshy upper and lower eyelids, the turtle has a transparent **nictitating membrane** which closes over the eyeball from the

Hugh Spencer   *American Museum of Natural History*

Fig. 31-15. The snapping turtle (*left*) is dangerous to handle because of its powerful jaws. The soft-shelled turtle (*right*) is about to enjoy a tasty meal of a frog.

front corner of the eye. A smooth **tympanic membrane** lies just behind the angle of the upper and lower jaws.

The limbs of most turtles are short and, in most species, have five toes provided with claws. The feet vary in the amount of webbing between the toes. The skin covering the limbs is tough and scale-covered. The tails of turtles vary greatly in length and are of little use.

North American turtles. About 65 species of turtles live on the continent of North America and in its coastal waters. They inhabit the oceans, lakes, rivers, ponds, woodlands, plains, and deserts.

The *green turtle, hawksbill,* and *leather turtle* are large sea turtles which reach weights of several hundred pounds. These turtles have limbs in the form of flippers and are powerful swimmers. The sea turtles come to land only to lay eggs, which are buried in sandy beaches.

The *diamondback terrapin,* prized for its flesh, lives in the salt marshes of our southeastern states. Several varieties of the *painted turtle* live in rivers and ponds of the East, Midwest, and South.

The *Cumberland terrapin, Mobile terrapin, Florida terrapin,* and *red-bellied terrapin* are large hard-shelled turtles widely used for food. They are often sold in markets as " sliders."

The *common snapping turtle* and *alligator snapping turtle* are the most dangerous of the turtles. The powerful jaws of these turtles can amputate a finger or limb. The long neck and tail with vertical plates are reminders of reptile life in ancient times.

The *soft-shelled turtles* live almost entirely in the waters of rivers and streams. The upper shell of these turtles is leathery and pliable and lacks protective shields. The lower shell is small and offers little protection. This turtle often lies buried in the bottom of a stream with only its long neck protruding, ready to seize a passing fish with its small but powerful jaws.

Various forms of the *box turtle* range over eastern, central, and southern United States. These turtles have the greatest shell protection of all the forms. They can draw the head and neck, limbs, and tail into the shell and close the lower shell against the upper shell, by means of a leathery hinge running across the plastron in the region of the bridge. Most of the box turtles live in wooded areas. Certain of the southern species are much more aquatic.

The tortoises are represented in North America by the *gopher tortoise* of the southeastern states, the *desert tortoise* of the Southwest, and *Berlandier's tortoise* of southern Texas and Mexico.

In Conclusion

The vast expanses of the tropics have been a refuge for many rare reptile species. But in most regions, reptiles are secondary to birds and mammals.

Long ago when reptiles ruled the earth, a strange creature about the size of a crow glided from the trees. Biologists found its fossil remains and named it *Archaeopteryx* (ar-kee-*op*-ter-iks), a name meaning " ancient bird." It had some characteristics of a bird and some of a reptile. In the next chapter, we shall see that nature modified certain vertebrates for life in the air, and made them capable of flying.

BIOLOGICALLY SPEAKING

antivenin	oviparous	side winding
bridge	ovoviviparous	terrapin
carapace	parietal eye	tortoise
caterpillar movement	plastron	true turtle
fang	quadrate bone	venom
Jacobson's organ	scute	viviparous
lateral undulatory movement	shield	

QUESTIONS FOR REVIEW

1. Name and describe a plant-eating and a flesh-eating dinosaur.
2. What four orders of reptiles are represented in the world today?
3. List seven characteristics which distinguish reptiles from other vertebrates.
4. In what respect is *Sphenodon* an unusual reptile?
5. What use does the snake make of its forked tongue?
6. Describe three methods used by various snakes in capturing prey.
7. How is the snake's jaw structure adapted for swallowing large prey?
8. Describe three forms of movement in snakes.
9. Distinguish oviparous and ovoviviparous snakes.
10. Name three nonpoisonous snakes of your region.
11. What four groups of poisonous snakes are found in North America?
12. List, in order, the steps which should be followed in treating a victim of a poisonous snake bite.
13. What characteristics of a crocodile distinguish it from an alligator?
14. Describe the structure of the shell of a turtle.

APPLYING FACTS AND PRINCIPLES

1. In what respects are reptiles better suited to life on land than are amphibians?
2. Make a list of possible reasons for the disappearance of the dinosaurs.
3. Why do you think the eggs of reptiles require a shell, while those of fish and frogs do not?
4. Account for the fact that many unusual and rare animals are found today only on islands.
5. What arguments can you give for conservation of snakes, especially the nonpoisonous species?
6. Why do turtles whose normal habitat is water come on land to lay eggs?

CHAPTER 32

Birds—Vertebrates Adapted for Flight

F OR centuries, man watched birds soaring easily through the sky and wished that he, too, could fly. Several early inventors even made large wings which they strapped to their arms in the hope that they could imitate birds. But such experiments only ended in exhaustion and disappointment. With all our adaptations and abilities, we lack the power in our shoulders and arms to fly, even with perfectly designed wings.

Blue-winged teal ducks cut through the air with outstretched necks at 90 miles an hour. The ruddy turnstone flies each autumn from Alaska to Hawaii in a single flight. And the golden plover flies from northern Canada to southern South America, a distance of 8,000 miles, and later makes a return trip. These records compare favorably with those of transcontinental planes, even in this age of jet propulsion.

No forms of life have challenged the birds in the air. Birds have an advantage over all other living things in that they are able to change environments as conditions require. They have been so successful that they have spread their numbers from the jungles of the tropics to the wastelands of the polar regions, and from mountain top to valley.

Birds vary in size from the tiny hummingbird to the ostrich. The food of various birds includes the nectar of flowers, seeds, insects, worms, fish, and even other birds and smaller animals. The variation in the form and use of the beaks and feet, protective coloration, nesting habits, care of the young, migration, and many other phases of the lives of birds are interesting studies in adaptation. Nature has given the birds many advantages in the struggle for survival in the living world.

Characteristics of birds. While birds vary greatly in form, size, diet, and life habits, they have certain characteristics in common. The following distinguish them easily from the other vertebrates: (1) body covering of feathers; (2) bones light, porous, and air-filled; (3) forelimbs (arms) developed as wings for locomotion (in most birds) and never for grasping; (4) body supported on two limbs; (5) mouth provided with a horny, toothless beak; (6) eggs with a protective shell and, in most cases, incubated in a nest; (7) maintenance of constant body temperature (warm-blooded); and (8) a heart that is divided into four chambers.

Adaptations for flight. Did you ever compare a bird to an airplane? We probably got our first ideas for airplane design from the birds.

The body is streamlined and cuts through the air with a minimum of resistance. The beak and head are pointed and also serve to reduce air resistance. The body itself is made smooth by feathers. The body tapers at the tail, where large feathers act as a steering device.

Fig. 32-1.   These flamingos illustrate some of the special adaptations birds possess for flight, enabling them to travel easier and farther than other animals.

The legs are attached on the body at the center of gravity. "Fore-and-aft" balance is provided by the head and neck and the posterior part of the body, legs, and tail.

The wings are rounded and thicker on the front edge and taper on the rear edge. We have duplicated this general shape in the airplane wing. The wings of a bird can be tilted to give upsweep or downsweep or act as a brake. The wings of an airplane have ailerons, and the airplane tail has a rudder and elevators to accomplish the same purpose. The porous bones of the bird give maximum support with minimum weight, while we have learned to use aluminum and magnesium, both strong, light metals, in airplane construction. Most birds pull their feet against the body in flight. Did you ever watch an airplane fold its landing gear? If you compare a bird and an airplane, you may find still other similarities in these two flying machines.

Structure and functions of feathers. Strange as it may seem, feathers are modified scales. Some unchanged scales remain on the feet and legs of birds and remind us of the relationship of birds to reptiles. Feathers develop from pits in the skin. They grow in lines which lie in only certain regions of skin. However, the feathers spread out to cover featherless regions.

There are four kinds of feathers. Soft **down feathers** form the plumage of newly-hatched birds. In older birds, especially waterfowl, they form an insulation close to the skin. Down reduces heat loss so efficiently that a bird can fly through cold winter air and still maintain a body temperature of over 100° F. The slender hairlike feathers with a tuft on the end are known as **filoplumes**.

Contour feathers cover the body and round out the angles, giving the bird a smooth outline. They also form an effective shield against injury and provide the coloration so important in the life of a bird. Often the female blends more closely with the surroundings than her brightly-colored mate. **Quill feathers** grow in the wing and tail. These large feathers provide the surface the bird needs in flying and steering in flight.

Fig. 32-2 shows the structure of a quill feather. A broad flat **vane** spreads from a central axis, the **rachis** (*ray*-kis). The rachis ends in a hollow **quill**. If you magnify the vane, you can see the many rays or **barbs**. Each barb is like a tiny feather with many projections, the **barbules** (little barbs). These are held together with tiny interlocking hooks. This complicated arrangement makes the vane strong, light, and elastic. If a vane is " split," the bird shakes its feathers and locks the barbules together again. Or it may preen the feather by drawing it through its beak, making it whole again. The rachis is grooved and the quill hollow, a condition which gives a feather the greatest strength with the least weight. At the base of the quill is an opening through which nourishment is supplied while the feather is growing.

The vane of the wing feather is wider on one side of the rachis than the other. When the wing strikes the air in a power stroke, the vane turns up and rests against its neighbor. On the return stroke it is free to turn back. The air passes through the wing as each feather turns slightly on its axis (feathering) and the wing meets less air resistance.

You have probably noticed birds oiling their feathers after a bath or a swim. They transfer oil from a gland at the base of the tail and spread it over the surface of the feathers, which makes them waterproof. Oil on the feathers is vital to swimming and diving birds such as ducks, geese, swans, loons, and grebes. Not only does water not penetrate the feathers to the skin, but also this oil makes the birds buoyant and prevents chilling of the body.

Molting in birds. The bird sheds its feathers at least once a year. Feathers, especially those of the wings and tail, may be lost or broken, and since molting usually occurs in the late summer, the bird is provided with new quills before the fall migrations. A second partial molt often occurs in the spring before the breeding season. This molt provides the bright breeding plumage of many birds. In some species, including the ptarmigan, two complete seasonal molts occur. The early summer molt provides a plumage which blends with rocks and soil. The fall molt arrays the bird in a snow-white winter plumage.

The new feathers grow from the same

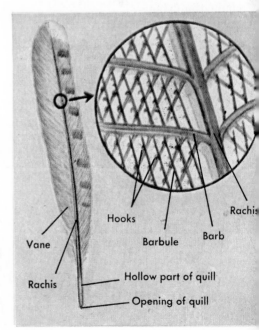

Fig. 32-2. This diagram shows the structure of a quill feather. The enlarged section on the right illustrates a portion of the rachis and the vane as seen under a microscope.

Rachis

Hooks

Barbule

Barb

Vane

Rachis

Hollow part of quill

Opening of quill

pits from which the old ones are shed. In most species, the wing feathers are shed gradually and in pairs, thus allowing the bird to fly during the molt.

A bird's wing is a modified forelimb adapted entirely for flight. You can see the resemblance to your own arm if you examine a chicken wing closely. The upper arm is a large single bone which is attached to the shoulder at a ball-and-socket joint (Fig. 32-3). The part corresponding to the lower arm has two bones like your own. The end section includes the wrist and the hand. This is covered with skin and contains the partial bone structure of a thumb and two fingers.

The shoulders are braced by three bones in a tripod arrangement: (1) the *shoulder blades* are embedded in the muscles of the back above the ribs; (2) the *collarbone* (wishbone) extends from each shoulder and fuses in front of the breastbone forming a V-shaped bone; and (3) the *coracoid* (*kor*-uh-koyd) *bones* also brace the shoulder against the breastbone. Thus the wing is firmly braced to withstand the tremendous force required in flying.

The muscles necessary to power the wings are enormous. Let's see how much power a human body would need to fly, by using a one-pound pigeon as a basis for comparison. Such a pigeon has a wing spread of about two feet. By comparison, a person weighing 110 pounds would have to swing through the air a pair of wings, each one from 50 to 70 feet long. And he would have to swing these wings at a rate of 100 to as many as 500 strokes per minute! Try to swing your arm at this rate for a minute!

The muscles of the lower arm bend the hand at the wrist. Those of the upper arm move the lower arm. These muscles are involved in folding the wings. But the movement of the wings in flight is largely a movement at the shoulder. These muscles are enormous and in many birds make up one-third or more of the whole body weight. The breast muscles are attached to the greatly enlarged breastbone and form the white meat. These muscles of a chicken or turkey are tender and light in color because the birds do not fly. Tendons from these muscles pass over the shoulders like ropes over pulleys, giving tremendous leverage.

Fig. 32-3. The wing of a bird shows a greatly lengthened " hand " region and a reduced number of " fingers."

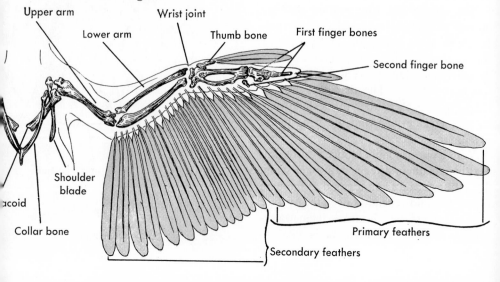

Upper arm

Lower arm

Wrist joint

Thumb bone

First finger bones

Second finger bone

Shoulder blade

coid

Collar bone

Primary feathers

Secondary feathers

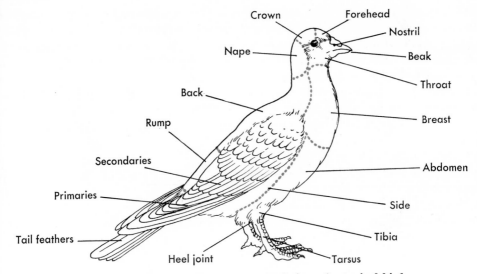

Fig. 32-4.   **This drawing is an external view of a typical bird.**

The longest quill feathers, the *primaries,* grow from the end section of the wing or modified hand, where leverage is the greatest. *Secondaries* grow from the second section of the wing, or modified forearm. The lower portion of both of these sets of quill feathers is covered with smaller feathers, known as **coverts.** The secondaries, in turn, are covered by other rows both above and below. The outline of the wing as a whole is concave on the lower side, thick on the forward edge, and thin and flexible on the rear edge and tip — a perfect design for flight.

Motion of the wings in flight. We might compare the motion of a bird's wings in flight to a horizontal figure eight — down and back, up and forward. The down stroke is the power stroke. The upward movement returns the wing to position for another power stroke. These two actions of the wing require two sets of muscles, arranged in layers on the breast. You may have noticed that these layers separate on the breast of a chicken. The tougher muscles of the outer layer pull the wing down in a power stroke. Those of the more tender inner layer raise the wing for the next stroke.

Structure of the legs and feet. The hip joint of a bird is high on the back. The body hangs suspended between the legs. This arrangement gives ideal balance and lets the bird bend easily to pick up food.

Though you may not realize it, man has a much greater balance problem than does the bird. A baby has to learn to walk and falls many times in the process, but walking or hopping is natural with the young bird.

The thigh extends from the hip to the knee joint. The lower leg is the familiar drumstick. The second bone of the lower leg is the small, long "sliver" you find along the drumstick. The heel joint is just below the feather line. What appears to be the leg is really a greatly lengthened foot, covered with scales in most birds but bearing feathers in many species.

The feet of various birds differ widely in structure, depending on the particular purpose required. Some are adapted for perching or climbing. Others are adapted for swimming or for scratching or, like the hawk, for catching food. See Fig. 32-5 and the table on page 380 for examples of these foot adaptations.

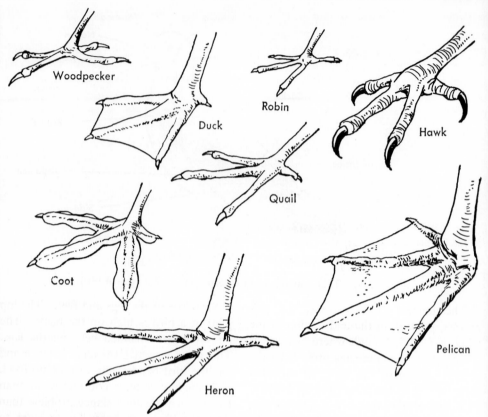

Fig. 32-5. The feet of birds vary with the type of activity. Name the activity for which each type of foot is best adapted.

TYPES OF FEET

STRUCTURE OF TOES	EXAMPLES	ADAPTED FOR
3 front; 1 rear	Songbirds	Perching
2 front; 2 rear	Woodpecker	Climbing
All webbed, separate	Coot	Swimming
All webbed, united	Pelican	Swimming
3 webbed, united	Duck, goose, loon	Swimming
3 front; 1 rear (heavy claws)	Hawk, owl, eagle	Catching prey
Small, weak	Hummingbird, swift	Little used
Long, separate	Crane, heron, snipe	Wading
Legs short, far back	Loon, duck	Diving

How a bird perches. When at rest or asleep, the bird usually perches on a support. The tendon that closes the claws passes over the leg joints; hence the more the leg is bent, the tighter the claws close up. Thus, when the bird settles down on a branch to sleep, the more it relaxes and the more its legs bend, the closer the the claws grasp the perch. This arrangement coupled with the balancing adaptations mentioned above enable birds to cling to a swinging twig when awake, or to a perch when asleep.

The structure of the bird's head and neck. With the forelimbs developed as wings, the head and neck must assume most of the functions performed by the hands or forefeet of other animals. The bird's neck is long and flexible, which aids in balance and permits free movement of the head.

Sense organs are located on the head. The eyes are large and the sense of sight is very keen. It is said that some birds, especially hawks and owls, have vision eight times as keen as that of man. Owls and certain other birds have excellent vision in the dark. Birds have a remarkable ability to judge distance, both at close range and at great height. They can drop out of the sky and light on a rock in a stream, fly through a deep woods, or swoop down onto a slender perch. The eyes are protected by an upper and a lower eyelid as well as a thin transparent third eyelid, or **nictitating membrane.**

Ear canals are covered by a tuft of feathers. Eustachian tubes lead from the ears to a single opening in the upper wall of the throat. The sense of hearing is very keen and the ears are especially sensitive to high notes.

The senses of smell and taste are very poor, a fact which is due in part to the horny nature of the mouth.

The **beak** is light, strong, and horny.

The tongue of most birds is small and serves as an organ of touch. The beaks of various birds vary greatly with the nature of the food and the manner in which the bird catches it. Like the feet, the beak has special adaptations, as you can see by referring to Fig. 32-6 and the table on page 382.

Birds eat various kinds of food. Certain birds eat animal food exclusively, others are strict vegetarians, while many have a mixed diet. Their intense activity requires large amounts of food.

Since birds require so much food, they seem to be eating nearly all the time. Watch any common bird, such as a robin, for a few minutes to observe the way it eats. Robins are ground-feeders and you can see them searching the lawn for insects and earthworms. Both sight and hearing seem to be used to locate their quarry. A swift motion of the beak usually secures it, though an earthworm, with its tail securely anchored in its burrow, sometimes requires a considerable amount of pulling.

Most birds drink by taking a beakful of water and tilting back the head so that it will run down their throat. They drink large quantities of water, especially in hot weather, and they also frequently enjoy bathing their feathers. One of the easiest ways to attract birds is to provide them with a shallow dish of water for a bird bath. The edges and bottom should be rough enough to afford safe footing and the bath should be put where cats or birds of prey cannot attack its visitors.

Among birds using animals for food are large birds of prey, such as hawks and owls, which feed on rats, rabbits, field mice, and other small animals, as well as on some other birds. There are many whose diet is largely fish, which they catch by diving. Such birds as the loon, grebe, pelican, and kingfisher do this. Some, like the vulture or buzzard,

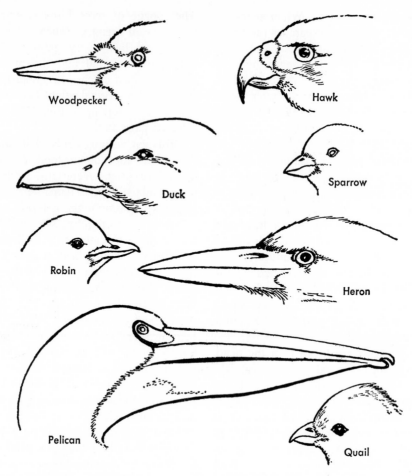

Fig. 32-6.   The diet of birds varies according to the type of beak.

TYPES OF BEAKS

KINDS	EXAMPLES	ADAPTED FOR
Hooked	Hawk, owl	Catching prey
Chisel-shaped	Woodpecker	Drilling in trees
Wide but weak	Nighthawk, swift	Catching insects on wing
Broad and notched	Duck	Scooping and straining
Slender and sensitive	Snipe	Probing in mud
Short and straight	Sparrow, finches	Crushing seeds
Notched and hooked	Parrot	Climbing
Crossed mandibles	Crossbill	Opening pine cones
Slender tube	Hummingbird	Sucking nectar

FOOD USED BY SOME OF OUR COMMON BIRDS

NAME OF BIRD	INSECT FOOD	VEGETABLE FOOD	RODENTS, ETC.	POSSIBLE HARM
Quail	Potato bugs, etc., 14%	Weed seed, 63%		
Woodpecker	Wood borers, ants			
Nighthawk	Grasshoppers, flying ants, fleas			
Kingbird	Flies, bees, beetles	Wild fruit		
Phoebe	Beetles, spiders, 93%	Wild fruit		
Bluejay	Harmful insects, 19%	Nuts, acorns	Mice, fish, salamanders	Eats some corn and eggs and young of birds
Crow	Grasshoppers, beetles	Corn, wild fruit	Mice	Pulls corn, eats birds' eggs, chicks, frogs
Red-winged blackbird	Grasshoppers, weevils	Weed seed, 57%		Grain, peas, fruit, corn
Meadow lark	Grasshoppers, etc., 73%	Weed seed, 12%		
Grackle	Insects, 35%	Grain, fruit	Mice and snails	Some fruit, grain
Junco	Beetles, caterpillars	Weed seed		
Field sparrow		Weed seed, mainly		
Swallow	Flies, ants, wasps, in enormous numbers			
Cedar waxwing	Insects, including caterpillars	Wild fruit, seeds, 74%		Cherries 5% Cultivated fruit, 13%
Wren	Insects, 98%			Some cultivated fruit
Robin	Grasshoppers, 43%, caterpillars	Wild fruit, 47%		
Bluebird	Insects, 76%	Wild berry seed		
Great-horned owl			Rabbits, rats, mice	Some native birds
Cooper's hawk			Rabbits, birds	Chickens, grouse
Sharp-shinned hawk			Mice, birds	Chickens, other birds

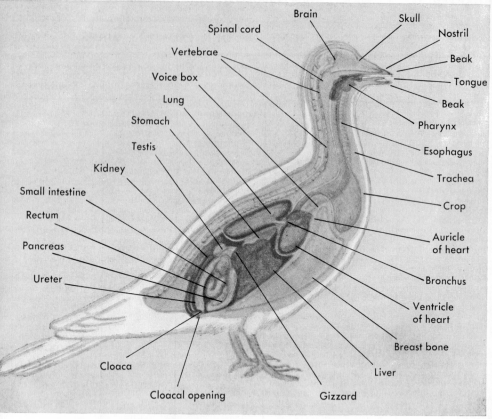

Fig. 32-7. The internal organs of a bird are shown above.

are scavengers and eat any dead animal they can find; such birds have a very keenly developed sense of sight. Probably the largest number of birds which enjoy an animal diet live chiefly on insects which they catch in the air (swifts), in wood (woodpeckers), on the ground (robins), or on trees (warblers).

Many birds live almost exclusively on seeds, doing much good by the destruction of weed seeds, while others, such as blackbirds and bobolinks, do considerable damage by their preference for grain, peas, and rice. Various kinds of both wild and cultivated fruits, especially berries, are preferred by certain birds.

Sometimes birds eat the same seeds or fruits that man raises, or they may at times rob his yard of a stray chicken. But careful study has proved that there

are only three or four birds which do more harm than good. The rest many times repay for eating fruit by destruction of insects and vermin. Birds in whose favor little can be said are the Cooper's and sharp-shinned hawks, great horned owl, starling, and English sparrow. The first three destroy poultry and useful birds, while the sparrow drives away many valuable and attractive native songbirds.

The digestive system of the bird. The bird is the first warm-blooded animal we have studied. A constant body temperature as high as 112° F is maintained in some species. The maintenance of this high temperature, together with the tremendous muscular exertion during flight, requires that the bird's body be a highly efficient living power plant. The systems which supply this great energy need are highly developed. As with an engine running at full throttle much of the time, the fuel need of a bird is proportionately greater than that of other animals. Birds spend much of their time eating. To say that someone has an " appetite like a bird " is actually no compliment.

Food is swallowed whole down a long *esophagus* into a large *crop,* located just below the base of the neck (Fig. 32-7). Here the food is stored and moistened. The crop permits a bird to eat a large amount of food and digest it later on. From the crop, food passes into the first division of the *stomach* where glands in the thick walls add *gastric fluid,* a digestive secretion. The stomach content then passes into the second stomach region, the *gizzard.* Here the thick muscular walls, aided by pebbles, churn and grind the food. A U-shaped loop of intestine joins a short *rectum,* or large intestine, which leads to a *cloaca* somewhat like that of the frog.

The two-lobed *liver* is large and may or may not have a *gall bladder* on the lower side, depending on the species of bird. Bile is poured into the small intestine through two ducts. The *pancreas* lies along the U-shaped portion of the intestine and pours its secretion into the intestine through three ducts.

Respiration, circulation, and excretion in the bird. The lungs of a bird lie in the back against the ribs, in the anterior region of the body cavity. The capacity of the lungs is greatly increased by a system of *air sacs* which extend from the lungs into the chest area and the abdomen and connect with cavities in the larger bones (Fig. 32-8).

Air is drawn through the nostrils in the beak and down the *trachea* (*tray-*kee-uh) and its lower divisions, or *bronchi* (*bron-*kye) [sing. *bronchus*], to the lungs and air sacs by relaxation of the thoracic and abdominal muscles. Contraction of these muscles forces air out. Though the lungs are small, a rapid rate of respiration fills them often and supplies the blood with the great amount of oxygen necessary to carry on the high rate of oxidation in the body tissues.

The bird's respiratory system is also its principal temperature-regulating system. It has no sweat glands and cannot eliminate heat through its skin. Most excess heat is discharged from the body through the lungs. The air sacs are believed to assist in heat elimination. You may have noticed that birds often pant with their mouths open on a hot day. At times like these, the insulation provided by feathers is more a liability than an asset.

Fig. 32-8. Since birds are so active, they need a specially adapted respiratory system to accomplish rapid oxidation of food and release of energy.

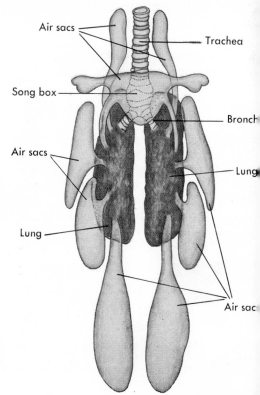

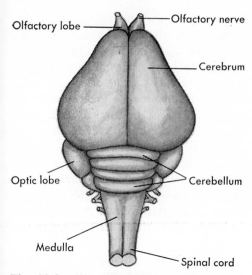

Olfactory lobe

Olfactory nerve

Cerebrum

Optic lobe

Cerebellum

Medulla

Spinal cord

Fig. 32-9. What does the size of the olfactory and optic lobes of the bird's brain reveal about the development of senses in the animal?

The lungs also supply air for singing. The bird's song is not produced in the throat, but at the base of the trachea, where the bronchi begin. Here the **song box**, a delicate and highly adjustable structure, is located.

The **kidneys** are dark brown, three-lobed organs lying along the back. They excrete *uric acid,* a waste product of cell activity. This uric acid is discharged with very little water through the ureters into the cloaca, and is then excreted along with intestinal waste.

The **heart** of a bird is large and powerful. It consists of two thin-walled **auricles** and two muscular **ventricles.** The right side of this four-chambered heart receives blood from the body and pumps it to the lungs. Blood returns from the lungs to the left side and is pumped to the body. The heart of the bird beats at an amazing rate. With the bird at rest, the beat is several hundred times per minute. Under exertion, the heart may beat as many as a thousand times a minute.

The nervous system of a bird. In birds, the brain is large and broad, completely filling the cranial cavity. The **olfactory lobes** are small, indicating a poorly developed sense of smell (Fig. 32-9). The **optic lobes** are large, thus accounting for the keen vision of the bird. The hemispheres of the **cerebrum** are the largest of any animal we have discussed thus far. The highly developed instincts of birds center in this brain region. The large **cerebellum** accounts for the excellent muscular coordination of the bird, especially in flight. The **medulla** joins the spinal cord, which extends down the back, encased in vertebrae.

The reproductive system. The oval **testes** of the male bird lie in the back in about the same position we found them in the male frog. Tiny tubes carry sperm to openings in the cloaca. During mating, sperm are deposited in the cloaca of the female.

The female reproductive organs include a single **ovary** in which eggs develop, and a long, coiled **oviduct** which leads to the cloaca (Fig. 32-10). In most birds, the right ovary disappears early in life. The absence of one ovary and oviduct is another of the interesting modifications of birds for life in the air.

If you examine a hen you are preparing for dinner, you will find a mass of orange spheres in the region of the back — these are developing **yolks.** On the surface of each yolk is a tiny **egg cell** surrounded by protoplasm. When a yolk has grown to full size, it is drawn into the upper end of the oviduct by lashing cilia. As the yolk travels down the oviduct, it is surrounded with layers of **albumen** or "white of egg." Two enclosing membranes form around the albumen. Sometimes an egg is laid in this condition. We refer to it as a soft-shelled egg. Normally, a hard shell is secreted around the membranes by **lime-producing glands**

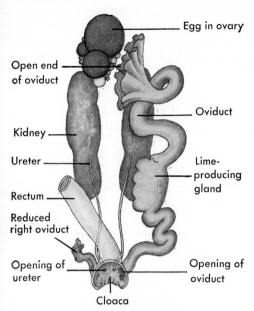

Egg in ovary

Open end
of oviduct

Oviduct

Kidney

Ureter

Lime-
producing
gland

Rectum

Reduced
right oviduct

Opening of
ureter

Opening of
oviduct

Cloaca

**Fig. 32-10. In this drawing of the repro-
ductive system of the hen, the ovary is
shown with immature eggs.**

in the lower part of the oviduct, before
the egg is laid.

Thus, we must distinguish between an
egg and an *egg cell*. The tiny spot surrounded by protoplasm on the side of the
yolk will develop into a new organism.
It is the only living part of an egg. The
protein of the albumen and oils of the
yolk are stored nourishment for the developing embryo. The shell prevents
drying out, but must be porous enough
to admit air. The pores are also large
enough to admit bacteria, which accounts
for the spoilage of eggs, especially in
warm weather.

Incubation and development of a bird.
An embryo can develop in an egg only
if a sperm has fertilized the egg cell before the shell is formed. Development
begins as soon as the egg is *incubated* or
kept continuously warm. The mother
provides this warmth by sitting on the
egg. The incubation temperature of
most birds is slightly above 100° F.

The time of incubation varies from 13

to 15 days in smaller birds to as many as
40 to 50 days in a large bird. The hen's
egg is incubated 21 days (Fig. 32-11,
page 388), while that of a duck requires
28 days. It is usually the female which
sits on the eggs. However, the male bird
takes his turn in some species, including
the ostrich. Just before hatching, the
baby bird absorbs the remainder of the
yolk. The shell is " pipped " in a line,
after which the baby bird pushes the
shell halves apart and works itself out.
Some birds have hardly any body covering when they are hatched. Others are
covered with a dense coat of down.

Egg number and parental care. Birds
like the robin, bluebird, sparrow, and
warbler usually lay less than six eggs.
Incubation starts when the last egg is
laid. Thus the baby birds hatch at about
the same time, but they are helpless and
must be fed almost continuously by their
parents. They remain in the nest until
they are able to fly.

Hawks and owls usually lay only one
to four eggs and incubate them as soon
as each is laid. This results in a " stair-
step " family. The young of these birds
are also fed in the nest until they are
feathered and able to fly.

Ducks (except the wood duck), geese,
quail, grouse, turkeys, chickens, and
other fowl-like birds lay a much larger
number of eggs in a nest on or close to
the ground. The eggs are not incubated
until the last one is laid. As many as 12
to 15 birds may hatch at the same time.
Within a day or two the mother bird takes
her family walking or swimming in search
of food.

Getting acquainted with birds. In
1810, John James Audubon, an American naturalist who was also an artist,
began his famous study of birds. He
roamed the fields and forests for several
years, making life-size drawings of each
species he met. Then he took his work

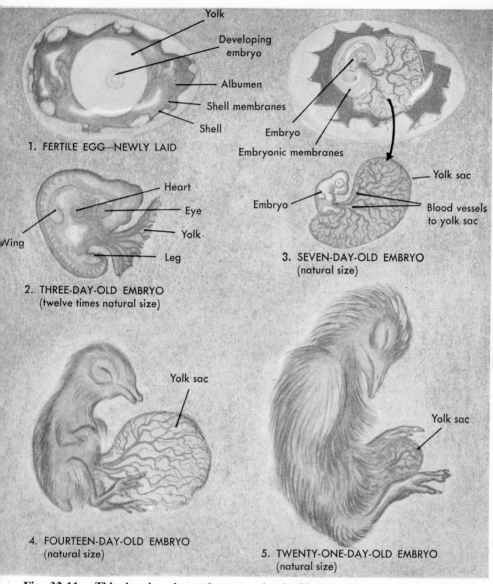

1. FERTILE EGG—NEWLY LAID

Yolk
Developing embryo
Albumen
Shell membranes
Shell

Embryo
Embryonic membranes

Wing
Heart
Eye
Yolk
Leg

2. THREE-DAY-OLD EMBRYO
(twelve times natural size)

Embryo
Yolk sac
Blood vessels to yolk sac

3. SEVEN-DAY-OLD EMBRYO
(natural size)

Yolk sac

4. FOURTEEN-DAY-OLD EMBRYO
(natural size)

Yolk sac

5. TWENTY-ONE-DAY-OLD EMBRYO
(natural size)

Fig. 32-11. This drawing shows the parts of a fertilized hen's egg and also illustrates some of the stages in the development of the chick embryo.

to England where he supervised the coloring of each drawing to be sure it was accurate. These were published a few years later as *The Birds of America,* in two large volumes.

From the time of Audubon, scores of other great **ornithologists,** or students of birds, have added contributions to the study of bird life. Today, bird study is a highly organized science. National, state, and local bird societies list thousands of members in their rolls.

Bird study is a delightful challenge. Distinctive marks like wing bars, white outer tail feathers, a black band under the throat, or white lines on the crown may be a means of identifying a bird with only a brief glimpse. A good pair of field glasses will greatly help you in the identification of birds, since even the trained ornithologist often has difficulty approaching them closely.

In addition to size, shape, and color, you can recognize birds by the way they fly, walk, hop about, and seek their food. Songs, too, are very characteristic. At first, most bird notes may sound alike, but you will soon learn to associate certain calls with the birds which make them. When you have reached this advanced stage in bird study, you can stand quietly in the woods and identify the birds merely by listening to their sounds.

Bird habitats are varied. In selecting the places for your bird study, you will want to include a variety of habitats. Birds, like all other animals, are restricted in their surroundings. Large bodies of water are inhabited by certain species of ducks, loons, and gulls, while sandpipers and other shore birds wade in the shallow water along the beach looking for food. In the marsh, you will find the rails and herons, the bitterns, coots, swamp ducks, and red-winged blackbirds. Woodland species include the thrushes and orioles, thrashers, and warblers. In the open field, one finds the goldfinches, sparrows, and meadow larks.

Bird migration. One of the most wonderful instincts of birds is that which controls their migration. *Migration* is the periodic moving from one home to another. Many birds fly long distances in spring, nest and raise their young in a new home, and then return to warmer climates in the fall. We do not understand all the causes of migration, but many facts are known about it.

Migration may be caused by food needs, climatic changes, or breeding habits. It is not easy to find out why some species leave abundant food and warmth in the tropics and migrate to breeding grounds in the far North. Much more

easily explainable is the southward migration of insect-eaters when cold weather kills their prey, and the southward flight of water birds before the ponds and lakes freeze over. It is logical, too, that fruit- and seed-eaters would tend to follow the crops.

Some make their migratory flights at night and some during the day, depending on the species. Some of you are familiar with the flights of geese during the spring and autumn nights when they become confused by the lights of a city and circle about, honking noisily. The daylight flights of thousands of red-winged blackbirds and grackles are familiar sights during spring and fall.

While many birds migrate slowly, feeding by the way and averaging only 20 to 30 miles a day, others are marvels of speed and endurance. As you read in the introduction to this chapter, the ruddy turnstone travels each autumn from Alaska to Hawaii in a single flight, and the golden plover travels from Canada to South America, more than 8,000 miles (Fig. 32-12, page 390).

Migratory routes. We do not know much about the instinct which governs the time and routes of migration. Any given species follows the same routes year after year and may be expected to arrive at a certain point within a few weeks of the same time each season, depending on the weather.

As though to vary the scenery, certain species travel northward along one route and return by an entirely different route. How do they know the way? Keen sight may help, but not over water or through dark nights and fogs. Even the memory of old birds which have made the flight before cannot account for unescorted flights of young birds. In an effort to explain the sense of direction in migrating birds, biologists have long suspected that the sun guides them on their

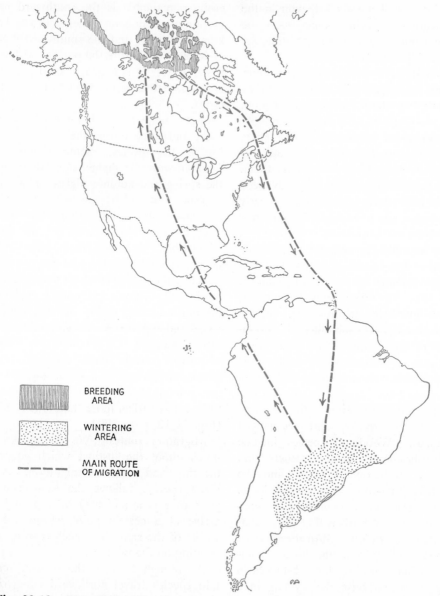

BREEDING
AREA

WINTERING
AREA

MAIN ROUTE
OF MIGRATION

Fig. 32-12. **The golden plover travels more than 8,000 miles during its migratory flight.**

daylight flights. This theory does not infer that birds understand intellectually their position in relation to the sun. Sun navigation would involve an instinct in a bird which we can observe but cannot explain. Furthermore, it would involve some time instinct to allow for the shift in position of the sun in the sky.

What about the migratory flights of birds at night? Recent studies of night flights reveal even more amazing possibilities. Birds seem to be directed by the position of the stars. This celestial navigation has been studied extensively, especially in Europe. Investigators have used caged birds in a planetarium in which star patterns of different seasons and various places in the earth can be projected on a dome representing the heavens. They have found that certain birds, including warblers, make a definite response to the position of stars during the normal season for migration. Under a fall star pattern, they face the winter migratory home in their cages. On the other hand, they face the summer home when a spring star pattern is projected on the planetarium dome.

Much more work remains to be done in this area. If, however, biologists discover that birds migrate by celestial navigation, this discovery will be yet another of the wonders of the living world.

Bird banding. An interesting phase of bird study called *bird banding* is carried on by ornithologists all over the country. Individuals of certain species are caught in special cage traps, removed carefully,

and marked with a light aluminum band (Fig. 32-13). Each band contains the date of banding, the place, and the name of the individual who caught the bird. It is then released to go its way. Later, it may be caught by another bird bander who examines the band and reports its new location. Through the *Bird Banding Association* and other bird societies, records of banding and observations of banded birds are assembled. Bird banding is also valuable to determine the age to which a certain species may live.

Seasonal bird study. Migration adds much to the study of birds, for new species are arriving during many seasons of the year. Each locality has *permanent residents* which remain the year round. In addition, certain species may be present in the winter only, moving farther north with the coming of spring. These species are called *winter residents*. The

Fig. 32-13.   **How does bird banding help the ornithologist trace migratory routes?**

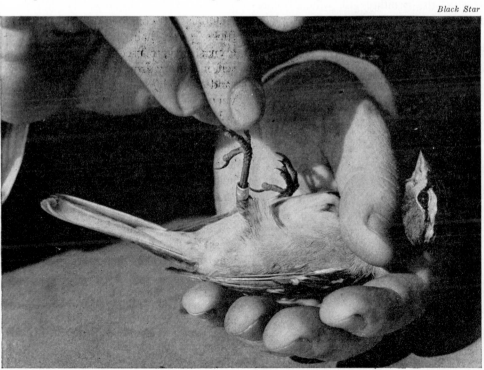

Fig. 32-14. The blue herons shown at the left are about 22 inches long. Their broad, flat nests are constructed of twigs and are often found near the tops of large trees.

General Biological Supply House

summer residents spend summers in a given locality and migrate southward with the approach of fall. Many species are found only at certain times in the spring and fall. These are the *migratory birds* which are passing through a given locality on their journey between wintering areas farther south and breeding areas farther north.

Nest building. During the breeding season, the ornithologist watches carefully for nests in the variety of places

birds choose to rear their young. The skilled observer may study nests and young birds with no annoyance to the parent birds. The place selected, form, and size of the nest, color and number of the eggs, and the way in which the parents rear the young are as characteristic as the birds themselves.

Next to migration, the highest development of bird instinct is shown in nest construction. Nests differ widely both as to materials and construction. Earth, clay, sticks, grass, hair, feathers, moss, and even string are used. The structure itself may vary from a mere hole in the sand (ostrich) to the dainty nest of a vireo.

Kinds of nests. Water birds usually lay their eggs on rocks with only sticks enough to keep the eggs from rolling. The kingfisher and bank swallow dig holes in clay banks (Fig. 32-17). Owls and woodpeckers live in excavated homes in dead trees.

Ducks and wading birds make simple grass nests. Orioles and vireos build long nests which hang securely from

Fig. 32-15. The goldfinch is about 4½ inches long, and is closely related to the familiar canary. It has a faint but pleasant song. Its neat nest is constructed of dried grasses and small twigs.

Cruickshank from National Audubon Society

Fig. 32-16. Notice the striking difference between the red and black male and the yellow female scarlet tanager. These birds make their delicate nests in oak or other trees.

Harrison from National Audubon Society

limbs. They weave these from horsehair and various plant fibers.

Each species builds its own nest in its own way, in the same general type of location, and of the same type of materials. See the table on page 394 and the photographs on page 392 and this page for details.

Birds destroy many insects. Birds are the chief enemies of insects. There are about 13,000 species of birds in the world, of which about 850 live in North America. About 200 kinds may usually be found in one region. On the other hand, there are, for instance, 15,000 species of insects within 50 miles of New York City, many of which are harmful to man. The fact that such hordes of insects are even partially held in check by birds shows the services birds render to man.

Nature tends to establish a balance. Unfortunately, man often disturbs it. Native birds could completely regulate native insects, but man has introduced many insects from other countries, such as the gypsy moth and corn borer.

Fig. 32-17. The kingfisher makes its nest in a hole in a clay bank that has been formed by some burrowing animal. The floor of the nest is covered with the bones of the fish on which the adult kingfisher preys.

These, not having their natural enemies to check them, multiply almost beyond the power of bird or man to control, and constitute one of our greatest problems. Without our bird allies, it would be insolvable.

Destruction of weed seeds. Look at the food table on page 383 and note that weed seeds constitute a large portion of the food of many birds.

Weeds cost the farmer many dollars to keep down. But sparrows, juncos, quail, and finches help him by destroying thousands of tons of weed seeds each year. Ornithologists have estimated that the tiny tree sparrow eats nearly one ounce of weed seeds every day. It is hard to say how much money this bird alone saves farmers of our country. Without birds, weed control would probably be a losing battle.

NESTS OF SOME COMMON BIRDS

NAME	LOCATION OF NEST	MATERIAL AND DESCRIPTION
Kingfisher	Hole in bank	6 to 8 ft. deep; eggs on ground or on feathers.
Woodpecker	Holes in trees	Usually cut into hollow or dead tree through side.
Crested flycatcher	Holes in trees	Bulky, of grass, etc.; may use a snake-skin.
Robin	On branch or crotch	Bulky, case of mud, grass-lined, heavy.
Bluejay	On branches	Bulky, ragged, of twigs, leaves, rags, string, etc.
Crow	In trees	Very bulky, of sticks, cedar bark, sod, hair, etc.
Grebe	In bogs	Decayed swamp plants.
Red-winged blackbird	In bushes and reeds	Deep, mouth contracted, of grass and rushes.
Phoebe	Under bridges, on houses or rocks	Moss, cemented with mud and lined with hair.
Barn swallow	Hollow trees or eaves	Mud and straw, lined with hay or feathers.
Chimney swift	Hollow trees, chimneys	Sticks glued with "saliva," cup-shaped.
Whippoorwill	Dead leaves	No real nest, slight depression.
Quail	Underbrush	Arch of vegetation over nest made of grass.
Meadow lark	Underbrush	Similar to above, but smaller.
Marsh wren	On reeds in swamps	Made of reeds and grass, down-lined; many dummy nests.
Hummingbird	On high branches	Tiny, shallow nest, saddled onto branch, lichen-covered.
Oriole	Overhanging branch of elm tree	Pendant, woven of hair, string, and grass.
Oven bird	On ground	Under arch of grass, entrance at side.

Destruction of harmful mammals. Hawks, owls, and other birds of prey were formerly regarded as harmful, but recent studies have proved this conception to be false. Only five species are harmful, six are wholly beneficial and thirty chiefly so, and seven others do about equal amounts of good and harm.

Their eating of mice, rats, squirrels, rabbits, and other harmful animals more than pays for any poultry these birds may take. Of the diet of the *red-tailed hawk,* commonly called a "hen hawk," harmful mammals comprise 66 per cent, while poultry forms only 7 per cent. *Cooper's hawk* really should be called a "hen hawk," since poultry and wild birds constitute much of its fare. This hawk and the *sharp-shinned hawk, goshawk, great horned owl,* and *snowy owl* do more harm than good.

Harm done by birds. Three hawks and two owls have been mentioned as killers of wild and domestic birds. To this list should be added the English sparrow, which drives away native birds, kills the young, and breaks up nests, especially of bluebirds and swallows.   The starling is a similar pest in some regions.   Both are immigrants and, lacking their natural enemies, have multiplied fast in their adopted country.   Crows do considerable harm to corn and, together with their cousins, the bluejays, destroy eggs and young of other birds.   To balance this damage, both birds destroy many insects and it is doubtful whether they ought to be killed except in regions where the harm they do is really serious.

Birds could hold their own against natural enemies if man would not interfere.   Remember that exterminating birds is likely to produce disastrous results because it upsets a normal biological balance.   Harmful animals should be killed only to the extent demanded by control.

In Conclusion

Birds are a subject of never-ending interest.   Their bright colors and songs add beauty to the landscape.   Their instincts have long been a subject of scientific study.   Their bodies are models of flight engineering and aerodynamics.   They contribute so much to the balance of nature that we cannot do without them.   Protection of our birds is a major phase of conservation.   We shall discuss what you can do to help them in Chapter 56.   Our study of vertebrates now shifts to the highest class, the mammals.

BIOLOGICALLY SPEAKING

air sac	egg cell	quill feathers
albumen	filoplume	rachis
barbs	incubation	rectum
barbules	lime-producing glands	secondaries
contour feathers	ornithologist	song box
coverts	primaries	vane
down feathers	quill	yolk

QUESTIONS FOR REVIEW

1. What are some characteristics of birds which make them ideally suited for life in the air?
2. Give the functions of the four kinds of feathers on a bird.
3. How do birds oil their feathers?
4. Describe the location of the bird's powerful flight muscles.
5. How does the attachment of the bird's legs provide excellent balance?
6. In what ways are air sacs important in the bird?
7. What advance in structure over the reptile is shown in the bird heart?
8. At approximately what temperature are the eggs of most birds incubated?
9. Describe several field identification marks which are used in distinguishing various birds.
10. For what purpose are birds banded?
11. What are some materials used by birds in making nests?
12. In what ways do birds render a valuable service to man?

APPLYING FACTS AND PRINCIPLES

1. Compare the amount of food consumed, rate of respiration, and oxidation in the bird with other vertebrates that you have studied.
2. Explain the meaning of the term *warm-blooded* as it applies to birds.
3. Discuss the development of the special senses of birds.
4. Discuss the relation between parental care and the number of eggs laid.
5. Discuss several possible explanations for bird migration.

CHAPTER *33*

Mammals—The Highest Forms of Animal Life

FROM early times, mammals have served mankind as sources of food and clothing, as beasts of burden, and as pets and companions. Man has controlled the breeding of domestic mammals to produce types and breeds suitable to nearly every need and pleasure. In countless ways, mammals, both wild and domesticated, have been essential to the progress of mankind through the ages.

In many ways, the mammals are a " super " group of chordates, including from 15,000 to 20,000 species. Fish are still the most abundant chordates of the seas and waterways; the birds are not surpassed in the air; but on land, mammals are supreme. The high development of their nervous systems has placed mammals above all other forms of life. But it remained for man, the most intelligent of all mammals, to gain domination of the earth. In this respect, man is far superior to even the most highly developed of the mammals.

The rise of mammals. Compared with other animals, mammals are recent forms of life. Fossils indicate that the earliest mammals appeared about 60 million years ago. At that time, the earth was undergoing geological changes which mark the end of the Mesozoic Era and the dawn of the Cenozoic Era. Prior to this time, a warm, humid climate had prevailed over much of the earth. Shallow inland seas and swamps were numerous among the flat land masses. These conditions had favored the giant reptiles which dominated animal life for ages. Then, as though nature were closing one chapter of life to make way for another, continents were uplifted and mountain ranges and high plateaus arose. These topographic changes altered the climate of the continents, resulting in seasonal

Fig. 33-1. These mastodons were prehistoric mammals that became extinct. They could not adapt to climatic changes, as did the early horses in the background.

temperature variations and differences in the precipitation in various continental areas. Forest lands, prairies, plains, arid lands, and deserts came into being. Within a short time, most of the reptiles died out, yielding their dominance among land animals to the mammals.

The earliest mammals were small and included forerunners of the squirrel, rat, and mouse. Another of the earliest mammals was a little ancient horse, known as *Eohippus,* which was no larger than a small dog. This curious ancestor of the modern horse had five toes. Other early mammals resembled monkeys. One of the few early mammals which has survived to the present day is the opossum.

From these early beginnings, mammals increased in size and became more abundant. Hoofed mammals, including ancient species of the rhinoceros, camel, wild pig, and a larger three-toed horse roamed the forests and grasslands in great herds. Still later, flesh-eating mammals, including the great bear dogs and terrible sabre-toothed cats, flourished, destroying large numbers of hoofed mammals. Near the close of the Cenozoic Era, further cooling of the climate resulted in the Glacial Age. Then prehistoric elephants, called mastodons and mammoths, migrated to Africa through Europe, Asia, and North America.

Many species of ancient mammals perished long ago. However, a large number survived the changing conditions and served as the ancestral stock of the mammals we find today.

Characteristics of mammals. Modern mammals vary in size from the tiny shrew, less than two inches long, to the enormous blue whale, over 100 feet long. In their widely varied forms, mammals are found in all parts of the world except a few Pacific islands. They are, for the most part, land animals, although some, like the whale, porpoise, and sea cow, are adapted to life in the sea. The bat is one of the few mammals which is capable of flight.

While mammals vary greatly in body form, size, and mode of living, all have certain characteristics in common which distinguish them from all other chordates:

1. Body mostly covered with hair.

2. Young born alive and nourished during development in the body of the mother, in most mammals; hence, **viviparous.**

3. Young nourished after birth by milk secreted by the **mammary glands** of the female, a characteristic for which the class is named.

4. Cerebrum highly developed.

5. Diaphragm (breathing muscle) separating the thoracic (chest) cavity from the abdominal cavity.

6. Lungs used for breathing throughout life.

7. Four-chambered heart and high circulatory development with left aortic arch only.

8. Ability to maintain constant body temperature (warm-blooded).

9. Seven cervical (neck) vertebrae, except in the sea cow (manatee) and sloth.

10. Two pairs of limbs, except in the whales, porpoises, and sea cow.

The body covering of mammals. The skin of a mammal consists of two layers, an outer **epidermis** and an inner **dermis.** Hairs grow from pits, or **follicles,** which lie deep in the skin. Hair shafts protrude from these follicles and form a protective covering in most mammals. Oil glands in the follicles lubricate the hair shafts.

Many mammals have thick coats of hair, especially during cold seasons. The fine, dense fur of the mink, beaver, muskrat, and fur seal makes their skins especially valuable commercially. There are usually two types of hair composing the coat of a mammal. The thick, soft **under hair** lies next to the skin and insulates the body preventing heat loss. Longer and more coarse **guard hairs** form a protective outer coat.

Tiny muscle fibers attach to the hair follicles of many mammals. These muscles contract in times of fear and anger or when the body surface is chilled, changing the angle of the follicles and causing the hair to " stand on end." You have probably seen the hair on the back of a dog or cat bristle when the animal was annoyed. The same mechanism causes " goose pimples " on your skin in areas where hairs are small or lacking.

The amount and structure of body hair varies greatly among mammals. The whale has no body hair, with the exception of a few bristles. On the other hand, modified hairs grouped in quills are the chief defense of the porcupine. Contrary to common belief, the porcu-

Fig. 33-2. The porcupine, a rodent, has stiff, sharp spines mingled with its hair.

Goodpaster from National Audubon Society

pine cannot throw its quills. However, a quick flip of the tail can sink a mass of quills deep into the skin of an annoying animal.

Many horny structures grow from the skin of various mammals. The armadillo has an armor formed by overlapping plates between which coarse hairs protrude. The horns of the rhinoceros are composed of hard masses of modified hair. *Fingernails* and *toenails* are other outgrowths of the skin of mammals. They grow from roots and lie on nailbeds of the fingers and toes. In mammals such as the dog, cat, bear, and squirrel, nails form powerful claws used in running, tearing flesh, and climbing.

Hair coloration in mammals. The color of mammals is due, primarily, to pigmented hairs. In most cases, the hair colors blend with shades of the environment. Most mammals which live in deserts and dry plains are pale brown or grayish in color. Those of forest areas tend to be darker, with more pronounced color patterns.

Certain mammals undergo curious color changes during different seasons. The weasel sheds its brown fur in the late fall and grows a white coat which remains until spring. This white coat provides nearly perfect protective coloration with the winter snow as a background. Similar color changes occur in the arctic fox and the snowshoe rabbit.

Color phases occur in many species of mammals. For example, most red foxes have the characteristic rusty red coat with white at the tip of the tail. However, a black phase known as the *silver fox* may appear in a litter of young produced by two red foxes. A color phase between red and black is known as a *cross fox*. Similarly, the black squirrel is a color phase of the gray squirrel.

Many mammals produce occasional **albinos** which lack pigmentation en-

American Museum of Natural History

Fig. 33-3. The special body covering of the armadillo acts much like a coat of armor. The shell is actually composed of modified hairs.

tirely. These animals have white hair in addition to pink eyes. Albino mice, rats, and rabbits are commonly bred. Albinos have also been seen among deer, raccoons, skunks, squirrels, woodchucks, and porcupines.

Antlers and horns — special structures for defense. Various mammals have interesting body structures which are used in defense. The **antlers** of the deer family are examples of such structures. All male members of the deer family have antlers. In the case of the caribou, they are produced by both males and females. Antlers are bony outgrowths of the bones at the front of the skull. They are shed and re-formed each year. Antlers grow from the skull bones during the late spring and summer. For a time, they are covered with skin having a velvet surface. By fall, the skin is rubbed off and the antlers are hard and bony. Male deer use their antlers in fierce battles with other males during the fall mating season. Several months later, the antlers loosen at the base and are shed. The eastern whitetail deer and the western blacktail deer develop additional prongs on the new antlers each year. The antlers of the moose are large and flattened and are referred to as *palmate*. While these antlers are valuable in defense, they may also be a handicap because their great size and weight makes them cumbersome.

Hollow **horns** are found on cattle, bison, sheep, and goats. Horns are permanent bony structures which grow from the base throughout life. They are covered with a horny material which grows from the skin, much like a fingernail. The horns of the pronghorn antelope of the western plains region, while true horns, are unique in that they are forked and shed annually.

The limbs of mammals are as varied as their environments. Limb modifications, especially of the forelimbs, have contributed much to the success of mammals in the world of life.

Have you ever considered how much you owe to the marvels of the human hand? Teamed with the brain, it can repair a watch, paint a portrait, play a

Fig. 33-4. Gazelles are small and very graceful antelopes. Notice their horns, and their long, hoofed limbs modified for running.

Lanks from Monkmeyer

musical instrument, rivet the girders in a skyscraper, or perform a delicate surgical operation. Much of the progress of the human race has involved the hand. The limbs of the other mammals are just as vital to their lives.

Most mammals have two pairs of limbs, but there are exceptions even to this. Whales and sea cows have lost all external evidence of hind limbs. The forelimbs are modified into finlike organs for swimming. Unlike the fins of a fish, however, these fins contain the bone structure of a hand.

Seals and walruses have limbs in the form of flippers, which make these mammals powerful and graceful swimmers. But on land the flippers serve as little more than props and levers to propel the animals with a clumsy, bouncing motion.

In the bat, long bony fingers support a thin membrane which forms a winglike organ for flight. The hind limbs are small and of little use, except to grasp a perch when the bat folds its wings, hangs upside down, and sleeps through the day.

The horse, cow, bison, antelope, and deer have limbs modified for running on hard ground. The toes form a hard hoof capable of supporting great weight. Smaller animals like the dog, fox, and wolf, have separate toes adapted for running on land. The lynx, lion, tiger, and other members of the cat family use their limbs for running, climbing, defense, and food-getting. Strong toes equipped with sharp claws rip the flesh of an enemy or prey. The squirrel, raccoon, and opossum have flexible claws adapted for climbing. Squirrels, especially, are masters in climbing, running through treetops, and leaping from tree to tree.

The teeth of mammals are of four kinds. We classify the teeth of mammals as: (1) *incisors;* (2) *canines;* (3) *premolars;* and (4) *molars.* These four kinds of teeth are developed about equally in the human mouth. The front teeth are incisors. The canines, sometimes called "eye teeth," are near the corners of the mouth. Next in order come the premolars, and finally the "jaw teeth" or molars.

Gnawing mammals like the beaver, porcupine, and rat have enormously developed incisors. These chisel-shaped teeth in the front of each jaw grow rapidly and replace the cutting edges as they wear down. Greatly enlarged canine teeth form the "fangs" of the dog, cat, bear, and weasel. These powerful teeth are used for ripping flesh. The large premolars and molars found in the vegetarian mammals, like the horse and cow, serve for grinding hard plant substances.

Internal organs of a mammal. The internal systems of a mammal are more highly developed than those of other animals you have studied. Fundamentally, these systems are similar to those of other vertebrates. However, the gradual advance you have seen in the structure of the heart, respiratory organs, reproductive organs, brain, and other body structures in the various classes of vertebrates reach their point of highest development in the mammal.

All mammals have well-developed lungs for air breathing. Air is drawn into the lungs by expansion of the chest cavity. This is accomplished by the rib muscles and diaphragm. The large lungs of the mammal are essential in supplying the great amount of oxygen required by the blood stream for meeting the respiration requirements of the tissues.

The mammalian heart is four-chambered and is similar to that of a bird. Rapid circulation is necessary to supply the needs of active cells and to remove their waste products. It is necessary, also, to distribute heat throughout the body tissues and maintain a constant

Davidson from National Audubon Society

Fig. 33-5. The bat is a mammal which has limbs curiously modified for flight. Notice, however, that the finger bones are present, although very elongated.

body temperature. Many mammals have sweat glands which cool the surface of the body. Others discharge heat through the respiratory organs by way of the mouth and nasal openings.

Mammals have a highly efficient method of reproduction. Development of the embryo takes place within the mother's body (except in one order) and may require from only 13 days to nearly two years. The mother's blood supplies nourishment to the developing young until they are born.

Eggs develop in the two *ovaries,* which are located in the lower abdominal cavity. Several eggs may mature at the same time, coming from both ovaries, a situation which results in multiple births as in the case of dogs, cats, rabbits, swine, and other mammals. Or, in most cases, a single egg develops, as it does in horses, cows, and elephants.

When an egg matures, it leaves the ovary by passing through a tube called the *oviduct.* Many tiny cilia fan the egg into the funnel-like opening of the oviduct which connects the ovary with the *uterus* (*yoo*-ter-us). The uterus is the

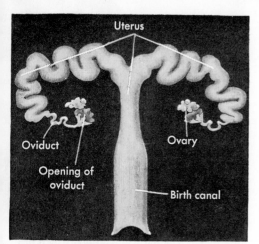

Fig. 33-6. The reproductive organs of a typical female mammal are shown in this drawing.

organ in which the young organisms are nourished until the time when they are born. In some mammals the uterus is divided into a left and a right portion which join at the lower ends (Fig. 33-6). In others, both oviducts lead to a single uterus.

If the animal has mated, sperm from the male have migrated through the uterus and up the oviducts. The mature egg meanwhile passes down an oviduct. Thus the union of egg and sperm, known as **fertilization,** takes place somewhere in the oviduct.

Division of the fertilized egg begins immediately. The first division results in a two-celled condition. These cells divide to form four, and so on until a many-celled, ball-shaped structure is produced. As growth of the mass continues, it moves down the oviduct and enters the uterus, where it becomes attached to the wall of the uterus. As the embryo continues to develop, an absorbing structure, known as the **placenta** (pluh-*sen*-tuh) spreads over the inner membrane of the uterus. A cord called the **umbilical** (um-*bil*-ih-kul) **cord** leads from the placenta to the embryo. Blood flows from the embryo

in arteries which lead through the umbilical cord to the placenta. The arteries branch into numerous thin-walled capillaries in the placenta. Here the blood of the embryo comes into close contact, but *does not mingle,* with the blood of the mother. Blood returns from the placenta to the embryo through a vein in the umbilical cord.

As blood from the embryo circulates through the placenta, it receives oxygen and dissolved food materials from the mother's blood. Carbon dioxide and cell wastes enter the mother's blood stream.

Later in its development, the embryo is called a **fetus** (*fee*-tus). At the end of its term of development in the uterus, or **gestation** (jes-*tay*-shun) **period,** the fetus is forced through the birth canal leading from the uterus. Soon after the young mammal is born, the placenta is loosened from the wall of the uterus and passes through the birth canal. This is sometimes referred to as the "afterbirth." The mother cuts the cord with her teeth and thus separates the young animal from the placenta.

Birth brings a sudden change in the life of the young animal. Its lungs fill with air for the first time. Body nourishment must now come from its own digestive system. However, the mother will supply this nourishment for some time in the form of milk secreted by the mammary glands in her breasts.

There are variations in periods of gestation. Among the shortest periods of gestation is that of the opossum, which lasts about 13 days. The young are born prematurely and are so small that several can rest in the bowl of a teaspoon. They continue to develop in a brood pouch of the mother containing the mammary glands.

The table at the top of page 403 shows the approximate gestation periods of several well-known mammals.

GESTATION PERIODS

MAMMAL	PERIOD	MAMMAL	PERIOD
Opossum	13 days	Human	36 weeks
Mouse	21 days	Cow	41 weeks
Rabbit	30 days	Horse	48 weeks
Cat	63 days	Whale	20 months
Dog	63 days	Elephant	20 to 22 months
Pig	120 days		

Young mammals must have parental care. The fact that a young mammal is nearly helpless and dependent on its mother's milk for a time after birth makes *parental care* necessary. Parental care permits smaller families among mammals. The number of young is usually proportionate to the length of parental care. Mice, rabbits, and other small mammals bear several litters, often numbering ten or more, each season. Larger mammals produce smaller numbers of young and provide parental care over a longer period.

Mammals vary greatly in their degree of development at birth. Mice and rats are born hairless and blind. A baby bear weighs less than a pound when it is born during the winter hibernation.

On the other hand, a cow, horse, deer, or bison is born in a much more advanced condition and can stand and walk with the mother a few hours after birth. The young whale is born in a well-developed condition in the water after a long gestation period. The newborn porpoise is half as long as its mother.

Development of the nervous system. The high degree of development and specialization of the nervous system is the primary factor that places mammals above the other classes of vertebrates. The brain of the mammal is larger, in proportion to the body weight, than that of any other animal.

In the mammalian brain, the **cerebrum** is the largest brain region. It is, as in all animals, the region that directs all of the higher-level activities. It fills most of the cranial cavity and spreads out over the other brain regions. The cerebrum is composed of two large hemispheres, joined at a central fissure. The surface is greatly increased by rounded ridges, or **convolutions** (con-voh-*loo*-shuns). The outer region, or **gray matter**, consists of the bodies of countless nerve cells. The **white matter**, deeper in the brain, consists of masses of nerve fibers which carry impulses to and from the brain cells.

The olfactory region of the mammalian brain consists of two bulbs extending from the front of the cerebrum on the lower side. The optic region, largest of the brain areas in lower vertebrates, lies in the posterior region of the cerebrum.

The **cerebellum** is large and lies below and posterior to the cerebrum. The high development of this brain region accounts for the excellent muscular coordination of the mammal. The short **medulla,** a center of control of many vital body processes, lies below the cerebrum and extends to the **spinal cord.** Cranial nerves extend from the brain to the sense organs and other head structures. Spinal nerves extend from the spinal cord to all regions of the body.

Senses of a mammal. Perhaps you would expect the mammal, with its highly developed nervous system, to have equally efficient sense organs. This is often true. However, there are many mammals in which one of the senses may be poorly developed while another sense is especially acute as a compensation for the deficient one.

The mole is a good example of such compensation. It has nearly lost its sight (Fig. 33-7). However, a keen sense of smell and touch directs its activities efficiently in its underground burrows. Similarly, the bat depends little on its sense of sight and can even fly through the passages of caves in total darkness, relying on its " radar " system for direction. The bat emits a series of clicking sounds in flight. The waves produced by these sounds rebound from objects and are received by the bat's highly sensitive ears, thus locating objects and indicating their distance.

Members of the dog and cat families have an extremely keen sense of smell. These mammals can track the scent of a prey left where its feet touched the ground. The deer is one of the many mammals which can detect the odor of an approaching animal at a considerable distance by sniffing the air.

Monkeys, squirrels, and other tree-dwelling mammals have large eyes and depend greatly on keen vision for survival. Many mammals, including the cat, raccoon, skunk, and opossum have excellent night vision and are most active in dim light or darkness.

Body hair increases the sense of touch in many mammals. The hairs are not sensitive to touch. However, when the hairs are pressed against an object, the skin is moved and a sensation of pressure is experienced.

Automatic behavior in mammals. As we discussed in Chapter 28, the automatic behavior called *instinct* can be observed in many common mammals. The house cat still follows the instinctive law of the jungle when it crouches for a leap or stalks a mouse — even a catnip mouse. *Self-preservation* instincts can be observed when any mammal is faced with sudden danger. A rabbit dashes in a zigzag path for the nearest clump of grass or undergrowth; a squirrel races up the nearest tree trunk. These escape movements are automatic and the mammal never makes a mistake by seeking a shelter it cannot use. *Species-preservation* instincts direct mating activities at certain seasons. They may drive the male mammal to bloody combat with other males, or cause the animals to seek special surroundings in which the young can be produced and reared in the greatest possible safety. These instincts also govern care of the young and their defense. They may cause an otherwise harmless mammal to fight fiercely when its young are threatened.

Emotional responses grow out of instincts. The mammal shows affection for its mate. Similarly, the mammal may express anger when its mate is disturbed or threatened. Biologists have found that many wild mammals become friendly if they have never associated man with danger. However, when they are hunted, annoyed, or teased by man, they soon associate him with danger and fear him.

Fig. 33-7. The senses of smell and touch of the nearly blind mole enable it to live its underground life successfully. The feet of the mole are adapted for digging.

Mohr from National Audubon Society

Fig. 33-8. The beaver shows great ingenuity in constructing its lodges, or " houses," and dams across streams.

A domesticated mammal associates food, comfort, and security with the one who cares for it. A feeling of affection can cause a mammal such as a dog to give its life for a kind and considerate master.

Mammals respond to training. The mammal has an advantage over other animals in having a capacity for learning. This capacity is possible because of superior development of the cerebrum and the lengthened period of immaturity during which the animal can learn. The Alaskan fur seal, for instance, has to be taught to swim. Similarly, parent black bears teach their cubs to climb trees.

The mammal's capacity for learning makes *training* possible. During training the animal learns to associate a signal with a given activity, after which the trainer expresses pleasure or gives the animal its reward. Biologists classify the results of such training as **conditioned reactions** — activities which become automatic after a period of training. You can compare them with such activities as riding a bicycle or driving an automobile. While conditioned reactions in mammals involve the brain, they are not on the level of intelligent acts, resulting from reason. The animal trainer does not teach his lions to jump through hoops in the way your teacher taught you to read. During a long training period, the lions associate the leap with a command or the crack of a whip.

Homes of mammals. Many mammals range over a wide area and have no permanent shelter. However, certain kinds of mammals build more or less permanent homes.

The circular lodge of the beaver has a floor just above the water level. The walls are made of sticks, plastered with mud and grass (Fig. 33-8). Ten beavers may live in a single lodge. The woodchuck constructs a series of underground tunnels leading to grass-filled chambers. The nest usually has more than one exit.

One of the most familiar sights to visitors of the marsh is the muskrat house. These dome-shaped mounds of willow branches, sedge, cattail stems and leaves, grasses, and mud vary from the size of a bushel basket to eight or ten feet in diameter. The hollow interior may accommodate six or more muskrats. A hole near the water line serves as a door.

The fox squirrels and gray squirrels of eastern United States build bulky nests of branches and leaves in treetops. The cottontail rabbit makes a fur-lined nest in a shallow depression, but conceals it so perfectly that a person can step on it without noticing it.

Many mammals make long journeys from one place to another. In some cases, a migratory journey is necessary for mammals because of seasonal changes in the food supply. Other mammals migrate to a more favorable climate regardless of food supply. Still others make seasonal journeys to regions where they can produce their young under the most favorable conditions.

Among the most remarkable migrations is that of the fur seal. During the winter, females, young males, and pups roam the waters of the Pacific Ocean to as far south as California. The older males winter in the cold waters near Alaska and the Aleutian Islands. With the approach of the breeding season in the spring, the males migrate to the Pribilof Islands, north of the Aleutians. The males arrive several weeks before the females and battle for a " territory." The females and young seals start their long journey of 3,000 miles or more to the Pribilofs in the spring and arrive in June. A herd of 50 or more females gathers around each male. Pups from the past year's breeding are born almost immediately and within a week, breeding occurs again. After this, the seals migrate southward.

The seasonal migration of the elk is easily observed in the Yellowstone Park region. During the summer, elk live on the higher mountains at altitudes above 8,000 feet. Early in September small herds move down the mountains to winter quarters in protected valleys. As spring approaches, the herds move back up the slopes in long, single-file processions.

Some mammals hibernate. Various mammals differ in degree of inactivity and hibernation during the winter months. The woodchuck (groundhog) and ground squirrels enter a period of true *hibernation* during which the body processes slow down to a point near death. The heartbeat may slow down to four or five beats per minute. The body temperature may drop to as low as 45° F. Breathing may occur at a rate as low as once in five minutes. The animal lies in a stupor and cannot be awakened.

The bear enters a period of *winter sleep,* but does not hibernate in the true sense. Heartbeat and respiration slow down and the animal lives on stored food in its body. However, a high body temperature is maintained. The bear may wake up on a mild day and even walk about before continuing its winter nap. The skunk, raccoon, and opossum undergo a similar winter hibernation.

Orders of mammals. Biologists do not agree as to the exact number and arrangement of orders of mammals, but there are generally considered to be at least thirteen. We shall discuss each of these briefly in the following pages.

Egg-laying mammals. The order **Monotremata** (mon-oh-tree-*may*-tuh) is represented by the *duckbill* and the *spiny anteater.* These mammals are of great interest to the biologist because they are so different from other members of the class. The duckbill is a small brown animal, about 12 to 18 inches in length. It has waterproof fur like a beaver, webbed

Fig. 33-9. Examples of eleven orders of mammals found in the Western Hemisphere.

Philip Gendreau

Fig. 33-10.   Why is the platypus considered an unusual type of mammal?

feet like a muskrat, and a horny bill like a duck (Fig. 33-10).   It lives in the streams of Australia and New Guinea, where it probes in the mud with its bill in search of insects.   Its home is a burrow, dug several feet into a bank, which ends in a grass-filled nest.   The duckbill usually lays two or three eggs which resemble those of reptiles.   After hatching, the young are nourished on milk.   This milk, which is secreted by the mammary glands, is licked from the mother's fur.

The spiny anteater has a tubular bill and a long tongue, used in catching ants. Its body is covered with long spines resembling those of a porcupine.   It lays two eggs which are placed in a brood pouch on its lower side.   The eggs remain in the brood pouch several weeks before hatching.

Pouched mammals. What do the opossum and the kangaroo have in common? They certainly do not look alike, nor are their diets similar.   One lives in North America and the other in Australia and islands close by.   But they do have one thing in common.   Both have a brood pouch in which the young develop after premature birth.   This characteristic sets the **Marsupialia** (mar-soo-pee-*ay*-lee-uh) in an order by themselves.   An *opossum* is born as a tiny, hairless creature less than an inch long.   It could not possibly live outside its mother's brood pouch. Here it is nourished on milk from mammary glands for about two months before it is large enough to leave the pouch. From six to fifteen young are produced in one litter and a female usually bears two or three litters a year.   The opossum usually sleeps curled up in a tree through the day.   At night it roams the countryside in search of small birds and mammals, eggs, insects, and fruit.

The *kangaroo* is a helpless, naked creature about an inch in length at birth.   It spends four months in the mother's brood pouch before venturing out (Fig. 33-11). Even then, it scampers back to the protection of the pouch when frightened.

Toothless mammals.   In the order **Edentata** (ee-den-*tay*-tuh) we include the *armadillo, sloth,* and *anteater*.   Actually, these are not entirely toothless, but teeth are absent in front. If we were to rate the mammals on the basis of brain development, this group would be far down the scale. Various species of armadillos live in our southwestern states, Mexico, Central and South America. Our North American species is known as the nine-banded armadillo. It hides in a burrow during the day and spends its nights digging in the ground for insects. The young of the armadillo are identical quadruplets. They start life as a single egg. Separation of cells early in development results in four individuals which ordinarily would have been one.

The sloth is a bearlike creature of the jungles of Central and South America. It hangs upside down on tree limbs with long claws and moves in slow motion in search of leaves, its chief diet. In some species, the hair is green due to the presence of minute algae which grow in it.

Insect-eating mammals. Moles and shrews are the best-known mammals of the order *Insectivora* (in-sek-*tih*-vor-uh). The *mole* spends its life underground, digging long burrows just below the surface. Its long nose is adapted for rooting out grubs and worms in the soil. Its small sightless eyes are covered with skin. Its soft fine fur is valuable for making coats and capes. While the mole is valuable in destroying many harmful beetle grubs, it is a pest in lawns and golf courses because it digs up the turf.

The *shrew* is a tiny mammal resembling both a mole and a mouse. It is a bloodthirsty killer, feeding on insects, mice, and even other shrews. We seldom see the shrew because it runs along tunnels in the grass and hides easily under a leaf.

Flying mammals. The name *Chiroptera* (ky-*rop*-ter-uh) means, literally, " hand-winged." This order includes more than 600 species of bats and vampires. True flight is accomplished by membranous wings formed by the greatly lengthened finger bones. *Bats* are insect feeders and fly mostly at night when insects are abundant in the air. They spend the days hanging upside down in a cave or hollow tree, and use the " radar " system we mentioned earlier in the chapter for direction. *Vampires* are large bats which live in tropical America. They pierce the skin of cattle and other warm-blooded animals including humans, and draw blood flowing from the wound.

Marine mammals. It is highly probable that the members of the **Cetacea** (see-*tay*-shuh) and **Sirenia** (sy-*ree*-nee-uh) orders developed from mammals which originally lived on land and then took up life in the sea at some early period.

Whales, dolphins, and porpoises belong to the order Cetacea. The *blue whale* is the largest living animal and probably the largest which ever lived.

Fig. 33-11.   Marsupials, such as the kangaroo, have a brood pouch in which the young develop after birth.

Goro from Monkmey

Specimens may reach a length of 100 feet or more and weigh as much as 150 tons.

The head of the *sperm whale* contains an enormous reservoir of oil which is used commercially as a lubricant and as a base for cosmetic creams. The most valuable product of this whale is **ambergris** (*am-ber-greese*), a secretion of the intestine. For centuries sailors have watched for ambergris floating on the ocean. Its principal use is in the manufacture of perfumes.

Dolphins are smaller relatives of the whale, usually under ten feet in length. They travel in herds in the ocean bays and mouths of rivers. *Porpoises* also travel in herds, often close to moving ships, and delight the passengers with their graceful leaps. They feed on fish which they catch in their narrow tooth-lined jaws (Fig. 33-12).

Sea cows belong to the order Sirenia. These large-bodied mammals reach a weight of one ton. The large rounded head resembles that of a walrus. The tail is fishlike. Sea cows live in shallow stretches of warm oceans close to the coast. They feed on algae and other marine plants.

Flesh-eating mammals. All of the members of the order **Carnivora** (kar-nih-vor-uh) have enlarged canine teeth for tearing flesh, and their other teeth are pointed for cutting it. Most of them are predatory animals, feeding on birds, insects, and other small animals. Some, like the bear, feed on vegetable matter as well. Variations in foot structure are used in dividing the order into families, many of which are familiar to everyone. In addition to the families of *terrestrial* carnivores, several forms, including the seal, sea lion, and walrus, are *aquatic* (Fig. 33-12).

A glance at a few typical carnivores. The *black bear* lives in the northern and western forest states and at one time was common throughout eastern North America. In regions where it lives one may be seen perched high in a tree. The *grizzly* is larger and more dangerous than the black bear. It lives in the Northwest,

Kenyon from National Audubon Society

Fig. 33-12. The white porpoise shown at the left is a marine mammal belonging to the order Cetacea. The porpoise is from five to eight feet in length. The seal shown above is an aquatic carnivore which, unlike the porpoise, does not spend all its time in the water.

Leahey from Shostal

and is especially abundant in Yellowstone Park. It frequently wades the shallow water of streams in search of salmon and other fish. The *brown bears,* especially the Kodiak bear of Alaska, are the largest of all bears. The *polar bear* of the Arctic region is an expert swimmer. Its snow-white coat, slender head, and long neck are different from those of other bears.

The *raccoon,* with its black mask and long-ringed tail, is a favorite of many people because if captured young it makes a nice pet. The raccoon prefers fish and clams as its food but will eat other things as well if these are unavailable. It has a habit of washing its food before eating. This is probably to moisten the food rather than to clean it.

The weasel family includes some of the most blood-thirsty carnivores and some of the most valuable fur-bearing mammals. The *mink* especially is prized for its fur. These long-bodied, short-legged animals live along streams. The *ermine* is an Arctic weasel which grows a coat of white fur except for a black-tipped tail in winter, but is brown in summer. The largest and most destructive member of the family is the *wolverine* of the northern forest. Its body, including its bushy tail, is about 36 inches long and weighs between 30 and 35 pounds.

The dog and cat families are not as well represented in America as in other lands. The *mountain lion* (puma or cougar) was found over the majority of North America at one time, but civilization has driven it to the remote regions of the southwest. Its chief harm lies in its destruction of livestock, especially young horses. Both the *bay lynx,* or bobcat, and the *Canada lynx* live in deep forests and are seldom seen.

The *gray wolf,* or timber wolf, is most frequently found in the northern forests and may be dangerous during the winter when it runs in packs. The *coyote,* or

Haddon from U. S. Fish and Wildlife Ser

Fig. 33-13. Why has it become necessary to import coyotes in some regions of this country?

prairie wolf, has been more successful than its larger cousin in surviving the effects of civilization. It is still abundant on the western plains (Fig. 33-13). However, in some regions, too many have been destroyed and their natural prey, including rodents and jack rabbits, have become pests. It has therefore been necessary to import coyotes into these regions.

The *red fox,* and the other foxes that are color phases of the red fox, ranges over much of the United States. It is sly and a very fast runner for short distances. The gray fox resembles the red fox but lives in the warmer regions of the South.

Gnawing mammals. The gnawing mammals are grouped in the order **Rodentia** (roh-*den*-shuh) and include some of our most valuable as well as some of our most destructive mammals. All have very strong chisel-shaped incisor teeth. These teeth have sharp edges which

Rush from U. S. Fish and Wildlife Service

Fig. 33-14.   The cottontail rabbit is a common North American wood rabbit.   Its name comes from the white-tufted underside of the tail.

become even sharper with use because the front edge is harder than the back edge, causing the biting surface to wear on an angle.

Rats and *mice* are among the most common rodents.   Others include the *squirrel, woodchuck, prairie dog, chipmunk,* and *gopher*.   The *beaver* is the largest North American rodent.   The great value of beaver pelts brought the early trappers to the Northwest Territory.   Another rodent, the *muskrat,* is an important fur-bearing mammal of North America.

The rodentlike mammals.   *Rabbits, hares,* and *picas* resemble rodents in many ways, but differ from them in tooth structure.   They are included in the order **Lagomorpha** (lag-oh-*mor*-fuh).   These mammals have four enlarged incisor teeth in each jaw, rather than two as in the rodents.   They grind plant foods with a characteristic sideways motion of the lower jaw.

The *cottontail rabbit* is the most widely

hunted mammal of the United States, and supplies more flesh than any other wild mammal (Fig. 33-14).   But even though preyed upon by man, predatory birds, and other animals, these rabbits have been able to hold their own in most localities. The *jack rabbit* is common in the broad expanses of the western prairies and plains.   It reaches a length of nearly 30 inches and has characteristic long ears and large powerful hind legs.   Both sight and hearing are especially keen, enabling it to escape from its enemies.

The hoofed mammals.   Man has lived in close association with the **Ungulata** (ung-gyou-*lay*-tuh) since prehistoric times. The goat was probably the first to be domesticated.   For ages man has depended on the horse, camel, ox, llama, and other hoofed mammals as beasts of burden. The cow, pig, and sheep are our principal food animals.   Deer, elk, caribou, moose, and antelopes are our most important big game ungulates.

Biologists classify the ungulates as follows: (1) *odd-toed,* including the *horse, tapir,* and *rhinoceros;* (2) *even-toed non-ruminants,* or non-cud-chewers, including the *pig* and *hippopotamus;* and (3) *even-toed ruminants,* or cud-chewers, including the *cow, ox, bison, sheep, goat, antelope, camel, llama, giraffe, deer, elk, caribou,* and *moose.*

The **ruminants** (*roo*-mih-nunts) have a four-chambered stomach.   While grazing, they eat large quantities of food which pass into a large paunch, or **rumen,** the first of the stomach divisions.   Here food is stored for later chewing.   Later, the food is forced back into the mouth for leisurely chewing as **cud.**   After thorough chewing, the cud is swallowed into the second stomach, where digestion begins.   From there it passes through the other stomach regions to the intestine.

Trunk-nosed mammals.   Only two species of elephants remain as representatives of the order **Proboscidea** (proh-boh-*sih*-dee-uh). The *Asiatic elephant* is the familiar performing elephant of the circus. In many parts of the world, it is used as beast of burden. The *African elephant* is a taller, more slender animal with a sloping forehead and enormous ears. African elephants travel in herds in the deepest parts of Africa and are not as easily domesticated as their Indian cousins. Elephants reach a weight of seven tons or more.

During the glacial and pre-glacial eras, more than 30 species of elephantlike mammals lived in Asia, Europe, Africa, and North America.

Erect mammals. None of the wild forms of the order **Primates** (pry-*may*-teez) lives in the United States. Biologists usually include man in the primates, but place him in a family by himself, namely the Hominidae (hoh-*mih*-nih-dee), which sets him completely apart from the monkeys and apes. He belongs to the genus *Homo,* the species *sapiens,* which makes his biological name *Homo sapiens.*

Superior brain development places the primates at the top of all groups of living organisms. Primates have well-developed arms and hands. Their fingers are used for grasping and one or more fingers or toes are equipped with nails. Primates walk erect. Most live in South America, Africa, or the warm regions of Asia.

The *anthropoid apes* are most like man in body structure. They have no tails. The arms are longer than the legs. When walking, the feet tend to turn in. These primates, especially the chimpanzee, respond to a very high degree of training. They include:

1. The *gorilla,* the largest of the apes, which lives in Africa. It walks on two feet and certainly is one of the most powerful animals (Fig. 33-15).

2. The *chimpanzee* also lives in Africa.

It is smaller than the gorilla and when trained reveals much intelligence.

3. The *orangutan* lives in the East Indies. It is a droll animal with red hair.

4. The *gibbon* is a long-armed type found in Asia.

5. The *Old World monkeys* have long tails, but do not use them in climbing. They sit erect. Food is stored in cheek pouches. The baboon, an Old World monkey, has a long, doglike nose.

6. *New World monkeys* have flat, long tails which are used for grasping. The septum between the nostrils is wide and they lack cheek pouches.

7. *Marmosets* are small primates ranging from Central America to South America. They resemble squirrels in appearance and activity.

8. *Lemurs* are primates found in Madagascar.

Fig. 33-15. The gorilla, an erect primate, is one of the most powerful of animals.

New York Zoological Society

In Conclusion

As you might expect, the greatest threat to the survival of our native mammals is another mammal — man. With much of our land given over to expanding cities, farms, and ranches, many wild mammals have retreated farther and farther into the wilderness. Some face possible extinction. Our generation faces a major conservation problem in restoring our wild mammal population and, at the same time, continuing to expand our civilization. This can be done with proper education, game management, and public cooperation. Chapter 56 will discuss measures which can accomplish this aim.

The next unit presents a more thorough study of mammalian anatomy and physiology. The subject will probably be the most interesting of all to you — the human body.

BIOLOGICALLY SPEAKING

albino	gestation period	parental care
ambergris	gray matter	placenta
antler	guard hair	premolar
canine	horn	rumen
convolution	incisor	ruminant
cud	mammary gland	umbilical cord
fetus	medulla	under hair
follicle	molar	white matter

QUESTIONS FOR REVIEW

1. What characteristic of mammals is referred to in the class name *Mammalia?*
2. List several modifications of hair in the body covering of mammals.
3. Most mammals have two pairs of limbs. Name two exceptions.
4. Describe the brain structure of mammals.
5. In what respect is the brain structure of the mammal higher than that of any other vertebrate?
6. Describe four kinds of teeth present in mammals.
7. Name several problems of existence which are solved by the migration of various mammals.
8. Give several reasons why parental care is necessary among mammals.
9. (a) What do we mean by the term *gestation period?* (b) Give examples of gestation periods of several mammals.
10. How does true hibernation in the ground squirrel differ from the winter sleep of a bear?
11. In what respect are the duckbill and spiny anteater exceptions to the rule among mammals?
12. Why can kangaroos and opossums be born prematurely and yet survive?
13. (a) Describe the specialized tooth development of a rodent. (b) What uses are made of these teeth?
14. Make a list of six or more ungulates raised by man as domestic animals.

APPLYING FACTS AND PRINCIPLES

1. Discuss possible reasons for the disappearance of reptiles and the rise of mammals in past ages.
2. How do many mammals illustrate compensation in the special senses?
3. Discuss instinctive behavior in mammals and give several examples.
4. Discuss the capacity of a mammal for learning and training.
5. What is the relation between parental care and mortality and the number of young produced by various mammals?
6. Compare mammalian reproduction with that of lower vertebrates and list ways in which mammalian reproduction is more efficient.
7. The rodents, carnivores, ungulates, and primates are the most abundant orders. Give reasons why each of these orders has gained supremacy.
8. Account for the fact that carnivores are often hard to domesticate.

RESEARCH ON YOUR OWN

1. Place a living fish (a goldfish can be used) in a large jar or an aquarium and watch its movements carefully. Notice the action of the operculum in pumping water into the mouth and through the gill chambers. Watch the fish rise and sink in the water, swim forward, and rest quietly. List the various fins and the use the fish makes of each. You may wish to make a drawing, showing the general form of the fish, its head structures, fins, and some of the scales. Label all of the parts you show.
2. In your classroom, make a community aquarium of small native fish. Include such species as sunfish, bullheads, and minnows (not small game fish). An aquarium of this type should have an air pump or an abundant supply of oxygenating plants.
3. Put a living frog in a large jar or an aquarium containing enough water to submerge the frog, and a rock or other object for the frog to rest on. Study the movement of the throat and the sides of the body and movement of the nostril flaps when the frog is out of the water. Watch it closely while under water. Notice the structure and use of the front and hind legs. Touch the eyes and see what happens. Open the mouth carefully. Examine the tongue and the lining of the mouth. Notice the rich blood supply to the mouth lining. You should be able to locate the internal nostril openings, and the openings of the Eustachian tubes, gullet, and glottis, as well as the vomerine teeth.
4. Make a study of a living turtle. Include a sketch of the arrangement of plates forming the upper and lower shells. You can find the names of the various plates (shields) in a reptile or turtle book. Study the head and limbs of a turtle and compare them with other reptiles.
5. Prepare a table of data for twelve common birds of your region. Include the name of each bird, a small drawing of the bird (taken from a bird book), its resident classification, diet, nesting habits, number and description of eggs, and general economic importance.
6. Dissect the joint end of a chicken foot to expose the tendons. See if you can find the tendon which bends each toe and the one which closes the entire foot.
7. Make a table of the common native mammals of your region. Include the name of each, the order to which it belongs, habitat, diet, whether it migrates, hibernates or remains active through the winter in your locality, economic importance, and any other data you might be able to include.

MORE ABOUT BIOLOGY

Bevans, Michael. *The Book of Reptiles and Amphibians.* Garden City Books, Garden City, N.Y. 1956

Breland, Osmond. *Animal Facts and Fallacies.* Harper and Brothers, New York. 1948

Burt, William and Grossenheider, Richard. *A Field Guide to the Mammals.* Houghton Mifflin Co., Boston. 1952

Burton, Maurice. *Animal Legends.* Coward-McCann, Inc., New York. 1957

Ditmars, Raymond L. *Reptiles of the World.* The Macmillan Co., New York. 1933

Earle, Olive L. *Birds and Their Nests.* William Morrow, New York. 1952

Eddy, Samuel. *How to Know the Fresh-Water Fishes.* William C. Brown Co., Dubuque, Iowa. 1958

Guyer, Michael F. *Animal Biology.* Harper and Brothers, New York. 1949

Hall, E. Raymond and Kelson, Keith R. *The Mammals of North America.* The Ronald Press Co., New York. 1958

Hegner, R. W. and Stiles, D. A. *College Zoology.* 6th ed. The Macmillan Co., New York. 1951

Hegner, R. W. *Parade of the Animal Kingdom.* The Macmillan Co., New York. 1935

Hoke, Helen, *The First Book of Tropical Mammals.* Franklin Watts, Inc., New York. 1958

Innes, William T. *Exotic Aquarium Fishes.* 19th ed. Innes Publishing Co., Philadelphia. 1955

Kauffeld, C. *Snakes and Snake Hunting.* Doubleday and Co., Inc., New York. 1957

LaMonte, Francesca. *North America Game Fishes.* Doubleday and Co., Inc., New York. 1952

Moyer, John W. *Practical Taxidermy.* The Ronald Press Co. New York. 1958

Oliver, James A. *Snakes in Fact and Fiction.* The Macmillan Co., New York. 1958

Peterson, Roger Tory. *A Field Guide to the Birds.* Rev. ed. Houghton Mifflin Co., Boston. 1941

Pope, Clifford H. *The Reptile World: A Natural History of the Snakes, Lizards, Turtles, and Crocodilians.* Alfred A. Knopf, Inc., New York, 1955.

Romer, Alfred Sherwood. *The Vertebrate Story.* Rev. and enl. ed. The University of Chicago Press, Chicago. 1958

Scharff, Robert. *Look for a Bird's Nest.* G. P. Putnam's Sons, New York. 1958

Scheele, William E. *Prehistoric Animals.* World Publishing Co., Cleveland. 1954

Sterling, Dorothy. *The Age of Reptiles.* Garden City Books, Garden City, N.Y. 1958

Verrill, A. Hyatt. *Strange Animals and Their Stories.* L. C. Page and Co., Boston. 1939

Wood, Laura N. *Raymond L Ditmars: His Exciting Career with Reptiles and Insects.* Julian Messner, Inc., New York. 1944

Zim, Herbert and Gabrielson, Ira N. *Birds — A Guide to the Most Familiar American Birds.* Simon and Schuster, Inc., New York. 1956

Zim, Herbert, and Hoffmeister, Donald. *Mammals — A Guide to Familiar American Species.* Simon and Schuster, Inc., New York. 1955

How Biology Applies to Ourselves

Nature is not all one; men have one nature, the beasts an-other, the birds another, the fishes another; so too, there are bodies that belong to earth and bodies that belong to heaven. . . . Do you not understand that you are God's temple, and that God's Spirit has His dwelling in you? — I Cor. 15:39; 3:16

Good health is a priceless possession. It reflects in our per-sonalities, our success, and in the enjoyment we get out of living. Still, we often take good health for granted and as-sume that we shall always have it. It is normal to be healthy, but we may either abuse our health or safeguard it.

Science has given us a wonderful opportunity to be healthy. We can expect to live longer than has any genera-tion before us. And we expect to live this long life without worry about many of the health problems which plagued our ancestors. What better reason could there be for finding out more about the marvels of your own body?

Our study of plant and animal life has led to the climax of biological study — your own body.

CHAPTER 34: **STRUCTURE OF THE HUMAN BODY**
CHAPTER 35: **THE NATURE OF FOODS**
CHAPTER 36: **DIGESTION OF FOODS**
CHAPTER 37: **RESPIRATION AND EXCRETION**
CHAPTER 38: **THE BLOOD AND CIRCULATION**
CHAPTER 39: **THE NERVOUS SYSTEM**
CHAPTER 40: **THE SENSE ORGANS**
CHAPTER 41: **THE BODY REGULATORS**
CHAPTER 42: **ALCOHOL, NARCOTICS, AND TOBACCO**
CHAPTER 43: **RADIATION AND BIOLOGY**
CHAPTER 44: **SPACE BIOLOGY**

CHAPTER 34

Structure of the Human Body

MAN is not structurally adapted for skill in climbing, running, flying, and swimming, as are many vertebrate animals. Although he has these skills, they are not developed as well as in certain animals. In fact, without the aid of his intelligence, there is nothing that man can do which many animals cannot do much better. But with his intelligence to direct him, there is no animal that can compete with man. He has learned the use of tools, devised a spoken and written language, found a means of controlling fire, and developed mental faculties and social habits that put him in a position far above that of any of the animals.

Man's highly developed brain is the organ that has made him more advanced than any other living organism. The human brain is larger in proportion to body size than the brain of any other mammal, and is much more highly specialized. This brain has enabled men to form habits more easily, to think out problems and reach satisfactory solutions, and to acquire skills by constant practice.

Man and mammals. The study of the various vertebrate classes in Unit 6 revealed an interesting development in the complexity and efficiency of body organs and systems which climaxed in the mammal, the most advanced of the vertebrates. This background knowledge of vertebrate anatomy and physiology will make the study of the human body far more interesting and meaningful.

The organs and systems of the human body resemble those of other mammals closely. The structural similarity of man and the other primates is especially striking. Almost every detail in their anatomy is similar. You can observe this fact in the form of the skeleton and muscles, tooth structure, position and structure of the eyes, form of the hand and foot and, even, in the facial expressions. Similarities in the internal structure of man and the other primates are equally striking. They may be seen in the structure of the heart and blood vessels, lungs, digestive organs, excretory organs, glands, and nearly all other internal organs.

Equally striking are the similarities in the chemical secretions of man and other mammals. The digestive enzymes are the same. The chemical substances known as *hormones,* which are secreted by the endocrine glands, are also similar among mammals. The insulin used to save the lives of diabetics is extracted from the pancreas of the hog. Furthermore, the Rh factor, so important in matching human blood types, was discovered, originally, in the blood of the Rhesus monkey. The structural, physiological, and chemical similarity of man and the other mammals is of great biological importance.

Fossil men of ancient times. One of the most fascinating branches of biology is the science of **anthropology,** which includes the study of primitive forms of man, long extinct. The anthropologist has acquired his knowledge of these ancient people from fossils, bone fragments, complete or nearly complete skeletons, utensils, weapons, tools, drawings on the walls of caves, and other sources of evidence. By piecing together this valuable information, he can determine the nature of the people, the degree of mental development and intelligence, and their living habits.

Perhaps the most primitive of the known forms of ancient man is the *Java man,* who is believed to have lived more than 500,-000 years ago. The first evidence of this man was a portion of a cranium, a piece of a jaw, and the upper leg or femur bone discovered in an excavation on the Island of Java in 1891. The remains of this man lay in a deposit of sand and gravel transported by an early glacier, thus dating his existence. Other remains of this man were found in the same general region in 1937. The Java man is believed to have walked erect. He was about five feet in height. He had a slanting forehead and heavy brow ridges. The skull of the Java man indicates that his brain, while only about half the size of modern man's, was more than one-third larger than that of a gorilla. Anthropologists believe that the Java man learned to make use of crude stone weapons. If he used wood weapons and utensils, they decayed long ago.

During the period of the Java man, an-other primitive man was living in China. *Peking man,* as he is known today, was discovered in deep excavations of ancient caves near Peking, China. Many partial skeletons of this primitive man have been unearthed. While the brain of the Peking man was nearly the size of that of modern man, he was far less intelligent. Apparently, he used stone implements and weapons and had learned the use of fire. Many of the skulls of Peking man which have been discovered are broken open near the base, which suggests that the Peking man was a savage head hunter.

A portion of a lower jaw of an extremely ancient and primitive man was found near Heidelberg, Germany in 1907. Little is known of the *Heidelberg man* except that his body was heavy and apelike, although his teeth were definitely human. Since no weapons have been found with the remains of the Heidelberg man, little is known of his intelligence or mode of life. However, he is believed to have lived in forest regions of Germany.

Much more is known about the *Neanderthal man,* who lived in Europe, Asia Minor, Siberia, and Northern Africa.

Fig. 34-1. Neanderthal man lived in family groups in caves. He had discovered the value of fire, and used stone tools and weapons.

Scientists believe that the Neanderthal man disappeared about 25,000 years ago, near the close of the Glacial Epoch. Information about the Neanderthal man has been acquired from careful study of nearly 100 skeletons, many of them nearly complete. He was about five feet tall and walked in a stooped position. His bone structure indicates that he was powerfully built. His facial features were coarse. His forehead sloped backward from heavy brow ridges. His mouth was large, and he had little or no chin.

The Neanderthal man lived in caves from which he journeyed on hunting expeditions in search of the hairy mammoth, saber-toothed tiger, and woolly rhinoceros. His brain was as large or larger than that of modern man. However, lack of brain development placed him far below modern man in intelligence. The Neanderthal man used stone tools and weapons, made

Fig. 34-2. The bottom photographs of those below show, from left to right, the skulls of Java, Neanderthal, and Cro-Magnon men. The dark portion of the skull at the far left is the fragment from which the rest of the skull was restored. The other two skulls were constructed entirely from original material, except for the jaws and teeth. The models in the top photograph were reconstructed on the basis of the skulls, and represent what these primitive men are believed to have looked like.

American Museum of Natural History

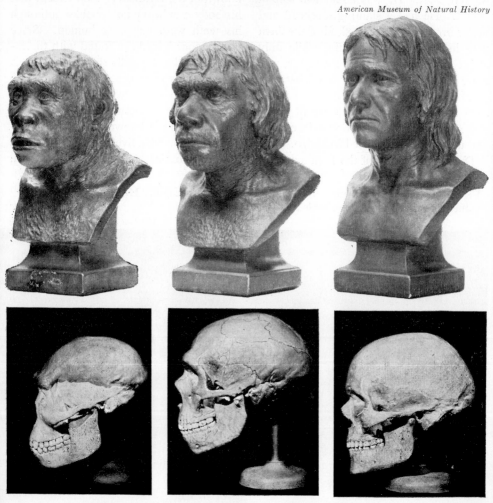

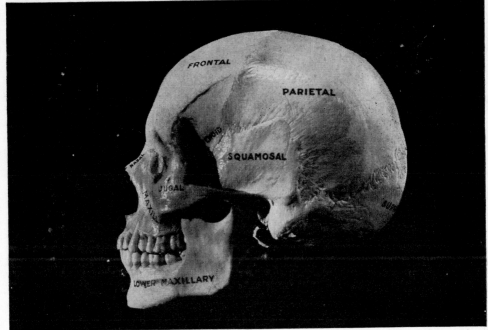

Fig. 34-3.   In this skull of modern man, notice the large brain capacity, the high-brow type of forehead, the small jaw, and the well-defined chin.

use of fire, buried his dead and lived in a family group (Fig. 34-1, page 419).

The *Cro-Magnon man* was, probably, the first " modern " man.   He lived in Europe, especially in France and Spain, perhaps 50,000 years ago.   This man is often referred to as the " cave man."   He had a high forehead and a well-developed chin and lacked the heavy brow ridges of more primitive men.   Several caves along the southern coast of France have yielded abundant remains of the Cro-Magnon man.   Here, scientists found weapons of stone and bone as well as skeletons.   The walls of these caves bear drawings of animals of the region (Fig. 34-4, page 422).   These drawings have been valuable in dating the period of his existence.   Anthropologists believe that the Cro-Magnon man, living at the same time as the Neanderthal man and being superior to him in intelligence, may have exterminated him.   There is evidence, also, that the Neander-

thal man mixed with the Cro-Magnon man and, in time, lost his identity.

Modern man.   All people living today belong to the species *Homo sapiens,* referred to as *modern man.*   Racial groups are types or stocks of this single species.   Human types are distinguished on such characteristics as body build, bone structure (especially formation of the skull), facial features, eye color, and the texture, color, and distribution of body hair.   Skin pigmentation may vary greatly among members of a single type.

Racial groups are very complex and variable.   Furthermore, people have traveled far and wide in recent times with the result that basic stocks are becoming more and more mixed.

The *Mongoloid* type is represented by people from most of Asia, the East Indies, and the Philippines.   This type is well represented in the Western Hemisphere by the Eskimos, and Indians of North

Fig. 34-4. The wall paintings found in certain caves in southern France are believed to have been made by skilled artists among Cro-Magnon men, in the manner depicted by the above illustration.

America as well as Central and South America. Anthropologists believe that the Mongoloid people came to North America from Asia in very early migrations through Alaska.

Natives of North Africa, South Africa, East Africa and the Congo pigmies are of the *Negroid* type. Negroid stock is found, also, in New Guinea, the Philippines, and islands in the region of Australia.

People of the *Caucasoid* type are, largely, from Europe, Southwestern Asia, and North Africa. Caucasoid people vary greatly. They include the Teutonic types of Northern Europe and Iceland, Southern Europeans, Slavs, Hindus, Gypsies, Arabs, Jews, Egyptians, and Ethiopians.

A fourth type of modern man is represented in the *Australoid* type. These people do not fit any of the three major types. This small group includes the original people, or aborigines, of Australia and Ceylon. These primitive people live in Australia and still maintain the life of the

early Stone Age. The sloping forehead and prominent brow ridge characteristic of the Australoids suggest a relationship to ancient man. However, the hand structure and body form are definitely like those of modern man. Anthropologists still have much to learn about these interesting people.

Modern man dominates the biological world. A comparison of modern man and ancient man shows the triumph of "brain over brawn." Few people today could match the strength of primitive man, nor could they endure the hardships of life in those primitive times. Yet, modern man, while he may have lost some of his physical development through the ages, lives three or four times as long as primitive man. Modern man used his hands, along with his great capacity for learning, to construct the civilization we live in.

Intelligence has permitted us to control our environment. We have removed ourselves, largely, from the struggle for existence in nature. Heating and air-conditioning allow us to live in any climate at any season of the year in a comfortable, uniform temperature. We grow an abundance of food and, if necessary, enrich it with vitamins. Modern medicine prevents most infectious diseases and aids greatly in overcoming those we cannot avoid. Machines have removed most of the toil and drudgery from living. Life is, for the most part, easy, pleasant, and enjoyable.

With all of the benefits and comforts of modern living, however, we still have many biological problems to face. Far too often, we overwork the nervous system and work or worry ourselves into a mental or emotional crisis. As we enjoy the benefits of science and technology, our bodies grow weaker from inactivity. We slump in comfortable chairs and enjoy an evening of television or drive a block or two to the corner grocery or drug store. It is probably more important today than ever before that we have a thorough knowledge of our bodies. We are living in the most advanced and exciting age the world has ever known. We have every advantage and opportunity for health and happiness. Certainly, then, no topic you will ever study is more important to you than your own body.

Two major divisions in the study of the human body. *Anatomy* is the study of the structure of an organism. *Physiology* probes the functions of the various parts. In order to understand *how* our body works, we shall, first, have to know *what* it is composed of.

The cellular structure of the human body. Like any other organism, the body of a human being is composed of cells and their products. All of these cells are not alike in shape or function. As we mentioned in Chapter 22, a *tissue* is a structure composed of cells which are alike in structure and in duty performed. Various kinds of tissues are grouped to-

gether into **organs.** Various kinds of organs are grouped together into **systems.** Each system is specialized to perform certain processes with the highest degree of efficiency. The **organism** is composed of all the systems.

Tissues of the human body. All the cells which compose the human body can be placed into four groups: (1) **connective tissue,** (2) **muscle tissue,** (3) **nerve tissue,** and (4) **epithelial tissue.** (Refer to the table on page 424 for subdivisions of connective tissue.) Connective tissue lies between groups of nerve, gland, and muscle cells and beneath epithelial cells. It fills up spaces in the body which are not occupied by specialized cells, and it forms protective layers with fat cells (Fig. 34-6, page 425).

Connective tissue, in addition to serving as a " filler tissue " of the body, also binds together many softer tissues and gives them strength and firmness. Fibrous tissues in the walls of organs, the

Fig. 34-5. This photomicrograph is of epithelial cells in the lining of the small intestine.

General Biological Supply House

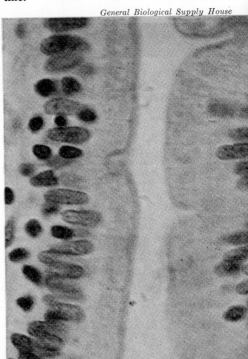

TISSUES IN THE HUMAN BODY

TISSUE	OCCURRENCE	FUNCTION
1. CONNECTIVE TISSUE		
a. BONE	Skeleton	Composes framework and allows for movement
b. CARTILAGE	Outer ears, ends of long bones, larynx, tip of nose, between vertebrae, juncture of ribs and breastbone, trachea	Acts as cushion, lends rigidity to structures which lack bones, provides slippery surface to some joints
c. DENSE FIBROUS CONNECTIVE TISSUE		
(1) Regularly arranged	Tendons, ligaments	Joins muscles to bones or bone to bone to aid in movement
(2) Irregularly arranged	Membrane around bone (periosteum), one of the membranes around spinal cord and brain (dura mater), inner layer of skin	Provides protection and carries blood supply
d. LOOSE FIBROUS CONNECTIVE TISSUE		
(1) Fibro-elastic (elastic — strong, closely woven)	Capsules of organs	Holds organ together
(2) Fibro-areolar (areolar — loosely woven)	Facial area beneath skin	Acts as "filler" tissue
(3) Reticular	Surrounding individual cells and muscle fibers	Acts as "filler" tissue
(4) Adipose	Around organs, beneath skin	Cushions and insulates, stores fat
e. LIQUID TISSUE		
(1) Blood	In heart and vessels (arteries and veins)	Has essential part in: respiration, nutrition, excretion, regulation of body temperature, protection from disease
(2) Lymph	Fluid in tissue spaces between cells, cerebrospinal fluid	Bathes the cells, has part in nutrition and protection from disease
2. MUSCLE TISSUE		
a. SMOOTH	In internal organs	
b. STRIATED	Attached to bones, tendons, and other muscles	Produces either voluntary or involuntary movement
c. CARDIAC	In heart	
3. NERVE TISSUE	Brain, spinal cord, nerves	Carries impulses which cause muscles to contract, carries messages to brain to inform individual about the environment
4. EPITHELIAL TISSUE	(1) Covering surface of body (skin), lining nose, throat, and windpipe, lining all of digestive tract (2) Many glands	Provides protection, produces secretions in some cases

tendons of muscles and ligaments binding bones, as well as the bones themselves, are all types of connective tissue.

Tissues are organized into organs and systems. Familiar examples of organs in the human body include the arms, legs, ears, eyes, heart, liver, and lungs. Each of these organs is specialized to perform a definite function or a group of related functions involving several different tissues. The arms, for example, are composed of epithelial tissue, bone tissue, cartilage, muscle tissue, blood tissue, nerve tissue, and other tissues. All these function together to perform such acts as grasping, writing, and sewing.

Organs are grouped together into ten *systems* as follows:

1. Skeletal (bones)
2. Muscular (muscles)
3. Digestive (teeth, mouth, esophagus, stomach, intestines, liver, pancreas)
4. Respiratory (lungs, trachea, nose, pharynx)
5. Circulatory (heart, arteries, veins, capillaries)
6. Endocrine (glands)
7. Excretory (kidneys and bladder)
8. Integumentary (skin and hair)
9. Nervous (brain, spinal cord, nerves, eyes, ears)
10. Reproductive (testes, ovaries, uterus, oviducts)

The body regions in man. The general form of the human body is similar to the other vertebrate animals. It includes the limbs (in the form of arms and legs), the head, neck, and trunk. The head includes the *cranial cavity,* which is formed by the bones of the skull and safely encloses the brain. The head also contains the sense organs which are located close to the brain, to which they transmit impulses.

The *thoracic* (thor-*as*-ik) **cavity** is formed by the ribs, breastbone, and spine. It encloses the lungs, the trachea, the heart, and the esophagus. A dome-shaped

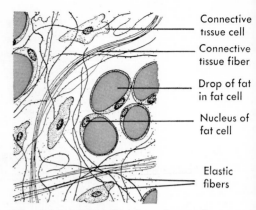

Fig. 34-6. **This drawing shows the way some of the connective tissues in the human body appear under the microscope.**

partition, the *diaphragm* (*dy*-uh-fram), separates the thoracic cavity from the abdominal cavity which is included in the lower part of the trunk. Inside the abdominal cavity are the *stomach, liver, pancreas* (*pan*-kree-us), *intestines, spleen, kidneys,* and in the female, the *ovaries.* While the abdominal organs lack the bony protection of the cranial and thoracic cavities, they are protected by the vertebral column along the back and by layers of skin and muscle on the front.

The body framework. When building a model airplane, the framework of the body is usually built first. Then comes the covering and painting, and finally the motor, wheels, and accessories. The strength of the entire structure depends upon the framework to which all the other parts are fastened. Man and the other vertebrates, like the model airplane, have a very efficient system of support in the form of an internal skeleton, or *endo-skeleton.* You will recall that the arthropods have an exoskeleton. Many of the other invertebrates have other methods for the support of their bodies. Man's bony framework gives him the greatest support with the least amount of weight. It also permits movement far

SKELETON Front View

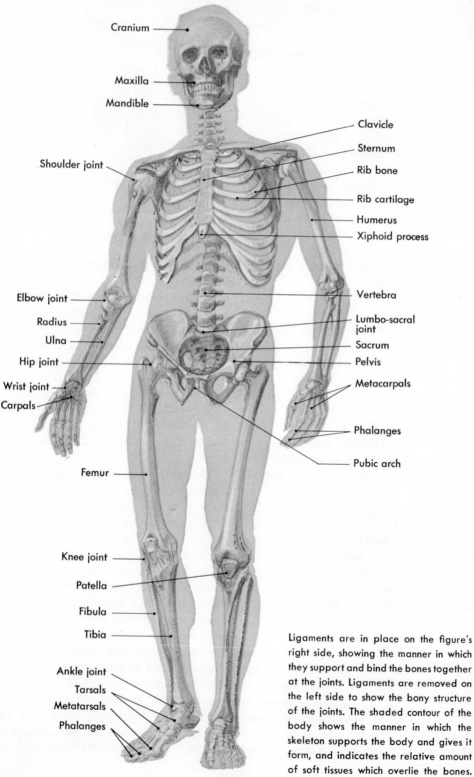

Cranium

Maxilla

Mandible

Clavicle

Sternum

Rib bone

Shoulder joint

Rib cartilage

Humerus

Xiphoid process

Elbow joint

Vertebra

Radius

Lumbo-sacral joint

Ulna

Sacrum

Hip joint

Pelvis

Wrist joint

Metacarpals

Carpals

Phalanges

Pubic arch

Femur

Knee joint

Patella

Fibula

Tibia

Ankle joint

Tarsals

Metatarsals

Phalanges

Ligaments are in place on the figure's right side, showing the manner in which they support and bind the bones together at the joints. Ligaments are removed on the left side to show the bony structure of the joints. The shaded contour of the body shows the manner in which the skeleton supports the body and gives it form, and indicates the relative amount of soft tissues which overlie the bones.

Fig. 34-7, page 426

SKELETON Back View

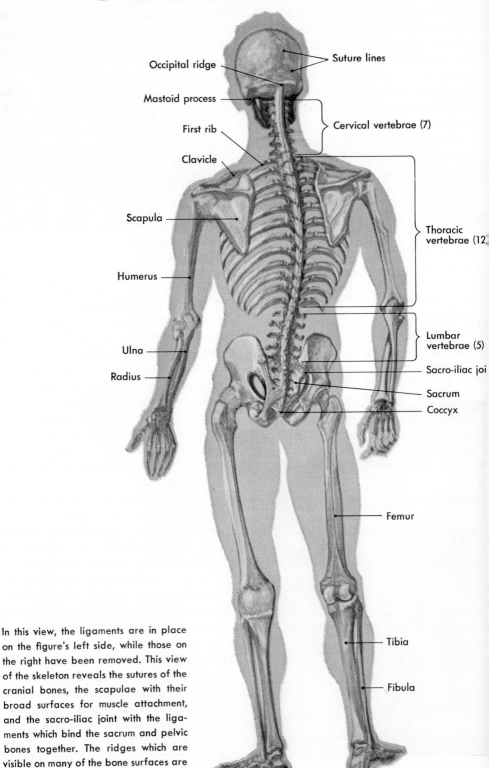

Occipital ridge

Suture lines

Mastoid process

First rib

Clavicle

Cervical vertebrae (7)

Scapula

Thoracic vertebrae (12)

Humerus

Ulna

Radius

Lumbar vertebrae (5)

Sacro-iliac joi

Sacrum

Coccyx

Femur

Tibia

Fibula

In this view, the ligaments are in place on the figure's left side, while those on the right have been removed. This view of the skeleton reveals the sutures of the cranial bones, the scapulae with their broad surfaces for muscle attachment, and the sacro-iliac joint with the ligaments which bind the sacrum and pelvic bones together. The ridges which are visible on many of the bone surfaces are for the attachment of muscles.

Fig. 34-8, page 4

better than any other type of framework. The animal with an internal skeleton is, however, at one great disadvantage. It does not have much of the protection against injury from the outside that is given by an external skeleton. Many soft parts of the body are exposed. Consequently, the organism must rely on its nervous system and sense organs to make up for the protection which the skeleton does not provide.

The functions of the skeleton. The functions of the bones of the body are classified as follows: (1) support and form for the body; (2) place for the attachment of muscles; and (3) protection for delicate organs.

Many of the 206 bones which compose

Fig. 34-9. This is an X-ray photograph of a complete fracture and separation of the lower end of the femur (thighbone) just above the knee joint. This fracture resulted from the impact of an automobile bumper.

Indiana University Medical Center

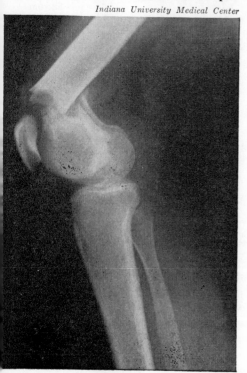

the human skeleton have more than one function. For example, the vertebral column, the shoulder girdle, the hip girdle, the bones of the legs, and those of the arms both support the body and give it definite form. Some of these bones also have muscles attached to them, permitting the many types of movement (Figs. 34-7 and 34-8, pages 426 and 427).

Certain delicate organs lie under special protective bones. Examples are the brain, which is encased by the cranial bones; the heart, which lies under the sternum; and the lungs, which are protected by the ribs.

Bone is composed of living tissue. We use the expression " dry as a bone," and assume that living bone is like a dried-out bone. Actually, living bone is far from dry. It is moist and active and requires nourishment as does any living organ. True, part of what we call bone is nonliving, for bone tissue is a peculiar combination of living cells and their products and mineral deposits.

The development of bone tissue. The formation of bone involves not only bone substances but cartilage as well. Among some of the lower vertebrates the skeleton is composed entirely of cartilage, which lasts throughout their lives, and results in a tough, flexible skeleton.

In the early stages of the development of the human embryo, the skeleton is composed almost entirely of cartilage, with a few membranes taking the place of bone in some regions. After about the second month of development, however, certain of the cartilage cells disappear and are replaced by bone cells. These cells deposit minerals in the form of *calcium phosphate* and *calcium carbonate* in the spaces between them. This process is called **ossification** (os-ih-fih-*kay*-shun), and occurs throughout childhood. In fact, it continues at a reduced rate throughout a person's entire life.

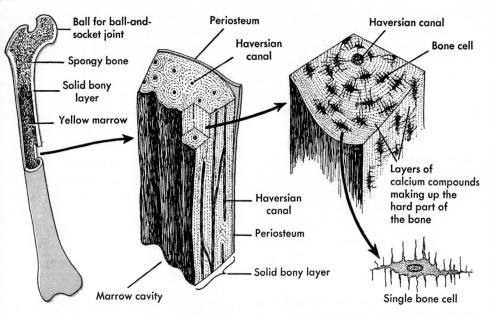

Fig. 34-10.   A cutaway view of the human femur is shown on the left.   The center drawing is an enlarged section of that bone.   The Haversian canal system and a single bone cell are shown enlarged on the right.

Certain factors control mineral deposit in bone.   Since ossification involves the deposit of calcium compounds between the bone cells, it results in an increase in the strength of the bone.   Naturally, this deposition cannot occur unless the proper minerals are present.   Calcium compounds enter the body with food and are carried to the bone tissues by the blood. The diet is therefore an important factor in governing the mineral deposition in bone.   Especially in childhood, the diet must be controlled carefully to be sure that the proper supply of minerals is available to the body.   Milk, the natural food of all young mammals, is the ideal source of these calcium compounds.

Developing bone tissue must assimilate the minerals after they have been supplied by a proper diet.   Certain vitamins, especially vitamin D, are necessary for the normal growth of bone.   We shall study these in Chapter 35 under vitamins.

Bones grow along lines of stress.   In other words, they become heaviest and strongest where the strain is greatest. This fact is important in dealing with bone fractures (Fig. 34-9).   If a broken bone is protected by a cast and is unused during that period of repair, the fact that it is under no stress delays healing.

For example, if a leg bone is broken, the patient is provided with a walking cast, which puts a broken bone under limited stress during the healing period, and speeds up the repair process.   If, on the other hand, a limb is paralyzed or made useless, the minerals are reabsorbed by the blood and deposited elsewhere.

The structure of a bone.   If a long bone, such as a bone from the leg or arm, is cut lengthwise, several distinct regions can be seen (Fig. 34-10).   The outer covering is a tough membrane called the *periosteum* (pair-ee-*os*-tee-um).   This membrane aids in nourishing the bone (due to its rich blood supply), in repairing injuries, and also provides a surface to which muscles are attached.   Beneath the periosteum is a *bony layer* containing the deposits of mineral matter. This layer may vary in hardness from an extremely hard to a spongy material, depending on its location in the bone. The bony layer is very hard through the mid-region of the bone, but becomes porous and spongy at the ends.

The bony layer is penetrated by numerous channels, the *Haversian* (huh-*ver*-shun) *canals,* which form a network extending throughout the region. These canals carry nourishment to the living cells of the bony layer. The blood vessels of the Haversian canals connect with those of the outer membrane from which nourishment is received.

Fig. 34-11. What are the advantages of each type of joint shown here?

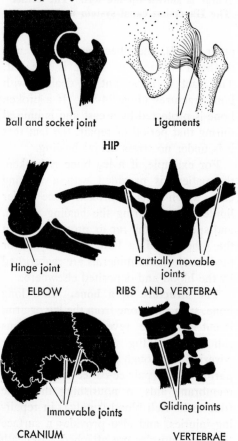

Ball and socket joint   Ligaments

HIP

Hinge joint   Partially movable joints

ELBOW   RIBS AND VERTEBRA

Immovable joints   Gliding joints

CRANIUM   VERTEBRAE

Many bones have hollow interiors and contain a soft tissue called *marrow.* The marrow is richly supplied with nerves and blood vessels. There are two distinct types of marrow, *red* and *yellow.* The **red marrow** is found in flat bones such as the ribs and sternum, as well as in the ends of long bones and vertebrae. It is active in forming the red corpuscles and some of the white corpuscles. The **yellow marrow** fills the central cavity of long bones and extends into the Haversian canals of the bony layer. It is normally inactive, and primarily composed of fat cells, but may produce corpuscles in time of great blood loss and in certain blood diseases.

The smaller bones are solid rather than hollow and vary considerably in the amount of spongy bone tissue present. Though they are solid, they are completely penetrated with blood vessels.

Parts of the body are supported by cartilage rather than bone. *Permanent cartilage* remains as such and is not replaced by bone as is *temporary cartilage.* Permanent cartilage forms such structures as the end of the nose, the external ear, and the walls of the larynx and trachea. The inner surfaces of the joints, too, are covered with layers of cartilage. A secretion called *synovial* (sih-*noh*-vee-ul) *fluid* serves to lubricate the joints. In some joints such as the knee or shoulder, a sac, called the *bursa* (*bur*-suh), serves as a cushion between the bones.

The joints of the body. The point at which two separate bones meet is called a *joint.* The various bones of the human body are connected by several different kinds of joints (Fig. 34-11).

The elbow is an example of a *hinge joint.* Such a joint moves as a hinge in one plane only, but has the ability to give great power because there is little danger of twisting. When certain muscles of the upper arm contract, the lower arm is pulled upward only. The knee is another example of a hinge joint. The hip and shoulder joints are examples of **ball-and-socket joints.** Here the bone of the upper arm ends in a ball which fits into a socket of the shoulder girdle. Such a joint has the advantage of universal movement, or movement in any direction within the limits imposed by the muscles. The hip joint is similar to the shoulder, with a ball on the end of the **femur** (*fee-mer*), or thighbone, fitting into a socket of the hipbone, the **pelvis.**

Ball-and-socket and hinge joints are held in place by tough strands of connective tissue called **ligaments.** Ligaments may be stretched with exercise, thus " loosening " joints and permitting freer movement.

The ribs are attached to the **vertebrae** (*ver*-tuh-bree) by joints which are only **partially movable.** Long strands of cartilage attach the ribs to the breastbone in front to allow for chest expansion during breathing. The junction between the spine and pelvis, the sacroiliac joint, is a well-known example of partial movability. It is a frequent place for injuries from sudden falls. Some joints, as in adult skull bones, are **immovable.**

Other joints include the **angular joints** of the wrists and ankles, the **gliding joints** of the vertebrae, and the **pivot joint** of the head on the spine.

How do muscles produce movement? Bones, even in a living body, have no power to move by themselves because their hard layers of calcium prevent contraction. Muscles, however, can contract, causing movement. There are about 400 different muscles, making up about one-half of the body weight (Figs. 34-14 and 34-15, pages 434 and 435).

We can move our arms whenever we desire. This fact shows that certain muscles are under the control of our will.

Such muscles are called **voluntary** muscles. There are many others which help in the operation of our digestive, respiratory, circulatory, and excretory systems, which are never controlled by our will. They are the **involuntary** muscles. Some muscles are both voluntary and involuntary, as, for instance, those that operate the eyelids and the diaphragm.

Types of muscle cells. There are three kinds of muscle cells: (1) *unstriated,* or *smooth:* spindle-shaped cells with one nucleus (involuntary); (2) *striated,* or *skeletal:* long cylindrical cells with many nuclei (voluntary); and (3) *cardiac:* branched, striated fibers (heart muscle) (Fig. 34-12, page 432).

Smooth, or *unstriated,* **muscle** form the walls of many internal organs. The stomach and intestinal walls contain layers of smooth muscle cells which contract in waves to churn food or pass it along through the digestive tract. Artery walls also contain layers of smooth muscle. Impulses from the nervous system cause the artery walls to constrict and raise the blood pressure during danger or emotional upset. All action of smooth muscle is controlled by parts of the nervous system over which we have no conscious control.

Striated, or *skeletal,* **muscle** cells (fibers) do not run the entire length of most muscles but are bound together in small *bundles* by connective tissue sheaths. These small bundles are then held together by a heavier sheath which encloses the entire muscle. This structure gives most voluntary muscles a spindle shape. The body of the muscle is called the **belly.** Some muscles attach directly to bones, some attach to other muscles, and some attach to bones by inelastic **tendons** extending from the tapered end. These tendons are dense bands of fibrous connective tissue. Since muscles are organs of movement, they

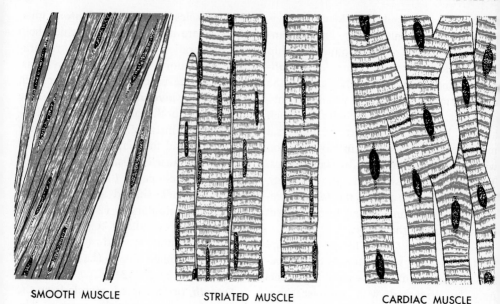

SMOOTH MUSCLE   STRIATED MUSCLE   CARDIAC MUSCLE

Fig. 34-12. There are three different kinds of muscle cells, each having a different function.

must attach at two points. The **origin** is stationary while the **insertion** is the attachment of the muscle on the movable part. Determine the origin and the insertion of the biceps in Fig. 34-13.

Cardiac, or *heart,* **muscle** is similar to striated muscle when one views it under the microscope. The cells, however, are branched and contain specialized disks or bands of materials at varying intervals. Like striated muscle, cardiac muscle is capable of rapid movement, but it does not tire easily. In this respect it is like smooth muscle.

The action of heart muscle is unlike that of any other muscle. It has an *automatic beat* which is conducted from cell to cell throughout the muscle. The beat originates in a small mass of tissue on the top of the heart, called the **sinoauricular** (*sy*-noh-or-*ih*-kyoo-lur) **node.** From this point, the beat is carried through the muscle of the upper chambers to another node, the **auricular-ventricular node,** where it is relayed through the muscles of the lower chambers. Conduction of

the beat through the cells of heart muscle results in the rhythmic wave of contraction characteristic of the heart.

Muscle action. When a nerve impulse stimulates a muscle fiber, the fiber has only the power to shorten, or contract. A period during which the fiber relaxes must follow before another contraction can occur. However, since a muscle is composed of many fibers, a steady contraction can be maintained by alternating contractions of individual fibers or bundles of fibers. Since muscle tissue is very active, it requires a rich blood supply. Abundant food and oxygen must reach the muscle, and waste products of cell activity must be removed from it rapidly in order to prevent fatigue.

The skeletal muscles which move joints of the trunk and limbs are always arranged in pairs. Muscles which bend joints are called **flexors,** while those that straighten them are called **extensors.** For instance, when you bend your elbow joint, the tendon of the contracted biceps muscle raises the radius bone of the forearm. The other end of this muscle is securely anchored at the shoulder. During this contraction you can feel the belly of the biceps muscle swell on the front side of your upper arm. The extensor muscle involved in this movement is called the triceps. It is on the back side of the upper arm. When you lower the arm, the triceps contracts and the biceps relaxes. If you straighten your arm completely, you can feel the belly of this muscle contract.

Even when a joint is not being moved, flexor and extensor muscles oppose each other in a state of slight contraction called **tone**. Increased use of muscles results in enlargement and increased tone. When totally unused, muscles become weak and flabby, decrease in size, and lose tone.

Muscular coordination. The skeletal muscles, like all other muscles, contract as a result of nerve impulses. Any body activity involves many impulses and many muscles. The combined action of muscles to produce a movement results in *muscular coordination*. The skill with which movement is produced depends on the coordination of nerve impulses and muscular contractions. To a great extent, muscles may be trained to produce a particular kind of movement by practice. One must learn to play tennis, drive a golf ball, dribble a basketball, or play a piano. As one's nervous system and muscles become accustomed to the activity, a skill is developed.

Muscular exercise. Normal body activity is a balance between physical and mental exertion. However, the average person today, surrounded by laborsaving devices, uses less than one-tenth of his muscles in the course of a day's activity.

Relief of tension fatigue is probably the greatest benefit to be obtained from physical exercise, a fact which emphasizes the importance of your participation in physical activities.

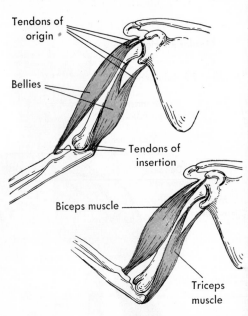

Fig. 34-13. In the upper drawing, the arm is straightened by the contraction of the triceps muscle, while the biceps is relaxed. In the lower drawing, the biceps contracts to flex the arm, while the triceps relaxes.

America has a well-deserved reputation as a nation of sportsmen. It is well to support your school athletic program, but your interest in sports should not be confined to a seat on the side lines. An exciting contest may even increase tension fatigue, except in the players themselves.

Extreme exertion in an individual who has been inactive for some time is unwise and may be dangerous. Heart action, respiration, and other vital activities have been geared to a sluggish existence and may have difficulty adjusting to a sudden great increase in muscular activity. For this reason, muscular exercise should be increased gradually and maintained at a fairly constant level.

Competitive athletics is a valuable experience for at least two reasons. In the first place, it requires gradual but regular attainment of a physical peak under a trained coach. In addition, it trains

SKELETAL MUSCLES Front View

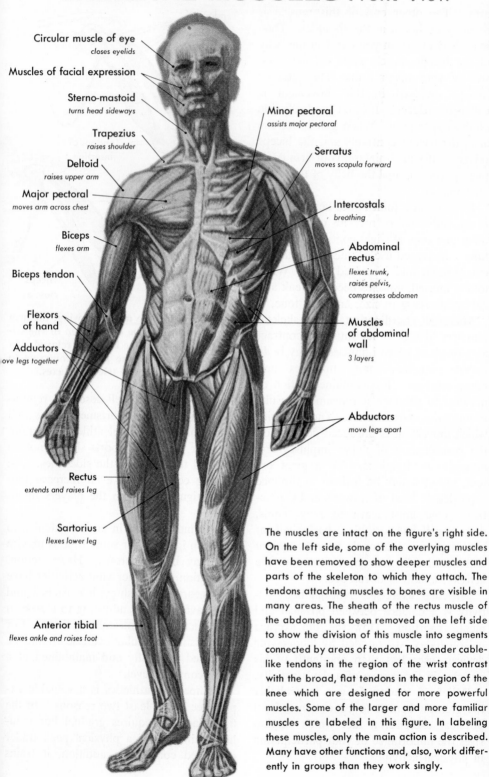

Circular muscle of eye
closes eyelids

Muscles of facial expression

Sterno-mastoid
turns head sideways

Trapezius
raises shoulder

Deltoid
raises upper arm

Major pectoral
moves arm across chest

Biceps
flexes arm

Biceps tendon

Flexors
of hand

Adductors
move legs together

Rectus
extends and raises leg

Sartorius
flexes lower leg

Anterior tibial
flexes ankle and raises foot

Minor pectoral
assists major pectoral

Serratus
moves scapula forward

Intercostals
breathing

Abdominal
rectus
*flexes trunk,
raises pelvis,
compresses abdomen*

Muscles
of abdominal
wall
3 layers

Abductors
move legs apart

The muscles are intact on the figure's right side. On the left side, some of the overlying muscles have been removed to show deeper muscles and parts of the skeleton to which they attach. The tendons attaching muscles to bones are visible in many areas. The sheath of the rectus muscle of the abdomen has been removed on the left side to show the division of this muscle into segments connected by areas of tendon. The slender cable-like tendons in the region of the wrist contrast with the broad, flat tendons in the region of the knee which are designed for more powerful muscles. Some of the larger and more familiar muscles are labeled in this figure. In labeling these muscles, only the main action is described. Many have other functions and, also, work differently in groups than they work singly.

Fig. 34-14, page 434

SKELETAL MUSCLES Back View

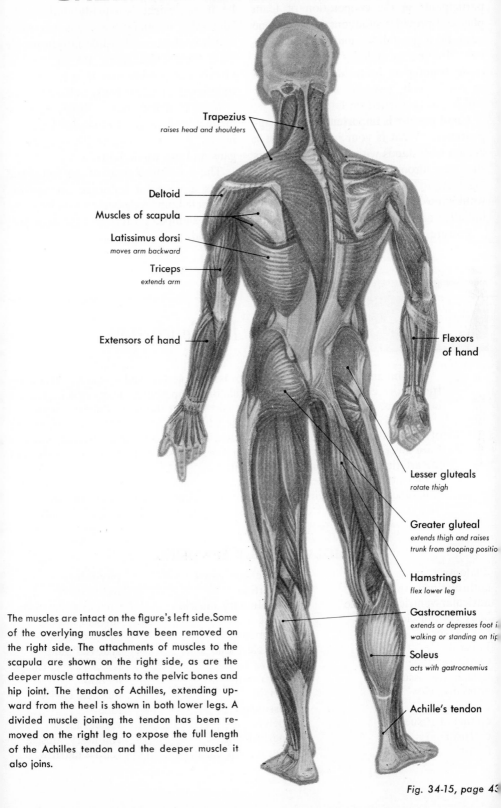

Trapezius
raises head and shoulders

Deltoid

Muscles of scapula

Latissimus dorsi
moves arm backward

Triceps
extends arm

Extensors of hand

Flexors of hand

Lesser gluteals
rotate thigh

Greater gluteal
extends thigh and raises trunk from stooping positio

Hamstrings
flex lower leg

Gastrocnemius
extends or depresses foot i walking or standing on tip

Soleus
acts with gastrocnemius

Achille's tendon

The muscles are intact on the figure's left side. Some of the overlying muscles have been removed on the right side. The attachments of muscles to the scapula are shown on the right side, as are the deeper muscle attachments to the pelvic bones and hip joint. The tendon of Achilles, extending upward from the heel is shown in both lower legs. A divided muscle joining the tendon has been removed on the right leg to expose the full length of the Achilles tendon and the deeper muscle it also joins.

Fig. 34-15, page 43

participants in the cooperation of team play and provides situations in which one must be a good loser and graceful winner. Interest in athletics should also include training in individual sports, such as tennis, golf, bowling, and swimming, which can be carried on later in life.

Good posture is important for good appearance. What is your impression of a person who stands with his back bent, his shoulders drooping, and his head hanging forward? If you were an employer, would you hire him to fill a job requiring initiative and leadership?

Posture which demands that the spine be held straight is equally undesirable. The spine normally has a distinct curve which is often more visible in thin people than those with more fat or muscle. Overly stiff posture may lead in later life to inflexibility of the back. Good posture is hard to define, but in brief, it is the maintenance of good muscular tone giving the most flexibility to the internal organs and the whole body.

The emotional state of an individual exerts a powerful influence on posture. A dejected, unhappy person usually maintains a slumped posture and the poor posture adds to his dejection.

In Conclusion

The human body is organized into tissues, organs, and systems. The body framework consists of an internal skeleton composed of bones which give the body form, act as levers for muscles, and protect the more delicate organs.

Muscles produce movement. Those which are attached to bones by means of tendons are skeletal, or striated, muscles. Smooth, or unstriated, muscles form layers in the walls of such internal organs as the stomach, intestines, and the arteries. Their control is involuntary.

Our attention will next be focused on the nature of foods, which have several functions in a living organism. If we know what foods are and what they do, we can then study the digestive system with better understanding.

BIOLOGICALLY SPEAKING

anatomy	Haversian canal	physiology
anthropology	insertion	red marrow
auricular-ventricular node	involuntary muscle	sinoauricular node
belly (of muscle)	joint	smooth muscle
bony layer	ligament	striated muscle
bursa	muscle tissue	synovial fluid
cardiac muscle	nerve tissue	temporary cartilage
connective tissue	organism	tendon
cranial cavity	origin	thoracic cavity
diaphragm	ossification	tone
epithelial tissue	pelvis	vertebrae
extensor	periosteum	voluntary muscle
flexor	permanent cartilage	yellow marrow

QUESTIONS FOR REVIEW

1. Name the racial groups found in the world today and give their place of origin.
2. How do the tissues, organs, and systems of the human body illustrate division of labor?
3. (a) What are the three body cavities? (b) By what structures are they enclosed? (c) Name some of the organs found in each.
4. (a) What are the principal functions of bones? (b) Give an example of a bone serving each purpose.
5. What are some important functions of the Haversian canals?
6. Describe some of the tissues surrounding a joint.
7. Describe four kinds of joints found in the body.
8. How do we classify muscle cells as to (a) appearance, (b) control, and (c) location?
9. Why are muscles often found in opposing pairs in the body?
10. Describe the process of an individual muscle contracting.

APPLYING FACTS AND PRINCIPLES

1. Compare the skull of modern man with those of Java, Neanderthal, and Cro-Magnon man.
2. Explain why an organism with an internal skeleton must have a highly-developed nervous system.
3. Proper diet alone does not insure good teeth and healthy bones. Explain what other factors are involved.
4. How does a walking cast speed up the repair of a bone fracture?
5. Why can the heart of some lower animals be removed and kept beating in a nutrient solution?

CHAPTER 35

The Nature of Foods

THERE is no more dramatic chapter in the study of biology than the story of foods. Radiant energy from the sun, streaming through space, enables green plants to combine the air, water, and minerals of the earth into substances that animals use for foods.

The story of food began in Chapter 5, where inorganic and organic substances were discussed. It continued in the study of green plants and their vital role as food producers. Now we conclude the study of foods and nutrition as they apply to human life.

What is food? **Food** is any substance which, when absorbed into the body tissues, yields materials for the production of energy, the growth and repair of tissue, and the regulation of life processes, without harming the organism. This is another way of saying that you eat to be active and to grow and maintain your body. Six classes of substances meet the requirements of this definition:

(1) water; (2) minerals; (3) carbohydrates; (4) fats; (5) proteins; and (6) vitamins.

Water has many uses. *Water* is inorganic, and does not yield energy to the tissues. However, it is so vital in the maintenance of life that a person deprived of it dies sooner than he would if deprived of other types of food.

If you weigh 100 pounds, your body contains between 60 and 70 pounds of water. Much of this water is organized into your body protoplasm and into the spaces between the cells. As water is lost, first from the intercellular spaces and then from the cells themselves, the protoplasm becomes more and more solid and finally dies. This water loss is part of the process called **dehydration.**

The fluid part of blood, called *plasma,* is 91 to 92 per cent water. Water is essential in the plasma as a solvent for the food and waste products that are transported to and from the body tissues. Water serves further as a solvent in the movement of dissolved foods from the digestive tract to the blood and in the removal of tissue wastes from the skin and kidneys. The kidneys alone pass two to five pints of excess water daily; this water contains many cellular wastes which the body must eliminate.

The flow of sweat is essential in the regulation of heat loss from the body. **Evaporation,** or the change of a substance from a fluid to a gas, requires heat. When perspiration evaporates from the body surface, heat resulting from internal oxidation is lost.

Water requirements of the body are met in three ways: (1) some water is present in the food you eat; (2) some is a by-product of oxidation in cells; and (3) some is consumed as drinking water. The amount required varies with the temperature and humidity of the air and the amount of body activity.

Mineral salts are important for body functions. Table salt, or *sodium chloride,* is consumed directly and in considerable quantities in the diet. Other salts (chemical compounds composed of a mineral and one or more other elements) are also present in food. Since salts are lost in perspiration, persons exposed to excessive heat over long intervals must either increase the salt in the diet or supplement the normal diet with salt tablets.

Calcium and *phosphorus* are required in greater abundance by animals than other mineral elements because of the importance of calcium phosphate in the formation of bones and teeth. These two elements form about five per cent of animal tissue when combined with others in the form of proteins. Milk is an ideal source of these two elements; other sources include whole-grain cereals, meat, and fish. Calcium is necessary to insure the proper clotting of blood and, together with *magnesium,* to nerve and muscle action. *Potassium* compounds are essential to growth.

Iron compounds are essential for the formation of red blood corpuscles. Meats, green vegetables, and certain fruits such as plums or prunes and raisins are important sources of iron in the diet. *Iodine salts* are essential in the formation of the secretion of the thyroid gland. Iodine may be obtained from drinking water or by eating sea foods.

Minerals are vital to the body in many ways. Each of them, however, must be in a compound form before it can be used by the body. If we ate chemically pure elements, such as sodium or chlorine, it would be fatal. When these elements are in a compound form, such as sodium chloride, however, they are harmless and in fact essential to the body.

What are organic nutrients? We call carbohydrates, fats, and proteins **organic nutrients** because they are originally

Fig. 35-1. Many vegetables and fruits are good sources of mineral salts in the diet.

formed by living cells and contain the element carbon. Carbohydrates and fats supply energy. The tissue-building value of foods cannot be measured except by observing growth in animals when they are fed. But the energy value can be measured in heat units, called *Calories*. A *Calorie* (large Calorie) is the amount of heat required to raise the temperature of 1,000 cubic centimeters (about one quart) of water one degree centigrade. This is 1,000 times as great as the small calorie used in physical measurements of heat. Notice that the two are distinguished by the fact that the large Calorie is capitalized.

The number of Calories required in an average day's activity varies with the kind of activity and with the age and body build of the person concerned. A daily requirement of 2,500 to 3,500 Calories is probably about average. The calorie needs for persons of different ages performing different activities are shown in the table on page 440.

More than half of your total diet is carbohydrate food. Regardless of this high percentage, the accumulated carbohydrate reserve in your body is less than one per cent of your total weight. This is evidence that carbohydrates are primarily fuel foods, and that they are oxidized rapidly to supply the energy required for body activity.

Sugars and starches. A *saccharide* (*sak*-uh-ride) is any one of a group of **carbohydrates,** which includes the sugars and starches. A saccharide unit is called a **hexose.** It is composed of six atoms of carbon and six molecules of water. *Monosaccharides* are composed of *one hexose molecule,* and they are called

DAILY CALORIE NEEDS (APPROXIMATELY)

1. For child under 2 years	1,000 Calories
2. For child from 2 to 5 years	1,300 "
3. For child from 6 to 9 years	1,700 "
4. For child from 10 to 12 years, woman (not working)	2,000 "
5. For girl from 12 to 14 years, woman (light work)	2,200 "
6. For boy (12–14), girl (15–16), man (sedentary)	2,600 "
7. For boy (15–20), man (light work)	3,000 "
8. For man (moderately active)	3,200 "
9. For farmer (busy season)	3,500 to 4,500 "
10. For excavator, hard laborer, etc.	4,500 to 5,000 "
11. For lumberman (winter)	5,000 to 8,000 "

simple sugars. Simple sugars are obtained from fruits in the form of grape sugar (glucose) or fruit sugar (fructose). These sugars require no further simplification, since they are already in the chemical form in which carbohydrates are absorbed into the blood from the organs of the digestive system.

More **complex sugars** come from cane, beets, maple trees (sucrose), and from milk (lactose). These are *disaccharides* as they consist of *two hexose molecules.* They require conversion to simple sugars before absorption. We shall discuss them in the next chapter.

Polysaccharides. Starches are *polysaccharides,* which consist of many hexose molecules joined together. Starches are abundant in cereal grains, such as wheat, corn, rye, barley, oats, and rice. Breakfast foods, bread, pastry goods, macaroni, and many other food items are made from these. Potatoes and tapioca are other sources of starch.

One class of carbohydrates, the **celluloses,** come from the cell walls of plants. Celluloses are indigestible in man and many animals and are, therefore, non-energy foods. However, they provide bulk or roughage in the digestive system. They expand the intestine and stimulate the movement of food by muscular contractions of the intestine wall. Without this stimulation, there would not be normal movement of food.

Carbohydrates are stored in the liver and muscles of man as **glycogen** (*gly-koh-jen*), or animal starch. This activity is essential in maintaining the proper sugar content of the blood. If it were not for the liver, we would probably have to eat a small quantity of food continuously. However, sugar (dextrose or glucose) is absorbed from the digestive system and is carried by the blood directly to the liver. Here excess sugar is converted to glycogen and stored until needed. As the level of blood sugar decreases, glycogen is converted back to sugar and the supply in the blood is replenished.

Fats are highly concentrated energy foods. The **fats** yield more than twice as much energy by weight as carbohydrates. They may be formed in the body by conversion of excess carbohydrates or may be used directly as fat from plant or animal origins. The chief storehouses of fat are the tissue spaces just beneath the skin, the region of the kidneys, and the liver.

Fat in the diet is obtained largely from butter, cream, cheese, oleomargarine, lard, and other shortenings, oils, nuts, and meats. They undergo digestion slowly and delay the hunger sensation between meals. However, excess fats should be avoided, especially by individuals with limited physical activity, and during warm weather. Also, fats should be avoided if a person has a tendency to gain weight.

What are proteins? The *proteins* are extremely complex chemical compounds which might be compared to buildings. The " blocks " which form the building are called *amino acids.* During digestion, the proteins which a person has consumed are broken down and the products, or amino acids of several kinds, enter the blood stream.

Cells absorb these amino acids and then build new proteins. These proteins then become part of protoplasm and growth or repair of tissue is accomplished. During childhood, growth is important, but the adult uses protein principally for the replacement of protoplasm which has worn out. Protoplasm can be constructed *only* from protein.

Amino acids not required in the growth and maintenance of protoplasm may be oxidized to supply energy. These excess amino acids are carried to the liver where separation of the molecule takes place. The carbon-containing part is sent to the tissues, and it is oxidized there. The nitrogen-containing part is changed to *urea,* delivered by the blood to the kidneys, and excreted in the urine. This urea is in addition to that which is formed during the breakdown of tissue protein.

In a normal diet, carbohydrates and fats supply the body's energy needs, although a little protein is usually oxidized. However, when carbohydrates and fats are lacking in the diet, the body draws on its reserve of glycogen and fat or increases protein oxidation. At this point a person begins to lose weight.

The most valuable protein sources include: lean meat, eggs (albumen), milk (casein), cheese, whole wheat (gluten), beans, and corn.

Vitamins should not be neglected in the diet. Many years ago, when sailing vessels rode the high seas for months between ports, sailors often developed a disease called *scurvy.* British sailors found that if they ate limes during the course of these voyages, they avoided scurvy. Today we know that these fruits contain vitamin C and that scurvy results from lack of it.

In 1911, Dr. Casimir Funk found that certain substances, apart from ordinary nutrients, are present in foods. They seemed to be necessary for normal growth and body activity and in the prevention of certain diseases called *deficiency diseases.* He called these substances *vitamins.*

Vitamins were first designated by letters — A, B, C, etc. Later it was discovered that certain vitamins thought to be simple were made up of many different components such as, for example, the vitamin B complex. Then such names as B_1, B_2, and so forth were adopted. Today, most of the vitamins have names that indicate their chemical composition, although letters are still used as a means of easy and simple reference.

Some vitamins may be stored in the body, while others must be supplied constantly because they are excreted in the urine when present in excess quantities in the diet. Only one vitamin, vitamin D, can be produced in body tissues. Others must be supplied by the diet or taken in the form of extracts, if the normal diet lacks them. In the final analysis, the best source of vitamins is a balanced diet.

FUNCTIONS AND IMPORTANT SOURCES OF VITAMINS

VITAMINS	BEST SOURCES	ESSENTIAL FOR	DEFICIENCY SYMPTOMS
Vitamin A (oil soluble)	Fish liver oils Liver and kidney Green and yellow vegetables Yellow fruit Tomatoes Butter Egg yolk	Growth Health of the eyes Structure and functions of the cells of the skin and mucous membranes	Retarded growth Night blindness Susceptibility to infections Changes in skin and membranes Defective tooth formation
Thiamin (B_1) (water soluble)	Sea food Meat Soybeans Milk Whole grain Green vegetables Fowl	Growth Carbohydrate metabolism Functioning of the heart, nerves, and muscles	Retarded growth Loss of appetite and weight Nerve disorders Less resistance to fatigue Faulty digestion (beriberi)
Riboflavin (B_2) (water soluble)	Meat Soybeans Milk Green vegetables Eggs Fowl Yeast	Growth Health of the skin and mouth Carbohydrate metabolism Functioning of the eyes	Retarded growth Dimness of vision Inflammation of the tongue Premature aging Intolerance to light
Niacin (P–P) (water soluble)	Meat Fowl Fish Peanut butter Potatoes Whole grain Tomatoes Leafy vegetables	Growth Carbohydrate metabolism Functioning of the stomach and intestines Functioning of the nervous system	Smoothness of the tongue Skin eruptions Digestive disturbances Mental disorders (pellagra)
Folic acid (B_{12}) (water soluble)	Green vegetables Liver	Preventing pernicious anemia	A reduction in number of red blood cells
Ascorbic acid (C) (water soluble)	Citrus fruit Other fruit Tomatoes Leafy vegetables	Growth Maintaining strength of the blood vessels Teeth development Gum health	Sore gums Hemorrhages around the bones Tendency to bruise easily (scurvy)
Vitamin D (oil soluble)	Fish liver oil Liver Fortified milk Eggs Irradiated foods	Growth Regulating calcium and phosphorus metabolism Building and maintaining bones, teeth	Soft bones Poor teeth development Dental decay (rickets)
Tocopherol (E) (oil soluble)	Wheat-germ oil Leafy vegetables Milk Butter	Normal reproduction	Undetermined
Vitamin K (oil soluble)	Green vegetables Soybean oil Tomatoes	Normal clotting of the blood Normal liver functions	Hemorrhages

Fig. 35-2. *Milk Group.* Teen-agers should have four or more cups of milk daily, occasionally replacing one or two of them with a serving of butter, ice cream, or cheese.

Photos from National Dairy Council

Meat Group. Two or more servings from this group should be eaten daily, using the beans, peas, and nuts only occasionally as alternates.

Vegetable-Fruit Group. Four or more daily servings, including one of a citrus fruit and one dark-green or deep-yellow vegetable, are necessary.

Bread-Cereal Group. Four or more servings of whole-grain, enriched, or restored foods from this group are essential in your daily diet.

FOOD SUBSTANCES

SUBSTANCE	KIND OF SUBSTANCE	ESSENTIAL FOR	SOURCE
Water	Inorganic compound	Composition of protoplasm and blood Dissolving substances	All foods (released during oxidation)
Sodium compounds	Mineral salts	Blood and other body tissues	Table salt, vegetables
Calcium compounds	Mineral salts	Deposition in bones and teeth Heart and nerve action Clotting of blood	Milk, whole-grain cereals, vegetables, meats
Phosphorus compounds	Mineral salts	Deposition in bones and teeth Formation of protoplasm	Milk, whole-grain cereals, vegetables, meats
Potassium compounds	Mineral salts	Blood and cell activities Growth	Vegetables
Iron compounds	Mineral salts	Formation of red blood corpuscles	Lettuce, leafy vegetables, liver, meats, raisins, prunes
Iodine	Mineral salts	Secretion by thyroid gland	Sea foods, water, iodized salt
Carbohydrates	Organic nutrients	Energy (stored as fat or glycogen) Bulk in diet	Cereals, bread, pastries, tapioca, fruits, vegetables
Fats	Organic nutrients	Energy (stored as fat or glycogen)	Butter, cream, cheese, oleomargarine, lard, oils, nuts, meats
Proteins	Organic nutrients	Growth, maintenance, and repair of protoplasm	Lean meats, eggs, milk, wheat, beans, peas, cheese
Vitamins	Complex organic substances	Regulation of body processes Prevention of deficiency diseases	Various foods, especially milk, butter, lean meats, fruits, leafy vegetables; can also be made synthetically

Vitamins seem to act in a similar way to the digestive enzymes. Chemically, they can be called *catalysts*. The best sources, functions, and deficiency symptoms of the better-known vitamins are summarized in the table on page 442.

Synthetic vitamins. Most of the vitamins listed in the table on page 442 are available in highly concentrated synthetic form. These preparations are very important in supplementing the natural vitamins of the diet when deficiency occurs. However, even with all the publicity given commercial vitamin preparations, you should keep in mind the fact that a normal, balanced diet is much more valu-

Fig. 35-3. The rat on the left is suffering from a deficiency of vitamin B_1. The same rat is shown below after being given sufficient vitamin B_1 to restore it to normal health.

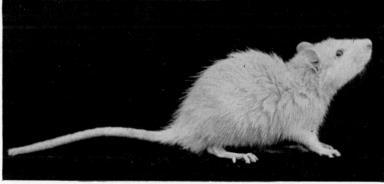

U. S. Dept. of Agriculture

able than supplementary doses. Your doctor can diagnose vitamin deficiency and prescribe concentrated vitamins if he thinks you need them. If a proper diet is followed, additional vitamins are a waste of money and unnecessary for the average person.

What is a balanced diet? The body needs carbohydrates, fats, and proteins in the approximate proportions of 4:1:1. In addition, the diet must contain adequate mineral salts and vitamin sources. One food cannot supply all these, so a mixed diet is necesary. A *balanced diet* is one in which foods in proper proportion conform to all the body needs.

People who are trying to lose or gain weight by dieting should still aim for a balanced diet. Otherwise severe nutritional diseases can result.

The table on page 444 summarizes the functions and sources of the various food substances which are necessary in a well-balanced diet.

The Basic Four foods. Probably the simplest guide to proper eating is the *Basic Four* (Fig. 35-2, page 443), determined as a result of research by the United States Department of Agriculture in cooperation with many other agencies and noted food authorities. These four groups of foods contain all the essentials for a well-balanced diet.

If you eat the proper amount from each group daily, as suggested in the captions for Fig. 35-2, your diet will automatically include a minimum of all the essential vitamins and minerals, and the right proportions of protein, fat, and carbohydrate foods.

In Conclusion

In order to be healthy, the human body requires a variety of complex organic nutrients as well as water, minerals, and vitamins. The organic nutrients are divided into three groups: proteins, carbohydrates, and fats.

The most interesting story is yet to come. In the next chapter we shall see how the many organs of the alimentary canal break down food substances so that they can be absorbed and used by the body.

BIOLOGICALLY SPEAKING

amino acid
ascorbic acid
balanced diet
Calorie
carbohydrate
celluloses
complex sugar
deficiency diseases

dehydration
evaporation
fat
folic acid
food
glycogen
hexose
niacin

organic nutrients
protein
riboflavin
simple sugar
thiamin
tocopherol
vitamin

QUESTIONS FOR REVIEW

1. List six classes of foods and the general use of each by the body.
2. Explain several ways in which your body depends on water.
3. List three mineral salts and state the use of each by the body.
4. Name and define the unit used to measure the energy value of foods.
5. Explain how the carbohydrates can be classified upon the basis of hexose molecules. Give an example of each carbohydrate.
6. Explain the double role of proteins in the diet.
7. Why are fats considered to be highly concentrated energy foods?
8. How do vitamins act as catalysts in various activities of the body?

APPLYING FACTS AND PRINCIPLES

1. Why is it advisable that most people reduce the fat content of their diets during warm weather?
2. Why do you think carbohydrates are reduced to monosaccharides before they can be absorbed?
3. Discuss the role of the liver in maintaining a constant level of blood sugar.
4. Why must age and occupation be considered in determining daily calorie needs?
5. Explain how a vitamin deficiency is possible even if an adequate amount of all the vitamins is taken daily.
6. Discuss the value of the Basic Four food groups as a guide to eating.

CHAPTER 36

Digestion of Foods

W HEAT and corn growing in the fields draw water and minerals from the soil and carbon dioxide from the atmosphere. These plants have the ability to utilize the radiant energy from the sun in the manufacture of substances essential to their life. All this takes place in the plants' remarkable cell factories. Since plants store energy in the form of carbohydrates, proteins, and fats, we can use them for food. We use the wheat for flour; the corn is used for food for cattle and hogs as well as for us. From this plant-stored energy, the cattle grow, thus producing our meat; the cow produces milk and cream; the flour is mixed with other ingredients and put into ovens, thus giving us our bread. Much time and many chemical processes have taken place before you can have a roast beef sandwich and glass of milk served to you for lunch.

Some time after you eat this sandwich and drink the milk, these substances are still in your tissues. But in what form — as bread, beef, milk, and butter? No. These foods are found as glucose, amino acids, and fatty acids. What has happened to the sandwich? As it passed through the **alimentary canal,** a 30-foot tube, several organs broke it down chemically in a series of changes that make up the process of digestion. Your digestive system is like an assembly line in reverse. It starts with the many complex foods you eat and simplifies them to a few basic foods. This remarkable system allows you to enjoy the wide variety of foods in your daily diet and, still, to send your tissues the basic, simple foods you would find no real pleasure in eating.

The phases of digestion. There are two reasons why tissues cannot use most foods in the form in which you eat them. First, many substances are insoluble in water and could not enter the cells if they reached them. Second, they are too complex chemically for tissues to use, either in oxidation or for growth and repair. Digestion brings about changes in both of these conditions, with the result that cells can absorb and use the products. These complex foods we eat are broken down into smaller molecules of water-soluble substances through a long and complicated process.

How are these chemical changes, which we call digestion, brought about in the body? The first part of the change occurring during digestion is *mechanical.*

This phase involves the chewing of food in the mouth, and the constant churning and mixing action. This mixing action is caused by the muscular movement of the walls of the digestive organs. The breaking of food into small particles and thorough mixing with various juices aid the second phase of digestion, which is *chemical.* This phase is accomplished by *digestive enzymes.* These substances are present in various secretions produced by the digestive *glands.*

The anatomy of the digestive system will be taken up first in order that the mechanical phase of digestion may be understood. In studying digestion, it will be very helpful for you to refer to the "Trans-Vision" of the human torso between pages 470 and 471.

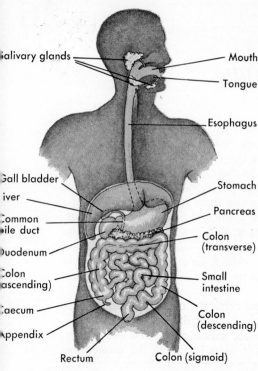

Fig. 36-1. The organs of digestion in the human body.

The special organs of digestion. The digestive system includes the organs which form the *alimentary canal,* or *food tube* (Fig. 36-1). It also includes those organs which do not actually receive undigested food, but act on foods in the alimentary canal by means of secretions delivered to it by tubes, or **ducts**.

The mouth first receives the food. The chief function of the mouth is to prepare the food for digestion. It is also an organ of sensation and an organ of speech. The organs for digestion in the mouth are the salivary glands, the tongue, and the teeth.

The **hard palate** forms the roof of the mouth in the chewing area. It consists of a bony structure, covered with several membranes. The **soft palate** lies just back of the hard palate. It is formed by folded membranes which extend from the rear portion of the hard palate and fasten along the sides of the tongue. You can see a knoblike extension of the soft palate

called the **uvula** (*you*-vyoo-luh) when the mouth is opened wide (Fig. 36-2).

The back of the mouth opens into a muscular cavity which is called the **pharynx**. This cavity extends upward, above the soft palate, to the nasal cavity. The soft palate partly separates the nasal cavity from the mouth cavity and extends into the pharynx, somewhat like a curtain, as you can see in Fig. 36-3.

The inside of the cheeks forms the side walls of the mouth cavity. The cheek linings are mucous membranes, containing numerous mucous glands. **Mucus,** a lubricating secretion, mixes with food in the mouth and aids in chewing and swallowing. The lining of the mouth turns outward to form the lips.

Three pairs of salivary glands secrete saliva. (1) The **parotid** (puh-*rot*-id) **glands** are the largest of the **salivary** (*sal*-ih-very) **glands.** One lies on each side of the face below and in front of the ears. Ducts from these glands empty saliva into the mouth opposite the second upper molars. An infection of the parotid glands, causing swelling and irritation, is the disease called *mumps.* (2) The

Fig. 36-2. Digestion begins in the mouth, which is the most anterior organ of the alimentary canal.

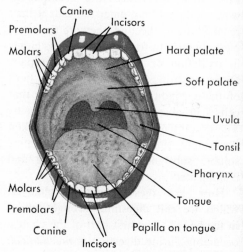

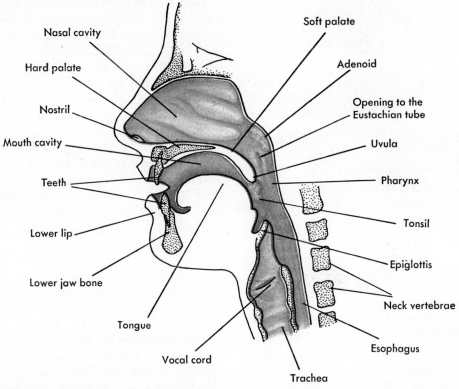

Fig. 36-3. You can see the internal structures of the mouth and throat in this cutaway diagram.

submaxillary glands lie within the angles of the lower jaws. (3) The **sublingual** (sub-*ling*-wul) **glands** are embedded in the mucous membranes in the floor of the mouth, under the tongue (Fig. 36-4). Ducts from both of these glands open into the floor of the mouth under the tongue. The smell of food, the sight of it, the presence of it in the mouth, and the taste of it stimulate the secretion of saliva. In other words, your mouth " waters."

The tongue and its functions. The **tongue** lies in the floor of the mouth and extends into the throat. This muscular organ performs several different functions, as follows:

1. It acts as an organ of taste. Scattered over the surface of the tongue are

numerous tiny projections called *papillae* (puh-*pil*-ee). These papillae contain **taste buds.** Nerve endings lie at the base of the taste buds. When food is mixed

Fig. 36-4. Three pairs of salivary glands aid in producing saliva.

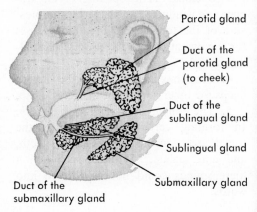

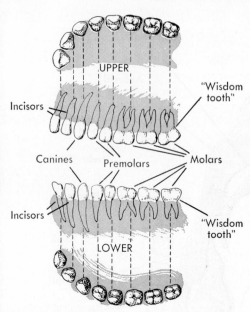

Incisors

Canines   Premolars   Molars

Incisors

UPPER

"Wisdom tooth"

"Wisdom tooth"

LOWER

Fig. 36-5. Permanent teeth, of which there are thirty-two, form in the gums under the primary teeth.

with mucus and saliva, it contacts the taste buds, and the nerve endings are stimulated. The result of this stimulation is that we taste. These buds are sensitive to only four tastes: salty, sour, bitter, and sweet.

2. The tongue aids in chewing by keeping the food between the teeth.

3. During swallowing, food is worked to the back of the tongue. When the tongue is jerked downward, food lodges in the pharynx and passes into the esophagus opening. The opening of the trachea, or windpipe, is closed by the pressure of the tongue and breathing ceases for a moment during the process of swallowing.

4. The tongue rolling in the mouth keeps the inner surface of the teeth clean.

5. The tongue is essential in *speech*. In forming certain word sounds, the tongue acts together with the lips, teeth, and hard palate. Without such action these sounds could not be formed into words.

Each kind of tooth has a definite function. If you start between the two front teeth and count back, the permanent teeth are arranged in the following order: the first two are the flat **incisors** with sharp edges for cutting food. Next, near the corner of your lips, is a large conical **canine**, or *cuspid,* tooth. These teeth are often called " eye " teeth, although they have no connection with the eyes. Behind the canine teeth are two **premolars,** or *bicuspids*. Next come three **molars** (two, if you have not " cut " your " wisdom teeth "). The premolars and molars have large surfaces and are grinding and crushing teeth. Many jaws are too small to provide space for the third molars, or wisdom teeth. In such cases, they may grow in crooked, lodge against the second molars, or remain impacted in the jawbone (Fig. 36-5).

The structure of the teeth. A tooth is composed of three general regions. The exposed portion above the gum line is called the **crown.** A narrow portion at the gum line is called the **neck,** while the **root** is encased in a socket in the jawbone, and holds the tooth securely in place. Roots vary in form in the different kinds of teeth. They may be long and single, or may consist of two, three, or four projections. The crown is covered with a hard white substance, the **enamel.** The covering of the root is called **cementum** and holds the tooth firmly together. The root is anchored firmly in the jaw socket by the fibrous **periodontal** (pair-ee-uh-*don*-tul) **membrane.**

If you cut a tooth lengthwise, you can see the *dentine* beneath the protective layers of enamel and cement (Fig. 36-6). **Dentine** is a relatively softer substance than enamel and forms the bulk of the tooth. The **pulp cavity** lies within the dentine area. It contains small nerves and blood vessels, which join larger nerves and blood vessels in the jawbone through the *nerve canal*.

The number and kinds of teeth. The first set of teeth, sometimes called *milk teeth,* are temporary and are replaced by the permanent teeth. The first temporary tooth usually appears between the sixth and ninth month after birth. The "cutting" of teeth continues for about two years, when the last of the *twenty* temporary teeth appear. The first permanent teeth usually appear during the sixth year. They are the first molars, and erupt behind the temporary molars. The last permanent teeth, or wisdom teeth, usually appear between the ages of 17 and 25. The full adult or permanent set of teeth consists of *thirty-two* teeth of four different kinds.

The permanent teeth form below the temporary teeth and push these temporary teeth out as they come up. The temporary incisors and canines are replaced by corresponding permanent teeth. The permanent molars occupy a portion of the jaw which did not produce temporary teeth.

Temporary teeth should be given the same dental care as permanent teeth. Decay of the temporary teeth may cause damage to the permanent teeth forming under them. Of course, care of the permanent teeth is a basic rule of good health. Loss of teeth interferes with normal chewing and puts an extra burden on the digestive organs.

Hygiene of the teeth. The mouth provides ideal conditions for the growth of bacteria. It is warm and moist, and particles of food between the teeth supply the necessary organic food for the growth and development of bacteria. Decay of food in the mouth by bacteria releases acids which dissolve the enamel of the teeth and permits the formation of a cavity. Such a cavity, unchecked, will deepen and may result in loss of a tooth.

Many dentists have wondered why certain people experience no tooth decay for long periods and then suddenly develop many cavities. Careful checks have revealed no diet deficiency or neglect of oral hygiene in most of these patients. In studies being conducted on this problem, dentists have found that many patients have undergone a period of great emotional tension coinciding with the period of greatest decay.

Dentists speak of a period of increased tooth decay as "galloping caries," a condition that often occurs in adolescence. It is probably no mere coincidence that this period is one of increased emotional stress. Many of us have noted a dry mouth during emotional stress. The salivary glands are underactive at such times. The flow of saliva has a considerable cleansing effect and, being alkaline, neutralizes corroding acids in the mouth which damage tooth enamel.

Fig. 36-6. This vertical section through a cuspid tooth shows its various parts.

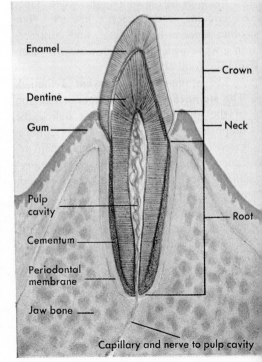

Enamel
Dentine
Gum

Crown
Neck

Pulp cavity
Cementum
Periodontal membrane
Jaw bone

Root

Capillary and nerve to pulp cavity

Mouth hygiene demands that you include abundant minerals in your diet, brush your teeth regularly, and visit your dentist twice a year for a check-up.

Fluorine may help fight the battle of tooth decay. In certain areas of our country where the fluorine content of the soil and water is high, natives of the region experience less tooth decay than those of other areas. This has led public health officials to recommend that dentists apply fluorine compounds to the teeth of children. They have also suggested that these compounds be added to the water supply. However, research on the effectiveness of fluorine is still going on and it is too early to determine the possible results.

The food leaves the mouth. After food has been mechanically ground by the teeth and mixed with saliva, it leaves the mouth and enters the **esophagus.** This is a tube which is about a foot in length and connects the mouth to the stomach. Food travels to the stomach with the aid of layers of smooth muscle in the wall of the esophagus. One layer is circular, and squeezes inward. The other layer is longitudinal, and contracts in a wave which travels downward, pushing the food ahead of it.

The stomach is somewhat J-shaped. The **stomach** lies in the upper left region of the abdominal cavity just below the diaphragm. The stomach walls contain three layers of smooth muscle, each arranged differently. One layer is *longitudinal,* one is *circular,* and one is angled, or *oblique.* Contraction of the smooth muscle fibers of the various layers in different directions causes the twisting, squeezing, and churning movement of the stomach.

The lining of the stomach is a thick, wrinkled membrane. Numerous **gastric glands** are embedded in the stomach lining. Each gland is a tiny tube with an opening into the stomach (see Fig. 4-8, page 36). The walls of each gland are lined with cells which secrete **gastric fluid** containing an enzyme and **hydrochloric acid.** This secretion passes directly into the stomach.

Food usually remains in the stomach two to three hours. During this period, rhythmic contractions of the stomach muscles churn the food back and forth in a circular path. This action separates the food particles and mixes them thoroughly with the stomach secretions. At the completion of stomach digestion, the valve at the intestinal end, the **pyloric valve,** opens and closes several times. With each opening of the valve, food squirts into the small intestine. This mixture is called **chyme** (*kyme*). Finally, the stomach is relieved of its content and begins a period of rest. After several hours without food, contractions start again and cause the sensation of hunger.

The small intestine. When food leaves the stomach through the pyloric valve, it enters the **small intestine,** a tube about one inch in diameter and 23 feet in length. This division of the alimentary canal is the most vital of all digestive centers. The upper ten inches of the small intestine are referred to as the **duodenum** (doo-oh-*dee*-num). The duodenum curves upward, then backward and to the right, beneath the liver. Beyond the duodenum is a second and much longer region, the **jejunum** (jeh-*june*-um). This portion, about seven and one-half feet in length, is less coiled than the other regions. The lower portion of the small intestine is referred to as the **ileum** (*il*-ee-um). This portion, about 15 feet long, coils through the abdominal cavity before joining the large intestine.

The liver is the largest gland in the body. The **liver** weighs about 3½ pounds and comprises about 1/40th of the body weight. It is a dark chocolate color

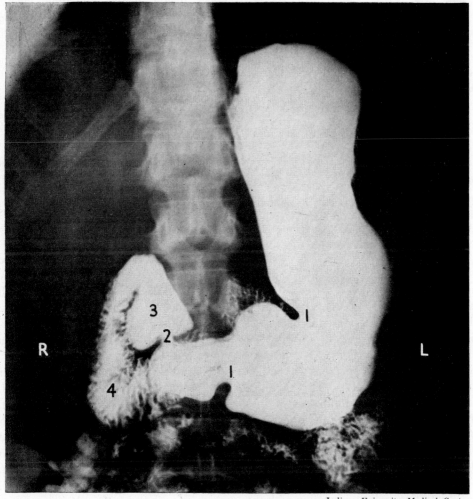

Indiana University Medical Center

Fig. 36-7. **This X-ray photograph is of a normal stomach that is filled with barium to make the parts visible on a film. Note contractions (1); pyloric valve (2); beginning of the small intestine (3); and region of villi in the small intestine (4).** *R* **indicates right side;** *L* **indicates left.**

and lies in the upper right region of the abdominal cavity.

Bile is a brownish-green fluid. It passes from the liver in a series of bile ducts which form a Y. As bile is secreted in the liver, it passes down one branch of the Y, then travels up the other branch to the **gall bladder.** Here the bile is stored and concentrated as part of the water is removed. The base of the Y is the **com-mon bile duct.** This tube carries bile from the gall bladder to the upper end of the small intestine, or duodenum. If the common bile duct becomes clogged by a gallstone, or a plug of mucus, bile enters the blood stream and causes a yellowing of the eyes and skin, known as *jaundice.*

The pancreas and pancreatic fluid. The **pancreas** is a many-lobed, long,

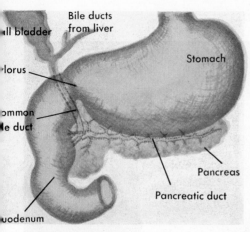

Bile ducts from liver
ll bladder
Stomach
lorus
ommon
le duct
Pancreas
Pancreatic duct
uodenum

Fig. 36-8. The pancreas and its digestive fluid play an important role in digestion. What four enzymes does pancreatic fluid contain?

whitish gland, quite similar in general appearance to a salivary gland. It lies behind the stomach and the upper end of the small intestine, against the back wall of the abdominal cavity. It performs two entirely different functions. The production of insulin by the pancreas will be discussed in Chapter 41. The digestive secretion, *pancreatic fluid*, passes into the small intestine through the *pancreatic duct*, which leads to a common opening with the bile duct in the wall of the duodenum.

The large intestine, or colon. The small intestine ends at a junction with the *large intestine* in the lower right region of the abdominal cavity. Below the point of junction is a blind end of the large intestine called the *caecum* (*see*-kum). The *vermiform appendix* is a fingerlike outgrowth of the caecum. When the appendix becomes inflamed, appendicitis results.

The colon is usually five to six feet long and about three inches in diameter. It forms an inverted U in the abdominal cavity. The *ascending colon* runs upward along the right side, where it curves abruptly to the left to form the *transverse colon.* This portion extends across the

upper region of the abdominal cavity. Another curve leads to the *descending colon* on the left side. At its lower end, the descending colon forms an S, called the *sigmoid colon.* The *rectum* is a muscular cavity at the end of the large intestine. The lower end of the rectum forms the *anal opening.* A *sphincter muscle* in the lower end of the rectum controls elimination of intestinal waste.

The chemical phase of digestion also occurs in the alimentary canal. Each organ in the digestive system has a particular task to perform. The result is that all foods are not *digested* (chemically broken down into simpler substances) in all the digestive organs. The digestion which occurs in the alimentary canal is *extracellular digestion,* which means that it occurs outside the cells. *Intracellular digestion* refers to the chemical changes which take place within a single cell.

The mouth is more than an organ for the mechanical breaking apart of food. *Saliva* from the salivary glands is a thin, alkaline substance. It is more than 95 per cent water, and contains dissolved mineral salts and the enzyme *ptyalin* (*ty*-uh-lin). Ptyalin converts starch, especially cooked starch, to maltose, which is a disaccharide. It is necessary to cook starchy foods, such as potatoes, to burst the cellulose cell walls which enclose the starch grains. Otherwise, the ptyalin does not come in contact with the starch. Saliva also contains mucus, which lubricates the food. Unlike starches, neither fats nor proteins are altered during mouth digestion.

The composition of gastric juice. Gastric juice contains the enzyme pepsin and hydrochloric acid. *Pepsin* splits the complex protein molecules into simpler groups of amino acids called *peptones* and *proteoses* (proh-tee-*oh*-seez). This chemical change is the first in a series involved in protein digestion. Pepsin acts only in the presence of hydrochloric acid. Contrary to common opinion, the stomach has to be somewhat sour, or acid, to function properly.

For many years another enzyme called *rennin* was thought to be present in gastric juice. Recent research indicates that there is none in adult gastric juice, but that it may be present in infants. Rennin acts on milk, changing *casein* (*kay*-see-in), or milk protein, to a curd. It has been found in the stomachs of calves.

Hydrocholic acid, in addition to providing the proper medium for the action of pepsin, dissolves insoluble minerals and kills large numbers of bacteria which enter the stomach with the food. It also causes the valve at the base of the stomach to open, allowing food to enter the small intestine.

The food which passes from the stomach to the small intestines contains: (1) fats, unchanged; (2) sugars, unchanged; (3) some starches which were not acted upon by the ptyalin of saliva; (4) some proteins unchanged by the pepsin of the gastric fluid; and (5) peptones and proteoses formed from the action of pepsin on protein.

Functions of the liver and bile. The liver performs several vital functions. In receiving glucose from the blood and changing it to glycogen, it serves as a *chemical factory.* It serves as a *storehouse* in holding reserve carbohydrates as glycogen. In acting on amino acids and forming urea, it is an *organ of excretion.* All these changes involve food *after* digestion. As a *digestive gland,* the liver secretes bile which acts on food in the small intestine. In the formation of bile, the liver plays a part in using what might otherwise be discarded as waste. Part of the bile is formed from worn-out hemoglobin that the blood system can no longer use.

Bile has several important functions:

1. It is partially a waste substance containing material from dead red blood corpuscles filtered from the blood stream by the liver.

2. It increases the digestive action of *lipase* (*ly*-pase), an enzyme produced in the pancreas, by breaking globules of fat into small droplets, in the process called *emulsification.*

3. It helps to neutralize the hydrochloric acid from the stomach so that digestion can take place in the intestine.

Actually, bile is not a digestive secretion. In emulsifying fats, it splits large fat particles into smaller ones, producing a milky liquid called an *emulsion.* In this form, pancreatic fluid can act on fats more readily.

The role of the pancreas in digestion. *Pancreatic fluid* acts upon all three classes of organic nutrients. This digestive fluid contains the following three enzymes: (1)*trypsin;* (2) *amylase;* and (3) *lipase.*

Trypsin (*trip*-sin) continues the breakdown of proteins which began in the stomach, by changing peptones and proteoses to still simpler amino acid groups called *peptids.* In addition, it may act upon proteins which were not simplified during stomach digestion. Peptids are not the final product of protein digestion. Only one additional step is necessary to form the amino acids which are used by the body tissues.

Amylase (*am*-ih-lase) duplicates the action of the ptyalin in saliva by changing starch into maltose. This is how the potatoes you did not chew enough are changed to sugar.

Lipase splits fats into *fatty acids* and *glycerin.* This is the only digestive action on fats which reduces them to the form in which they are absorbed.

The intestinal glands secrete intestinal fluid. The mucous lining of the small intestine contains many tiny embedded

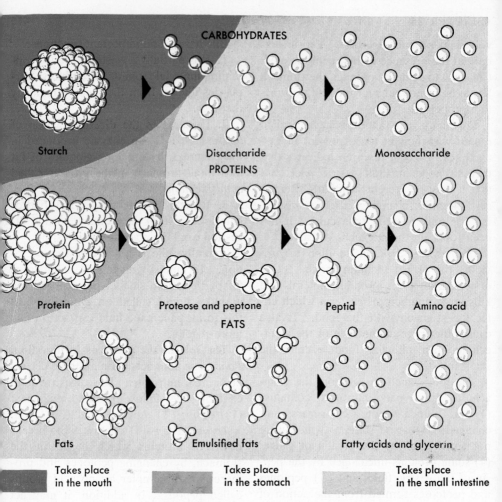

CARBOHYDRATES

Starch | Disaccharide | Monosaccharide

PROTEINS

Protein | Proteose and peptone | Peptid | Amino acid

FATS

Fats | Emulsified fats | Fatty acids and glycerin

Takes place in the mouth | Takes place in the stomach | Takes place in the small intestine

Fig. 36-9. This diagram shows phases in the digestion of carbohydrates, fats, and proteins. Why can they not be used by tissues in the form in which you eat them?

glands that are called **intestinal glands.** They secrete **intestinal fluid,** a highly alkaline substance containing four principal enzymes: (1) *erepsin;* (2) *maltase;* (3) *lactase;* and (4) *sucrase.*

Erepsin (ee-*rep*-sin) completes protein digestion by changing peptids, formed by the pancreatic fluid, to *amino acids.* **Maltase** splits the double sugar, maltose, into the simple sugar, *glucose,* the final product of carbohydrate digestion. **Lactase** has a similar action on lactose, or milk sugar, in changing it to glucose. **Sucrase** acts on sucrose and changes it to the simple sugars, glucose and fructose.

Thus, with the combined action of bile, pancreatic fluid, and intestinal fluid in the small intestine, all three classes of foods are completely digested. As simple sugars, fatty acids and glycerin, and amino acids, they leave the digestive system and enter the blood and lymph (*limf*).

Absorption takes place in the small intestine. A magnified portion of the small intestine shows that its irregular lining gives rise to great numbers of fingerlike projections called **villi** (*vil*-eye) [sing. *villus*]. These projections are so numerous that they give a velvety appearance to the intestinal lining. Within the villi are branching lymph vessels, called **lac-teals** (*lak*-tee-uls), and blood vessels (Fig. 36-10, page 458). The villi bring blood and lymph close to the digested food and increase the absorption surface of the intestine enormously. Absorption is increased further by a constant sway-ing motion of the villi through the intestinal content.

Glycerin and fatty acids enter the villi and are carried away by the lymph. They eventually reach the general circulation and travel to the tissues. Glucose and amino acids, however, enter the blood

SUMMARY OF DIGESTION

PLACE OF DIGESTION	GLANDS	SECRETION	ENZYMES	DIGESTIVE ACTIVITY
Mouth	Salivary	Saliva	Ptyalin	Changes starch to maltose, lubricates
	Mucous	Mucus		Lubricates
Esophagus	Mucous	Mucus		Lubricates
Stomach	Gastric	Gastric fluid	Pepsin	Changes proteins to peptones and proteoses
		Hydrochloric acid		Activates pepsin Dissolves minerals Kills bacteria
	Mucous	Mucus		Lubricates
Small intestine	Liver	Bile		Emulsifies fats Activates lipase
	Pancreas	Pancreatic fluid	Trypsin	Changes proteins, peptones, and proteoses to peptids
			Amylase	Changes starch to maltose
			Lipase	Changes fats to fatty acids and glycerin
	Intestinal glands	Intestinal fluid	Erepsin	Changes peptids to amino acids
			Maltase	Changes maltose to glucose
			Lactase	Changes lactose to glucose
			Sucrase	Changes sucrose to glucose
	Mucous	Mucus		Lubricates
Large intestine (colon)	Mucous	Mucus		Lubricates

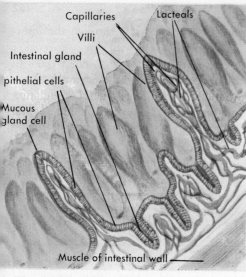

Capillaries Lacteals

Villi

Intestinal gland

pithelial cells

Mucous
gland cell

Muscle of intestinal wall

Fig. 36-10. How do the villi increase absorption in the small intestine?

vessels of the villi. From the villi they are carried directly to the liver through the portal vein.

The large intestine absorbs water. The large intestine receives a watery mass of undigestible food bulk from the small intestine. As this mass progresses through the colon, water is absorbed and taken to the tissues. The intestinal content, or *feces,* becomes more solid as the water is absorbed.

Fig. 36-9 on page 456 and the chart on page 457 summarize the digestive processes that occur in the various organs. The chart also reviews the enzymes in the glandular fluids as well as the chemical changes they bring about.

In Conclusion

The digestive system is a tube which is divided into various regions. Each particular region of the tube is a specialized organ adapted for carrying on certain phases of the digestive process. Many glands pour their enzymatic secretions into the digestive organs. These enzymes bring about the chemical changes, while muscular contractions bring about the mechanical changes.

The next chapter deals with respiration and the excretion of waste products.

BIOLOGICALLY SPEAKING

alimentary canal	ileum	pyloric valve
amylase	intestinal gland	rennin
bile	intracellular digestion	saliva
caecum	jejunum	sigmoid colon
cementum	lactase	soft palate
chyme	lacteal	sphincter muscle
crown	lipase	sublingual gland
dentine	maltase	submaxillary gland
ducts	parotid gland	sucrase
duodenum	pepsin	taste buds
enamel	peptone	trypsin
erepsin	periodontal membrane	uvula
extracellular digestion	proteoses	vermiform appendix
gastric gland	ptyalin	villi
hard palate	pulp cavity	

QUESTIONS FOR REVIEW

1. Name the regions that can be distinguished in a tooth cut lengthwise.
2. Name and locate the various salivary glands.
3. Why is it especially important that you chew bread and potatoes thoroughly, even if the potatoes are mashed?
4. In what two general ways must foods be changed during digestion?
5. List, in order, the divisions of the alimentary canal, or food tube.

6. Discuss five or more uses of the tongue.
7. Suppose that a person had a glass of milk and a sandwich consisting of bread, butter, and ham. Tell what would happen to each of these foods as they go through the process of digestion.
8. List four functions of bile.
9. Name two important functions of the large intestine.

APPLYING FACTS AND PRINCIPLES

1. Plot a diagram of the tongue and label the areas of the four tastes.
2. Why is chyme acid in the stomach and alkaline in the small intestine?
3. Explain how interference with the

rhythmic waves of the walls of the large intestine may cause either constipation or diarrhea.
4. Why is it easier to digest sour milk than fresh milk?

CHAPTER *37*

ℛespiration and Excretion

W HEN a newborn child first fills his lungs with air, it is a dramatic event. From the moment when his breathing movements first begin, the process continues 16 to 24 times per minute throughout life, and when the person is under exertion the movements are much faster than they are when he is at complete rest or asleep.

Each living cell takes in oxygen, uses it in the oxidation of foods, and gives off carbon dioxide and water. Without oxygen, cells are unable to carry on their life processes.

Respiration is a life process common to all living organisms. We define **respiration** as the intake of oxygen and elimination of carbon dioxide associated with energy release in living cells. In some of the simple organisms, such as the Protozoa, sponges, and jellyfish, the cells are in direct contact with the environment, and an exchange of gases between the cells and their surroundings occurs directly. Plant cells, too, respire in this way. In an insect, air is delivered directly to the tissues through the tracheae. However, as animals become more complicated in their structure, the cells are deprived of direct contact with the external

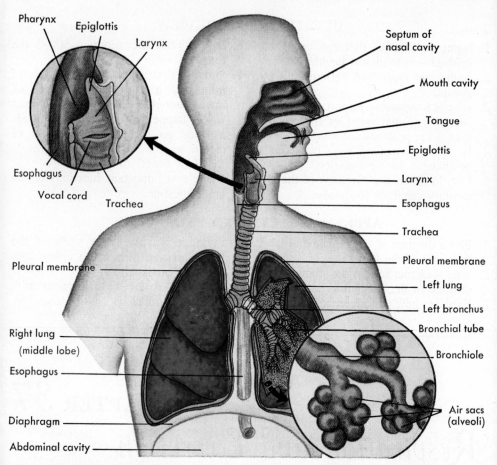

Fig. 37-1. The air passages increase in number and decrease in size as they enter the lungs. They end in tiny membranous sacs called alveoli. The inserts are enlargements of the areas indicated.

environment. Some means of receiving oxygen at one place and carrying it to the body tissues becomes necessary.

Respiration in man involves two phases. *External respiration* concerns the exchange of gases between the atmosphere and the blood. This phase involves the lungs. *Internal respiration* concerns an exchange between the blood and the body tissues. It occurs in every living cell. *Breathing* is merely a mechanical process involved in getting air containing oxygen *into* the body and air containing waste gases from respiration out of the body.

The respiratory system in man. We can divide the organs concerned with breathing and external respiration into two groups. The first group includes the passages through which air travels in reaching the blood stream: the nostrils, nasal passages, pharynx, trachea, bronchi, bronchial tubes, and lungs (Fig. 37-1).

The second group is concerned with the mechanics of breathing by changing the size of the chest cavity. This group includes the ribs and rib muscles, the diaphragm, and the abdominal muscles.

The nose and nasal passages. Air enters the nose through two streams, because the nostrils are divided by the **septum.** From the nostrils, air enters the nasal passages, which lie above the mouth cavity. The nostrils contain hairs which aid in filtering dirt out of the air. Other foreign particles may lodge on the moist mucous membranes in the nasal passages. The length of the nasal passages allows warming of the air and adds moisture to the air before it enters the trachea. All these advantages of nasal breathing are lost in mouth breathing.

The trachea. From the nasal cavity, the air passes through the **pharynx** and enters the **trachea.** The upper end of the trachea is protected by a cartilaginous flap, or lid, the **epiglottis** (ep-ih-*glot*-tis). During swallowing, the end of the trachea is closed by the epiglottis. At other times, the trachea remains open to permit breathing. The **larynx,** or "Adam's apple," is the enlarged upper end of the trachea. Inside it are the **vocal cords.** The walls of the trachea are supported by horseshoe-shaped rings of cartilage which hold it open for the free passage of air.

The trachea and its branches are lined with **cilia.** These are in constant motion, and carry dust or dirt taken in with air upward toward the mouth. This dust, mixed with mucus, is removed when you cough or clear your throat.

The bronchi and air cells. At its lower end, the trachea divides into two branches called **bronchi** (*bronk*-eye). One extends to each lung and subdivides into countless small **bronchial** (*bronk*-ee-ul) **tubes.** These, in turn, divide into many small tubes called **bronchioles,** which end in air sacs. These air sacs are called **alveoli** (al-*vee*-oh-lye) and compose most of the lung tissue. The walls of the alveoli are very thin and elastic. Through their thin walls, gases are exchanged between the capillaries and the alveoli (Fig. 37-2). Thus the lungs provide enough surface to supply air by way of the blood for the needs of millions of body cells having no direct access to air. The total area of the alveoli in the lungs is about 2,000 square feet, or more than 100 times the surface area of the body.

The **lungs** fill the body cavity from the shoulders to the diaphragm, except for the space occupied by the heart, trachea, esophagus, and blood vessels. They are spongy and consist mainly of the air tubes and alveoli and an extensive network of blood vessels and capillaries, held together by connective tissue.

The lungs are covered by a double **pleural membrane.** One part adheres tightly to the lungs, and the other covers the inside of the thoracic cavity. These membranes secrete mucus so that there is free motion of the lungs in the chest for breathing.

The blood supply. The **pulmonary artery** brings dark (deoxygenated) blood to the lungs. There it divides into an extensive network of capillaries, completely surrounding each air cell (Fig. 37-3, page 462). The thin moist walls of both cell and capillary aid the gaseous exchange of

Fig. 37-2. **This diagram illustrating external respiration shows a bronchiole ending in an alveolus. The small red ovals in the capillaries represent red corpuscles.**

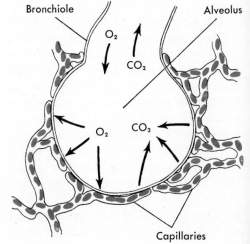

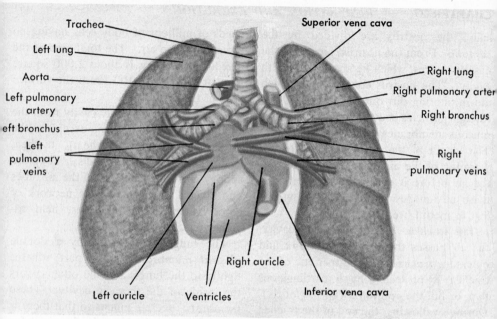

Fig. 37-3. In this back view of the lungs and heart, you can see the branches of the pulmonary artery and the pulmonary veins. Which vessels are carrying oxygenated blood?

Labels in figure:
Trachea
Left lung
Aorta
Left pulmonary artery
Left bronchus
Left pulmonary veins
Superior vena cava
Right lung
Right pulmonary artery
Right bronchus
Right pulmonary veins
Right auricle
Left auricle
Ventricles
Inferior vena cava

oxygen from air to blood and of carbon dioxide and water from blood to air. The **pulmonary veins** return to the heart the bright (oxygenated) blood for the tissues. Carbon dioxide in the lung capillaries has a higher concentration than that in the connecting air cells. Hence, carbon dioxide diffuses outward into the area of lower concentration in the air cells. Water passes out of the blood for the same reason.

The air capacity of the lungs. When the lungs are completely filled, they hold about 300 cubic inches of air. However, only about 30 cubic inches are involved each time we inhale and exhale. The air involved in normal, relaxed breathing is called *tidal air*. However, air movement is increased with forced breathing.

To illustrate forced breathing, inhale normally without any forcing. Your lungs now contain about 200 cubic inches of air. Now exhale normally. You have moved about 30 cubic inches of tidal air from the lungs. Now, without inhal-

ing again, force out all the air you can. You have now exhaled an additional 100 cubic inches of *supplemental air*. The lungs now contain about 70 cubic inches of *residual air* which you cannot force out.

When you inhale normally again, you replace the supplemental and the tidal air, or about 130 cubic inches. However, if you inhale with force, you can add 100 cubic inches of *complemental air,* raising the total capacity of the lungs to about 230 cubic inches. In other words, the *vital capacity* of the lungs, which does not include the residual air, consists of:

Tidal air	= 30 cu. in.
Supplemental air	= 100 cu. in.
Complemental air	= 100 cu. in.
Vital capacity	= 230 cu. in.

The mechanics of breathing. Many people think that the lungs draw in air, expand, and bulge the chest. Actually, this is the opposite of what happens.

The lungs contain no muscle, and cannot expand or contract of their own ac-cord. They are spongy, air-filled sacs, anchored in the chest cavity. Breathing is accomplished by changes in size and air pressure of the chest cavity. This fact can be shown by substituting apparatus for the body parts (Fig. 37-4).

A Y-tube (*trachea* and *bronchi*) is in-serted in a stopper and set in a bell jar (*chest*). Balloons (*lungs*) are fastened to the Y-tube. A piece of rubber sheet (*di-aphragm*) is fastened securely to the open base of the bell jar. When you pull the rubber sheet downward, you increase the volume of the bell jar and decrease the pressure within it. Air moves through the Y-tube and inflates the balloons. When you release the rubber sheet, the volume of the bell jar is decreased and the pressure within it is increased. Again air moves to equalize the pressure. But this time it leaves the balloons and passes through the Y-tube to the atmosphere.

Although the apparatus described above is a good model, notice that only one thing is being changed — the rubber sheet representing the diaphragm. As you will see, the ribs also play an impor-tant part in changing the size and pressure of the chest cavity.

Breathing movements. *Inspiration*, or the intake of air, occurs when the chest cavity is increased in size and therefore decreased in pressure. Enlargement of the chest cavity involves the following movements:

1. The rib muscles contract and pull the ribs upward and outward. If you inhale with force, you carry this action even further with the aid of the shoulder muscles.

2. The muscles of the resting, dome-shaped diaphragm contract. This action straightens and lowers the diaphragm and increases the size of the chest cavity from below.

3. The abdominal muscles relax and

allow compression of the abdominal or-gans by the diaphragm.

The enlargement of the chest cavity re-sults in decrease of the air pressure with-in. In an equalizing movement, air passes through the trachea and inflates the lungs.

Expiration, or the expelling of air from the lungs, results when the chest cavity is reduced in size. The action involves the following four movements:

1. The rib muscles relax and allow the ribs to spring back.

2. The diaphragm relaxes and rises to assume its dome-shaped position.

3. The compressed abdominal organs push up against the diaphragm. This ac-tion is increased during forced exhala-tion by contraction of the abdominal mus-cles.

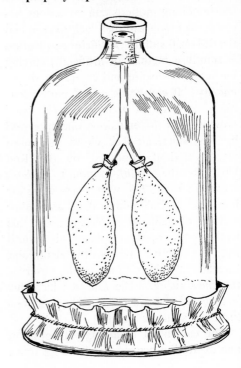

Fig. 37-4. Identify the parts of the re-spiratory system that are represented in this apparatus. What breathing structures are *not* properly represented?

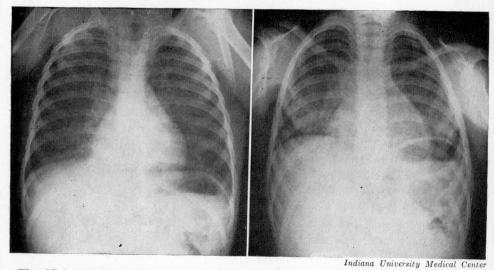

Fig. 37-5. These two X-ray photographs show the chest during exaggerated breathing. The left-hand photograph shows the lowering of the diaphragm and the spread ribs during inspiration. The photograph on the right was taken after expiration. Compare the shapes of the chest, especially in the shoulder region.

4. The elastic lung tissues, stretched while the lungs are full, shrink and force air out.

Artificial respiration. Any stopping of the breathing motions can be serious because the blood will then lack oxygen and the cells will suffer. *Artificial respiration* is simply a method of artificially forcing the lungs to inspire and expire air rhythmically. It can be described more accurately as *artificial breathing.* The *back pressure-arm lift method* is one approved by the American Red Cross. A more recent method approved by the Red Cross is the *mouth-to-mouth method,* shown in Fig. 37-6, which gets more air into the victim's lungs than any other method of artificial respiration. In this method, the operator places his mouth over the mouth or nose of the victim and breathes into the victim until he observes the chest rising. The rate at which this is repeated depends on whether the victim is an adult or a child.

The control of breathing. Inspiration and expiration occur from 16 to 24 times per minute, depending on the body activity, position, and age. The greater the oxygen need in the tissues, the more rapidly the lungs must function to supply the necessary oxygen. This is automatically regulated by the amount of oxygen or carbon dioxide present in the blood. Abundance of carbon dioxide stimulates breathing. Oxygen surplus in the blood has the opposite effect.

Air changes in breathing. Oxygen is absorbed from the alveoli of the lungs by blood in the lung capillaries. It combines with the *hemoglobin* of the red blood corpuscles. The amount of oxygen which is absorbed from the blood by the body tissues is smaller than you might think. In the first place, the air we breathe is only one-fifth oxygen. Of this amount, only about one-fourth is absorbed by the blood in the lungs. Furthermore, the hemoglobin gives up only about one-third of the oxygen it is carrying to the tissues.

The use of oxygen by the cells. In the tissues, oxygen is used by each cell in the oxidation of food to release energy. This

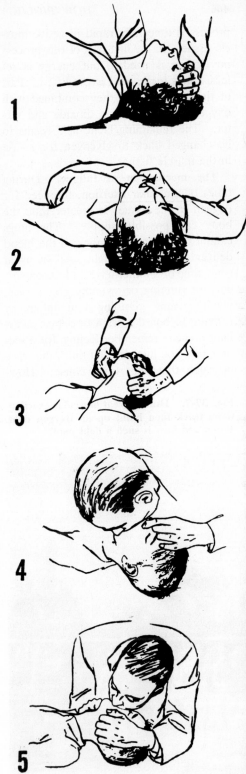

Fig. 37-6. Before starting the mouth-to-mouth method of artificial respiration, look to see if there is any foreign matter in the victim's mouth. If so, wipe it out with your fingers, then proceed according to the following steps:

First, tilt the head back so the chin is pointing upward (1). Pull or push the jaw into a jutting-out position (2 and 3). These maneuvers should relieve obstruction of the airway by moving the base of the tongue away from the back of the throat.

Second, open your mouth wide and place it tightly over the victim's mouth. At the same time pinch the victim's nostrils shut (4) or close the nostrils with your cheek (5). Or close the victim's mouth and place your mouth over his nose. Blow into the victim's mouth or nose.

Third, remove your mouth, turn your head to the side, and listen for the return rush of air that indicates air exchange. Repeat the blowing effort. For an adult, blow vigorously at the rate of 12 breaths per minute. For a child, take relatively shallow breaths appropriate for the child's size at the rate of about 20 per minute.

Fourth, if you are not getting air exchange, recheck the head and jaw position. If you still do not get air exchange, quickly turn the victim on his side and administer several sharp blows between the shoulder blades to dislodge any foreign matter in the airway.

American National Red Cross

process is especially rapid in active muscle tissue. In the first part of this process no oxygen is needed, but energy is released and *lactic acid* is produced. Part of the lactic acid is then combined with oxygen to form carbon dioxide and water. The remaining lactic acid seems to be changed back to glycogen for re-use in the muscle tissues.

The mechanism of fatigue. During times of muscular exertion, the need for oxygen in the tissues is greater than the body can possibly supply. The lungs cannot take in oxygen nor can the blood deliver it rapidly enough. All of us at some time or another have had the experience of running or swimming in a race, playing tennis, climbing a mountain, or running to board a train or a bus. Perhaps you can remember feeling, for a second, that you just couldn't finish that race or catch that departing vehicle. How-

Fig. 37-7. During great muscular exertion, these track men build up an oxygen debt. When and how is such a debt paid?

Cyr from Shostal

ever, with a final surge of reserve energy, you succeeded. You felt limp, light-headed, and completely exhausted. You may recall how your heart pounded and your breathing was deep and rapid. After 20 or 30 minutes you were ready for another race, another tennis match, or the long hike back.

What happens in one's body to cause these changes, and how is this rapid recovery brought about? During mild exercise the supply of oxygen meets the demands of the cells. However, during exertion, there is not enough oxygen. Therefore, the lactic acid produced is not oxidized or changed to glycogen. As a result, lactic acid builds up in the tissues and in the blood stream. The breathing becomes rapid and the heart speeds up in order to supply the tissues with enough oxygen, but even with these efforts, the lactic acid accumulates in the body, and the body is in a state of **oxygen debt**. During a 20- or 30-minute rest, some of the accumulated lactic acid is oxidized, and some is converted to glycogen. Carbon dioxide and excess water are excreted, and the debt is paid. The body is then ready for more exercise.

Respiration problems at high altitudes. The oxygen content of air remains at approximately 21 per cent of the total volume of the air at sea level in our atmosphere. In a sense, we are living at the bottom of a large sea of air. However, as we increase our altitude the amount of air on top of us is decreased, and thus the pressure is reduced. The pressure of the air is an important factor in how we breathe and how oxygen combines with the hemoglobin of the blood. Thus, mountain climbers and airplane pilots experience increasing difficulty in breathing and progressive weakness as they increase their altitude. At elevations near 12,000 feet they almost approach exhaustion.

A pilot can fly much higher than a

man can climb because the plane motor is doing the work and his oxidation requirements are much reduced. However, when a pilot nears 20,000 feet, the oxygen becomes so reduced that he experiences difficulty in seeing and hearing. This condition, called **anoxia** (an-*ok*-see-uh), is the result of oxygen starvation in the tissues. It is a dangerous condition and will cause death if not corrected within a short time. Anoxia may be avoided by equipping the pilot with an oxygen tank and a mask.

Passengers in modern air liners can fly at high altitudes in the safety and comfort of pressurized cabins. These cabins maintain an internal pressure and oxygen content equivalent to an altitude of approximately 5,000 feet.

However, man traveling at supersonic speeds in the new aircraft and rockets finds that the problems involved are similar to those experienced by divers under high pressure. Force produces profound changes in the circulatory system, too, and aviation research scientists are working hard to find effective methods of coping with them.

Metabolism concerns all the vital body processes. Respiration and oxidation are part of a complex series of body processes which are included in **metabolism** (meh-*tab*-oh-lizm). All processes, both physical and chemical, which are concerned with the activity, maintenance, and growth of an organism make up metabolism.

Growth and maintenance are concerned with the assimilation of food. During assimilation, food substances are reorganized in the tissues to form new protoplasm. In some way, the new protoplasm is given the power of life from the protoplasm which organized it. The building-up activities of metabolism are called **anabolism.**

These processes, like all other types of

U. S. Air Force

Fig. 37-8. This suit has been designed to provide a comfortable level of pressure and oxygen for high-altitude flying.

protoplasmic activity, require energy. This must come from food and must be released through the process of oxidation. Thus the energy exchange between food and living matter constitutes another important phase of metabolism. The tearing-down activities, for example, those in energy production, are called **catabolism.**

Body oxidation and its measurement. The rate of oxygen intake, respiration, and energy released increase in proportion to the activity of the body. This activity may be muscular, as in the case of walking, running, or some other form of exertion, or it may be mental. Other factors governing the rate of oxidation include exposure to cold, and activity of the digestive organs during digestion of food. The rate of oxidation in the body may be measured directly by determining the amount of heat given off from its surface. This may be measured by a device called a **calorimeter** (kal-or-*im*-ih-ter).

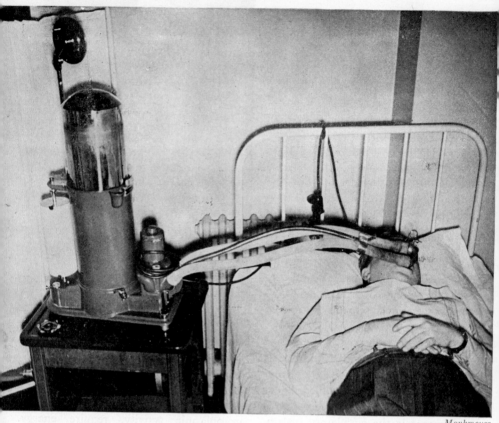

Fig. 37-9. The basal metabolism test determines the rate at which oxidation occurs in the body.

The person to be tested enters a closed compartment which is equipped to measure accurately all the heat which is given off by his body. He may lie quietly in bed during the process, or he may sit in a chair, or exercise vigorously, depending on the nature of the activity to be tested. The amount of heat energy given off during each type of activity is a direct indication of the rate of oxidation in the body tissues. Calorimeter tests are important in determining the energy needs of various individuals in order to adjust a diet to their specific requirements.

Basal metabolism and its measurement. Even when the body seems completely inactive as it does in sleep, respiration, oxidation, and energy release are continuing. With the cessation of muscular and, to a great extent, nervous, activity, the rate of oxidation is greatly reduced. The activities required to maintain the body and to supply energy necessary to support the basic life processes are included in the term *basal metabolism.* But it must be remembered that the term metabolism refers to the total activity of the individual cell. When the amount of oxygen intake is measured for the whole body, this is termed the *basal metabolic rate.*

The rate of basal metabolism may be determined by means of the calorimeter test. Another method, widely used in hospitals, measures the amount of oxygen consumed in a definite period (Fig. 37-9). The patient rests for at least an hour before the test. The test is usually run in the morning and the patient is instructed to eat no food until after the test is completed. After a rest period, during which the body is completely relaxed, the nose is plugged to avoid breathing from the atmosphere. A mouthpiece, connected to a tank of oxygen, is fitted into the mouth.

Thus all oxygen inhaled during the test period is from the measured tank. The amount of oxygen used from the tank is recorded on a graph. From these data, the rate of oxidation is determined. The rate of basal metabolism is calculated from the rate of oxidation in the tissues during complete rest.

External influences upon breathing and respiration. External factors, such as temperature, moisture in the air, and oxygen and carbon dioxide content of air, are very important influences on the rate of breathing and respiration. Certain of these factors are involved in *ventilation*.

Stuffiness in a room is due mainly to increase in the temperature and moisture content of the air, rather than to accumulation of carbon dioxide and decrease of the oxygen content. Movement of air in a ventilating system increases its flow over the body surfaces and speeds up the evaporation of perspiration. Modern air-conditioning systems not only circulate air, but remove moisture and heat as well.

The air in most homes, especially those equipped with a central heating system, becomes too dry during the cold months. This condition dries out mucous membranes and lowers their resistance to infection. The moisture content of the air, therefore, should be kept as high as possible by means of humidifiers or other devices.

Many people carry the ventilation of bedrooms at night to extremes. Your body requires less oxygen while you are asleep than at any other time. If the windows are open too much during cold weather, your body may chill during the night. There is little logic in piling covers on a bed to keep part of the body warm while at the same time chilling the exposed parts with cold air from an open window.

Carbon-monoxide poisoning. Far too often, we read of people who have died in a closed garage where an automobile engine was running or in a house filled with gas from an open stove burner or a defective furnace. The cause of death is given as *carbon-monoxide poisoning*. Actually, the death is not due to poisoning, but to *tissue suffocation*.

Carbon monoxide will not support life. Yet it combines with the hemoglobin of the blood 250 times more readily than oxygen. Thus a small concentration of carbon monoxide in the air will be absorbed in preference to a much larger concentration of oxygen. Furthermore, when carbon monoxide combines with hemoglobin, the two are very difficult to separate. As a result, the blood becomes loaded with carbon monoxide and decreases its oxygen-combining power. As tissues suffer from oxygen starvation, the victim becomes lightheaded and ceases to care about his condition. Soon paralysis sets in and he cannot move even if he wants to. Death follows from tissue suffocation.

Excretion of waste products produced by metabolism. The oxidation of foods involved in metabolism produces waste products which must be given off by the body in the process called **excretion**. In the case of protein metabolism, waste products result from the separation of the carbon and nitrogen parts of amino acids before oxidation of the carbon part. Other waste products result from the organization of amino acids to form protoplasm during growth processes. These nonprotein **nitrogenous wastes** include *urea* and *uric acid*.

(*Text continued on page 472*)

Description of the
Anatomical Transparencies
THE HUMAN BODY

Plate 1. This view shows the skin and muscle walls of the front of the body removed from the figure on the opposite page. You are looking at the inner side of the front half of the chest and abdominal cavities. The muscles in the neck, including the sterno-mastoid (1), which turns the head, and the pectoral muscles (2) of the chest, have been sectioned with the ribs (3) and clavicles (4). You are seeing the inside of the sternum (5) to which the rib cartilages (6) attach. The pleural membrane (7) lining the chest cavity is intact on the left side of the figure and has been removed on the right side to show the intercostal muscles (8) between the ribs. The diaphragm (9), a dome-shaped muscle, divides the chest and abdominal cavities. The abdominal cavity is lined with a membrane, the peritoneum (10), which is shown on the left side. It has been removed on the right side to expose the transverse abdominal muscle (11) and the vertical rectus muscle (12), which is partially enclosed in tendonous sheaths (13) pierced by the umbilicus (14).

Plate 2. In this view, most of the skin has been removed from the head to show the temporal (15) and masseter (16) chewing muscles attached to the skull and the large parotid salivary gland (17) with its duct. Around the mouth are the muscles of facial expression. The neck muscles have been removed to expose the thyroid cartilage (18) surrounding the larynx, the thyroid gland (19), the carotid artery, and the internal jugular vein. The numerous veins of the arms and legs lying close to the skin are shown in this view. With the front portion of the pleural membrane (7) removed, the lobes of the lungs (20) and the pericardium (21) covering the heart are visible. Below the diaphragm (9), in the abdominal cavity, are the organs of digestion. On the right side are the liver (22) and gall bladder (23). The stomach (24) is on the left side. The ascending, transverse, and descending regions of the colon (25) surround loops of the small intestine (26).

Plate 3. In this view, the head is sectioned along the midline and you are looking toward the inside of the right half of the cranial cavity (29) and the spinal canal (30) with its dural lining intact. On the side wall of the nasal cavity (31) are the three nasal turbinates. Two sectioned nasal sinuses are above the nasal cavity. The sectioned tongue (32) reveals its muscular structure. The pharynx (33) leads to the esophagus and the larynx at the upper end of the trachea. At the top of the larynx (34) are the vocal folds and epiglottis. The lungs (20) are sectioned. The pericardium (21) has been lifted off the heart and you are seeing its inner surface. The superior vena cava (35) has been cut above the heart. The back view of the liver (22) shows the cut ends of the hepatic veins above and the end of the portal vein entering the liver from below. The gall bladder (23) and bile ducts are clearly shown. The stomach (24), a portion of the transverse colon (25), and the small intestine (26) with its blood supply and anchoring root of the mesentery (36) are viewed from the back. The muscles shown are portions of the deltoid (27) of the shoulder and the sartorius (28) and a side muscle of the thigh. These are removed to expose deeper views on Plate 6.

Plate 4. This view shows the brain. You are seeing the outer surface of the right hemisphere of the cerebrum (37) and the cerebellum (38). The pons, medulla, spinal

(Continued on page following Anatomical Transparencies)

THE HUMAN BODY
IN ANATOMICAL TRANSPARENCIES

By GLADYS McHUGH, Medical Artist
Associated with the University of Chicago Clinics

The "Trans-Vision" process presents the human body in a unique manner in which you can perform a "dissection" and proceed through the depths of its structures by turning transparent pages. You can see organs overlying other organs in a three-dimensional effect. As you turn the pages, a layer of anatomy is removed and a deeper layer comes into full view. The right pages give you a front view of the structures. To see the same structures from the back side, you turn the page. Thus, you can see the relation of organs to the body as a whole and to each other. You can single out an individual part for more detailed observation.

The pages preceding and following the anatomical transparencies give you a description of each view—how it was made and what it shows. The numbers you find on many of the structures refer to an identification key on the back of Plate 6. This will identify any structure you wish quickly and easily. Numbers have been omitted where they would detract from structural detail. Many such structures are referred to in the description of the various plates.

The structures shown are detailed and accurate. This presentation of the human body will serve as an adequate basis for anatomical study in any degree of thoroughness and complexity you may desire.

Key identifying numbered structures on back of Plate 6.

1

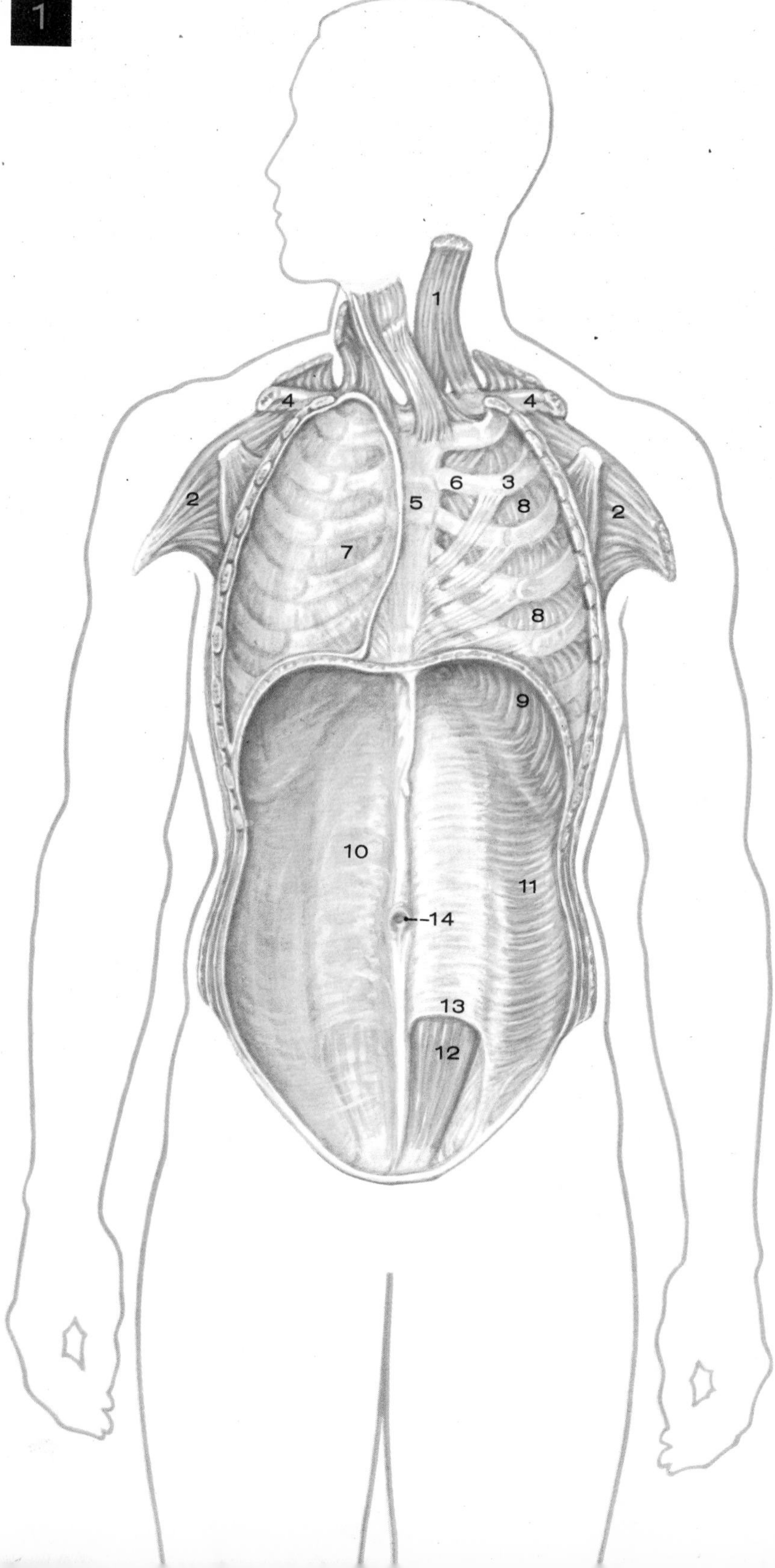

6

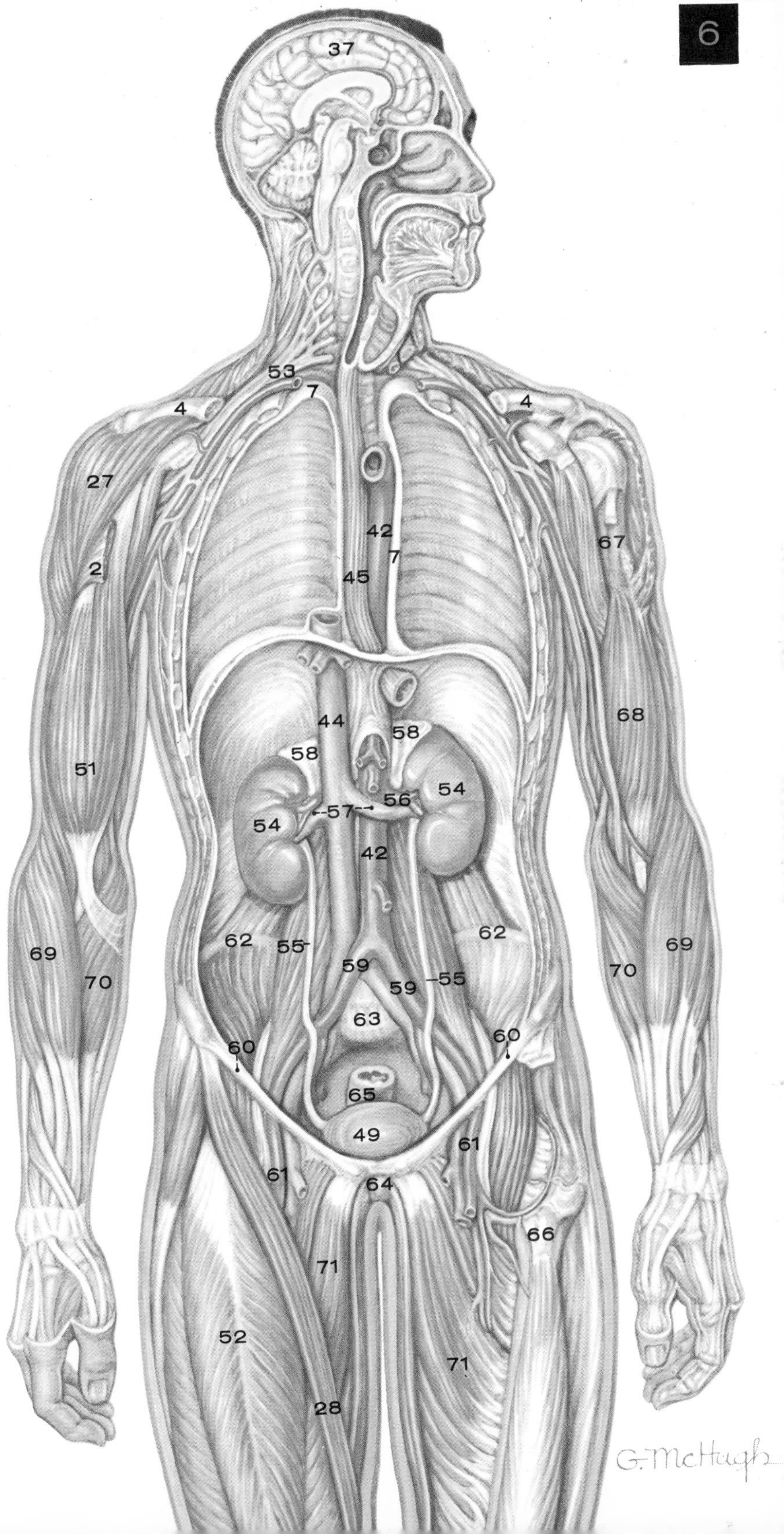

37
53
7
4
4
27
2
42
7
45
67
68
44
58
58
51
54
56
57
54
42
62
62
55
55
59
59
69
70
69
70
63
60
60
65
49
61
61
64
66
71
52
71
28
G. McHugh

Key to the Structures of the Human Body

1. Sterno-mastoid muscle, used in turning the head
2. Pectoral muscle, used in moving the arm across the chest
3. Rib
4. Clavicle
5. Sternum
6. Rib cartilage
7. Pleural membrane
8. Intercostal muscles, used in breathing
9. Diaphragm
10. Peritoneum
11. Transverse abdominal muscle, supporting the abdominal wall
12. Rectus abdominal muscle, used in flexing the trunk
13. Rectus sheath
14. Umbilicus
15. Temporal muscle, used in chewing
16. Masseter muscle, used in chewing
17. Parotid salivary gland
18. Thyroid cartilage
19. Thyroid gland
20. Lung
21. Pericardium
22. Liver
23. Gall bladder
24. Stomach
25. Colon
26. Small intestine
27. Deltoid muscle, used in raising the arm
28. Sartorius muscle, used in crossing the leg
29. Cranial cavity
30. Spinal canal
31. Nasal cavity
32. Tongue
33. Pharynx
34. Larynx
35. Superior vena cava
36. Root of the mesentery
37. Cerebrum
38. Cerebellum
39. Nasal septum
40. Trachea
41. Heart
42. Aorta
43. Pulmonary artery
44. Inferior vena cava
45. Esophagus
46. Duodenum
47. Spleen
48. Pancreas
49. Urinary bladder
50. Cerebral septum
51. Biceps muscle, used in flexing the arm
52. Flexor muscles of front of thigh
53. Brachial plexus
54. Kidney
55. Ureter
56. Renal artery
57. Renal vein
58. Adrenal gland
59. Iliac artery
60. Inguinal ligament
61. Femoral artery
62. Crest of hip bones
63. Lumbo-sacral joint
64. Pubis
65. Rectum
66. Femur
67. Humerus
68. Brachial muscle, which works with biceps as a flexor of the arm
69. Extensor muscles of hand
70. Flexor muscles of hand
71. Adductor muscles which bring legs together

cord, and spinal nerves are visible. The nasal septum (39) is the central partition of the nasal cavity. The trachea (40) is an airway to the lungs, where it divides into the bronchi. The sectioned lungs reveal the numerous branches of the bronchial tree (white), the pulmonary arteries (blue), and the pulmonary veins (red). You are looking at the heart (41) and its great vessels: the aorta (42), pulmonary artery (43), superior vena cava (35), and inferior vena cava (44). The cut ends of the hepatic veins are seen entering the inferior vena cava just below the diaphragm. In removing the stomach, the lower end of the esophagus (45) and the beginning of the duodenum (46) were cut. The spleen (47) and pancreas (48), along the back wall of the abdominal cavity, are visible. After removal of the transverse colon and the small intestine, the peritoneum (10), lining the back of the abdominal cavity and carrying blood vessels to the colon, can be seen. The lower end of the small intestine (26) is sectioned close to its junction with the colon. Just below this junction is the appendix, which extends from the caecum, or beginning portion of the colon (25). The lower end or sigmoid portion passes behind the urinary bladder (49).

Plate 5. In this view, the hemispheres of the cerebrum are divided along the midline. You are seeing the cerebral septum (50), which divides the hemispheres. Below the cerebrum you see the sectioned interbrain, pons, medulla, cerebellum (38), and spinal cord. You are viewing the lungs (20) from the back with sections removed to show the bronchial divisions of the trachea (40). With the posterior peritoneum removed, the spleen (47), pancreas (48), and duodenum (46) are visible from the back. The portal vein, which receives blood from these organs and the intestinal tract, is seen entering the liver close to the bile duct. A portion of the pancreas has been dissected to show the pancreatic duct, which enters the duodenum beside the common bile duct. The biceps muscle (51) and three thigh muscles (52) are removed and are seen from the back.

Plate 6. In this view, the cerebral septum is removed and you are seeing the inner side of the left hemisphere of the cerebrum (37) with its surface blood supply. Notice the spinal nerves emerging from between the vertebrae of the neck and forming the brachial plexus (53), the nerve supply to the shoulders and arms. The arteries supplying these regions follow the same course as the nerves. With the lungs and trachea removed, you can see the full length of the esophagus (45) and its relation to the aorta (42). The inferior vena cava (44) is cut at the entrance to the heart, just above the junction with the hepatic veins. The kidneys (54), ureters (55), and bladder (49) form the urinary tract. A renal artery (56) enters each kidney from the aorta (42). The renal veins (57) drain into the inferior vena cava (44). On top of the kidneys are the adrenal glands (58). In the lower abdominal region, the aorta divides into the iliac arteries (59), which divide further into internal and external branches. The internal iliac arteries supply the pelvic organs. The external iliacs encircle the pelvic region, pass under the inguinal ligaments (60) in company with the femoral veins and nerves, and emerge as the femoral arteries (61). Portions of the bone structure of the pelvis are visible as the crests of the hip bones (62), the joint between the sacrum and spine (63), and the pubis (64). The upper end of the rectum (65) can be seen behind the bladder. The shoulder and hip joints are partially exposed on the left side, showing bone and muscle structures not visible on the right side. Additional muscles and bones of the arms and legs are identified in the Key to the Structures of the Human Body.

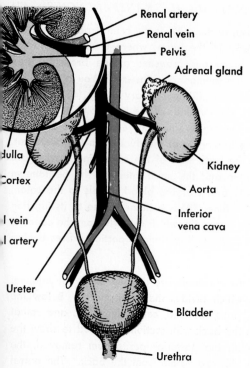

Renal artery
Renal vein
Pelvis
Adrenal gland

Kidney
Aorta
Inferior
vena cava

ledulla
Cortex

l vein
l artery

Ureter

Bladder

Urethra

Fig. 37-10. The kidney on the left has been cut away and enlarged to show the internal structures. The cortex contains millions of microscopic glomeruli.

(Text continued from page 469)

Waste products must pass from the tissues to the blood, and from the blood to the organs of excretion. Accumulation of wastes, especially nonprotein nitrogens, in the tissues causes rapid tissue poisoning, starvation, and suffocation. Tissues filled with waste products cannot absorb either food or oxygen. Fever, convulsions, coma, and death are inevitable if nonprotein nitrogen wastes do not leave the tissues.

Further complications arise if the mineral acids and salts accumulate in the body because of excretory failure. This accumulation disturbs certain delicate acid-base balances in the body. It also upsets the osmotic relationships between blood and lymph and the tissues. When excess salts are held in the tissues, water accumulates and causes a swelling.

The kidneys are bean-shaped organs, about the size of your clenched fist. *The kidneys* lie on either side of the spine, in the " small " of the back. Deep layers of fat around them form a protective covering. Their concave side is toward the spine. (See the " Trans-Vision " between pages 470 and 471.)

If you cut a kidney lengthwise (Fig. 37-10), you can see several different regions. The firm, outer region is called *cortex.* The cortex composes about one-third of the kidney tissue. The inner two-thirds, or *medulla,* contains conical projections called *pyramids.* The points of the pyramids extend into a saclike cavity, the *pelvis* of the kidney. The pelvis, in turn, leads into a long, narrow tube (one for each kidney) called the *ureter* (you-*ree*-ter). The two ureters empty into the *urinary bladder.*

Fig. 37-11. This is an X-ray photograph showing the kidneys and ureters. The kidneys lie on either side of the spine. Notice the renal pelves and the ureters leading to the urinary bladder.

New York Presbyterian Hospital

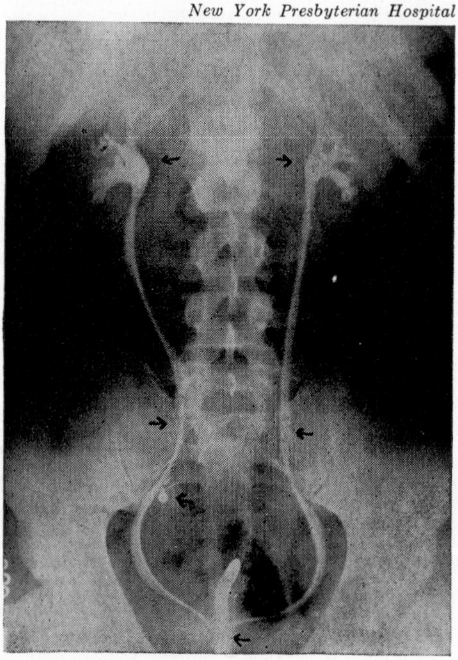

The kidneys act as filters. Each kidney contains about 1,250,000 tiny filters called **nephrons.** The function of these nephrons is to control the chemical composition of blood. Each nephron consists of a small, cup-shaped structure called a **Bowman's capsule** (Fig. 37-12). A tiny, winding **tubule** comes from each capsule. This tubule becomes very narrow as it straightens out and goes toward the renal pelvis. Characteristically, this tubule widens out again and goes back into the cortex. This loop of the tubule is so typical of a nephron that it has been named *Henle's loop,* after the man who discovered it. Once this tubule has passed back into the cortex, it becomes very crooked again and then enters a larger straight tube called the **collecting tubule.** The collecting tubule is a straight tube which receives the tubules of many nephrons. It carries fluid to the renal pelvis. If all these tubules were straightened out and put end to end, they would extend over 200 miles.

How does the nephron function? Blood enters each kidney through a large **renal artery,** which branches directly from the aorta. It is the largest artery in the body in proportion to the size of the organ it supplies. In the kidney, the renal artery branches and rebranches to form a maze of tiny **arterioles,** which penetrate all areas of the cortex.

Each arteriole ends in a coiled, knob-like mass of capillaries, the **glomerulus** (gloh-*mair*-you-lus). Each glomerulus fills the cuplike depression of the Bowman's capsule. In the first stage of removal of waste from the blood, far too much of the blood content leaves the blood stream and enters the capsules of the kidney. However, this is soon corrected in a second stage, in which valuable substances return to the blood.

The first stage takes place in the coiled capillaries of the glomeruli. Here water,

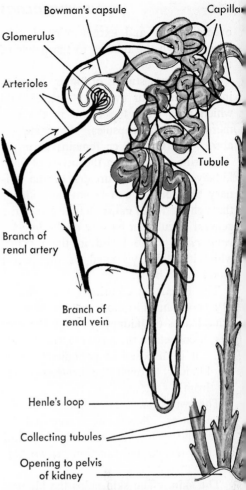

Fig. 37-12. **The kidneys act as filters. As blood flows through the glomeruli, substances from it pass into the Bowman's capsule, where they then flow through the tubules. Some of the substances are reabsorbed into the blood stream. Collecting tubules carry wastes to the pelvis of the kidney.**

nitrogenous wastes, glucose, and mineral salts pass through the walls of the capillaries and into the surrounding capsule. This solution resembles blood plasma without blood proteins. Complete loss of this much water, glucose, and minerals would be fatal. However, after this fluid leaves the capsule through the tubules, it passes a network of capillaries. Here, many of the substances are reabsorbed into the blood. Only nitrogenous wastes, excess water, and excess mineral salts pass through the tubules to the pelvis of the kidney as **urine.**

Some recent studies of kidney function indicate that, for every 100 cc of fluid which pass from the blood in the glomeruli into the capsules, 99 cc are reabsorbed. Only 1 cc remains as urine. The urine passes from the pelvis of each kidney through the ureters to the urinary bladder. Blood leaves the kidneys through the **renal veins** and returns to the general circulation by way of the *inferior vena cava.* The blood in these veins, while it is deoxygenated, is the purest blood in the body.

The formation of urine by the kidney is a constant filtration process. After urine leaves the kidneys through the ureters, it collects in the large muscular bladder. It is disposed of periodically from the bladder through the **urethra** (you-*ree*-thruh).

The two kidneys have tremendous reserve power. When one is removed, its mate enlarges to twice its normal size and assumes the normal function of two kidneys.

The skin. The skin helps the kidneys in the excretion of water, salts, and some urea, in the form of *sweat* (*perspiration*). However, this fluid is much more important in regulating body temperature than it is as an excretory substance.

Skin consists of an outer portion, or **epidermis,** composed of many layers of cells (Fig. 37-13). The outer cells, or **horny layer,** are flattened, dead, and scalelike. The inner ones, or **germinative layer,** are more active and larger. The epidermis serves largely for protection of the active tissues beneath it. It is rubbed off constantly, but active cells in the lower layers replace cells as fast as they are lost. Friction and pressure on the epidermis stimulate cell division, and may produce a *callus* more than a hun-

dred cells thick. Hair and nails are special outgrowths of the epidermis.

The **dermis** lies under the epidermis. It is a thick, active layer, composed of tough, fibrous connective tissue, richly supplied with blood and lymph vessels, nerves, sweat glands, and oil glands.

The functions of the skin. The varied functions of the skin include:

1. Protection of the body from mechanical injury and bacterial invasion.

2. Protection of the inner tissues against drying out. The skin, aided by oil glands, is nearly waterproof. Little water passes through it, except out through the pores.

3. Location of the nerve endings which respond to pressure, or touch, pain, and temperature changes.

4. Excretion of wastes present in sweat.

5. Control of the loss of body heat through the evaporation of sweat.

This last statement needs further explanation. In an earlier discussion about water and its uses, we mentioned that heat is used during the change of liquid water to water vapor. Thus as sweat evaporates from the body surface, heat is withdrawn from the outer tissues. The skin is literally an automatic radiator. It is richly supplied with blood containing body heat withdrawn from the tissues. As the body temperature rises, the skin becomes more flushed with blood, and heat is conducted to the surface. At the same time, secretion of sweat increases and bathes the skin. This increases the rate of evaporation and the amount of heat loss becomes greater.

The skin and its care. It is obvious that personal cleanliness is a vital part of grooming. We all expect to see clean hands and a skin free of dirt. However, there are certain unfortunate skin conditions which are not dependent on cleanliness.

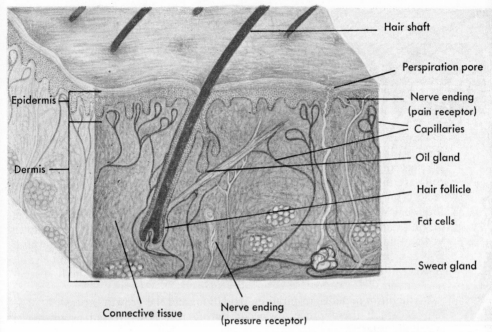

Fig. 37-13. Under a microscope, a thin section of skin reveals many cell layers and specialized structures.

Acne (*ak*-nee) is a condition in which the skin erupts in numerous blackheads, pimples, and boils. It is especially prevalent among young people. During the teen years, hormones, especially from the reproductive organs and the adrenal glands, are being secreted in greater quantity than at any previous time. This increase may result in a hormonic imbalance which often is expressed by acne and other disorders.

Acne is not a dangerous or permanent condition. But it does bring distress and embarrassment to a person at the time when he is most sensitive about his personality and social acceptability. A vicious circle may result. The condition causes emotional tension, and emotional tension increases hormone secretion and aggravates the condition.

There are several things to do to improve an acne condition. Eat foods that are low in fats. Avoid ice cream and butter especially. If chocolate aggravates the condition, stop eating it. Frequent washing of the spots with mild soap is helpful. By all means, because of the danger of infection, do not squeeze or try to open any pimple.

Eczema (*ek*-zuh-muh) is a condition of allergic or emotional origin which results in scaling of the skin. Such diseases require treatment for emotional tension in addition to local treatment of the skin itself.

Other organs of excretion. During expiration, the *lungs* excrete carbon dioxide and considerable water vapor. The excretory function of the *liver* in forming urea has been discussed earlier. The bile secreted by the *gall bladder* is also a waste-containing substance.

The large intestine removes undigested food. This, however, is not cell excretion in the strict sense, since food refuse has never actually been absorbed into the tissues. As you will recall, earlier in the chapter excretion was defined as the giving off of waste products resulting from *metabolism*.

In Conclusion

Respiration is the exchange of gases between living matter and its surroundings. It is closely related to the chemical process, oxidation, in which energy is released during the breakdown of foods. In lower forms of life, individual cells are in direct contact with their surroundings. In higher animals, blood is necessary as a conducting medium between the body tissues and a respiratory center which is in contact with the outer environment. The movement of air in and out of lungs is accomplished by the mechanical process known as breathing, which consists of inspiration and expiration. External respiration and internal respiration are concerned with the actual exchange of gases between the lungs and blood and between the blood and body tissues respectively.

Metabolism includes respiration, oxidation, and the growth processes. The rate at which these processes occur during rest is expressed as the basal metabolic rate.

Various wastes that result from metabolism are removed from the body through actions of the kidneys, skin, lungs, liver, and large intestine. The kidneys, the most vital organs of excretion, serve as blood filters. They are responsible for the removal of practically all the nitrogenous wastes resulting from protein metabolism, excess water, and mineral acids and salts. Skin also has a complex role. It excretes large quantities of water as sweat. It also functions as the " radiator " of the body in eliminating heat during evaporation of sweat.

In the next chapter we shall study the composition of blood, the structure and functions of the heart and blood vessels, and the vital role the circulatory system plays in maintaining the life processes of the body.

BIOLOGICALLY SPEAKING

alveoli	excretion	pelvis
anabolism	expiration	pharynx
anoxia	external respiration	pleural membrane
artificial respiration	germinative layer	pulmonary vessels
basal metabolism	glomerulus	pyramids
Bowman's capsule	horny layer	renal vessels
breathing	inspiration	respiration
bronchi	internal respiration	septum
bronchioles	kidney	trachea
calorimeter	lactic acid	tubule
catabolism	larynx	ureter
collecting tubule	medulla	urethra
cortex	metabolism	urinary bladder
dermis	nephron	urine
epidermis	nitrogenous wastes	vocal cords
epiglottis	oxygen debt	

QUESTIONS FOR REVIEW

1. What are the differences between respiration and breathing?
2. How do pressure changes within the chest cavity cause inspiration and expiration of air?
3. What is the purpose of artificial respiration?
4. What factors influence the rate of breathing?
5. (a) How can you build up an oxygen debt? (b) How can it be repaid?
6. Explain the physiology of carbonmonoxide poisoning.

7. In what way do the kidneys regulate blood content?
8. What are the differences in composition between the glomerular fluid and the urine which finally leaves the kidneys?
9. Why may a person who is not sweating in the hot sun be in danger of a sunstroke?
10. What are the chief functions of the skin?
11. What are other organs of excretion besides the kidneys?

APPLYING FACTS AND PRINCIPLES

1. What happens to the respiratory system of a pilot who is in a power dive or in a supersonic speed plane?
2. After several very deep breaths, breathing stops for a time. Explain.
3. People who live in dry climates, such as the southwestern parts of our country, report that high temperatures are easier to take there than the same temperatures in the more humid parts of the United States. Why?
4. If plants produce oxygen in photosynthesis, how do you explain the fact that they also respire?

5. Why is increased salt intake recommended in hot weather?
6. What happens to water in the blood if it does not enter the glomerulus? If it enters the glomerulus but is reabsorbed? If it enters the glomerulus but is not reabsorbed?
7. Explain what is probably wrong if, during an analysis of the urine, red blood cells are found? Albumin is found? Glucose is found? Excess of water is discovered?
8. What is the chief difference in composition between sweat and urine?

CHAPTER *38*

The Blood and Circulation

THE movement or flow of nutritive fluids, waste materials, and water in living organisms is called *circulation.* The sponges accomplish circulation by literally pumping the ocean into their bodies! The sea water supplies each cell with its individual oxygen needs and washes its wastes away. Actually, the cells in man's body are bathed in a fluid which has a salt content very much like sea water. We call this solution *tissue fluid.*

However, man's circulatory system is far more complex than that of the invertebrates.

Man produces his own " sea water," and adds other vital substances to it. Then it is piped through his body, and circulated with a pump — the heart. If the pump stops working, man's cells are in the same predicament as a sponge would be when thrown up on the beach.

What is blood? *Blood* is a *fluid tissue.* It is a peculiar tissue in that the cells are scattered among the nonliving substances composing the fluid portion. The average person has about 12 pints of blood, which compose about nine per cent of the body weight. The fluid portion of the blood is the **plasma,** and the blood cells are called the *solid components,* or the **corpuscles.**

Blood plasma. If you remove the cells from whole blood, the straw-colored, sticky plasma remains. Nine-tenths of plasma is water.

The proteins in plasma give it the sticky quality. One of them, **fibrinogen** (fy-*brin*-oh-jen), is essential in the clotting of blood. When fibrinogen is removed from plasma, two other proteins remain. One is **serum albumin** (al-*byou*-min), which is necessary to normal blood and tissue relationship during absorption. The other is **serum globulin** (*glob*-you-lin), which gives rise to antibodies causing immunity to various diseases.

Prothrombin (proh-*throm*-bin) is an enzyme produced in the liver when vitamin K is present in the body. It is inactive normally, but active during clotting.

Inorganic minerals, dissolved in water, give plasma a salt content of approximately one per cent, while that of sea water is approximately three per cent. These compounds include carbonates, chlorides, and phosphates of the elements calcium, sodium, magnesium, and potassium. They are absolutely essential to the blood and to the normal functioning of the body tissues. Without calcium compounds, blood will not clot in a wound.

Digested foods are present in plasma in the form of glucose (*blood sugar*), fats, and amino acids. They are received in the digestive organs, liver, and other places of storage, and travel to the tissues.

Nitrogen-containing wastes, from protein metabolism in tissues, and *urea,* produced largely in the liver during the breakdown of amino acids, travel in the plasma to the organs of excretion. Since these nitrogen compounds are no longer part of a protein molecule, we call them **nonprotein nitrogens.**

The solid components. The **red blood cells** (red blood corpuscles, or erythrocytes), the **white blood cells** (white blood corpuscles, or leucocytes), and the **platelets** (thrombocytes) are the three solid components of blood (Fig. 38-1).

The red blood cells. The red corpuscles are shaped like disks with both sides concave. Sometimes they travel in the blood in rows which resemble stacks of coins, although they may separate and float individually. The red cells are so small that ten million of them can be spread in one square inch. They are so numerous that, placed side by side, they would cover an area of 3,500 square yards. It is estimated that the blood of a normal person contains 25 trillion (25,000,000,000,000) red blood cells, or enough to go around the earth four times at the equator, if they were laid side by side.

The pigment in the red blood cell is

hemoglobin. This protein substance gives blood its red color. As you will see later, it is a very important pigment.

The red blood cells are produced in the red marrow of bones. During their development, they have nuclei, as do all other cells. Normally, by the time they are ready to be released into the blood stream, they have lost their nuclei. Recent research shows that the average life span of the red corpuscle is 21 days. The worn-out red cells are filtered out of the blood in the spleen and liver. At the same time, certain valuable compounds are released into the blood stream and used in the manufacture of new red blood cells.

What do the red blood cells do? The hemoglobin within the cell membrane of the red blood cell is a complex protein containing iron. This iron gives the pigment hemoglobin the ability to carry oxygen. Perhaps you have seen an iron nail turn red with rust. It has *oxidized,* which means that it has combined with the oxygen in the air. The iron of hemoglobin combines with oxygen in the lungs. There is, however, an important difference. The iron of the nail, which has rusted, will not easily give up its oxygen. The iron in hemoglobin easily gives up its oxygen at the proper time and place in the body. We say the blood is **oxygenated** when the hemoglobin has combined with oxygen. In this form the hemoglobin is a bright red color and is called **oxyhemoglobin.** Oxygen is carried from the lungs to the tissues in this form.

In the tissues, the pigment gives up its oxygen and is called **reduced hemoglobin,** which is a darker color than oxyhemoglobin. The carbon dioxide, formed in the tissues, now combines with the reduced hemoglobin, and the product is called **carbhemoglobin.** In this form much of the carbon dioxide is carried to

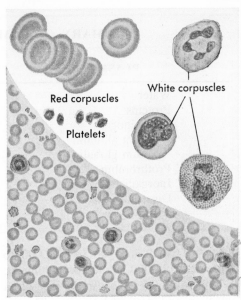

Red corpuscles

Platelets

White corpuscles

Fig. 38-1. The solid components of the blood include red corpuscles, white corpuscles, and platelets.

the lungs to be released and the cycle is repeated.

The white blood cells. White blood cells are, on the average, larger than red blood cells and differ from them in three ways: (1) white corpuscles have nuclei; (2) white corpuscles do not contain hemoglobin and are, therefore, nearly colorless; and (3) some white corpuscles can move much like the ameba. The white blood cells are less numerous than the red cells, the ratio being about one white cell to every 600 red cells. White corpuscles are formed in the red bone marrow and in the lymph glands. Normally there are about 8,000 in one cubic millimeter of blood as against four and one-half to five million red cells.

The white blood cells that can move about are able to ooze through the capillary walls into the tissue spaces. Here, they engulf solid materials, including bacteria. They are an important defense of the body against infection. Whenever an infection develops in the tissues, the

SUMMARY OF COMPOSITION OF BLOOD

PLASMA	BLOOD CELL

Water
Proteins
  Fibrinogen
  Serum albumin
  Serum globulin
Prothrombin
Inorganic substances
Digested foods
Tissue wastes
	Red corpuscles
	White corpuscles
	Platelets

white-cell count may go from 8,000 to more than 25,000 per cubic millimeter. White corpuscles collect in the area of an infection and destroy bacteria. The remains of dead bacteria, white corpuscles, and tissue fluid is *pus*.

Blood platelets. Platelets are irregularly shaped, colorless bodies, much smaller than the red corpuscles. They are probably formed in the red bone marrow. Platelets are not capable of moving on their own but float along in the blood stream. They have an important function in the formation of a blood clot.

The functions of blood. Blood is the transporting medium for all substances in the body. Its functions as such are summarized in the table below.

BLOOD AS A TRANSPORTING MEDIUM

TRANSPORTA- TION OF	FROM	TO	FOR THE PURPOSE OF
Digested food	Digestive organs and liver	Tissues	Growth and repair of cells and supplying of energy
Cell wastes	Active tissues	Lungs, kidneys, and skin	Excretion
Water	Digestive organs and tissues	Kidneys, skin, and lungs	Excretion and equalization of body fluids
Oxygen	Lungs	Tissues	Oxidation
Heat	Tissues	Skin	Equalization of the body temperature
Secretions	Ductless glands	Various organs, glands	Regulation of body activities

THE CLOTTING OF BLOOD

Thromboplastin + prothrombin + calcium = thrombin
Thrombin + fibrinogen = fibrin

How blood clots. When you cut small blood vessels in a minor wound, blood oozes out. Such an injury is not alarming because a clot will soon form and the blood flow will stop. You probably take this for granted, without considering what would happen if the flow did not stop.

Clotting results from chemical and physical changes in the blood. When blood leaves a vessel, the platelets disintegrate and release **thromboplastin.** This substance reacts with *prothrombin* and with *calcium* to form **thrombin.** The thrombin changes *fibrinogen,* a blood protein, to **fibrin** (*fy*-brin). The fibrin is a mesh or network of tiny " threads " which will entrap blood cells, thus forming a clot, and prevent further escape of blood (Fig. 38-2). These entrapped

corpuscles dry out and form a scab. Healing takes place as the edges of the wound grow toward the center. If *any* of the substances mentioned above is not present, clotting will not occur. Clotting is summarized in the table above.

If blood vessels are broken under the skin in a bruise, a " black and blue " spot may appear, because clotting occurs under the skin. Gradually, the clotted blood is absorbed and the color of the bruise changes and finally disappears.

Blood transfusions have saved many lives. Conditions like **hemorrhage** (*hemor-idge*), wound shock, severe burns, and various other illnesses may require **blood transfusions.** If *whole blood* is used, the patient receives both the necessary plasma and blood cells. However, the blood of the donor must be typed and matched with that of the patient. The matching is done by adding a drop of the patient's blood to a drop of the donor's blood. If the red cells *agglutinate* (clump together), the bloods are **incompatible** (Fig.

Fig. 38-2. This diagram shows the microscopic changes which occur during the clotting of blood: *A*, before clotting has started; *B*, formation of threads of fibrin; *C*, shortening of the fibrin threads and trapping of the blood cells in the mesh.

Fig. 38-3. This diagram of a blood smear shows the agglutination reaction that occurs when incompatible types of blood are mixed. When two compatible types of blood are mixed, there is no such reaction.

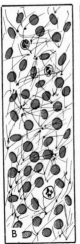

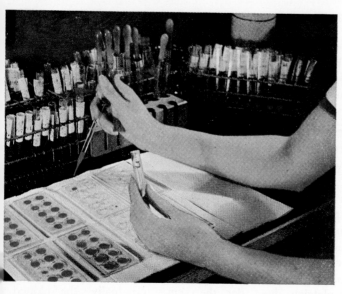

Fig. 38-4. After whole blood has been donated for transfusions, it must be grouped and typed. Here a technician is testing various samples for accurate determination of blood groups and Rh factor.

38-3). If, however, the red cells remain in suspension, the samples are **compatible,** and it is possible to perform the transfusion. Blood types are designated *A, B, AB,* and *O.* There is also an *Rh* type. You can see why using the wrong type might result in serious blood reactions, clotting, and death of the patient.

Often the patient needs an immediate increase in the volume of liquid in the blood stream and does not require additional blood cells. This condition is called **shock.** The red corpuscles form rapidly if the blood volume is maintained. In such cases, *plasma* may be transferred in preference to whole blood. Typing is not necessary in the use of plasma because of the absence of the cells.

The Rh factor in blood. Two scientists, Landsteiner and Wiener, discovered the **Rh factor** in the blood of a *Rhesus* monkey. They named the factor *Rh,* as an abbreviation for *Rhesus.* When they added a portion of blood taken from a *Rhesus* monkey to a rabbit and later some of the rabbit's blood into a human, it was discovered that the corpuscles of the human blood were affected. Further studies showed that this effect on human

corpuscles occurred in 87 per cent of the persons tested in New York City. The reaction had no relation to the common blood groups designated as A, B, AB, and O. They discovered that the blood of the *Rhesus* monkey contained the Rh factor, and that the rabbit's blood formed an antibody against it. All the people whose blood was affected by the antibody had Rh-positive blood.

The Rh factor may be any one of six or more protein substances, **antigens,** present in the red corpuscles of 87 per cent of all the people. A person with one of these antigens is *Rh positive.* The 13 per cent lacking any one of them are *Rh negative.*

If a patient is Rh negative and receives Rh-positive blood in a transfusion, he produces an antibody against the factor. This particular antibody causes the corpuscles of the Rh-positive blood to agglutinate and to dissolve. There is little danger during the first transfusion because the antibody is not present when the Rh-positive blood is added. However, the patient now builds antibodies against this Rh-positive blood. Therefore, a second transfusion results in serious fatal complications.

How the Rh factor may affect childbirth. Complications from the Rh factor occur with childbearing in about one case in three or four hundred mothers. In such cases, the mother is Rh negative and the father is Rh positive. The child has inherited Rh-positive blood from the father. During development, blood from the child, containing the factor, may seep into the mother's circulation through tiny ruptures in the membranes which normally separate the two circulations. Blood from the mother seeps into the child through the same channels.

Such seepage is uncommon, and explains why many Rh-negative mothers bear normal Rh-positive children. However, if seepage occurs with a second Rh-positive child, the antibody in the mother's blood enters the child's circulation and causes serious damage.

Occasionally, the child dies before birth. But if the damage to the child is not too extensive, an immediate transfusion after birth may save its life. In some cases, the child's blood is almost entirely removed and replaced by transfused blood. Blood used in such a complete transfusion is Rh negative but does not contain the antibody. In other words, the donor has never received positive blood.

Now you can see why a mother whose blood contains the antibody because of an Rh-positive transfusion may sometimes lose even her first child. For this reason, blood used in a transfusion for a woman under 40 is checked carefully.

Blood banks store blood. In recent years, great advances have been made in the preservation of whole blood and plasma for use in transfusions. Whole blood can be safely kept in vacuum bottles under refrigeration (at 40° F) for as long as a month. Each bottle contains 500 cubic centimeters, or about one pint of blood, mixed with sodium citrate, citric acid, and dextrose. The sodium citrate prevents the blood from clotting. When a transfusion is needed in a hospital, blood of the correct type is immediately available in the **blood bank.** Or a friend or relative of the patient may supply the kind of blood he needs, if a direct transfusion appears advisable.

Plasma may be prepared in powdered form. When used in a transfusion, it is dissolved in sterile distilled water. Since the dried plasma and water can be carried without the necessity of refrigeration,

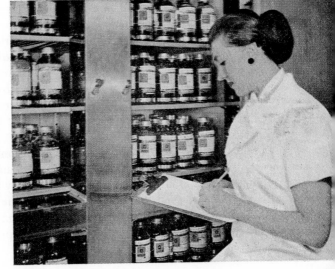

Fig. 38-5. In a blood bank, whole blood is kept in a refrigerator that preserves it for three to four weeks. Each container of blood is very carefully classified and labeled according to type.

it can be administered at once. This was practiced during World War II and saved the lives of many wounded men.

What is anemia? *Anemia* (uh-*nee*-mee-uh) results from a reduction in either the number of red corpuscles or the quantity of hemoglobin, depending on the type of the disease. The many types of anemia may be due to one of the following causes: (1) loss of blood; (2) deficiency of iron in the diet; (3) failure of the blood-forming organs to produce red blood cells (pernicious anemia); (4) destruction of red blood cells by chemical poisons; and (5) loss of red blood cells during infection.

A diet rich in iron is valuable in correcting forms of anemia in which the hemoglobin content of the red blood cells is low. *Pernicious anemia,* in which the number of red blood cells is low because of a defect in the red bone marrow, is a much more serious condition.

Leukemia is a disease of the blood. When the white cell-forming elements of the bone marrow or lymph glands " go wild " and produce white cells in enormous numbers, *leukemia* (lew-*kee*-mee-uh) results. This is a malignant condition. Bone marrow, which normally produces both red and white blood cells, becomes so crowded with white cells that the red corpuscle-forming elements are literally crowded out. The white-corpuscle count rises rapidly as the red-cell count decreases. The liver enlarges as it filters out white blood cells in an effort to correct the condition. Leukemia is of several types: it may be chronic, with alternate periods of illness and relief; or it may be acute, resulting in death in a fairly short time.

The heart. The *heart* is a cone-shaped muscular organ situated under the breastbone and between the lungs (Fig. 38-6). It is enclosed in a sac called the *pericardium* (pair-ih-*kar*-dee-um).

It usually lies a little left of the mid-line of the chest cavity with its point extending downward and to the left between the fifth and sixth ribs. Since the beat is strongest near the tip, many people have the mistaken idea that the entire heart is on the left side.

The heart is composed of two sides, right and left. The two halves are entirely separated by a wall called the **septum.** Each half is composed of two chambers, a relatively thin-walled **auricle,** and a thick, muscular **ventricle.** The auricles act as reservoirs for the blood entering the heart. Both auricles contract at the same time, filling the ventricles rapidly. Next, the thick muscular walls of the ventricles contract, forcing the blood out through the great arteries.

Flow of blood from the ventricles under pressure and maintenance of pressure in the arteries between beats require two sets of one-way heart valves. The valves between the auricles and ventricles (**a-v** or **auricular-ventricular valves**) are flap-like structures which are anchored to the floor of the ventricles by tendons (Fig. 38-7, page 486). When the auricles contract, blood passes through these valves freely into the ventricles. However, the valves cannot be opened from the lower side because of the tendons which anchor them. Thus blood is unable to flow backward into the auricles during contraction of the ventricles. Other valves (**s-l** or **semilunar valves**) are located at the openings of the arteries. These cuplike valves are opened by the force of blood passing from the ventricles into the arteries, and they prevent blood from returning to the ventricles.

Circulation of blood through the heart. Blood first enters the right auricle of the heart by way of the **superior** and **inferior venae cavae** (*vee*-nee *kay*-vee). The superior vena cava carries blood from the head and upper parts of the body. The

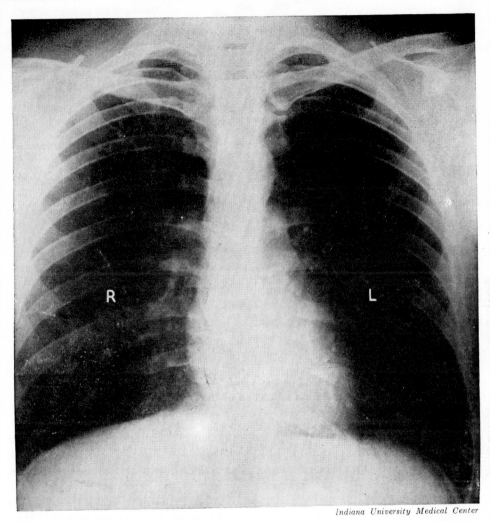

Indiana University Medical Center

Fig. 38-6. The X-ray photograph above shows a normal heart and lungs as seen from the front. Notice that the heart points toward the patient's left side. The curved area below the heart is the diaphragm.

inferior vena cava returns blood from the lower body regions. From the right auricle, blood then passes through the right auricular-ventricular valve into the right ventricle. When the right ventricle contracts, blood is forced through a set of semilunar valves into the **pulmonary artery,** which carries the blood to the lungs. After the blood has passed through the lungs, it is returned to the heart through the right and left **pulmonary veins.** These vessels open into the left auricle, from which the blood passes through the left auricular-ventricular valve into the left ventricle. From here, blood passes out the **aorta** (the largest artery of the body) and is distributed to all parts of the body.

Although the heart is an organ filled with blood, the muscle layers are too thick to benefit from it. The cells receive special nourishment through arteries of the heart or **coronary arteries.** There is an enlargement of the aorta as

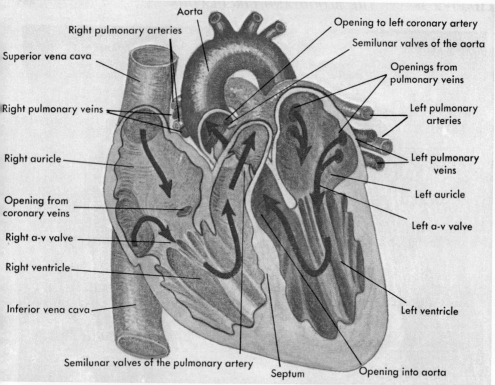

Fig. 38-7. Notice the locations of the valves in relation to the heart chambers and blood vessels. The arrows indicate direction of the flow of blood.

it leaves the heart. This is called the **aortic sinus.** From the aortic sinus, two arteries (*right* and *left coronary*) branch off. These arteries curve downward around each side of the heart, sending off smaller vessels which penetrate the heart muscle.

Heart action. A complete cycle of heart activity, or beat, consists of two phases. During one part of the cycle, or **systole** (*sis*-toh-lee), the ventricles contract and force blood into the arteries. During the other part, or **diastole** (dy-*as*-toh-lee), the ventricles relax and receive blood from the auricles.

The sounds you hear in a stethoscope when you listen to a normal heart sound like the syllables " lub " and " dup " repeated over and over in perfect rhythm. The " lub " is the sound of the contraction of the muscles of the ventricles and

the closing of the auricular-ventricular valves. The " dup " is the closing of the semilunar valves at the base of the arteries.

At rest, the heart of an average man beats about 70 times per minute. During strenuous work or exercise the heart rate may be as high as 180 beats per minute.

Activity speeds up heart action. With the body at rest, the heart pumps about 10½ pints of blood per minute. If your body contains 12 pints of blood, it would make a complete circulation through the body in slightly over a minute, at this rate of heart action. However, mild exercise, such as walking, speeds the heart output to about 20 pints per minute and strenuous exercise may increase it to as much as 42 pints per minute. If you were to use a hand pump to move blood, you could not possibly keep up with a heart under exertion. This will give you some idea of the efficiency of this organ which weighs only a quarter of a pound and works every day and night of your life.

The blood vessels. Blood moves in a system of tubes of varying sizes (Fig. 38-8, page 488) that are classified as: (1) **arteries** and **arterioles,** which are vessels carrying blood *away* from the heart; (2) **capillaries,** which are very small thin-walled vessels; and (3) **veins** and **venules** (*ven*-yooles), which are vessels carrying blood back *toward* the heart.

The aorta branches into several large arteries. These arteries branch and become arterioles. As the arterioles branch, they soon become capillaries, which are the smallest vessels in the body. After passing through a tissue or organ, the capillaries come together to form venules. As the venules join they become veins, which take the blood toward the inferior or superior vena cava and into the right auricle of the heart.

Arteries have elastic, muscular walls and smooth linings. *Arteries* must be elastic to expand and absorb part of the pressure resulting from contraction of the ventricles. This expansion can be felt in the wrist and in other parts of the body where arteries are near the surface. It is known as the **pulse.** The muscles of the artery walls are controlled by nerves. When these muscles contract, they reduce the size of the artery and raise the blood pressure.

Blood pressure in the arteries. Blood leaves the heart ventricles under terrific pressure. Pressure in the aorta leading from the left ventricle to the body is greater than that in the pulmonary artery pumped by the smaller right ventricle. If the aorta were cut, blood would spurt out in a stream six feet or more.

With each contraction of the ventricles, blood surges through the arteries with enough force to bulge their elastic walls. At this point, arterial blood pressure is greatest. We refer to this as **systolic** (sis-*tol*-ik) **pressure.** The recoil of the artery wall maintains part of this pressure while the ventricles are at rest. This is the time of lowest pressure in the arteries, or **diastolic** (dy-as-*tol*-ik) **pressure.** When you take a pulse at the wrist or temple, you feel the bulge in an artery wall caused by systolic pressure. The pulse taken at any part of the body has the same rhythm as do the heart beats.

How a doctor measures blood pressure. A doctor uses a simple device consisting of an air bag, a small pump, and a mercury gauge attached to the bag. He wraps the bag around your arm just above the elbow. Then he lays his stethoscope against the bend of your elbow and inflates the bag until he collapses the artery in your arm. While releasing air from the bag, he listens for the return of a pulse in the artery. At this point, he reads his gauge and records the *systolic* blood pressure.

The doctor continues releasing air from the bag until he hears a sudden change in the tone of the pulse or until the sound disappears completely. At this point the heart is at rest. This is the *diastolic* blood pressure. The blood pressure is referred to as a fraction. The upper figure, usually between 110 and 140, is systolic pressure. The lower figure, or diastolic pressure, is usually between 70 and 90.

What are capillaries? As arterioles penetrate the tissues, they branch into *capillaries* (Fig. 38-8). Capillaries differ from arterioles in that their walls are only one cell layer thick. Capillaries are only slightly greater in diameter than the red blood cells. Red corpuscles must pass through them in single file and may even be pressed out of shape by the capillary walls. The size of the capillary is controlled by nerves and chemicals.

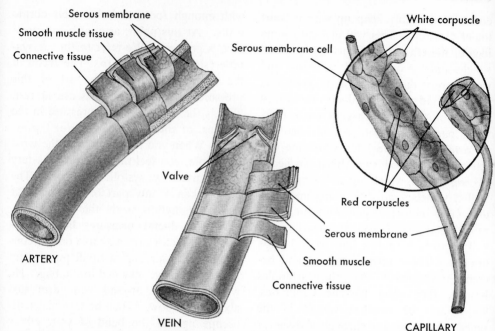

Fig. 38-8. Notice the difference in structure of the three types of blood vessels. In the drawing of the capillary the white corpuscle is squeezing through the wall between cells in order to pass into the tissue spaces.

Various chemical substances, including *histamines* (*his*-tuh-meens), cause the capillaries to enlarge, or dilate. Do you see what this would do to blood pressure?

Dissolved foods, waste products, and gases pass freely through the thin walls of capillaries, in and out of the tissue spaces. Tiny openings in the walls are penetrated by white corpuscles as they leave the blood stream and enter the tissue spaces. Also in the capillaries, part of the plasma diffuses from the blood and becomes *tissue fluid*. Thus, all the vital relationships between the blood and the tissues occur in the capillaries and not in arteries and veins.

On leaving an organ, capillaries unite to form veins. *Veins* carry dark-red blood; that is, blood lacking oxygen. In the skin the veins have a bluish color due to the fact that the skin contains a yellow pigment which changes the appearance of the dark-red blood.

The walls of veins are thinner and less firm than those of arteries, and their internal diameter is proportionally larger.

Many of the larger veins are provided with cuplike **valves** which prevent the backward flow of blood. Veins are often close to the surface, as on the back of the hand, and show the dark color of the blood they carry.

Veins have no pulse wave and the blood pressure within them is much lower than that of arteries. Blood pressure resulting from heart action is almost completely lost as blood passes through capillaries. Blood from the head may return to the heart with the aid of gravity, but in the body regions below the level of the heart other factors are required. Venous flow from these regions is aided by the working muscles, the vacuum created in the chest during inspiration, and, to a small extent, by a sucking action caused by contractions of the heart.

Circulations in the body. A four-chambered heart, such as the human heart, is really a double pump in which the two sides work in unison. Each side pumps blood through a major division of the circulatory system.

The right side of the heart receives dark, deoxygenated blood from the body and pumps it through the arteries of the **pulmonary circulation.** The great pulmonary artery, extending from the right ventricle, sends a branch to each lung. (See the " Trans-Vision " between pages 470 and 471). These arteries, in turn, branch within the lungs, forming a vast number of arterioles which lead to the networks of capillaries surrounding the alveoli. Here, the blood discharges carbon dioxide and water and receives oxygen. Oxygenated blood, now bright scarlet in color, leaves the lungs and returns to the left auricle of the heart through the pulmonary veins.

Oxygenated blood passes through the left heart chambers and out the aorta under great pressure. The blood is now in the **systemic circulation,** which supplies the body tissues. This extensive circulation includes all of the arteries which branch from the aorta, the capillaries which penetrate the body tissues, and the vast number of veins which lead to the venae cavae. The systemic circulation also includes several shorter circulations which supply or drain special organs of the body.

The **coronary circulation,** referred to in the discussion of the heart muscle, supplies the heart itself. This short but vital circulation begins at the aorta and ends where the coronary veins empty into the right auricle. Every beat of the heart depends on the free flow of blood through the coronary vessels.

The **renal circulation** starts where a renal artery branches to each kidney from the aorta. It includes the capillaries which penetrate the kidney tissue and the renal veins, which return blood from the kidneys to the inferior vena cava. Blood on this route nourishes the kidneys and discharges water, salts, and nitrogenous cell wastes. Thus, even though it is low in oxygen content, blood in the renal veins is the purest blood in the body.

The **portal circulation** includes an extensive system of veins which lead from the spleen, stomach, pancreas, small intestine, and colon. The large veins of the portal circulation unite to form the portal vein, which enters the liver. Blood flowing from the digestive organs transports digested food and water. Blood laden with food for the body tissues flows from the liver in the hepatic veins, which, in turn, empty into the inferior vena cava, thus ending this vital branch of the systemic circulation.

Return of tissue fluid to the circulation. The tissue fluid which bathes the cells is collected in tubes and is called **lymph.** These tiny lymph tubes join one another and become larger lymph tubes in the same way that capillaries join to form venules. *Lymph nodes,* which are enlargements in the lymph tubes, are located along the lymph tubes much like beads on a string. In these lymph nodes, the lymph tubes break up into many fine vessels once again. Here certain white corpuscles collect and destroy bacteria which may be in the lymph. The lymph glands, then, act to strain, or to purify, the lymph before returning it to the blood. The greatest concentrations of these lymph nodes are in the neck, the armpit, the bend of the arm, and the groin. Often when there is an infection in the hand or arm, the lymph nodes of the armpit will swell and become painful. The *tonsils* and *adenoids* in the throat are both masses of lymphatic tissue which often become inflamed during childhood and have to be surgically removed.

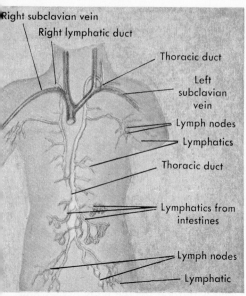

Right subclavian vein
Right lymphatic duct
Thoracic duct
Left subclavian vein
Lymph nodes
Lymphatics
Thoracic duct
Lymphatics from intestines
Lymph nodes
Lymphatic

Fig. 38-9.   The lymphatics course throughout the entire body.   At what point does the lymphatic system join the blood stream?

The lymph of the right side of the head, neck, and right arm enters into a larger vessel named the **right lymphatic duct.** This vessel returns the lymph to the blood by opening into the **right subclavian vein.** The lymphatics from the rest of the body drain into the **thoracic duct,** which, in turn, empties into the **left subclavian vein** (Fig. 38-9).

In the walls of the larger lymph tubes are valves to control the flow of lymph. These valves are similar in structure to those found in the veins. In inactive tissues, lymph flows very slowly or is completely stagnant. When activity increases, the fluid flows faster. The return of lymph to the blood stream is aided by the contracting movements of many of our body muscles.

In Conclusion

The circulatory system is the transportation system of the body and its vehicle is blood. Blood is a fluid tissue, composed of plasma and solid components. Plasma contains water, blood proteins, prothrombin, inorganic substances, digested foods, and cell wastes. The solid parts of the blood are of three types: red corpuscles, white corpuscles, and platelets. Red corpuscles are essential in carrying oxygen to the body cells, and carrying carbon dioxide away as a waste product. White corpuscles aid in fighting disease bacteria. Platelets are an essential factor in the process of blood clotting.

The heart is a pump which forces blood through the arteries to all parts of the body. It consists of two auricles which receive blood from the veins, and two ventricles which force blood through the arteries by contractions. Arteries carry blood from the heart to the tissues, and veins return it. The arterial and venous systems are connected by countless microscopic networks of capillaries.

Once part of the plasma has seeped into the tissue spaces, it is collected as lymph and filtered by the lymph nodes. Then it is returned to the blood stream.

We have seen how food is digested, absorbed, and circulated in the human body. In the next chapter we shall discuss the marvelous mechanism that controls these processes, the human nervous system.

BIOLOGICALLY SPEAKING

anemia	fibrinogen	Rh factor
antigen	hemoglobin	semilunar valves
aorta	hemorrhage	septum
aortic sinus	incompatible	serum albumin
arteriole	leukemia	serum globulin
artery	lymph	shock
auricular-ventricular	nonprotein nitrogen	subclavian vein
valves	oxyhemoglobin	systemic circulation
auricles	oxygenated	systole
blood	pericardium	thrombin
blood bank	plasma	thromboplastin
blood transfusion	platelets	thoracic duct
capillary	portal circulation	tissue fluid
carbhemoglobin	prothrombin	vein
circulation	pulmonary circulation	vena cava
compatible	pulse	ventricles
coronary circulation	red corpuscles	venule
diastole	reduced hemoglobin	white corpuscles
fibrin	renal circulation	

QUESTIONS FOR REVIEW

1. What materials are found in blood plasma?
2. What is the origin of the cells found in blood?
3. What condition in the body does a high white-blood count usually indicate?
4. What are the various steps in the clotting of blood?
5. (a) Why is plasma more quickly and easily used in a transfusion than whole blood? (b) Which method is better and why?
6. Trace the path of a drop of blood from the right auricle to the aorta.
7. At the time the ventricles contract, where is the blood going?
8. Why can you feel the pulse in an artery and not a vein?
9. (a) What is tissue fluid? (b) How does it get back to the blood stream?
10. How does lymph differ from blood?

APPLYING FACTS AND PRINCIPLES

1. What is the basis for the following statement: " A man is only as young as his arteries "?
2. Alcohol has a dilating effect on the skin arteries. What would be its effect, then, on the temperature control of the body?
3. What could be the possible explanations for a blood pressure reading which was consistently low at both systole and diastole? One high at systole but normal at diastole?
4. Why might a second transfusion with Rh-positive blood be fatal in an Rh-negative patient, while the first transfusion with Rh-positive blood caused no complications?
5. How does the manufacture of red blood cells demonstrate conservation of resources by the body?
6. What would be some of the results you would predict if a patient received a blood transfusion of incompatible blood?

CHAPTER 39

The Nervous System

TODAY you can pick up your telephone and talk to 95 per cent of all the people in the world who have telephones. You can phone to or from a ship at sea, or a moving train. You can watch a World Series game in your own living room or hear Big Ben in London strike the hours.

Marvelous as are the telephone, radio, and television, none of them compares with the communication system of your own body. The nervous system receives impressions from your surroundings, stores them in the brain, originates activity, and carries impulses to all parts of the body. It coordinates the activity of several million cells into a single functioning unit.

The nervous system. The nervous system functions as the control center for body activities. Activity of the nervous system involves impulses carried along nerves. It is a two-way communication system. Impulses are sent from the body tissues and organs to nerve centers, and from these centers to the tissues and organs.

Fig. 39-1. The meninges and the three regions of the brain are shown in this lengthwise section.

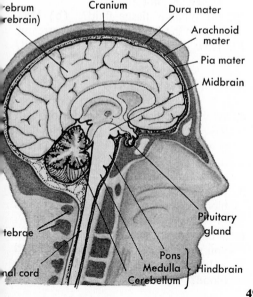

-ebrum rebrain)
Cranium
Dura mater
Arachnoid mater
Pia mater
Midbrain
tebrae
Pituitary gland
nal cord
Pons
Medulla } Hindbrain
Cerebellum

The brain and spinal cord comprise the **central nervous system.** They communicate with all parts of the body by means of the **peripheral** (peh-*rif*-er-ul) **system.** Another division is the **autonomic** (aw-toh-*nom*-ik) **system,** which regulates certain vital functions of the body almost independently of the central nervous system.

The brain and its membranes. The *brain* (Fig. 39-1) is probably the most highly specialized organ of the human body. It weighs about three pounds and fills the cranial cavity. It is composed of soft nervous tissue covered by three membranes, together known as the **meninges** (meh-*nin*-jeez). The inner membrane, or **pia mater** (*pee*-uh *mah*-ter), is richly supplied with blood vessels which carry food and oxygen to the brain cells. It is a delicate membrane which closely adheres to the surface of the brain and into all the grooves, which are called **convolutions.** The middle membrane, or **arachnoid mater,** consists of fibrous and elastic tissue. This membrane does not dip down into the convolutions of the brain but bridges them. The space between these two membranes is filled with a clear liquid, the **cerebrospinal** (sair-uh-broh-*spy*-nul) **fluid.** The outermost layer of

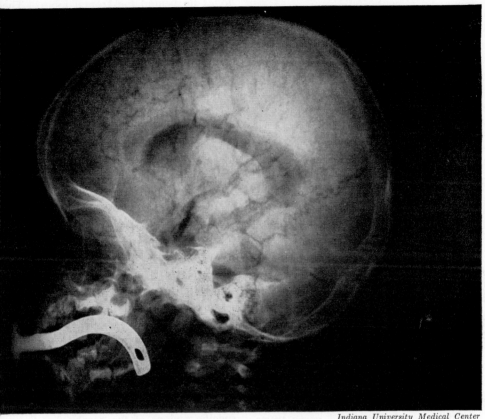

Fig. 39-2. In this " air " X-ray photograph of the brain, the cerebrospinal fluid has been drained through the spine and replaced by air. Since the patient was under anesthetic the white " airway " was placed in the mouth to avoid having the tongue fall back and cut off the air supply (" swallowing the tongue "). The convolutions of the cerebrum and large ventricular cavities are visible only because of the injected air. Notice the zigzag sutures of the cranial bones in the lower back area of the skull.

protective membranes is a thick, strong, fibrous lining, the **dura mater.** This layer serves as a lining for the inside of the cranium as well as a membrane of the brain. The meninges protect the brain from jarring by acting as a cushion. A **concussion** is the result of a violent jar or shock that causes damage in spite of the protective meninges. These three membranes extend down the spinal column to cover and protect the spinal cord.

Cavities of the brain. There are four spaces called **ventricles** within the brain. Two *lateral ventricles* open into the *third ventricle,* which leads to the *fourth ven-*tricle. From the fourth ventricle the cavity is continuous with the *subarachnoid space* and the central canal of the spinal cord. The cavities of the brain and the central canal are lined with ciliated epithelium which keeps the cerebrospinal fluid, with which the cavities are filled, in motion.

The regions of the brain. Each region of the brain is made of several parts. Although each part of the brain has a specific function, it works closely with the others. There are three main regions — the *forebrain,* the *midbrain,* and the *hindbrain* (Fig. 39-1).

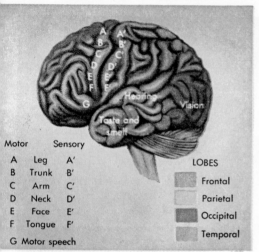

Motor   Sensory

A	Leg	A'
B	Trunk	B'
C	Arm	C'
D	Neck	D'
E	Face	E'
F	Tongue	F'
G	Motor speech	

LOBES

Frontal
Parietal
Occipital
Temporal

Fig. 39-3. These are the control areas of the cerebrum. Notice that some are for the origin of action and some for the termination, or interpretation, of senses.

The cerebrum is the largest of the brain regions. The **cerebrum** composes the **forebrain** and is proportionally larger in man than in any animal. It consists of two halves, or hemispheres, securely joined by tough fibers and nerve tracts. The outer surface, or **cortex,** is deeply folded in irregular wrinkles and furrows, the *convolutions,* which greatly increase the surface area of the cerebrum.

The cerebral cortex is composed of countless numbers of nerve cells not covered by sheaths. We frequently refer to this area as **gray matter** because of the color of these cells. The cerebrum below the cortex is composed of **white matter,** formed by masses of fibers covered by sheaths and extending from the nerve cells of the cortex to other parts of the body.

Deep grooves divide the cerebral hemispheres into lobes. The *frontal lobes* are situated on the front of the hemispheres and extend well back along the top of the cerebrum. These lobes are much more highly developed in man than in animals. The *parietal* (puh-*ry*-eh-tul)

lobes lie behind the frontal lobes. The *temporal lobes* are below the frontal and parietal lobes, along the sides of the cerebral hemisphere. The *occipital* (ok-*sip*-ih-tul) *lobes* occupy the lower back region of the cerebrum (Fig. 39-3).

The functions of the cerebrum. So far as we know, there is no consciousness unless an impulse reaches the cortex of the cerebrum. However, the study of the cerebrum does not tell us how ideas expressing intellectual, moral, or spiritual values originate. Thought is not secreted like bile or hormones; it is not a material substance. We can explain the activity of our body organs in terms of nervous and chemical stimulation and response. But the origin of thought is something quite different. The study of brain cells does not explain how thoughts or emotions originate, or how memory is possible. Neither does it explain how we distinguish right from wrong. Our knowledge of the nervous system is inadequate to explain such experiences.

Different activities are controlled by specific regions of the cerebrum. Some of the areas of the cerebral cortex are **motor areas,** which means that they are centers which control voluntary movement. The motor area of the cerebrum controls the muscles of the legs, trunk, arms, shoulders, neck, face, and tongue, in this order, from the top of the lobes downward. Some of the areas of the cerebral cortex are **sensory areas,** which means that the various senses, such as seeing, hearing, touching, tasting, and smelling, are interpreted here. We interpret what our eyes see in the vision center of the occipital lobes. If these lobes were destroyed, we would not be able to see anything, although our eyes might be perfect. The frontal lobes are centers related to emotion, will power, and self-control. These functions, however, are shared by other areas of the cerebrum.

The things we see and hear and feel are registered as impressions in different areas of the cerebral cortex. These areas are, in turn, connected by a vast number of **association fibers.** Constructive imagination becomes possible as the result of the association of impressions. Your intellectual capacity is aided by the ability of your cerebral cortex to register impressions, the activity of your association fibers, and the sum of your experiences.

The cortex of the brain never loses an impression. Many impressions of past experiences cannot be recalled in consciousness, but are retained in what we call the *unconscious mind.* In other words, these impressions are covered up by more recent or more outstanding impressions which dominate conscious activity. When, however, an individual is hypnotized and skillfully questioned, these impressions may be recalled vividly from the recesses of the mind. Individuals under hypnosis can review the details of childhood experiences just as they occurred. This could never be done in normal conscious activity.

Brain waves. In 1929, Hans Berger, a German doctor, showed that living brains produce electrical impulses in the form of waves. These impulses may be converted into sound waves by vacuum tubes. Research workers discovered that so-called **" brain waves "** in normal people may vary in pattern when the person is undergoing different emotional or intellectual experiences. Nervous disorders like epilepsy, however, produce a special type of pattern. This knowledge of brain waves is used to study the interrelations between the mind and the body.

The electrodes used to detect brain waves may be little metal disks which are attached to the scalp by a special glue. After the test is made, a solvent dissolves the glue, and the disks are thus removed. Waves from definite locations can be made by the proper placement of these electrodes (Fig. 39-4).

The midbrain. The *midbrain* is a very short region of the brain, consisting of nerve fibers which connect the forebrain to the hindbrain. It is often considered a part of the brain stem, along with the pons and the medulla. Some of the fibers of the midbrain connect the cerebrum to the cerebellum, and some connect the cerebrum to the pons and medulla.

Fig. 39-4. By attaching electrodes to the head (*left*), activities of the cerebral cortex can be measured as electrical impulses with an electroencephalograph. The " brain wave " pattern is then recorded on a tape (*right*).

Patzig from Monkmeyer   *Goro from Monkme*

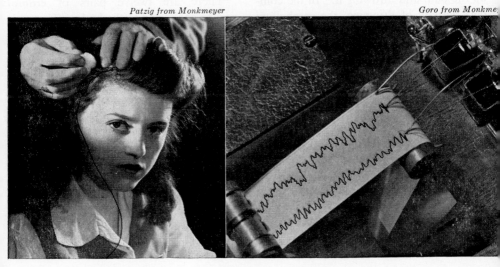

The hindbrain consists of the cerebellum, the pons, and the medulla. The *cerebellum* is a structure that lies below the back of the cerebrum and is part of the *hindbrain*. Like the cerebrum, it is composed of hemispheres but its convolutions are shallower and more regular than those of the cerebrum. The surface of the cerebellum is composed of gray matter. Its inner structure is largely white matter, although it contains some areas of gray matter. Bundles of nerve fibers connect the cerebellum with the rest of the nervous system through the midbrain.

In a sense, the cerebellum acts as an assistant to the cerebrum in controlling muscular activity. Nervous impulses do not originate in it nor can one control its activities. The chief function of the cerebellum is to coordinate the muscular activities of the body. Thus, without the help of the cerebellum, the impulses from the cerebrum would result in disorganized body motions.

For example, you may decide to pick up a ball and throw it. From the motor area in the frontal lobe of the cerebrum, a series of nerve impulses proceeds to the cerebellum. The cerebellum sorts out these impulses. It stimulates just the right muscles required in bending over, picking up the ball, and throwing it. In the complex activity of throwing, the cerebellum coordinates many different movements: those of the fingers in grasping the ball, those of the arms, shoulders, and trunk in throwing it, and those of the legs in helping maintain the general balance of the body.

Other functions of the cerebellum. The cerebellum functions further in strengthening impulses to the muscles. This action is a little like picking up a weak radio or television signal and amplifying it before broadcasting it.

Another function of the cerebellum is maintenance of tone in muscles. The cerebellum cannot originate a muscular contraction, but it can cause the muscles to remain in a state of partial contraction. Otherwise you would collapse. You are not aware of this because the cerebellum operates below the level of consciousness.

The cerebellum functions also in maintaining balance. In this activity, it is assisted by impulses from the eyes and from the organs of equilibrium, or semicircular canals of the inner ears, which you will study in the next chapter. Impulses from both of these organs inform the cerebellum of your position in relation to your surroundings. The cerebellum in turn maintains contraction of the muscles necessary to balance your body. If you close your eyes, the task is more difficult and you may sway or lose your balance.

The brain stem. Nerve fibers from the cerebrum and cerebellum enter the *brain stem*, an enlargement at the base of the brain. The *midbrain* is usually considered to be the upper portion of the brain stem. The lowest portion of the stem, the *medulla oblongata,* is located at the base of the skull and protrudes from the skull slightly where it joins the spinal cord. Another part of the brain stem is the *pons* (*pohnz*), whose function is too specialized for our study here.

There are twelve pairs of *cranial nerves* connected to the brain. These act as direct connections with certain important organs of the body. One pair, for example, called the *optic nerves*, connects the eyes with the brain. Another cranial nerve, the *vagus* (*vay*-gus), connects the brain with the lungs, heart, stomach, and other abdominal organs.

The medulla oblongata controls the activity of the internal organs. It regulates the rate of respiration and heart action, muscular action of the walls of the digestive organs, secretion in the glands, and other automatic activities.

The spinal cord. The *spinal cord* extends from the medulla oblongata through the protective bony arch of each vertebra, almost the length of the spine. Its outer region is white matter, made up of great numbers of nerve fibers covered by sheaths. Nerve cells, composing the gray matter, lie inside the white matter in a form similar to the shape of a butterfly with its wings spread (Fig. 39-5). The pointed tips of the wings of gray matter are called *horns*. Two of them, the **posterior horns**, point toward the back of the cord while a pair of **anterior horns** point toward the front.

Thirty-one pairs of **spinal nerves** branch off the spinal cord. These nerves are large trunks, similar to a telephone cable in that each contains many nerve fibers. Some of the fibers carry impulses into the spinal cord, while others lead impulses away from it. Nerve impulses travel along these fibers in only one direction. Thus fibers bringing impulses into the cord cannot carry outgoing impulses. Each spinal nerve divides just outside the cord. The fibers which carry impulses from the body into the spinal cord branch to the posterior horns of the gray matter. This branch of each spinal nerve has a swelling, or **ganglion** (*gang*-glee-un), near its point of entry to the cord. The other branch at the junction leads from the anterior horns of gray matter. These fibers carry impulses from the spinal cord to the body.

If the spinal cord were cut, all parts of the body controlled by nerves below the point of severance would be totally paralyzed. Such an injury might be compared to cutting the main cable to a telephone exchange. Anesthetics are now being used on the cord to deaden temporarily entire sections of the body by chemically blocking nervous impulses. Under these conditions, there is no effect on the brain or consciousness. In addi-

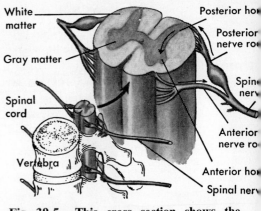

Fig. 39-5. **This cross section shows the structures of the spinal cord. Notice that, unlike in the brain, the cortex is the white matter. What do the small arrows indicate?**

tion to linking the brain and the body, the spinal cord is the center of reflex actions, a type of nervous activity which will be discussed later.

The nerves. If all the other tissues of the body could be dissolved, the outline of the body would be preserved by the network of nerves which would remain (Fig. 39-7, page 499).

Nerve cells are called **neurons** (*new*-ronz). Each has a rounded, star-shaped or irregular **cell body**, containing a nucleus and cytoplasm, from which thread-like *processes* extend (Fig. 39-8, page 500). The branching treelike processes which carry impulses *toward* the cell body are called **dendrites** (*den*-drytes). The number of dendrites entering a cell body may range from one to 200. Impulses travel *from* the nerve cell body along a single process enclosed in fatty sheaths. We call these outgoing processes **axons** (*aks*-onz). Dendrites and axons branch at their tips in tiny brushlike structures.

The bodies of nerve cells are most often found only in the gray matter of the brain and spinal cord, in scattered masses called **plexuses** (*plek*-suh-seez), and in the ganglia of the spinal nerves. Sheathed fibers penetrate the body tissues and also form the white matter of the brain and spinal cord.

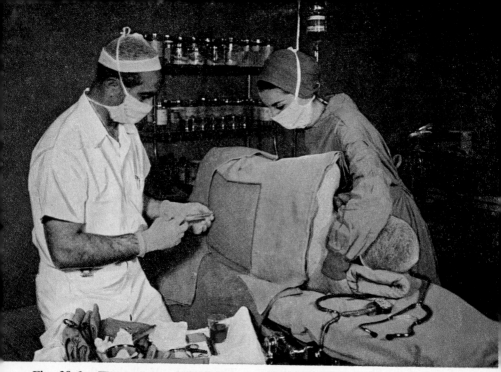

Fig. 39-6. The patient is being given a spinal anesthetic to deaden the lower part of the body. He will have both sensation and motor control above the area of the injection, and will even be able to watch the operation.

Sensory and motor neurons. *Sensory neurons* carry impulses from the skin and other sense organs to the spinal cord and brain. These nerves have dendrites with numerous branched endings. They may be short or very long, depending on their location. For example, an impulse from a sensory nerve in a toe travels along a dendrite from the toe to a nerve body in a ganglion just outside the spinal cord. It enters the cord through the axon of the same nerve cell.

Motor neurons carry impulses from the spinal cord and brain to muscles and glands. When you wiggle a toe, impulses travel from the brain through the spinal cord and along an axon leading from the spinal cord to the toe muscles. The endings of sensory and motor nerves in the spinal cord and brain mingle with many **central,** or *association,* **neurons** that have short processes. The processes of one neuron never touch those of another neu-

ron. The space between endings of nerve-cell processes is called a **synapse** (*sih*-naps). Impulses must pass over these synapses as they travel from one neuron to another. Furthermore, an impulse never travels from one motor neuron to another. It is received by the dendrite of a sensory or a central neuron. Nor do impulses travel from one sensory neuron to another.

Mixed, motor, and sensory nerves. A **nerve** is a cordlike structure which contains bundles of nerve fibers. A **nerve fiber** is a nerve-cell process, either an axon or a dendrite. In the peripheral nervous system, any nerve which is composed *only* of axons is a **motor nerve.** Any nerve composed *only* of dendrites is a **sensory nerve.** Some nerves contain both axons and dendrites. These are **mixed nerves,** as they carry impulses either *to* the central nervous system or *away* from it.

498

CENTRAL NERVOUS SYSTEM AND MAJOR NERVE TRUNKS

1. Cerebrum
2. Cerebellum
3. Spinal cord
4. Cervical plexus
5. Brachial plexus
6. Sympathetic ganglionic chain
7. Intercostal nerves
8. Lumbar plexus
9. Sacral plexus
10. Sciatic nerve

This diagram shows the central nervous system and the major nerve trunks of the peripheral nervous system. For clarity, only a few of the branches from the major nerve trunks and nerves are shown. Actually, if all the nerve branches were shown, they would solidly fill this outline of the body, so that if a pin were put anywhere on this outline it would strike a nerve. The central nervous system and posterior peripheral nerves are drawn in gray, the anterior ones in brown.

Fig. 39-7, page 499

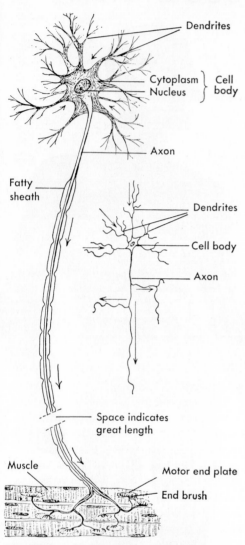

Fig. 39-8.   The drawing on the left is of a typical motor neuron.   That on the right is of a typical neuron in the brain.

Nerve impulses.   A *nerve impulse* is known to be an electrochemical impulse which brings about a change in the nerve processes.   It is not a flow of electricity, for nerve impulses are much slower.   A nerve impulse travels at a rate of about 272 miles per hour, while electricity travels at a rate of 186,000 miles per second.   Also, when a nerve impulse passes along a nerve, carbon dioxide is liberated, which

indicates that a chemical reaction is involved.

For a long time scientists were in doubt as to how a nerve impulse causes a muscle to contract.   Now we know that the stimulation is indirect.   An impulse, traveling along the axon of a motor nerve, ends at the **motor end plates** at the tips of the brushlike structures.   Here the impulse causes the release of a minute amount of a chemical called **acetylcholine** (uh-seet-il-*koh*-leen).   This substance transmits the impulse to muscle fibers, which begin a series of chemical reactions resulting in contraction.   Following a brief period of contraction, the nerve releases another substance, **cholinesterase** (koh-lih-*nes*-ter-ase), which neutralizes acetylcholine and causes the muscle fibers to relax, all in 0.1 second or less.

Nervous reactions.   Nervous reactions vary greatly in form and complexity. The simplest of these is the **reflex action** (Fig. 39-9).   It is an automatic reaction involving the spinal cord or the brain.

The knee jerk is an excellent example of a simple reflex action.   If you allow your leg to swing freely and strike the area just below the kneecap with a narrow object, the foot jerks upward.   This reaction is entirely automatic.   Striking the knee stimulates a sensory nerve from the lower leg.   An impulse travels along the dendrite to the spinal cord.   Here the impulse is sent to a central neuron.   This neuron, in turn, stimulates the dendrite endings of the motor nerve to the leg muscles, causing a jerk.   The entire reflex takes only a split second.

When you touch a hot object, you experience a similar reflex.   Your hand jerks away almost instantly.   After the reflex is completed, the impulse reaches the brain and registers pain.   However, if the muscle response had been delayed until the pain impulse had reached the

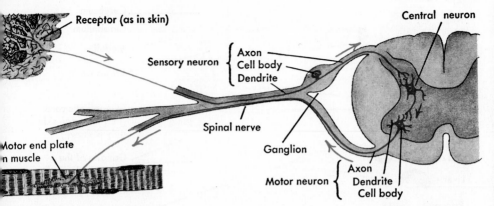

Receptor (as in skin)

Central neuron

Sensory neuron { Axon
                 Cell body
                 Dendrite

Spinal nerve

Motor end plate in muscle

Ganglion

Motor neuron { Axon
               Dendrite
               Cell body

Fig. 39-9.   **Trace the path of this impulse from the stimulus to the response.   Why are reflex actions said to be automatic?**

brain and a motor impulse traveled down the spinal cord from the cerebral motor area, the burn injury would have been much greater. Other reflex actions include: sneezing, coughing, blinking the eyes, laughing when tickled, and jumping when frightened.

Voluntary activities involve the cortex of the cerebrum.   When you learn to ride a bicycle, every movement is controlled by the cerebral cortex. You are aware of pedaling, guiding, and balancing. This is quite a muscular undertaking, and you may fall a few times during the learning period. As you practice riding, the pathways along the nerve fibers become well established. Furthermore, the cerebellum becomes more skilled in coordinating the muscular activity involved. After a time, riding your bicycle becomes a habit.

The motor area of the cerebrum and the cerebellum, after training, controls the impulses without any help from other areas of the brain cortex. You are no longer conscious of riding and can concentrate on other things. The same thing applies to playing a piano, after you have learned the fingering technique, the position of the keys, and the notes on the printed music.

Another division of the nervous system. The *autonomic nervous system* is entirely involuntary and automatic.   It is partly independent of the rest of the nervous system.   The autonomic system is, in turn, composed of two parts: (1) the *sympathetic system;* and (2) the *parasympathetic system* (Fig. 39-10, page 502).

The *sympathetic system* includes two rows of nerve tissue, or *cords,* which lie on either side of the spinal column.   Each cord has *ganglia,* which contain the bodies of nerve cells.   The largest of the sympathetic ganglia is the **solar plexus,** located just below the diaphragm.   Another is near the heart, a third is in the lower part of the abdomen, and a fourth is in the neck.   Fibers from the sympathetic nerve cords enter the spinal cord and connect with it and the brain, as well as with each other.   The sympathetic nervous system helps to regulate heart action, the secretion of ductless glands, blood supply in the arteries, the action of smooth muscles of the stomach and intestine, and the activity of other internal organs.

The *parasympathetic system* opposes the sympathetic system and thus maintains a system of check and balance.   The principal nerve of the parasympathetic

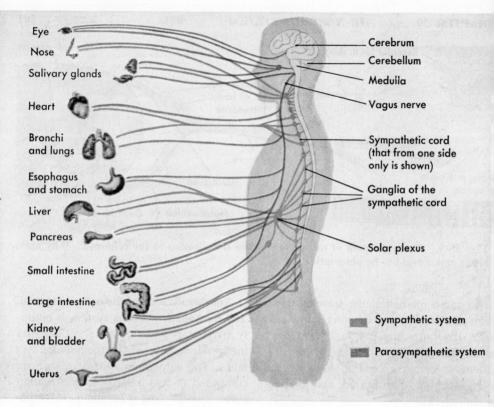

Fig. 39-10. The autonomic nervous system regulates the internal organs of the body. What are the functions of its two divisions?

Labels (top to bottom, left):
Eye
Nose
Salivary glands
Heart
Bronchi and lungs
Esophagus and stomach
Liver
Pancreas
Small intestine
Large intestine
Kidney and bladder
Uterus

Labels (right):
Cerebrum
Cerebellum
Medulla
Vagus nerve
Sympathetic cord (that from one side only is shown)
Ganglia of the sympathetic cord
Solar plexus

Sympathetic system
Parasympathetic system

system is the *vagus nerve,* one of the cranial nerves which extends from the medulla oblongata, through the neck, to the chest and abdomen. The check-and-balance system is illustrated by the fact that the sympathetic system speeds up heart action, while the vagus nerve slows it down.

What is tension fatigue? *Tension fatigue,* often called nervous fatigue, is actually a state of muscular tension. It is produced by mental activity continued to the point of boredom. A person with tension fatigue is literally tense and tired. He cannot relax and sleep like a person who is physically fatigued. The obvious remedy for tension fatigue is change in mental activity or the substitution of some enjoyable physical activity.

Mental fatigue. *Mental fatigue* is related to tension fatigue, but the result is not usually so long-lasting. Sometimes people feel it when they have been concentrating on some kind of mental activity for too long. Mental fatigue, like tension fatigue, can be relieved by changing activity.

The human body needs sleep. The human body cannot endure continued activity without regular periods of complete rest. During sleep the brain and nerve cells, aside from those which continue impulses to the vital organs, slow their activity. Heart action slows, blood pressure decreases, secretion is greatly reduced, and tissue oxidation drops to a low rate. During this period, waste products are removed and body tissues undergo growth and repair without competition with rapid body activity. The amount of sleep a person needs varies with the individual.

In Conclusion

The brain and spinal cord compose the central nervous system. They communicate with all parts of the body by nerves. The brain consists of the forebrain, midbrain, and hindbrain.

The cerebrum is of great importance in all conscious activities. It contains both sensory and motor areas. Impulses from the cerebral motor area pass through the cerebellum, where coordination of impulses takes place. The medulla oblongata controls the activity of internal organs and is the center of control of respiration.

Remarkable nerve endings which are specialized to act as receptors of sense organs are the subject of the next chapter. We shall see how some are organized so as to be sensitive to light, others to sound, some to pressure, and still others to chemicals. Without sense organs, our life would be quite dull.

BIOLOGICALLY SPEAKING

acetylcholine
arachnoid mater
association fibers
autonomic nervous
    system
axon
brain stem
brain wave
central nervous system
central neurons
cerebellum
cerebral cortex
cerebrospinal fluid
cerebrum
cholinesterase
concussion
convolutions
cranial nerves
dendrite
dura mater

forebrain
ganglion
gray matter
hindbrain
medulla oblongata
meninges
mental fatigue
midbrain
mixed nerve
motor end plate
motor nerve
motor neuron
nerve
nerve cell body
nerve fiber
nerve impulse
neuron
optic nerve
parasympathetic nervous
    system

peripheral nervous
    system
pia mater
plexus
pons
reflex action
sensory nerve
sensory neuron
solar plexus
spinal cord
spinal nerve
sympathetic nervous
    system
synapse
tension fatigue
vagus nerve
ventricles of brain
white matter

QUESTIONS FOR REVIEW

1. Name the parts of the human nervous system and state the function of each.
2. Name the parts of the brain and state the functions of each.
3. Describe the meninges of the brain and state the function of each.

4. (a) What is cerebrospinal fluid? (b) What are its functions?
5. Of what advantage are the convolutions of the brain?
6. Why is it harder to maintain balance when you close your eyes?
7. How can concussion cause blindness?

8. What advantage would a spinal block have over other forms of anesthesia in which complete unconsciousness results?

9. Why are brain waves so regular during the time of sleep?

10. In what way is the autonomic nervous system really two systems?

11. Why are peripheral nerves containing only axons considered to be motor nerves?

12. Why does the body need sleep?

APPLYING FACTS AND PRINCIPLES

1. Why is the naming system of the lobes of the brain logical?

2. Compare the nervous system to a telephone exchange by tracing an incoming call, a connection by an operator, and a conversation with your party in both systems.

3. What is intelligence?

4. How can the brain store impressions below the level of consciousness?

5. Explain the value of hypnosis in determining some kinds of mental illnesses.

6. What reasons can you give to explain the fact that the sympathetic nervous system is sometimes called " the system for fight or flight "?

7. Explain the activity that occurs after a chicken has its head cut off.

8. How can brain waves be accounted for by comparing the nervous system to an electronic calculating machine?

CHAPTER 40

The Sense Organs

L IFE without the sense organs would be even more meaningless than that of a prisoner condemned to live and die in solitude in a dungeon. The nervous system would control the basic life processes, but for what purpose? Most of our pleasure in living results from being able to see, hear, feel, smell, and taste the things around us. Such sensations are registered in the brain and are given meaning in the thought areas of our cerebral cortex. They provide the storehouse of impressions we associate with intelligent behavior. Indeed, there is some doubt whether the nervous system could operate without the sense organs.

Irritability is a fundamental process of living protoplasm. It is a quality possessed by every living organism. It may be expressed in the slow reaction of a stem to light or a root to water. In our study of plants, simple animals, and more complex animals, we have seen an increase in the efficiency of this life activity, irritability. In the higher animals certain cells are highly specialized by being sensitive to certain stimuli.

The sensations of the skin. The skin has five different types of nerve endings, each associated with a different sensation. Since the nerve endings in the skin are terminal branches of dendrites, they are called **receptors.** Some receptors are many-celled, some consist of only one specialized cell, and some are the bare nerve endings themselves. Each receptor is suited to receive only one type of stimulus and to start impulses to the central nervous system. The skin has five different types of receptors. Certain of these respond to *touch,* while others receive stimuli of *pressure, pain, heat,* or *cold* (Fig. 40-1).

Normally, no one receptor reacts to more than one stimulus, and thus the five sensations of the skin are distinct and different. The pain receptor, for example, is a bare dendrite. If the stimulus is strong enough, these pain receptors will react to mechanical, thermal, electrical, or chemical stimuli. The sensation of pain is a protective device used to signal a threat of injury to the body. Pain receptors are distributed through the skin.

The sensory nerves of the skin are distributed unevenly over the skin area in spots and lie at different depths in the skin. For instance, if you move the point of your pencil over your skin very lightly, you stimulate only the nerves of *touch.* These nerve endings are close to the surface of the skin in the region of the hair sockets. The finger tips, the forehead, and the tip of the tongue contain abundant nerve endings which respond to touch.

Nerve endings which respond to *pressure* lie deeper in the skin. If you press the pencil point against the skin, you feel pressure in addition to touch. Since the nerves are deeper, a pressure stimulus must be stronger than a touch stimulus. We usually do not distinguish touch and

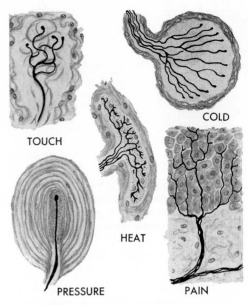

Fig. 40-1. The five types of receptors shown here are found in the skin. The nerve fibers are in solid black and the accompanying structures are in gray.

pressure. However, the fact that you can distinguish the mere touching of an object from a firm grip on it indicates that separate nerves are involved.

Heat and *cold* stimulate separate nerve endings, which is an interesting protective device of the body. Actually, cold is not an active condition. Cold results from a reduction in heat energy. If temperature stimulated a single nerve, impulses would be strong in the presence of great heat and would become weaker as heat decreased. There would be no impulses in greatly reduced heat (intense cold). However, since some nerves are stimulated by heat and others by the absence of it, we are constantly aware of both conditions.

Taste results from the chemical stimulation of certain nerve endings. Since nearly all animals prefer some food substances to others, we must assume that they can distinguish different chemical substances. The sense of taste in man is

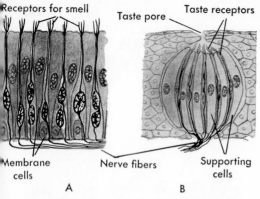

Receptors for smell

Taste pore

Taste receptors

Membrane cells

Nerve fibers

Supporting cells

A   B

Fig. 40-2. Diagram *A* shows how a section of the membrane of the nose would appear under a microscope. Diagram *B* shows a section of the tongue through a taste bud.

centered in the **taste buds** of the tongue. These flask-shaped structures, containing groups of nerve endings, lie in the front area of the tongue, along its sides, and near the back. Foods, mixed with saliva and mucus, enter the pores of the taste buds and stimulate the hairlike nerve endings (Fig. 40-2).

Our sense of taste is poorly developed. We recognize only four common flavors: *sour, sweet, salty,* and *bitter.* A fifth, *alkaline,* is difficult to describe but is not unlike salty. Taste buds are distributed unevenly over the surface of the tongue. Those sensitive to sweet flavors are at the tip of the tongue. Doesn't candy taste sweeter when you lick it than when you

Fig. 40-3. This drawing shows the surface of the inner wall of the nose. What is the function of the Eustachian tube?

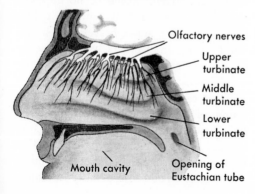

Olfactory nerves

Upper turbinate

Middle turbinate

Lower turbinate

Mouth cavity

Opening of Eustachian tube

chew it far back in the mouth? The ti of the tongue is also sensitive to salt flavors. You taste sour substance along the sides of the tongue. Bitte flavors are detected on the back of th tongue, which explains why a bitter sub stance does not taste bitter at first. If substance is both bitter and sweet, yo sense the sweetness first, then the bitter ness. Substances such as pepper an some other spices have no distinct flavor but irritate the entire tongue and produc a burning sensation.

Much of the sensation we call " taste is really smell. When you chew foods vapors enter the inner openings of th nose and reach nerve endings of smell If the external nasal openings are plugge up, many substances lack the flavor w associate with them. Under such condi tions, onions and apples have an almos identical sweet flavor. You have prob ably noticed the loss of what you though was taste sensation when you had a hea cold and temporarily lost your sense o smell.

Smell also results from the chemica stimulation of nerves. Odors are air borne. Some are strong and some are weak, but they must all make contact with our olfactory nerve endings before we can smell them (Fig. 40-2).

Our sense of smell is poorly developed compared to many animals. The nasal passages are arranged in three tiers, or layers, of cavities, separated by bony lay ers called **turbinates** (*tur*-bih-nates). The upper turbinate (Fig. 40-3) con tains branched endings of the **olfactory nerve.** Stimulation of these endings by odors results in the sensation of smelling.

Smell involves several interesting fac tors. When you breathe cold air into the nostrils, air warmed in its passage over the lower and middle turbinates is forced into the area above the upper turbinate, where the olfactory receptors are located.

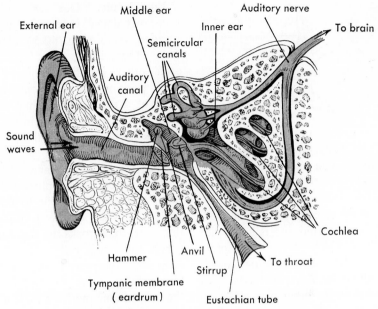

External ear
Middle ear
Auditory nerve
Inner ear
Semicircular canals
Auditory canal
To brain
Sound waves
Cochlea
Hammer
Anvil
Stirrup
To throat
Tympanic membrane (eardrum)
Eustachian tube

Fig. 40-4.   The structure of the human ear.

This accounts for the fact that your ability to smell increases when you sniff several times in succession. Furthermore, receptors which are exposed to a particular odor over a long period of time become deadened to the odor, although they are receptive to other odors. Nurses are not usually aware of the odor of iodoform in a hospital, but a visitor notices it.

Hearing. Hearing brings us into contact with our surroundings through the medium of sound waves carried in air. By means of this well-developed sense, we become aware of a large portion of our environment. Furthermore, it is through hearing that we communicate with each other.

The structure of the human ear. Our ears, and those of other mammals, are wonderfully complex organs. The external ear opens into an auditory canal embedded in the skull (Fig. 40-4). The canal is closed at its inner end by the **tympanic** (tim-*pan*-ik) **membrane,** or *eardrum,* which separates it from the middle ear.

The middle ear connects with the throat through the **Eustachian** (you-*stay*-kee-un) **tube.** This connection equalizes the pressure in the middle ear with that of the atmosphere.

When the connection between the middle ear and throat is blocked by a cold that involves the Eustachian tube, the pressures outside and inside do not equalize. For this reason, divers and fliers do not work when they have a cold. In the case of the diver, the outside pressure increases as he dives. But with a blocked Eustachian tube, the middle-ear pressure would remain the same and the difference might cause damage to the eardrum. The flier's situation would of course be in reverse.

Three tiny bones, the **hammer, anvil,** and **stirrup,** form a chain across the middle ear. They extend from the inner face of the eardrum to a similar membrane that covers the *oval window,* which is the opening to the inner ear.

The inner ear is composed of two general parts. The **cochlea** (*kok*-lee-uh) is

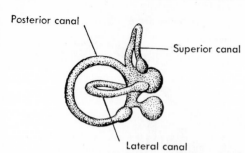

Posterior canal

Superior canal

Lateral canal

Fig. 40-5. The semicircular canals of the inner ear function in maintaining balance. They are not concerned with hearing.

a spiral passage resembling a snail shell. It is filled with a liquid and is lined with nerve endings which receive the sound impressions. The *semicircular canals* consist of three loop-shaped tubes, each at right angles to the other two.

How we hear. If sound were visible, we would see irregular waves with peaks and valleys traveling through the air. The higher the pitch of a sound, the greater its wave frequency. This means that high notes have more peaks and valleys during a given unit of time, such as a second, than low notes. When sound waves reach the ear, they are gathered by the external ear and directed through the canal to the eardrum. Here they cause the eardrum to vibrate in time with the peaks and valleys of the sound wave. As the drum vibrates, the hammer, anvil, and stirrup bones of the middle ear are vibrated. The vibration is transmitted to the membrane of the inner ear and causes the fluid in the cochlea to vibrate. Vibration of the fluid, in turn, irritates the nerve endings in the cochlea. Impulses travel through the *auditory nerve* to the cerebrum, where the translation of sound waves occurs. If the auditory nerves are destroyed, or if the auditory region of the cerebrum ceases to function, a person cannot hear, even though his ear mechanisms receive vibrations normally.

Equilibrium. Our sense of *equilibrium,* or balance, is centered in the *semicircular canals* (Fig. 40-5) of the inner ears. These canals lie at right angles to each other in three different planes. Their position has been compared to the parts of a chair. One canal lies in the plane of the seat, another in the plane of the back, and a third in the plane of the arms.

The semicircular canals contain a great number of receptors called **hair cells,** and a fluid similar to that of the cochlea. When the head changes position, the fluid rocks in the canals and moves these hair cells. Impulses travel from these receptors through a branch of the auditory nerve to the medulla and the cerebellum, and from there to the cerebrum. We then become aware of the position of the head. Since the canals lie in three planes, any change in position of the head moves the fluid in one or more of them. If you spin around rapidly, the fluid is forced to one end and strong impulses travel to the brain. When you stop spinning, the fluid rushes back the other way, giving you the sensation of twirling in the opposite direction, so that you feel dizzy. Regular rhythmic motions produce unpleasant sensations that involve the whole body. These sensations are what we call *motion sickness.* Disease of the semicircular canals results in temporary or permanent dizziness and loss of equilibrium.

Care of the ears. Fortunately, the most important parts of our ears are situated within the protection of the skull. However, you can injure the eardrum by probing the ear canal with hard, sharp instruments. Excess wax can accumulate in the eardrums, but it should not be removed by probing. Only a physician should attempt to remove any excess wax.

Earache and discharge from the middle ear indicate an infection. Such a condition should receive the immediate attention of your doctor. Middle-ear infections may occur during a head cold, especially if you blow your nose too hard and force mucus and infectious organisms into the Eustachian tubes.

The structure of the human eye. The normal eye is spherical and slightly flattened from front to back (Fig. 40-6). The wall of the eyeball is composed of three distinct layers. The outer, or *sclerotic* (sklair-*ot*-ik), *layer* is tough and white. This layer shows as the white of the eye. It bulges and becomes transparent in front, and is called the *cornea* (*kor*-nee-uh) (Fig. 40-9, page 511).

The middle, or *choroid* (*kor*-oid), *layer* is richly supplied with blood vessels. It completely encloses the eye except in front where there is a hole. This small opening, lying behind the center of the cornea, is the *pupil.* Around the pupil the choroid contains pigmented cells. This area is the *iris* and may be colored blue, brown, black, or hazel. Change in size of the circular pupil is accomplished by muscles in the iris. This adjustment in size of the pupil opening to the intensity of light is an automatic reflex. When the light is reduced, the pupil becomes large, or *dilates.* In bright light it *constricts,* or becomes small. The eye doctor uses drops to dilate the pupil. By doing this, the automatic reflex is blocked and he can use a bright pinpoint of light to see inside the eye. This is the only place in the body where the blood vessels may actually be seen. The black pigment of the choroid layer may also be seen inside the eye. This black pigmentation prevents reflection of light rays within the eye.

A convex, crystalline *lens* lies behind the pupil opening of the iris. The lens is supported by the *ciliary* (*sil*-ee-air-ee) *muscles* fastened to the choroid layer.

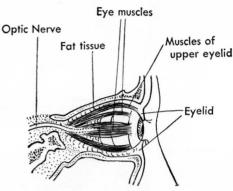

Fig. 40-6. This is a diagram of the human eye, showing the muscles that control its movements.

Contraction of these muscles changes the shape of the lens. In this way varying light rays are focused on the surface of the retina in the eye.

The space between the lens and the cornea is filled with a thin, watery substance, the *aqueous* (ay-kwee-us) *humor.* A thicker, jellylike transparent substance, the *vitreous* (*vih*-tree-us) *humor,* fills the interior of the eyeball. This fluid aids in keeping the eyeball firm and preventing its collapse.

The inner layer, or *retina* (*reh*-tih-nuh), is the most complicated and delicate of the eye layers. The terminals of the *optic nerve* are found in the retina. This large nerve extends from the back of each eyeball to the vision center in the occipital lobe of the cerebrum. Some of the fibers cross as they lead to the cerebrum. This means that some of the impulses from your right eye, for example, go to the left occipital lobe and some go to the right occipital lobe. Thus, what you see with each eye is interpreted in both lobes.

The structure of the retina. The retina is less than 1/80th of an inch thick. Yet it is composed of seven layers of cells, receptors, ganglia, and nerve fibers. The purpose of all of the structures of the

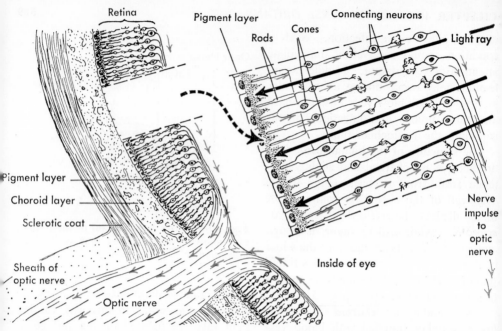

Retina | Pigment layer | Connecting neurons
Cones
Rods
Light ray

Pigment layer
Choroid layer
Sclerotic coat

Nerve impulse to optic nerve

Sheath of optic nerve

Inside of eye

Optic nerve

Fig. 40-7. This is a drawing of the structures at the back of the inside of the eye. The enlargement illustrates the arrangment of the rods and cones (photoreceptors) on the retina.

eye is to focus light on the retina. The specialized receptors which are stimulated by light are called *photoreceptors* and are of two types, **cones** and **rods** (Fig. 40-7). *Cones* are sensitive to bright light and are responsible for color vision. The *rods* act in reduced light but do not respond to color. Perhaps the phrase, " cones color, rods reduced," will help you to keep the two straight. They lie deep in the retina, pointing toward the back surface of the eyeball. Impulses from the cones and rods travel through a series of short nerves with brushlike endings to ganglia near the front part of the retina. More than half a million nerve fibers lead from the ganglia over the surface of the retina to the optic nerve. There are no rods or cones at the point where the end of the optic nerve joins the retina. Since there is no vision at this point, it is called the *blind spot*.

How we see. Cones occur throughout the retina, but are especially abundant in

a small sensitive spot called the **fovea** (*foh*-vee-uh). When we see in daylight, light rays pass through the cornea, aqueous humor, pupil, lens, and the vitreous humor to the cones of the retina. The lens focuses rays on the fovea, the point at which we see an object clearly. As light rays pass through the lens, they cross and strike the retina in an inverted position (Fig. 40-8). Cones outside the fovea register vision only indistinctly.

Fig. 40-8. Light rays enter the eye, cross in the lens, and focus on the retina. Why is the image inverted on the retina?

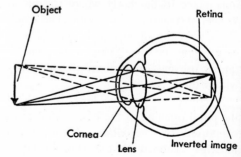

Object | Retina

Cornea
Lens | Inverted image

Thus, if you focus your eyes on an object, you see it clearly. In addition, you see objects contained in a hemisphere of vision indistinctly, or " out of the corner of your eye."

During the late evening or at night, the light is too reduced to stimulate the cones. This quality of light stimulates the rods. Rods produce a substance we call **visual purple,** which is necessary for their proper functioning. Bright light fades visual purple, which causes the rods to be insensitive to further stimulation by light. This explains why, when you leave a bright room at night, you are temporarily night blind. As visual purple is restored, the rods begin to function, and you can see objects in dim light.

The human eye contains fewer rods than many animal eyes, so our night vision is relatively poor. The cat, deer, owl, and many other animals see well at night because they have many rods. The owl, however, lacks cones and is day blind.

The fovea of your retina contains many cones, but no rods. This explains why you can see an object " out of the corner of your eye " at night, but when you focus on it, it disappears.

The eye and the camera. By understanding the eye and how it produces vi-

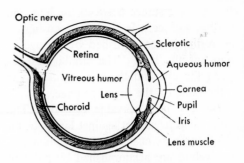

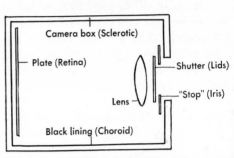

Fig. 40-9. Explain how the parts of the eye correspond to those of a camera. How do the eye and the camera differ?

sion, we can compare it to a camera in certain respects (Fig. 40-9). There are, however, several fundamental differences between an eye and a camera. In a camera the image of a picture is recorded on the film in the back of the camera. In the eye, this image is recorded on the retina and in the brain. Furthermore, when you focus light rays on a film, you

COMPARISON OF THE EYE AND THE CAMERA

PART OF THE EYE		PART OF THE CAMERA
Eyeball	corresponds to	Camera box
Lens	corresponds to	Lens
Lids	corresponds to	Shutter
Iris	corresponds to	Stops or diaphragm
Pupil	corresponds to	Lens opening
Lens muscles	corresponds to	Focusing devices
Pigment of choroid and retina	corresponds to	Black lining
Retina	corresponds to	Plate or film

change the distance between the lens and the film surface. In the eye, focusing on the retina is accomplished by change in shape of the lens. The similarities between the eye and the camera are given in the table on the previous page.

The eye is a movable camera. The eye rests in its socket against layers of fat which serve as cushions. Movements of the eyeball are accomplished by pairs of muscles (Fig. 40-6, page 509) which attach to its sides and extend back into the eye socket. The sclerotic layer is supplied with nerve endings which register pain when a foreign object touches it. The eye is further protected by its location deep in the recesses of the eye socket, by bony ridges, by the eyelids, and by the tear glands which keep its surface moist. Tears wash over the eye and drain into the tear ducts in the lower corner of the eye socket, which leads to the nasal cavity. Because of their high salt content, tears are mildly antiseptic.

Defects of the eye. Certain structural defects of the eye and changes which occur as you get older result in incorrect vision. Many defects result from improper shape and irregularities of the eyeball. In such cases, the lens is unable to focus light rays sharply on the surface of the retina. These conditions

Fig. 40-10. In the nearsighted eye, the image focuses in front of the retina. In the farsighted eye, the image focuses in back of the retina.

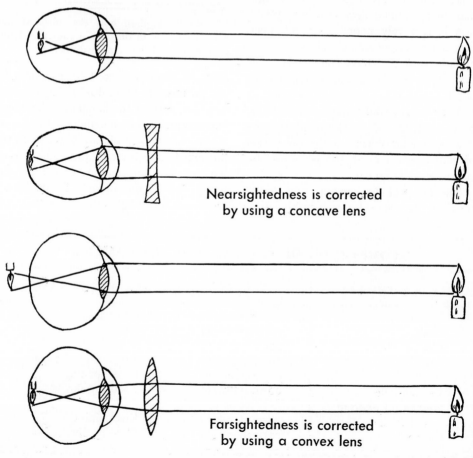

Nearsightedness is corrected
by using a concave lens

Farsightedness is corrected
by using a convex lens

SOME COMMON EYE DEFECTS

CONDITION	DEFECT OF THE EYE	CORRECTIVE MEASURE
Nearsightedness	Eyeball lengthened from front to back, or lens too curved	Concave lens glasses
Farsightedness	Eyeball shortened from front to back, or lens too flat	Convex lens glasses
Astigmatism	Irregularities in the shape of the lens or cornea	Special prisms or cylinders in lens glasses
Old age	Loss of lens flexibility, resulting in farsightedness	Convex lens glasses

may be remedied by altering the path of the light rays to the retina by means of glasses. It is highly important, however, that glasses be prescribed *only* by a person trained to do so.

The doctor of medicine who specializes in the treatment of eye defects, the correction of improper vision, diseases of the eye and their treatment, and eye surgery, is called an *ophthalmologist* (off-thul-*mol*-uh-jist). The old name for this physician was *oculist* (*ok*-you-list). The *optometrist* (op-*tom*-uh-trist), on the other hand, corrects defects of focus by means of glasses and eye exercises. He is trained in the use of mechanical instruments for the measurement of vision. Since he is not a medical doctor, he refers cases of eye injury or suspected disease to an ophthalmologist.

An *optician* (op-*tih*-shun) is an expert in the grinding of lenses and the fitting of glasses. He fills the prescription written by the ophthalmologist or optometrist. It is very important for you to have your eyes examined at regular intervals.

Fig. 40-10 and the table above summarize some common eye defects, their causes, and the type of lens used to correct each.

In Conclusion

Sensory nerves carry impulses from their receptors in sense organs to the central nervous system. The numerous minute sense organs of the skin respond to touch, pressure, pain, heat, and cold. The endings involved in the sense of smell contact gases that have reached the upper turbinate region of the nasal passages. The ears are highly developed sense organs which receive air-borne vibrations and carry them to the receptors in the cochlea in the inner ear. They also contain the semicircular canals, which control our sense of equilibrium.

The eye is the most highly specialized of the sense organs. It receives light rays through the pupil and directs them to the retina by means of the lens. In the retina, the photoreceptors send impulses through the optic nerve to the visual center in the occipital lobes of the brain.

BIOLOGICALLY SPEAKING

anvil bone	hair cell	rod
aqueous humor	hammer bone	sclerotic layer
auditory nerve	iris	semicircular canals
choroid layer	lens	stirrup bone
ciliary muscles	olfactory nerve	taste buds
cochlea	optic nerve	turbinate
cone	photoreceptor	tympanic membrane
cornea	pupil	visual purple
Eustachian tube	receptor	vitreous humor
fovea	retina	

QUESTIONS FOR REVIEW

1. (a) Name the five sensations of the skin. (b) In what ways are the receptors different?
2. Why is it important to have both heat and cold receptors in the skin?
3. Account for the fact that we think we distinguish more than the five tastes the tongue can perceive.
4. Why does sniffing help to detect an odor?
5. Describe how a sound wave in the air is able to stimulate the receptors in the cochlea.
6. How can an infection in the middle ear produce temporary deafness?
7. Describe the movements of the head which would be necessary to stimulate each semicircular canal separately.
8. Why is our vision at night relatively poor when compared to the eyes of an owl?
9. What structures of the eyeball do light waves pass through as they enter the eye and finally reach the retina?
10. Why is it that you can see an object out of the corner of your eye at night, but when you focus on it, it disappears?
11. Why couldn't a nearsighted person use convex lenses?

APPLYING FACTS AND PRINCIPLES

1. Why is it that you can become so used to a particular odor that you do not notice it until you go outside and come back later?
2. How does the ear transmit sound waves so that there is a difference in the pitch, the quality of the tone, and the volume of the sound?
3. How would you go about designing an experiment to prove whether or not the eye really receives an image upside down, while the mind interprets it oppositely?
4. Describe the exact path an impulse travels to reach the brain when a rod or cone is stimulated.
5. Make a diagram to show which fibers of the optic nerve cross over to the opposite cerebral hemisphere and which do not.

CHAPTER 41

The Body Regulators

S INCE the dawn of medicine in ancient Greece, men have searched for the strange and powerful chemical substances which regulate all vital activities of the body. Someone discovered that goiter could be treated successfully with a concoction of burnt seaweed and sponges. But not until many centuries later, armed with a knowledge of iodine and the thyroid gland, were scientists able to explain why this early treatment worked.

Now we know that an amazing system of glands, operating like the balance wheel of a watch, controls the vital activities of the body. It can cause your organs to function in perfect harmony, or struggle against each other in a desperate effort to survive. It can save your life in time of need, or lead to its destruction.

What are the ductless glands? You are already familiar with glands, such as the salivary glands of the mouth and the gastric glands of the stomach. These pour secretions into a digestive organ through a tube, or duct. However, the *ductless glands* which we shall study in this chapter are entirely different from the digestive glands. The name *ductless* indicates that they have no ducts leading from them; their secretions enter the blood stream directly. With blood as a transporting medium, these secretions reach every part of the body and influence all the organs. Ductless glands are also called **endocrine** (*en*-doh-krin) **glands.**

We call the secretions of this group of ductless glands **hormones.** These powerful chemicals are formed from substances taken from the blood. They control the activity of all the body processes. Thus the circulatory system is vital to the endocrine system, both in supplying the raw materials and in delivering the finished product. For the most part the endocrine glands are small. They are entirely out of proportion to the vital influence they exert on the body.

Endocrine glands operate in a state of *dynamic balance,* which means that the secretion of one gland may influence the activity of other glands. If one gland becomes overactive, the balance is upset and the other glands become overactive. For this reason, glandular disorders may be very complex.

Our study of endocrine glands will include the following six glands known to secrete hormones and their products: (1) *thyroid* (*thy*-roid) *gland;* (2) *parathyroid* (*pair*-uh-thy-roid) *glands;* (3) *pituitary* (pih-*tew*-ih-tair-ee) *gland;* (4) *adrenal* (ad-*reen*-ul) *glands;* (5) *pancreas* (*pan*-kree-us); and (6) *ovaries* and *testes* (Fig. 41-1, page 516).

The *thymus* and *pineal* (*pin*-ee-ul) *body* may also function as endocrine glands. However, we do not know too much about the part these structures play in the body.

The thyroid gland. You are probably more familiar with the **thyroid** than with any of the other endocrine glands. It is relatively large and close to the body surface, lying in the neck, near the junction of the lower part of the larynx and the trachea. The thyroid consists of two lobes

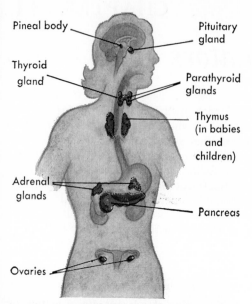

Pineal body

Pituitary gland

Thyroid gland

Parathyroid glands

Thymus (in babies and children)

Adrenal glands

Pancreas

Ovaries

Fig. 41-1. **This diagram shows the location of the endocrine glands in the body. Why are they called ductless glands?**

connected by an " isthmus " (Fig. 41-2). The lobes lie on either side of the trachea and extend upward along the sides of the larynx. The isthmus extends across the front surface of the trachea. As Fig. 41-2 illustrates, the complete thyroid gland somewhat resembles a butterfly with its wings spread.

The secretion of the thyroid gland is known as the **thyroid hormone,** but its exact chemical composition is not entirely known. We do know, however, that it contains two distinct chemical substances and that both of these are composed of amino acids, combined with large amounts of *iodine.*

The concentration of iodine in the thyroid gland is greater than in any other tissue of the body. This concentration is about one part of iodine to 1,000 parts of thyroid tissue. While this may appear to be a very small amount, it is actually very high. Since both parts of the thyroid hormone contain large quantities of this element, you can understand why

iodine is essential for normal functioning of the thyroid gland.

The thyroid and metabolism. Thyroid hormone regulates the rate of metabolism. In this way it influences growth and oxidation. Overactivity of the thyroid gland, or **hyperthyroidism** (hy-per-*thy*-roid-izm), increases the rate of oxidation and raises the body temperature. Heart action increases and blood pressure rises. Sweating, when the body should be cool, is a common symptom of this condition. In addition, the individual becomes extremely nervous and irritable. In some cases, victims may develop characteristic bulging eyes and a staring expression.

Underactivity of the thyroid gland, called **hypothyroidism** (hy-poh-*thy*-roid-izm), produces the opposite symptoms. The rate of oxidation is decreased and activity of the nervous system is reduced. This produces characteristic physical and mental retardation. Heart action decreases and in many cases the heart enlarges. Both overactivity and underactivity of the gland may be determined by measuring the rate of basal metabolism.

If the thyroid is defective during infancy, **cretinism** (*kree*-tin-izm) results. This condition produces a stunted body. The face usually becomes bloated, the lips greatly enlarged, and the tongue thick and protruding from the mouth. Cretins are mentally dull and stupid. If the condition is not corrected early in life by giving thyroid extract, the victim becomes a mental defective. If the cretin has passed from infancy to childhood without treatment, the dwarfism and certain other symptoms can never be corrected.

What is goiter? Iodine deficiency is the major cause of enlargement of the thyroid gland, known as **simple goiter.** This condition is rare along the seacoast where people eat an abundance of sea foods containing iodine. It is more common in mountainous regions and in the Great Lakes basin where the iodine content of the soil is low. The addition of iodine compounds to table salt and to the water supply in certain regions is an adequate preventive measure.

How is thyroid hormone prepared? Commercially, thyroid hormone is prepared by extraction from the dried thyroid glands of sheep. After being purified, it is called *thyroid extract* and is used in treating thyroid disorders. Thyroid extract is the least expensive of any commercial endocrine preparation.

The parathyroid glands. The *parathyroids* are four small glands embedded in the back of the thyroid, two in each lobe (Fig. 41-2). Their secretion, *parathormone* (pair-uh-*thor*-mone), controls the use of calcium in the body. Bone growth, muscle tone, and normal nervous activity are absolutely dependent on a constant, stable calcium balance.

The pituitary gland. The small *pituitary gland,* about the size of an acorn or cherry, lies at the base of the brain. It was once thought to be the "master gland" of the body, since its secretions appeared to influence the activity of all other endocrine glands. However, it is now known that other glands, especially the thyroid and adrenal glands, also influence the pituitary gland.

The pituitary gland consists of two lobes: *anterior* and *posterior*. The *anterior lobe* secretes several different hormones. One of these, the **somatotropic** (soh-mat-oh-*troh*-pik), or growth, **hormone** regulates the growth of the skeleton.

Another hormone secretion of the anterior lobe of the pituitary gland, the **gonadotropic** (goh-nad-oh-*troh*-pik) **hormone,** influences the development of the reproductive organs. It also influences hormone secretion of the ovaries and testes. The gonadotropic hormone, together with the sex hormones, cause the

Fig. 41-2. Note the position of the thyroid gland in relation to the trachea. Note also the four parathyroid glands imbedded in the back of the thyroid.

Fig. 41-3. A magnified section of human thyroid tissue. The large areas are secretion; the small dots are nuclei of cells.

General Biological Supply House

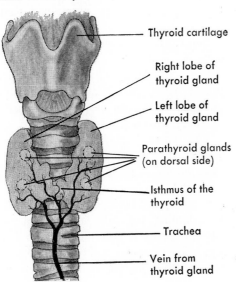

Thyroid cartilage

Right lobe of thyroid gland

Left lobe of thyroid gland

Parathyroid glands (on dorsal side)

Isthmus of the thyroid

Trachea

Vein from thyroid gland

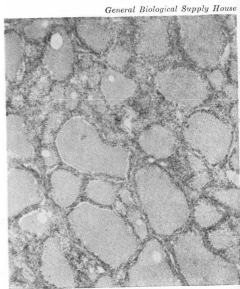

Ewing Galloway

Fig. 41-4. **If the anterior lobe of the pituitary gland produces too little of the somatotropic hormone, midgetism may result. What happens when there is oversecretion of this growth hormone?**

sweeping changes which occur during adolescence, when the child becomes an adult.

Other secretions of the anterior lobe of the pituitary gland include hormones which stimulate the secretion of milk in the mammary glands (*lactogenic hormone*), the activity of the thyroid gland (*thyrotropic hormone*), and the parathyroid glands (*parathyrotropic hormone*).

What is ACTH? *ACTH* (*adreno-cortico-tropic-hormone*) is a secretion of the *anterior lobe* of the pituitary gland; it stimulates the outer part, or cortex, of the adrenal glands. ACTH has been used in the treatment of leukemia and more successfully in the treatment of arthritis.

Good results in the treatment of asthma and other allergies with ACTH have also been reported. Even though ACTH may not give permanent cures to these diseases, its use may lead the way to the discovery of their actual causes.

The *posterior lobe* of the pituitary gland produces two hormones: (1) **pitressin** (pih-*tres*-in), which helps regulate the amount of water in the blood and the blood pressure; and (2) **pitocin** (pih-*toh*-sin), which stimulates smooth muscles. Pitocin is administered after childbirth to cause contraction of the muscles of the uterus, thus preventing blood loss.

Disorders of the pituitary gland. The most frequent disorder of the pituitary involves the *somatotropic hormone*. If an oversecretion of this hormone occurs during the growing years, a condition called *giantism* may result. There are circus giants over 8 feet tall, who weigh over 300 pounds, and wear size 30 shoes. If the oversecretion occurs during adult life, the bones of the face and hands thicken, since they cannot grow in length. However, the organs and the soft tissues enlarge tremendously. This condition is known as **acromegaly** (ak-roh-*meg*-uh-lee). Victims of this disorder have greatly enlarged jawbones, noses, and hands and fingers.

Somatotropic hormone deficiency results in a pituitary dwarf, or *midget*. These individuals are perfectly proportioned "men in miniature." They are quite different from the thyroid dwarf in that they have normal intelligence.

The adrenal glands. The **adrenal glands,** also called *suprarenals,* are located on top of each kidney (Fig. 41-5). They are composed of an outer region, the **cortex,** and an inner part, the **medulla.** Unlike the adrenal medulla, the adrenal cortex is absolutely essential for life. It secretes a hormone-complex called **cortin** (*kor*-tin). These hormones are responsible for the control of certain phases of carbohydrate, fat, and protein metabolism as well as of the salt and water balance in the body.

The adrenal cortex also yields hormones which control the production of some types of white corpuscles, and the structure of connective tissue. When ACTH is given to patients with leukemia, a dramatic but unfortunately temporary improvement occurs. Other possible effects of the cortical hormones have been discussed in connection with ACTH.

The medulla secretes a hormone called **epinephrine** (eh-pih-*nef*-reen), or *adrenaline* (ad-*ren*-uh-leen). The adrenal glands have been called the *glands of emergency* because of the action of this hormone. Many people have performed superhuman feats of strength during periods of anger or fright, with the help of epinephrine. This strength of desperation results from a series of rapid changes in body activity:

1. The person becomes pale, because of constriction of the blood vessels in the skin. The rapid movement of blood from the body surfaces reduces loss of blood in case of a surface wound. It also increases the blood supply to the muscles, brain, heart, and other vital organs.

2. The blood pressure rises, because of constriction of surface blood vessels.

3. The heart action and output are increased.

4. The liver releases some of its stored sugar and provides material for increased body activity and oxidations.

Your life may have been saved on several occasions by these rapid changes in body activity.

The pancreas. The production of pancreatic fluid in connection with digestion is only part of the function of the **pancreas.** Special groups of cells, called **islets of Langerhans,** secrete a hormone, **insulin.** This hormone enables the liver to store sugar as glycogen and regulates the oxidation of sugar in the tissues.

A person who lacks insulin cannot store or oxidize sugar efficiently. Thus the tissues are deprived of energy food, and sugar collects in the blood. As the blood sugar rises, some of it is excreted in the urine. Doctors call this condition **diabetes mellitus** (dy-uh-*bee*-teez meh-*lye*-tus).

However, diabetes mellitus is probably not only simple failure of the islet cells of the pancreas to produce insulin. The pituitary, thyroid, and adrenal glands, as well as the liver, are known to play an important part in the disease. Body weight also influences the appearance of this condition. Diabetes mellitus is definitely hereditary. If you have it in your family, regular periodic check-ups for sugar in the urine should be made by your family doctor. There is no cause for alarm if the disease appears, for once discovered, it usually can be controlled successfully. If treatment is begun in the early stages, the patient can lead a perfectly normal life.

Fig. 41-5. Notice the position of the adrenal glands in relation to the kidneys. What two important hormones do these glands secrete?

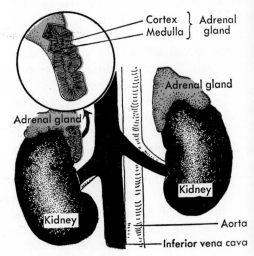

New York Diabetes Assoc.

**Fig. 41-6. A diabetic learns to inject insu-
lin herself and to control her diet, so that
she may lead a normal life.**

The ovaries and testes. The **ovaries**
of the female and the **testes** of the male
have dual functions. We think of them
primarily as organs for the production of
eggs and sperm. However, certain cells
of the ovaries and the testes serve as ductless glands. These ovary cells secrete the
female hormone **estrogen** (*es*-troh-jen),
while special cells of the testes produce
the male hormone **androgen** (*an*-droh-
jen).

Testosterone (tes-*tos*-ter-ohn), one of
the active parts of androgen, can now be
produced artificially, and is used in treating sex hormone disturbances in both
males and females. Furthermore, the
production of this hormone is not limited
to the testes. It is secreted by the cortex
of the adrenal glands in *both males and
females*. In the female, the estrogen secreted in the ovaries normally neutralizes

the effects of the androgen from the adrenal glands. However, if the estrogen
secretion in the ovaries is reduced, the
female may become mannish. Similarly,
reduced production of androgen in the
testes of the male can result in feminine
tendencies. Thus different individuals
may represent various degrees of maleness
and femaleness.

Sex hormones control the development
of secondary sex characteristics which appear in the change from childhood to
adulthood. The time of the first appearance of these changes with the maturation of the ovaries and testes is called
puberty (*pyoo*-ber-tee). In the animal
world, these characteristics may appear
as the large comb of the rooster, the
bright plumage of most male birds, and
the antlers of the deer.

Many secondary characteristics are appearing and have appeared in your own
body. As a boy approaches puberty, his
voice cracks and then deepens. His
beard appears along with a general increase in body hair. The chest broadens
and deepens. Rapid growth of the long
bones adds to his height. As a girl matures, her breasts develop, her hips
broaden, her body contours become more
rounded, because of the formation of fat
deposits under the skin, and menstrua-
tion begins. These physical changes in
both boys and girls are accompanied by
sweeping mental and emotional changes.
Compare your present personality with
that of a child ten to twelve years old and
you will see how these glands have influenced you.

The pineal body and thymus. The
pineal body is a mass of tissue about the
size of a pea, located at the base of the
brain. It lies directly behind the junction
of the spinal cord and brain tissue. As
we stated on page 515, this body may or
may not be a ductless gland. No hormone secretion from the pineal body has

DUCTLESS GLANDS AND THEIR SECRETIONS

GLAND	LOCATION	HORMONE	FUNCTION OF HORMONE
Thyroid	Neck, below larynx	Thyroid hormone	Accelerates the rate of metabolism
Parathyroids	Back surface of thyroid lobes	Parathormone	Controls the use of calcium in the tissues
Pituitary Anterior lobe	Base of brain	Somatotropic hormone	Regulates growth of the skeleton
		Gonadotropic hormone	Influences development of sex organs and hormone secretion of the ovaries and testes
		ACTH	Stimulates secretion of hormones by the cortex of the adrenals
		Lactogenic hormone	Stimulates secretion of milk by mammary glands
		Thyrotropic hormone	Stimulates activity of the thyroid
		Parathyrotropic hormone	Stimulates activity of the parathyroids
Posterior lobe		Pitressin	Regulates water in blood and blood pressure
		Pitocin	Stimulates smooth muscles
Adrenal Cortex	Above kidneys	Cortin (a hormone-complex)	Regulates metabolism, salt, and water balance Controls production of certain white corpuscles and structure of connective tissue
Medulla		Epinephrine	Causes constriction of blood vessels, increase in heart action and output, stimulates liver and nervous system

Pancreas
  Islets of
  Langerhans
	Below and behind stomach	Insulin	Enables liver to store sugar and regulates sugar oxidation in tissues

Ovaries
  Follicular
  cells
	Pelvis	Estrogen	Produces female secondary sex characteristics; influences adult female body functions

Testes
  Interstitial
  cells
	Below pelvis	Androgen	Produces male secondary sex characteristics

yet been discovered, so we do not know what its function is.

The *thymus,* too, may be a ductless gland, but its function is unknown. It lies just above the heart, under the breastbone. At birth, the thymus weighs less than half an ounce. It increases in size during childhood and reaches its maximum size between the ages of 12 and 14.

During the time when it is of maximum size, the thymus gland usually weighs about one ounce, or twice its weight at birth. During adulthood, it gradually grows smaller and finally shrinks to the size it was at birth. The fact that it grows larger during childhood and then decreases in size, shows that it may influence development of the reproductive organs. We have no real proof of this at the moment, but research workers with the assistance of prominent doctors are investigating the possibility.

Many questions regarding the action of these glands remain unanswered. However, a great deal of research on the endocrine glands and the specific effects of hormones is being done today to find the answers.

In Conclusion

Ductless, or endocrine, glands secrete hormones directly into the blood stream. These hormones have a powerful influence over the activity of body organs, including the glands of the endocrine system themselves. Ductless glands function in a state of dynamic balance. Overactivity of any one gland may result from overactivity of other glands or may cause it. This is especially true of the pituitary, adrenal, and thyroid glands. The pineal body and thymus may function as ductless glands, although the activity of neither one is understood.

BIOLOGICALLY SPEAKING

acromegaly	estrogen	pineal body
adrenal cortex	goiter	pitocin
adrenal glands	gonadotropic hormone	pitressin
adrenal medulla	hormone	pituitary gland
ACTH	hyperthyroidism	puberty
androgen	hypothyroidism	somatotropic hormone
cortin	insulin	testes
cretinism	islets of Langerhans	testosterone
diabetes mellitus	ovaries	thymus
ductless gland	pancreas	thyroid gland
endocrine gland	parathormone	thyroid hormone
epinephrine	parathyroid glands	

QUESTIONS FOR REVIEW

1. What role does the blood play in the function of endocrine glands?
2. How does the thyroid gland regulate the rate of metabolism?
3. Explain how hyperthyroidism and hypothyroidism can affect personality.
4. In what ways do the pituitary and thyroid gland influence growth?
5. How does the pituitary gland affect the sex glands?
6. (a) What is ACTH? (b) What is its function?
7. In what ways are puberty and adolescence a result of glandular activity?
8. Why does sugar appear in the urine of a diabetic?
9. Compare the body characteristics of a thyroid dwarf and a pituitary dwarf. How do they differ and in what ways are they similar?

APPLYING FACTS AND PRINCIPLES

1. What gland may have a hormone which influences intelligence?
2. How do you account for the fact that the heartbeat of a basketball player increases a great deal before the game as well as during it?
3. Why is a study of the endocrine glands often included with a study of the nervous system?
4. What hormone injected into the blood stream of a male rat will often result in a mothering instinct? Why?

CHAPTER 42

Alcohol, Narcotics, and Tobacco

PROBLEMS resulting from alcohol and narcotics are as old as civilization. But they are more acute today because automobiles, firearms, and other mechanical devices become implements of destruction in the hands of an intoxicated or drug-addicted person.

We shall consider alcohol, tobacco, and narcotics together, because they are all harmful substances when used habitually. Young people who see a large proportion of the adult society smoking without any *apparent* effect may arrive at the wrong conclusions, because the long-term effects of tobacco are not always visible. While there is no real justification for the use of tobacco, its influence on the human mechanism is not to be compared with the physical, emotional, and mental damage resulting from the habitual and excessive use of alcohol or narcotics.

This chapter will show you some of the effects of these substances on the body. It will be up to each of you, as an individual, to form your own opinion and your own personal habits.

Is alcohol a food? We defined food in Chapter 35 as any substance which, when taken into the body, yields material valuable for the growth and repair of tissue, production of energy, or regulation of the life processes, without harming the organism. Alcohol yields no material which can be used in growth and repair of tissues. Actually, its presence in tissue may interfere with growth and repair involving protein foods. While large amounts of heat are released during oxidation of alcohol in the tissues, this heat cannot be used as energy for carrying on the life processes. In fact, energy derived from real foods must be used up in ridding the body of the excess heat from the alcohol. Even if there were energy value in alcohol, the anesthetic effect of alcohol on the body would rule it out as a food classification. Thus we must rule out any possible nutritional value of alcohol.

Is alcohol a stimulant? Many people excuse moderate drinking on the grounds that it stimulates them. A " shot " before an important conference does not sharpen the mental processes. In fact, it dulls them. Actually, *alcohol is a **depressant**,* a substance which dulls the senses. Any feeling of uplift a person may claim to feel is a mistaken impression or an attempt to justify the act in his own mind.

What happens when alcohol enters the body? When alcohol is consumed, it passes to the stomach and starts to enter the blood within two minutes. Since no change in form or composition occurs before absorption begins, absorption is very rapid.

Absorption continues in the stomach and in the upper region of the small intestine until all the alcohol has reached the blood. This absorption is more rapid when the stomach is empty than when it contains food. The blood carries it to all tissues where it is combined with water.

Oxidation begins immediately and large amounts of heat are released. Because the rate of oxidation of alcohol has no relation to the energy needs of the body tissues, the heat produced has no value. As heat is released, it is picked up by the blood and delivered to the skin where it causes the flush on the body surface that is associated with the presence of alcohol in the system. In this manner, the body rids itself of the excess heat. The body tissues oxidize alcohol at the rate of approximately one ounce in three hours.

Since the receptors of heat are in the skin, the rush of blood to the skin gives a false impression of warmth in the body. During this feeling of warmth, however, the internal organs are deprived of adequate blood supply and become chilled.

Some effects of alcohol on the body organs. Since alcohol is absorbed by all the body organs, all of them are affected by its presence. However, certain organs seem to be affected more than others. The kidneys are overworked in eliminating excess water consumed with certain beverages. In other cases, alcohol dehydrates the tissues and causes the skin to excrete large quantities of water during heat elimination. This loss of water concentrates nitrogenous wastes in the kidneys and interferes with normal elimination.

One kind of liver degeneration, *cirrhosis* (sir-*oh*-sis), is often associated with heavy drinking and alcoholism. All heavy drinkers do not develop cirrhosis nor do all people with cirrhosis consume alcohol. The evidence indicates, however, that there is a correlation between the two.

When beverages with high alcoholic content are taken into the stomach and intestine, damage may occur in the linings. Inflammation of the stomach lining causes a painful condition called *gastritis* (gas-*try*-tis).

Fig. 42-1. The "balloonometer" demonstrated in this photograph is one of several breath-test devices used by policemen to determine the amount of alcohol in a person's blood.

National Safety Council

Effects of alcohol on the nervous system. Alcohol has an anesthetic effect on the nervous system. The influence may appear as temporary impairment of the mental faculties and abnormal behavior. Or it may exert an influence over a period of time which will lead to permanent mental illness. It can even cause death.

The first effects of alcohol occur in the brain cortex. *Reaction time* for muscular activity is increased. The association of sensory and motor impulses is retarded because of the dulling effects of alcohol on brain tissue.

Another early effect is difficulty in making judgments and exercising self-control, as a consequence of changes in the brain cortex. With loss of judgment, cares seem to vanish and the person becomes gay and lightheaded. Influence on the frontal lobe alters emotional control and may lead to a feeling of great joy, shown by foolish laughter, or to sadness and weeping. As the effects of alcohol progress through the brain tissue, the vision area of the cerebrum and the eyes themselves become involved. Blurred vision, double vision, and lack of ability to judge distance occur.

As the cerebellum becomes involved, coordination of the muscles is affected. The victim becomes dizzy when standing, and if he is able to walk at all, does so with a clumsy, staggering gait. Even the muscles of the tongue become involved, and speech becomes thick and hesitant.

In the final stages of drunkenness, a person becomes completely helpless. The brain cortex ceases activity, resulting in complete unconsciousness. The skin becomes pale, cold, and clammy. Body oxidation is reduced and alcohol remains in the tissue fluids. Heart action, digestive action, and respiration slow up and the victim lies near death.

Addiction to alcohol. There is a sharp distinction between a *habit* and an *addiction*. We may make a habit of eating candy, chewing gum, or carrying on some other type of activity. By exerting self-control, we can break the habit. The break may cause some nervous tension and a temptation to resume the activity. Other than this, however, there is no serious effect upon the body.

An *addiction* is much more serious and acute. If a person is addicted to alcohol, his system reacts violently if he is deprived of it. Nervous reactions may be acute, and hallucinations and violent craving may result, conditions we refer to as **withdrawal symptoms.**

Alcoholism is a disease. *Alcoholism* produces both mental and physical symptoms. It results also in complete destruction of the personality.

Six to seven per cent of the adult users of alcohol develop into alcoholics. Alcoholism may begin with occasional social drinking. As distressing situations and problems arise and life seems temporarily unpleasant, the individual uses alcohol as an escape from reality. The problems remain unsolved, and alcohol is used for a definite purpose — to try to escape from the problems. With loss of judgment and will power, the chances of solving them are further reduced. The alcoholic then resorts to solitary drinking for the pure effects of alcohol.

Alcohol is the tool and not the underlying cause of alcoholism. Thus the alcoholic seeking a cure must first find the reason for his problem drinking. Then he must solve the problem and not resort to alcohol as an escape from it. Sympathetic understanding and cooperation of his family and friends will help greatly in overcoming the problem.

Thirty-four states and the District of Columbia have clinics and hospitals to assist alcoholics in curing their condition. They supply both medical treatment and counseling necessary to deal with the problem.

If alcoholism is allowed to progress to an acute condition, serious deterioration of brain tissue may result. This may cause terrifying hallucinations known as **delirium tremens,** or " D.T.'s." The victim has visions of snakes, rats, and other vermin crawling over his body, and becomes violent with fear. By this time, his alcoholism has reached the proportions of alcoholic insanity.

Frequently, the heart muscle degenerates and the arteries harden. Almost constant digestive upsets occur due to the damage caused to the stomach walls by large quantities of alcohol. Such a person is extremely ill and requires medical care and hospitalization.

Alcohol and the length of life. Life-insurance companies ask applicants for insurance about their use of alcohol and drugs, which is evidence that heavy drinkers are poorer risks than those who abstain.

It is difficult to say that limited or moderate use of alcohol shortens life. However, no one can deny that even moderate drinking of alcoholic beverages increases the possibility of accidental death. It also lowers body resistance and increases the possibility of death from infectious disease, especially tuberculosis. There is no question that heavy drinking shortens life considerably.

Alcohol and society. The effects of alcohol are much more far-reaching than damage to the habitual drinker himself. His family and all society pay a price for his shortsightedness.

Often a man or woman addicted to alcohol will neglect a family to satisfy the desire. Child neglect, home neglect, divorce, and other acute domestic problems frequently result. Anxiety, frustration, and insecurity in children are a terrible price to pay for alcoholism.

Alcohol must also answer for much of the crime committed in America. In a recent study of the records of 13,402 convicts in 12 states, alcohol was found to be a contributing factor in 50 per cent of the crimes committed, and a direct cause of 16.8 per cent of the crimes.

Alcohol and driving. Automobile accidents, resulting from driving while intoxicated, take a huge toll of life on our highways. Many people think a drink or two could not possibly affect their driving. In fact, such a person may feel that he is a more skilled driver than usual.

As a result, he takes chances because he is so sure of himself.

Important experiments have recently been carried on in Pennsylvania to test thoroughly, under actual road conditions, the relation of drinking to driving a car. Motorists who have been given measured amounts of alcohol but who were not drunk (all but one passed the standard police sobriety tests) were found to make all sorts of accidental errors. Not only did most of these drivers have a slower braking reaction time, but they were also inaccurate in performance. Yet every one of these drivers thought that he was doing well. The fundamental trouble, graphically proved by psychological tests, was found to be the *impairment of judgment after only one or two drinks.*

The death toll from automobiles is over 100 per day with over 3,000 more injured per day. Safety officials attribute from 7 to 10 per cent of fatal highway accidents directly to the use of alcohol, while competent traffic officials state that one-third of these accidents are indirectly caused by alcoholic indulgence by the driver.

The effects of alcohol on a driver of a car are:

1. Less attention to signals and driving hazards.

2. Slower responses of eyes, hands, and feet, due to increased reaction time.

3. Increased self-assurance which causes a driver to take chances and be less considerate of other drivers.

Narcotic drugs. By discussing problems relating to alcohol and narcotic drugs in the same chapter, we do not mean to imply that the problems are similar. Many people consume alcoholic

Fig. 42-2. Alcohol lowers every aspect of driving efficiency.

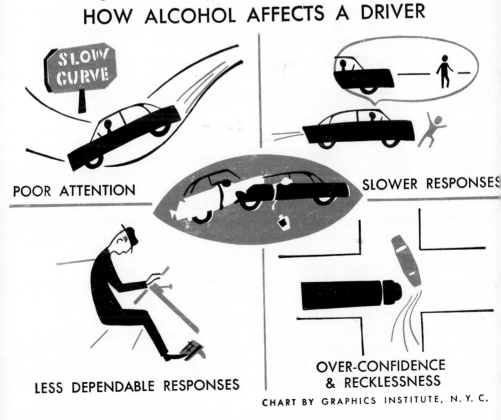

HOW ALCOHOL AFFECTS A DRIVER

POOR ATTENTION

SLOWER RESPONSES

LESS DEPENDABLE RESPONSES

OVER-CONFIDENCE & RECKLESSNESS

CHART BY GRAPHICS INSTITUTE, N. Y. C.

National Safety Council

Fig. 42-3. **" If you drive, don't drink; if you drink, don't drive."** **Accidents such as this one often result when drinking and driving are mixed.**

beverages without becoming habitual drinkers or alcoholics. However, continued use of narcotic drugs results in both mental and physical addiction. That is, the victim becomes dependent on the mental and emotional effects of the drug and his body develops a need for it. When not under the influence of a narcotic, the addict develops violent withdrawal symptoms. These include sleeplessness, difficulty in breathing, irregular heart action, and acute suffering. Mental symptoms include severe depression and derangement. Withdrawal sickness may be severe enough to cause death. The longer an addict uses a narcotic, the greater amount he must take to ward off the withdrawal sickness. The situation becomes so desperate that an addict will commit a crime to get a supply of a narcotic drug.

It is hard to define a narcotic accurately. Generally, we include a group of drugs classified as **narcotics** by the fed-

eral government. They have a powerful effect on the nervous system and are dangerous to use except under strict medical supervision. For this reason, the sale of narcotics, except on a doctor's prescription, is illegal.

Opium (*oh*-pee-um) is the source of a family of narcotic drugs. It is extracted from the juice of the white poppy. *Morphine* (*mor*-feen) and *codein* (*koh*-deen) are derived from opium. *Heroin* (*hair*-oh-in) is a synthetic compound prepared from morphine. Morphine is used to reduce pain. Codein has similar uses and is an ingredient in special kinds of medicines, including some cough syrup. Heroin is so dangerous and addiction-forming that its possession or use in the United States, even for medicinal purposes, is illegal.

Cocaine (koh-*kain*) is a narcotic drug extracted from the leaves of the South American coca plant (not connected with the beverage cocoa). Cocaine deadens skin and mucous membranes. A doctor may use it to deaden the area around a wound before he cleanses it or takes stitches. When taken internally, cocaine causes a temporary stimulation of the nervous system and a feeling of pleasure. Later, however, the victim is seized by a feeling of great fear and may even become violent.

A weed called *marijuana* (mar-ih-*wah*-nuh) often receives considerable attention in the newspapers as a narcotic. Its strength is so great that it has to be mixed with tobacco before it can be smoked. The marijuana user develops an emotional addiction to the effects of the drug, but does not experience physical addiction. However, marijuana addicts usually continue down the narcotic road to ruin, as they eventually turn to opiates.

People may become narcotic addicts in several ways. In some cases, people become addicted after an illness in which a narcotic drug was used medically to relieve pain. Highly nervous or distressed people may use certain narcotics as depressants and continue purchase of the drugs illegally. Still others who are emotionally disturbed or maladjusted deal with dope peddlers who are associated with the organized and unlawful sale of narcotics. This has become a serious problem in certain sections of the country.

Tobacco is the nation's leading habit. More than 60 million people in the United States use tobacco in some form. Over 50 million of these are cigarette smokers.

The smoker actually becomes a slave to two habits: the *smoking habit* and the *tobacco habit*. The first is indicated by reaching for a cigarette at regular intervals, lighting it, and going through various movements associated with smoking. Through habit, heavy smokers often light a second cigarette even before finishing

Fig. 42-4. Painful, grotesque withdrawal symptoms occur when a narcotic addict is taken away from his drug.

Wide World

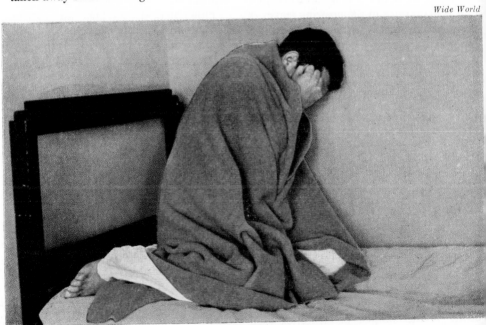

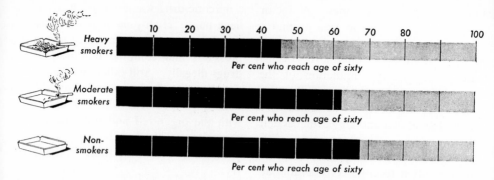

Fig. 42-5.   Statistics indicate that nonsmokers live longer than heavy smokers.

the first one. The heavy consumers of tobacco also acquire a physiological craving for tobacco — the tobacco habit.

Most young people who start smoking feel that it makes them seem more mature. Yet, if they asked the advice of an older person who has smoked for several years, his advice would probably be not to start. Certainly several things should be considered before deliberately starting a practice as habit-forming as smoking.

Tobacco contains a strong alkaloid, nicotine. *Nicotine* is a natural chemical that concentrates in the growing leaves of the tobacco plant. In its pure form it is a poison. A person who smokes a pack in one day absorbs an amount of nicotine which might well prove fatal if taken at one time. About ten per cent of the absorbed nicotine is excreted in the urine within 24 hours. The remaining 90 per cent is probably chemically changed by the liver.

Fortunately, about 60 per cent of the nicotine in a cigar or cigarette is burned during smoking. About 30 per cent of it is exhaled with the smoke, and about 10 to 12 per cent is absorbed by the body.

Recent research indicates a possible link between smoking and lung cancer. In fact, medical authorities have been warning smokers either to quit or to cut down on the number of cigarettes used

each day. The Public Health Service has stated that evidence indicates that excessive smoking is one of the causative factors in lung cancer. Some of the tars formed by the burning tobacco have been found to be *carcinogenic* agents — that is, capable of producing cancer.

The harmful effects of tobacco are not as definite as those of alcohol and narcotics. The harm depends on: (1) the amount one smokes; (2) the depth to which the smoke is inhaled; (3) the nervous make-up and general health of the individual.

Other than the possible link with lung cancer, the principal damage to the body as a result of smoking includes:

1. *Throat irritation.* The fact that smoke is irritating to the eyes indicates that it is irritating also to the mucous membranes of the throat. This may lower the resistance of these membranes to invasion by bacteria.

2. *Depression of heart action* for a period and increase in the rate of beat following this period. This effect varies in different people.

3. *Constriction of arteries and increase in blood pressure.* This condition also varies in different people. It is the result of tension due to the effect of nicotine on the nervous system.

4. *Stomach discomfort.* Smoking increases the flow of gastric fluid at a time

when it is not required. This is especially injurious to a person with a stomach ulcer. Many people develop spasms of the stomach wall as the result of nervous tension due to smoking.

Why do people smoke? People who smoke give several reasons to justify their habit. They say that it quiets their nerves. The nervous condition would probably not exist if they did not smoke. Others say it gives them something to do. This is quite apparent in the case of chain smokers who light a cigarette, smoke it a few minutes, then lay it down and forget it. Perhaps the tension which requires them to do something is aggravated by the fact that they use tobacco.

There are certainly more reasons why you should *not* smoke than excuses for smoking.

1. *It is expensive.* The average moderate smoker smokes a package of cigarettes per day. At a cost of about 24 cents a package, this amounts to $1.68 per week, or $87.36 per year. The cost of tobacco to the entire population is well over $3,500,000,000 each year.

2. *Smoking is often annoying to other people.* The smoker is sometimes nervous if he finds himself in a place where smoking is forbidden. Or if he insists upon smoking, he is being discourteous to those around him.

3. *Tobacco may mar the appearance.* Teeth may become stained and discolored. Breath can become strong and objectionable. Certainly, no one's appearance is improved by a cigar or cigarette hanging from his mouth. And good appearance is worth a great deal.

In Conclusion

Your ambitions, plans, and hopes for future years depend on good health. You have every reason to look forward to many years of health and happiness. The highly advanced medicine of modern times is at your service.

As you assume more and more of the responsibilities of adult life, you will feel the pressure of the complex age we live in. Hustle and bustle — hurry and worry — these are signs of the times. Maybe they account for a large number of the millions of smokers. They might explain too why many become maladjusted and emotionally disturbed and seek an escape in problem drinking.

Certainly, tobacco is a blind alley leading nowhere. Alcoholism is a dangerous detour which leads only to misery and failure. The narcotic road leads all too suddenly to complete physical, moral, and mental ruin.

Your opportunities for success are almost unlimited today if you have the desire, the drive, the ability, and the good health to claim your place.

BIOLOGICALLY SPEAKING

addiction	depressant	nicotine
alcoholism	gastritis	opium
cirrhosis	habit	reaction time
cocaine	marijuana	withdrawal symptoms
delirium tremens	narcotic	

QUESTIONS FOR REVIEW

1. Why is alcohol not considered a stimulant?
2. Why is alcohol not considered a food?
3. What happens when alcohol enters the body?
4. What organs of the body are especially affected by cirrhosis?
5. Where in the body do the first effects of alcohol occur?
6. (a) Is there a difference between habit and addiction? (b) If so, what is the difference?
7. Why is it dangerous for a person who has had an alcoholic drink to drive an automobile?
8. Name six definite narcotic drugs as defined by the federal government.
9. In what ways is it possible to become a narcotic addict?
10. What are the harmful effects of using tobacco?

APPLYING FACTS AND PRINCIPLES

1. Why does the presence of alcohol in the body give a person a feeling of warmth?
2. The narcotic addict follows a definite pattern. What are the steps in the narcotic road to ruin?
3. Why do life-insurance companies always ask the applicant if he drinks or smokes, and to what extent?
4. Why is drinking alcohol on an empty stomach more injurious than drinking with meals or after eating?
5. Why is inhaling smoke more injurious than not inhaling?
6. Explain the possible relationship between drug addiction and juvenile delinquency. How do drug addicts and alcoholics show character weakness?

CHAPTER *43*

Radiation and Biology

IN 1895, Wilhelm Konrad von Roentgen was working in his laboratory in Bavaria when he observed a strange phenomenon. He was focusing an electron beam on a metallic plate in an evacuated tube, when he noticed that the plate was emitting some form of energy that passed through black paper, caused a phosphorescent screen to glow, and even traveled to the next room. Later he found that the invisible radiations could pass through the hand and cast shadows of the bones on that same glowing screen. He named these radiations, which seemed to travel in waves, *X rays*. His observation was the beginning of the series of discoveries that has led to our present knowledge of nuclear energy and radiation.

The next year, in France, Antoine Henri Becquerel discovered that uranium gave off waves which resembled Roentgen's X rays. With this background, Pierre and Marie Curie began their celebrated work on the radioactivity of radium in Paris.

During this time, between 1895 and 1909, all of the research on radioactivity concerned the physics and chemistry of radiation. Although many uranium miners died of a strange disease (later diagnosed as lung cancer), and many workers suffered from skin burns that would not heal, the biological effects of radiation were not studied until 1909. At this time it was definitely established that skin burns, followed by cancer and death 6 to 30 years later, could be caused by radiation. It is still too early to know all the effects of the Hiroshima and Nagasaki atomic bombs of 1945, but an increase in cancer has been observed in the survivors.

In order to use radiation beneficially in medicine, public health, industry, power, and warfare, it is important that we know something of its harmful effects. A knowledge of the principles of radiation and its effects on organisms involves physics and chemistry as well as biology.

The Nuclear Age has increased our awareness of radiation as a form of energy. As we shall see in this chapter, every living thing is affected by it. Our increased use of nuclear energy will create more radiation and in turn more problems. For this reason, it is very important that we know something about the nature and biological effects of radiation.

Transmission of energy. *Radiation* is a means by which energy moves from one place to another. Light and heat are forms of radiation which travel from the sun to the earth in *waves*. Sound energy travels from a speaker's mouth to the listener's ear in the form of waves. As you will see, some of these forms of energy which travel in waves are essential for life (Fig. 43-1).

A second form of radiation consists of a stream of minute particles. Electrons, radiating from a hot wire, provide, for instance, the energy that produces the picture in a television set. This type of energy is in the form of *rays*.

Electromagnetic radiation is the name given to the first form of energy mentioned above, which does not travel in a straight line, as do the particles of the second type, but in waves. The major kinds of electromagnetic radiations are: (1) *radio waves;* (2) *infrared waves;* (3) *visible light;* (4) *ultraviolet waves;* (5) *X rays;* (6) *gamma rays.* All of these radiations travel at the same speed (about 186,000 miles a second). They differ only in wave length (see table on page 534). The shorter the wave length,

the greater the amount of energy the wave carries.

Radio, or wireless, waves. Television, radar, and radio are made possible by *radio waves.* Of the types of waves named above, these have the longest wave lengths.

Energy from the sun. *Infrared waves* have a shorter wave length than wireless waves; therefore they have more energy. These radiations are called *heat waves*

Fig. 43-1. These are representations of three energy waves, each having a different wave length. The energy travels from point *A* to point *B* in each case, following the dark black line. Which wave represents the most energy?

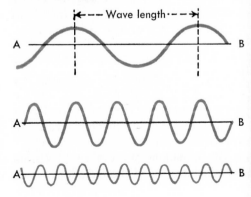

TABLE OF WAVE LENGTHS OF ELECTROMAGNETIC RADIATION

TYPE OF RADIATION	SUB-DIVISION	WAVE LENGTH IN ÅNGSTROM UNITS		AMOUNT OF ENERGY
Radio (Hertzian waves)	Television	10^{10}–10^{12}	(Longest)	(Least)
	Radar	10^7–10^{10}		
	Radio	10^7–10^{13}		
Infrared		7800		
Visible (3900–7800 Å)				
	Red	6200–7800		
	Orange	5900–6200		
	Yellow	5600–5900	Spectrum	
	Yellow-green	5300–5600		
	Green	5000–5300		
	Blue-green	4700–5000		
	Blue	4300–4700		
	Violet	3900–4300		
Ultraviolet		150–3900		
X rays		.005–200		
Gamma rays		.001–1.4	(Shortest)	(Greatest)

because their energy is converted to heat when they strike an object. Naturally occurring infrared radiation comes from the sun. These radiations are responsible for the climates of the world. Infrared waves that strike the earth perpendicularly are almost completely absorbed, but those which strike the earth at an angle are reflected — an important fact which is responsible for the higher temperatures at the equator and the colder temperatures at the poles. Infrared radiation is also responsible for the evaporation of water from the surface of lakes, oceans, and plants, and for winds. The heating of the earth's surface causes the air above it to warm up and rise. As the warm air rises, it is replaced by cooler air brought in from surrounding areas. In this way breezes and winds are caused.

The radiations we can see. *Visible light* includes all of the radiations which we can see. They are made of wave lengths varying from 3900 Å to 7800 Å. An *angstrom unit* (Å) is one ten-millionth of a millimeter. As you refer to the table above, you will notice that our eyes can easily distinguish between wave lengths that differ as little as 300 Å. When you consider all of the shades of color that we are able to perceive, you can appreciate the wonderful complexity of the human eye.

The existence of all organisms depends upon visible light. You have read how the process of photosynthesis enables green plants to make their food by using the energy from sunlight. Plants use certain wave lengths of visible light for photosynthesis.

Dependence of animals on light. Animals are able to see where they are going and search for food by using visible light radiations. The organs which function to receive light energy and change it into chemical energy are called *photorecep-tors*. Photoreceptors vary in complexity from the simple eyespot of the euglena to the intricate human eye. Fig. 43-2 shows several types of photoreceptors. The eyespots of the euglena or the planaria enable the animal to find the desirable light intensity, and to distinguish light from dark. Many simple marine organisms migrate to certain depths during the daylight but come to the surface at night.

The *Nautilus* has an eye which functions like a pinhole camera. Although lacking a lens, this eye enables the animal to distinguish some form. The snail has an eye with a lens covering the surface. The eyes of the squid, octopus, and man are very similar in structure and function. The insect's compound eye is best suited to detect movement.

The flowering of many plants is dependent upon the length of light in relation to the length of darkness. This phenomenon is called *photoperiodism*.

Some people speak of long-day plants and short-day plants. The winter-blooming plants of the chrysanthemum, for example, would be called short-day bloomers. The summer-blooming sunflower and petunia would be considered long-day blooming plants. Nurserymen who raise flowers for the florist make use of this fact, and by varying the length of the light period can cause plants to bloom earlier and longer.

One of the factors causing the migration of birds is thought to be the length of daylight. It has been observed that at low temperatures small birds may lose weight rapidly. This weight loss seems to be as dependent on the length of daylight as it is on temperature. If the length of the daylight period is shortened, as it is in winter, the birds may not be able to find sufficient food each day. When this happens, the birds migrate to places where the temperature and day length are sufficient to supply their needs.

Visible light radiations are partially responsible for changes in the behavior

Fig. 43-2. The photoreceptors of different animals vary in complexity. Refer to Fig. 40-9, page 511, for a diagram of the human eye, the most complex type of photoreceptor.

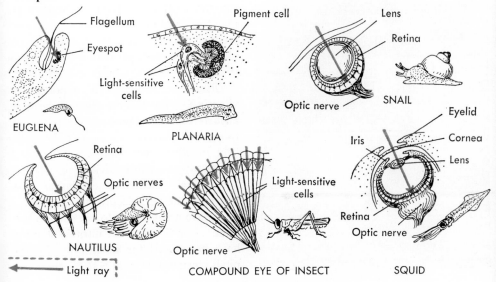

patterns of many animals. For instance, the molting of birds has been controlled, in some cases, by varying the amount of light. The poultry producer keeps lights in his hen houses where the egg-laying hens are living. The increase in the " day-length " increases the number of eggs laid.

Ultraviolet light. *Ultraviolet waves* have wave lengths which vary from 150 Å to 3900 Å. Although the human eye cannot perceive ultraviolet light, many animals, such as the bees, can. Much of the ultraviolet radiation which comes to the earth from the sun is filtered out by

Fig. 43-3. In this photograph of a fluoroscope screen, the esophagus shows up because the patient drank barium, which is opaque to X radiation. Refer to Fig. 37-5, page 464, for X-ray photographs of the same area, in which the esophagus does not show up because the patient did not drink barium.

Indiana University Medical Center

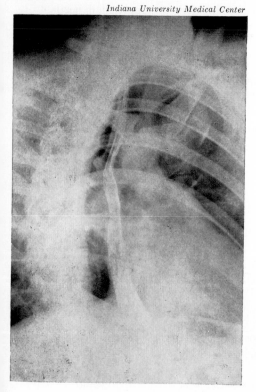

clouds, smoke, and fog. Walls, glass, and clothing stop much of the ultraviolet radiation for the human.

One effect of ultraviolet waves is that they produce **sunburn.** Ultraviolet waves with shorter wave lengths are absorbed by the protective, noncellular, horny layer of the skin (see Fig. 37-13, page 475). However, cells of the germinative layer of the epidermis are injured by radiations which have a wave length of more than 2500 Å. The injured cells release chemicals which cause the surface capillaries to open. This brings the blood near the surface and causes the skin to redden. If the burn is not serious, the red color will soon disappear and a small amount of pigment will develop (tanning). If the injury is more severe, the upper part of the germinative layer will be destroyed. Serum and white blood cells will accumulate in this area to form a blister. When the blister dries up, the skin is sloughed as a new epidermis forms.

Snow-blindness is caused by ultraviolet waves on the cornea of the eye. Surface cells are injured, causing the cornea to become opaque. This results in blindness for a few days until the new cells have formed and the injured cells are sloughed. If the exposure is long, scars may form and produce permanent impairment of vision. Because glass filters out ultraviolet waves, plain sunglasses aid in preventing snow-blindness.

Ultraviolet radiation is important in vitamin-D production by the body. **Ergosterol,** a substance present in various foods, is converted to vitamin D in the skin by ultraviolet radiation. The lack of this vitamin causes rickets.

Although ultraviolet radiation does not penetrate very deeply into the body, it does have great power to kill surface bacteria. For this reason, ultraviolet lamps have been used for sterilization in hospitals, restaurants, and rest rooms.

X rays are extremely short waves of radiation. **X rays** range in wave length from .005 Å to 200 Å. Injuries do not follow brief exposures to them, such as those used to treat various skin diseases. Small doses of X rays may cause a reddening similar to that caused by ultraviolet radiation. However, with increased length of exposure, severe burns result as the germinative layer of the epithelium is destroyed. New epithelium cannot be reproduced, therefore healing produces scars. The shorter wave lengths are called "hard" X rays. These hard X rays are able to penetrate the body and expose a film or can be seen on a fluoroscope screen (Fig. 43-3). However, all the X-ray waves do not pass through the body. Some of them are stopped by bone, which is why bones show up on a film as a shadow (see Fig. 34-9, page 428). Since different cells absorb X rays to a different extent, some tissues are affected more than others. Rapidly growing tissues are considerably more sensitive to X rays than connective tissues, for example. It is this fact that makes X ray a valuable treatment in cancer, where the cells are rapidly growing (refer to Chapter 48, page 602). In bone exposed to X rays, the blood-forming tissues are affected. In the gonads (ovaries and testes), the forming gametes are destroyed.

Gamma rays are electromagnetic waves that are extremly short. **Gamma rays** vary in wave length from .001 Å to 1.4 Å. They are given off from radioactive substances and are like X rays in their properties and actions on the body. In general, these penetrating gamma rays from a radioactive body consist of groups of electromagnetic radiations of different frequencies.

It is one of the important discoveries of modern physics that the shorter the wave length of any radiation, the more energy carried by each unit. Therefore, X rays and gamma rays possess many times more energy than light. They will also produce greater effects as they can penetrate farther into all kinds of matter.

How radiations affect the body. As radiation passes through the tissues, it collides with atoms. Each time an atom is hit, an electron is knocked loose and, in turn, usually becomes attached to another atom (Fig. 43-4). This electron removal and reattachment is known as **ionization**. The original radiation travels on to cause

Fig. 43-4. Ionizing radiations are those which collide with atoms and dislodge electrons which, in turn, attach to other atoms. This ionization is the factor responsible for the damage done to cells by radiation.

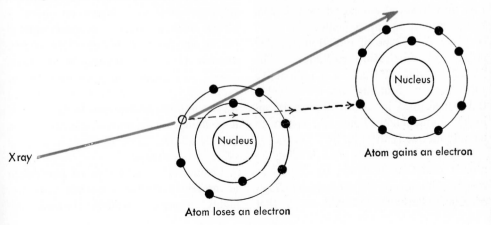

X ray

Nucleus

Nucleus

Atom gains an electron

Atom loses an electron

more ionizations until its energy is dissipated. In the process of ionization, chemical changes occur which cause biological effects such as burns, killed cells, or altered mechanisms of heredity.

As you read on you will see that different types of radiation can produce ionizations. Those that can are called *ionizing radiations.* The extent to which cells are killed is determined by the strength of radiation (the energy it possesses and the length of time to which the tissue is exposed).

Overexposure to ionizing radiations causes symptoms of burned areas on the surface which do not heal properly (such as we mentioned in connection with X rays), a decrease in the production of white blood cells, an increase in the susceptibility to infection, and bleeding into the intestines and lungs. Since many reproducing cells are destroyed, the body is not able to heal properly and death may result from infection, leukemia, or cancer. Many of these symptoms are similar to those associated with radiation sickness caused by the atomic bomb.

The effects of radiation on inheritance in animals and man are discussed in detail on pages 633 and 654.

Streams of minute particles. The second group of radiations involves streams of particles all moving in the same direction. Unlike electromagnetic waves, these rays may travel at almost any speed from nearly zero up to approximately the speed of light. This type of radiation is called *atomic,* or **particulate radiation.** The particles given off from such radioactive substances as uranium are unbelievably tiny (measured in 100-trillionths of an inch), unimaginably light, and known to us only indirectly through their effects.

Before you continue your reading on atomic radiation, it would be helpful to review Chapter 5, *The Chemical Basis of Life.* Perhaps you will recall that every atom has a tiny positively charged *nucleus* surrounded by one or more rings of negative *electrons.* The nucleus contains protons (positively charged particles) and neutrons (particles that are neither positive nor negative).

The number of protons and the number of electrons determine the chemical properties of an atom. Therefore, every element is different because its atoms have a proton number and an electron number different from any other element. Every atom of the same element has the same number of protons. The number of protons and neutrons together determine the weight of the atom. Two atoms with the same number of protons but different numbers of neutrons are **isotopes** of the same element (Fig. 5-3, page 46).

Atoms that are giving off particles (such as electrons, neutrons, or protons) are said to be **excited.** Some atoms, such as those of radium, are naturally excited and are constantly giving off particles. Other atoms can be excited by being struck by a projectile. If we were to shoot a rifle at a metal target, for example, energy would be added to the target — the target would be excited. The energy added to the target would be radiated away in the form of waves which carry sound and heat of the impact. If some pieces of the target were knocked out, this situation would be similar to particle radiation. When an atom is struck by a projectile, energy is carried off in the form of waves (X rays and gamma rays), or streams of particles (which are pieces from the target), or both. Since each atom is characterized by the number of particles in its nucleus, it is changed into another element or an isotope of the same element if it gives off atomic radiation.

Cosmic rays are a type of particulate or atomic radiation. *Cosmic rays* are highly charged protons (which are charged hydrogen nuclei). These rays enter the earth's atmosphere from outer space. In passing through the atmosphere many collide with other particles and change to neutrons, gamma rays, and charged particles other than protons. Many cosmic rays reach the surface of the earth where they are striking all living things every second. Since cosmic rays are able to penetrate many centimeters of lead, all organisms are being bombarded by them constantly.

Little is known about the effects of cosmic rays on living things, however, because it would be extremely difficult to provide a habitat which would screen out the rays. The measurement of cosmic rays at various altitudes was an important part of the program in which the first United States satellite, 1958 Alpha, was sent up from Cape Canaveral, Fla.

Radium is an example of an element with naturally excited atoms. As *radium* constantly emits (gives off) particles, it is changed to the element lead. In this gradual change to lead, called *radium decay,* three types of radiations are emitted: (1) *alpha particles* (Fig. 43-5); (2) *beta particles;* and (3) *gamma rays.*

Helium nuclei. *Alpha particles* are charged nuclei of helium atoms that are projected at velocities of 10,000 miles a second. Each alpha particle consists of two protons and two neutrons. Although these particles travel at such a tremendous speed, they are easily absorbed and even a sheet of paper will stop them. In living tissue damage is done when a particle, acting like a bullet, passes through the cells and disrupts the molecules with which it collides. These alpha particles are not able to enter the tissues because they are stopped and absorbed by the skin. They are dangerous, however, if breathed in with dust or moisture and in this manner allowed to reach the delicate tissues of the lungs. Alpha particles are

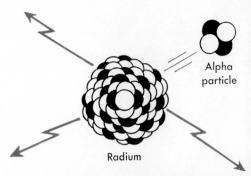

Fig. 43-5. Radium is a naturally excited element which constantly gives off radiations, one form of which is alpha particles.

also dangerous if they are ingested with food or water. In this way they can reach other vital organs.

High-speed electrons. *Beta particles* are streams of electrons. They have different velocities, but some approach the speed of light. These particles, like alpha particles, do not penetrate deeply but are dangerous if inhaled or ingested.

The effects of atomic radiation are similar to those of the shorter electromagnetic waves. The rapidly growing tissues (which have many dividing cells) are the most sensitive.

How is radiation produced? Radiation occurs *naturally,* and it can also be produced *artificially.* One source of naturally occurring radiation is the sun, which emits the waves of electromagnetic radiations which are so important to life as we know it on the earth. Everywhere on earth there is also a small amount of background radiation which comes from two sources: cosmic rays, and naturally radioactive elements, such as radium and uranium, that are found in rocks and in the soil. The strength of exposure of organisms to these radiations will vary widely since these elements are not evenly distributed over the surface of the earth. These are naturally excited atoms which are constantly throwing off "bullets" which may strike other atoms, causing

Atomic Energy Commission

Fig. 43-6. During the chain reaction of an atomic bomb blast, alpha particles, beta particles, gamma rays, visible light waves, and heat are produced. Radioactive material may be carried for thousands of miles before it returns to the earth in the form of fallout.

them to break apart and, in turn, throw off more bullets.

Radiation has been of value in tracing the history of life on the earth. Biologists have taken advantage of natural radiation to determine the age of extinct or preserved animals and plants. The normal carbon atom, carbon-12, has 6 protons and 6 neutrons in its nucleus. One isotope of carbon, *carbon-14*, has 6 protons, but it has 8 neutrons in its nucleus. The nucleus of this isotope is unstable and therefore radioactive. C^{14} can be made artificially, but it also exists in the atmosphere. As cosmic rays strike the earth's atmosphere, some carbon molecules are produced which have two additional neutrons in their nuclei.

A low but constant level of radioactivity is maintained in plants and animals through the carbon atoms involved in the carbon dioxide-oxygen cycle. However, when living things die, the carbon atoms within their cells are no longer replaced. The radioactivity of the carbon atoms slowly diminishes. It is known that half of the C^{14} in a dead organism will be converted to C^{12} in 5,570 years. This figure is called the **half-life** of C^{14}. A wooden beam taken from the tomb of an Egyptian Pharaoh was found to have about half the radioactivity of wood in living trees. How old would this make the beam?

Artificial radiations. Artificial radiations have been produced by atomic explosions and in atomic reactors. In every atomic explosion, radioactive particles are formed in a huge cloud (Fig. 43-6). Some of these particles are carried great distances by the wind and gradually settle over the earth as " fallout." Radioactive material from Nevada has been carried to grass in England, where it had been ingested by cattle.

In some nuclear explosions, *strontium-90* (Sr^{90}) is produced. Some of this Sr^{90} makes up very fine particles which are blown up into the stratosphere (higher than 40,000 feet). This material stays in the upper air so long that it is eventually carried to all parts of the earth. We do not know how long it is actually stored in the stratosphere, or how it returns to the lower atmosphere and then to the ground. The mixing of the upper and lower layers of air is one of the major questions with which meteorology is concerned today.

Since this isotope of strontium has a half-life of about 27 years, it can accumulate in various ways before its radioactivity is dissipated. Even in small concentrations, it is taken up from the soil in plants. It may be then concentrated more when animals eat these plants. Thus it is possible that a person eating the meat or drinking the milk from a cow that has fed on contaminated grass could be taking in more Sr^{90} than he would be exposed to in fallout from a nuclear explosion. Since Sr^{90} is chemically similar to calcium, it accumulates in bones. Once a certain level of concentration is reached, Sr^{90} can destroy tissues, cause cancer, and death. Most scientists believe that the Sr^{90} formed from nuclear explosions to date is not yet large enough to be a danger.

Atomic reactors use particles from a radioactive isotope, such as uranium-235, to cause other atoms to disintegrate. This disintegration produces more atomic particles, which may, in turn, causes other atoms to disintegrate, resulting in a continuous process called a *chain reaction.* This reaction also releases large amounts of heat. Throughout the United States, as well as in England and other countries, there are many of these atomic reactors which use this heat to produce steam for turning large turbines that produce electricity.

It is probable that the principal source of harmful radioactive material in the future will be the generation of electricity by stations that are powered by nuclear energy. One of the problems to be solved will be the disposal of wastes containing radioactive material. Simply dumping the wastes into the rivers or the ocean will involve the exposure of many living things to radiation. In turn, some of these organisms may be used by man for food. Algae in the North Sea have been contaminated by radioactive material which has been dumped there. Where did it go? What fish ate it? Who ate the fish? These are still unanswered questions. Thus, contamination by radioactive wastes is not the problem of a single country but is a topic of international concern.

Sterilization of foods by radiation. Radiation can also be used to sterilize certain foods. This practice would reduce the need for refrigeration and enable foods to be kept for longer periods of time. Experiments have shown that foods can be sterilized by radiation without becoming radioactive. From a health standpoint this procedure may become valuable, as foods can be sterilized after packaging, thus preventing contamination.

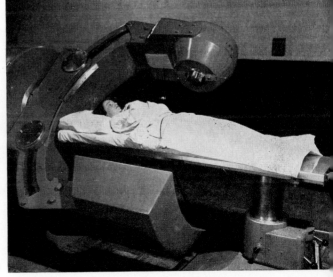

Fig. 43-7. Radioactive materials are used effectively in the treatment of cancer in its early stages. This patient has a good chance for complete recovery because her case was diagnosed and treated at an early stage.

Hajjar from Monkmeyer

Use of radioactive isotopes. Isotopes have been widely used in studies of physiology, chemistry, and botany. A radioactive isotope of oxygen, for example, can be followed by a Geiger counter throughout a plant, an animal, or a chemical reaction. By using this oxygen isotope, which we call a *tracer element,* we can learn many things about the respiration of plants and animals. For example, if this oxygen atom is combined with two atoms of hydrogen, a tagged molecule of water is produced. By following it through the experimental plant, we can learn many things about what the plant does with water it takes in through its roots. Thus radiation has given us a tool which can be used to gain a better understanding of the chemistry of living things.

Medical uses of radiation. In medicine, X rays, radium, and isotopes produced in reactors have proved to be a valuable treatment for skin diseases, tumors, and cancer. Since tumors and cancer are rapidly growing tissues, they are especially sensitive to radiation treatment. However, our studies of the physics of radiation and its effects on life have shown us that these waves and rays must be used with great care. The direction, strength, and time of exposure must be carefully calculated to obtain effective treatment with minimum damage to surrounding tissues.

Special precautions against radiation. Those who work in industries producing or using radioactive materials have an additional radiation problem. In these installations, workers are checked regularly by means of radiation indicators worn at all times in danger areas. Thus, the worker always knows the total amount of radiation to which he has been exposed. He also wears protective garments, and is shielded from the radioac-

Fig. 43-8. The atomic energy worker on the left is carrying ion chambers in his breast pocket, and a film meter on the lapel of his coat. The small meters on his tie, finger, and wrist are worn to detect radiation at specific body areas. The worker on the right wears a plastic suit for protection when handling radioactive materials.

Westcott from Oak Ridge　　　　　　　　　　*General Electric Co.*

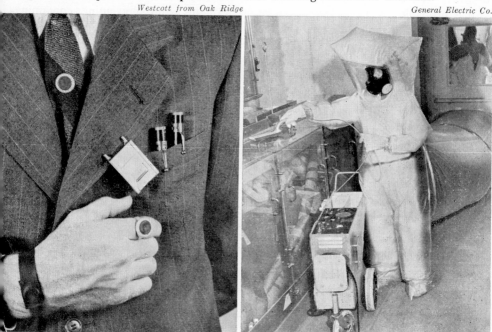

tive materials with which he works by cases or walls of radiation-resistant lead. Dentists and physicians who specialize in radiology also take special precautions not to expose themselves to X rays for any length of time. Recently, many shoe stores have removed the machines that X ray childrens' feet, and the U. S. Public Health Service now recommends that chest X rays be given only when there is a positive indication of some disorder in the lungs.

In Conclusion

We are exposed to certain electromagnetic and particulate radiations every day. Many of these are vital to health and essential for life. Without visible radiations from the sun all plants would die, and soon after that, all animals. Although many radiations are not necessary for life, they have been used in medicine for the diagnosis and treatment of disease.

Since we are now in the beginning of the Nuclear Age, more will be learned about radiation and its effects on life. The increased use of atomic energy will present many unforeseen problems which will require a knowledge of the basic nature of radiations.

BIOLOGICALLY SPEAKING

angstrom unit	gamma rays	radio waves
alpha particles	half-life	radium
atomic reactor	infrared waves	snow-blindness
beta particles	ionization	strontium-90
carbon-14	isotopes	sunburn
chain reaction	particulate radiation	tracer element
cosmic rays	photoperiodism	ultraviolet waves
electromagnetic radiation	photoreceptors	visible light
ergosterol	radiation	X rays
excited atom		

QUESTIONS FOR REVIEW

1. What were some of the dangers of which the earlier workers on radioactivity were unaware?
2. What fields of science are brought together in the study of the biological effects of radiation?
3. Make a table listing the types of electromagnetic radiations, some sources of each, and the effect of each on living things.
4. Make a table listing the types of atomic radiations, some sources of each, and the effects of each on living things.
5. How has radiation been valuable in determining the age of fossils embedded in the earth?
6. Would plain sunglasses prevent snow-blindness? Explain your answer.

7. What do radiations have to do with breezes? Which radiations are involved in breeze formation?
8. Which radiations do you consider to be essential for life? Explain.
9. Which radiations are most widely used in the treatment of cancer? Is healthy tissue also destroyed during this type of cancer treatment? Explain.
10. When can alpha and beta particles be dangerous?

APPLYING FACTS AND PRINCIPLES

1. Explain how radiation can be used in the treatment of cancer even though it is capable of producing cancer.
2. If you had a patio or a porch covered by glass, which radiations would reach you inside? Which would not? Would the temperature of this area differ from a similar area covered by wood? Explain.
3. Find a diagram of an atomic reactor and make a sketch of it. In your own words, explain the basic parts.
4. Can you think of any suggestions for methods of disposal of atomic wastes?

CHAPTER 44

Space Biology

MEN of all ages have gazed into the vastness of space, longing to explore both the ocean of air which blankets the earth and the limitless expanse beyond. They have dreamed of reaching the moon and looking back at the earth, or landing some strange machine on another planet, perhaps to find life in a totally different form.

Although the conquest of space has long been a dream, very soon it should become a reality. Today we stand on the threshold of the Space Age. At any time, a giant rocket may streak upward, carrying the first spaceman into a realm never entered before by a human being. Such rockets are now nearing perfection. But what about the spaceman? Can he survive such a mission? What of the psychological effects of such an exciting ordeal as a journey into space? Can he return safely from outer space to the earth?

We know that life cannot exist in the void of outer space. Thus, we must propel both the spaceman and his life-sustaining environment within the space vehicle.

This chapter will discuss many unique problems which must be solved before man can conquer the most challenging of all frontiers — the vast expanse of outer space.

Various definitions of space. Specialists in practically every branch of science have their own questions and problems about space. The biologist wants to know if organisms can survive in space; the engineer wants to know what kind of craft must be built to reach outer space and to travel in it; the meteorologist wants to determine better methods for predicting the weather by the study of cloud formations

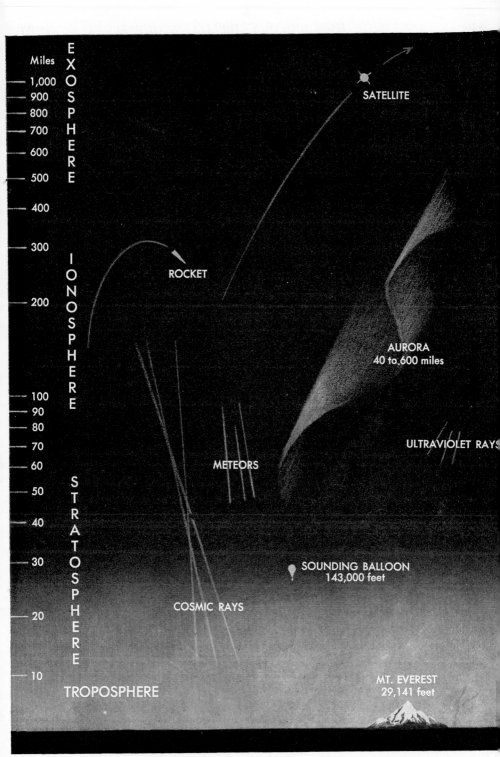

Fig. 44-1. This diagram illustrates the different layers which make up the earth's atmosphere. Notice the altitudes of the different types of radiation, and the relative heights to which various man-made vehicles have been sent.

Wide World

Wide World

Fig. 44-2. The nose cone of the Jupiter rocket (*left*) carried the two monkeys, Able and Baker, to an altitude of 300 miles. On the right, you can see where one of the monkeys was strapped into position in the interior of the cone, with wires leading to recording instruments from the electrodes that were placed on his body.

and wind patterns high in the earth's atmosphere; the physicist wants to prove theoretical data; the physician wants to study the behavior and physiology of man under the stresses of space travel. Each of these scientists has a different concept of what constitutes space. For instance, the biologist might choose an altitude of 100,000 feet as the beginning of outer space, because at this height the low pressure causes the fluids of the body to vaporize; there is no air to breathe; and even reflected light cannot be viewed without protection for the eyes. The rocket engineer, on the other hand, might think of outer space as beginning at the altitude at which there would be almost no interaction between a space ship and the gas molecules in the atmosphere. A meteorologist might consider that outer space begins just above the lower layers of the stratosphere, because above this level the weather is always " clear and sunny." The physicist defines space in the terms of the number of gas molecules found in a given volume. To a physicist, outer space contains about a dozen molecules per cubic inch. This is a very small number when you consider that the best vacuum man has ever created contains several billion molecules per cubic inch.

What do we know about space? Our present information regarding space has come to us from mountain climbers, balloonists, pilots, and recording instruments sent aloft in balloons, rockets, and satellites. Fig. 44-1 illustrates some of the physical and geographic aspects of space, and also shows some of the heights to which various man-made objects have ascended in the pursuit of vital information. The current data collected by these vehicles indicate that space is by no means a friendly environment. There is no air; there is no light as we know it because there is no atmosphere to scatter light rays. There is only a blazing glare from the sun — all else is dark. There is no matter to transmit sound waves; there is no orientation by gravity; dangerous radiations prevail; and hurtling rocks and dust in the form of meteors are present.

The best instruments, however, are no substitute for determining the precise effects that space travel will have on a living organism — especially man. To gather such information, scientists have sent various mammals to high altitudes in rockets. Two monkeys named Able and Baker were fired in the nose of a Jupiter rocket to an altitude of 300 miles on May 28, 1959 (Fig. 44-2). The nose cone was later recovered after re-entry into the earth's atmosphere with the monkeys still alive inside. The data collected showed that the monkeys suffered no ill effects from the experience and their body processes continued to function normally during all stages of the flight. This event was noteworthy because it was the first time a living organism had ever ascended to such heights and then returned to the earth alive, and in good physical condition as well. The implications are obvious — if monkeys can do it, why can't man?

Plans for space travel. Despite the many problems still to be solved, scientists now believe that it will be possible for man to travel in space in the near future. Vehicles capable of escaping the earth's gravitational field have already been built and launched successfully. It now remains to devise a vehicle with a suitable environment for human passengers and capable of returning them to earth safely. But first, let's examine some of the biological problems that must be solved before man can safely travel in space.

Effects of acceleration upon leaving the earth's atmosphere. In order for a vehicle to orbit around the earth at an altitude of 300 miles, it must travel at 18,000 miles per hour; to leave the gravitational field of the earth, the vehicle must obtain a speed of about 25,000 miles per hour. We know that many of the problems of physics and chemistry involved in both such feats have been solved with the successful launching of earth satellites and lunar probes.

One of the biological factors to be considered in man's conquest of space is that of the effects of *acceleration,* or the rate of change of speed, to attain velocities of 18,000 and 25,000 miles per hour. When you are taking off in an airplane, or even when your car starts to move, you can feel your body press lightly into the back of the seat. This accelerating force,

Fig. 44-3. This man is shown being subjected to an increasing number of *g*'s, to test his ability to endure rapid acceleration. Why does this rapid acceleration cause the contortions in his face?

Wide World

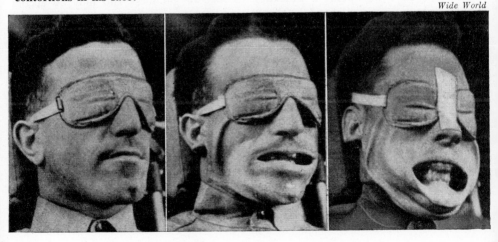

Fig. 44-4. These men are shown being subjected to a condition of zero gravity, which gives them the sensation of weightlessness. Notice that they are floating in air.

which has the effect of increasing your weight, is measured in units called **g's**. At a force of two g's, for example, your body would weigh twice what it normally does. A pilot making diving or gunning runs may black out between five and seven g's because his heart cannot pump sufficient blood to his brain against the extreme force of acceleration. However, recent experiments indicate that men lying down can take up to 14 g's without blacking out. Above this point a **blackout** may occur because the weight of the blood is increased to such an extent that the heart can no longer keep it circulating through the arteries and veins. The brain and retinas of both eyes also fail because of lack of vital blood and oxygen. Since the rockets now in use seldom exceed 10 g's during their greatest acceleration, scientists now believe acceleration is not the problem is was once thought to be.

Weightlessness in space. The period of a space ship's rapid acceleration with the accompanying g-factor lasts only a few minutes. Once the desired velocity

and height have been reached, the power is shut off. At this moment, the g-factor ceases, whereupon the passengers begin to experience the sensation of **weightlessness** (Fig. 44-4). Because the earth is so far away, its gravitational pull now exerts practically no effect on the body, hence the body lacks weight in this state of **zero gravity.** The sensation is similar to one you have probably experienced in a rapidly descending elevator. The feeling is one of giddiness and may be accompanied by nausea. However, your experience was only momentary. Imagine the same sensation continuing over a prolonged period of time, as it would in a long space flight.

The body lacks all **kinesthetic sense,** which is the awareness of the whereabouts of your body parts when you move them. The sense of balance is also lost, as the semicircular canals can no longer function properly. However, most body processes continue normally in spite of weightlessness, and scientists believe that men can be trained to adjust to the experience.

There are other peculiar problems that accompany weightlessness. Liquids cannot be poured, hence the space traveler will have to drink with a straw, or the liquid will have to be in a container which can be squeezed to force the liquid into the mouth. Passengers will have to be strapped down while sitting or sleeping to avoid floating about the ship. Magnetic shoes will have to be worn for walking.

Respiration — a vital problem. Respiration problems at high altitudes were discussed in connection with the respiratory system on pages 466 and 467. The space traveler would encounter the same problems, but to a much greater degree. At 16 miles above the earth, the density of the air is only about four per cent of its density at sea level; beyond an altitude of 70 miles, there is practically no atmosphere and therefore practically no oxygen. It is now known, however, that after training man can exist in an atmosphere of approximately one-half the normal oxygen content on earth without discomfort, and still be reasonably efficient. Scientists came to this conclusion after studying the activities of a tribe of Indians who live at high altitudes in the mountains of Peru. These Indians were able to carry on normal physical activities that would quickly exhaust a healthy individual who is accustomed to the atmosphere at sea level. On further investigation, scientists learned that the reason these tribesmen could carry on such activities was because of their greater lung capacity and a higher red blood cell count. These factors enabled them to take in a larger air supply with each breath, thereby obtaining more oxygen; and the greater number of red blood cells could distribute this oxygen more efficiently to the tissues of the body. The scientists then concluded that similar body changes could be induced in a person by doing considerable exercise at high altitudes. Further tests

bore this fact out, as men were trained at high altitudes and it was found that both the red blood cell count and the air capacity of the lungs had increased considerably. Hence these men were able to carry on normal activity in an atmosphere much reduced in oxygen content. Nevertheless, even in a reduced oxygen atmosphere, the entire cabin of the space ship must be supplied with oxygen, or masks connected to oxygen tanks must be worn, since there is practically no oxygen in the outer reaches of space.

As you know, carbon dioxide is a byproduct of respiration. On earth it is reused by plants in the process of photosynthesis. In a sealed space ship, however, it will be necessary to devise a method of utilizing the carbon dioxide exhaled by the travelers. On page 102, we mentioned that certain algae are now being considered for use in space travel. One of the algae that has indicated considerable promise in this regard is the green alga *Chlorella*. Not only does *Chlorella* give promise of being extremely efficient in utilizing the carbon dioxide exhaled by the crew, but it also will probably serve as an excellent source of oxygen to replenish the supply on the space ship. Another factor that is being considered, and one which is extremely important, is the possibility that *Chlorella* can be cultured while the space ship is in flight to serve as a possible source of food for the passengers. Hence, it is not beyond reason that the same *oxygen-carbon dioxide cycle* that goes on continuously on earth may be simulated in a space ship.

Pressure problems in space. At sea level, the air pressure is approximately 14.7 pounds per square inch. We are not aware of this pressure because our bodies are adapted to it. When we climb a mountain or fly in an airplane, however, the pressure is less than that on the surface of the earth, as there is less air above us. In a rocket, the effects of this decrease in pressure would be drastic, because at altitudes above 60,000 feet the blood would boil at normal body temperature. This boiling is caused by the formation of bubbles of the gases normally dissolved in blood and other body fluids as a result of the decrease in pressure on the blood. These bubbles would tear through capillaries and damage delicate brain tissues, resulting in death in 15 minutes at an altitude of only 11 miles.

There are several methods being considered for attacking this particular problem. One is the obvious method of a pressurized cabin such as used in a modern airplane; another method is to alter the atmosphere within the space craft. Scientists have found that the atmosphere can be altered by replacing the normal nitrogen content in the air with helium, which helps to solve the pressure problem because helium is not nearly as soluble in the blood as is nitrogen. If helium is substituted for nitrogen in the space ship's atmosphere, the formation of gas bubbles in the blood and body tissues is greatly reduced.

Scientists have learned a great deal about the problem of gas-bubble formation, since the same problem is also encountered in deep-sea diving. In this occupation, divers can work at great depths because they wear air-pressurized diving gear. However, if the air pressure on the diver's body is reduced too quickly as he ascends, nitrogen bubbles form in his blood and tissues. This results in a crippling occupational disease known as the **bends.** The same disease could be suffered in a space ship following an **explosive decompression** of the atmosphere in the ship as a result of a break in the space ship's wall. A sudden outrush of the atmosphere with the resulting drop in the pressure of the cabin would cause bubbles to form in the blood, as they would if there were no pressure control at all. However, with helium used in the atmosphere, this danger is greatly reduced, since fewer bubbles are formed.

Another method for reducing the dangers of low pressure in outer space is by the use of a specially developed pressure suit (Fig. 44-5). The purpose of such a suit is to supply pressure to the body to make up for that which the atmosphere lacks. This suit is so constructed that if there should be a severe decompression as the result of a break in the wall of the cabin, a barometric device on the suit would automatically cause it to press against the body at a pressure quite close to normal. This would then maintain the

Fig. 44-5. The type of space suit shown here is designed to afford maximum comfort while allowing body processes to function normally. The man is feeding himself through a tube connected to a squeeze bottle.

normal flow of blood and prevent it from boiling.

There is also the possibility that the atmospheric pressure in a space ship will, by design, be much less than that to which the passengers are accustomed at sea level. It has been found that a man can carry on normal body functions and conduct activities with a reasonable efficiency at a pressure of only 10 pounds per square inch rather than a normal sea-level pressure of 14.7 pounds per square inch. A cabin so pressurized at a level of 10 pounds per square inch would greatly reduce the hazards that come with any sudden decompression. However, a combination of all the methods mentioned above will probably be used so as to provide the crew and passengers with the greatest possible protection, should such an explosive decompression ever occur.

Extremes of temperature. One of the principal functions of our atmosphere is to insulate the earth from the radiations of the sun. As such an insulating blanket, the atmosphere keeps the temperature on most parts of the earth within reasonable limits. However, in outer space this insulating blanket is lacking, with the result that there is nothing present to ward off the high temperatures produced by the sun's radiations. And since outer space lacks an atmosphere, there is nothing there to conduct the heat away from the space ship. Thus a ship in outer space would absorb the high intensity of the sun's rays on that side of the ship facing the sun, whereas the side away from the sun would be extremely cold. This would obviously present considerable discomfort to the occupants within the ship. Physicists believe that imparting a slight spin to the ship might distribute these temperatures evenly. It might also be possible to construct the ship so that there would be insulating barriers between the outside hull and the inside of the cabin.

However, the greatest danger from heat would probably be not from the severe temperature differences in outer space but in the re-entry of the ship into the earth's atmosphere. At the great speed the space ship will be traveling, high temperatures will be built up around the ship as soon as it begins to collide with the gas molecules of the atmosphere. The heat generated by this friction will have to be reduced in order to prevent the ship from burning up, much as a meteor does on entering the earth's atmosphere. This could be done by slowing down the ship in stages as it returned to the earth's atmosphere, and also by covering the ship with heat-resistant materials.

Naturally, air conditioning will also be necessary to distribute the heat evenly throughout the entire ship, as well as to provide the proper humidity for the evaporation of body moisture in the atmosphere of the ship. The air-conditioning system will also serve as part of an artificial *water cycle* to replenish the water supply. Thus the water vapor expelled into the air by both the algae cultures and the passengers would be condensed and distilled for reuse, and at the same time the humidity would be maintained at a comfortable level.

Cosmic rays. In Chapter 43 we learned that cosmic rays are constantly entering the earth's atmosphere from outer space, and that they are composed of high-speed protons. It has been thought these cosmic rays would imperil the space traveler by causing undersirable genetic mutations. However, recent experiments seem to indicate that we need not fear such damage in space. Monkeys have spent as long as 35 hours in balloons at altitudes of 17 miles, with no observable genetic damage. Balloons have also carried black mice to altitudes of 100,000 feet and exposed them to cosmic rays. When these mice were returned to the earth,

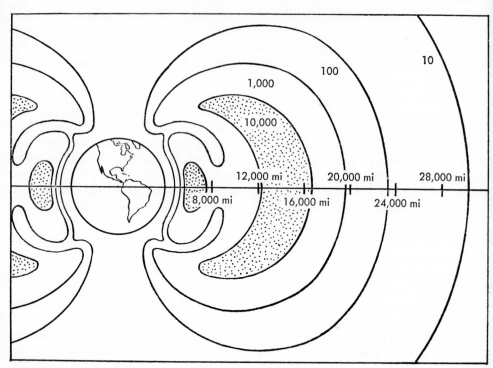

Fig. 44-6. **The stipple areas in this diagram are the Van Allen Radiation Belts. The numbers above the mileages indicate the radiation counts per second.**

their coats had turned white, but in two or three succeeding generations, no detrimental genetic effects were observed.

A more recent discovery indicates that there are two belts of high-energy radiations around the equatorial regions of the earth. These have been named the *Van Allen Radiation Belts,* after the scientist who predicted their existence. At present, it is thought that the first manned space ship will be launched at an altitude either north or south of these radiation belts, in an effort to avoid their harmful effects (Fig. 44-6).

Psychological effects of space travel. Man traveling in space will need sufficient food to sustain him until he returns to earth. However, instruments and fuel to allow for a return trip must make up the greatest weight of the rocket. Hence the food supply will have to consist of the basic nutrients in their most condensed

form — not a very tasty menu! The diet of the space traveler will of necessity have to consist of some bulk foods. These will be supplemented by multivitamin pills and others containing various nutrients. As has been previously mentioned, algae may be cultured during a prolonged space flight to serve also as a possible food source. Nevertheless, the diet of the space traveler will be considerably different in form and content from the one he is accustomed to on earth. This will necessitate an adjustment and training to new tastes.

Man is used to alternating periods of light and dark. Tests indicate that he cannot tolerate either day or night indefinitely. Space ships therefore will have to be equipped with apparatus capable of producing artificial day and night cycles in order to accommodate this psychological need.

The sensation of weightlessness and the long periods of time spent in cramped quarters are other psychological problems of space travel. However, scientists now believe that most of these psychological problems can be reduced in intensity by an adequate training program which the spacemen will undergo.

What makes a good spaceman? Because of the numerous psychological and physical stresses that will be encountered in space travel, the men who will be the first to attempt it must be extremely well adjusted, stable, and physically fit. In preparation for the first manned space flight, seven men have already been selected by the National Aeronautics and Space Administration to undergo the training needed for such a venture (Fig. 44-7). These seven *astronauts,* as they are called, were selected from thousands of candidates screened for the purpose.

Many tests have been given to the candidates to determine their physical fitness and psychological stability. One of the initial tests is to place a man in a chamber completely devoid of light and sound and leave him there alone for 48 hours. The purpose of this test is to determine how well the man can tolerate such absolute quietness and isolation. Following this are tests to determine how a candidate will react to the severe acceleration to which his body will be subjected during the initial period after a rocket's blast-off. This is done by placing the man in a special centrifuge and whirling him around at great speeds. Another test is to place the candidate in a room in which the temperature is raised to 130° F, whereupon the candidate then performs specific tests to determine how well he can maintain his reactions at such high temperatures. The candidate is also subjected to ear-splitting noises and is required to perform specific functions during the noises. He is also put in a special room in which various altitudes can be simulated. By means of a series of vacuum pumps, the atmosphere is removed from the room so the candidate

Fig. 44-7. The seven men shown were chosen from over 100 candidates to be the first astronauts. Testing proved them physically and emotionally fit to withstand space travel when it comes.

Wide World

is placed at an " altitude " anywhere up to 100,000 feet. At one stage of this altitude ascent the air is suddenly removed from the room to simulate an explosive decompression. The candidate's reactions are then tested as a special pressure suit immediately takes over the function of the space ship's pressure chamber. These are only a few of the tests that the candidates must undergo to determine their fitness and to train them for what they will encounter during long periods of space flight.

The shape of things to come. Much remains to be done before man can be successfully sent into space and returned to the earth. However, space capsules to carry human astronauts are now well beyond the designing stage. It is believed that the launching of a manned space capsule may be accomplished in the not-too-distant future. If all plans are successful, this capsule will probably be launched by rockets to an altitude of 125 miles, will circle the earth for a day, and will then return to the earth by parachute. Reaching a speed of approximately 18,-000 miles per hour, the capsule is expected to circle the earth 18 times during the initial 24-hour period. Food, water, a two-way radio, and an atmosphere of endurable pressure, temperature, and humidity will be provided. A man lying on his back on a padded couch will experience about 7 g's on blast-off. When in orbit, he will be in a sitting position. During the time the capsule is orbiting the earth, the man will be in a state of weightlessness, and will not begin to feel the effects of gravity until the capsule re-enters the earth's atmosphere.

It is not yet certain which rocket will carry the manned capsule into space. Before this can be done, however, a series of tests with instrument-carrying capsules is planned. These will be followed by a series of capsules carrying primates and other mammals on increasingly long rides. Eventually, a man will be sent to an altitude of about 70 miles before landing about 200 miles away from the blast-off site. The next step will then be to send a manned capsule into orbit to circle the earth once, and finally, to remain in orbit for the full 24 hours But all this is just the prelude to a prolonged space trip.

In Conclusion

We are proceeding cautiously in our plans to visit vast, limitless space. Research data from all branches of science must be carefully calculated before sending a human being on this exciting journey. Some of the steps which have already been taken to collect these data include: high-altitude rockets and lunar probes; earth-orbiting satellites; and mammals sent up in artificial satellites and rockets.

All these initial tests are, of course, for the purpose of eventually launching man into space and returning him to earth successfully. The timetable for this future manned flight is still rather tentative, but there are various stages by which it will be accomplished. These include: a manned journey to various altitudes in rockets; placing a man in a satellite for a certain period of time; and sending a man into space for a short period of time. Then, it is hoped, man will be ready for interplanetary travel.

BIOLOGICALLY SPEAKING

acceleration	blackout	kinesthetic sense
astronaut	explosive decompression	weightlessness
bends	g's	zero gravity

QUESTIONS FOR REVIEW

1. Why does man want to conquer space?
2. Describe some of the methods used to collect data on space.
3. What is acceleration and what effect does it have on the body?
4. Why does a person black out when subjected to a force of many g's?
5. Describe the causes and effects of weightlessness.
6. What body changes can be induced through training to make respiration easier at high altitudes?
7. Explain why the blood would boil at normal body temperature at altitudes above 60,000 feet. What can be done to prevent this?
8. Describe how artificial carbon dioxide-oxygen and water cycles can be created in a space ship.
9. What evidence exists to show that cosmic rays may not be as great a hazard to space flight as scientists once thought they were?
10. What are some of the special qualifications and training that will have to be met by the first man to attempt a trip into space?

APPLYING FACTS AND PRINCIPLES

1. Using the steps in the research method for solving a problem, make an outline entitled "Man Attempts to Conquer Space," giving the principal steps that scientists have taken to date.
2. If you were a passenger in a space ship, could you talk to a fellow passenger? Explain your answer.
3. Do you believe the present qualifications and training for the first man to travel in space will always be necessary? Explain your answer.
4. Why can the wearer of a pressure suit withstand many more g's than a person without such protection?
5. Name several everyday occurrences which might be difficult to perform in a condition of zero gravity. Tell what might occur in each case. Can you suggest any solutions?

RESEARCH ON YOUR OWN

1. Using either prepared slides or fresh mounts, examine several kinds of muscle tissues. Record your results in sketches. If fresh mounts are made, use fibers of heart muscle and lean beef as skeletal muscle. Stomach or intestine wall is a good subject for smooth muscle. Spread the fibers apart and stain them with methylene blue.
2. Keep an accurate check on all of your meals for one week. Calculate the number of Calories you take in each day by consulting a Calorie chart. Calculate the number of Calories you need each day, based on your weight and activity. Make a bar graph showing the number of Calories consumed each day and draw a line across the graph to show what your intake should have been.
3. Test various foods, such as apple, potato, cane sugar, raisins, lean meat, etc., for simple sugar, starch, fat, and protein. Use Fehling's solution, iodine, carbon tetrachloride, and the nitric acid-ammonia test for the various types of foods. Review the procedure

for using each of these before making the tests.

4. Fill a quart jar with water and submerge it, mouth down, in an aquarium or a large, deep pan. Put the end of a rubber hose into the mouth of the jar. When you blow through the hose, the air you exhale will displace water in the jar. Exhale normally, then blow all of the air you can into the jar. Mark the level of the water in the jar. Fill the jar again and repeat, blowing out all the air you can after normal inhalation. Repeat after a forced inhalation.

5. Place a drop of blood on a microscope slide and stain it with Wright's blood stain. Examine it under high power.

6. Prepare a set of corks (about six) with a pair of pins stuck through each one. One cork should have the pins touching each other. The second should have them slightly separated, the third still farther apart, etc. Have someone touch the pins to various areas of your skin to see how far apart the points must be before you feel both of them and to discover if all areas of the skin have similar reactions to touch.

7. Make a list of some problems which must be solved in order to make space travel possible. This list should include such factors as temperature extremes, weightlessness, food, water, wastes, and oxygen. After you have compiled the list, choose any one item and find out as much as you can about this particular problem by using your library. When you feel that you are up to date on this phase of space travel, prepare a short report and present it to the class.

MORE ABOUT BIOLOGY

Alexander, P. *Atomic Radiation and Life.* Penguin Books, Baltimore, Md. 1957

Ames, G. *The First People of the World.* Harpers and Bros., New York. 1958

Asimov, Isaac. *Chemicals of Life: Enzymes, Vitamins, and Hormones.* Abelard-Schuman, Ltd. New York. 1954

Best, Charles A. and Taylor, Norman B. *The Living Body.* 4th ed. Henry Holt and Co., Inc., New York. 1958

Boyd-Orr, John. *The Wonderful World of Food, the Substance of Life* Doubleday and Co., Inc., New York. 1958

Cosgrove, M. *Wonders of Your Senses.* Dodd, Mead, New York. 1958

Glemser, B. *All About the Human Body.* Random House, New York. 1958

Glynn, John H. *The Story of Blood.* A. A. Wyn, Inc., New York. 1948

Hunter, I. *Memory: Facts and Fallacies.* Penguin Books, Baltimore, Md. 1958

Ley, Willy. *Rockets, Missiles, and Space Travel.* Viking Press, New York. 1957

Mathison, R. *The Eternal Search: The Story of Man and His Drugs.* G. P. Putnam's Sons, New York. 1958

Morrison, Cornett, and Tether. *Human Physiology.* Henry Holt and Co., Inc., New York. 1959

Pierce, John R. and David, Edward E. Jr. *Man's World of Sound.* Doubleday and Co., Inc., New York. 1958

Pollack, Luby. *Your Normal Mind: Its Tricks and Quirks.* Wilfred Funk, Inc., New York. 1951

Reidman, Sarah R. *Our Hormones and How They Work.* Abelard-Schuman, Ltd., New York. 1957

Schneider, Leo. *Lifeline: The Story of Your Circulating System.* Harcourt, Brace and Co., Inc., New York. 1958

Schubert, Jack and Lapp, Ralph. *Radiation: What It Is and How It Affects You.* Viking Press, New York. 1958

Stine, G. Harry. *Rocket Power and Space Flight.* Henry Holt and Co., Inc., New York. 1957

Sutton-Vane, S. *The Story of Eyes.* Viking Press, New York. 1958

Vogel, V. *Facts About Narcotics.* Science Research Assoc., Chicago. 1958

Wynder, E. *The Biologic Effects of Tobacco.* Little, Brown, Boston. 1955

Biology and the Problems of Disease

Study thy health before ever thou fallest sick. . . . And when the sun was going down, all those who had friends afflicted with diseases of any kind brought them to Him: and He laid His hands upon each one of them and healed them . . . and great multitudes came together to listen to Him, and be healed. — Eccl. 18:20, Luke 4:40, Luke 5:15, 16

Can you imagine what it would be like if an epidemic swept through your community and killed half the population? How would you like to live in constant fear of smallpox, typhoid fever, or diphtheria?

You have been spared the dread of smallpox because an English country doctor made a great discovery and dared to defend his idea in the face of ridicule. We have waged a successful war against the microbe world because a French chemist discovered bacteria and a German doctor devoted his life to the study of germ diseases. An English biologist discovered penicillin, a German scientist gave us sulfa drugs, and an American produced a polio vaccine.

Step by step, scientists of the world have developed a highly organized medical science. As new discoveries are made, more infectious diseases are brought under the control of your doctor, and life expectancy is lengthened.

You, your doctor, the staff of your hospital, your public health workers, and all the others who deal with the prevention and treatment of disease form a team. You as a part of this team need to understand the problems involved.

CHAPTER 45: **MICROBES—MIGHTY MITES OF INFECTION**
CHAPTER 46: **BODY DEFENSES AND AIDS AGAINST DISEASES**
CHAPTER 47: **THE CONQUEST OF DISEASE**
CHAPTER 48: **THE PREVENTION OF DISEASE**

Microbes—Mighty Mites of Infection

A FEW tiny bacteria, so small that thousands can occupy the point of a needle, are able to multiply in your body and give you an infectious disease. They can be carried through the air in a drop of spray from a cough or sneeze, be present in the food you eat, or enter a wound you did not wash and treat.

You can perhaps understand why infectious diseases swept through whole communities years ago before microbes were finally tracked down. No one thought of looking for an invisible, living organism as the cause of scarlet fever, tuberculosis, or typhoid fever. Actually, bacteria were identified by a chemist, not a biologist, and he found them in a beet sugar solution.

But this was only about 100 years ago. Let's go back many centuries before the microbe was unmasked and see how ancient people struggled to find an answer to the riddle of infectious disease.

Demons, devils, and disease. Primitive man lived at the mercy of nature. He had little or no understanding of the natural events he witnessed daily. Fear and superstition crowded out reason in his efforts to account for the many things he could not understand.

Primitive man lived in constant terror of disease. He could fight off an attack by an enemy or a wild beast, but when infection struck him down he was bewildered and helpless. He had no basis for associating infectious disease with invisible microbes. Such knowledge has come to us only in recent times. Lacking this knowledge, early peoples could not understand that an infection could spread from one person to another.

Fig. 45-1. Here a " medicine man " is shown performing the ritual for frightening away the " evil spirits " that were believed to cause disease.

It is little wonder that primitive man linked disease with the supernatural world. He thought a victim of infection was "possessed" by a demon or evil spirit. This concept, which we refer to as the **demonic theory,** exists today in areas where people still live in primitive societies beyond the reach of civilization. To deal with these evil spirits, primitive people turned to one of their number who was supposed to have supernatural power — the witch doctor, or medicine man. This strange person usually lived apart from the rest of the tribe. He dressed in weird clothing and often wore a headdress made from the head of an animal. He treated the sick with strange rituals and dances intended to frighten away the evil spirits. In some tribes, a victim of disease was half-buried in hot sand or soil for several days as a means of driving out the demon which had possessed him. Among the most extreme of treatments was the chipping of holes in the skull to release the tormenting evil spirit.

The demonic theory and association of disease with evil lasted many centuries, until a famous figure in medical history took the first step in the conquest of infectious disease.

Medicine among the ancients. In ancient Greece, during the fourth century B.C., one early physician, Hippocrates (hih-*pah*-kruh-teez), began to look for natural causes for disease. His great wisdom in dealing with the sick marks him as the Father of Medicine.

Hippocrates had many mistaken ideas about the body and about disease. He thought the brain was a radiator to cool the head, and that food was cooked in the digestive system. He believed that health was determined by four body fluids. He named these fluids *blood, phlegm, black bile,* and *yellow bile.* But while he was wrong in some of his ideas, he was amazingly right in others. He recognized that

The Bettmann Archive

Fig. 45-2. Hippocrates is remembered today as the Father of Medicine because he was the first of the ancients to attempt scientific explanations for disease.

pain, cough, and fever were reactions of the body to disease. He noticed that hollow eyes, sunken temples, and dry skin, especially on the forehead, were signs of grave illness and usually approaching death. He emphasized the need for proper diet, rest, fresh air, and exercise for maintaining good health. When patients came to him, he made careful records of their symptoms, his treatment of the disease, and the progress of the case. While he made mistakes, he tried not to repeat them.

The wisdom of Hippocrates established a new era in medicine. His influence remains today in the **Hippocratic Oath** taken by young doctors when they receive their M.D. degrees. This is an oath to uphold the high ethical standards of the medical profession, and to give all knowledge acquired to new generations of doctors.

In the second century, another famous

Fig. 45-3. This painting is an artist's conception of the epidemic of bubonic plague which occurred in Florence, Italy, in the 14th century, and killed over 100,000 people.

Greek physician, Claudius Galen (*gaylen*), came upon the scene. Galen was appointed surgeon to the Roman gladiators following his study of medicine in Alexandria. Later he went to Rome where he served as a doctor, teacher, and medical experimenter. Galen was the most honored physician of his time. Galen's writing became the basis for medical instruction and his influence lasted for hundreds of years.

Disease in the Middle Ages. Following the decline of Rome in the 5th and 6th centuries A.D., the civilized world entered the Dark Ages. Progress in medicine as well as in other fields was halted until the 15th and 16th centuries. Epidemic diseases stalked the civilized world. Rats swarmed through the streets and in open sewers carrying the fleas which harbored the deadly microbes of the " Black Death," or bubonic plague. One epidemic of the plague between 1347 and 1350 killed 60 million people in Europe, Asia, and Africa. Over 100,000 people died in Florence, Italy alone during a single year of this dreadful epidemic. As the plague spread through France, it took the lives of 50,000 people. A short time later, it killed half of the population of London. Influenza, cholera, smallpox, and typhus fever swept through the civilized world in other epidemics.

Many theories of disease came out of the Middle Ages. Doctors believed that " bad blood " was the chief cause of infectious diseases. They called it *" bad humor,"* harking back to the humors of Hippocrates. This belief led to the practice of *bloodletting,* or bleeding, as a means of removing " bad blood " and allowing the body to produce more " good blood." Bloodletting was done by barbers, who also performed surgical operations. The barber opened a vein in the patient's arm, which was held over a basin to catch the flowing blood. Blood spiraled down the arm in wide, red streams — a pattern which is duplicated even today before the barber's shop as a symbol of his trade. At the end of the treatment, the patient was sent home, weak from loss of blood and with the probability of infection from the wound in his arm made by the barber's dirty knife.

Another theory of infectious disease prevalent in early times was based on *"seeds of vermin."* According to this idea, various kinds of filth could change to living matter by spontaneous generation. This material, in turn, invaded the body and caused an infection. While this notion had no basis, it was a step forward in that infection was associated with filth and unsanitary conditions.

" Bad air " was once thought to cause infectious disease. This notion about infection was prevalent until recent times. Our ancestors thought malaria (the name means literally " bad air ") was caused by air coming from swamps and marshes, especially in the evening.

Still another notion about infectious disease which was generally accepted by doctors at one time was the **disposition theory.** According to this theory, certain people were " disposed " to certain infections because of something in their make-up. Those who were spared the infection lacked this " disposition."

Such were conditions in the middle of the 19th century when one of the outstanding scientists of all time made a startling discovery.

Fig. 45-4. The practice of bloodletting to remove " bad blood " was common in this country even as late as the 19th century.

The Bettmann Archive

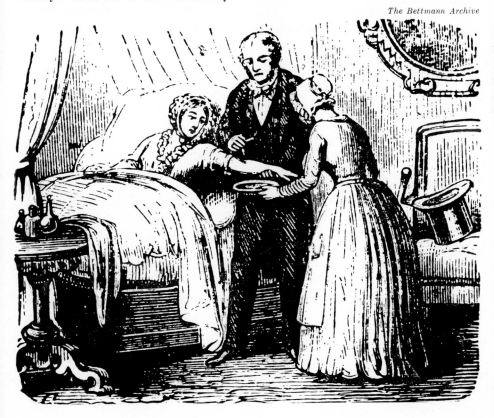

Fig. 45-5. Louis Pasteur's identification of microorganisms as the cause of fermentation and decay contributed to his reputation as one of the greatest biologists in history.

Louis Pasteur, the father of bacteriology. Our scene now shifts to France in the year 1854. Louis Pasteur, a young chemist, was a professor of chemistry. One day a local distiller asked him to investigate the process during which alcohol is produced in the fermentation of sugar in beet pulp. As part of the investigation, Pasteur examined sugar solutions in various stages of fermentation. He was amazed to find numerous rod-shaped bodies which seemed to be alive. He noticed, too, that the number of rods increased during fermentation. Thus, in his study of the fermentation of a beet sugar solution, Pasteur identified bacteria. He made one of the greatest scientific contributions of all time.

He continued his study of fermentation with the souring of milk. He found similar organisms in sour milk and discovered that they changed milk sugar to lactic acid during the souring process. When he transferred some of the organisms to a sugar solution, he found that they soured the solution and produced acid just as they had in milk. He reasoned that microorganisms caused fermentation and disproved the theory that fermentation and decay produced living things by *spontaneous generation.*

Robert Koch, the father of bacteriological technique. Robert Koch (1843–1910) was born in Germany, the son of a poor miner and one of 13 children. His first outstanding contribution to medicine was in the study of **anthrax,** an epidemic disease of animals and often contracted by man. From early times, anthrax had spread through sheep, cattle, and other herds in epidemics. Anthrax was the first disease definitely linked to bacteria. In the examination of the organs of animals dead from anthrax, Koch found numerous rod-shaped bacteria swarming in the blood vessels (Fig. 45-6). His next problem was to find out if these organisms caused the disease. He transferred some of the living bacteria into a cut made at the base of the tail of a healthy mouse. The mouse developed anthrax and died. Koch found the same bacteria greatly increased in number in the blood stream of the dead mouse.

Koch was not satisfied until he had actually watched this multiplication. Accordingly, he obtained a drop of sterile fluid from the eye of a freshly killed ox and put into the drop a small portion of the spleen of a mouse containing anthrax germs. He patiently watched through his microscope until the germs spread entirely through the drop. He transferred germs from one drop to another and succeeded in growing them in the complete absence of any mouse spleen or blood. His next step was to try inoculating healthy mice with his laboratory-grown organisms to see if they would produce the disease. The mice died soon after inoculation and microscopic examination of the blood disclosed the same abundant rod-shaped organisms.

Koch's brilliant procedure is summarized in four steps called the **Koch postulates:**

1. Isolate the organism probably causing the disease. (Koch found anthrax organisms in the blood stream of infected animals.)

2. Grow the organisms in laboratory cultures. (Koch used sterile fluid from the eyes of oxen.)

3. Inoculate a healthy animal with the cultured organisms. (Koch inoculated mice with the eye fluid containing germs.)

4. Examine the diseased animal and recover the organisms which produced the disease. (Koch found that the organisms with which he had inoculated the mouse had multiplied enormously in the blood stream.)

Koch's discovery of tuberculosis organisms. Koch discovered the causative organism in the lungs of victims of tuberculosis. In 1882 he announced that tuberculosis was caused by a tiny rod-shaped organism (Fig. 45-7). His announcement was based on long hours of research during which he inoculated experimental animals with the disease by using pieces of infected lung tissue.

He had trouble growing tuberculosis organisms in his laboratory, for they failed to grow on any of the many kinds of media he had perfected. Finally he produced a successful medium by adding blood serum to agar. Thus, he was not only the first person to see the tuberculosis organism, but the first to grow it under laboratory conditions.

Forms of disease. We may define **disease** as any condition which actively impairs the health or interferes with the normal functioning of the body of an organism. It may be due to various causes which can be classified in distinct groups:

1. Diseases caused by microorganisms (*infectious*).

2. Organic diseases due to abnormalities in the structure of body organs, abnormal growths, etc. (*noninfectious*).

Fig. 45-6.   Robert Koch saw a microscopic field similar to this one of *Bacillus anthracis* when he examined smears of organs of animals dead from anthrax.

Fig. 45-7.   *Mycobacterium tuberculosis,* the form of bacterium that causes tuberculosis, is shown here. Koch cultured it in agar with blood serum added.

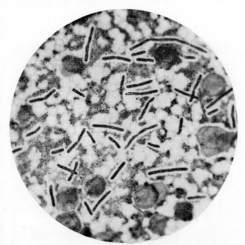

General Biological Supply House

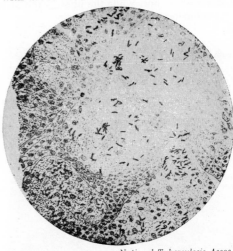

National Tuberculosis Assoc.

3. Functional diseases due to abnormalities in the functioning of body organs (noninfectious).

4. Diet-deficiency diseases due to a lack of proper diet, especially of vitamins (noninfectious).

Organisms which cause disease. We use the term **pathogenic** to distinguish disease-causing organisms from harmless forms. These pathogenic organisms include various kinds of plants as well as certain small forms of animal life. The following types of organisms are associated with disease: (1) viruses; (2) Rickettsiae; (3) bacteria; (4) spirochetes; (5) protozoans; (6) molds and moldlike fungi; (7) yeasts; and (8) parasitic worms.

We shall limit our discussion to viruses, Rickettsiae, bacteria, and spirochetes and the infectious diseases associated with them.

What are viruses? Most everyone is familiar with the group of organisms known as *viruses* because of their association with many well-known human infectious diseases. Among these are smallpox, chickenpox, influenza, colds and sinus infections, a form of pneumonia mumps, measles, German measles, polio rabies, and yellow fever.

Biologists are still trying to discover the true nature of a virus. These tiny forms of life, if they are alive, are the smallest living things. They are invisible under the optical microscope but have been photographed by means of the high magnification of the electron microscope (Fig. 45-8). Viruses are so small that they pass through the fine pores of a clay filter used to separate bacteria from substances in solution by filtration. This property gave them their real name, **filtrable virus.** The first virus was isolated from tobacco plants infected with leaf mosaic in 1935. Dr. Wendell Stanley of the Rockefeller Institute earned the Nobel Prize for his work with this virus. In studying the virus, he found that it could be crystallized into a nonliving form. In this condition, it could be stored on a laboratory shelf. However, when the crystals were injected into a healthy tobacco plant, the plant became diseased. The virus crystals had been transformed from a nonliving substance into an active

Fig. 45-8. The left-hand photograph shows one type of polio virus as seen under an electron microscope, while the photograph at the right is an electron micrograph of one type of influenza virus.

National Foundation

Wide World

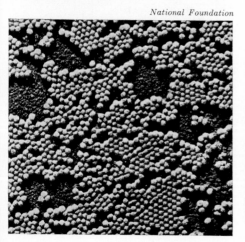
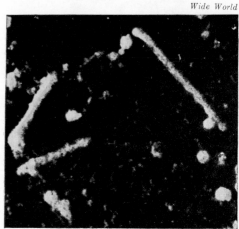

organism. Biologists are now exploring that mysterious gulf between living and nonliving matter. The viruses seem to shuttle back and forth between the two.

Viruses cannot grow outside of living cells. Thus, the only laboratory media used in their culture are living plants and animals, chick and duck embryos, and tissue cultures of living cells. Recent studies indicate that virus particles enter living cells and cause both chemical and physiological changes in the cell substance, which alters the cell or destroys it entirely. Certain of the cell substances may be used in organizing more virus particles. Each virus particle may be a single protein molecule in combination with a molecule of nucleic acid. Or, a virus may be a single hereditary particle, known as a **gene** (*jean*). Viruses are difficult to study since they have a way of changing their characteristics just as an investigator believes he has completed an accurate analysis of one of their number.

Rickettsiae and their carriers. The *Rickettsiae* (rih-*ket*-see-eye) seem to be midway between the viruses and bacteria. They are like viruses in that they cannot live outside of a host organism. They resemble bacteria in form, but are much smaller (Fig. 45-9).

Rickettsiae were first discovered in the blood of victims of Rocky Mountain spotted fever. A short time later Dr. Howard T. Ricketts, in whose honor they were named, found these organisms in cattle ticks which transmitted them to humans. Dr. Ricketts died of typhus fever, caused by another of the Rickettsiae, in 1910.

For some strange reason, Rickettsiae seem to be carried only by certain arthropods, including the human body louse, tick, and mite. In addition to Rocky Mountain spotted fever and typhus fever, Rickettsiae cause the mysterious " Q " fever and trench fever.

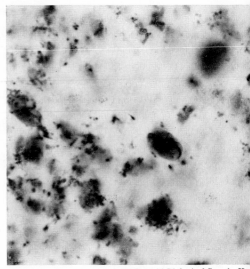

General Biological Supply Ho

Fig. 45-9. The tiny black bodies shown in this photomicrograph are Rickettsiae. They are smaller than bacteria and larger than viruses.

Bacteria and spirochetes. By far the largest number of pathogenic organisms are **bacteria.** They may be coccus, bacillus, or spirillum forms. Pathogenic bacteria do not differ in appearance from the harmless forms you studied in Chapter 10. Pathogenic bacteria cause disease when they invade a living host and damage its tissues. Among the well-known bacterial diseases are: diphtheria, scarlet fever, tetanus, typhoid fever, tuberculosis, lobar pneumonia, anthrax, and cholera.

Spirochetes (*spy*-roh-keets) resemble both bacteria and protozoans and seem to be forms of life midway between the two. They are long, spiral organisms resembling corkscrews. The syphilis organism is probably the best known of these.

The spread of infectious organisms. Bacteria and other pathogenic organisms may be transferred from one person to another almost instantly during a cough or sneeze or contact with an infected person. Or they may be carried on particles in the air, lie on objects, or live in water or food a long time before reaching a new victim.

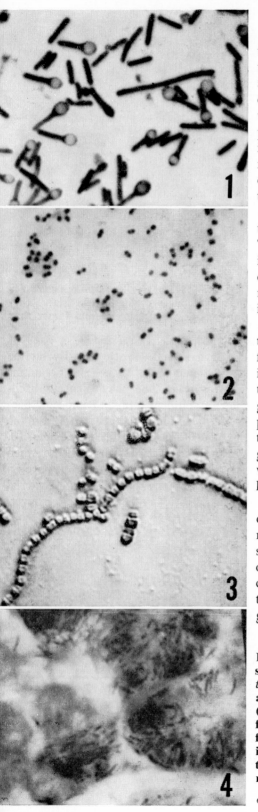

Food-borne infections. Food, contaminated with pathogenic bacteria, Protozoa, and other organisms, is a common agent of infection. The organisms that cause such *food-borne infections* enter the digestive organs with food and multiply rapidly during an incubation period in the intestine. In some cases, they reach the blood and lymph. Symptoms of infection appear following the incubation period.

Typhoid fever may be spread in food through handling by infected persons. Tuberculosis and various streptococcus infections may travel in milk. Epidemics of undulant fever have been traced to raw milk from cows suffering from a specific infection of cattle.

Food poisoning. We must be careful to distinguish between food infection and food poisoning. In *food infection*, food is merely the agent in which bacteria enter the body. In *food poisoning*, bacteria grow in the food and produce poisonous products. The poisons are absorbed into the blood stream from the digestive organs. They act on the body suddenly and within a period of a few minutes to a few hours after eating.

Botulism (*bot*-you-lizm) is the most deadly of all food poisoning. Most cases result from home-canned foods, especially string beans, which are eaten before thorough cooking. The botulism organism, a close relative of the deadly tetanus bacterium, thrives in an airtight container. It gets into the food as a spore before can-

Fig. 45-10. The four types of bacteria shown are all pathogenic. (1) *Clostridium tetani* **causes tetanus. Notice the drumstick appearance of the spore-containing cells. (2)** *Diplococcus pneumoniae* **causes one form of pneumonia. Notice that this type is found in pairs. (3)** *Streptococcus pyogenes* **is responsible for the " strep " throat infection. (4)** *Mycobacterium leprae* **causes leprosy.**

General Biological Supply House

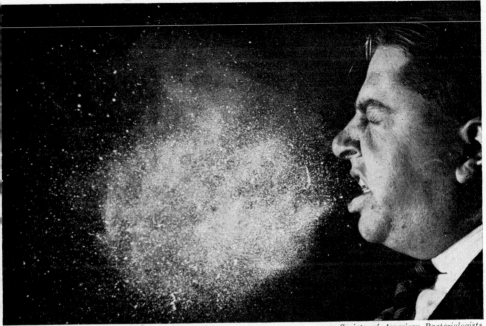

Society of American Bacteriologists

Fig. 45-11.   Every time a person sneezes, he throws out a spray that fills the air around him with droplets of mucus.   Riding these droplets may be the viruses of colds and sinus infections, or bacteria from a " strep " throat, pneumonia, or other bacterial disease.

ning and multiplies during the period of storage.   Powerful poisons are released from the bacteria into the food.   Symptoms of botulism usually appear within 12 to 36 hours after the food is eaten. They include double vision, weakness, and paralysis which creeps from the neck region to other parts of the body.   Death may result from respiratory failure or heart failure.   Mortality occurs in about 65 per cent of cases.   Since the poison is destroyed by heat, botulism can be avoided by cooking home-canned vegetables before eating them.

Water-borne infections.   Certain bacteria remain alive for days or even weeks in water.   Most *water-borne infections* are intestinal and are introduced into water through sewage contamination.   Many lakes and streams near heavily populated regions are dangerously contaminated with typhoid, dysentery, and other in-

testinal parasites.   Shallow wells are especially dangerous because they are usually located in low areas and are exposed to surface drainage.   You should be careful to drink water only from deep, tested wells.   If you have to use water from a spring or a stream, be sure to boil it for at least ten minutes.

Droplet infection.   Fig. 45-11 shows a photograph of a sneeze.   Each of those tiny *droplets* could contain bacteria and viruses which were dislodged from the nasal membranes, throat, and respiratory passages.   They might be diphtheria, scarlet fever, tuberculosis, pneumonia, measles, mumps, influenza, or common cold organisms.

Diseases spread through *droplet infection* include colds, sinus infections, " strep " throat, measles, scarlet fever, pneumonia, and tuberculosis.   They are most common in winter and spring, partly because of the fact that people are confined indoors at these seasons. The air in buses, stores, theaters, and other public places becomes heavily laden with droplets from coughing and sneezing as well as from normal breathing. Many of the droplets are inhaled. Others settle on objects where the microbes remain alive. These objects may be handled and later transferred to the mouth by someone who did not wash his hands before eating or perhaps by someone who puts his fingers to his mouth or bites his nails.

Various health measures have cut the number of droplet-borne infections greatly. Sanitary disposable cups have replaced the public drinking cup. Paper towels are far more sanitary than the old "family" towel. Even the pocket handkerchief has given way to disposable tissues which can be thrown away and burned after use.

Diseases spread by contact. Certain diseases produce sores or lesions on the skin and mucous membranes. Direct contact with material from these lesions or sores spreads the infection. Ringworm of the scalp and barber's itch, or impetigo, may be spread by such **contact infection.** In earlier times, smallpox was spread rapidly by contact with the virus present in skin lesions. Chickenpox virus may be transmitted by direct contact or through the air. Diseases spread by direct contact also include syphilis, gonorrhea, and other venereal diseases.

Wound infections. The unbroken skin is an effective barrier against the entrance of bacteria. However, breaks in the skin frequently become **wound infections** unless they are cleansed by bleeding and properly treated with antiseptic. Puncture wounds are especially dangerous because of the possibility of tetanus. These anaerobic bacteria enter the wound as spores, clinging to some object. When the wound heals on the surface, it leaves an airtight cavity ideally suited to the tetanus organisms.

Various staphylococci commonly infect wounds and produce a characteristic yellow pus. Streptococcus infections in wounds are highly dangerous and may lead to general blood poisoning and death. Wounds resulting from animal bites are sometimes dangerous. Rabies, or hydrophobia, is a dreaded virus disease transmitted through wounds resulting from the bites of rabid animals, most commonly dogs. Any serious or extensive wound should be treated by a doctor immediately. Minor wounds should be washed, treated with antiseptic, and covered.

Human carriers of disease. Certain diseases are spread by human **carriers,** who are themselves immune but who harbor the organisms in their bodies. In some cases patients who recover from an infectious disease carry the organisms in their bodies for weeks or even months. Sometimes a diphtheria patient recovers from the illness, but the organisms continue to grow in tonsils or nasal passages.

The carrier problem is especially great in the case of typhoid fever. Certain apparently healthy people harbor typhoid bacteria in their gall bladders and intestines and spread them through intestinal waste. When a carrier is found, his family is given immediate typhoid immunization treatments and he is not permitted to handle the food or eating utensils of others.

Diseases spread by insects. Insects spread disease in two entirely different ways. The housefly carries germs on its sticky feet and hairy body. When it flies from sewage to your home, it can be carrying typhoid fever organisms, dysentery, or other intestinal infections. Respiratory infections can be carried by flies when they lap up droplets. Houseflies, roaches, and certain other insects are agents, or *vectors,* of infection.

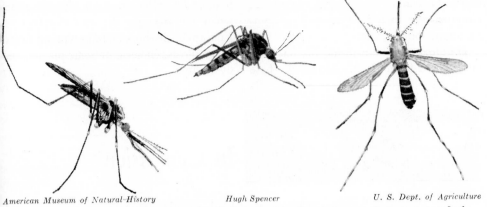

American Museum of Natural-History   Hugh Spencer   U. S. Dept. of Agriculture

Fig. 45-12. The *Anopheles* mosquito (*left*) is host to the protozoan that causes malaria. *Culex* (*middle*) is the annoying but harmless household mosquito. The genus *Aëdes* (*right*) carries the virus that causes yellow fever.

Other insects carry bacteria internally and transmit them in bites. Typhus is associated with the human body louse, bubonic plague with the rat flea, and African sleeping sickness with the tsetse fly. As we mentioned earlier, Rocky Mountain spotted fever is carried by ticks, which are relatives of the spider. Yellow fever virus is carried by the *Aëdes* mosquito of Central and South America (Fig. 45-12).

Still other insects serve as *hosts* of infectious organisms. Malaria organisms spend part of their life cycle in the body of a female *Anopheles* mosquito and part in the human blood stream, as you learned on pages 238 and 239.

How microbes cause disease. Various microbes damage the body in several ways. The damage may be mechanical or chemical. It may occur at the place of the infection or in other parts of the body, depending on the kind of pathogen present and the ability of the body to control the infection. Direct causes of body damage due to the activity of infectious organisms include: (1) *tissue destruction;* (2) *production of soluble toxins* (exotoxins); and (3) *production of insoluble toxins* (endotoxins).

Tissue destruction is illustrated by tuberculosis. The organisms usually infect the lungs, although other organs may be affected. As tuberculosis bacteria multiply in the lung tissue, they destroy cells and produce lesions. These allow blood to seep from the capillaries into the air passages, resulting in the hemorrhages characteristic of advanced tuberculosis.

Many organisms, including streptococci, destroy blood cells. During meningitis, the membranes covering the brain or spinal cord are attacked by bacteria.

Viruses act chiefly through tissue destruction. The polio virus attacks the cell bodies of motor nerves in the spinal cord. This damage may be temporary or it may be permanent. The deadly virus of rabies attacks the brain substance.

Many bacteria produce powerful chemical substances which are absorbed by the surrounding tissue or are transported through the blood stream with damaging effects. We refer to these poisons as **exotoxins.** Such toxins may cause serious damage far from the seat of the infection. For example, tetanus organisms living in a wound in the foot produce toxins which cause paralysis in the upper regions of the body. Other diseases that involve exotoxins include scarlet fever, diphtheria, streptococcus infections, as well as botulism food poisoning.

Endotoxins remain inside the bacterial cells which form them. However, these toxins are released with deadly effect when the bacteria die and disintegrate. Endotoxin diseases include typhoid fever, tuberculosis, cholera, bubonic plague, and dysentery.

In Conclusion

We have considered the various kinds of microbes which cause infectious diseases, the many ways in which they enter the body, and several ways in which they cause disease.

To produce an infection, the germs must be able to multiply in the body. Undoubtedly, you have pathogenic bacteria in your mouth, sticking to your nasal membranes, and lurking in your respiratory passages at the present moment. Many enter your body with the food you eat. You aren't sick with an infection because the organisms have not been able to multiply in enough numbers to overcome the body's natural defenses.

Your body has a marvelous system of defense. It keeps out most of the microbes you contact and destroys many others before an infection develops. The way your body does these things is the subject of the next chapter.

BIOLOGICALLY SPEAKING

anthrax	endotoxin	Koch postulates
" bad humor "	exotoxin	pathogenic
botulism	filtrable virus	Rickettsiae
carrier	food infection	" seeds of vermin "
contact infection	food-borne infection	spirochete
demonic theory	food poisoning	tissue destruction
disease	gene	water-borne infections
disposition theory	Hippocratic Oath	wound infection
droplet infection		

QUESTIONS FOR REVIEW

1. Explain why primitive people turned to magic and superstition in an effort to deal with infectious diseases.
2. Name four body fluids described by Hippocrates.
3. Which of the Greek physicians, practicing in Rome, was most influential in medicine through the Middle Ages?
4. Name several infectious diseases which swept through the civilized world in epidemics during the Middle Ages.
5. Upon what theory of disease was bloodletting practiced?
6. Explain " seeds of vermin " and the disposition theory of disease.
7. List the Koch postulates and explain how Robert Koch used these steps in his investigation of anthrax.
8. List eight groups of infectious organisms.

9. In what ways are the Rickettsiae organisms similar to both viruses and bacteria?
10. Explain the difference between a food-borne infection and food poisoning.
11. Explain why deep puncture wounds are especially dangerous.
12. Name four insect carriers of disease and the diseases they carry.
13. What are the five various causes of diseases in the body?

APPLYING FACTS AND PRINCIPLES

1. Explain how Pasteur's work in investigating the causes of fermentation disproved the idea of spontaneous generation, thus beginning the world's fight against harmful microorganisms.
2. Give reasons for the prevalence of colds, influenza, pneumonia, and other droplet-borne infections during the winter.
3. What measures have been taken in your community to protect you from water-borne infections?
4. Why may exotoxins cause damage far from the seat of infection?

CHAPTER 46

Body Defenses and Aids Against Diseases

WITH bacteria and viruses present outside and inside your body, you may wonder how anyone escapes infection to live to a ripe old age. Some do lose the battle of infection, but the human body has marvelous defenses against disease. When microbes invade, the tissues set up a counterattack and usually win — for they can only lose once.

Today the doctor knows how to mobilize defenses against some diseases before they strike. He can send reserves into the blood stream to aid the body's natural defenses by means of a hypodermic needle, as well as drugs and antibiotics.

In this chapter, we shall examine the body's defenses against disease and tour the doctor's arsenal of defensive weapons with which he prevents many infections and deals effectively with others when they strike.

The first line of defense. The most effective way of avoiding an infection is to prevent the organisms from entering the body — the function of the first line of defense. *Skin* covers all the external parts of the body and, if unbroken, is bacteria-proof. Unfortunately, it is not virus-proof, hence we have little protection against the entry of this group of pathogenic organisms. The openings of the body are lined with *mucous membranes,* which serve as a protective lining. Mucous

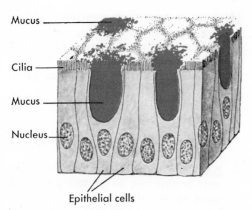

Mucus

Cilia

Mucus

Nucleus

Epithelial cells

Fig. 46-1. The mucous membrane is one of the first-line defenses. Notice the cilia, which aid in expelling foreign matter.

membranes are much thinner than skin, usually consisting of a single layer of cells. Those membranes lining the trachea and nasal passages are covered with cilia which sweep foreign particles, including bacteria, upward toward the throat (Fig. 46-1). When the particles irritate the throat membranes, a cough results and the particles are blown out into the air. Irritation of the membranes of the nasal passages results in sneezing.

Other first-line defenses include the *acid* of the stomach which destroys large numbers of bacteria taken in with food. *Tears* which protect the eyes are slightly antiseptic and cleanse the eyeballs continually, washing foreign matter through the tear ducts into the nasal passages.

Normally these first-line defenses prevent bacteria from gaining entrance into the body. However, skin may be broken or mucous membrane may become irritated, thus allowing the organisms to enter the body.

A factor called **general resistance** also seems to play an important part in maintaining the defenses against disease. It concerns not only the first line, but the other lines as well. We know that exposure to cold air or wet weather may cause irritation of the mucous membranes

and permit cold germs, pneumonia organisms, or even tuberculosis organisms to gain entrance and start an infection. But general resistance seems to affect this first-line defense, because lack of sleep and a general run-down condition makes the entrance of disease germs much easier.

The second line of defense. Once the bacteria have passed the first line of defense, they are met with a second line which operates within the body. This line is defended by the *white corpuscles* of the blood stream.

When disease-producing bacteria pass the first line of defense, as, for example, through a break in the skin, the white corpuscles leave the blood vessels and migrate through the tissue fluids to the site of infection. They make a wall around the invading germs and begin to engulf them (Fig. 46-2). A race starts between the multiplication of bacteria and their destruction by the white corpuscles. During the infection, which is still local, the tissues involved often swell and become inflamed. Redness often results from the increased flow of blood to the area to promote healing. The lymph aids in the struggle by carrying bacteria to nodes, where they are filtered out and destroyed by white blood cells.

This struggle with the second-defense line may cause a fever (rise in the body temperature). **Fever** is a body reaction against infection, and is beneficial unless it becomes too high for too long a period. The dead bacteria and white corpuscles collect at the site of the infection as **pus**. This is later discharged externally, or carried to the organs of excretion for elimination.

The third line of defense. If the bacteria overcome the army of white corpuscles, a "break-through" occurs and the organisms enter the blood stream. The infection then becomes general and the patient begins a fight for his life.

Bacteria or their poisons are carried by the blood throughout the body with damaging effects. The fever usually rises sharply and the patient becomes increasingly weak.

The infection becomes a battle between bacteria and their products and various substances which are produced by the blood to destroy the bacteria or neutralize the effect of their poisons. These blood substances are generally called **antibodies**. Antibodies are of an extremely complex nature and are not entirely understood. They seem to be **specific** — that is, a single kind of antibody is effective against a specific kind of organism or its products.

The types of antibodies. While antibodies are numerous, the principal types include: (1) *antitoxins;* (2) *agglutinins* (uh-*gloo*-tih-nins); (3) *bacteriolysins* (bak-tear-ee-oh-*ly*-sins); (4) *precipitins* (pree-*sih*-pih-tins); and (5) *opsonins* (*op*-soh-nins).

Antitoxins serve to neutralize toxins. In the case of diphtheria, for example, the organisms in the throat pour toxins into the blood stream which cause most of the symptoms of diphtheria. The blood is stimulated by the infection to produce diphtheria antitoxin which neutralizes the effect of the toxins. If the blood produces antitoxin faster than toxins are formed, recovery is assured.

Agglutinins are substances formed in the blood which cause bacteria to gather in clumps. When they are congregated, white corpuscles may surround them and devour them. **Bacteriolysins** are strange chemical substances formed in the blood, which cause bacteria to dissolve. **Precipitins** are little understood, but seem to cause bacteria or their products to precipitate in the blood, which makes it easier for the blood stream to filter them in the lymph glands and various organs and for the white corpuscles to destroy them.

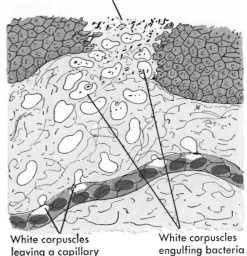

Bacteria entering through a break in the skin

White corpuscles leaving a capillary   White corpuscles engulfing bacteria

Fig. 46-2. As one of the second-line defenses, white corpuscles gather in an area of infection and immediately begin to engulf the accumulated bacteria.

Opsonins are peculiar substances which prepare bacteria for ingestion by white corpuscles.

Immunity to disease. We call the resistance of the body to disease **immunity**.

Immunity may be of several types. It may be **natural**, or it may be **acquired** within the lifetime of the organism. Acquired immunity may be more or less permanent (*active*) or only temporary (*passive*).

Natural immunity. Man is not subject to most animal diseases because of differences in structure. A different type of environment exists in the human body than in bodies of animals. Consequently, we are not usually plagued by diseases of horses, cattle, swine, and other animals. This type of immunity is **species immunity** since it includes all members of species. Notable exceptions to species immunity are: *tuberculosis* and *undulant fever,* which may be transmitted from cattle to man through milk; *anthrax,* which may cause lesions on the human body in addition to infecting animals; *tularemia* (too-luh-*ree*-mee-uh), which may be carried from rabbits to man; and *psittacosis* (sit-uh-*koh*-sis) from parrots.

Acquired immunity. As the name implies, *acquired immunity* is established during the lifetime of the individual. It may be *active* or *passive,* depending on the way in which it is acquired.

Active immunity results from having had a disease. The infection stimulates the body to form its own specific antibodies against the germs or their products, depending on the type of the disease.

For example, a person with diphtheria produces diphtheria antitoxins, while one who has typhoid forms typhoid agglutinins. Active immunity may be acquired artificially by using biological preparations consisting of weakened or dead bacteria or products removed from living cultures. In this way, the body is stimulated to form its own antibodies without actually having the disease.

Passive immunity is acquired artificially by the injection of antibodies that have been formed by the blood of other individuals or from animals. For example, tetanus antitoxin is taken from the blood of the horse and may be injected into the blood of man to give immediate immunity in the case of deep wounds. The horse antibodies remain only temporarily and, when destroyed, no longer make the individual immune. In the same manner, human blood serum containing antibodies for scarlet fever may be used to give immediate, but only temporary, immunity.

Immune therapy. One vital phase of the treatment and prevention of infectious diseases is based on the bolstering of the body's natural defenses. We refer to it as *immune therapy.* It involves two kinds of weapons and a two-pronged attack. One weapon is **serum** (*sear*-um), a blood protein containing specific antibodies

against disease. A serum is used to reinforce the body's production of antibodies during an infection. It is also used to give an immediate passive immunity to someone who has been exposed to a disease. The other weapon is **vaccine** (*vak*-seen), a product which stimulates the blood to produce antibodies and to develop active immunity against a specific disease.

Serum production. Serum usually comes from the blood of an animal which has been inoculated with a disease and has produced antibodies against it. Horses, cattle, sheep, goats, and rabbits are frequently used in serum production. In general, serums are of two types: (1) some contain agglutinins or precipitins, which act against the bacteria themselves; and (2) others contain antitoxins against their toxins.

The production of diphtheria antitoxin is an excellent example of serum production. The horse is used because it has a powerful resistance to the disease and produces a large quantity of antitoxin in its blood. The horse is given a large dose of diphtheria toxin. It responds with the immediate production of antitoxin. After several days, blood is drawn from the external jugular vein in the neck into sterile containers. It is then processed to remove the serum containing the antitoxin from the rest of the blood. This method of producing antitoxin is quite painless to the horse.

Similar antitoxins are prepared against scarlet fever and tetanus. They are given to patients who have been exposed to one of these infections. In the case of diphtheria and scarlet fever, they are used to assist the recovery of a victim of the disease.

Vaccine production. Vaccines are prepared by biological companies under carefully controlled conditions. The vaccines must be strong enough to cause

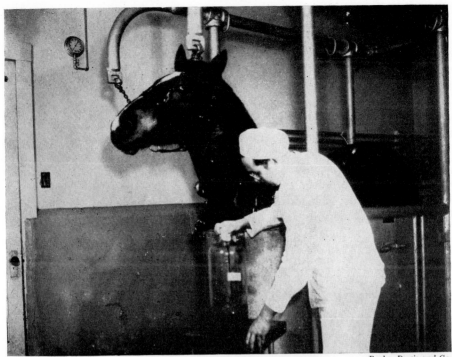

Parke, Davis and Co.

Fig. 46-3. Diphtheria antitoxin is prepared by first injecting quantities of diphtheria toxin into the blood of a horse. After removal of the blood from the external jugular vein in the neck, it is processed to remove antitoxins from the rest of the blood substances.

blood to produce antibodies, yet weakened sufficiently to be safe to use. Vaccines vary with the nature of the organisms or products involved. They may contain:

1. Virus weakened by growth in an animal (animal passage), aging, heat, or chemical treatment.

2. Bacteria killed by heat or chemicals (bacterins or bacterial vaccines).

3. Living bacteria in small numbers.

4. Bacteria weakened by adding weak antiseptics.

5. Bacterial products which have been weakened, as in the case of toxin-antitoxins and toxoids.

The *toxin-antitoxin,* used until recent years to produce active immunity against diphtheria and other toxin diseases, was made by weakening toxin taken from cultures of bacteria with antitoxin from the horse blood serum. Doctors found it hard to give products containing such serum to some patients because of a serious reaction caused by sensitivity to the protein in serum. This problem has been solved by using a newer product called a *toxoid.* A **toxoid** is a toxin which has been weakened by treatment with heat and chemicals to render it safe to inject into human tissues. Thus it can be used as a substitute for antitoxin. Today, doctors immunize with toxoids and reserve the use of serum for a time when a patient needs an immediate transfer of antibodies.

Chemotherapy. The conquest of disease is not a war of biology alone, for chemistry plays a very significant part. **Chemotherapy** is a recent field in which specific chemicals are used to destroy germs. It is of great importance because it assists the natural body defenses.

The development of chemotherapy is associated with the work of a brilliant German chemist, Paul Ehrlich, in connection with his long search for a cure for syphilis. Ehrlich spent many years attempting to discover a drug which would kill the organisms in the blood stream without damaging the blood or other parts of the body. After 605 unsuccessful attempts, he finally succeeded. His 606th drug was an arsenic compound called *salvarsan*. It was used in treating syphi-lis many years before penicillin was discovered.

Other scientists began experimenting with chemicals in the treatment of disease. Dr. Gerhard Domagk (*doh*-mag), another German scientist, discovered in 1932 that a red dye called *prontosil* had remarkable germ-killing powers. Soon after his discovery of prontosil he tried it on his own daughter, who was dying with a streptococcic infection which had progressed beyond medical control. It proved to be effective in halting the infection and saved the child's life.

Fig. 46-4. Each of these dishes contains the same four strains of bacteria, arranged in the same order. An antibiotic has been added to each culture, using an increasingly potent dose on the respective dishes. The bacteria in the upper right-hand corner of each dish are least inhibited by the antibiotic. Which strain is most easily inhibited?

Society of American Bacteriologists

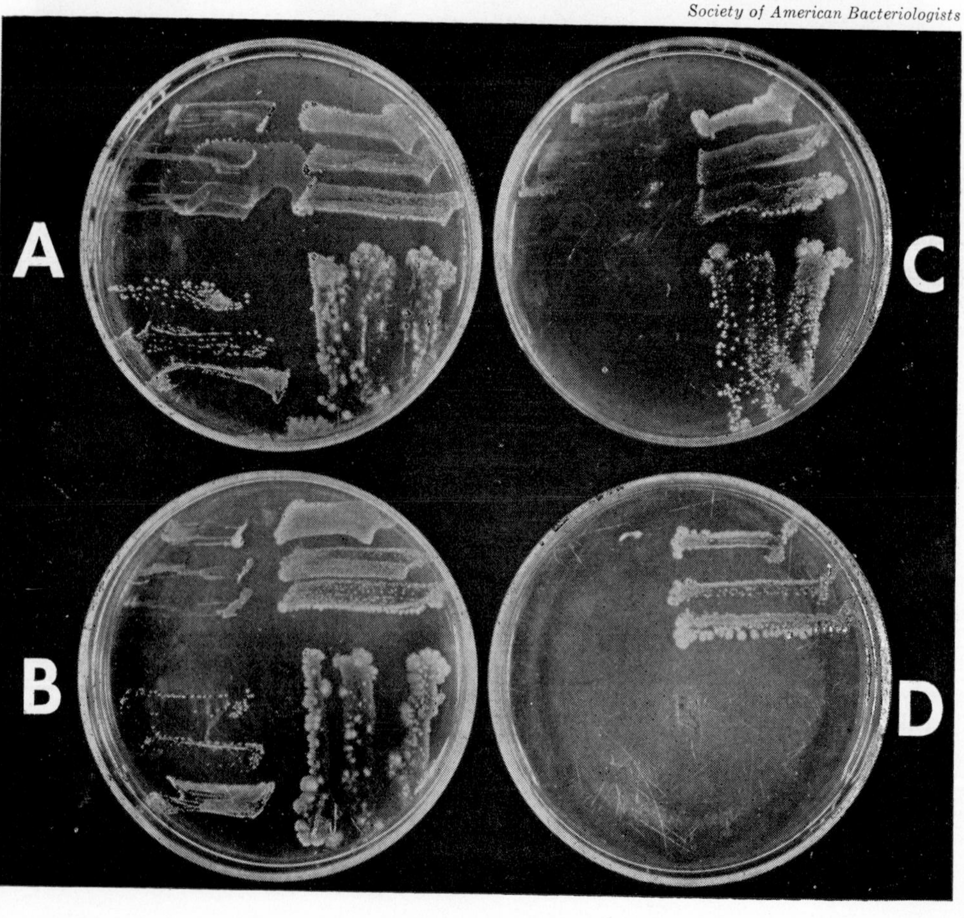

Further investigations on prontosil proved that only a part of the drug had germ-killing powers. This part was isolated and called *sulfanilamide* (sul-fuh-nil-uh-myde). It was the first of an important family known as the **sulfa drugs**. There are many different ones now, and they are used in the treatment of certain infectious diseases. These drugs should be taken only on the advice and recommendation of a physician. They are by no means cure-alls and are often dangerous.

Antibiotic therapy. Powerful chemical substances, call **antibiotics** (an-tee-by-*ot*-iks), are now quite commonly used in the treatment of disease. Antibiotics are products of living organisms. In this respect they are different from the drugs used in chemotherapy. We can sum up the use of antibiotics by saying, " bugs produce drugs which kill bugs," for our supply of these substances comes from bacteria, molds, and moldlike organisms.

Penicillin. The " wonder drug " of World War II, *penicillin,* was the first of the antibiotics. As we mentioned in Chapter 11, it was discovered accidentally by Sir Alexander Fleming, a British bacteriologist, in 1929. Fleming was working with staphylococcus bacteria in a London hospital. While examining plate cultures of staphylococci, he noticed that several of them contained fluffy masses of mold. Later the mold colonies turned dark green and were identified as *Penicillium notatum,* a relative of the mold found on oranges (Fig. 46-5, top).

In the opening days of World War II, Dr. Howard Florey and a group of Oxford workers began a search for antibacterial substances which would be useful in combating wound infections. Their attention turned to Fleming's work and, in cooperation with him, penicillin was developed and thoroughly tested. The result of this work is history.

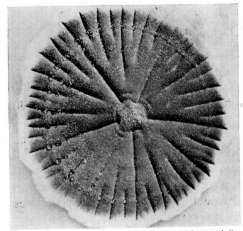

Chas. Pfizer and Co.

Fig. 46-5. The photograph above shows a culture of the mold *Penicillium notatum* as it grows in a Petri dish. The antibiotic, penicillin, is obtained from this mold and others of the same genus. In the photograph below, disks have been soaked in four different strains of penicillin and placed in a bacteria culture. Notice that the strain at the lower left has no inhibiting action on these particular bacteria.

Chas. Pfizer and Co.

Today a penicillin ten times as powerful as Fleming's is available in unlimited quantity and at low cost. New strains of *Penicillium notatum,* produced by exposure to X rays, yield far more penicillin than earlier strains. Biological companies have devoted vast factories to penicillin production. It is given effectively in large doses by injection with a slowly absorbing procaine salt. It can be taken by mouth in tablet form and inhaled into the nasal passages in powder form. Ointments are available for use locally and in the eyes. However, it should *never be used in any form unless recommended by a physician.*

Streptomycin. Dr. Selman Waksman became interested in the soil and its relation to life when he was a boy in Europe. Later he came to the United States and enrolled in Rutgers University. His interest in soil led him to New Jersey Agricultural Experiment Station at Rutgers. While still a student, Waksman discovered a filamentous soil fungus which he named *Streptomyces griseus.*

After graduate study, Waksman returned to Rutgers as a member of the faculty. With the aid of students, he continued the investigation of soil organisms. Together they studied the problem of the

Fig. 46-6. This photograph, taken through an electron microscope, shows two gold-shadowed conjugating bacteria. The left-hand bacterium has minute bacteriophage particles clinging to it, while the right-hand bacterium, which is of a different strain, does not have any particles clinging to it as it is resistant to the bacteriophage. Notice that the scale is marked at the upper left: 1 μ stands for one micron, and is equivalent to 0.000039 inch.

Society of American Bacteriologists

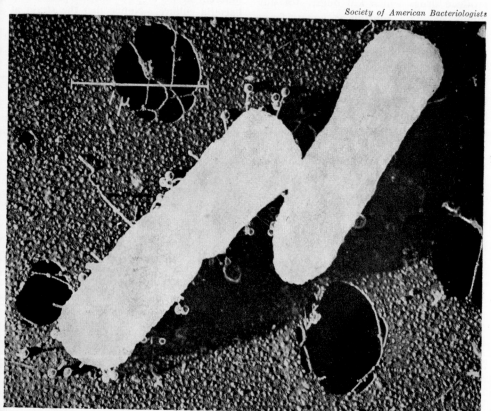

disappearance of disease organisms when the body of a diseased animal is buried, and found that products of soil organisms destroyed the organisms. After years of testing the effect of soil organisms on various pathogens, *streptomycin* (strep-toh-*my*-sin), an antibiotic substance produced by *Streptomyces griseus,* was discovered.

Streptomycin proved to be an effective drug against tuberculosis. In addition, it is partially effective against whooping cough, some forms of pneumonia, dysentery, gonorrhea, and syphilis. The streptomycin industry grew rapidly, and this valuable antibiotic took a place with penicillin.

Other antibiotics. Today, many new antibiotics have been added. Among these are *aureomycin* (*or*-ree-oh-my-sin) and *chloromycetin* (klor-oh-my-*see*-tin), both of which are effective against a wide range of diseases including the Rickettsia diseases, typhus fever, Rocky Mountain spotted fever, and virus pneumonia. *Terramycin* (tair-uh-*my*-sin), another recent addition, promises to be of great value because of its wide range of effectiveness and low toxicity in the body.

Erythromycin (eh-*rih*-throh-my-sin), one of the more recent antibiotics, is similar in action to penicillin. This substance is especially valuable in dealing with organisms which have a resistance to penicillin. *Tetracycline* (teh-truh-*sy*-kleen), another recent one, is produced under a variety of commercial names. It resembles aureomycin in its action. The search for new and better antibiotics continues. An ideal antibiotic has a broad spectrum, or range, of organisms against which it is effective. It must also destroy pathogenic organisms without injury to the body tissues or disturbance of body functions.

Bacteriophage, a possible weapon for future use. Scientists have conducted extensive studies of an extremely small virus known as a **bacteriophage** (bak-*tear*-ee-oh-fahj). This tiny virus has been found to lodge against the wall of certain bacteria (*E. coli*) and inject a substance known as DNA (desoxyribonucleic acid) into the cell (Fig. 46-6). This injection results in disorganization of the bacterium and production of more virus. It is possible that this bacteriophage might prove effective against pathogenic organisms. To some extent, this treatment has proved effective in certain external infections. However, this phase of the treatment of disease is still in the experimental stages.

In Conclusion

You might think of your body as a fort, with defenses set up against sneak attacks by invading microbes. Your skin is the outer wall. Mucous membranes, tears, and other first-line defenses guard the entrances. If microbes break through these defenses, white corpuscles rush to the attack and engage the invaders in a local battle. If the battle grows and becomes a general war, the reserves are called out in the form of antibodies which develop in your blood stream.

With the doctor as your ally, you can be spared much of this desperate struggle. When an infection strikes, he can send you immediate help against some enemies in the form of a serum army, fully equipped and ready to fight beside your natural antibody soldiers. Better still, he can send a preventive vaccine to prepare and train a horde of defensive soldiers to be ready without delay if a certain microbe strikes.

BIOLOGICALLY SPEAKING

acquired immunity	fever	pus
active immunity	general resistance	serum
agglutinin	immune therapy	species immunity
antibiotic	immunity	specific antibodies
antibody	natural immunity	sulfa drugs
antitoxin	opsonin	toxin-antitoxin
bacteriolysin	passive immunity	toxoid
bacteriophage	precipitin	vaccine
chemotherapy		

QUESTIONS FOR REVIEW

1. List various first-line defenses of your body. Would you say that one is more important than another? Why or why not?
2. Explain the role that the white blood corpuscles play in the second line of defense.
3. What is the composition of the pus which forms at the site of an infection?
4. (a) List five specific blood antibodies. (b) Explain briefly the function of each kind in combating bacteria or their products.
5. Explain why a serum gives immedi- ate passive immunity against a specific disease.
6. List five different products contained in various vaccines.
7. Which disease was first controlled by a specific drug discovered by Paul Ehrlich?
8. What important family of germ-killing drugs was isolated from the red dye, prontosil?
9. In what respect are antibiotic drugs different from those used in chemotherapy?
10. Name four widely used antibiotics other than penicillin.

APPLYING FACTS AND PRINCIPLES

1. Explain why exposure to the weather, getting wet, overtiredness, or improper eating may bring on a cold, sore throat, or other infection.
2. A fever is considered beneficial unless it gets too high or lasts too long. Of what benefit might a fever be in the struggle against an infection?
3. Why is active immunity more permanent than passive immunity?
4. How did World War II speed the dawn of antibiotic therapy?
5. Explain the principle of the bacteriophage in dealing with infections.
6. What is the chief limitation in the use of the sulfa drugs?

CHAPTER 47

The Conquest of Disease

LESS than 200 years ago, infectious diseases swept through cities and across the countryside in terrifying epidemics. Few escaped the scourge of smallpox. A face which did not show deep pockmarks as a grim reminder of a life-and-death struggle with the deadly smallpox virus was unusual. Diphtheria, scarlet fever, and pneumonia were fatal to many children. Typhoid fever, influenza, tuberculosis, and other dangerous infections took a heavy toll of those who were fortunate enough to escape the infections common during childhood.

Today many of the infectious diseases your recent ancestors feared rarely appear in communities with high standards of health. Smallpox, diphtheria, whooping cough, tetanus — your doctor probably sees to it that you will never have these infections. We can do this because he has the knowledge and products of nearly 200 years of work contributed by scientists of all nations, teamed together in the conquest of disease.

In this chapter you will review some of the well-known infectious diseases and the measures we can take to control them.

Edward Jenner — country doctor. It was during one of the most dreadful smallpox epidemics in England that Edward Jenner, a country doctor, made a discovery which was to alter the course of history. Epidemics took their greatest toll in cities. Jenner noticed that the disease seldom struck people who lived in rural areas and worked around cattle. Most farmers and dairy workers had contracted cowpox and had recovered with nothing more serious than a pustule which left a scar. Were they immune to smallpox? If so, why not vaccinate people with cowpox to protect them from smallpox?

The first vaccination. On May 14, 1796, Dr. Jenner had a chance to test his vaccination theory. His patient was James Phipps, a healthy boy about eight years old. James's mother, with great confidence in Dr. Jenner, allowed her son to be used in the test with the hope that he could be spared the danger of smallpox. Dr. Jenner took his young patient to a dairy maid, Sarah Nelmes, who had a

cowpox pustule on her hand resulting from an infection from one of her master's cows. Dr. Jenner made two shallow cuts about an inch long on James Phipps's arm and *inoculated* them with matter taken from the cowpox sore. A pustule developed on the boy's arm, formed a scab and healed, leaving only a scar. Was James Phipps now immune to smallpox? There was only one way to find out. He must be inoculated with smallpox.

In July of the same year, Dr. Jenner deliberately inoculated James with matter from a smallpox pustule. During the next two weeks, the doctor watched his patient anxiously for signs of smallpox. They did not appear. Several months later he repeated the inoculation. Again, the disease did not develop. The vaccination was successful. James Phipps was definitely immune to smallpox!

Following this famous experiment, Dr. Jenner wrote a paper explaining his method of *vaccination.* At first, the doctors were hostile and would not listen to

Teaching Films Custodian

Fig. 47-1.   This scene, taken from a movie based on Dr. Jenner's life, shows him ready to inject cowpox into James Phipps's arm.   Dr. Jenner's discovery of how to produce artificial immunity to smallpox marked a milestone in the history of medicine.

such a ridiculous procedure. Many townspeople even organized anti-vaccination campaigns. Gradually, however, the doctors and their patients accepted vaccination and smallpox epidemics were eliminated.

Smallpox immunization. Smallpox and cowpox, or *Vaccinia* (vak-*sih*-nee-uh), are closely related viruses. Cowpox virus produces a mild infection in humans. But even a single cowpox pustule is enough to stimulate the body to produce active immunity against smallpox.

Young heifers are used in the commercial production of vaccine virus used in vaccination. Before inoculating the animals with virus, they are examined

thoroughly by a veterinarian for signs of disease. Then the abdomen is shaved and sterilized. Cowpox virus is placed in numerous scratches made on the abdomen. The virus is grown on the heifer for six or seven days, after which the animal is killed under anesthetic. The virus, growing in the scratches in white, pulpy patches, is scraped off and put into sterile containers. After harvesting the virus, the animal is examined internally for symptoms of any other disease.

The pulp containing cowpox virus is frozen temporarily before processing. Later, it is ground and mixed with 50% glycerin and salt solution in a ratio of one part virus to four parts glycerin and salt solution. In this condition, the processed virus can be held at subzero temperature. The virus preparation is placed in sealed capillary tubes for distribution to the doctor. After being tubed, it can be stored for three months. The resulting product is the vaccine the doctor rubs in scratches on your arm or leg when he vaccinates you to protect you from smallpox.

Pasteur's famous immunization experiment. About 80 years after Dr. Jenner vaccinated James Phipps, Louis Pasteur conducted his famous immunization experiments. Previous to these experiments, Pasteur had made a vaccine containing the weakened microbes of chicken cholera. He found that he could inject the vaccine into healthy chickens and produce active immunity against the disease. This led him to try a similar procedure against anthrax at about the same time Robert Koch was conducting his famous work on the disease.

Pasteur made an anthrax vaccine from weakened bacteria taken from the blood of infected animals. He claimed this vaccine would immunize animals against the disease. Scientists challenged him to prove his theory. This challenge was the opportunity he had waited for. He selected 48 healthy animals (mostly sheep) and divided them into two groups. He gave the animals in one group injections containing five drops of anthrax vaccine. Twelve days later, he gave the same animals a second injection of vaccine. Fourteen days later he gave all 48 animals an injection of living anthrax bacteria. Two days later the scientists met at the pens to laugh at Pasteur. Imagine their amazement to find all Pasteur's immunized animals alive and healthy, and all the untreated animals dead or dying of anthrax. This famous experiment was an important milestone in the conquest of disease.

Pasteur's greatest contribution to mankind. During the latter years of his life, Pasteur turned his genius to experimentation with one of the most dreadful of all diseases, *rabies* (ray-beez), or *hydrophobia* (hy-droh-*foh*-bee-uh). This disease was common among dogs, wolves, and other animals during his time. If the virus was transmitted to a human by a bite, a human victim was certain to suffer an agonizing death after an incubation period of a few weeks to six months or more. During this time the virus slowly destroyed brain and spinal cord tissue.

The restlessness, convulsions, great thirst, and throat paralysis which climaxed a rabies infection led Pasteur to believe that the infection centered in the brain. However, microscopic examination of the brain tissue of an animal victim did not reveal any microorganisms. We can understand why today, for the rabies virus is invisible under the ordinary microscope.

Fig. 47-2. Louis Pasteur's controlled experiment with anthrax vaccine on sheep proved that active immunity could be produced against the disease.

Teaching Films Custodia

The Bettmann Archive

Fig. 47-3.   This scene in Pasteur's laboratory shows a child being vaccinated against rabies.   Until Pasteur made his contribution toward conquering rabies, it was one of the three or four most dreaded diseases.

Pasteur found that he could transmit rabies by injecting infected brain tissue from a rabid dog to a healthy one. He repeated the inoculations with rabbits and discovered that the virus gained strength as it was passed from one animal to another. However, if spinal cord tissue taken from a dog or rabbit was dried for 14 days, the virus lost its strength and could no longer produce the infection. Thirteen-day-old virus was only slightly stronger. The discovery that the virus weakened with drying and aging led to experiments to find out if rabies immunity could be produced. Pasteur injected 14-day-old brain tissue into a healthy dog, then followed this injection with 13-day-old material.

The injections were continued day after day until the dog was given an injection of full-strength virus in the 14th injection. The animal suffered no ill effects. The series of injections with material of increasing strength had produced immunity to rabies. The question now was whether he dare try the series of injections in human victims. A decision was forced on Pasteur a short time later.

Pasteur's treatment of rabies. On July 6, 1885, a frantic mother brought her son to Pasteur's laboratory, pleading that he use any method to save her boy's life. The boy had been attacked by a rabid dog two days before they reached Pasteur's laboratory. Pasteur had no time to lose, and no choice except to give the boy the treatment which had worked on dogs. The physicians and laboratory assistants he consulted agreed with his decision. On the evening of this important day, the boy was given an injection of rabbit-grown virus which had aged 12 days. Injections were repeated each day, using successively fresher virus. On the 12th day he received full-strength virus. After several weeks of observation, he was sent home, the first human being immunized against rabies.

This series of injections, known as the *Pasteur treatment,* is used today to immunize victims of bites by rabid dogs. The virus used in making the vaccine was once grown in rabbits. However, a recent method of growing the virus in the embryos of developing duck eggs has proved more satisfactory because there is no danger of serious body reaction to the substances present in nerve tissue of the rabbit.

The conquest of diphtheria. From the earliest times, diphtheria was one of the worst epidemic killers, especially among children. The effects of diphtheria on the body are twofold. The germs grow in a thick, grayish-white membrane on the back wall of the throat. As the membrane spreads, it may block the glottis opening and cause death by strangulation. In addition, powerful toxins are given off by the living bacteria and are absorbed through the infected tissues into the blood. They often cause severe damage to the heart, nervous system, and other organs.

The conquest of diphtheria some 50 years ago involved the work of several scientists. One found the rod-shaped bacteria growing in the throats of patients with diphtheria. Another worker cultured the bacteria in a medium containing blood serum and developed a stain used in microscopic study of the organisms. However, much of the credit for the conquest of this disease belongs to Emil von Behring (*bear*-ing), a German bacteriologist.

Von Behring was puzzled by the fact that, even though diphtheria organisms remained in the throat, the effects of the disease appeared in distant organs. When bacteria were grown in culture media, they produced a toxin which, when injected into guinea pigs, produced the symptoms of diphtheria even though no germs were present.

While conducting such experiments with diphtheria toxin, von Behring discovered that guinea pigs and rabbits could be used only once. They developed immunity to the disease. Could this immunity be transferred to animals which had never been given doses of toxin? In an effort to answer this question, von Behring took blood from immune animals, separated the blood serum from other substances in the blood, and injected it into other animals. They too were made immune to diphtheria toxin. Von Behring named this immune body present in serum *antitoxin.*

Sheep were used first in the production of diphtheria antitoxin. After extensive testing of the antitoxin in guinea pigs, it was first used with great success in the Children's Hospital in Berlin. As we mentioned earlier, the antitoxin used today is produced in greater quantity in the blood of the horse.

Von Behring found that immunity resulting from injections of sheep antitoxin lasted only a few weeks. Apparently, the antitoxin is destroyed slowly in the human blood stream. If children could be made to produce their own antitoxin, immunity would be as lasting as though they had recovered from diphtheria. To give diphtheria toxin would be as dangerous as inoculating them with the disease itself. Von Behring reasoned that a mixture of toxin and antitoxin might be safe to use. World War I prevented von Behring from finishing his work. However, it was completed in the United States by Dr. William H. Park and other workers. Until the recent development of the toxoid, *toxin-antitoxin* was used in producing active immunity against diphtheria.

The Schick test for diphtheria. The *Schick test* is used to determine the presence of immunity to diphtheria. A small amount of dilute diphtheria toxin is injected under the skin on the inside of the lower arm with a hypodermic needle. If the test is negative, there is no reaction. Diphtheria antitoxin in the blood neutralizes the toxin. A positive test shows as a reddened area with a raised, dark red center at the point of injection. This indicates that the patient is susceptible to diphtheria and that he should have toxoid immunization. The wide use of the Schick test in small children as well as those of school age has nearly eliminated diphtheria.

Tetanus immunization. The tetanus organism is an anaerobic spore-forming bacillus. The cells are not active in the presence of air, but remain alive as resting spores. Tetanus organisms live normally in the intestinal tract of horses and other animals. The spores are therefore most abundant in soil on which manure has been used as a fertilizer. Some of these spore forms may live 60 or more years in contaminated soil.

Fig. 47-4. The diagram below illustrates a positive reaction to the Widal test, which determines whether or not typhoid agglutinins are present in a person's blood.

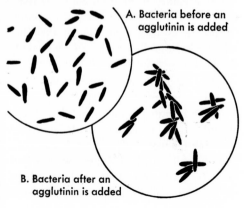

A. Bacteria before an agglutinin is added

B. Bacteria after an agglutinin is added

When spores are introduced into the body in a deep puncture wound, they germinate and become active cells. Within a short time they multiply and pour powerful toxins into the tissue and blood. The toxin causes grave illness, including fever, chills, and paralysis, usually first evident in the jaw, face, and neck muscles. This led to the name "lockjaw." Mortality is over 50 per cent. Many cases do not respond to any treatment after the symptoms have appeared, following a three- to five-day incubation period.

Horse antitoxin serum is used immediately to give passive immunity to a victim of a deep wound. However, the use of serum involves the possibility of serum sickness or may cause development of allergy to serum which would make the use of a serum in treating another disease difficult and dangerous. Instead of serum, tetanus toxoid is widely used today to produce active immunity against tetanus. Injections are given as a preventive measure and not at the time of an injury. If an immune person has an injury which requires further immunization, it is given in the form of a toxoid booster shot. Everyone should have toxoid immunization as a safe prevention against this dangerous infection.

Typhoid fever. Typhoid fever organisms live in the intestine, causing lesions in the intestine wall. They reach the lymph nodes of the mesentery from the intestine and enter the general circulation. From the blood, they may invade the spleen, lungs, bone marrow, liver, and gall bladder.

Typhoid vaccine, used in immunization, is made from dead bacteria. The vaccine is usually injected into the arm. A slight redness appears and may remain for a few days. Active immunity lasts for about three years.

The *Widal test* is widely used in diagnosing typhoid and in locating immune

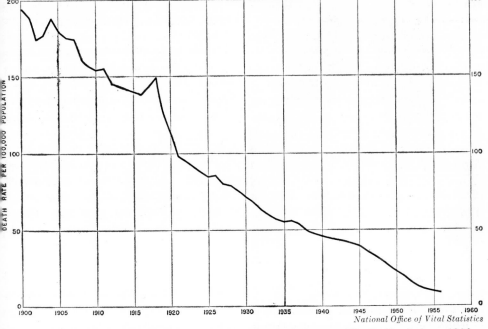

National Office of Vital Statistics

Fig. 47-5. Note how the death rate from tuberculosis has steadily declined since 1900.

carriers. A typhoid patient or carrier has typhoid agglutinins, the principal defense against the disease, in his blood stream. A small drop containing typhoid bacteria is put on a microscope slide. A drop of the patient's blood is added. If agglutinins are present, the typhoid germs clump, or agglutinate (Fig. 47-4). This is a positive reaction and shows that typhoid fever is present, or that the patient is immune.

Tuberculosis — its treatment. Until recently, *tuberculosis* was the most fatal disease, causing one-seventh of all deaths. While we usually think of it as an infection of the lungs, it may infect the bones, glands, and other organs, too. Tuberculosis is caused by tiny rod-shaped organisms which may enter the body with food or travel down the air passages. Damage to the body is slight at first and usually goes unnoticed. The bacteria destroy tissue at the place of the infection and produce a lesion. Endotoxins, released into the blood from dead bacteria, cause general weakness, loss of weight and appetite, and fever.

When Koch grew tuberculosis organisms on blood agar, he discovered the endotoxin, which he named **tuberculin.** He had hoped to use this product to produce active immunity, but discovered that it produced a dangerous abscess when injected into the body. However, we use tuberculin today to test for active tuberculosis. If a small square of filter paper, saturated with tuberculin, is laid against the skin, a red spot appears within two or three days if the patient is sensitive to tuberculin. Such a positive **patch test** means that a person has, or has had, active germs in his body. It does not mean that he has active tuberculosis.

A positive patch test is followed by an X ray of the chest to check for a lesion. A **sputum** (*spyou*-tum) **test** may also be made to see if the organisms are present in fluid from the lungs. Many people develop a slight tuberculosis infection

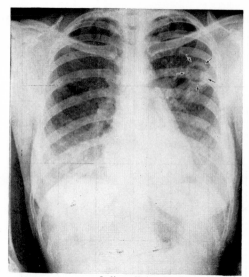

Fig. 47-6. Chest X rays verify the suspected presence of tuberculosis in the lung. Notice the circular lesion that has formed around invading bacteria in the left lung shown here.

following a severe cold, influenza, pneumonia, or some other condition which lowers their resistance to infection. They recover without knowledge of the infection. For this reason many people have a positive reaction to a patch test and show no evidence of tuberculosis in X ray and other tests.

Progress in preventing tuberculosis. Sparked by the untiring efforts of the National Tuberculosis Association and numerous county associations, a campaign has been conducted for several years to prevent tuberculosis. The work of these organizations has been financed through the sale of the familiar Christmas seals as well as private donations. The associations have sponsored educational campaigns and measures to remove conditions which lead to tuberculosis. They have stressed the importance of adequate rest, proper food, sanitation, healthful working and living conditions. Every case of human tuberculosis comes from

an existing case, and if every one of these were located, tuberculosis would be stamped out.

Colds and cold shots. We are fortunate that the common cold is not a dangerous infection or few would survive. Colds are caused by a number of viruses which attack the mucous membranes of the nasal passages and respiratory tract. They are highly contagious in most cases and usually follow a period of weakened resistance. After recovery, there is a brief period of immunity to that virus which caused the particular infection. But a cold caused by another virus may follow. Streptococcus infections, pneumonia, and other diseases may follow a cold.

Many investigations of colds and their causes have been made in recent years in an effort to produce a vaccine. One problem is the distinction between a cold and a noninfectious nasal allergy. Another is isolation and classification of the many cold organisms. Oral vaccines, to be taken by mouth, have not proved effective. The best preventive measure seems to be adequate rest, proper diet, and other health practices. These insure a maximum amount of resistance to the virus.

A group of drugs called **antihistamines** (an-tee-*his*-tuh-meens) has become popular during the past few years because of their possible relief of nasal congestion during a cold. Success with antihistamines has been reported in some cases, while others seem not to respond.

Influenza, a highly contagious virus infection. Influenza, or "flu" as we commonly call it, is a respiratory infection caused by a virus. It may occur in epidemic form, spreading rapidly from one person to another. Symptoms appear suddenly with fever, general weakness, aching pain in the back, arms, and legs, and inflammation of the mucous membranes of the respiratory passages.

One reason for the rapid spread of influenza during an epidemic is the fact that many people continue their daily work and mingle with others. The greatest danger from influenza is secondary complications which often follow. These include bronchitis, pneumonia, and other respiratory infections. Treatment includes rest in bed, abundant fluids, and protection against possible sources of secondary infection.

An influenza vaccine is prepared by growing the virus in fertilized hens' eggs (Fig. 47-7). Three injections of the vaccine are given at intervals of a week.

Various forms of pneumonia.. *Lobar pneumonia* is an infection of the lungs by a specific pneumonia organism known as *pneumococcus* (new-moh-*kok*-us). This bacterium is a tiny ball-shaped organism, often found in pairs and frequently enclosed in a thick, slimy capsule. At least 30 types of the pneumococcus organism are known to exist.

Specific sera have been replaced by the use of penicillin and various sulfa drugs in recent years. These new drugs are highly efficient in the treatment of pneu-

monia and bring about a dramatic response. When given at the start of the infection, penicillin usually brings the infection under control within 12 hours, and promotes a crisis with sudden lessening of symptoms within 48 hours.

Bronchial pneumonia results from invasion of the lungs by a variety of organisms which infect the respiratory tract. *Virus pneumonia* is an infection of the lungs by a single virus, or group of viruses. It usually is not as serious as other forms of pneumonia, but it may last much longer. Aureomycin, one of the antibiotic drugs, seems to be the most effective treatment in this case.

Childhood diseases. Certain infections are so common during childhood that we often think of them as *childhood diseases*. However, they are by no means limited to children, nor is it necessary that all children have them.

Whooping cough is a bacterial disease most common in childhood. About half of the cases occur in children under two years of age. Whooping cough is most common during the winter and spring.

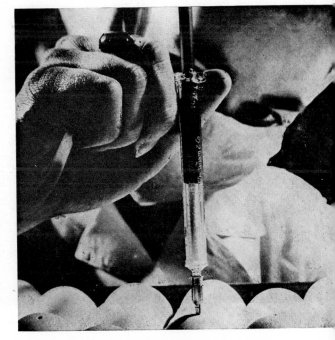

Fig. 47-7. Influenza vaccine is produced by injecting influenza virus into chick embryos, which act as a culture medium and promote rapid growth of the virus.

Epidemics occur at two- to four-year intervals. Severe coughing, vomiting, and the characteristic gasping "whoop" are common symptoms. The disease is very dangerous in infants under one year of age. In fact, it is one of the most fatal diseases because they may strangle from an accumulation of mucus. For this reason, three injections of whooping cough vaccine are given usually one week apart to infants within a few months after birth.

Chickenpox is a highly contagious virus infection of children. The disease is usually mild, starting with a slight fever, weakness, and nasal congestion. Within 24 to 48 hours, raised areas appear over the trunk, shoulders, and face. These open, and fluid seeps out a short time later. If a child scratches these small pustules, a permanent scar may be left on the skin. The most common complication is infection of the skin eruptions.

Measles and *German measles* are virus infections. Both diseases are spread rapidly through nasal discharges. Serious complications, including ear infections

and pneumonia, may follow measles. Serum may be given to provide passive immunity to an exposed child or to reduce the seriousness of the disease if it develops. Complications from German measles are less frequent.

Mumps is a virus infection of the salivary glands, although it may involve other tissues, especially the reproductive organs. It is more serious in an adult than in a child.

What is polio? Polio is a shortened name for poliomyelitis, a disease well known to the public today. Its common name, infantile paralysis, is poorly chosen for it is not a disease of infants, nor does it always cause paralysis. From 40 to 60 per cent of polio cases result in no permanent damage. There is a slight paralysis in 25 to 35 per cent of the cases, and extensive, permanent paralysis in 14 per cent of cases.

The polio virus attacks the anterior motor nerve roots of the spinal cord. These are the great nerve trunks which lead to the muscles. If there is destruc-

Fig. 47-8. To make polio vaccine, minced kidney cells of monkeys are first put into bottles containing a nutrient solution (*below*). The bottles are then rocked for six days in an incubator room (*right*), where the kidney cells grow and multiply.

Eli Lilly Co.

Eli Lilly Co.

tion of nerves by the virus, the muscles they control become paralyzed. In some severe cases of polio (*bulbar* type), the virus attacks the spinal bulb at the base of the brain, causing paralysis of the breathing muscles. When this occurs, the victim has to be put into an "iron lung," a mechanical breathing device.

The polio virus lives only in the tissue of primates and was first transmitted from humans to monkeys in 1908. The path of the virus into the body has been a subject of study for several years. Until recently it was thought to enter the nasal cavity and travel along the olfactory nerves to the brain. More recent research indicates that it enters the alimentary tract with food or water. It then passes into the blood stream and finally reaches the nerve tissue of the spinal cord where it starts to grow. Three specific types of polio virus are known to exist.

A patient who recovers from polio has a lifetime immunity to the type, or types, he has experienced. Many adults appear to have immunity to polio without being aware of having had a mild polio infection. For some years, scientists worked frantically to find either a serum which would give temporary passive immunity or a vaccine which would give permanent active immunity. These efforts have been supported through the tireless work of the National Foundation for Infantile Paralysis (now called simply the National Foundation) and other health agencies and an interested, generous public.

The conquest of polio. The first major victory came a few years ago with the production and first use of GG, or **gamma globulin**. It resulted from the work which had been done in the pooling and preservation of blood in blood banks during World War II. Gamma globulin containing antibodies against polio is separated from other parts of blood by quite complicated chemical processes. A large pooling of blood is necessary to be sure that antibodies against all three types of polio virus are present. These come from many adults who have experienced mild and probably undiagnosed infections of

Eli Lilly Co.

Fig. 47-9. The nutrient solution is then removed and a medium containing live polio virus is added to the kidney cells (*left*) and reincubated for four days. After this, the polio virus is inactivated in formaldehyde (*below*), filtered, and stored.

Eli Lilly Co.

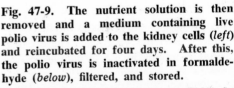

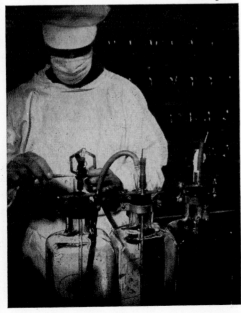

polio. Gamma globulin serum gives a short passive immunity against polio, which lasts about five weeks. For this reason, its use is limited to the protection of children during a polio epidemic and to members of a family who have been exposed to polio.

The long-awaited polio vaccine was announced in the spring of 1953. While many scientists had an important part in developing the vaccine, much of the credit for its discovery has been given Dr. Jonas Salk and his colleagues at the University of Pittsburgh. As a result of widespread inoculation by the **Salk vaccine**, the overall incidence of reported poliomyelitis has gone down 90 per cent.

The production of Salk vaccine was possible because of advances in the area of tissue culture, or the growing of animal tissues in nutrient solutions outside of the animal's body. During the latter part of 1953, biological companies started the production of the vaccine in tissue cultures made from the kidneys of monkeys. Kidney cells are used because they are more successfully cultured than nerve cells, and because certain irritating proteins present in nerve tissue might be introduced into the vaccine. These cause serious reactions in a few people.

The production of the vaccine starts with thorough examination of a monkey to be used to determine whether it has tuberculosis. If the tuberculin test is negative and the monkey appears to be in good health, it is given a fatal anesthetic, during which time the kidneys are removed. This is followed by a complete examination of the internal organs for evidence of disease. If the animal is healthy, the kidneys are cut into fine pieces and put into flasks containing a nutrient solution to which antibiotics have been added to prevent bacterial growth. These tissue cultures are incubated for six days at 98.6° F. Then the nutrient solution is drained off and replaced with new solution containing all three types of polio virus. Incubation continues four more days, during which the virus multiplies rapidly in the kidney cells. The cultures are filtered three times to remove all cells and any bacteria which may be present. The virus is then made inactive by treating it with a weak solution of formaldehyde. The inactive virus is then tested in another tissue culture as well as in monkeys. Before the vaccine is released for use, the manufacturing company's tests are duplicated in the laboratories of the National Institutes of Health in Washington.

In Conclusion

In the lobby of a mid-western children's hospital, bronze tablets bearing the names Edward Jenner, Robert Koch, Louis Pasteur, and other great men of science are set among the stone slabs of the floor. Because these men lived, few if any cases of smallpox, diphtheria, rabies, and other dangerous infectious diseases need be admitted to this hospital. The ward for the treatment of polio cases is nearly empty because of the work of Dr. Jonas Salk and the many others who contributed to the research in tissue culture and the production of polio vaccine.

The conquest of infectious diseases continues. The death rate in the United States from the four principle communicable diseases of childhood — measles, scarlet fever, whooping cough, and diphtheria — fell from 143 per 100,000 in 1910 to 1.5 in 1956, or 99 per cent! But only part of the battle is fought in doctors' offices, clinics, hospitals, and research centers. Prevention of disease is equally important. We shall explore this phase in the next chapter.

BIOLOGICALLY SPEAKING

antihistamines
gamma globulin
inoculation
patch test

Salk vaccine
Schick test
sputum test

tuberculin
vaccination
Widal test

QUESTIONS FOR REVIEW

1. Why is the fact that Edward Jenner was a country doctor important in the discovery of vaccination against smallpox?
2. What false belief regarding the danger of vaccination in Jenner's time led to violent objections and campaigns against it?
3. Discuss modern methods in producing and processing smallpox vaccine.
4. Against what disease of poultry did Pasteur make a successful vaccine before making his famous anthrax vaccine?
5. What characteristics of rabies led Pasteur to believe that it centered in the brain?
6. Describe the treatment Pasteur gave the boy who was bitten by a mad dog. Do we use the same treatment today?
7. Describe the two-fold effect of diphtheria on the body.
8. What condition in a patient is indicated by a positive reaction to the Schick test for diphtheria?
9. Describe the Widal test for typhoid fever.
10. Of what medical use is the endotoxin tuberculin?
11. Describe the several different forms of pneumonia.
12. What medical use is made of antihistamine drugs?
13. What living host is used in growing influenza virus?
14. Explain why muscle paralysis occurs in some cases of polio.

APPLYING FACTS AND PRINCIPLES

1. Explain how the production of virus for smallpox vaccination illustrates the weakening of a virus by animal passage.
2. Discuss the source and medical use of diphtheria toxin, antitoxin, toxin-antitoxin, and toxoid. Which product is used in immunization today?
3. Explain why the patch test for tuberculosis, while valuable for children, is of little value in testing adults.
4. Under what conditions might gamma globulin be used against polio?
5. Why did the production of a vaccine for polio (Salk vaccine) depend on advances in the field of tissue culture?

CHAPTER 48

The Prevention of Disease

I T is reassuring to know that your doctor is standing by to help you with effective biological products and powerful drugs and antibiotics if infection strikes. He is highly trained in the use of these weapons of *curative medicine,* but the cure of infectious disease is only one phase of the health program today. *Preventive medicine* fights infection at the source by removing the cause. It is in this phase of the health program that you, your doctor, and others concerned with maintaining the health of the community work as a team in protecting your health and the health of others.

In this chapter we shall discuss the prevention of infection in various areas of your community. Then we shall explore the problems of heart disease and cancer to find out what you may be able to do to prevent these major killers of our time.

Lister and antiseptic surgery. A hundred years ago few patients survived the ordeal of major surgery. Anesthetics were just coming into use. Because of the high mortality rate, operations were avoided, except in cases of severe wounds or those requiring amputation of limbs. Doctors often performed operations with unscrubbed hands and instruments which had not been sterilized. Wounds were covered with non-sterile dressings and bandages. Under conditions like these serious infection almost always followed surgery. The mortality rate was at least three out of four patients, if not from shock and loss of blood during surgery, then from infection a few days later.

These conditions in hospitals were alarming to a famous English surgeon, Sir Joseph Lister, a century ago. Lister had studied Pasteur's accounts of air-borne organisms and the possibility of infection during surgery. He applied this knowledge to his surgical procedures. He scrubbed the walls and floor of his operating room and covered his operating table with clean linen. Splints and bandages were soaked in a carbolic acid solution

and surgical instruments were boiled in water. Those present in the operating room were required to scrub thoroughly. He even devised a carbolic acid spray which produced a fine germ-killing mist over the area of operation. By these methods Lister introduced *antiseptic surgery.* His success in reducing surgical infection changed the practice of surgery all over the world.

The modern hospital operating room uses germ-free methods known as *aseptic surgery.* The rooms are scrubbed with germicides. The air is sterilized with lamps which give off germ-killing rays. All linens, dressings, and bandages are sterilized. The surgeon and his assisting doctors and nurses wear sterile gowns, head covers, and face masks. Those actually performing the surgery and handling instruments and dressings wear sterile gloves over thoroughly scrubbed hands. These aseptic conditions have removed much of the risk of an operation and now most surgical wounds heal with no infection whatever.

Antiseptics and disinfectants. Since Lister's first use of carbolic acid as a dis-

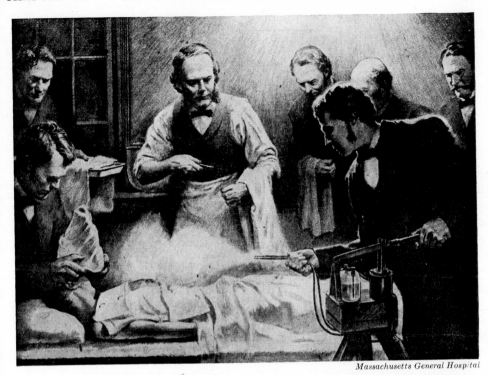

Massachusetts General Hospital

Fig. 48-1. Lister was the first to realize the importance of antiseptic surgery. His assistant is shown spraying carbolic acid on the skin of a patient just before an operation.

infectant (germicide), many chemical substances have been developed for use in the destruction of microbes. They are of two general types. **Antiseptics** destroy some bacteria and prevent the growth of others. They are used locally in contact with body tissues, and must not be of such strength that they damage the tissues. Do not confuse antiseptics with **disinfectants,** which are powerful germ-killers used in chemical sterilization.

The perfect antiseptic, which would have powerful effect on germs without injury to living tissue, has not been found. A 1% iodine solution is reliable for treating ordinary wounds and cuts. Solutions up to 3½% are used as antiseptics. Hydrogen peroxide (if fresh), potassium permanganate, camphor, thymol, and even common salt and soap are of definite antiseptic value. Some of the most recent

antiseptics work on the cleansing principle rather than by chemical destruction.

Disinfectants are used in sterilizing instruments, utensils, bedding, clothing, and walls and floors of rooms which have been exposed to infection. Some disinfectants may be used in diluted form on hands, but only with extreme care. They should never be used on other parts of the body without specific medical instructions. Among the widely used disinfectants are 5% carbolic acid (phenol) solution, creosol, lysol, creolin, and formaldehyde. All of these are used in solution, according to directions supplied.

Preventive medicine in the community. Much of the responsibility for protecting the community from infectious disease is assigned to the local and state boards of health. One of the major activities of these **public health** organizations is to protect the community through the enforcement of quarantine in certain contagious diseases. This work of the Board of Health prevents contagious diseases from sweeping the community in epidemics as they did in earlier times.

The Board of Health gathers statistics on diseases in a community which are valuable to doctors. These data serve further in tracing epidemics and removing the cause whenever possible. The local food supply, water supply, public restaurants, hotels and motels, and other public places are under the Board's constant observation.

Inspection of the food supply. Almost every city and state has regulations in regard to food inspection. The stores, bakeries, meat-packing plants, and milk companies are under supervision of official inspectors. Meat which is to be sold outside the state must be inspected

by the Bureau of Animal Industries of the United States Department of Agriculture. You have probably noticed the purple stamp of the inspector on meat you buy.

Milk can be a dangerous source of infection, especially in small children. Many cases of tuberculosis, undulant fever, streptococcus infections, intestinal infections, and typhoid fever have been traced to contaminated milk. For this reason, every precaution is taken to be sure the cows of a dairy herd are free of disease and that milk does not become contaminated during milking, handling, and bottling for delivery.

Safeguarding our water supply. The water supply is one of the most critical factors, especially in cities where great numbers of people use a common source. Under such circumstances, infected water could cause an epidemic almost overnight. The water supply for a large city repre-

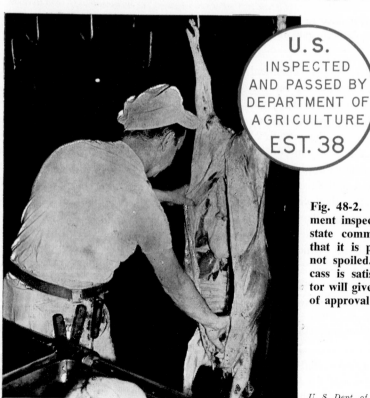

Fig. 48-2. The federal government inspects all meat in interstate commerce to make sure that it is properly labeled and not spoiled. If this lamb carcass is satisfactory, the inspector will give it the official stamp of approval shown above.

U. S. Dept. of Agriculture

U. S. Public Health Service

Fig. 48-3.   On the left a local health department sanitary inspector is shown checking dishes in a restaurant to see that they have been washed according to the required standards.   The health department bacteriologist shown on the right is making a bacteria count of samples taken from restaurant utensils.

sents an enormous investment. The watershed, or original source of the water supply, the streams or lakes from which the water is obtained, and the wells driven deep into the ground must be checked continually.

Chemical and bacteriological tests are run almost constantly. Thus, one living in a large city may be sure that his water supply is a safe and healthful one.

In smaller communities and individual farms, wells usually serve as water supply. Water from these sources should be checked regularly by the Board of Health to guard against infection.

Sewage and garbage disposal. Disposal of waste products, especially of sewage and garbage, is an important problem in most cities. The old way was to dump the garbage in special areas outside the city and carry the sewage through sewers to rivers and streams. Both measures

created serious health hazards. Garbage dumps created breeding places for flies and general offensive conditions. Streams and beaches polluted by sewage became dangerous areas of infection for bathers. It also made water unfit for other uses, even to the extent of killing fish and other aquatic animals.

The best method of garbage disposal consists of converting it into useful fertilizer for distribution to agricultural regions for use on fields. In the same way, sewage may be treated and either reduced to fertilizer or treated to stimulate the growth of bacteria of decay. This is done to destroy its harmful properties before it is piped into rivers and streams.

Other agencies concerned with the fight against disease. To some extent, disease is an individual problem. But the effects of disease are much more far-reaching. The life of every individual has a direct bearing on his community, his state, and even the nation as a whole.

In 1912 the United States Public Health Service was established as a national agency to assist in the control of disease. It grew out of a much older organization, the Marine Hospital Service.

In addition to national and state agencies, numerous local and private agencies are doing extremely important work in the control and prevention of disease.

Insurance companies have made exhaustive studies in connection with the life expectancy of their insured. This information is available to the public in the form of numerous pamphlets and is valuable in health education. The Rockefeller Foundation maintains an extensive program of research in the fields of medicine and prevention of disease. Public health nursing associations, both privately and in connection with the local boards of health, provide nursing care to those who could not otherwise afford it. In most cities, public health nurses are available for people of all economic circumstances and no one is denied proper care during illness because of inability to pay for nursing care.

Patent medicines. Home prevention of disease is highly desirable, but home treatment of disease is an entirely different matter. In this day of highly advanced and efficient medicine, one is extremely foolish to attempt self-diagnosis and treatment of disease.

The Federal Food, Drug, and Cosmetic Act has done much to eliminate quack medicines. While it does not forbid the sale of these medicines, it does make the following requirements:

1. That the manufacturer put on the label the amounts of alcohol and other ingredients in the medicine.

2. That he make no false or misleading statement about cures or other virtues in using the medicine.

Effectiveness of recognized drugs and antibiotics is proven in large numbers of clinical tests, performed under medical supervision. Curative value is not determined by testimonials of private users. If a drug is found to be of questionable value, it is withdrawn from public use.

Our greatest threats to health today. During the past 50 years, the conquest of infectious diseases has been a series of victories, one after another. Diphtheria no longer takes its toll of infants. Public health and community hygiene measures have largely removed the typhoid menace. Tuberculosis, once a leading cause of death, especially among young people, seems well under control. The control of polio is one of the most recent milestones in our record of medical achievement. Each new discovery has given your doctor an additional weapon with which to guard you against infectious disease. But the battle against disease is not yet won.

As infectious diseases have been removed from leading causes of death, other killers have moved in to take their places. We have entered a new phase of the struggle against disease. The conquest of organic and functional disease is our prime objective. These are the leading killers today.

Organic and functional diseases. The *organic* and *functional* diseases present quite a different problem from infectious diseases. They are not due to microorganisms and cannot be treated like infectious diseases.

At the present time, diseases of the heart are the leading cause of death. Cancer and other malignant tumors, cerebral hemorrhage, arteriosclerosis (hardening of the arteries), and diseases of the nervous system also have become prominent.

These diseases are of a personal nature. They cannot be prevented through efforts of public agencies the way infectious diseases can. The individual must understand them and use every possible precaution against their occurrence.

Diseases of the heart and related organs. Heart disease leads all others today as a cause of death, especially among people of middle and old age. We usually think of heart disease as developing suddenly because death from certain forms of this ailment is almost immediate. Actually, heart disease develops over a long period of time and often involves other organs.

Various kinds of heart damage and diseases are associated with different periods of life. We can divide them according to age and cause as follows: (1) childhood and adolescence — rheumatic fever; (2) middle age — hypertension, or high blood pressure, and coronary heart disease; and (3) old age — hardening of the arteries, or arteriosclerosis.

Heart disease can result from rheumatic fever. *Rheumatic fever* develops as a complication in approximately three per cent of the cases of scarlet fever and related streptococcic throat infections. The powerful exotoxins absorbed from the infected throat tissues cause an allergic reaction in the connective tissues of certain people. This reaction is most common in the joints where the tissues become inflamed, reddened, and painfully swollen. The condition travels from one joint to another during several weeks or months of the illness.

In about one-third of the cases of rheumatic fever, the valves and ligaments of the heart, especially on the left side, become similarly inflamed. This inflammation may cause scar tissue to develop and leave the valves defective. The bicuspid, or mitral valve, between the auricle and ventricle on the left side of the heart, is most frequently involved. In some cases, the valve does not open enough to allow a normal flow of blood from the auricle to

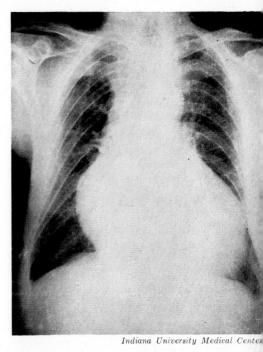

Indiana University Medical Center

Fig. 48-4. Compare this X-ray picture of the enlarged heart of an elderly person with the normal heart in Fig. 38-6, page 485.

the ventricle. In others, the valve does not close properly and allows blood to flow back into the auricle each time the ventricle contracts, thus lowering the blood pressure and adding greatly to the work of the heart.

The use of penicillin and other antibiotics, as well as sulfa drugs, has reduced the amount of heart damage in rheumatic fever. These drugs lessen the seriousness as well as the duration of streptococcic infections.

Children who have valvular heart damage resulting from rheumatic fever should be taught to live with their heart conditions as normally as possible, and should not become overcautious heart invalids. A heart specialist should be consulted. He may advise nothing more than a little extra rest and a little less exertion than usual.

Hypertension is the great enemy of middle age. *Hypertension,* or high blood pressure, has been increasing in

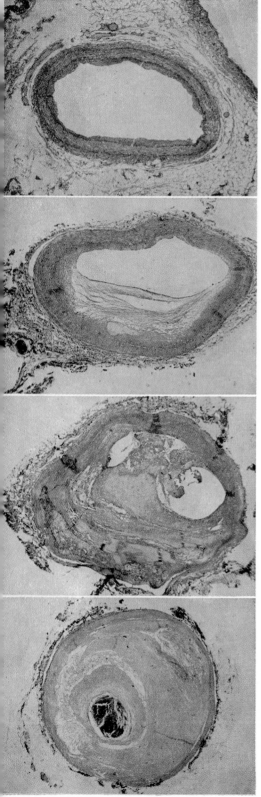

recent years. It is far more common in men than in women. It is commonly related to emotional stress resulting from worry, fear, and anxiety. Emotional stress causes various body changes, including constriction of the artery walls and increase in blood pressure. When arteries remain in this condition for long periods, their walls die slowly and harden with internal deposits (Fig. 48-5). This situation reduces the internal diameter of the arteries and also reduces the flow of blood, just as lime deposits in a pipe reduce the flow of water. As a result, the blood pressure remains high.

In some cases, hypertension results in slow destruction of the tiny arteries of the kidneys, resulting in *chronic nephritis*. In others, the coronary arteries of the heart become involved. For this reason, hypertension is sometimes referred to as **cardiovascular-renal disease**, referring to the heart, blood vessels, and kidneys.

Coronary heart disease. Constriction and hardening of the coronary arteries which supply the heart muscle reduce the blood supply to the heart. This condition may not be noticed at first, especially if the person does not exert himself physically. However, as the condition grows worse, he may experience a crushing pain in the chest which extends into one or both arms at times of exertion. The pain and feeling of pressure in the chest at these times result from insufficient circulation to the heart muscle when the work of the heart is increased because of body exertion.

In some cases of coronary heart disease, a sudden flow of blood into the constricted coronary arteries at a time of exertion may cause a clot to form and block one of

Fig. 48-5. These photographs show four successive stages of internal deposit in a blood vessel of the brain. As the flow of blood becomes slower, clots may form and completely close the vessel.

American Heart Assoc.

the arteries. Such a stoppage in a coronary artery is called a **coronary occlusion.** When the clot causing the occlusion forms in the heart vessel, we refer to it as a **coronary thrombosis.** Occasionally a clot may form in a vessel in some other part of the body, travel through the circulation, and lodge in a coronary artery, resulting in a **coronary embolism.**

When a coronary artery becomes blocked, the portion of the heart muscle it supplies dies. A " heart attack " results. The seriousness of the condition depends on the location of the occlusion and the amount of heart muscle involved. Absolute rest is necessary during the period the heart is repairing the damage. A doctor can determine the amount of heart damage by means of an instrument known as an **electrocardiograph** (ee-lek-troh-*kar*-dee-oh-graf).

Hardening of the arteries. Hardening of the arteries, known medically as **arteriosclerosis,** is primarily a disease of older people. It results from permanent change in the artery walls. In some cases, calcium deposits form in the walls of the vessels and make them rigid. The arteries do not expand freely with the surge of blood following each contraction of the ventricle of the heart, causing a rise in blood pressure. Hardening of the arteries puts the heart under constant strain and may cause it to enlarge and, in time, to go into failure.

We are in the midst of extensive research in an effort to find the causes of heart diseases. When they are eventually found, many years will be added to the present human life span.

Cancer is one of the chief killers today. The difficulty in dealing with cancer is that it is a " normal abnormality." It seems to be a mass of tissue in which cell division has gone wild, resulting in an abnormal growth which soon invades other organs.

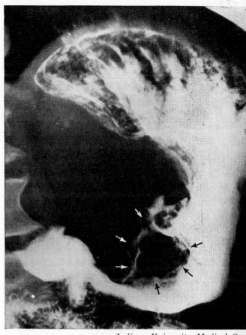

Indiana University Medical Cen

Fig. 48-6. This X-ray photograph shows cancer of the stomach. If you compare it with the normal stomach shown in Fig. 36-7, page 453, you will notice that much of the wall along the inner curvature is replaced by cancer tissue.

Cancer appears most frequently in the colon, stomach, throat, lungs, liver, and, in the case of women, in the uterus and breast. Cancer is most common in people between the ages of 40 and 60.

The disease can be treated effectively if found in its early stages. Consequently, one should report any suspicious symptoms to the doctor immediately. The following symptoms *may* mean cancer, although they are not necessarily indications and should not cause undue alarm: (1) any sore that does not heal in a few weeks; (2) bleeding from any body opening; (3) a lump on the surface of the body which changes shape or becomes enlarged; (4) persistent indigestion; (5) persistent change in bladder or bowel habits; (6) progressive change in the color of a wart or mole; and (7) continued hoarseness or cough.

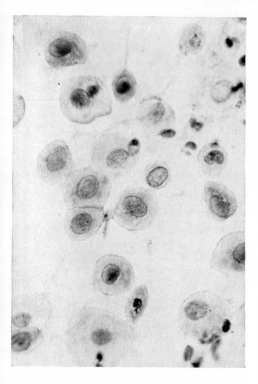
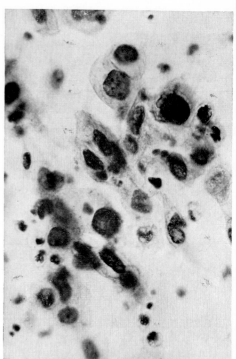

Fig. 48-7. The left-hand photomicrograph shows the regular cell outlines and orderly distribution of cells in normal tissue. The right-hand photograph shows the characteristic growth and arrangement of cancer cells in the same type of tissue.

The diagnosis and treatment of cancer. External cancers of the skin are readily diagnosed and treated. However, internal forms are often very difficult to detect. X rays are used to determine the extent and location of the growth, although even this method is not positive evidence. The proof of cancer is based on the presence of characteristic giant cells in the abnormal growth.

There are *only three recognized methods of treating cancer:* (1) the entire growth may be removed by *surgery;* (2) *X ray* may be used to destroy the rapidly dividing cells; and (3) *radium* and other radioactive substances which give off radiations that destroy cancerous cells more rapidly than normal ones may be used in treatment.

Cancer is not considered contagious, as it is not yet known if microorganisms are involved. It cannot be inherited directly, although statistics seem to indicate that certain types of cancer are more prominent in some families than in others. An individual may inherit a constitutional make-up which tends toward cancer, although the disease is never inherited as such. Furthermore, cancer tendency in a family may be altered in offspring through marriage with individuals in which the tendency is not present.

Mental diseases. The average individual today lives under great stress and strain which is apt to affect his nervous system in some way or other. Although mental disorders may result from disease in other parts of the body or from organic conditions, the greatest number of cases are the result of functional disturbances.

We look on **mental disease** as we would on any other disease, except that in affecting the nervous system it necessarily influences the actions of the individual. We know now that by far the majority of cases may be cured and restored to normal life if treatment is begun early. While some forms of mental disorders may require institutional care for long periods of time, seven out of ten patients could avoid institutional commitment if treated in time.

The great need in the country now is for more mental hospitals with emergency wards where critical mental cases of short duration may receive extensive treatment.

If a patient who has " cracked up " could be sent to a hospital *at once,* he would have the skilled care of a psychiatrist. A **psychiatrist** (sy-*ky*-uh-trist) is a physician who has been specially trained

to handle mental cases. The mentally ill patient who can be put under the care of a psychiatrist immediately will seldom have to return to an institution later in life.

Our trouble has been in disregarding early symptoms of mental and nervous disease and then committing the patient to an institution when he is advanced beyond anything private care can do. Consequently, many patients fail to receive treatment at a time they need it most and are put into overcrowded mental hospitals or state or local institutions.

Mental diseases can be prevented. Most cases of mental illness could be avoided if the individual understood something about the cause of these disorders. Frequently, mental disease begins with attitudes on the part of the individual. These attitudes, in turn, put a strain on the nervous system which may

Fig. 48-8.   X-ray therapy is frequently used effectively in the treatment of cancer. The X rays destroy the rapidly dividing cells.

Monkmeyer

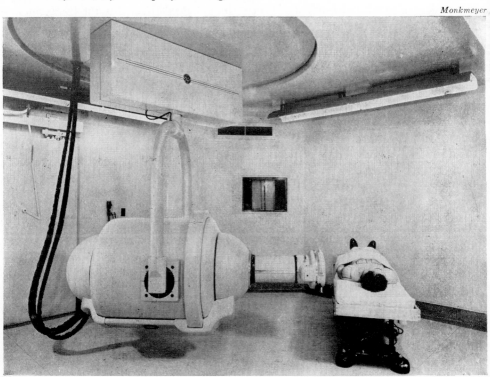

Fig. 48-9. The psychiatrist is shown obtaining the complete case history of a patient who is being admitted to a mental hospital.

affect the mental processes. Even as high school pupils you should guard against damaging attitudes and types of behavior. Study the following list carefully, then see if you are tending toward any of the attitudes which may possibly lead to trouble in later life:

1. Avoid thinking too much about yourself. Think in terms of other people and make their happiness your chief goal. Avoid selfishness and self-pity.

2. Don't allow all your activity to center around one thing. The person with varied interests changes activities from time to time and is able to relax.

3. Strive to get satisfaction from your work. Don't look on things you must do as chores, but rather as opportunities.

4. Maintain hobbies which have little to do with your routine life. These activities are as important to you as your chief occupation.

5. If possible, engage in sports and other outdoor activities which tend to tire you physically.

6. Develop adaptability. Learn to adjust yourself to new friends and situations. Don't live in a rut by excluding new acquaintances.

7. Learn to accept disappointments willingly and cheerfully. Look beyond present reverses to future successes.

8. Develop admiration for those who are more successful in certain things than you are. Avoid the attitude that " some people get all the breaks " while you have more than your share of bad luck.

9. If you have any handicaps, disregard them and develop superiority in some other line. If you have no physical handicaps yourself, be sure to disregard them in others.

10. Be conscientious in what you do, but don't worry excessively.

When nervous and mental disorders are treated with the same degree of efficiency as infectious diseases, we shall have reached a high standard in the conquest of disease.

In Conclusion

One reason the percentage of deaths from heart disease, cancer, and other diseases of middle age and beyond has been increasing in recent years is the reduction in the number of deaths from infectious diseases earlier in life. Most of the dangerous killers of childhood have been eliminated. Tuberculosis and pneumonia, which once took a heavy toll of young people and adults, are under control. When we finally conquer heart disease and cancer, the average life span will rise suddenly from the present 68–70 years to perhaps 100 or more. Some day, perhaps soon, science will make this possible.

BIOLOGICALLY SPEAKING

antiseptic
antiseptic surgery
arteriosclerosis
aseptic surgery
cardiovascular-renal disease
coronary embolism

coronary occlusion
coronary thrombosis
curative medicine
disinfectant
electrocardiograph
functional disease

mental disease
organic disease
preventive medicine
psychiatrist
public health

QUESTIONS FOR REVIEW

1. What did Lister do to create antiseptic conditions in his surgery?
2. What practices in a modern operating room produce an even more desirable aseptic condition?
3. List several commonly used antiseptics and disinfectants.
4. List various health regulations observed by dairies in protecting the milk supply.
5. Why must drinking water be pure?
6. Classify the major forms of heart and blood vessel diseases according to age groups.

7. What specific parts of the body are involved in cardiovascular-renal disease?
8. How can a coronary occlusion cause heart damage or death?
9. Explain how hardening of the arteries may cause high blood pressure, heart strain, and heart failure.
10. Name several body organs in which cancer frequently develops.
11. What are the three recognized treatments for cancer?
12. Discuss several ways of maintaining good mental and emotional health.

APPLYING FACTS AND PRINCIPLES

1. What are some of the methods various communities use in disposing of sewage and garbage? Point out good and bad practices.
2. Discuss problems relating to the use of patent medicines.
3. Why are organic and functional diseases more personal and difficult to control than infectious diseases?
4. Discuss the relation of valvular heart disease and rheumatic fever.
5. Make a list of suggestions that you think could possibly help prevent mental illness.

RESEARCH ON YOUR OWN

1. Using prepared slides of pathogenic bacteria which cause well-known diseases, make drawings of the organisms under high power of your microscope. Prepared slides of pathogenic bacteria can sometimes be supplied through your local Board of Health or a hospital.

2. Make a table of insect carriers of disease, listing the insect, the disease carried, the way in which the insect carries the disease, and the way in which it transmits the organisms to man.

3. Make a diagram showing three lines of defense against disease and include as forts in each line the proper agents of defense.

4. Send to a biological supply company for a culture of *Penicillium notatum*. Grow it in a moist chamber or a large covered dish containing a recommended culture medium. The mold is started in the culture dish by transferring spores and fragments from the stock culture. After about two weeks at room temperature, the mold should have grown enough for microscopic examination.

5. Assume that you are investigating an unknown disease. Outline the procedure you would follow in conducting your research according to the Koch postulates.

6. Get figures showing the five diseases causing the greatest numbers of deaths today. Make a block graph, showing the number of deaths resulting from each disease last year, or in the most recent year you can show. In each case, indicate whether the disease is infectious, organic, or functional.

MORE ABOUT BIOLOGY

Calder, Ritchie. *Medicine and Man.* The New American Library of World Literature, Inc., New York. 1958

Calder, Ritchie. *The Wonderful World of Medicine.* Doubleday and Co., Inc., Garden City, N.Y. 1958

Clifford, C. E. *Introduction to Bacteria.* McGraw-Hill Book Co., Inc., New York. 1958

Cook, J. Gordon. *Virus in the Cell.* Dial Press, Inc., New York. 1957

Cook, James. *Remedies and Rackets: The Truth about Patent Medicines Today.* W. W. Norton and Co., Inc., New York. 1958

DeKruif, Paul. *Microbe Hunters.* Harcourt, Brace and Co., New York. 1926

Fox, Ruth. *Milestones of Medicine.* Random House, New York. 1950

Garland, Joseph. *The Story of Medicine.* Houghton Mifflin Co., Boston. 1949

Haydock, Kay S. *Your Allergy and You.* Henry Holt and Co., Inc., New York. 1958

Hill, Ralph N. *The Doctors Who Conquered Yellow Fever.* Random House, New York. 1957

Marriott, Henry L. *Medical Milestones.* Williams and Wilkins Co., Baltimore, Md. 1952

Morgan, Murray. *Doctors to the World.* Viking Press, New York. 1958

Reinfeld, Fred. *Miracle Drugs and the New Age of Medicine.* Sterling Publishing Co., Inc., New York. 1957

Rider, Elizabeth. *The Story Behind the Great Medical Discoveries.* Dodd, Mead and Co., New York. 1946

Rosenau, Milton J. *Preventive Medicine and Public Health.* 8th ed. Appleton-Century-Crofts, New York. 1956

Roueche, Berton. *The Incurable Wound and Further Narratives of Medical Detection.* Little, Brown and Co., Boston. 1958

Shippen, Katherine. *Men of Medicine.* Viking Press, New York. 1957

Sutherland, Louis. *Magic Bullets.* Little, Brown and Co., Boston. 1956

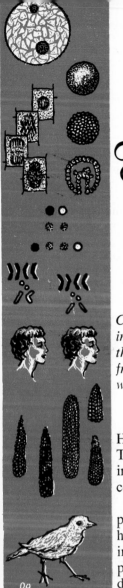

The Biology of Heredity

Can grapes be plucked from briers, or figs from thistles? so, indeed, any sound tree will bear good fruit, while any tree that is withered will bear fruit that is worthless; that worthless fruit should come from a sound tree, or good fruit from a withered tree, is impossible. — Math. 7:16–19

Have you ever wondered why people resemble their parents? The answer to this question and others about inheritance lies in the science of **genetics** (jeh-*net*-iks), one of the most recently developed branches of biology.

Knowledge of the heredity of plants and animals is important in many phases of modern life. The gardener and horticulturist apply the principles of heredity to plant breeding in the production of new varieties of garden flowers, crop plants, and fruit trees. The agriculturist has used them in developing his beef cattle and dairy cattle, hogs, sheep, and other highly productive farm animals.

CHAPTER 49: **THE BASIS OF HEREDITY**
CHAPTER 50: **THE PRINCIPLES OF HEREDITY**
CHAPTER 51: **PLANT AND ANIMAL BREEDING**
CHAPTER 52: **GENETICS APPLIED TO HUMAN INHERITANCE**
CHAPTER 53: **THE CHANGING WORLD OF LIFE**

The Basis of Heredity

PERHAPS you have never stopped to realize that no other hand is quite like your right hand — except your left one! Nor will there ever be another face, body, or personality just like yours.

At one time people believed that all characteristics were controlled by the blood. Doubtless you have heard some of your friends say that they are "related by blood" to some famous person. Breeders of dogs, cats, and farm animals always refer to "blood lines."

Actually, the blood has nothing to do with the qualities an organism inherits from its parents. A child's blood frequently is quite unlike that of either his father or mother. Nor are the characteristics of an individual changed in any way by receiving blood from another person during a transfusion.

Heredity is the transmission of characteristics from the parents to the offspring. In this chapter you will see that the determiners of heredity are included in every cell. You will learn how they are passed on to new cells during cell division, and how they are paired with one another in forming a new organism.

Hereditary and environment. Two sets of factors have great influence on the makeup of an individual. The first of these is **heredity**. Such traits as body size, hair color, skin color, eye color, and even some traits which contribute to personality may be inherited.

The second set of factors is **environment**. It is hard to say, however, where hereditary influences end and environmental ones begin. For example, body size is controlled by heredity. But it is also determined partially by diet, by the action of the glands, and by the type of activity in which the person engages.

We speak of "born criminals," but no one is really born a criminal. Instead, some people become criminals because of bad social influences in a poor environment.

Perhaps these arguments about the influences of heredity versus those of environment seem pointless. However, they are really of tremendous importance because environment can be changed, while heredity is fixed.

What kinds of characteristics are inherited? In certain respects, all members of a single species are alike. For example, man normally inherits the characteristics of the human race which make him like other human beings. These **species characteristics** include hands with fingers for grasping, the ability to walk erect, and a highly developed nervous system with a brain that is superior to that of all other organisms.

In addition to species characteristics, man inherits **individual characteristics** which make him different from all other people. Many of these individual characteristics are passed on from parent to offspring. The result is that the individual resembles his parents to a certain degree, but differs from each because he has inherited characteristics from both.

The cell is the unit of heredity. You know that the cell is the unit of structure.

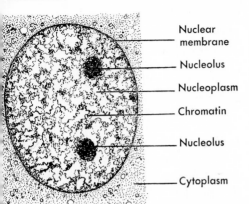

Nuclear membrane

Nucleolus

Nucleoplasm

Chromatin

Nucleolus

Cytoplasm

Fig. 49-1. The nucleus of the cell contains chromatin, the substance of heredity.

Similarly, the cell is the unit of function, for it is the seat of all the activities of the organism. We shall now discuss the cell as the center of another phase of the life of an organism — *the cell as the unit of heredity.* The characteristics of an organism are expressed through its cells. That is, every cell is controlled individually by the factors of heredity.

The nucleus is the center of cell heredity. As you recall, the nucleus is a spherical body of protoplasm usually lying near the center of the cell. It consists of a *nuclear membrane,* one or more small bodies called *nucleoli,* and a mass of living substance called *nucleoplasm.* A twisted mass of threadlike material lies in the nucleoplasm. The material itself, which is called **chromatin,** is the substance of heredity. The entire mass of threads is termed the **chromatin net,** or *nuclear net* (Fig. 49-1). The *chromatin in all the nuclei of the body cells of a single organism is identical.* Thus, the individual functions as a single unit and carries the same hereditary characteristics in all parts of his make-up.

Chromosomes and genes. The chromatin material in the nucleus becomes more apparent during division of the nucleus prior to division of the cell. At this time the chromatin condenses and forms a number of rod-shaped bodies called **chromosomes** (*kroh*-muh-sohms). When cells are treated with special stains for microscopic examination, chromosomes take more of the stain than do other nuclear substances and thus appear darker. This property gave them the name *chromosome,* which means " color body."

Chromosomes vary in shape. They may be slender, threadlike rods of different lengths or may be shaped like a horseshoe, a letter J, or a letter S. Furthermore, chromosomes are present in pairs in the body cells of any organism. Thus, any particular chromosome will have a mate somewhere in the nucleus.

The number of chromosomes varies in different plants and animals but it is constant for *every organism of a particular species.* For example, all corn plants have 20 chromosomes, consisting of 10 pairs; all pigeons have 16; all bullfrogs, 26. It is now believed that all humans have 23 pairs of chromosomes, or 46

Fig. 49-2. This stained section of the nucleus of one cell from the salivary gland of a fruit fly (*Drosophila*) clearly shows the chromosomes, each made up of many genes.

Bausch and Lomb

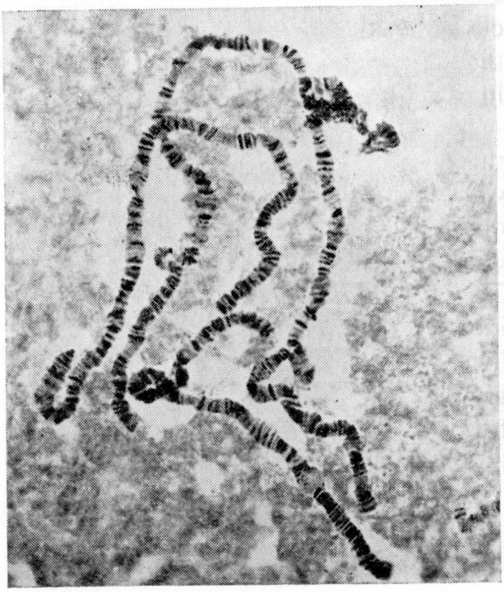

altogether. Until recently, this number was thought to be 48.

When a chromosome is enlarged under extremely high magnification, it appears to have granules arranged in a linear order, like beads in a strand. These granules are known to contain still smaller bodies, known as **genes.** These tiny particles are the individual bearers of heredity. A single chromosome may contain several thousand genes. Thus, your own heredity is determined by many thousands of pairs of genes, contained in your 23 pairs of chromosomes. An individual gene influences the development of one or more **hereditary traits,** such as eye color, hair color, or nose shape. Biologists do not know how a gene exerts an influence on the development of a trait. However, they do know that such an influence exists and that most hereditary traits are influenced by numerous genes. Furthermore, it has been found that a particular gene may influence more than one trait.

The arrangement of genes in chromosomes is always the same among members of a particular species. Thus, if a gene influencing the development of hair color is situated at the end of a particular chromosome, the other chromosome of the pair will have the same kind of gene in this identical location.

Perhaps you have already figured out that half of your chromosomes and genes came from one parent and half from the other. The original egg cell contained 23 chromosomes and one full set of genes. The sperm which fertilized it provided an identical set of chromosomes and genes. Thus the pairs of chromosomes and genes present in all of the cells which now form your body are descendants of those in the original fertilized egg. The growth of your body from the original cell has required a vast number of cell divisions. These divisions have, in turn, involved continuous growth and division of your genes. The manner in which genes divide and supply identical hereditary substance to the two cells resulting from a division of a cell is, truly, a remarkable process.

The formation of body cells is called mitosis. Immediately after it has been formed, a cell enters a period of growth and other activities. We refer to this period in the life of a cell as the **interphase.** The length of the interphase depends largely on the rate of growth. In some cases, such as in the embryonic region of a root and other rapidly growing tissues, it may last only a few hours. On the other hand, some cells of the human body grow very slowly and may spend a year or more in the interphase stage.

At the close of the interphase stage, the cell begins its nuclear division, a process which is called **mitosis** (my-*toh*-sis). During this remarkable process, the chromatin of the nucleus is duplicated. Thus, the two new cells resulting from the division of the old one have identical hereditary material. Mitosis always precedes division of a body cell. It can be seen in many plant and animal tissues under the microscope. It is very easily seen in rapidly growing embryonic tissue, such as the tip of a root or stem, or in an animal embryo.

The stages of mitosis. While mitosis is a continuous process, we often group the changes which occur into four stages, or phases, as follows: (1) *prophase;* (2) *metaphase;* (3) *anaphase;* and (4) *telophase* (Fig. 49-3).

1. **Prophase.** The first evidence that nuclear division is about to occur is the gradual condensing of the chromatin net into double ribbons. These are *chromosomes* and this stage is called the *early prophase,* the first stage of mitosis. The chromosomes then become shorter and

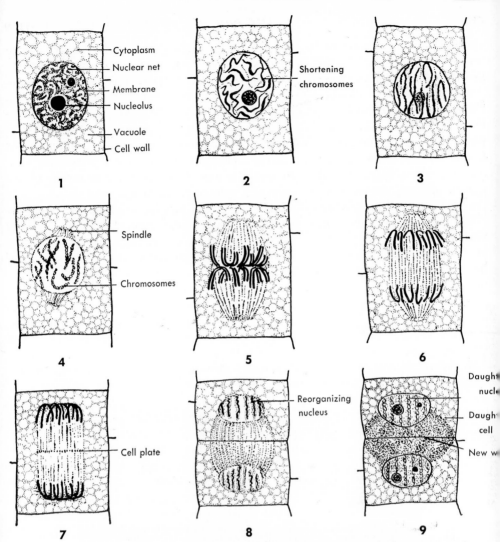

Fig. 49-3. The four stages of mitosis as it occurs in a plant cell are shown here. *1*, resting cell in interphase; *2–4*, various prophase stages; *5*, metaphase; *6–7*, two anaphase stages; *8*, telophase; and *9*, the two new daughter cells.

thicker until they appear as distinct rod-like bodies. We refer to this stage in the process as the *middle prophase*. With the shortening of chromosomes, the nuclear membrane gradually disappears and numerous fine threads composing the **spindle** form from poles above and below the nucleus. During *late prophase,* the nuclear membrane and other parts of the nucleus are no longer visible.

2. *Metaphase.* This is an easy stage to identify, but the hardest to find in tissue prepared for microscopic study because it is the shortest of the four stages. The chromosomes arrange themselves along the imaginary center of the cell in the region referred to as the **equator.** As though attracted by some mysterious force at each of the opposite poles, the chromosomes are pulled apart lengthwise into two identical halves. The metaphase stage is now complete.

3. *Anaphase.* During the anaphase stage, the two sets of chromosomes move

along the spindle threads in opposite directions toward the respective poles. Bear in mind that each group of chromosomes is a full set, identical with the set which is moving in the opposite direction toward the other pole. Late in the anaphase stage in a plant cell, a **cell plate** begins to form across the middle of the spindle, which splits the cell into two halves. During the next stage, each of the new cells will form a wall along this cell plate. In an animal cell, indentations appear in the outer membrane and gradually deepen, cutting the cell in half. The anaphase stage ends when the chromosomes have reached their poles.

4. *Telophase.* The final, or telophase, stage includes the formation of two daughter nuclei. The spindle fibers dis-

appear gradually. The rod-shaped chromosomes reverse the process of shortening and become long, loosely tangled threads that have the appearance again of a chromatin network. The other nuclear contents reappear and become surrounded by a nuclear membrane. As each daughter nucleus is reorganizing, division of the cell in the region of the equator is completed.

Each daughter cell enters the interphase period during which it will carry on its normal activities, including growth. When maturity is reached, the process of mitosis starts again.

Chromosome content of gametes. During sexual reproduction, a *sperm*, produced in a testis of the male parent, combines with an *egg*, formed in an ovary of

Fig. 49-4.   Identify the four stages of mitosis indicated by the letters *A*, *B*, *C*, and *D* in this photomicrograph of stained cells of an onion skin.

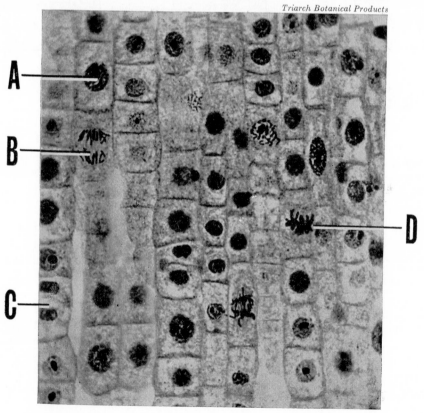

Triarch Botanical Products

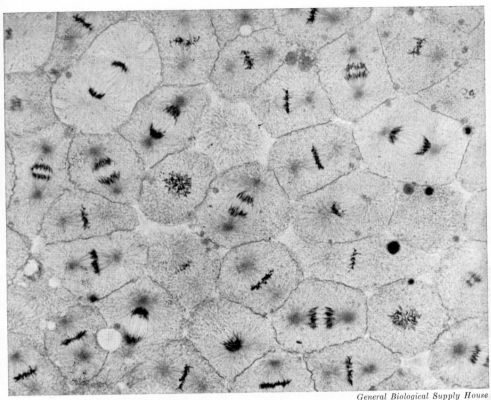

Fig. 49-5.   Locate as many different stages as you can of mitosis as it occurs in an animal cell in this photomicrograph of stained cells from a whitefish blastula.

the female parent. The two germ cells unite in the process of *fertilization* and produce the new individual. The sperm and egg carry hereditary characteristics of both parents and combine them in the offspring. Both germ cells contribute equally to the heredity of the new individual.

Perhaps you have already wondered why, with both parents contributing to the heredity of the offspring, it does not receive twice the number of genes and chromosomes that either parent possessed. That is, if both parents have 46 chromosomes in all of their cells, like all other humans, why doesn't the offspring have 92 chromosomes?

Remember that chromosomes are always present in pairs. Human body cells have 23 pairs of chromosomes and not 46 different ones. One set of 23 chromosomes came from one parent, while the other set came from the other parent. A sperm with its 23 chromosomes is only half an individual. The egg with the other set of 23 chromosomes is the other half. You can see already that a child is equally related to both parents even though it may resemble one more than the other.

The cells of the testes which form human sperm have 46 chromosomes (23 pairs) like all other body cells of the human being. Similarly, the cells of the ovaries which form eggs have 46 chromosomes (23 pairs). What happens to the missing set of chromosomes not present in an egg or sperm?

Reduction division is called meiosis.
Eggs and sperm are formed as a result of a complicated series of cell divisions in the ovaries or testes. These divisions are shown in Fig. 49-6. As we describe each division, study the diagrams closely to note the chromosome changes.

We shall start with a cell in an ovary or testis which contains a full set of chromosomes with both members of a pair present. The biologist refers to this, the double number, as the **diploid** (*dip*-loid) **number** of chromosomes. During one of the divisions, the chromosome pairs separate so that each new cell receives only one chromosome of each pair. This process is called *reduction division, or* **meiosis** (my-*oh*-sis). We refer to the chromosome content, at this point, with only one of each pair present, as the **haploid** (*hap*-loid), or *half, number.* In order to make it easier to show the changes in the chromosomes, only three pairs of chromosomes have been shown. The various stages in egg formation are shown on the right of the drawing in Fig. 49-6. You should compare these carefully with the stages in the formation of the sperm, as shown on the left.

1. The original germ cells divide and form many oögonial cells (we have shown only one such cell in Fig. 49-6). These oögonial cells have the same chromosome composition as the germ cells because they were formed by mitosis.

2. Each oögonial cell matures and then becomes a **primary oöcyte** (*oh*-oh-syte). An *oöcyte* is an egg before maturation, a process which includes the formation of the polar bodies. Important changes in the chromosomes take place during maturation. Pairs come together. Then each chromosome divides and becomes double. This division thus produces groups of four chromosomes, called *tetrads.*

3. The primary oöcyte then divides un-

equally. This division forms a large **secondary oöcyte** and a smaller cell which is called the *first polar body.* This division is the real **reduction division.** The pairs of divided chromosomes separate from each other. One member of each pair goes to the secondary oöcyte. The other member of each pair goes to the first polar body.

4. The secondary oöcyte divides to form an **oötid** (*oh*-oh-tid), which will mature into the egg and a *second polar body.* During this division, the halves of each divided chromosome separate from each other, one-half going into each of the new cells. Thus the oötid and second polar body each have a haploid set of chromosomes, with only one member of each pair present. The first polar body divides similarly to form two other polar bodies. None of the polar bodies is involved in fertilization.

5. The oötid matures into the egg, ready for fertilization.

6. A mature sperm unites with a mature egg during fertilization, each contributing a set of chromosomes. This combination restores the original diploid number of chromosomes, with a pair of each kind present in the fertilized egg, or *zygote.*

Notice that sperm are formed as a result of similar divisions. However, the *primary* **spermatocytes** form two functioning *secondary spermatocytes* by meiosis. The secondary spermatocytes give rise to four **spermatids,** all of which mature into sperm.

From fertilized egg to many-celled organisms. After fertilization, the zygote begins a period of division. The cell divides by mitosis to form a two-celled stage (Fig. 49-7, page 616). Since chromosomes are split in the process, both cells of the two-celled stage have identical chromosome make-up. Soon these cells divide to form a four-celled stage, then an eight-

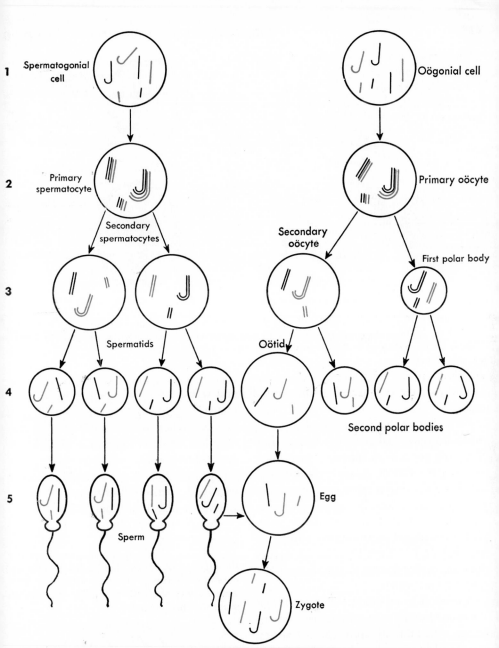

1 Spermatogonial cell

Oögonial cell

2 Primary spermatocyte

Primary oöcyte

Secondary spermatocytes

Secondary oöcyte

First polar body

3 Spermatids

Oötid

4 Second polar bodies

5 Sperm

Egg

Zygote

Fig. 49-6. This diagram shows the various chromosome changes that occur during reduction division, or meiosis, which results in the formation of eggs and sperm. The last phase of the diagram represents fertilization.

celled stage, and so on until a large number of cells are produced and form a hollow sphere. We refer to this sphere of cells as the **blastula** (*blas*-tyoo-luh). A short time later, the wall of the blastula fold inward on one side, forming a deep pocket. An inner layer, or **endoderm**, as well as the outer layer, or **ectoderm**, form. A third layer, or **mesoderm**, forms between the other two layers. We refer to the stage in which the germ layers are formed as the **gastrula** (*gas*-troo-luh).

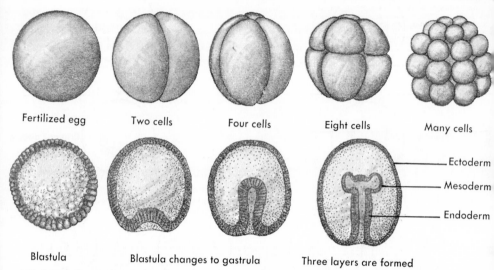

Fertilized egg   Two cells   Four cells   Eight cells   Many cells

Blastula   Blastula changes to gastrula   Three layers are formed

— Ectoderm
— Mesoderm
— Endoderm

Fig. 49-7. Cells divide repeatedly, as shown in the top drawings, and then form a hollow ball, or blastula (*bottom left*). The last three stages, or gastrula, develop to form germ layers which give rise to organs and tissues of the embryo.

As development continues, the various layers form the organs and tissues of the embryo.

Note that all the cells are related to the original zygote and have descended from it by the process of mitosis. Each new cell receives part of the chromosomal material which was present in the original fertilized egg. Thus, the hereditary makeup of the individual is determined the instant the egg and sperm unite. From that moment on it cannot be changed, except very rarely by disease or injury that destroys certain genes.

Variation in offspring. We know that the same parents may produce several offspring with quite different characteristics. It is evident, therefore, that the eggs or sperm formed by a single individual may vary. This variation is due to the *chance distribution* of genes in the chromosomes of the germ cells.

This chance distribution is shown in Fig. 49-8. Two pairs of genes on separate chromosomes are shown. These pairs are shown as *Aa* and *Bb*. During the reduction division that forms eggs or

sperm, these pairs may separate in several ways. *A* may segregate with *B*. *A* and *b* may go together, or *a* and *B*, or *a* and *b*. When you consider the fact that man has 46 chromosomes in all and that each chromosome has numerous genes, the possibilities of gene combinations in eggs and sperm following reduction division are almost without limit.

This chance distribution of genes dur-

Fig. 49-8. The diagram below illustrates the manner in which chance distribution occurs during the process of reduction division, or meiosis, with two pairs of genes on separate chromosomes.

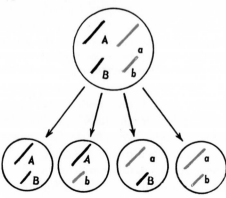

ing reduction, and the resulting variation in characters of offspring are the phenomena on which the science of genetics is based. This same chance distribution of a large number of genes makes you different from any other person. Your particular combination of genes will never occur again, so as a result there never has been and never will be another person exactly like you.

In Conclusion

Only in recent years have we known how family traits are passed on from parent to offspring. "Like father, like son," is only a very small part of the story. You might have your grandfather's nose, or you might have certain artistic talents neither parent had but which resemble some aunt's.

As you continue the study of genetics, you will discover how genes can be carried without indicating their presence for several generations, and may then appear at a later time in some member of the family.

There is nothing strange about inheritance. It follows laws, the first of which were discovered by an Austrian monk, about whom you will learn in the next chapter.

BIOLOGICALLY SPEAKING

anaphase	gastrula	primary oöcyte
blastula	genetics	oötid
cell plate	haploid number	prophase
chance distribution	heredity	reduction division
chromosome	individual characteristics	secondary oöcyte
diploid number	interphase	species characteristics
ectoderm	meiosis	spermatid
endoderm	mesoderm	spermatocyte
environment	metaphase	spindle
equator	mitosis	telophase

QUESTIONS FOR REVIEW

1. What is the difference between hereditary and environmental characteristics?
2. Why is the cell the unit of heredity?
3. What is the relationship between chromatin, chromosomes, and genes?
4. (a) How many chromosomes are present in every human body cell? (b) How many in eggs and sperm?
5. Describe the migration of chromosome halves from equator to poles during mitosis.
6. What is the difference between an unfertilized egg and a fertilized egg with respect to genetic make-up?
7. List the stages in the formation of an egg, starting with the oögonial cell.
8. List the stages in sperm formation, starting with a spermatogonial cell.
9. Name three cell layers which form during the gastrula stage.
10. List four possible gene combinations which may result from chance distribution of two pairs, *AaBb*, during reduction division in egg or sperm formation.

APPLYING FACTS AND PRINCIPLES

1. To what false idea of early times does the term " blood line " refer?
2. Account for the fact that all of your cells have identical genetic make-up.
3. In terms of chromosome number and structure, explain why unrelated organisms cannot be crossed.
4. You know that a single oöcyte gives rise to only one egg, whereas a single spermatocyte gives rise to four sperms. Explain why.
5. Explain, in terms of chance distribution of genes, how the same parents can produce a variety of offspring.

CHAPTER 50

The Principles of Heredity

IN 1865, Gregor Mendel, an Austrian monk, published the results of a masterful piece of work on the laws of heredity. He was not the first to experiment in the field of inheritance, but his findings were the first of any scientific consequence. His paper, representing years of work with garden peas, was published by the Natural History Society of Brünn, Austria. Mendel had been dead for 16 years when three other scientists discovered his work and began to make use of his findings. It is, however, a great tribute to Mendel that the laws he formulated from his experiments with garden peas stand today, practically unchanged, as the basis of the science of genetics.

Mendel's experiments with the garden pea. There were good reasons why Mendel selected the garden pea for his experiments. Mendel noticed that garden peas differed in certain definite characteristics. Some plants were short and bushy, while others were tall and climbing. Some produced yellow seeds, some green seeds; some had colored flowers and some white ones. Mendel discovered that garden peas differed in seven respects altogether. He also found that the characteristics of any one kind of pea were preserved in generation after generation because the plants normally carried on self-pollination. However, cross-pollination could be performed easily by transferring pollen from the stamens of one flower to the pistil of another. Because of the seven different characteristics to follow, and because cross-pollination was easy to perform, Mendel had selected an ideal subject.

His first task was to find out whether or not the seven characteristics which he observed were always handed down from parent to offspring. To establish this fact, Mendel collected seeds from each of the various types of plants and planted them in his garden. The generation that resulted proved that the seven characteristics he was considering were transmitted from parent to offspring. Seeds from tall plants produced other tall ones and yellow seeds produced plants with yellow seeds. He called each of these a **pure characteristic.**

Mendel discovers the principle of dominance. Mendel's next step was to see what would happen if he crossed two plants with contrasting characteristics. Accordingly, he selected one tall parent and one short one. He took pollen from the tall one and put it on the pistil of the short one. When the seeds matured on the short plant, he sowed them to find out the results of his cross. Would they be short like one parent, tall like the other, or of medium height, with characteristics of both? He discovered that all the plants were tall like the plant from which he had taken the pollen in making the cross.

His next step was to determine if it made any difference which plant he used for pollen and which he used to produce seeds. Accordingly, he reversed the process of pollination, using a short plant for pollen and a tall one for seed production. The results were as before — all the offspring were tall.

Mendel then experimented with crosses involving other characteristics. He crossed plants which had yellow seeds with those which had green seeds. He found that all of the first generation of the cross had yellow seeds. Similarly, he discovered that round-seeded varieties crossed with plants with wrinkled seeds produced a generation with round seeds. He repeated these crosses until he had tested seven different characteristics.

Mendel was surprised to find that, in all seven crosses, one of the characteristics present in a parent plant seemed to be lost in the next generation. What would a second cross produce? This step in the experiment was destined to make history, since it led to the discovery of two important laws of heredity.

In keeping track of his generations of crosses, Mendel designated the *parent plants* used in the first cross as **P**. He referred to the generation resulting from this cross as **F₁**, which stands for *first filial*.

The Bettmann Archi

Fig. 50-1. Gregor Mendel's interpretations of his carefully controlled experiments with garden peas made him the founder of the science of genetics and one of the greatest biologists that has ever lived.

By crossing two tall peas of the F_1 generation, he produced an **F₂**, or *second filial,* generation. To produce this generation, Mendel proceeded as before. He selected two F_1-generation plants, both of which were tall, cross-pollinated them, and planted the seeds which bore the F_2 generation. The results of this cross were quite striking. Some plants were tall, while others were short. None was in between. Furthermore, three-fourths of the plants were tall, while only one-fourth was short. The reappearance of short plants in this generation was of great significance to Mendel. The F_1 plants had possessed a character for shortness without showing it.

Exactly the same results were obtained in crossing F_1-generation plants having other characteristics. The yellow peas

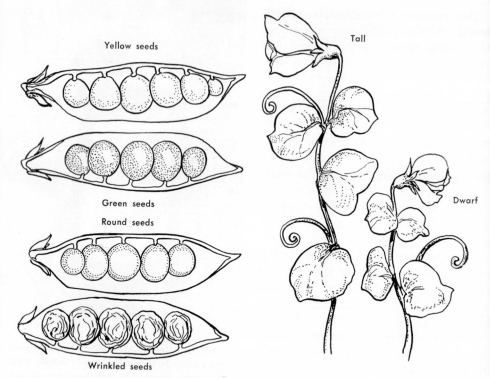

Fig. 50-2. These are contrasting traits that appear in garden peas. Which traits shown are dominant and which are recessive?

which had been produced by crossing parent plants with yellow seeds and those with green seeds, when crossed with each other, produced peas of which three-fourths were yellow, and one-fourth green.

Mendel's first laws of heredity. The fact that tall peas crossed with short peas produced an F_1 generation of tall peas and that short peas reappeared in the F_2 generation led Mendel to reason that something within the plant controlled a characteristic such as height. He called these unknown influences *factors*. Today, we call them *genes*. He reasoned, further, that height in peas was controlled by a pair of factors, since some peas were short while others were tall. On this basis, he formulated his first law of heredity, the **Law of Unit Characters.** This law states that *the various hereditary characteristics are controlled by factors (genes), and that*

these factors occur in pairs. Of course, Mendel did not know of genes or even chromosomes, which makes even more remarkable the fact that his Law of Unit Characters remains a basic principle in genetics today.

Mendel reasoned further that the tall plants of his F_1 generation were not like the pure tall parent plants. These peas were carrying a factor for shortness which did not appear but which would reappear in the next generation. This reasoning led to the discovery of his second law of heredity, the **Law of Dominance.** This law states that *one factor (gene) in a pair may mask or prevent expression of the other.*

In the case of garden peas, height is controlled by one pair of genes. A gene for tallness is **dominant** over a gene for shortness, which we refer to as a **recessive** gene.   In Mendel's crosses, one parent was pure tall, having both genes for tallness.   The other was pure short, having both genes for shortness.   The members of the F_1 generation were all tall but were **hybrid,** a term we use to designate the offspring of a cross between two parents which differ in one or more traits.   The members of this generation had one gene for tallness and one for shortness, but appeared tall because the gene for tallness was dominant over the one for shortness.

You will recall that chromosomes are always present *in pairs* and that as a result of fertilization each parent contributes *one member of each pair.*   In dealing with tallness and shortness in peas, Mendel was actually concerned only with one pair of genes located on *one pair* of chromosomes.   If we let the letter T stand for tallness, a pure tall plant would be written TT, indicating that both its genes for this character were for tallness.   The capital T indicates that tallness is dominant over the contrasting character, shortness.   In like manner, the small letter t stands for short, and a pure short individual would be designated as tt.

While all the body cells contain diploid sets of chromosomes and genes, you remember that reduction division occurs only during the formation of sex cells.

Consequently, the egg cell in the pea ovule and the sperm nuclei formed from the pollen grain have only one gene for each character.   When eggs or sperm are formed by a pure tall pea plant, one sperm nucleus receives one T and the other receives the other T.   In like manner, the tt genes present in all body cells of a pure short plant are separated in reduction division to t and t in the formation of eggs or sperm.

Mendel's Law of Segregation.   Mendel based his third law of heredity, referred to as the **Law of Segregation,** on the reasoning above.   According to this law, *a pair of factors (genes) is segregated, or separated, during the formation of gametes (spores in lower plants) in reduction division.*   That is, a gamete contains only one gene of a pair, the other having gone to another gamete.   Furthermore, the composition of one gene is not altered by the presence of another gene in a pair.   For example, a recessive gene in a hybrid is not altered by the presence of a dominant gene.   If, in an offspring of the hybrid, the recessive gene is paired with another recessive gene, the recessive character will reappear (Fig. 50-3, page 622).

Methods of diagramming Mendel's crosses.   In the study of genetics, we use special charts resembling checkerboards

MENDEL'S LAW OF DOMINANCE

THE SEVEN PAIRS OF CONTRASTING TRAITS	DOMINANT TRAIT IN OFF— SPRING (F_1 HYBRIDS)
1. Round seeds, wrinkled seeds	Round seeds
2. Yellow seeds, green seeds	Yellow seeds
3. Colored seed coat, white seed coat	Colored seed coats
4. Inflated pod (unripe), constricted pod	Inflated pod
5. Green pod, yellow pod	Green pod
6. Axial flowers, terminal flowers	Axial flowers
7. Tall stem, short stem	Tall stem

Fig. 50-3. This diagram illustrates Mendel's Law of Segregation. Although the F_1 generation in this cross consists of only tall plants, the recessive gene responsible for shortness reappears in the F_2 generation, to produce plants in the ratio of three tall to one short. What kind of plants would result from a cross between the two F_2 plants shown at the bottom left? Give the probable ratio of tall plants to short plants, and the genetic make-up of each type.

to determine the possible results of various crosses. We refer to these charts as **Punnett squares.** Possible gene combinations which may occur in the eggs produced by the female are shown in the spaces at the top of the chart. Possible gene combinations in the sperm of the male parent are shown in the spaces on the left side of the chart. Combinations of the various eggs and sperm during fertilization appear in the squares of the chart. Mendel's work with tall and short peas can be shown more clearly by diagramming his crosses on Punnett squares, such as the various ones that follow in this chapter.

In the chart below, a cross between pure tall, *TT,* and pure short, *tt,* is diagrammed as follows:

RESULTS OF CROSSING TT AND tt

Female → GENES Male ↓	t	t
T	Tt	Tt
T	Tt	Tt

All the offspring are hybrids, with a gene for tallness, *T,* and a gene for shortness, *t.* They appear equally as tall as the tall parent plant, however, because the gene for tallness is dominant over the one for shortness.

If the *Tt* hybrids are bred together, it is easy to see that four possible combinations of genes may occur, as shown in the following chart. The chart also shows how the genes *T* and *t* from hybrid parents, though they combine by chance, will logically result in offspring that are ¼ pure dominant (*TT*), ½ hybrid (*Tt, Tt*), and ¼ pure recessive (*tt*).

RESULTS OF CROSSING Tt AND Tt

Female → GENES Male ↓	T	t
T	TT	Tt
t	Tt	tt

The same scheme explains the ratios resulting from other crosses:

RESULTS OF CROSSING TT AND Tt

Female → GENES Male ↓	T	t
T	TT	Tt
T	TT	Tt

RESULTS OF CROSSING Tt AND tt

Female → GENES Male ↓	t	t
T	Tt	Tt
t	tt	tt

Dominant and recessive genes in guinea pigs. The same results Mendel obtained in crossing tall and short peas are shown in the inheritance of color in guinea pigs. In this case, the color black is dominant over white.

Let's see what happens when we cross a pure black guinea pig (*BB*) with a pure white (*bb*) one. All the offspring in the

F_1 generation are black. They differ in genetic make-up, however, in that they are hybrid blacks (Bb). When two hybrids are crossed, the F_2 generation will show a ratio of ¼ pure black (BB), ½ hybrid black (Bb), and ¼ pure white (bb). The cross between two hybrids of the F_1 generation to produce the F_2 generation may be diagrammed as in the chart below (see also Fig. 50-4).

RESULTS OF CROSSING
Bb AND Bb

Female → GENES Male ↓	B	b
B	BB	Bb
b	Bb	bb

The same ratios occur after the crossing of rough- and smooth-coated guinea pigs. In this case, the rough-coat gene is dominant over that for smooth coat.

Crosses involving two characters. Crosses involving two characters become more complicated than simple crosses in which only one pair of contrasting characters is considered. The same principles apply, but the possible gene combinations are increased. When two pairs of characteristics are involved, the individuals possessing mixed genes for both characters are called **dihybrids** (dy-*hy*-brids).

If a pea with round green seeds (two characters) is crossed with a pea having wrinkled yellow seeds, all members of the F_1 generation have round and yellow seeds. The recessive characters of green color and wrinkled seed coat are overshadowed by the two dominant traits. In this cross, R will stand for a gene for

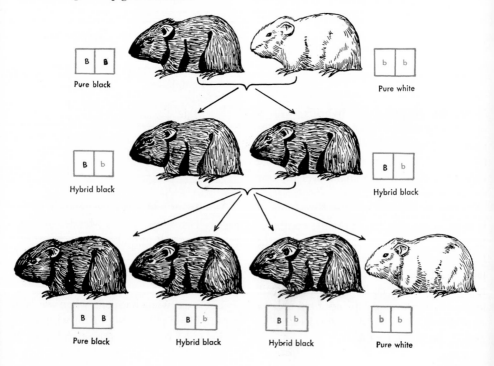

Fig. 50-4. The F_1 generation of a cross between a pure white guinea pig and a pure black one produces hybrid black animals. What results are obtained when the two hybrid black guinea pigs are mated?

Pure black   Pure white

Hybrid black   Hybrid black

Pure black   Hybrid black   Hybrid black   Pure white

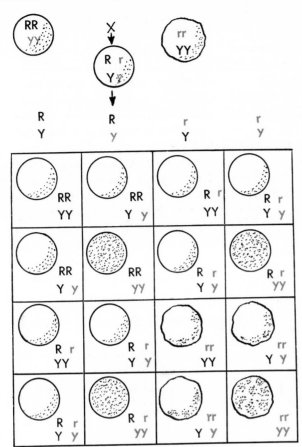

Fig. 50-5. This Punnett square shows the various types of seeds that can result in the F_2 generation from a cross between a pea plant with round (R) and green (y) seeds and one with wrinkled (r) and yellow (Y) seeds. The possible female gene combinations are printed across the top of the table, while the possible male gene combinations are printed down the left side of the table. Dominant genes appear in black, recessive ones in color.

round seed coat, r for wrinkled, Y for yellow color, y for green. The F_1 hybrids would all possess the genetic make-up *RrYy,* a gene for round seed coat (R) having come from one parent, and a gene for wrinkled (r) having come from the other. In like manner, one parent supplied a gene for yellow color (Y), while the other supplied a gene for green (y).

When the two hybrid round yellow peas are crossed, the situation becomes more complicated. Each hybrid with the genetic make-up *RrYy* may produce four kinds of eggs or sperm. During reduction division, the pairs R and r as well as Y and y must separate and go into different cells. R may pair with Y to form *RY* or R may pair with y, resulting in *Ry.* Similarly, r may pair with Y to form *rY* or

with y to form *ry.* The nature of the offspring in such a cross depends on which eggs and sperm happen to unite during fertilization.

The possible offspring which may result from such a cross and the ratio of their occurrence may be diagrammed as in the case of a single character, except that space must be provided for more possible crosses. The diagram in Fig. 50-5 shows the result of such a cross. One of the parents was pure round green (*RRyy*), while the other was pure wrinkled yellow (*rrYY*). You will note that all the F_1 generation are alike, being hybrid round yellow (*RrYy*). In the F_2 generation, however, four different kinds of individuals have been produced, as follows:

1. %₁₆ of the offspring have seeds which

are round and yellow (both dominant traits).

2. ³⁄₁₆ have seeds which are round and green (one dominant and one recessive trait).

3. ³⁄₁₆ have seeds which are wrinkled and yellow (the other dominant and the other recessive trait).

4. ¹⁄₁₆ has seeds which are wrinkled and green (both recessive traits).

You will note, too, that yellow seeds may be either pure yellow or hybrid yellow; also that round seeds may be either pure round or hybrid round. The only case where a recessive character shows is when both genes for the recessive character are present. Both recessive charac-

ters appeared only once in the 16 possibilities.

When hybrid black, rough-coated guinea pigs are crossed (black and rough genes are dominant), similar results are obtained: ³⁄₁₆ of the offspring are black and rough, ³⁄₁₆ are black and smooth, ³⁄₁₆ are white and rough, and ¹⁄₁₆ is white and smooth.

The Law of Independent Assortment. The dihybrid crosses you have studied illustrate another of Mendel's laws, the *Law of Independent Assortment.* According to this law, *the separation of pairs of genes and distribution of the genes to gametes* (*spores in lower plants*) *during reduction division is entirely independent*

Fig. 50-6. **How is the principle of incomplete dominance illustrated by the crossing of pure red four-o'clocks with pure white ones?**

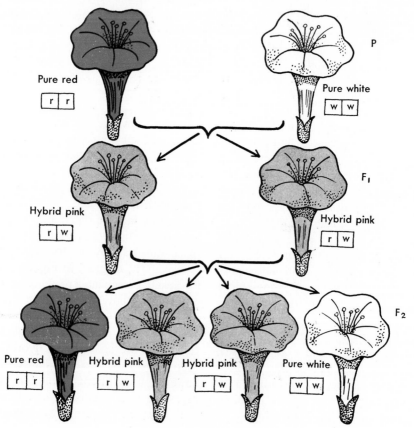

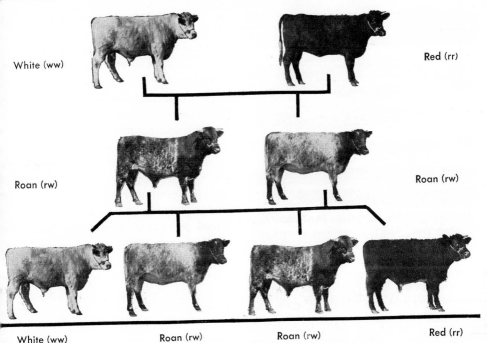

Fig. 50-7. The crossing of pure white and pure red shorthorn cattle produces results similar to those obtained by the crossing of the four-o'clocks shown in Fig. 50-6.

of the distribution of other genes. Actually, this law holds only when pairs of genes are situated on *different chromosome pairs,* since it is the chromosomes and not individual genes which are distributed during reduction division.

Blended characters. Genes are not always dominant or recessive. In some cases, different genes of a pair may both appear in a blended character. This blending, or **incomplete dominance,** as it is called, may be illustrated in crossing the flowers of four-o'clocks, zinnias, and some other plants.

When pure red four-o'clocks (*rr*) are crossed with pure white (*ww*) varieties, all of the first generation are pink (*rw*). Neither red nor white is completely dominant, so that both colors appear in the hybrid F₁ as a blend which is pink. However, when two of these hybrid pink (*rw*) flowers are crossed, the next generation includes ¼ red, ½ pink, and ¼ white in-

dividuals. The fact that red and white genes actually did not mix in the pink hybrid is indicated in the fact that both pure characteristics appear again in the second generation (Fig. 50-6).

Similarly, the color of shorthorn cattle illustrates incomplete dominance. A pure red animal crossed with a pure white animal results in a blend of red and white called roan. When two roan animals are crossed, ¼ of the offspring is red, ½ are roan, and ¼ is white, illustrating again the 1:2:1 ratio (Fig. 50-7).

Ratios are based on averages. The ratios obtained in breeding experiments represent *averages* and not definite numbers that will always appear. These ratios are accurate *only when large numbers of individuals are considered.* For example, two roan shorthorns bred four times will not necessarily produce one red calf, two roan ones, and a white one.

Two hybrid black guinea pigs will not

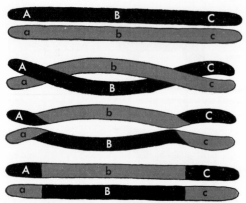

Fig. 50-8. This diagram illustrates how crossing-over, which sometimes occurs during meiosis, can result in a new grouping of genes on the chromosomes.

always produce one pure black, two hybrid blacks, and one white. If only four eggs and four sperm were involved in the process, the ratio would work out. But actually, the eggs may be more or less than four in number and the sperm usually number in the millions. Thus it becomes entirely a matter of chance as to how the eggs and sperm will unite.

Chance ratios may best be illustrated with two coins. If you flip two coins, they will light in these possible combinations: two heads, one head and one tail, or two tails. There is twice the chance of one head and one tail appearing as two heads or two tails. Consequently, if you flip them many times, they should appear in a ratio of 1 (two heads) : 2 (one head and one tail) : 1 (two tails). This ratio will only appear after flipping many times.

Gene linkage and crossing-over. Normally, an organism has no more pairs of genes which sort out independently of other genes than it has pairs of chromosomes. For example, the genes for hair color and hair texture in guinea pigs are on different chromosomes, as are height and seed-color genes in garden peas. For this reason, these genes sort out independently of each other. However, genes

on the same chromosome are linked together and are transmitted in groups, a situation referred to as **gene linkage.**

Sometimes two chromosomes of a pair exchange segments as they lie side by side during reduction division. If we designate a pair of chromosomes as *A* and *a* we can assume that both chromosomes separate at the same place. Chromosome *A* receives a segment of chromosome *a* while chromosome *a* receives the corresponding portion of chromosome *A*. This exchange results in a new combination of linked genes in both chromosomes. We call this process **crossing-over** (Fig. 50-8). When it occurs, an offspring receives a combination of characters not present in either parent. Double and even triple crossovers are known to occur.

Application of Mendel's laws to other organisms. Scientists have worked with numerous traits of plants and animals, and have shown that the truth of the Mendelian laws is beyond question. There is overwhelming evidence that inheritance in humans also follows the Mendelian laws. But it is impossible to experiment on humans. Therefore, geneticists have difficulty in finding "purebred humans" and in knowing what traits are the contrasting ones.

Determination of sex. Sex is determined at the time of fertilization. This is shown by the fact that identical twins, which began life as one individual but became separated in the two-celled stage, are always of the same sex.

Determination of sex is *purely the result of a chance union of sperm and egg.* Actually, in human beings and many animals, it is determined by the sperm alone. Two of the chromosomes in the cells of females are called **X chromosomes.** The cells of males, however, have only one X chromosome, and, in addition, have what is called a **Y chromosome.**

When an oöcyte becomes an egg, there

CHARACTERISTICS OF VARIOUS ORGANISMS

ORGANISM	DOMINANT TRAIT	RECESSIVE TRAIT
Corn	Yellow grain	White grain
Corn	Black grain	Yellow grain
Tomato	Tall stem	Short stem
Tomato	Spherical shape	Oval shape
Wheat	Late ripening	Early ripening
Wheat	Susceptibility to rust	Immunity to rust
Fowls	Black plumage	Yellow plumage
Fowls	Crest	No crest
Cattle	Hornless	Horned
Cattle	Black coat	Red coat
Horses	Trotting	Pacing

is a reduction in the number of chromosomes due to meiosis. Each egg cell receives an X chromosome. A similar reduction occurs when sperm are formed. Since each spermatocyte always contains one X chromosome and one Y chromosome, half of the sperms will receive an X chromosome, while the other half will lack the X and will receive the Y chromosome. If the egg is fertilized by a sperm with an X chromosome, the fertilized egg will have two X chromosomes and will be female. If, however, the sperm happens to be lacking an X chromosome, but has a Y chromosome, the fertilized egg will develop into a male (Fig. 50-9).

Sex determination may be shown easily by the following chart:

SEX DETERMINATION

Female → CHROMOSOMES Male ↓	X	X
X	XX	XX
Y	XY	XY

Although sex is *determined* at the time of fertilization, it may be altered under certain unusual conditions. These are due to stimuli called **primary sex determiners.** Destruction of an X chromosome would most certainly alter sex. Sometimes chemical changes occur in the egg due to variations in temperature, nutrition, or other causes which affect an X chromosome and thus change the sex. Occasionally, sex reversal occurs in animals during embryonic development, or even later, due to changes in the sex glands or variations in hormone production. But such instances are rare.

Fig. 50-9. The sex chromosomes of the fruit fly, *Drosophila*, are represented in color. The female (*right*) has two straight X chromosomes. The male (*left*) has one straight X chromosome and one bent Y chromosome. In mating, combinations of X and X chromosomes produce females; combinations of X and Y chromosomes produce males.

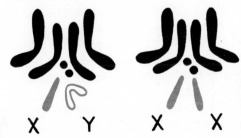

X   Y   X   X

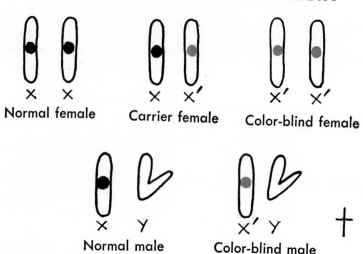

Fig. 50-10. The gene for color blindness is indicated in color, and the chromosome carrying it is designated as X'. Notice that two such chromosomes are necessary to produce a color-blind female, while only one will produce a color-blind male.

Sex-linked characters. The genes for certain characteristics are carried on the X chromosomes, which function in the determination of sex. Several abnormal characteristics are also carried by recessive genes on the X chromosomes.

Red-green color blindness, a condition in which these colors appear as shades of blue and yellow, is called a *sex-linked character.* The gene for color blindness is carried on an X chromosome, but it is recessive to a normal gene on another X chromosome. Thus, a female can carry a gene for color blindless (X') on one chromosome and a normal gene on the other (X). Such an individual (XX') will not show the characteristic, but will transmit it to offspring. In the case of a male, however, only one X chromosome is present. Hence, a single X chromosome having a color-blind gene, combined with a Y chromosome lacking a gene for the character, (X'Y), will produce the defect. This explains why red-green color blindness is much more common in males than in females.

Fig. 50-10 shows the genes on X chromosomes of a normal female, one carrying color blindness, and a color-blind female as well as a normal male and a color-blind male. The chart below shows how a female parent, carrying a gene for color blindness but not showing the trait, may produce a color-blind son even though the male parent is not color-blind. The ratio resulting from such a cross would be one female carrying color blindness; one normal female; one color-blind male; one normal male.

INHERITANCE OF SEX–LINKED CHARACTERS

Female → Sex Chromosomes Male ↓	X'	X
X	XX'	XX
Y	X'Y	XY

If a color-blind male marries a normal female, color blindness will not appear in any of the offspring, although all the females will carry the trait as a recessive

ene. The chart illustrating this is shown
below.

INHERITANCE OF SEX–LINKED CHARACTERS

Female → SEX CHROMOSOMES Male ↓	X	X
X'	XX'	XX'
Y	XY	XY

By diagramming a cross between a
color-blind male and a female carrying a
recessive gene for the character, you will
discover how color blindness may appear
in a female. Similarly, a color-blind female crossed with a normal male will produce all color-blind males, but with no females showing the trait, although all are
carrying it. Two color-blind individuals
will have all color-blind offspring.

**Other characteristics associated with
sex.** Certain genes produce a character in
one sex or the other, but not in both, even
though they are carried in both sexes. In
this respect, *sex-limited characters* are
different from sex-linked characters. It
seems that sex-limited characters develop
only in the presence of sex hormones.

One example of a sex-limited character
is the bright plumage of certain male
birds which does not appear in females of
the same species. The roosters of most
breeds of chickens develop a large comb
and wattles and characteristic male plumage, while hens of the same breed develop a different kind of female plumage (Fig.
50-11). Both result from the influence
that sex hormones have on the genes for
these characteristics that are present in
the variety.

Baldness is an example of a human *sex-
influenced character*. In this case, the
gene for baldness is dominant in males but
recessive in females. Thus a mother may
transmit baldness to her son without
showing it herself. If we represent a gene
for baldness as *B* and the one for normal
growth of hair as *b*, then a *Bb* male would
be bald, while a *Bb* female would have
normal hair. However, *BB* would represent a male or female with baldness, while
bb would produce a normal male and

Fig. 50-11. Notice the difference in plumage and in comb formation between the male
Brown Leghorn shown at the left and the female shown at the right.

U. S. Dept. of Agriculture

Halliday from National Audubon Society

Fig. 50-12.   The albino robin shown above has white feathers and pink eyes.   Albinism is a mutation that sometimes occurs as a result of gene changes.   It is transmitted to the offspring.

female. You can see from this explanation why baldness is more common in men than in women.

Mutations. Occasionally an offspring appears with a characteristic which was not inherited, but which can be passed on to future generations. This new characteristic is called a *mutation,* and the individual possessing it is called a *mutant.*

One of the most common examples of mutation is illustrated in *albino organisms,* which are completely lacking in color. Apparently the genes for color are destroyed or altered in such a way that they do not function. This characteristic will remain and can be passed on to new generations, although it may not reappear immediately because of its recessive nature.

Albino animals are always white and have pink eyes. The white body covering

is normal except that it lacks any pigmentation. The eyes, too, are normal but lack coloring in the iris so that the blood in the capillaries gives them a reddish appearance. You have seen albinos in the form of white rabbits, white rats, and white mice. All these animals, if they are true albinos, have pink eyes. In addition to these forms which are well known, albino squirrels, woodchucks, raccoons, deer, robins, crows, sparrows, and other kinds of animals have been found, although they are very rare. Albino humans are characterized by having very light skin, pure white hair, and pink eyes.

Other mutations have occurred from time to time in cattle. Occasionally, a calf belonging to a horned breed is born without horns. From such mutations, hornless, or polled, breeds have been developed, including the Aberdeen-Angus and polled shorthorn. Other mutations include tailless dogs, and hogs with " mule " feet.

Causes of mutations. The principles of mutation, in which genes may be lost or new combinations of genes may appear, were discovered by a famous biologist of recent years, Thomas Hunt Morgan. Much of his work was done with the fruit fly (*Drosophila*), a tiny insect which has been used extensively in research in genetics since his time.

In 1946, the Nobel Prize was awarded to another American scientist working in the field of genetics, Dr. H. J. Muller of Indiana University. Dr. Muller discovered that exposure of fruit flies to X rays caused various mutations. One mutation he produced was a change in eye color. A normal fruit fly with red eyes produced offspring with white eyes after exposure to X rays. In further studies, Dr. Muller produced mutants with entirely different body hair, wings, and eye structure. In fact, he produced a series of monstrosities the like of which has never been seen. And he found that all offspring of the mutants bore the new characteristics, since the X rays had altered the gene structure of the parents. Other radioac-tive substances also influence or destroy genes and cause mutations.

Lethal genes. Occasionally, characteristics appear as a result of mutation which cause death of the organism. For example, geranium and corn seedlings have been discovered which are entirely lacking in chlorophyll. Normally they could not live because the lack of chlorophyll means lack of the ability to make food by photosynthesis. However, if such colorless seedlings are partly woody and are grafted to normal plants as has been done in the case of the geranium, food may be obtained and the colorless plants may even bloom. Similar **lethal genes** have been known to appear in animals. When they appear, usually during the period of development, the animal dies suddenly.

These lethal characters have proved to be recessive ones in every case studied. They appear only when both of the parents are carrying recessive genes for the trait and the offspring happens to receive a recessive gene from each of the parents.

Biologists have discovered lethal characteristics in many different kinds of animals. Among them are mice, chickens, hogs, and certain breeds of cattle. They have also been known to occur in man.

In Conclusion

Who would have thought that an Austrian monk, working with peas in a monastery garden, would have made a discovery important enough to introduce a new branch of biology? This was the genius of Gregor Mendel. Among his tall peas and short ones, those with round seeds and wrinkled ones, green pods and yellows pods, he discovered that variations appeared in an orderly manner. Laws seemed to control the heredity of those peas — laws so exact he could predict the kind of peas the seeds would produce.

Remarkable indeed was this pioneer in genetics. We have gone far beyond Mendel, but we have never revised our understanding of his laws.

As we continue our study of genetics, we shall apply the principles of heredity to plant and animal breeding and to our own inheritance.

BIOLOGICALLY SPEAKING

albino organisms	Law of Dominance	primary sex determiner
crossing-over	Law of Independent	Punnett square
dihybrid	Assortment	pure characteristic
dominant gene	Law of Segregation	recessive gene
F_1 generation	Law of Unit Characters	sex-influenced character
F_2 generation	lethal gene	sex-limited character
gene linkage	mutant	sex-linked character
hybrid	mutation	X chromosome
incomplete dominance	P generation	Y chromosome

QUESTIONS FOR REVIEW

1. (a) List seven pairs of contrasting traits Mendel found in garden peas. (b) Which ones of these traits are dominant?
2. Black is dominant in guinea pigs. How is pure black different from hybrid black, even though the guinea pigs look alike?
3. When two hybrids are crossed, pure dominant, hybrid dominant, and pure recessive individuals appear. Account for this.
4. When two parents which are hybrid for one character are crossed, what ratio of offspring (F_1 generation) will show the dominant character and how many will show the recessive character?
5. In breeding experiments, why do the ratios obtained represent averages rather than definite numbers?
6. Explain the Law of Independent Assortment.
7. In what way is blending, or incomplete dominance, an exception to the Law of Dominance?
8. Why does red-green color-blindness occur much more frequently in males than in females?
9. Give an example of a sex-limited character.
10. Why is baldness more prevalent in men than in women?
11. Give an example of mutation and distinguish a mutation from an inherited character.
12. Name some of the causes of mutations.

APPLYING FACTS AND PRINCIPLES

1. Outline a possible cross to determine whether a black guinea pig is a pure black or a hybrid black.
2. How can you disprove the idea that some people have that the father determines the sex of a male child, while the sex of the female is determined by the mother?
3. Why do sex-limited characters appear only after sexual maturity?
4. Why should a hybridizer know which traits in plants or animals with which he is working are dominant or recessive?
5. Why does the Law of Independent Assortment apply only to certain pairs of genes?
6. How does crossing-over produce new gene combinations?
7. Lethal genes are rare in plants and animals. Give at least one reason to account for this.

CHAPTER 51

Plant and Animal Breeding

SELECTIVE breeding of plants and animals is an old practice. For centuries, man has made a constant effort to improve the varieties of plants and animals which supply his daily needs. Wheat was grown as a cereal crop by the early Egyptians. Garden flowers, fruit trees, domestic fowl, sheep, goats, cattle, and many other plants and animals have been domesticated longer than recorded history.

Genetics originated largely to explain the phenomena which resulted from plant and animal breeding. Selective breeding was a practice of chance selection rather than scientific application of principles. With the development of genetics as a science, established laws have greatly improved the efficiency of the process.

The laws of heredity, when applied directly to plant and animal breeding, are not always exact because of the extreme complexity of the inheritance of organisms. Not one or two, but hundreds of different characteristics are involved in each cross.

Luther Burbank, the genius of California. Plant breeding will always be associated with the genius of Luther Burbank. He produced many new and different plants on his farm in California.

Burbank's brilliant work began in the summer of 1871 in his native Massachusetts. While a young man, he was examining a crop of potatoes one day and happened to notice a fruit maturing on one of the plants. This was an unusual occurrence because the potato plant flowers regularly but seldom bears fruit. New plants are grown from cuttings rather than from actual seeds. Burbank saved that fruit.

When the seeds ripened, he planted each one in a separate hill. After the plants matured, he dug the potatoes and discovered that those from each plant were different. Some were large, some were small. Some hills had many tubers, while others had only a few. One hill had far better potatoes than any of the others. These were large, smooth, and numerous. Burbank sold them to a gardener for $150 — his first profit from plant breeding. They were named *Burbank potatoes* in his honor, and were the first of a strain which was destined to become popular all over the country.

With the profit from his first achievement, Burbank bought a ticket to California, where he established the farm that made him famous. From his experimental gardens came such varieties as the Shasta daisy and a new strain of poppies. By combining various fruits, he produced the plumcot, pitless plum, and the improved peach plum. Another of his famous developments is the thin-shelled walnut. The spineless cactus, used as fodder for cattle, is still another of his achievements.

Objectives in plant breeding. The plant breeder has several purposes in producing new strains or varieties of plants. One of the chief objectives is the production of *more desirable varieties*. Such characteristics as large fruit, large and abundant seeds, vigorous growth, early maturation of fruit, large leaf area

U. S. Dept. of Agriculture

Fig. 51-1.   The tobacco seedlings shown above have been exposed to the disease, black root rot.   Notice that, from left to right, each strain is increasingly resistant to the disease.   The seedlings at the right are practically immune to the rot.

in leafy vegetables, and vigorous root growth in root crops are highly profitable. Plant breeders work constantly to improve the quality and quantity of the yield of all crop plants.   In addition to the nature of the yield, resistance to disease is highly important.   Plant breeders also have been able to produce many varieties of *disease-resistant crops*.

A third objective is an *extension of crop areas* through the production of new varieties.   Wheat is an example of this extension through plant breeding.   Varieties of spring wheat grow well in the northern sections of the nation while winter wheat favors the climate of the central states.   Wheat growing has been extended even to the Great Plains by the production of varieties of hard wheat.   In a similar way, other crops which were once limited to small areas because of climatic requirements or soil conditions have now been extended to many other regions in the form of new varieties.

By means of hybridization, entirely *different kinds of plants* have been developed.   The hybrid may be the result of crossing two strains or varieties or two closely related species.

Mass selection is widely used in obtaining desirable varieties.   As the name implies, **mass selection** consists of the careful selection of parent plants from a great number of individuals.   Burbank practiced mass selection when he discovered his famous potato.   He selected the most ideal plant from all those he grew from seed.   The farmer who selects seed from his own crop always picks the most desirable plants for propagation. Thus he takes advantage of any natural, desirable variations which occur.

Mass selection is important, too, in the production of disease-resistant strains of plants.   To show how mass selection operates, let us assume that a cabbage disease has swept into an area, resulting in the destruction of almost all the crop.

As we examine the acres of diseased plants, we find two or three plants which, for some unknown reason, have withstood the disease. We carefully preserve the seeds from these plants and sow them the following season. Disease again strikes the crop, but a few more plants remain than the year before. Again, we use these plants for seed in the following season. Each year, more and more plants withstand the disease. The character of disease resistance, present in the original plant, becomes more and more strongly established in the offspring. Finally, an entire strain is developed in which this character appears (Fig. 51-1).

What is hybridization? We define **hybridization** as the crossing of two different varieties to obtain a new one, also called **outbreeding**. It is like mass selection in some ways because desirable traits are always sought. But it is a more rapid way of getting the desired results than selection of natural variations.

In hybridization, characteristics of two unlike, but closely related, parents are combined in a new individual by artificial cross-breeding. In getting a new hybrid strain, we might choose one parent because of vigorous growth. The other one might be selected because of the fine quality of its fruit or flower. Often a hybrid possesses qualities not shown in either parent, because of a new combination of genes.

Another advantage of hybridization is **hybrid vigor** in the offspring. Often the new hybrid has a natural vigor which neither parent had.

Line breeding is the opposite of hybridization. After the desired characteristics have been obtained by mass selection or hybridization, the next step is to propogate these new and different plants. This is a simple matter when vegetative multiplication is involved, because such reproduction in no way affects the hereditary make-up.

After Burbank had discovered his potato, propagation was simple. He used cuttings from the potato in order to produce more plants exactly like the parent. Had he been forced to grow more potatoes from seed, the situation would

Fig. 51-2.   Plant breeders have developed numerous varieties of corn, each suitable for a different purpose.

U. S. Dept. of Agriculture

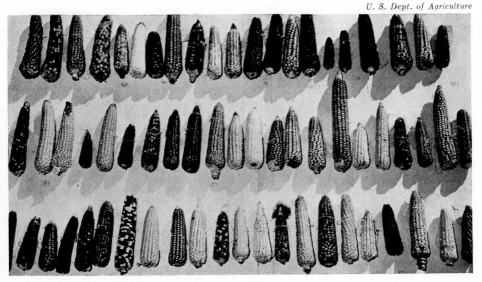

have been quite different because chromosomes from two parents would have been involved. In the same way, the grower can propagate a new variety of apple, peach, iris, or rose by grafting, cutting, or budding without altering the hereditary make-up.

In the case of plants like corn and wheat where seeds must be used for propagation, the problem is more difficult. Seed production involves a mixing of numerous characters. Plants produced from seeds are not necessarily like the parent, especially when they are crop plants which have been crossed by man for centuries.

This difficulty can be overcome by generations of **line breeding,** or **inbreeding.** This is the opposite of hybridization, or outbreeding. Self-pollination is carried on to avoid introducing any new characteristics from a new plant. Seeds resulting from self-pollination are planted and all individuals of the new generation are carefully sorted. Only those with the desired characteristics of the parent are selected as seed plants for the next generation. Again, self-pollination is carried on, after which the resulting plants are carefully sorted.

As you repeat this breeding method generation after generation, more and more plants bear the desired characteristics. Eventually, a pure strain which will be true to seed is established and is ready for the market. Even then all plants may not produce the pure-strain characteristics, but these individuals can be readily sorted out.

The production of hybrid corn. Years ago a farmer saved some of the best ears from his corn crop as seed for the next year. By the process of mass selection, he tried to produce more corn like his best plants of the previous season. But the plants which bore these ears were so mixed in their heredity that only some of the kernels bore the genes which had made them productive. And with no control over pollination, the farmer had no idea about the quality of the other parent. The seeds on a single ear might produce many different varieties of corn, some good and some poor. Some of the kernels might have resulted from self-pollination, while others were the result of cross-pollination from fields some distance away. It was not unusual to find ears of corn with a mixture of yellow, white, and red kernels. Often sweet corn and popcorn were mixed with kernels of field corn. Under conditions like these, a yield of 20 to 40 bushels per acre was all that could be expected.

Today hybrid varieties, produced by **artificial pollination** which is scientifically controlled, yield from 60 to 80 bushels of corn per acre. These hybrids have large root systems, sturdy stalks, broad leaves, and large ears. The energy which once produced the towering stalk now produces the full, long ear.

Much of hybrid corn planted today is the result of a **double-cross** in which four pure-line parents are mixed in two crosses. Each pure-line parent has been selected because of its vigor, resistance to disease, or some other desirable trait. However, plants resulting from the double-cross are superior to any of the parent strains.

Fig. 51-4 shows how hybrid corn is produced by the double-cross method. Four inbred plants, designated as A, B, C, and D, serve as the foundation. These varieties are the result of controlled self-pollination, or line breeding. This is accomplished by covering the developing ears with sacks until the silks are ready to receive pollen. Then pollen collected from the same plant is dusted onto the silks. The plant breeder carefully avoids any contamination of these inbred varieties. During the first cross, plant A is crossed

Funk Bros. Seed Co., Bloomington, Ill.

Fig. 51-3. These two photographs show controlled pollination of corn for the production of inbred lines required for hybridizing. Top: the tassel is being covered by a bag, which is fastened at the bottom where the pollen collects. Bottom: pollen obtained from a bag is blown into the silks of another plant. The ear is then covered with another bag to prevent contamination with pollen from other strains of corn.

with plant B, which produces a single-cross hybrid plant (*B* × *A*). In making this cross, the tassel from plant B is removed and the ear is covered with a bag. When the silks are mature, they are dusted with pollen from plant A. A similar first cross is made between plant C and plant D, resulting in a single-cross hybrid plant (*C* × *D*). The following season, plant B × A is detasseled. The developing ear is covered. This plant is cross-pollinated with C × D. Kernels resulting from this double-cross are designated as (*B* × *A*)×(*C* × *D*).

This seed is sold to the farmer for planting. However, he cannot plant the seed produced by this hybrid corn because the genes will sort out in new combinations in the next generation. He might get plants which would have different characteristics from those of the hybrid parents.

New plants are produced by crossing different species. One of the best known of Burbank's plant varieties is the Shasta daisy. He produced this beautiful garden flower by crossing a native oxeye daisy with a European variety. In a cross between a plum and an apricot, he produced the plumcot. Another hybrid plant was produced by crossing the squash and the pumpkin. One of Burbank's last experiments was an attempt to cross a tomato and a potato to produce a dual-purpose plant which would bear fruit above ground all season and form tubers which could be dug at the end of the season. Unfortunately, such a cross was never perfected. Many crosses of closely related species have been made in animals as well as plants.

Plant varieties resulting from mutations. While examining a bed of white tea roses one day, a grower happened to notice a branch which had produced a pink flower. He carefully removed the branch and set it in a cutting bed. The plant which grew bore all pink flowers. These were budded onto understock and propagated as a **bud-mutant,** or **sport,** of the white rose. These mutants appear from time to time in roses and other plants. For some reason, a mutation occurs in a cell which gives rise to the tissue of a branch. If the branch is propagated vegetatively, the mutation will remain.

Other varieties which have resulted from a *bud-mutation* include the California navel orange, the Delicious apple, and the smooth-skinned peach, or nectarine.

Plants with increased chromosome numbers. Have you ever noticed blueberries on a fruit counter which are twice as large as native blueberries? These blueberries have a double set of chromosomes. This condition, in which plants have some multiple of the diploid number of chromosomes, is called **polyploidy.** Other fruits that have been produced by plants with multiple chromosome numbers include varieties of plums, cherries, grapes, strawberries, and cranberries. A similar increase in the chromosome number occurred in the McIntosh apple. Apple trees usually have 17 pairs, or 34 chromosomes. The normal McIntosh has this number. However, one variety with a fruit more than twice as large as the normal McIntosh has four sets of chromosomes (the *tetraploid number*), or 68 in all.

It has been discovered recently that polyploidy can be artificially produced by the drug *colchicine* (*kohl*-chih-seen). Blueberries, lilies, and wheat are a few of the plants that have been improved by its application. It has also been discovered that the chemical *gibberellic* (jib-er-*el*-ik) *acid* will induce unusual and sometimes favorable growth patterns in plants. In view of these discoveries, it is hard to tell how many new varieties of fruits and vegetables will be available in future years.

FIRST YEAR

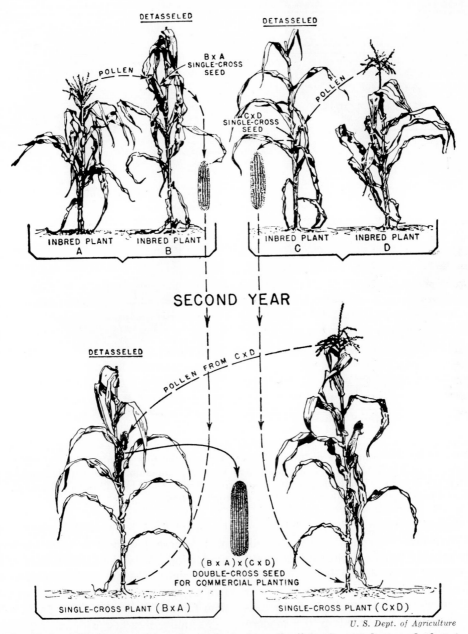

U. S. Dept. of Agriculture

Fig. 51-4. This diagram shows the method of crossing inbred corn plants and of crossing the resulting single crosses to produce double-cross hybrid seed. The four plants labeled *A*, *B*, *C*, and *D* represent the products of four different inbred lines. Strain *A* is crossed with strain *B* (*A* furnished the pollen and *B* was detasseled). Similarly, strains *C* and *D* are crossed. The products of these two lines are then crossed to produce the hybrid corn seed which is used in commercial planting.

U. S. Dept. of Agriculture

Fig. 51-5.   Different lines of breeding have produced the four breeds of poultry shown here.   The Black Minorca (1) has been bred for egg production.   The New Hampshire Red (2) is suitable for both egg and meat production.   The Light Brahma (3) and the Red Cornish (4) have both been bred for meat production.

Animal breeding.   The principles used in plant breeding apply to animal breeding as well.   Mass selection has long been a method of producing highly desirable breeds of animals.

The results of years of selective breeding are well illustrated in the modern breeds of poultry.   The Leghorn, for example, has been bred for its ability to lay large numbers of eggs.   All its energies are directed toward egg production rather than the production of body flesh.   The Plymouth Rock has been developed as a dual-purpose fowl and is ideal for egg production and meat.   Large breeds, like the Brahma, Cochin, and Cornish, are famous for their delicious meat rather than for egg production (Fig. 51-5).

The modern turkey, with massive body and broad breast covered with thick layers of white meat, is quite a contrast to the slender bird the Pilgrims found in the New England forest.   The modern turkey has been bred for the highest possible flesh production. It spends its life, often on wire, eating a scientifically prepared diet and building up large, little-used muscles, better suited to being eaten than to flying and perching high in trees.

Improvement in livestock. Using similar selective breeding methods, domestic cattle have been developed along two entirely different lines. Aberdeen-Angus, Hereford, and Shorthorn are breeds of beef cattle. Their low, broad, stocky bodies provide high-quality steaks and roasts for the nation's markets. Dairy breeds, including the Jersey, Guernsey, Ayrshire, Holstein-Friesian, and Brown Swiss have been bred as milk producers. A breed of Shorthorns, known as " milking Shorthorns," as well as Redpoll cattle, are classified as dual-purpose breeds because they were developed for milk production as well as beef.

Swine raising is one of the most important divisions of American agriculture, especially in the midwest Corn Belt. Heavy, or lard type, breeds include the Poland China and Berkshire, Hampshire, and Duroc-Jersey. The Yorkshire and Tamworth hogs have long slender bodies and are classified as lean, or bacon, type hogs (Fig. 51-6).

In livestock breeding, the records of outstanding individuals used in breeding are kept in pedigree and registration papers. Purebred animals may be registered at the headquarters of their respective breed. Papers must include the names and registration numbers of both *sire* (male) and *dam* (female) as well as part of the ancestry. In this manner, different strains of the same breed may be crossed without the danger of introducing undesirable characteristics or losing any good qualities.

True hybrid animals. Plant and animal breeders use the term hybrid loosely. They use it to indicate crosses between different strains of the same species as, for example, hybrid corn. A **true hybrid**, in the strict sense of the word, is the result of crossing two different species.

The mule is an example of a true hybrid animal. This hardy, useful animal is produced by crossing a female horse with a male donkey. The size is inherited from the horse. From the donkey the mule inherits long ears, sure-footedness, great endurance, and the ability to live on rough food and to endure hardships. However, with all of its hybrid vigor, the mule in most cases is sterile — that is, unable to reproduce.

Several hybrid strains have resulted

Fig. 51-6.   The Poland China breed shown at the left is the fat, or lard, type hog, while the Yorkshire shown at the right is the lean, or bacon, type.

U. S. Dept. of Agricultu

Fig. 51-7. Selective breeding has improved livestock as well as plants. The Guernsey cow has been bred as a milk producer.

U. S. Dept. of Agriculture

Fig. 51-8. The Hereford steer, with its low, broad, stocky body, provides prime beef for the consumer.

American Hereford Assoc.

Fig. 51-9. The hybrid Brangus combines the heat-resistant characteristics of the Brahman with the excellent beef qualities of the Aberdeen-Angus.

U. S. Dept. of Agriculture

from crosses between Brahman cattle from India and domestic breeds. Tourists in the southern and southwestern states are often surprised to see in pastures these large gray or brownish animals with long, drooping ears and shoulder humps. Brahman cattle can endure the hot, humid climate of the Gulf States as well as the dry summer heat of the Southwest much better than domestic breeds of beef cattle. In addition, they resist disease and insect attacks.

A cross between Brahman and Aberdeen-Angus cattle produced Brangus cattle, one of the most popular of the Brahman crosses. The Braford is another cross breed with Brahman and Hereford cattle as parent stock.

In Conclusion

Plant and animal breeding may seem far removed from you if you live in a large city. Actually it is no more removed than your next trip to the grocery store.

Scientific breeding has brought rust-resistant asters to flower beds of your home and city parks. Roses in clusters, long-stemmed tea roses, and climbing roses in great variety leave the growers by tens of thousands each season to beautify our gardens. Just name a size and color of tomato and the time in the summer you want it to ripen and a grower will supply it to you. Beef cattle and dairy cattle, fat hogs and lean hogs, horses for work and horses for pleasure — we have them all.

BIOLOGICALLY SPEAKING

artificial pollination	hybridization	outbreeding
bud-mutant	inbreeding	polyploidy
double-cross	line breeding	sport
hybrid vigor	mass selection	true hybrid

QUESTIONS FOR REVIEW

1. What are four objectives of plant breeding?
2. Why is line breeding practiced in plant and animal breeding?
3. Make a comparison of hybridization and line breeding as to methods and purposes.
4. How many pure-line parents are involved in the production of hybrid seed corn by the double-cross method?
5. Name several hybrid plants produced by the genius of the late Luther Burbank.
6. How is natural cross-pollination prevented during the growing of hybrid corn?
7. Name three general types of chickens and a breed representing each type.
8. Name a dual-purpose breed of cattle.
9. In what respect is the mule a true hybrid animal?
10. Why are Brahman cattle good parent stock for breeding purposes?

APPLYING FACTS AND PRINCIPLES

1. If line breeding is practiced too long, offspring may become weak and inbred. How might this condition be remedied?
2. A farmer does not use seed from his hybrid corn for the next year's crop. Explain why.
3. Outline the method by which poultry breeders have been able to increase egg production by developing 300-egg strains of chickens.
4. What is the importance of pedigrees and registration papers in breeding livestock?

CHAPTER 52

Genetics Applied to Human Inheritance

THE same laws and principles which govern heredity in plants and animals apply to human inheritance. However, human inheritance, in many instances, is far more difficult to study. For one thing, because we are thinking and reasoning organisms we respond more strongly to environmental conditions than do other forms of life. Genes may determine certain of our facial characteristics, but cares and worries, satisfaction and contentment leave their mark, too. Similarly, genes may influence certain characteristics of the form and size of the body. But so do the diet, the general health, and other environmental influences. None of your genetic make-up is quite as simple as tallness or shortness in peas, or black or white coat color in guinea pigs. Factors are often complex, and environmental influences make them even more so.

Much attention has been given to human inheritance in recent years. A specialized branch of genetics, called **eugenics** (you-*jeh*-niks), is now an organized science. It deals entirely with human inheritance.

Galton, the founder of eugenics. Eugenics dates its beginnings from 1883 when Sir Francis Galton pointed out the need for such a science. He even gave it the name *eugenics,* which means, literally, " good birth." Galton himself defined it as " the science which deals with all influences that improve the inborn qualities of a race."

He studied the family records of many English families and concluded that mental ability, scholarship, moral strength or weakness were subject to heredity just as were physical traits such as size and eye color. He based these ideas on the results of numerous case histories and mathematical investigations he had conducted in the field of heredity. Today we know that some of Galton's ideas were incorrect since he did not have the benefit of Mendel's work.

The nature of human heredity. The heredity of man is essentially like that of any other organism. Characteristics of the human race are carried by genes which are borne on the 46 chromosomes present in every cell. Furthermore, the genes are always paired in the same way as chromosomes are paired. A pair of genes concerned with a particular characteristic is located in identical places on corresponding chromosomes.

Human inheritance is difficult to trace for several reasons. For one thing, human characters are frequently not controlled by a single pair of genes as in the case of tallness and shortness in peas. In the human eye, for example, two colors seem to be involved. The infant's eye is blue, but in many individuals a brown layer appears later, resulting in a change in eye color. It seems that the number of genes present for brown determines the shade of the eyes. They may range from deep brown to shades of hazel, and greenish-blue to pure blue, which would indicate the presence of numerous genes, each exerting a definite influence on the color of the eyes.

Another complicating factor in human inheritance is the fact that most people come from a mixed ancestry. This means that few, if any, characters are pure. Therefore, it is almost impossible to trace one characteristic through a family. Each time a marriage occurs, the entirely different genetic backgrounds of two families are combined in the offspring.

The use of case histories in studying human inheritance. Mendel was able to trace the inheritance of garden peas through several generations within a few years. Other investigators have used fruit flies, rabbits, and guinea pigs because they, too, mature rapidly and can

Fig. 52-1. Identical twins have the same genetic make-up, while fraternal twins are usually no more alike than ordinary brothers and sisters.

A. Devaney

produce several generations of offspring in a relatively short time. But any one person can observe only three or four generations of human beings within a lifetime. Many times that number of generations would be necessary to demonstrate the principles governing human inheritance.

For this reason, the *eugenist* (you-*jeh*-nist) makes use of case histories in the study of human families. Eugenics is a young science and a case history soon outdates the science itself. Many descriptions of individuals of several generations ago may have been inaccurate and unreliable. The eugenist must take this into consideration in tracing various physical and mental characteristics through a family by the case-history method.

Much has been learned from the study of twins. Twins are of two types. *Fraternal twins,* the more common type, are two entirely different individuals. Often they are brother and sister. They develop from separate eggs which were fertilized by different sperm. They are no more closely related than any other brothers or sisters in a family. Fraternal twins usually live in identical environments. Yet they may be totally different in physical characteristics, personality, emotional make-up, and mental ability. These variations are valuable in helping to determine which characteristics are hereditary and which are environmental.

Fig. 52-2. The diagram below illustrates how identical twins develop from a single fertilized egg while fraternal twins develop from two fertilized eggs.

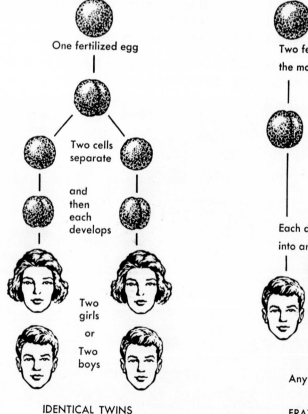

One fertilized egg

Two cells separate

and then each develops

Two girls or Two boys

IDENTICAL TWINS

Two fertilized eggs occur in the mother at the same time

Each develops separately into an individual

and

or

Any other combination

FRATERNAL TWINS

Fig. 52-3. These students have developed skill on their instruments through many years of practice. Will such skill be transmitted to their offspring?

Hays from Monkmeyer

Identical twins have been the subject of many interesting studies in human inheritance. Identical twins are nearly the same person *in duplicate*. They started life as the same fertilized egg. But after the first division, the two cells separated and started growth over again (Fig. 52-2). Sometimes this happens several times, resulting in identical triplets, quadruplets, or quintuplets.

Having started life as the same cell, identical twins have the same genetic make-up. Consequently, the similarities in identical twins indicate, for the most part, characteristics controlled by genes. Identical twins show a marked likeness not only in appearance, but in temperament, abilities, likes and dislikes, and many other personality traits.

Several studies have been made of identical twins who were separated early in life and reared in different environments. In these instances, home and family life, education, day-to-day experiences, friendships, and other environmental influences leave their mark on the personality of each. But the two persons usually remain amazingly alike in appearance, basic personality traits, and capacity for learning.

Can acquired skills be inherited? Man, more than any other organism, adjusts his life to his surroundings. High mentality makes these adjustments possible. The complex nature of human society requires that each individual develop his inherited abilities in the form of trades, skills, and professions. One may become a lawyer, a doctor, a musician, a carpenter, or a mechanic as a result of a long period of training and practice. The question is whether these **acquired skills** are transmitted to the offspring in any degree.

To answer this question, we must examine very carefully the nature of the skill. Certain individuals inherit tendencies which lead them toward a particular kind af activity. Certain characteristics such as coordination of finger movements essential in musical ability may be inherited, but a musician is the product of long hours of practice. Only the inherited, or native, ability may be passed on to the next generation. If such an ability is inherited but for some reason never developed further during life, the same ability may still be passed on to the next generation.

If, on the other hand, the individual uses his inherited ability to become a great musician, he will have in no way improved the inheritance of his children in that respect. In like manner, the acquired skills of great lawyers or expert

Fig. 52-4. Having six fingers is a dominant hereditary characteristic. Instances are known in which all members of a family have inherited this characteristic.

Wide World

mechanics cannot be passed on to the next generation. However, certain inborn characteristics, which had an important influence on the success of these individuals, may be passed on.

Is prenatal influence possible? Have you ever heard of a baby supposedly being " marked " before birth because of some thought or experience of the mother during its development? This idea has been handed down from early times as part of the superstition associated with human inheritance. Many people today believe in such *prenatal influence*.

According to this belief, prenatal influence could be either good or bad. If a mother wanted her child to be a musician, she might cause him to acquire musical genius by listening to music and attending concerts before his birth.

Thoughts, emotional upsets, and experiences, either good or bad, can in no way alter the heredity of a developing child. The heredity was determined at the time of the union of the egg and sperm before development started.

Inheritance of desirable and undesirable traits. Among the traits known to be inherited in the human race are eye color, skin color, and body structure. Others include the structure and color of the hair, length of the limbs, shape of the hands, finger length, facial features, and other factors which determine the form of the body. We notice features such as these in family resemblances. In addition to these physical traits, there is evidence that personality traits, native intelligence, and aptitudes may also be inherited. These characteristics are more difficult to determine and to trace than physical traits.

Finger deformities, including extra fingers, fingers grown together, and fingers lacking one bone occur as dominant traits. Other unfortunate defects include blindness from birth and deaf-mutism. These characteristics are carried by recessive genes or by genes which express a characteristic more in some people than in others. When paired with normal genes, the traits usually do not appear. For this reason many undesirable traits in humans do not appear when genes are mixed in the offspring of unrelated people. On the other hand, close intermarriage tends to make these characteristics appear more frequently.

Inheritance of blood type. In the mention of blood types in Chapter 38, we referred to them as type A, B, AB, or O. These letters refer to a protein substance known as an **antigen** (*an*-tih-jen). Some people have type-A antigen, while others have type B. Some have both (*AB*) while others have neither (*OO*). Blood type is an inherited characteristic, controlled by three kinds of genes.

If you have type-A blood, you could have received an A gene from each parent (*AA*) or an A gene from one parent and a recessive gene (*O*) from the other (*AO*). Similarly, a person with type-B blood may have BB genes or BO genes. If one parent transmits an A gene and the other a B gene, the offspring (*AB*) will produce both antigens, since neither is dominant over the other. Type-O blood, lacking both antigens, results when neither dominant gene is present (*OO*).

Inheritance of the Rh factor. There is evidence that as many as six pairs of genes may be involved in inheritance of the Rh factor. An Rh-negative person lacks all dominant genes which produce the various Rh antigens. Rh-positive persons have various combinations of dominant genes which produce the Rh antigens. For this reason, it is difficult to diagram the results of crosses between various Rh types.

Are diseases inherited? Many geneticists have explored the possibility that certain diseases which appear to run in families may be related to genes. In the case of infections such as tuberculosis, the disease itself cannot be inherited. However, evidence seems to indicate that a resistance to certain infections is hereditary. Lack of this resistance would increase the possibility of contracting the disease sometime during one's life. However, proper precautions can prevent tuberculosis, even in the most susceptible persons.

On the other hand, diseases resulting from abnormal structure or function of body organs are more likely to be hereditary. For example, sugar diabetes (*diabetes mellitus*) is known to run in families and is probably transmitted by a dominant gene. However, the gene does not seem to produce an equally serious diabetic condition in all people. Furthermore, regulation of the diet and body weight may prevent diabetes, even when the gene is present.

Case history studies indicate that many other human diseases and disorders are definitely associated with genes. Among these are respiratory allergies, farsightedness, nearsightedness, and night-blindness.

Sex-linked and sex-limited characters in human inheritance. *Hemophilia* (hee-moh-*fee*-lee-uh), or "bleeder's disease," operates as a *sex-linked character* in the same way as color blindness, which was discussed in Chapter 50. Hemophilia is the result of an inherited abnormality in the character of the blood. Normally, blood clots when exposed to the air. Clotting causes formation of a scab which stops the flow of blood through severed blood vessels. In the case of hemophilia, the blood does not clot properly because of the absence of fibrinogen, and bleeding may continue for a long time. Death

Fig. 52-5. Aptitude tests help to determine a person's capacity to think quickly and his ability to coordinate.

from loss of blood may occur as a result of slight wounds.

Hemophilia tends to run in families and to appear in males. It can appear in a female only when the father is a bleeder and the mother is a carrier.

The characteristics of the beard is a good example of a *sex-limited character*. A boy may inherit a heavy beard with a coarse growth around his chin and upper lip from his mother's side of the family. The mother never developed the trait, nor did the son until he reached sexual maturity and started producing male hormones in his reproductive organs.

Inheritance of mental ability. The phase of eugenics dealing with mental ability is complicated. For one thing, mental ability is difficult to determine. Just how much of what we call intelligence is hereditary and how much is due to environment is extremely difficult to measure.

One of the modern methods of determining mental ability is by the administration of *intelligence tests*. These are intended to evaluate the mental processes of the individual in various ways. The score on the intelligence test is used to calculate the **mental age.** Intelligence is then determined by dividing the mental age by the actual age, or **chronological age.** The result, multiplied by 100, is the **intelligence quotient,** or I.Q. A normal, or average, I.Q. is considered to be 100.

Actually, this method contains many flaws because of variable factors. The general physical and mental conditions such as slight illness or mental strain of the person taking an intelligence test may affect his mental processes temporarily. Furthermore, no test has yet been devised which will eliminate completely the effects of environment on the individual.

We must consider, too, that the mental age and I.Q. of a person may change through the years. Many children are late in maturing, both physically and mentally, but finally " catch up " with their chronological ages. Thus, a child may have a below-normal I.Q. in elementary school, a normal I.Q. in high school, and a superior I.Q. in his college years and adult life.

Inheritance of mental disorders. Extensive genetic studies have supplied evidence that several kinds of mental deficiency are hereditary. Among these are forms of arrested mental development resulting in idiocy. Such deficiencies may be the result of complex chemical disturbances or the lack of certain enzymes associated with mental development. In some cases, these disturbances may result from mutations.

Much more frequent are cases of feeble-mindedness. Recent figures from mental health agencies and hospitals indicate that there are about 3 million known cases of feeble-mindedness in the United

States today. This figure is probably low, since it does not include many cases cared for by families in private homes. Studies show that feeble-minded people usually seek other feeble-minded people for marriage. Thus, the condition may appear in increasing frequency in future generations.

Extensive studies are now being made of the occurrence of mental diseases in families. Manic-depressive psychosis is thought to be hereditary, at least to some degree. It seems to be related to a dominant gene, although presence of the gene may merely produce a tendency which can be avoided by environmental influences. Similarly, a tendency to develop schizophrenia may be associated with genes.

Environment is a powerful influence in human development. Who can say just what part of mental ability and other factors of a personality are due to heredity and which ones are products of environment? Fig. 52-6 shows two contrasting environments. If two children with identical hereditary characteristics came from these surroundings, wouldn't they have different social and educational backgrounds, attitudes, and desires? Living under conditions that are unfavorable, the individual has less chance and opportunity to improve his native intelligence. Good environment can bring out hidden desirable traits in an individual, while bad environment may stifle them.

Euthenics, a method of improving human life. It is impossible to control human heredity in the manner in which we control inheritance in plants and animals. Therefore, if we cannot control genes, we can alter the influence of genes by regulating the environment. This work is the area of *euthenics,* or scientific control of the environment. It implies more than improvement of the physical and social surroundings. It involves the altering of the influence of genes and correction of conditions they might otherwise produce.

For example, a child with an inherited thyroid gland deficiency would ordinarily become a cretin. He would suffer both physical and mental impairment. However, thyroid hormone given in regulated amounts from infancy on will allow such a person to live a reasonably normal life. Similarly, we can alter the effects of underactivity of the pituitary gland.

Fig. 52-6. **In which of the two environments shown would an individual have the best opportunity to develop?**

Meisel from Monkmeyer

Bloom from Monkme

While euthenics cannot alter genes or the occurrence of undesirable human traits, it can do much to promote human health and happiness. Euthenics will become more and more important in the years ahead as we discover more human traits controlled by genes, and the influence of these genes on human growth and development.

Genetic mutation and radiation. As we mentioned in Chapter 50, radiations can speed up the rate of mutation in many organisms, including man. Although these radiations can produce mutation in any of the cells of the body, the gene changes in the reproductive cells are the

ones of importance from the standpoint of heredity. If the mutation is of a recessive type, many generations may occur before a change is noticed. In general mutations are harmful — their effect range from early death to only minor impairment. Those mutations which cause the death of the organism are soon eliminated from the population, but those which cause minor defects remain in the population for a hundred or more generations. In man, this would represent over 3,000 years. For this reason, if for no other, it is important for the future welfare of man that we try to understand the effects of radiation.

In Conclusion

There never was a combination of genes just like those you carry in the chromosomes of every cell of your body. Each of those billions of cells is distinctly yours. Each is carrying your potential as an individual. What use will you make of your heredity? Lying in those tiny chromosomes may be genes bearing artistic talent, mechanical aptitude, athletic ability, or the qualities of great leadership. But genes alone will never produce the fine quality. This requires education, training, practice, and experience.

BIOLOGICALLY SPEAKING

acquired skill	euthenics	identical twins
antigen	fraternal twins	intelligence quotient
chronological age	hemophilia	mental age
eugenics		

QUESTIONS FOR REVIEW

1. What contribution did Sir Francis Galton make to the science of genetics?
2. Why are case histories essential to the study of human inheritance?
3. How does inheritance of human eye color and skin color indicate the presence of several pairs of genes?
4. (a) Can acquired skills be inherited? (b) Explain your answer.
5. How many kinds of antigens are involved in the common blood groups, A, B, AB, and O?
6. Account for the fact that certain infectious diseases may be more prevalent in some families than they are in others, even though the diseases are not inherited.
7. About how many Rh antigens are known to exist?
8. How do radiations sometimes affect human heredity?

APPLYING FACTS AND PRINCIPLES

1. How have identical twins supplied valuable data in the study of human heredity?

2. Distinguish between musical ability and musical skill and discuss the possible inheritance of either or both.

3. Using what you have learned about heredity, prove that prenatal influences from the external environment do not exist.

4. (a) Explain how an intelligence quotient is determined. (b) In what ways is an I.Q. determination valuable, and what are its limitations?

5. Discuss the role of heredity and environment in producing people of low mental ability and other undesirable qualities.

6. Discuss euthenics and eugenics as companion sciences.

CHAPTER 53

The Changing World of Life

IF we could somehow travel back in time for millions of years or even for thousands of years, our first exclamation would probably be, How different everything looks! We would see a variety of unfamiliar plants and animals. If we were to turn back our " magic time clock " 200 million years, we would see giant dinosaurs thundering over a strange landscape; we might see reptiles with wings soaring through the sky. We would see whole forests of giant ferns. What has caused the extinction of many of these species of plants and animals which once flourished for a time? Why have new species replaced them?

Earlier in your study of biology you learned that particular organisms can be found in certain environments. You also discovered that if organisms did not meet environmental changes by moving or adjusting, they would certainly perish. Many physical changes occur in the earth from day to day, from year to year, and from age to age. Rivers deepen their channels as they carry more land to the sea. Mountains rise, only to be leveled by winds and rain. Continents rise and sink back into the sea. The foregoing are gradual changes which are constantly altering the surface of the earth. They are the changes which alter the environment and cause the extinction of some species which cannot adjust or move.

The idea that all life in the world is in some way related is an ancient one. Throughout the ages man has noticed many similarities and differences among living things. The previous chapters have made you aware of some of the differences. However, if you will briefly review these chapters, you will see that similarities and relationships have also been pointed out to you.

Ewing Galloway

Fig. 53-1. Layers of sedimentary rock help geologists estimate the age of the earth. They are also an excellent source of fossils.

How old is the earth? When you look at the table of *geological eras* on page 661, you will see that life was possible over two billion years ago. Radiation studies have been very valuable in tracing the history of the earth and its life. As radium decays, it is changed into the element lead at a constant rate. By measuring the amount of radium as compared to the amount of lead in a particular rock, it is possible to determine the age of the rock. *Geologists* (scientists who study rocks and their formation) have used this method to study the age of parts of the earth. Some of the oldest rocks, which we have been able to date in this manner, have been estimated to be over two billion years old. There are rocks which are believed to be older, but they do not contain radioactive minerals which enable them to be dated. It is known, then, that the earth had a solid, cool crust over two billion years ago. This fact would indicate that the atmospheric conditions of the earth were much the same then as we know them today. This is significant, because it means that life was *possible* over two billion years ago.

Another method used in determining the age of the earth is to study the rate at which solid materials are deposited in water to form *sedimentary rocks* (Fig. 53-1). By knowing the rate of deposition and the thickness of the layers of these rocks, geologists can determine the length of time needed for their formation. Layers of sedimentary rock ten miles thick have been found. The formation of such a layer would require nearly two billion years. In such calculations a mistake of a million years or so is trivial! Whatever its actual age, we may be sure that the earth is extremely old, that it has changed from age to age, and that it continues to change at a gradual rate. We also believe that, along with the physical character of the earth, living organisms have changed and thus have survived in new environments.

Evidence that living things have changed through the ages. Science has turned to various sources to obtain evidence that organisms have become more complex through the ages and that plant and animal populations have changed with time. These sources include: (1)

fossil evidence; (2) *homologous structures;* (3) *vestigial organs;* (4) *evidence in embryology;* (5) *physiological similarities;* (6) *geographical distribution;* (7) *results of breeding;* and (8) *experiments in plant and animal genetics.*

Fossil evidence. Any impression or trace of an animal or plant of past geological ages which has been preserved in the earth's crust may be regarded as a **fossil.** The fossil record is not very complete, as the remains of very few organisms have been preserved. Most dead organisms decay or are eaten by scavengers which break up and scatter the skeletal parts. However, the few organisms that have become fossils give us valuable clues to life in past ages.

The most common type of fossils are those found in sedimentary rock which has formed on the floor of oceans or other large bodies of water. As the aquatic organisms died, they settled to the bottom and were covered by soft sediments. Here they were protected from scavengers and from oxidation. As the soft parts decayed and were removed by seepage of water, the bones remained. In some cases the skeletons were replaced by other minerals from the water — a process known as **petrifaction.** At times during the history of the earth, whole forests were covered by water, forming large seas or lakes, and even the big trees were preserved by petrifaction. With the passing of many ages, several layers of sediments containing organisms were built up. At various times, these large seas or lakes evaporated or were pushed up by earthquakes. Sedimentary rock exposed in such a way shows a record of life in the past, with the earliest living organisms at the bottom and the most recent ones near the surface.

Fig. 53-2. Geologists study the fossils found in sedimentary rock to form an idea of the nature and extent of life in past ages.

American Museum of Natural History

Fig. 53-3. **Fossils provide an invaluable record of past geological eras. This photograph shows fossils of early marine animals as found in a layer of limestone.**

The lowest layers in sedimentary rock contain few fossils, because the prevailing animal forms probably had no hard parts. Above these ancient layers, typical fossils found are marine invertebrates such as sponges, coral, the now unimportant *brachiopods* (*bray*-kee-oh-podz) and some gastropods.

Through the next layers fossils of higher invertebrates appear. The now extinct arthropods, the *trilobites* (*try*-loh-bytes), insects, armored fish, and amphibians are abundant, together with traces of tree ferns whose stems and leaves have for the most part been converted into coal. In later sedimentary rocks, one finds the remains of huge dinosaurs and other reptiles. As we approach more recent rocks, the land reptiles seem to have given way to flying reptiles and to true birds. The plants and trees of this era begin to look like the living forms of today. Finally, in the most recent layers, fossils of mammals, the highest form of animal life, can occasionally be found.

We know some strains or races of animals perished in the struggle for existence. It seems, however, that those groups which lived were the forebears of modern organisms. The organisms of today appear to be the descendants of those remote forms which we know only from fossil evidence.

Fossil remains of land animals. Dust storms and volcanic ash may have the same effect in creating fossils of terrestrial animals and plants as sedimentary rock does in creating fossils of water-living organisms. When Mount Vesuvius erupted in 79 A.D., Pompeii was buried with volcanic ash. Recent studies of this once thriving city have shown whole families and their domestic animals, preserved through these hundreds of years.

One of the best-known sources for well-preserved fossils of Pleistocene and recent mammals and birds (see the table on page 661) has been the tar pits at Rancho La Brea in southern California. These tar pits mark the location of a petroleum spring which formed thousands of years ago. As the oils of this spring evaporated, a mass of sticky tar and later one of thick asphalt was produced. When this happened, small rain pools accumulated on the surface. It seems that many mammals and birds were attracted to these pools and became trapped in the sticky asphalt. Larger predators attracted by the helpless victims soon found themselves trapped and sinking into the tarry ooze.

Insects preserved in amber furnish another type of fossil remains. Many specimens are extremely well preserved in the glasslike substance, so that even cellular detail can be studied. Larger animals, like the mammoths, have been found preserved in the frozen Arctic. Some fossils are merely footprints or casts formed from mud or sand which has been hardened into stone. Many imprints of leaves have been formed in this manner.

Homologous structures. In both plants and animals we find parts that are evidently of similar origin and structure, although they may be adapted for very different functions in different species. These parts are *homologous structures.* In many plants leaves are found modified as petals, tendrils, or thorns. Roots may likewise act as organs for climbing, anchorage, or storage.

Epidermal tissue of animals may be modified as hoofs, scales, nails, claws, feathers, and hair. The various appendages of the crayfish are greatly modified

for different functions in its relatives, yet the correspondence of these parts is evident. The bones of the bird's wing, the front leg of a horse, and the paddle of a whale are so similar in structure that, with slight exceptions, they are given the same names. Likewise, the muscles and internal organs of all mammals are, with certain modifications, basically alike.

The way in which comparative organs are modified for different uses throughout the animal kingdom indicates clearly how new species must have resulted, over the geological ages, from structural variations.

Vestigial organs. In certain animals structures exist which are well developed and perform an important function, while in the animals of related species the corresponding structure may be present, but poorly developed and not functioning. These remnants are called *vestigial* (ves-tij-ih-ul) *organs.* It is believed that such inadequate structures are the remains of organs that were well developed in

Fig. 53-4. Nonfunctional vestigial organs are common among animals, and provide one source of evidence that life has changed through the ages.

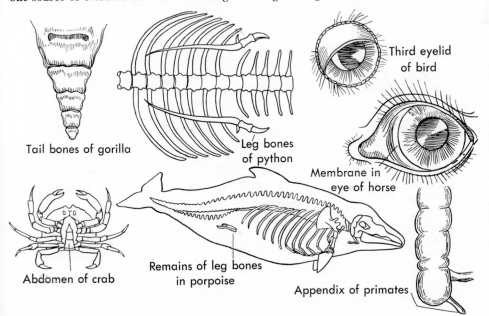

Tail bones of gorilla

Leg bones of python

Third eyelid of bird

Membrane in eye of horse

Abdomen of crab

Remains of leg bones in porpoise

Appendix of primates

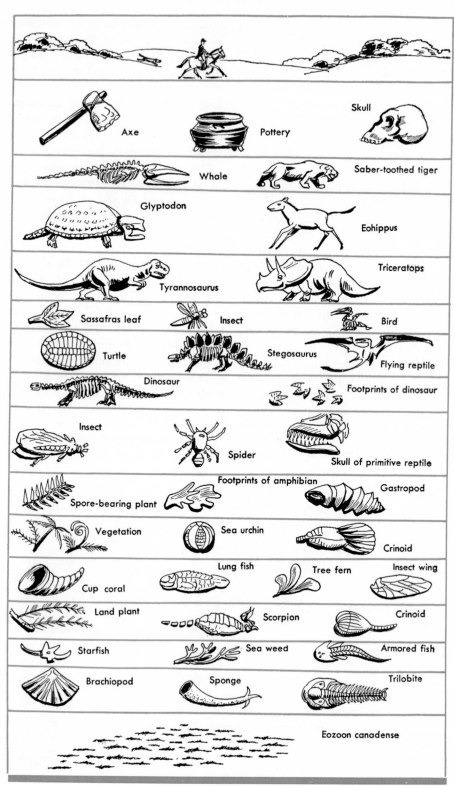

Axe

Pottery

Skull

Whale

Saber-toothed tiger

Glyptodon

Eohippus

Tyrannosaurus

Triceratops

Sassafras leaf

Insect

Bird

Turtle

Stegosaurus

Flying reptile

Dinosaur

Footprints of dinosaur

Insect

Spider

Skull of primitive reptile

Spore-bearing plant

Footprints of amphibian

Gastropod

Vegetation

Sea urchin

Crinoid

Cup coral

Lung fish

Tree fern

Insect wing

Land plant

Scorpion

Crinoid

Starfish

Sea weed

Armored fish

Brachiopod

Sponge

Trilobite

Eozoon canadense

GEOLOGICAL ERAS

Recent Period	**PSYCHOZOIC ERA** — about 25,000 years Beginning of man's dominance; domestication of animals
Pleistocene Period	**CENOZOIC ERA** — about 60,000,000 years Ice ages; extinction of mammoth and mastodon; rise of modern horse; man uses fire and makes implements
Pliocene Period	Rise of man; *Pliohippus*
Miocene Period	Saber-toothed tiger; *Protohippus;* whale
Oligocene Period	Primitive anthropoids and *Mesohippus*
Eocene Period	Primitive forms of modern mammals: sloths, armadillos, marsupials, *Eohippus*, rhinoceros
Cretaceous Period	**MESOZOIC ERA** — about 125,000,000 years *Tyrannosaurus* and other dinosaurs became extinct
Comanchean Period	Flowering plants; true trees; modern insects; true birds
Jurassic Period	Giant dinosaurs dominant; birds with teeth; turtles and flying reptiles; egg-laying mammals
Triassic Period	Rise of dinosaurs
Permian Period	**PALEOZOIC ERA** — about 350,000,000 years Rise of insects, spiders, and primitive reptiles; extinction of trilobites and other forms; glacial period
Pennsylvanian Period	Spore-bearing plants; sharks and large amphibians (first land vertebrates); coal formed
Mississippian Period	Rise of crinoids, brachiopods, and sea urchins; dense vegetation on land
Devonian Period	Tree ferns and other land plants; lung fish and primitive amphibians; fish and invertebrates dominant
Silurian Period	First air-breathing animals; crinoids; primitive sharks; scorpions; first land plants
Ordovician Period	Corals and clams; armored fish; starfish; first seaweeds
Cambrian Period	Marine invertebrates: sponges, jellyfish, trilobites, gastropods, brachiopods

Proterozoic Era and Archeozoic Era — about 1,450,000,000 years — Origin of life in form of one-celled organisms; fossil evidence scanty

Total number of years since life began — about 2,000,000,000 years common ancestors and therefore offer further evidence of the development of animal life and its relationship. The abdomen of the crayfish or lobster is homologous to the abdomen of the crab. Yet in the lobster, the abdomen forms a considerable part of the body, while in the crab it is a tiny V-shaped part and of little importance.

The appendix of some primates is a small structure without any known function. In other primates that eat a coarse diet with large amounts of cellulose, this pouch serves as an organ to store mixtures of food and enzymes over a long period of time. In rodents, for example, the appendix is the largest part of the intestine.

The majority of mammals have a well-developed tail. However, in all of the primates which do not have outwardly visible tails, the tail is represented by from three to five bones at the end of the spinal column. Even the muscles which other animals use to move the tail are present in all of the primates. See Fig. 53-4, page 659, for other examples of vestigial structures.

Evidence from embryology. Biologists have often compared the developmental stages of present-day mammalian embryos. The evidence from embryology seems to indicate that each animal in its individual development passes through stages which resemble those of its remote ancestors (Fig. 53-5). For instance, the embryos of mammals such as cows, dogs, and pigs, possess gill arches, although these animals are not aquatic. However, as mammalian embryos develop, two of these gill arches are modified to become the Eustachian tubes; the rest of them disappear.

Early in development, all land vertebrate embryos have a two-chambered heart and a circulatory system much like that of a fish. Later, the mammal's heart becomes four-chambered. The comparing of embryos of different animals also shows us that vertebrate lungs have developed from the swim bladder, or air bladder, of fishlike animals.

The similarity of structure found in developing organisms indicates the possibility that all animals represent modifications of a common ancestor.

Physiological similarities. Not only do the classes of vertebrates resemble one another in structure and in development, but there is also a marked similarity in function. For instance, the internal secretions of mammals are alike in many respects. The digestive enzymes are so similar that many commercial products such as *pepsin* have been extracted from cows, sheep, and hogs, and are used successfully in human medicine. *Insulin* and *thyroid hormone,* endocrine products taken from animals, have tremendous use in human treatment. Antitoxins produced by the horse are used in immunity treatments of human diseases such as diphtheria, scarlet fever, and tetanus.

Evidence from geographical distribution. It is known that animals on isolated islands usually differ from corresponding forms on the mainland, even though there is evidence that the two forms came originally from a common ancestor. The same differences are sometimes noticed among descendants of a common ancestor on different continents. For example, members of the camel family were at one time found throughout Asia, Europe, and North America. Today they are found only in parts of Africa and Asia, and in South America — the llama of the Andes is a member of the camel family. This redistribution has been explained by scientists in the following way. During part of the Cenozoic Era, North America and Asia were connected in the Bering Strait region. This strait appar-

Fish   Salamander   Turtle   Bird   Pig

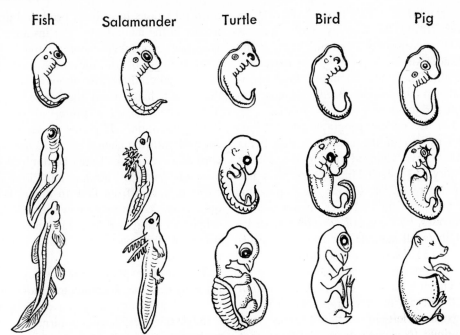

Fig. 53-5.   Stages in the development of five typical vertebrate embryos are shown. Note the long tails and gill slits in the early stages, as well as other structural similarities.

ently served as a " land bridge " for the spread of the camel group and many other organisms as well. However, with the climatic changes brought about by the ice ages that followed, extinction of the camels occurred in most regions. During the following 25,000 years, the characteristics of the remaining major groups of camels changed from those of the original population. The Asian camel has two humps, while the African (Arabian) camel has one. Both are well adapted for life on the desert. The llama of South America, on the other hand, has become a sure-footed beast well adapted for mountainous rocky areas.

The " land bridge " has sometimes been called a **corridor** because it is a pathway by which organisms can spread to a new territory. This same corridor, however, also acts as a filter, because certain organisms cannot reach the approach. The factors which prevent an organism from spreading to a new land are called **bar-**

riers. A mountain range, for example, is a barrier to species better adapted to growth on the lowlands. In turn, the lowlands may be barriers to the species which live on mountain ranges. The grasslands are barriers to forest animals, the cold ocean current is a barrier for warm-water species, the salt water is a barrier to fresh-water and some terrestrial organisms, and the land is a barrier to both fresh-water and marine animals and plants.

Although barriers cannot be crossed by a whole population, they are sometimes crossed by individual members. A dandelion seed, for example, may be blown across an ocean to a Pacific island. If by chance it lands in a suitable environment, it may be able to live, grow, and reproduce. A mouse may float on a log, cross the salt-water barrier, and find its way to an island where it may be able to live. But unless its mate goes along for the voyage, the mouse population will not be established. This type of distribution over strong barriers by individuals is called *sweepstakes dispersal* because the chances of its happening are extremely small. There are no native land mammals on any of the Pacific islands, except for those very near Australia.

Let us review geographical distribution as one of the evidences that living things have changed during the earth's history: (1) each kind of organism has a place of *origin;* (2) as the population of an organism increases, it spreads or *disperses,* by means of *corridors,* from its origin to all suitable environments available; (3) *barriers* often stop dispersal; (4) in time, geological changes, enemies, or climatic changes can cause *extinction* of the organism over large areas; (5) the organisms left in scattered areas may continue to change or *specialize* so that they become less like their ancestors.

Results of breeding. Domesticated plants and animals are examples of racial development. Over 25 kinds of dogs have been developed by man from wild wolflike progenitors. A dozen kinds of chickens have a common ancestor in the jungle fowl of India. The Percheron horse has been bred for draft purposes, the saddle horse for riding, and the thoroughbred for racing. In these cases the skeletons show striking differences in size and weight of bones and hoofs. Domestication and man's control of certain characteristics preserve variations that have arisen as mutations or as the result of hybridization.

The story of plant and animal breeding, while it does not prove that similar developmental changes have taken place naturally in past ages, does strongly point to that possibility.

Experiments in genetics. The rapid growth of the science of genetics has established mutation as one of the chief causes for the modification of life forms.

Such mutations have been produced artificially in the laboratory. For instance a you will remember from Chapter 50 when the eggs of fruit flies are exposed to X rays, alterations are observed in the flies which hatch from the treated eggs These alterations are preserved in the third generation. If plants or seeds are sprayed with the chemical *colchicine,* the chromosomes per cell may be doubled or even quadrupled. Similar mutations do occur in nature from time to time. It is quite possible that many new species have originated more or less suddenly as a result of this peculiar hereditary phenomenon.

Theories to explain racial development. As evidence was accumulated indicating that living things may have changed through the ages, scientists turned to the problem of explaining theories to account for *racial development.*

One of the first theories was presented by the French biologist Jean Baptiste Lamarck, in 1801. In 1859, the famous English scientist Charles Darwin published his theories. In 1901, just 100 years after Lamarck, a third great scientist, Hugo De Vries, announced another explanation for racial development.

Lamarck's theories. Lamarck proposed three theories as follows:

1. *Theory of need.* That the production of a new organ or part of a plant or animal results from a need.

2. *Theory of use and disuse.* That organs remain active as long as they are used, but disappear gradually with disuse.

3. *Theory of inheritance.* That all that has been acquired or changed in the structure of individuals during their life is transmitted by heredity to the next generation.

Most of Lamarck's ideas have been discarded. We know today that organisms cannot develop new organs as they are needed. We also know that environ-

Fig. 53-6. Compare the characteristics of the thoroughbred (*left*) and the Belgian (*right*), which have been developed for specific purposes by selective breeding.

mental variations acquired during the lifetime of a single organism cannot be inherited. Gradual modifications do appear in species over long periods of time, as we have pointed out in this chapter. Lamarck's theory of use and disuse has little if any scientific basis. However, we must admit that the human appendix is relatively small, and that it has no real use. Also, man does not need to use his third molars, or "wisdom teeth," and some individuals do not develop them at all. However, it is believed that these two phenomena are the result of natural selection, which is discussed below.

Darwin's theory of natural selection. In 1859 Charles Darwin, an English scientist, published his *Origin of Species by Natural Selection.* His theory is not confined to biology alone, but has influenced other branches of science. In its broader features it is accepted generally, although it still fails to account for all the known facts.

The chief factors, according to Darwin, that account for the development of new species from common ancestry are: (1) that all organisms produce more off-spring than can actually survive; (2) that because of overproduction, there is a constant struggle for existence among individuals; (3) that the individuals of a given species vary; and (4) that the "fittest," or the best-adapted, individuals of a species survive.

Overproduction. A fern plant may produce 50 million spores each year. If all the spores resulting from this **overproduction** matured, they would nearly cover North America the second year. A mustard plant produces about 730,000 seeds annually, which, if they all took root and matured, in two years would occupy an area 2,000 times that of the land surface of the earth. The dandelion would do the same thing in about ten years.

At a single spawning an oyster may shed 114,000,000 eggs. If all these eggs survived, the ocean would be literally filled with oysters. Within five generations there would be more oysters than the estimated number of electrons in the visible universe! There is, however, no such actual increase.

The elephant is considered to have a slow rate of reproduction. An average elephant lives to be a hundred years old, breeds from 30 to 90 years and bears about six young. Yet if all the young from one pair survived, in 750 years the descendants would number 19,000,000.

The competition for life. We know that in actuality the number of individuals of a species usually changes little in its native environment. In other words, regardless of the rate of reproduction, only a small minority of the original number of offspring reaches maturity. Each organism seeks food, water, air, warmth, and space, but only a few can obtain these needs in struggling to survive. This *struggle for existence* is most intense between members of the same species, as they compete for the same necessities.

Variation among individuals. With the exception of identical twins, every individual varies in some respects from other members of its species. Animal breeders take advantage of this fact when they choose the individuals with desirable characteristics to breed. Nurserymen are able to produce disease-resistant plants and control the size and color of the bloom by careful study and cross-fertilization of particular individuals. The *variations* within a species furnish the material for nature to use in her selection. Those forms whose variations tend to adapt them best to their environment survive, while the others perish. Consider the camels that migrated to the Andes at the time of the ice ages. Those individuals that had shorter legs, a heavier coat, and sure-footedness for traveling over rocky slopes were the ones that survived.

Natural selection — the survival of the fittest. The individual variations among the camel population that reached the Andes were probably not very great. But the ones with the slightly heavier coat had a better chance to survive cold winters and to reproduce the following year. Also, the animals with shorter legs and sure-footed ability had a better chance to survive by running away from enemies. The animals that did not possess these favorable variations were eventually wiped out. In general, offspring resemble their parents. If the parents reach maturity because of special fitness, those of their descendants which inherit most closely the favorable variation will in turn be automatically selected by nature to continue their species. Darwin called this part of his theory *the survival of the fittest*. In this way nature is selecting the characteristics of a certain population by favoring even the slightest variation which may be helpful. Nature, the breeder, and the nurseryman all have an ability in common — the ability to select!

New and better-adapted species. A continuation of the process of *natural selection* in time produces such differences in structure and habit that the resulting forms must be regarded as new species, genera, and finally higher groups. This process may be aided when developing species are separated by distance, mountain ranges, bodies of water, or climatic differences, so that they do not lose their favorable variations by interbreeding.

Conclusions from the theory. Natural selection, while recognized today as an important factor in the development of plant and animal life, does not seem to account for all the known facts. Scientists are turning to other theories to help explain things that natural selection fails to cover. This does not mean that scientists disbelieve Darwin's general conclusions. The main facts are becoming more strongly entrenched every year. The interpretation of these facts will continue to vary with new discoveries.

Mutation theory. We have already mentioned genetic mutation as one of the causes for the modification of life forms. The existence of mutation was unknown until Hugo De Vries, the Dutch botanist,

ORIGIN OF DOMESTIC ANIMALS

ANIMAL	PROGENITOR
Cat	Some wild type like European wildcat
Dog	An animal resembling the wild wolf, jackal, or possibly the fox. The first animal to be domesticated
Dove, Pigeon	Rock pigeon of England
Duck	Original wild progenitor unknown. Many wild species still living
Goat	Of uncertain origin. Wild relatives still alive: Angora of Asia Minor, Kashmir of Tibet, Egyptian goat of Nile
Goose	Graylag goose of north British Isles. Long domesticated
Hen	Jungle fowl of India, a kind of pheasant
Horse	Diminutive, five-toed *Eohippus*, progenitor of the *Orohippus*
Peacock	Some pheasant in Asia
Pig	European wild boar; Indian wild boar
Sheep	Domestic so long that previous history is lost; probably same type in Asia, possibly China
Turkey	Wild turkey of Central America and Mexico

startled the scientific world in 1901 by announcing his **mutation theory.** De Vries had found among a group of evening primroses two plants which were definitely different from the common type. He experimented for many years, finding that from 50,000 specimens of evening primroses at least 800 plants showed striking differences and that these characteristics were hereditary. To such new forms which arise suddenly and breed true for the new characteristic, De Vries assigned the name of *mutants.*

Most mutants are weaker than the normal stock because mutations are usually defects. But some mutations are advantageous. Both kinds of mutations can become permanent characteristics of a species, so that natural selection begins to operate, and the result may be an entirely new species. Hence De Vries' mutation theory supported Darwin's observations on the changing world of life.

Faith and evolution. " It remains for us now to speak about those questions which although they pertain to the positive sciences, are nevertheless more or less connected with the truths of Christian faith. . . . The teaching authority of the Church does not forbid that in conformity with the present state of human sciences and sacred theology research and discussions on the part of men experienced in both fields take place with regard to the doctrine of evolution in so far as it inquires into the origin of the human body as coming from pre-existent and living matter — for Catholic faith obliges us to hold that souls are immediately created by God. . . .

" When, however, there is question of another conjectural opinion, namely, polygenism, . . . the faithful cannot embrace that opinion which maintains either that after Adam there existed on this earth true men who did not take their origin through natural generation from him as from the first parent of all, or that Adam represents a certain number of first parents." Part of the encyclical letter, *Humani Generis,* of His Holiness Pope Pius XII.

In Conclusion

Through periods and eras representing millions of years, life on the earth has undergone gradual changes. This modification of life forms is termed *racial development*. Evidence has been accumulated through the study of fossils, homologous organs, vestigial organs, embryology, physiological similarities, geographical distribution, results of breeding, and genetics. Lamarck, Darwin, and De Vries advanced theories to explain racial development. Much of modern theory is based on their thinking.

In this unit we have studied the changes and hereditary mechanisms of life. Next we shall study how we can preserve the life that we now have on earth.

BIOLOGICALLY SPEAKING

barrier
corridor
fossil
geological era
geologist

mutation theory
natural selection
overproduction
petrification
racial development

sedimentary rock
struggle for existence
survival of the fittest
variation
vestigial organs

QUESTIONS FOR REVIEW

1. What methods have scientists used to determine the approximate age of the earth?
2. How are fossils formed?
3. What significance is attached to the order of the layers in which fossils are found in the earth?
4. How do homologous organs help explain the variety of forms found in related organisms?
5. Name several vestigial organs and discuss their probable origin.

6. How does embryology show the possible ancestry of organisms?
7. What are some of the physiological similarities found in animals?
8. Using your knowledge of genetics, discuss briefly how isolation is an important factor in forming new varieties of organisms.
9. How have the results of breeding shown that organisms may change because of variations in heredity?
10. What is meant by " the fittest "?

APPLYING FACTS AND PRINCIPLES

1. How do you account for the fact that squirrels found on the north rim of the Grand Canyon differ in many respects from those found on the south rim?
2. How is it possible for the fossil remains of salt-water organisms to be found many hundreds of miles from the ocean?
3. " Goose pimples " are caused by the action of little muscles attached to the hairs of the skin. Under what general

heading of the evidences for change would you place this fact?
4. How do you explain the fact that many plants and animals found in England and Japan resemble each other more than plants and animals found in Africa and Madagascar?
5. Explain the long neck of the giraffe according to Lamarck, according to Darwin, and according to modern theory.

RESEARCH ON YOUR OWN

1. Prepare a list of eight sketches showing successive stages of mitosis. Include the following: a cell at the close of the interphase and ready to start mitosis; early prophase; middle prophase; late prophase; metaphase; anaphase; telophase; and the beginning of a new interphase stage in the two daughter cells. If prepared slides showing mitotic stages are available, see how many you can find, using high power of your microscope.

2. Construct an imaginary cell containing three pairs of chromosomes. Make each pair a different shape and color. Diagram a mitotic division by drawing lines from the mother cell to two daughter cells. Show the three pairs of chromosomes in each of the cells.

3. Using the cell you constructed in Question 2, diagram egg formation (oögenesis) and sperm formation (spermatogenesis). Show the chromosome content of all of the cells produced during the series of divisions.

4. Diagram a cross between two trihybrid guinea pigs with the genetic formula *BbRrSs*. The parents are black, rough-coated, short-haired guinea pigs, with black (*B*) dominant over white (*b*); rough (*R*) over smooth (*r*); and short hair (*S*) over long hair (*s*). Each parent can produce eight different types of eggs or sperm. Sixty-four squares will be needed to diagram all of the possible egg and sperm combinations. Tally all of the offspring into various groups on the basis of appearance.

5. Make a study of eye color of the members of your class. List such colors as brown, hazel, green, blue, etc. Tabulate all colors represented and determine ratios of occurrence of each color.

6. Bring in a pedigree, or registration paper, for a dog, a cat, a horse, or some other purebred animal. Examine the ancestry shown and explain why this is important. Explain how this information can be used in either line or cross-breeding.

MORE ABOUT BIOLOGY

Adler, Irving. *How Life Began.* John C. Day Co., Inc., New York. 1958

Auerbach, Charlotte. *Genetics in the Atomic Age.* Oxford University Press, Fair Lawn, N. J. 1956

Beaty, John Y. *Luther Burbank, Plant Wizard.* Julian Messner, Inc., New York. 1943

Darwin, Charles. *The Origin of the Species.* The New American Library of World Literature, Inc., New York. 1958

Fenton, Carroll L. *The Fossil Book: A Record of Prehistoric Life.* Doubleday and Co., Inc., New York. 1958

Glass, B. *Genes and Man.* Columbia University Press, New York. 1943

Goldschmidt, Richard B. *Understanding Heredity: An Introduction to Heredity.* John Wiley and Sons, Inc., New York. 1952

Goldstein, P. *Genetics Is Easy.* Lantern Press, Inc., New York. 1955

Hill, J. and Hill, H. *Genetics and Human Heredity.* McGraw-Hill Book Co., Inc., New York. 1955

Mendel, Gregor. *Experiments in Plant Hybridization.* Harvard University Press, Cambridge, Mass. 1941

Scheinfeld, Amram. *The New You and Heredity.* J. B. Lippincott Co., Philadelphia. 1951

Snyder, L. H. and David, P. R. *Principles of Heredity.* 5th ed. D. C. Heath and Co., Boston. 1957

Sootin, Harry. *Gregor Mendel: Father of the Science of Genetics.* Vanguard Press, Inc., New York. 1958

U. S. Dept. of Agriculture. *Better Plants and Animals.* Supt. of Documents, Govt. Printing Office, Washington, D. C. 1937

Safeguarding Our Natural Resources

And God pronounced His blessing on them, Increase and multiply and fill the earth, and make it yours; take command of the fishes in the sea, and all that flies through the air, and all the living things that move on the earth. . . . Here all that lives shall find its nourishment. — Gen. 1:28; Gen. 1:30

The prosperity of cities depends on productive farms and ranches. Agriculture springs from the soil. Isn't soil, then, the basis for the prosperity of a whole nation? Hence, soil conservation is vital to all of us. But good soil is essential not only for prosperous agriculture. Conserve the soil, and you control the major water problems. Productive soil also aids in conserving forests, which, in turn, shelter our wildlife.

An active program of total conservation is vital to the future of our nation. Regardless of the brilliance of our scientists, the wisdom of our statesmen, the ingenuity of our industrialists, and the skill of our workmen, our country cannot continue in its role as a leading nation with its soil exhausted, its forests leveled, and its wildlife destroyed.

Conservation is actually everybody's business — yours, your state's, and your nation's. We are charged with preserving our natural heritage — the land and all it contains.

CHAPTER 54: **CONSERVATION OF SOIL AND WATER**
CHAPTER 55: **FORESTS AND CONSERVATION**
CHAPTER 56: **WILDLIFE CONSERVATION**

CHAPTER 54

*C*onservation of
Soil and Water

W HEN the first settlers came to America, they found a land of almost unbelievable opportunity. Climate, geographical location, and soil were ideal for crop production. Trees in almost endless quantity were at hand to supply materials for building a new nation. The greatest problem was the clearing of the land for agriculture. For generations, man was pitted against nature. The eastern forests fell to the woodsman's ax. Trains of covered wagons bore pioneer families through the eastern forest lands, across the prairies and Great Plains, and finally across the Rocky Mountains to the Pacific Coast.

The soil was the basis of all our early prosperity. It produced forests and grasslands where game abounded. As planted crops replaced native stands of timber, the soil yielded its fertility to fields of grain and vegetables. Herds of cattle and flocks of sheep fattened on the rich grasses of the prairies and plains.

The land today. What is our land like today? Can our soil continue to support such a rapidly growing nation? Can it supply the demands of a nation in which the average citizen enjoys a standard of living far above that of inhabitants of any other country? Unless large-scale conservation measures are taken immediately, the answer to these questions is definitely no! Our soil can support us if we rebuild it more rapidly than we deplete it and restore the natural controls that prevent its removal. Our task in rebuilding the land is doubly hard today. We must not only guard against further depletion in our age, but must repair the damage caused by past generations.

Soil and where it comes from. Think of the earth as a gigantic ball of rock. Soil lies in a thin film on the surface of this great ball. Season after season, running water, freezing and thawing, wind, and other forces of nature crumble the

rocks and form gravel, sand, or clay. These materials become mineral soil, or **subsoil**. In most regions, the subsoil forms a layer several feet in thickness, representing thousands of years of the slow disintegration of rock.

The organic part of the soil comes from the slow decay of roots, stems, leaves, and other vegetable materials, and the remains of animals. We refer to the organic remains of land plants as **humus** (*hyoo-mus*), while sphagnum moss and other aquatic plants form **peat** in lakes and bogs.

A mixing of mineral matter from the subsoil and organic matter combine to form **topsoil**, or *loam*. Topsoil is the most vital part of soil, the nutritional zone of plants both large and small. It forms very slowly, at a rate of about one inch in 500 years.

Topsoil supports great numbers of bacteria, molds, and other fungi which we

671

refer to as the **soil flora.** Activities of the many soil organisms are essential to fertility of the soil. Decay, ammonia production, nitrate formation, and many other chemical processes condition topsoil for the growth of higher plants.

If you examine a soil profile along a bank or the side of a ditch, you can see the dark topsoil and the lighter subsoil below. Under natural conditions, a small quantity of topsoil washes away or is blown away each season. This is replaced by additional topsoil formed by decaying vegetation added to the upper surface. Thus, topsoil formation is a continuous process. Remember, however, that this is an extremely slow one.

The original topsoil in America averaged nine to ten inches in depth. Today it averages about five inches. When topsoil is gone, land becomes a desert. In other words, we are now within five inches of being a desert. The conservationist refers to this situation when he says we have lost half the battle to save our soil. Conservation of topsoil is an extremely serious problem, but it can be solved.

Various kinds of soil loss. In some cases, soil is deprived of its essential minerals through continued planting of agricultural crops. We refer to such mineral exhaustion as **depletion.** Often, water seeping through deeply cultivated soil carries the soluble minerals far below the topsoil. We refer to this loss of fertility as **leaching. Erosion** is loss of the entire topsoil, due to water or to wind. It is the most critical of all the forms of soil loss.

In discussing the various kinds of soil loss, we shall refer to **row crops** and **cover crops.** As the name indicates, *row crops* are planted in rows in cultivated fields. The soil lies exposed between the rows. Corn, beans, tobacco, and tomatoes are examples of row crops. Wheat, oats, rye, clover, alfalfa, and various grasses are grown as *cover crops.* Here, the close-growing plants form a dense mat of roots which bind the soil and an aerial cover which protects the soil surface from wind and water. The relation of row crops and cover crops to the soil is very important in soil conservation.

Depletion of soil minerals. A century ago, abundant fertile land was still available to anyone who would " go West " and claim it. The soil contained a rich store of minerals, accumulated through centuries of the growth and decay of native vegetation. Year after year, corn, cotton, and other field crops were grown in the same fields with little thought about the condition of the soil. *Overproduction* was the order of the day. The object seemed to be to produce as much as possible in as short a time as possible. After a few seasons, the loss of fertility began to show in the form of reduced crop yield. Rather than heeding this danger signal, many farmers pushed the land even harder. When the soil finally became exhausted, the field was abandoned for a new and more profitable area.

A scientific view of the mineral depletion problem. It stands to reason that agricultural crops with a high food value would draw heavily on soil minerals. The most critical of these minerals are nitrates, phosphates, and potash. In a natural cycle, plants draw minerals from the soil and organize them into the various parts of the plant body. When the plant dies, these are returned to the soil through the process of decay. But a crop plant is harvested for its food value. The minerals contained in the crop are removed from the soil permanently. This removal can continue only a few seasons before the soil shows evidence of depletion of the most heavily used minerals.

Soil which is badly depleted of minerals usually becomes acid, or sour. To cor-

Fig. 54-1. These two plots show the difference in corn growth that can occur from different soil treatment. The soil on the right was treated with nitrogen, while that on the left was left untreated.

rect this condition, the farmer uses lime. Other minerals are restored by heavy applications of commercial fertilizer, especially superphosphate. In addition to this rapid method of restoring minerals, the scientific farmer avoids depletion by practicing **crop rotation.**

Principles of crop rotation. Various crops differ in the minerals they take from the soil. Furthermore, some crops must be grown in rows, while others are grown as cover crops. Many farmers prevent mineral depletion as well as serious erosion by rotating crops in each growing area. Many rotation plans follow a three-year cycle. The first crop might be corn, followed by wheat or oats, then by grass or clover. Clover, alfalfa, cowpeas, lespedeza, and other legumes are important in a rotation cycle because they support nitrogen-fixing bacteria on their roots. As we mentioned in the discussion of the nitrogen cycle, these bacteria produce nitrates from atmospheric nitrogen.

Mineral depletion and health. Have you ever heard a doctor speak of " hidden hunger "? It could happen to you without your knowing it. We assume that vegetables, meats, and other foods contain certain nutrients and minerals essential in our diets. But did you know that one bunch of carrots may be rich in mineral content, while another which looks just the same may be largely cellulose and water? Which type they are depends on the soil where the carrots grew.

" Hidden hunger " is a kind of hunger you do not feel because you have eaten sufficient bulk. But your body cells are not satisfied because the food did not contain sufficient proteins and minerals.

The problem of leaching. Before a field is planted, it is plowed and disked, which turns the weeds under the soil and conditions it for planting. Rains soak into the pulverized soil easily. This process is ideal for young plants, but it may cause a serious problem, especially in loose sandy loam. If the soil is properly cared for, the topsoil should be rich in minerals. These minerals must be dissolved in water or plants cannot absorb them. As water runs through the topsoil, it dissolves minerals and carries them down below the reach of the roots of many crop plants. By such leaching action, valuable fertility is lost.

We have always assumed that frequent cultivation is good for crops. But this may not be true. Row crops especially leave much of the soil exposed to soaking rains. One method of reducing leaching is minimum cultivation. Another is the planting of cover crops between row crops. Deep-rooted crops, like alfalfa, absorb minerals from the subsoil and bring them into the plant body. If such a crop is turned under, the minerals are thus returned to the topsoil.

Loss of organic matter. In a natural environment, the organic matter present in topsoil decays slowly as it is acted upon by bacteria and other soil organisms. In time it would disappear entirely were it not for the leaves, roots, and other plant parts which are added to the soil each season. However, in an agricultural situation, when hay crops are harvested or when stalks of wheat or oats are used for straw, little organic matter is left to return to the soil. In some cases, weeds and native grasses are even burned off fields before plowing. This procedure is a waste of valuable organic matter which should be plowed into the soil.

If fields are cleared season after season,

the organic part of the topsoil may disappear to the extent that much of the soil flora dies out. When these organisms are gone, many of the processes necessary for maintaining soil fertility cease. There are several ways in which organic matter can be added to soil. One is the addition of manure and decayed straw. An even better method is sowing grass or clover in a field, then plowing it under.

Erosion, the loss of topsoil. Of all forms of soil loss, erosion is the most advanced and the most destructive. Precious topsoil from millions of acres of our most productive land now lies in riverbeds and ocean bottoms. Some has been blown thousands of miles in violent dust storms. This destruction is the tragic result of man's carelessness and shortsightedness.

Some erosion has always occurred. We refer to this slow blowing away or washing out of soil as *geologic erosion*. Before any land was cultivated, soil formation kept pace with this type of erosion. But when land was stripped of its natural vegetation and poor farming methods exposed it to forces of water and wind, *accelerated erosion*, a far more dangerous condition, began.

Much of the land which is badly eroded today was abandoned for agriculture when the minerals became depleted — a result of overcultivation. With the rapid expansion of agricultural industry, more and more areas were cultivated for crops. In eagerness to make every inch of land pay, many farmers began cultivating hillsides, river bottoms, and all other available locations rather than increasing yields from land already cultivated.

In hilly forest lands, where oak and hickory trees were thriving in shallow topsoil, native vegetation was cleared to make available more tillable ground. Such lands were excellent for forests but were

Fig. 54-2. Notice the areas in this photograph where the removal of thin layers of soil, the process called sheet erosion, has begun to occur.

U. S. Dept. of Agriculture

Fig. 54-3. The rills on this exposed hillside were caused by the continuous downward flow of water carrying particles of soil.

U. S. Dept. of Agriculture

Fig. 54-4. If left unchecked, severe gully erosion can result in the formation of a canyon, such as the one shown in this photograph.

U. S. Dept. of Agriculture

Fig. 54-5. In contour strip cropping, one crop is alternated with another in strips, and both follow the contours of the land. How does this practice aid in conserving the soil?

entirely unsuitable for crops. Soon they were abandoned to the ravages of erosion or were left for families to eke out an existence from a few patches of dwarfed corn and vegetables.

Water erosion. One form of water erosion, known as *sheet erosion*, occurs when water stands in a field during a flood, then flows away gradually. The water carries a thin layer of soil with it as it flows away. When the water is gone, the land is left at a level much nearer the sterile subsoil. A few such floods may leave the land totally worthless.

In rolling and hilly sections where the rain falls on exposed soil, raindrops carry with them particles of soil, forming tiny channels or rills as they trickle down the slope. This process is the beginning of *rill erosion*. Each time water flows down the slope, it follows the same rills. These deepen and widen much as a stream increases the size of its bed. A more advanced stage known as *gully erosion* may follow. If the gully isn't checked, it may in time become a canyon, like the one pictured in Fig. 54-4, page 675. This can be avoided even on cultivated hillsides when proper conservation methods are used.

Contour farming. When land is cultivated up and down a slope, the furrows act as man-made rills and start rill erosion. Each time it rains, water pours down the furrows and enlarges them. They can become gullies in a short time.

The solution to this problem is logical. Plow around the hill rather than up and down, a method called *contour farming*. When furrows are plowed around the slope, each one serves as a small dam to check the flow of water. Water stands in each furrow and then soaks into the ground. If this simple practice had been followed long ago, our lands today would be richer and our rivers deeper and clearer.

Strip cropping. The extremely valuable soil conservation practice of *strip cropping* frequently combines two important measures. Broad strips are cultivated on the contour of a slope for growing row crops such as corn, cotton, potatoes, or beans. These strips alternate with strips in which cover crops, such as wheat, oats, clover, alfalfa, or grass, are grown. These cover crops completely cover the surface of the soil and hold it

securely. As water runs from the strip of row crop, it is checked upon entering the strip of cover crop.

Frequently, clover is used as a cover crop. Nitrogen-fixing bacteria, associated with roots of clover, alfalfa, and other legumes, return the various nitrogen compounds to the soil. Strips may be alternated every few years with the result that water erosion is checked continually and fertility of the soil is maintained.

Terracing. *Terracing* is used extensively to check the flow of water on steeply sloping land. A long slope is broken into numerous short ones by forming a series of banks. A type of machine, the terracing grader, is used to form flat strips on the contour of the slope. Each strip is

Fig. 54-6.   Check dams, such as those shown here, are often used to control gully erosion.

U. S. Dept. of Agriculture

Fig. 54-7. These terraces were made with a special tractor-drawn plow and finished with a grader. Trees will be planted later in the terraced channels.

divided from another by a bank. Drainage ditches at the base of each bank conduct the water around the slope.

Gully control. When large gullies have already formed, measures other than those discussed previously must be used. One of these is planting the slopes of the gully with trees, grass, or other plants to act as soil binders and prevent further widening. Deepening may be prevented by building a series of small dams. The dams slow the flow of water and soil gradually fills the gully.

The problem of wind erosion. *Wind erosion* is a critical factor in western Texas, Kansas, and Oklahoma. The prevailing strong winds blow from the south, especially during the spring and summer months. Originally, native grasses and other plants bound the soil firmly in place with their extensive, shallow root systems. Much of this land was extremely fertile and suitable for growing cereal crops and, as a result, extensive areas were plowed for agriculture.

During the spring and early summer months the soil was moist enough to hold its place, but with the late summer drought the strong hot winds blew the dry topsoil away. Entire fields were covered with fine particles of topsoil carried in dense clouds during a dust storm. Abandoned fields added to the growing desert. The farmer who was fortunate enough to hold his soil in check was powerless to stop the tons of soil which blew onto his land from other areas. There was nothing left but to abandon the homestead with its half-buried houses and barns and join the procession of landowners out of the growing " Dust Bowl."

Control of wind erosion. Wind erosion is an especially difficult problem because it involves such large areas. Any local wind erosion control could be wiped out in a single dust storm. Consequently, these projects must be undertaken on a very large scale and with the aid of the state and national agencies. One such measure is the planting of windbreaks, or *shelterbelts.* Extensive experiments have been conducted to find trees which can be planted at intervals to break the force of the wind. In addition to windbreaks, plants are needed as soil binders. Every inch of exposed land not used regularly for crop production must be anchored firmly by the roots of grasses and other soil-binding plants.

When land is cultivated, furrows should be *plowed at right angles to the prevailing wind*. Thus the wind does not blow down the furrows, but blows across them. Each furrow helps to stop the movement of soil. In sections where **irrigation** is possible, diversion of water into the fields during dry periods will check wind erosion because moist soil does not blow.

Problems in administering soil conservation. In 1935 the United States Soil Conservation Service was established as part of the Soil Conservation Act. This agency became a permanent part of the Department of Agriculture. This division of the Department of Agriculture has embarked on an extensive program of soil conservation. Expert agricultural engineers are investigating all phases of the problem. They travel throughout the country studying various problems and offering aid where needed.

Farmers have the opportunity to examine demonstration farms where soil conservation measures are in operation. If the farmers of a community wish to use these methods on their farms, they must first form a local soil conservation district under local control. Engineers from the Soil Conservation Service will then cooperate with the local district in applying soil conservation methods to the problem.

Soil problems and water problems — a vicious cycle. Disastrous floods and droughts, the two extremes in water problems, are inevitable results of misuse of soil and its plant cover. Rains which should soak into the ground and supply plant roots during drier periods pour off the surface of eroded land in torrents. Streams flood with muddy water from nearby fields. Then there is too much water, but later in the season, plants may die for want of ground water lost during the floods. During floods, water washes soil away and the wind blows it away. Soil erosion, floods, and droughts — these

Fig. 54-8. The rows of trees shown in this photograph were planted as a shelterbelt to help prevent wasteful wind erosion.

U. S. Dept. of Agriculture

three disasters form a vicious circle. Yet if we solve the soil problems, we will help correct the water problem. The wide flood plains of the streams and rivers of the Mississippi River drainage basin indicate that high and low water stages have always occurred. Rivers of this enormous system drain the land from the Appalachian Mountains in the east to the Continental Divide in the Rocky Mountains.

Prolonged droughts and desert conditions are normal in some sections of the country, too, because of uneven distribution of rainfall. But the past few generations are responsible for the mistakes which increased these natural conditions to the proportions of major disasters.

The water cycle. The **water cycle** is a continuous movement of water from the atmosphere to the earth and from the earth to the atmosphere. The movement in the water cycle from the atmosphere to the earth is **precipitation.** Eventually this water will return to the atmosphere by **evaporation** (Fig. 54-9).

When it rains, some of the water evaporates while falling or evaporates quickly from the surface of the ground. Much of it runs off the surface of the ground and enters the drainage systems of rivulets, streams, and rivers. This **runoff water** eventually reaches a pond, lake, or the ocean where it is stored. Water also evaporates constantly from the surface of both the drainage systems and the storage basins.

A large amount of the precipitation normally enters the soil and becomes **ground water.** This water will reach drainage systems through springs or underground streams or it will move upward through the soil during dry periods and pass into the atmosphere as *water vapor*. Our greatest problem in water conservation is the reduction of the amount of runoff water, and at the same time an increase in the amount of ground water.

Precipitation. The water vapor which passes from the earth to the atmosphere collects as mist in clouds. As warm air containing water vapor rises through the atmosphere, it cools. The mist then condenses as drops of water. The drops fall from the clouds as *rain*. If they freeze in falling, they reach the earth as *sleet*. Sometimes strong updrafts force falling sleet upward so that layers of ice deposit around the frozen drops, resulting in *hail*. *Snow* is frozen and crystallized mist which falls gently to the earth.

Ground water. Topsoil acts as a sponge in receiving and holding water during precipitation. As the topsoil becomes saturated, water moves into the subsoil, where it is held around the rock particles and in soil spaces. Some of the water moves downward and reaches the **water table,** the point at which water is standing in the ground.

The depth of the water table depends on the amount of precipitation, the condition of the soil surface for receiving water, and the nature of the rock and clay layers under the soil. Where depressions occur, as in basins of lakes and ponds, the water table is above the surface.

In hilly regions, ground water may strike a shelf of rock and travel along it to the side of the hill. Here it emerges as a *spring*. **Dug wells** are holes which reach to the water table. As the water table lowers during dry spells, these wells can become dry. **Driven wells** reach water far below a point where there is danger of surface drainage, but they are quite expensive to drill.

Movement of ground water. Plants do not wilt between rains because water moves from the water table up through the soil. Much of this water is absorbed by roots and passed to the atmosphere during transpiration. Some of it reaches the surface of the soil and evaporates into the atmosphere. This movement of water

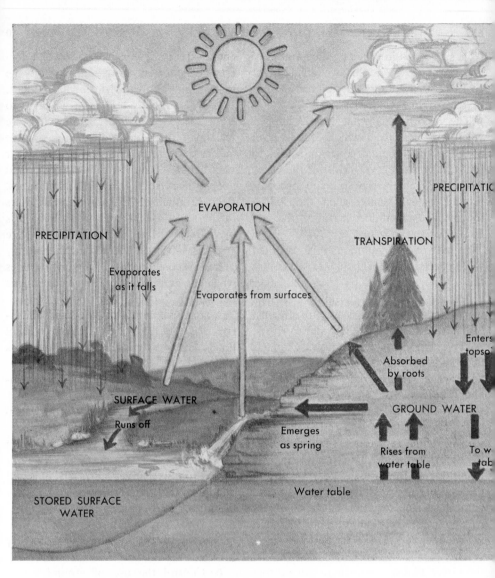

Fig. 54-9. Trace the steps in the water cycle as shown in the above diagram.

upward from the water table is an important part of the water cycle.

Depletion of ground water. The water table is lowering dangerously in many sections of the country, largely because of loss of water as runoff water during rainy periods and the increased use of ground water in cities. Numerous wells, necessary to supply drinking water, draw heavily on the supply of ground water. Industries require large quantities of water. Large cities must supplement their supply of ground water with treated surface water taken from rivers, lakes, and reservoirs.

In recent years, cities have tapped the supply of ground water heavily in supplying cold water for air-conditioning systems. After the water has been used to remove the heat in buildings, it enters the sewer system and adds to the amount of surface water. It cannot be returned to the ground from which it was taken.

Runoff water. The water problem in America can never be solved until we have succeeded in reducing the amount of runoff water. To do this, we must correct costly mistakes of the past and restore part of the original wilderness.

The following is what *should* happen when it rains. Rain which falls in level areas strikes the plant cover and drips to the surface of the soil. Most of the water which falls enters the soil and becomes ground water. Only when the soil is thoroughly soaked does it run off the surface or collect in pools.

In hilly and mountainous regions called **watersheds,** some of the water soaks into the topsoil, protected by trees and other vegetation. Much of it follows rivulets which lead down the slope to streams. Streams, in turn, carry the water to rivers. As rivers rise, water overflows channels and spreads into flood plains. Much flood water is received by sloughs and backwaters. As the crest of the flood passes, the flood plains feed water back to the channel. With the end of the rainy season, water is maintained in the river by the sloughs and backwaters and by numerous springs which feed streams in the watersheds. Thus the ground and natural surface reservoirs receive excess water during rainy periods and maintain the water supply during dry periods.

This condition is altered somewhat in the Great Plains where there are no forests or tall grasses to help hold water back during brief but heavy rainy periods. Flash floods and some soil loss cannot be avoided in these regions, which explains why De Soto saw muddy flood water in the Mississippi River. Much of this mud came from the Great Plains region. Farther east, the original tall grass prairies were dotted with sloughs and marshes during the rainy season.

But what *does* happen when it rains today? The spongy topsoil is gone in many regions. Rains pour onto hard subsoil clay, rush through deep gullies, and choke streams. In watersheds where forests have been cut away, nothing stops the rush of water downhill during flash floods. Rivers rise rapidly and have no place to store the excess water. Long ago we reclaimed their backwaters and swamps and extended our fields and cities to their very banks. Storm warnings go out and people flee from their lowland homes. Because much of our water supply roars to the sea, drought later in the season is inevitable. River channels which were swollen with flood waters during the rainy period become narrow, winding trickles when the rain stops. Crops bake in the fields.

Water conservation. We can summarize the measures necessary to control floods and prevent seasonal droughts as follows:

1. Control soil erosion and restore topsoil.

2. Restore forests, especially in watersheds.

3. Restore sloughs and backwaters along the rivers.

4. Prohibit cultivation of lowlands and flood plains of major rivers and restore the forests of these areas.

5. Build dams and reservoirs to hold back flood waters and store water for dry periods.

6. Control the use of ground water, especially in cities.

7. Maintain dikes and levees along major rivers. This measure, although the major flood control project in past years, is probably the least effective of all.

Dams and water power projects. As another means of controlling water, the government has constructed enormous dams in several sections of the country. These dams and the great reservoirs they form are important in preventing floods. In addition, they are the site of hydroelectric plants which use the water rushing over the dam to turn turbines attached to generators. In this way water power is converted into electricity for use in large areas of the nation. By raising the water level in the rivers, dams have made them navigable for long distances. In the west, water from reservoirs formed by dams is used for irrigation, and has made many semiarid regions ideal for crop production. Deep, clear lakes which lie above the dams are considered to be ideal recreation places for swimming, boating, and fishing.

In Conclusion

A soaking rain is a welcome sight to a farmer whose crops are flourishing in fertile fields. But to a family fleeing the flood waters of a river on a rampage, the sight of more rain only adds to their misery. It would seem that nature can be both kind and cruel. But when you examine our soil and water problems more closely, you discover that man cannot destroy nature's balance without paying a terrible price. Almost every dust storm, advancing gully, and disastrous flood is related somehow to man's carelessness or indifference. The forces of nature are powerful. They can produce a rich harvest or tremendous destruction. They can provide us with great wealth or great poverty.

Conservation is everybody's business. No nation can prosper on poor soil. Our economy depends on agriculture, and agriculture is geared to the water cycle.

BIOLOGICALLY SPEAKING

accelerated erosion	ground water	sheet erosion
contour farming	gully erosion	shelterbelt
cover crop	humus	soil flora
crop rotation	irrigation	strip cropping
depletion	leaching	subsoil
driven well	peat	terracing
dug well	precipitation	topsoil
erosion	rill erosion	water cycle
evaporation	row crop	water table
geologic erosion	runoff water	watershed

QUESTIONS FOR REVIEW

1. What are the several forces in nature which crumble rock and form subsoil?
2. From what sources are humus and peat formed?
3. Distinguish between depletion, leaching, and erosion. Mention the particular kinds of soil loss and the special cause of each.
4. Give several examples of row crops and cover crops.
5. How did overproduction in past years lead to soil depletion?
6. How can deep plowing and cultivation cause leaching, especially in sandy areas?
7. What are various methods of restoring organic matter to soil?

8. How can rill erosion lead to gully erosion?
9. Why are row crops alternated with cover crops in strip cropping?
10. In what kind of situation would terracing be used?
11. What are two methods of stopping the advance of a large gully?
12. What various methods can be used to prevent wind erosion? Can these be used in all parts of the country or are they adapted only to local situations?
13. Outline various phases of the water cycle.
14. List seven or more measures to reduce seasonal floods and prevent severe droughts.

APPLYING FACTS AND PRINCIPLES

1. Discuss the various parts of topsoil and their importance to plant life.
2. Outline a crop rotation program and explain why each crop is included.
3. How can loss of soil organic matter lead to the loss of another vital part of topsoil?
4. Discuss the combination of strip cropping, contour farming, and crop rotation in hilly agricultural areas.
5. Discuss various mistakes in past years which have led to disastrous floods and droughts. How do you think they might have been avoided?

CHAPTER 55

Forests and Conservation

AS you drive through many of our forest states, you may get the impression that timber trees are still abundant. The highways cut through grove after grove. And even in heavily farmed areas scattered woodlots and forested hillsides stretch across the horizon. But take a closer look. How far do unbroken forests extend from the highways? Do you still see extensive stands of large timber trees? How many trees are too small to cut or too crooked or damaged to be valuable as timber? How many are species which can never be used for saw logs or forest products? We have drawn heavily on our vast forest resources. Can our forests continue to meet the increased demands and still assure a supply of wood for the future? The idea of growing trees as a carefully regulated crop has been spreading rapidly in recent years. Foresters agree that we can produce all the wood we need if we get all of our forests under good management.

Some forest facts. The original forests covered nearly half our land — a total of more than 822 million acres. Forests occupied the eastern and western parts of our country. Prairies, plains, and arid lands covered much of the large central area.

The two great forest belts of the east and west were in turn divided into distinct types of forests. Then, as now, forests were greatly influenced by temperature, rainfall, soil, topography, and other physical factors of environment.

Today all of these same forest areas ex-

Fig. 55-1. These young pine trees are typical of the trees found in the forests of the Great Lakes region. Among the several different species of pine occurring here are red pine, white pine, and jack pine.

ist, although, for the most part, vigorous young second- and third-growth forests have replaced the original virgin stands. Let us take a brief trip into each forest area, so as to get a picture of the total forest lands of America.

Forest areas of America. Foresters divide our nation's forests as follows:

1. Northern forest
2. Central hardwood forest
3. Southern forest
4. Tropical forest
5. Rocky Mountain forest
6. Pacific Coastal forest

Northern forest. We shall begin our journey in the region of the Great Lakes and the St. Lawrence River Valley in the **northern forest.** This forest continues into Canada where it broadens out and extends from the Atlantic to the Pacific Ocean. It is the only forest extending across the entire continent. The Canadian section of the northern forest differs somewhat from the portion in the northern United States. However, both are dominated by evergreen (coniferous) trees. The Canadian forest consists largely of Canadian or white spruce, black spruce, and balsam fir. Foresters call this the **boreal** (*boh*-ree-al) **forest** to distinguish it from the *lake forest* region of the Great Lakes and the St. Lawrence River Valley.

The *lake forest* extends from Minnesota, through northern Wisconsin and Michigan, and northeast to Maine. Much of the lake forest grows on sandy soil. Here white pine, red or Norway pine, and jack pine grow in nearly pure stands and mingle with the spruce and fir of the

U. S. Dept. of Agriculture

Fig. 55-2.   This beautiful stand of loblolly pines is typical of those found in the southern forest.

Canadian forest.   Lakes and bogs are abundant in this forest area.   Their shores and the surrounding lowlands are often ringed with white cedar and larch, or tamarack.   In open places, the paper or canoe birch and aspen are abundant.   In more fertile soils, giant eastern hemlocks mingle with beech, maple, linden, yellow birch, and other hardwoods.   Northern hardwood forests would probably crowd out the pine in time if they were able to adapt themselves to the barren sandy soils of the area.

The *northern forest* has a long narrow arm which follows the mountain ridges from southeastern Canada, across the New England states, New York and Pennsylvania, through West Viriginia, Virginia, and North Carolina, to Tennessee and into northern Georgia.   At altitudes of from 3,000 to 5,000 feet, conifers mingle

with hardwood trees in a mixed forest. Among the conifers are white pine, hemlock, and red spruce.   Hardwood species are represented by red maple, oak, black gum, black birch, beech, linden, and yellow birch.   In the Allegheny Mountains of Pennsylvania, the wild black cherry, one of our most valuable hardwood trees, grows in great abundance.

Trees of the northern evergreen forest, especially the white pine, have supplied the nation and much of the world with highly valuable timber in past years and are one of our major sources of pulpwood.

Central hardwood forest.   Continuing southward from the lake forest, we enter one of the largest of forest areas.   It extends from the prairies west of the Mississippi River to the Atlantic Coastal states and from the lake forest nearly to the Gulf.   We call it the *central hardwood* forest. Most of the trees are *deciduous*. That is, most of the trees growing in it drop their leaves each fall.

The central hardwood forest area is a region of rich, deep soil for the most part. The climate is moderate. The rainfall averages about 40 to 50 inches each year. Trees towering more than 150 feet and with trunk diameters at eight feet or more were common in the original hardwood forest, especially in the Ohio River Valley. Among the many tree species found in this forest are the beech, oak, maple, buckeye, hickory, elm, ash, walnut, sycamore, cottonwood, tulip or yellow poplar, sweet or red gum, sour or black gum, and red cedar. Much of this forest was cleared early in our history because its soils were so fertile. Today, it is the center of very productive farmland.

Southern forest. The coastal plain extending from New Jersey to eastern Texas lies in a narrow belt along the Atlantic and Gulf Coasts. The sandy soils of the *southern forest* of this area support pine trees better than any other type. In the rich soils of the bottomlands and swamps, however, many commercially important deciduous, or hardwood trees, are found. The four principal species of pine which compose this forest are: (1) loblolly pine; (2) shortleaf pine; (3) longleaf pine; and (4) slash pine.

The leading hardwoods are black gum or tupelo, bald cypress, red and white oak, water oak, live oak, coast white cedar, willow, cottonwood, ash, and pecan. The bald cypress, a conifer which drops its needles each year, stands in the waters of swamps and backwaters. Farther north, along the river bottoms, the pin oak forms dense forests. The rich soils of the Mississippi River delta area have come down the large rivers draining the vast area between the Rocky Mountains and Appalachian ranges. Seasonal flood waters have added to these deposits for centuries.

The southern forest supplies more than a third of the nation's lumber and more than half its pulpwood. It also supplies nearly all of the nation's turpentine, rosin, and other by-products of the forest classified as *naval stores*.

Tropical forest. Farthest south is the smallest region, the **tropical forest**. It includes only the southern tip of Florida where mahogany, mangroves, and bay trees grow, and a small area in southeastern Texas in which no commercially important species grow.

Rocky Mountain forest. About half of the western forest belt occupies the slopes of the Rocky Mountain ranges and is called the **Rocky Mountain forest**. Deserts, sagebrush lands, and plains occupy the valleys between mountains while the mountains themselves support forests

Fig. 55-3. **Engelmann spruce, which is but one of many kinds of trees found in the Rocky Mountain forest, produces a valuable wood resembling white pine.**

U. S. Dept. of Agriculture

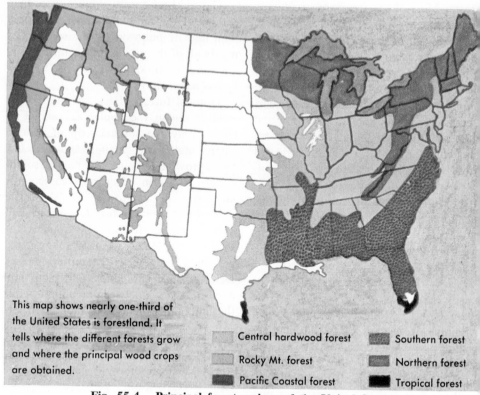

This map shows nearly one-third of the United States is forestland. It tells where the different forests grow and where the principal wood crops are obtained.

Central hardwood forest	Southern forest
Rocky Mt. forest	Northern forest
Pacific Coastal forest	Tropical forest

Fig. 55-4. Principal forest regions of the United States.

because of decreased temperature and increased rainfall due to elevation. The forests occupy definite zones, extending up the slopes to the tree line. Among the most prominent trees of the western forest are ponderosa pine, lodgepole pine, Engelmann spruce, Colorado spruce, Douglas fir, Idaho white pine, true firs, and aspen. Millions of tourists admire the beauty of the Rocky Mountain forest each year as they travel to national parks and other scenic areas.

Pacific Coastal forest. The most beautiful of all evergreen forests extends along the Pacific Coast from middle California to Alaska and is called the *Pacific Coastal forest.* This forest grows along the western slopes of the Cascades and on the coastal ranges. Here, clouds hang low and moisture-laden breezes blow in from the Pacific Ocean. The annual rain-

fall is more than 100 inches. The most famous trees of this magnificent forest are the tall redwoods found in a narrow belt along the northwest coast of California. Along the west slopes of the mountains in eastern California and Oregon are majestic pine forests in distinct ecological zones. Lodgepole pines form high altitude stands. At lower altitudes are forests of sugar pine, then ponderosa pine, followed by digger pine.

In separated groves at elevations of from 5,000 to 8,000 feet grow the giant sequoias, or "big trees," many of which are 4,000 to 5,000 years old and are the largest trees in the United States. Farther north, the Douglas fir, western red cedar, western hemlock, western larch, Idaho white pine, and true firs form the towering forests of Oregon and Washington. The Sitka spruce and western hemlock follow the coastal region to the far north, where they form dense forests in Canada and Alaska.

All these forests have contributed greatly to the building of America. The varied trees which form them have supplied wood for nearly every purpose. They constitute a major part of the natural heritage of America.

Lumber, our chief forest product. The greatest drain on the forests has been the demand for construction lumber. Once it was for log cabins and rail fences. Later, it was lumber for frame buildings. Even in this age of brick and stone buildings, four out of every five homes are still made of wood. Regardless of the exterior building material, the average home uses 10,000 board feet of lumber for flooring, trim, window casings, and other wooden construction parts.

The evergreen forests supply most of the construction lumber today because of the fact that our commercial forests have always contained more softwoods than hardwoods and also because of the ease with which the soft wood of conifers can be worked.

The most important timber trees now supplying lumber are given in the table on page 690.

Lumber for furniture. Much of the supply of hardwood timber now goes to the furniture industry. Among some of the hardwood trees supplying lumber for making furniture are: red gum, oak (white and red), maple (sugar, or rock), black walnut, wild black cherry, and birch. Mahogany is imported from the tropics. Rising production costs have increased the cost of furniture made of solid wood to the point that veneer finish

Fig. 55-5. This scene of a paper-pulp mill gives some idea of the tremendous quantities of lumber used in the manufacture of paper. After being cut, the logs are floated to the mill and stored in large piles.

Ray from Shostal

IMPORTANT TIMBER TREES

NAME OF TREE	FOREST REGION
Southern pine { loblolly, slash, shortleaf, longleaf	Southern forest
Douglas fir	Pacific Coastal forest
Ponderosa pine	Rocky Mountain forest
Oak	Central hardwood forest
Hemlock (eastern and western)	Northern and Pacific Coastal forest
Eastern white pine	Northern forest
Red Gum	Central hardwood and Southern forest
White fir	Rocky Mountain and Pacific Coastal forest
Poplar	Central hardwood and Southern forest
Maple	Northern forest and Central hardwood forest
Redwood	Pacific Coastal forest
Tupelo	Southern forest and Central hardwood forest
Spruce	Northern forest
Cottonwood and aspen	Northern forest and Rocky Mountain forest
Cedar	Pacific Coastal, Northern, and Southern forest
Sugar pine	Pacific Coastal forest
Beech	Northern and Central hardwood forest
Western larch	Rocky Mountain and Pacific Coastal forest
Idaho white pine	Rocky Mountain and Pacific Coastal forest
Cypress	Southern forest
Birch	Northern forest
Lodgepole pine	Rocky Mountain forest
Balsam fir	Northern forest

furniture is now much more popular. Less expensive furniture can be constructed of other wood, then covered with a layer of veneer.

Veneer is made by peeling a thin layer of wood from a hardwood log. The expensive wood shows on the surface, but is not used in the basic construction. Radio and television cabinets, pianos, and other pieces of furniture have beautiful grain designs produced by matching pieces of veneer.

Transportation and communication. Early in the history of our country, vast quantities of trees were used to build wooden ships and provide naval stores. The decks and planking of " Old Iron-sides," now anchored in Boston harbor, are native oak. But even though the wooden ships are gone, transportation and communication industries still need an enormous amount of timber.

Have you ever thought about how much wood our railroads use? There are about 3,000 crossties in a mile of track. Crossties have to be replaced as often as once in five to nine years. At this rate, railroads use an average of 40 million crossties each year. Add to this the wood used to construct and repair the countless buildings along the right-of-way. Then consider the wood used in certain freight-car construction.

Communication depends to a great exent on the countless telephone poles which run across the nation. An entire tree is required for a single pole. In the case of high-voltage lines, trees of great size are needed. The tall straight trunks of the spruce, fir, pine, and white cedar are ideal for use as telephone poles.

Newsprint for your daily paper. A single daily newspaper publisher in New York needs the paper produced from the **pulpwood** from 44 acres of timberland to print a single edition! When you consider the number of daily newspapers in the nation, the timber required for a day's supply of newsprint is almost staggering. In addition to newsprint, high quality book paper, stationery, packaging paper, toweling, and a great many other kinds of paper must be supplied daily.

Distillation products. Various hardwoods yield valuable products as a result of distillation. When certain kinds of wood are heated in closed iron cylinders, various products are given off as vapors. These vapors are condensed by cooling into a variety of substances called *distillation products*. The wood turns black during distillation and becomes carbon or charcoal. Some of the products of hardwood distillation include: wood alcohol, used as a solvent; acetic acid; lampblack, used in making certain inks; paints and varnishes; oxalic acid, used for dyeing and bleaching; and charcoal, used as a fuel and in water purification.

Beech, maple, and birch are commonly used in hardwood distillation. For this reason, the distillation industry centers are in Wisconsin, Michigan, Ohio, Pennsylvania, and New York.

Pine products. The South, as a region, leads the nation in the production of pine products. The fast-growing pines of the southeastern evergreen forest supply nearly two-fifths of our nation's lumber. Nearly half the pulpwood used in making paper comes from this productive forest.

Turpentine, rosin, and pine tar are products of southern pines. When certain species of pine are tapped, they yield a large quantity of **resin,** a thick gummy sap. Resin is removed from the trees by cutting diagonal gashes through the bark into the wood. Resin is collected in jars or pots. When the resin is boiled, *turpentine* comes off as a vapor. It is condensed to liquid form by cooling. After extraction of turpentine, tar and **rosin** remain. Do not confuse *pine tar* with the asphalt tar we use on streets and roofs.

Rosin has many uses. You've probably seen a baseball pitcher reach for the rosin bag or a batter dust rosin onto the bat handle.

Maple sugar. *Maple sugar* is an important product of Vermont, New York, Ohio, and other states of the northern

Fig. 55-6. This man is shown using an acid gun to stimulate resin flow from the new cut on the face of a pine tree that is being prepared for turpentining.

U. S. Dept. of Agriculture

region of the deciduous forest. Maple sugar comes from the sap of the sugar maple tree, which is collected in buckets attached to tapped trees in the early spring. The sap is boiled to remove the water, and it becomes a thick syrup.

Tanning materials. The tanning industry depends on the forests of the world for bark containing *tannic acid,* which is used in the tanning of hides. Chestnut wood, chestnut oak bark, eastern hemlock bark, and tanbark oak are the chief American sources. About 70 per cent of the nation's tanning supply comes from foreign woods, however. The tanning industry is centered mostly in the lake states, Appalachian, and northeast forest regions.

Control of the water supply. The forest area acts like a sponge by absorbing the rainfall in its layers of humus. The leaves of trees keep the rain from falling directly on the soil and washing it away. The network of roots binds the soil, and the deep layers of humus hold water, so that there is a gradual runoff of soil water rather than a flash flood.

Forested land helps to control the water supply in the following ways:

(1) Prevents floods and causes steady stream flow by reserve water held in humus; (2) prevents spring freshets by shading snow so that it melts slower; (3) prevents drought by storing water in the wet season; and (4) prevents washing of soil into rivers.

Benefits to soil. The early settlers regarded the forests as an enemy to agriculture because clearing had to be made to make room for farms. But in a larger sense, forests are a distinct benefit to soil. Erosion — the washing away of soil by rain — is one of the worst enemies of agriculture. But it is prevented by forests whose roots hold back the earth and whose leaves protect the surface. Furthermore, the humus which collects on the forest floor enriches the soil.

In some areas, the forest performs another function by preventing the spread of wind-blown sand over fertile areas which are thus saved for use.

Effect of forests on climate. While the effect of forests on climate may not rank in importance with the two preceding benefits, it is certain that by their retention of moisture, forests modify the climate over large areas and apparently influence rainfall. To a lesser extent forests affect climate by giving protection from wind and sun.

Homes for birds and animals. Forests supply shelter, homes, and food for a great many birds and animals which are of direct importance to man. Many valuable birds seek the shelter of forest trees for nests, and feed on the wild fruit and berries which grow there. Fur-bearing animals, like the raccoon, opossum, and squirrel, depend on the forest for food and cover. Forest streams supply cool clear water for many varieties of game fish, as well as smaller aquatic animals such as frogs and salamanders. Destruction of a forest destroys the entire woodland society of life. The loss of these forest birds and animals is nearly as tragic as the loss of the trees themselves.

Forests — their use and misuse. More and more Americans are learning to regard forests as a crop. We are learning to harvest trees when mature and to leave seed sources to replace them as they are used. Our forest lands could have supplied all the timber required for building America without their being seriously depleted if they had been used wisely. Instead, they were destroyed by a rapidly growing nation with little regard for the future.

As early as 1905 officials in Washington, among them President Theodore Roosevelt, became alarmed about the critical condition of the forests. Accordingly, Congress created the United States

Fig. 55-7. The piles of sawdust and limbs of trees in the above lumbering scene are a potential fire hazard unless they are removed, as companies now demand be done when the men have finished their cutting.

Forest Service under the control of the Department of Agriculture. When Theodore Roosevelt signed the act creating this agency on February 1, 1905, the forest conservation movement in America was begun. Vast tracts of timber, especially in the West, were set aside as national forests.

The United States Forest Service has built a splendid record through its years of activity. State and local agencies of conservation have looked to this agency for guidance and assistance in carrying out forest conservation programs. A well-trained staff of foresters works untiringly in research laboratories in an effort to discover better conservation methods, controls for forest diseases, more efficient lumbering practices, and new uses for timber products. Even more remarkable are the changes which have come on privately owned forest lands. Since it has

become possible to manage forests properly and still make a financial profit, forestry has been spreading rapidly. More professional foresters are hired by forest industries today than by the federal government. No small task in both the administration of the national forests and the management of millions of acres of private woodlands is the protection of these valuable timberlands from fire.

Fire — the forest's worst enemy. In a recent year, 83,392 fires burned over 3,409,038 acres of forest in the continental United States. This is a staggering loss to our nation. Fire protection has been extended to more and more forest areas in recent years, but as late as 1959, about 39,000,000 acres still lacked organized fire protection.

Aside from the danger to human life, a forest fire destroys standing timber and consumes the seeds and young trees of

MAJOR CAUSES OF FOREST FIRES

U. S. Forest Products Industries

Fig. 55-8.   Notice that natural causes constitute a relatively minor percentage of all the causes of forest fires.

the future forest. A large fire may even burn into the rich humus of the forest floor. The toll of animal life cannot be determined. Disaster continues as rains pour over the blackened earth and debris, washing the remaining humus into streams.

Causes of forest fires. According to reports of the United States Forest Service in recent years, the following are the most common causes of forest fires. The causes are listed in the order of frequency:

1. Incendiarists (those who set fires deliberately).

2. Debris burners (those who let brush fires get out of control).

3. Smokers (especially those who throw lighted cigarettes, cigars, and matches from automobiles).

4. Lightning.

5. Campers (especially those who leave live coals in a campfire).

6. Railroads.

7. Lumbering.

8. Miscellaneous.

It is shocking to learn that incendiarists are the leading cause of forest fires. Fires resulting from debris burners and smokers could be avoided if people were more careful and considerate of others. Lightning, the only natural cause, is responsible for less than 15 per cent of the forest fires a year (Fig. 55-8).

Fire prevention. In protected forests, fire towers are placed at strategic points. Usually all areas of the forest are visible from at least two towers. Trained rangers survey the forest from the towers and re-

port any evidence of fire to headquarters. A ranger cannot determine the exact distance of a fire from his tower, but he can report its direction. The same fire, spotted from another tower, will be reported from another angle. The point where the two lines of direction cross indicates the exact location of the fire. Fire fighters equipped with trucks, water tanks, and chemical fire extinguishers can often bring a fire under control before it becomes extensive. *Fire lines,* which resemble roads, penetrate the forest at regular intervals. They serve as avenues for reaching a fire and provide gaps at which a fire can be stopped. In some places, however, fires can be reached only by dropping fire-fighting crews from airplanes by parachute.

Our forests are protected from fire at a risk of many lives and at a cost of millions of dollars. It would seem a simple matter for all of us to cooperate in observing these simple rules in forest areas:

Fig. 55-9. Fire towers, set up in forest areas, enable forest rangers to locate fires before they have a chance to become too widespread.

Fig. 55-10. The men shown are preparing a fire line, which will be used both as a means of reaching a fire and as a gap to help stop it.

McPhearson from Monkmeyer

U. S. Dept. of Agriculture

U. S. Dept. of Agriculture

Fig. 55-11. Chestnut blight, the fungus that has destroyed the tree shown, has destroyed nearly all our American chestnut trees.

1. Never throw away lighted tobacco or matches.

2. Build campfires only in protected areas and *put the fire out completely*.

3. Watch for fire while driving through a forest. If you see a small one, stop and put it out. If the fire is too large to extinguish by yourself, report it at once.

4. Report any suspicious person attempting to start a fire.

5. Never burn a field or debris close to a forest or without adequate help to keep the fire from spreading.

6. Become acquainted with your state's forest-fire laws.

7. Get to know your nearest fire warden or foresters.

Insect enemies. In our study of insects we mentioned the damage some of them cause to trees. The saw flies, bark beetles, spruce budworm, woodboring beetles, western pine beetle, white pine

weevil, gypsy moth, hemlock looper, browntail moth, pine shoot moth, tent caterpillar, and tussock moth are among the worst forest pests. Sprays containing DDT and other powerful insecticides are effective against these pests. However, it is difficult to spray an extensive forest. We must depend principally on control by natural enemies of these insects.

Birds are valuable although assistance is rendered also by frogs, toads, snakes, ichneumon flies, and other insect destroyers.

Nearly all of the American chestnut trees still standing in our forests are dead. Not many years ago, these were common and valuable timber trees of the Northeast, Appalachian, and Ohio Valley regions. The chestnut tree fell victim to a blight, introduced accidentally from Asia in 1892. However, the wood of the dead trees is still being harvested for tannin extraction. Disease-resistant crosses of American and Chinese chestnut trees have been developed which show promise of restoring chestnuts to the American forest.

Dutch elm disease is also spreading through the Middle West. The only hope of saving this elm and several other species is control of a bark beetle which carries the disease. Such control cannot be done on a large scale. Individual infected trees must be cut down as soon as the disease has been diagnosed.

We mentioned the white pine blister rust when studying the fungi. This serious disease can be controlled by destroying the wild currant and gooseberry, since the rust alternates between these plants and the white pine.

A disease first diagnosed and classified in 1942 as *oak wilt* has now spread from Wisconsin to several surrounding states as far east as Pennsylvania and south to Arkansas. If left uncontrolled, it threatens to destroy all our great oak forests, sources of some of our most valuable wood. Recent research indicates, however, that a program of thorough identification and destruction of infested trees would bring it under control.

We depend on foresters and other specialists in the laboratories of the United States Forest Service, state forestry departments, universities, and private laboratories to find answers to the insect and disease problems.

Grazing and gnawing animals. In many of the deciduous forest states, pasturing is the greatest forest enemy. Pasturing of cattle, horses, sheep, or hogs in wood lots will completely destroy the trees in time. First, the animals eat or trample the young trees and reduce the woods to an open grove. Later they destroy the leaves on the lower limbs and injure roots and trunks. Aside from shelter, the animals receive very little value from a woods pasture. Trees and other plants of the forest are high in cellulose but very low in protein — an essential substance for the production of flesh and milk.

Weather conditions. Wind, ice, and snow are beyond our power to control. However, damage done to forests by natural forces should receive attention. Broken limbs open a tree to attack by fungus diseases and insect pests. Forest litter resulting from ice storms creates a fire hazard and should be cleared out regularly.

Reforestation. The return of a forest to an open area is a slow process. **Reforestation** is a lengthy and costly process, but it is a vital part of the conservation program. Large sections, useless for agriculture, have been cleared unwisely in past years. These regions, as well as eroded, heavily lumbered, and burned-out areas, should be returned to trees as rapidly as possible.

The various forest states, the United States Forest Service, and many private lumber and paper companies maintain large nurseries where seedlings of timber species are grown. Private landowners of nearly 48 million acres of forest land in 45 states are growing trees as a crop in the Tree Farm Program. Some associations of wood-using industries now grow their own seedlings and give them free of charge to forest landowners in their operating areas. Pine is being used in reforestation of many hardwood forest regions because it matures rapidly and yields valuable construction lumber.

Forest management. How valuable is a virgin forest? You may be surprised to learn that it is not as valuable as a planted and second-growth, managed forest. A virgin forest is always dominated by large, overripe trees. They have occupied their places for centuries — long past their period of rapid growth, and many of them are dying at the top. Some have been damaged by storms and are liable to attack by disease and insect pests. Much of the forest space is occupied by trees which have no commercial timber value. Other trees have grown crooked in their race for light. The floor is littered with fallen trees in various stages of decomposition.

Compare this forest with a managed forest, operated on a **sustained yield** basis. A forest so planned will yield trees for cutting regularly. All the trees are valuable timber species. Weed trees, damaged trees, crowded trees, crooked trees, and diseased trees are removed in **improvement cutting.** As timber trees mature, they are removed by **selective cutting.** The forest is a source of constant revenue to the owner and yet is never cut extensively. Every inch of space produces good timber, and every tree is a nearly perfect specimen.

Today, all national forests are using good cutting practices. Furthermore, the private owners that belong to the Tree

Weyerhauser Timber Co.

Fig. 55-12. The group of trees left standing will reseed the block of land around it from which trees have been harvested.

Farm Program mentioned above have pledged their cooperation.

Block cutting is another kind of lumbering used in stands of timber in which all the trees are about the same age. In such a case it is desirable to cut out a complete block and reseed it or replant it. In block cutting, stands of timber are left around the block for natural reseeding and protection of the exposed land. When small trees are established, another block can be cut. This method of lumbering is used in extensive stands of Douglas fir and a modified method called " strip cutting " is used in harvesting of spruce.

National parks and national forests. The six million acres of forest in the 29 national parks are to be preserved forever. They are part of game preserves and recreational areas dedicated to those who seek undisturbed natural beauty.

In addition, there are 149 national forests covering more than 181 million acres. The national forests supply timber for about 12 per cent of the nation's forest products. In addition, they supply homes for wildlife and aid greatly in restoring birds and animals which have been reduced in number in past years. During summer months, when drought strikes the Great Plains, they are opened to cattle and sheep as grazing areas under supervision. In addition, they are *recreational areas* which attract campers and sportsmen who fish in their lakes and streams.

In Conclusion

What will be the condition of tomorrow's forests? Will future generations be forced to find substitutes for wood and wood products because the forests were destroyed before their time? Or is there hope that the America of future years will receive a rich heritage in forest resources because our generations corrected the costly mistakes of the past?

The virgin forests of pioneer days will never be restored. But in their places even better forests are already producing crop after crop of trees. They are protected from fire and disease and are being scientifically managed to yield the maximum timber production. As this scientific management increases and spreads to all of our forests, our future wood supply will be assured. Little space will be wasted with over-age giants, diseased and injured trees, or species with low economic value. Trees will be a crop to be harvested when they are mature. Cutting will be a continuous process. At no time will the forest be completely destroyed.

Forestry today is a highly specialized science. Forest management and conservation is its most important business.

BIOLOGICALLY SPEAKING

block cutting	northern forest	selective cutting
boreal forest	Pacific Coastal forest	southern forest
central hardwood forest	pine tar	sustained yield
distillation products	pulpwood	tannic acid
fire line	reforestation	tropical forest
improvement cutting	resin	turpentine
lake forest	Rocky Mountain forest	veneer
maple sugar	rosin	

QUESTIONS FOR REVIEW

1. What are the forest areas of America?
2. (a) List at least ten valuable timber trees. (b) From what forests regions do we get each species?
3. How do the railroads make various uses of lumber?
4. Name several products of the distillation of hardwoods.
5. (a) List the principal products of pine resin. (b) What forest region supplies nearly all of these products?
6. What are some of the trees which supply bark for the tanning industry?
7. In what respects are forests essential to wildlife?

8. (a) What are the various causes of forest fires? (b) Indicate which ones are deliberate, the result of carelessness, or unavoidable. (c) How can forest fires be prevented?
9. How can two forest rangers, viewing a fire from towers, pinpoint the location of the fire?
10. List several of the worst insect enemies of forest trees.
11. What types of trees are removed from a managed forest during improvement cutting?
12. Under what conditions are whole sections of a forest cleared by block cutting?

APPLYING FACTS AND PRINCIPLES

1. The climate of the lake forest and southern forest regions is ideal for broadleaved trees. Yet, these areas support pine forests, for the most part. Account for this paradox.
2. Explain why the soil of the lower Mississippi region is different from the coastal plain areas to the east and to the west.
3. The largest conifers in the world grow in the Pacific Coastal forest. What

conditions in this forest area are responsible for these enormous trees?
4. Much of the forest wealth of our nation was wasted in past years. Find out various ways in which forests have been destroyed needlessly and discuss these.
5. Discuss the scientifically managed forest operated on a sustained yield basis and show how this forest is more productive than a virgin forest.

CHAPTER 56

Wildlife Conservation

W HEN the pioneers pushed westward through the North American wilderness, they found abundant wildlife at every turn. Inland waters teemed with fish, birds, and aquatic mammals. Large and small game roamed the forest and grassland. The woods bison, now extinct, lived in the forests as far east as New York State. Its western cousin, the plains bison (buffalo), thundered across the grasslands in herds numbering tens of thousands. The whitetailed deer thrived in millions of acres of forest lands and supplied the early settlers with both meat and buckskin. The wildcat and cougar (mountain lion), timber wolf and fox, beaver and muskrat, weasel and mink were some of the mammals of the wilderness.

As the settlers began their conquest of the wilderness, wildlife began its slow retreat. What caused this gradual decline? Was it the rifles of the pioneers? Was it the trapper or the market hunter? All these have been factors, but none has played a principal role. Silt and poisoned water, drained marshes and leveled forests did their damage as well. There was useless destruction of vast areas of natural habitat — areas man really did not need and should have left to the native wildlife.

We learned our lesson a few years ago. Deer now roam the forests of many states that had exterminated their native deer a century ago. Raccoons, opossums, squirrels, skunks, and many other small mammals are multiplying in every wilderness that is left to them within their natural ranges.

Can wildlife flourish in 20th-century America with its sprawling cities and vast agricultural lands? It can and will if we give it a chance. Conservationists are showing us how.

Divisions of wildlife. The term *wildlife* includes all native animals. However, the wildlife conservation program is concerned primarily with those native animals which have a direct food, fur, or sporting value. Divisions of wildlife include:

1. Fish, especially fresh-water game and food fish.

2. Birds, including our many song birds of forest, field, yard, and park.

3. Waterfowl, including ducks, geese, and wading birds.

4. Upland game birds.

5. Smaller game mammals with food, fur, and sporting value.

6. Big-game mammals.

Since management problems in each of these divisions differ, we shall consider each one separately.

Fish conservation. We often hear that a stream or a lake is "fished out." It would probably be more correct to say that a body of water is no longer suitable for a fish population. More rigid laws regulating fishing are not the solution, nor will restocking help in many cases. Give the fish the proper environment and they will hold their own and even increase in heavily fished streams and lakes.

In the study of fish conservation, we must first find out the characteristics of productive waters. Then we shall consider various practices which destroy fish

Fig. 56-1. A lake with vegetation such as this provides a spawning ground and a place for fry to grow.

and make waters unproductive. Finally, we shall discuss conservation measures which can restore ideal habitats and return the fish to our waters.

Characteristics of a productive lake and stream. A lake which supports a thriving fish population must supply many different environments suitable for large species and smaller ones, frogs, insects, and other vital parts of a complicated society and food chain. Deep channels and holes are necessary to protect fish during both the cold of winter and the extreme heat of summer. The depth at which fish live varies greatly with water temperature. During the spawning season, sunfish, bass, and many other species leave the deep water and enter clear, shallow pools and backwaters. Here the *fry* hatch and live protected by water plants in shallow areas.

Protozoa, tiny crustaceans, and larvae of various insects supply food necessary for small fish. As the smaller fish leave the shallow water and enter deep water,

they become food for predatory **game fish** such as the bass, pike, trout, and perch. **Forage fish,** including such species as shiners, chubs, and other minnows, while they have no sport or food value for man, are vital as a food for the game fish.

The productive stream has rapids and riffles, shallows and depths, channels and undercut banks. Larger rivers are fed from productive backwaters. Fallen logs and driftwood provide ideal habitats for many species. Abundant water plants are necessary to oxygenate the water, provide food for vegetarian fish and other aquatic animals, and supply the organic matter required by bacteria, protozoans, and organisms essential in the food chain.

Destruction of aquatic habitats. Many practices, some careless and others deliberate, have destroyed aquatic habitats. In regions where the water table has been lowered by removal of vegetation, soil erosion, and other misuse of the land and water resources, the level of lakes and ponds has fallen. Small ponds may dry out completely during the summer. The water in larger lakes may recede to the point that shallow areas and backwaters are left dry, thus destroying both spawning areas and regions where much of the food supply develops. In many cases, backwaters and marshes have been drained deliberately because they were thought to be useless wasteland.

The channels of many rivers have been dredged and straightened to increase the flow of water. Such open channels may be good from the standpoint of flood control, but they are not good surroundings for fish. Fish thrive better in a river with natural bends, rapids, and deep pools.

Dams across rivers interfere with fish migrations unless fish ladders are provided. A **fish ladder** is a channel around a dam through which fish can travel upstream. The fast flow of water is broken by a series of staggered plates projecting into the water from the sides. In other fish ladders, a long slope is broken into a series of steps like terraces, which can be leaped by fish traveling upstream.

Serious floods are tragic, not only to man, but to fish and aquatic animals as well. When flood waters overflow the lowlands, many fish follow the rising water. Large numbers are left stranded in isolated pools when the waters recede.

Water unfit for fish. Many game fish cannot survive in water containing a large amount of mud and silt. Mud coats the surface of the gill filaments and prevents oxygen from reaching the blood stream. This type of suffocation is common in species with a high oxygen requirement.

Sewage, garbage, cannery waste, and other organic refuse dumped into water kill fish for another reason. Organic matter decays in water as a result of bacterial action. Oxygen is used during this process and fish die for want of it in the water.

Fig. 56-2. The dead fish shown here could not survive in the water because it was polluted with sewage.

Del Vecchio from Washington Post

Industrial and chemical wastes poured into streams poison fish and other aquatic animals. Cyanide, acids, alkalies, and other industrial wastes may affect the stream's inhabitants for many miles downstream.

Hatchery programs. Both state and federal fish hatcheries produce large numbers of game fish in their rearing ponds. The hatcheries maintain a stock of adult breeders which are kept in special spawning pools. After spawning, the breeder fish are removed to prevent destruction of the small fish. Fry hatched in late spring reach stocking size by midsummer or early fall. Many hatcheries use special trucks equipped with aerated tanks for transporting small fish to distant streams and lakes.

Artificial propagation and stocking are essential parts of fish conservation programs. However, it is useless to stock polluted waters or those that lack conditions necessary to supply adequate food.

Private rearing ponds and lakes. Many farmers have constructed earthen ponds in low corners of fields by building up banks. These *farm ponds* are stocked with crappies, bluegills, catfish, and other species. The pond provides recreation,

Haddon from U. S. Fish and Wildlife Service

Fig. 56-3. These young bass are being sorted for size in a federal fish hatchery. Those that are large enough will be removed and used for stocking lakes and streams.

Fig. 56-4. Farmers frequently construct ponds on their land, such as the one shown below. List the purposes that these ponds serve.

U. S. Dept. of Agriculture

Fig. 56-5.   Fish ladders constructed around dams enable fish to travel upstream during the spawning season.

conserves water, helps prevent soil erosion, and supplies many strings of fish for the dinner table.

Great numbers of artificial lakes have been made by building dams and backing up water in valleys.   Lakes of this type are ideal for fishing and boating.

Laws protecting fish.   While laws governing fishing vary in different states, they usually contain the following provisions:

1. Closed seasons for certain species, usually during the spawning season.

2. Length limit, or a size under which a fish may not be kept.

3. Bag limit, or a limit to the number of individuals of a given species a person can take in a single day.

4. Possession limit, or the number of a species a person may have in his possession from several days' catch.

5. Laws prohibiting the use of explosives or the draining of ponds to kill fish.

6. Restriction as to the size, mesh diameter, and use of nets or mechanical traps.

7. Laws prohibiting or restricting the spearing of fish.

8. Laws requiring the construction of fish ladders at dams.

9. Laws prohibiting the dumping of chemical wastes and other polluting materials into streams, rivers, and lakes.

10. Laws requiring the purchase of a fishing license for use on inland waterways.

Importance of fishing.   You might think that one of the best ways to conserve fish is to prohibit fishing, but it is not.   A small lake or pond, especially, should be fished regularly to remove large fish and make food supply and space for new crops, and to prevent the fish population from growing beyond the available food supply.

Useless destruction of valuable allies, the birds.   The advancing tide of civilization has made dangerous inroads into the population of song birds and game birds. Much of this destruction is useless and avoidable.

The cutting of forests, clearing of underbrush and burning of fields have removed vast areas of bird homes. Unnecessary drainage of marshes and lowering of the water in ponds and lakes have deprived water birds and wading birds of both food and nesting sites.

In former years many thousands of birds were slaughtered for flesh or feathers. Fortunately, such **market hunting** is forbidden now, both by federal and state laws. But conservation measures came too late to save some species that were once common but are now extinct.

In the early 1800's Audubon described flocks of passenger pigeons so large they darkened the sky. When such flocks settled in trees to roost for the night, their enormous weight bent the branches and sent many crashing to the ground. We have reports of pigeon hunters who climbed the trees and knocked thousands of pigeons from their perches with clubs. Thousands of others were gathered in sacks to be sold for a few cents each or left on the ground as food for hogs. The last survivor of what is estimated to have been over 2,000,000,000 passenger pigeons died in the Cincinnati zoo in 1914. What caused the complete extermination of this valuable bird in less than 100 years? Perhaps the introduction of an epidemic disease hastened the end of those that escaped the ruthless market hunting. Certainly no thought was given to conservation until too late.

Rare birds we may still save. Bird societies are watching several other species which are nearing extermination, but which may still be saved.

Only a few ivory-billed woodpeckers remain in the forests of southern river bottoms. Anyone seeing one of these rare birds should report it immediately to the National Audubon Society.

The whooping crane is disappearing from the region of the Great Plains. In a recent count, only 26 adult whooping cranes were found. These were in the Aransas, Texas, National Wildlife Refuge, which is their wintering grounds.

The prairie chicken was hunted widely for market in earlier times. More recently its numbers have been further

Fig. 56-6. The California condor (*left*) and the northern bald eagle (*right*) are both nearing extinction. What measures can be taken to increase their numbers?

Koford from National Audubon Society   *Ambler from National Audubon Society*

U. S. Dept. of Agriculture

Fig. 56-7. The vegetation on a farm often provides shelter for such birds as the pheasant shown in this picture.

reduced by the plowing of native grasslands in the prairie states.

The California condor, a type of vulture, is a rare species of the mountainous regions of the far west. Less than 100 of these great birds are left. The condor, with a body three feet long and a wing spread of ten feet or more, lives on decaying flesh. Lack of food and the fact that it lays only one or two eggs each season may doom it to extinction.

Problems relating to game birds. Migratory ducks and geese have been favorite *game birds* for hunters. However, the decline in their populations during the past 50 years has been due only partially to hunters. The draining of marshes which supply natural food such as wild rice, as well as nesting places and cover, have presented a serious problem in con-

serving these birds. Large numbers of ducks die of alkali poisoning on ponds and lakes of the western prairies when the water is low and salts become concentrated. In some regions, thousands of ducks and geese have died of botulism when they consumed the deadly toxin while probing for food in the mud of ponds and lakes at low water. Lead poisoning takes its toll when game birds are wounded by lead pellets instead of being killed outright by hunters.

Upland game birds, including the quail, partridge, grouse, wild turkey and pheasant, are widely hunted by sportsmen. They can survive regulated hunting only if adequate food and cover are provided, especially during winter months. Many farmers allow trees, shrubs, and tall grass to grow along their fence rows and roadsides as cover. A few rows of grain left at the margin of fields provides winter food for these and other birds.

Laws to protect our birds. As early as 1885 the Ornithological Union drafted a law known as the *Audubon Law*. This law was adopted in most states.

In general, bird laws of the states and the federal government include the following provisions:

1. Non-game birds such as song birds may not be killed at any time.

2. Closed seasons are provided for game birds.

3. English sparrows, starlings, sharp-skinned hawks, Cooper's hawks, great horned owls, ravens, and crows are not protected in most states.

4. Laws protecting song birds apply to their eggs.

5. Birds and eggs may be taken for scientific purposes only with official permission.

The **Federal Tariff Bill** prohibits the importation of feathers, skins, plumes, wings, or quills of wild birds except for educational purposes.

The **Migratory Bird Treaty Act** is an international agreement between the United States and Canada. The Canadian Parliament approved it in 1917 after which our Congress approved it in 1918. This Act was amended by Congress in 1936 to include an agreement with Mexico to protect both migratory birds and animals.

The work of bird societies. One of the most active and best known of many bird societies is the **National Audubon Society** and its various state and local organizations. The Audubon Society supplies literature regarding birds and bird habits and other educational material including pictures, slides, and motion pictures. In addition, the society is a powerful influence in legislation to protect our wildlife. A yearly census is taken to determine the bird population. Many bird students and scientific workers support the activities of the **Wilson Society**, another national bird organization.

Private agencies work closely with the **Fish and Wildlife Service**, a department of the United States Department of the Interior. This important bureau has charge of the conservation of birds and other animals, controls the national wildlife reservations, administers laws regarding commerce in game, and publishes many educational bulletins and other information.

Destruction of fur-bearing animals. The first drain on the mammal population of North America occurred early in our history. Long before the pioneers began their journey westward, trappers had explored the wilderness in search of fur-bearing animals. As long ago as 150 years, trappers were penetrating the forests of the Pacific Northwest. Their prize was the beaver, highly valued in the eastern and European markets. " Empire builder " is an appropriate name for this valuable fur-bearer which played a major role in the settlement of this vast wilderness country. Fortunes were made in the fur business during these times. The pelts of beaver, mink, otter, muskrat, fox, skunk, and other fur-bearers brought an annual revenue of over $100,000,000. Early trappers were very ruthless hunters. They gave no thought to conservation of the animals they sought. The numbers of fur-bearing animals decreased rapidly. Later the settlers began clearing and cultivating the land. Mammals which had escaped the trappers retreated farther and farther into the remaining wilderness.

Destruction of larger mammals. The slaughter of the plains bison is a story of useless waste. In the middle of the last century, herds of bison numbering many thousands thundered across the Great Plains. For centuries, this noble animal

U. S. Dept. of Agriculture

Fig. 56-8.   The American bison is now protected in game preserves, and its numbers are slowly increasing.

had supplied both flesh and hides to plains Indians. But as calves replaced the mature animals taken from the herds by hunting, both the Indians and the bison flourished. Then came the buffalo hunters. Bison were slaughtered in tremendous numbers as food for workmen building railroads through the west or for pure sport. At one time, passengers on trains amused themselves by firing at bison from open platforms. It is shocking to learn that great numbers of bison were killed deliberately to starve the plains Indians into submission. Within 50 years, bison herds were reduced from tens of thousands to mere remnants. At one time it appeared likely that the bison might die out entirely.

The whitetail deer and black bear vanished from the remaining forests of most of the central and eastern agricultural states. Elk, mule deer, and antelope were slaughtered in the West.

What did the destruction of so much of the game resources profit America? It supported a rich fur trade for a time, and it provided food and clothing to pioneer families. But this could have been accomplished by sacrificing only a small portion of wildlife population. Much of the destruction of wildlife was useless, careless waste.

Wildlife restoration. Most small mammal and big-game mammal species have survived in greatly reduced numbers in the remaining wilderness regions. Can they return with our help to at least a portion of their former ranges? Can we make room for them among our many farms and ranches with their enormous population of domestic animals? This will require careful planning and scientific management. But it can be done.

Restoration of small animals. The residents of New England have noticed an increase in the population of raccoons, ox, opossums, squirrels, beavers, and other mammals in recent years. The increase in number of these species has been natural and not the result of artificial stocking from game farms. Why are they coming back? The answer can be found in the forests which have returned to hillsides once cleared for agriculture but since abandoned because they proved unprofitable. In other words, these mammals can live in heavily populated regions if cover and food supply are available.

Many residents of large cities are surprised to see an opossum, raccoon, groundhog, or even an occasional fox on a street at night. These animals are thriving in small sections of woodland in the vicinity.

Fur farming. Fur farms have spared large numbers of native fur-bearing animals which might otherwise have been taken to meet the demand for pelts. Many marshy areas have been converted to profitable muskrat farms. It is interesting to note that the muskrat is the most widely used fur-bearing animal, and that Louisiana leads all other states in fur production because of the number of these animals in the Mississippi delta.

Game management. You might think that the best way to conserve our native mammals is to establish large areas where hunting is prohibited. Unfortunately, the problem is not that simple. On several **game preserves,** deer and elk have multiplied to the point that they have exhausted the food supply. Large herds of starving animals defeat all the principles of conservation.

Those who manage game preserves know exactly how much food and cover are available for the various mammals in the area. A census at regular intervals tells them the size of the big-game population. When the numbers become too large, the preserve is opened to restricted hunting. Thus a managed game preserve supplies both food and sport in addition to conserving native mammals.

Destruction of game on highways. There seems to be no effective measure for preventing the slaughter of many thousands of animals on the highways each year. Vast numbers of birds are included

Fig. 56-9. The grey fox shown at the left and the mink shown at the right are both fur-bearing mammals which are now grown on fur farms.

Morton from National Audubon Society

Maslowski from National Audubon Soci

in this heavy loss of life, although the toll of small mammals is probably greatest. Many mammals are active at night. The bright lights of oncoming automobiles confuse animals on highways, causing them to stand motionless in the path of an automobile or dart to the side and back onto the highway in an effort to escape. This loss of game on highways will increase as more and more super highways increase the speed of night driving.

Many states warn motorists of the presence of big-game areas with such signs as " CAUTION — DEER CROSS‑ING AHEAD " or " ENTERING DEER AREA." These signs are a protection for animals and automobile passengers alike, since an automobile striking a large animal may demolish the car or drive it off the highway.

Public cooperation is the only method by which we can reduce the number of animals killed on highways. An alert driver can see an animal on a highway far enough ahead to give it warning. However, he must be careful not to swerve into another automobile or stop suddenly and endanger other motorists. Reduced speed in regions where game is abundant will save the lives of great numbers of night-roaming animals.

Conservation of plants. Many states have found it necessary to enforce laws protecting native plants from useless de‑struction. Native trees, shrubs, and herbs are not only beautiful in the natural land‑scape but are necessary to wildlife as food and cover. People are often tempted to dig native plants in an effort to establish them in yards, especially when the plants are in flower. In most cases, native plants do not survive well in cultivation, so noth‑ing is accomplished by removing them from their natural surroundings.

Millions of dollars are spent annually to beautify highways. Flowering trees set along the roadside add to the pleasure of driving and, in addition, serve to anchor the soil and prevent erosion. These plants should not, of course, be disturbed by motorists. Many states have signs along the highways warning against this. As in the case of wildlife, however, con‑servation of native plants requires public understanding, appreciation, and full co‑operation.

In Conclusion

The wildlife of America belongs to you. What can you do to conserve it? The most basic contribution you can make is an active interest in wildlife con‑servation. If you live on a farm or a ranch, think of the birds and animals along your fence rows or in the brush and woodland that you have not culti‑vated. If you are one of the many city dwellers, protect the squirrels in the park and the rabbits in the vacant lot. If you fish and hunt, respect the laws and limits. They protect your interests and add to your outdoor pleasures.

Have you thought of joining the Audubon Society or the Wilson Club? Have you heard of the Isaak Walton League? These organizations would welcome you if you are interested in wildlife and conservation. Ducks Un‑limited, The National Wildlife Federation, and The American Wildlife In‑stitute are other civilian agencies which are carrying on important work. They deserve your full support and cooperation.

BIOLOGICALLY SPEAKING

farm pond	fry	Migratory Bird Treaty Act
fish ladder	game bird	National Audubon Society
Federal Tariff Bill	game fish	upland game bird
Fish and Wildlife Service	game preserve	wildlife
forage fish	market hunting	Wilson Society

QUESTIONS FOR REVIEW

1. What six divisions of wildlife are important in wildlife conservation?
2. What are some features of a productive river or stream?
3. How has lowering of the water table caused serious loss of fish even in bodies of water which do not dry out?
4. Describe the operation of a fish ladder around a dam.
5. How are farm ponds made?
6. List six or more restrictions placed on fishing in most states.
7. Make a list of bird species which are now very rare or nearly extinct.
8. Discuss various problems relating to conservation of ducks and geese.
9. Name several species of upland game birds in your region.
10. List five provisions of the Audubon Law.
11. What mammal has been called the "empire builder" and why?
12. Name several valuable mammals which are raised profitably on fur farms.

APPLYING FACTS AND PRINCIPLES

1. Discuss the role of sportsmen in the wildlife conservation program.
2. Discuss the work of the Audubon Society and other societies in conservation.
3. List various problems in restoring big game mammals in the agricultural states.
4. Why are predatory birds and animals essential to proper game management?
5. Discuss the problem of destruction of wildlife on the highways.

RESEARCH ON YOUR OWN

1. Using soil or plaster of Paris, build models of slopes illustrating contour farming, strip farming, and terracing. Crops may be indicated with small straws or sticks, or painted (if plaster is used).
2. Prepare a soil profile in a glass cylinder, using gravel in the bottom, then sand, clay, and topsoil. Pour water through it and study its movement to the bottom of the cylinder. Add water until it stands about halfway from the bottom of the soil profile. Over a period of several days, study its movement up through the soil.
3. If a soil test kit is available, test various soils for the following: acidity, nitrates, phosphates, and potash. Individual kits are available for each of these tests; large kits include all of the tests.
4. Locate on an outline map of the United States the major dams and water power projects.
5. Conduct a wildlife census of a woods, a section of forest, a field, or a marsh in your area. Record the names of the various birds, mammals, and other animals you encounter and the number of each.

MORE ABOUT BIOLOGY

Allen, Durward. *Our Wildlife Legacy.* Funk and Wagnalls Co., New York. 1954

Baner, Helen. *Water: Riches or Ruin.* Doubleday and Co., Inc., New York. 1958

Bennett, H. H. *Elements of Soil Conservation.* McGraw-Hill Book Co., Inc., New York. 1947

Black, J. *Biological Conservation.* McGraw-Hill Book Co., Inc., New York. 1954

Butcher, Devereux. *Seeing America's Wildlife in Our National Refuges.* Devin-Adair Co., New York. 1955

Callison, Charles H., Ed. *America's Natural Resources.* The Ronald Press Co., New York. 1958

Dupuy, William A. *Our Bird Friends and Foes.* John C. Winston Co., Philadelphia. 1940

Greenway, James C. *Extinct and Vanishing Birds of the World.* American Committee for International Wildlife Protection, New York. 1958

Hogner, Dorothy. *Conservation in America.* J. B. Lippincott Co., Philadelphia. 1958

Holberg, Ruth. *Restless Johnny Apple-seed.* Thomas Y. Crowell Co., New York. 1950

Lathrop, Dorothy. *Let Them Live.* The Macmillan Co., New York. 1951

Morgan, Ann Haven. *Field Book of Animals in Winter.* G. P. Putnam's Sons, New York. 1939

Mountfort, Guy. *Wild Paradise.* Houghton Mifflin Co., Boston. 1958

Neal, Harry Edwards. *Nature's Guardians: Your Career in Conservation.* Julian Messner, Inc., New York. 1957

Osborn, Fairfield. *Our Plundered Planet.* Little, Brown and Co., Boston. 1948

Shippen, Katherine B. *Great Heritage.* Viking Press, New York. 1947

Smith, Guy-Harold, Ed. *Conservation of Natural Resources.* 2nd ed. John Wiley and Sons, Inc., New York. 1958

U. S. Dept. of Agriculture. *Water.* Supt. of Documents, Govt. Printing Office, Washington, D. C. 1938

White, Dale. *Gifford Pinchot: The Man Who Saved the Forests.* Julian Messner and Co., Inc., New York. 1957

Williams, J. H. *The Scent of Fear.* Doubleday and Co., Inc., New York. 1958

Appendix

A SIMPLIFIED CLASSIFICATION OF ORGANISMS

PLANT KINGDOM (Traditional Classification)

PHYLUM I. THALLOPHYTA (thal-*ah*-fih-tuh) [110,000 species]

One-celled or many-celled plants lacking usual tissues and without roots, stems, or leaves. Some possess chlorophyll; others do not. Reproduction by fission, spores, or gametes. Spore- and gamete-producing structures usually unicellular.

SUBPHYLUM 1. ALGAE: Thallophyte plants possessing chlorophyll, in addition to other pigments in certain groups.

Class 1. Cyanophyceae (sy-an-oh-*fy*-sih-ee): Blue-green algae [*Nostoc* (*nos*-tok); *Oscillatoria* (os-il-uh-*tor*-ee-uh); *Anabaena* (an-uh-*bee*-nuh); *Gleocapsa* (glee-oh-*kap*-suh)]

Class 2. Chlorophyceae (klor-oh-*fy*-sih-ee): Green algae [*Protococcus* (proh-toh-*kok*-us); *Chlorella* (klor-*el*-uh); *Spirogyra* (spy-roh-*jy*-ruh); *Oedogonium* (ee-doh-*goh*-nee-um); *Ulothrix* (*you*-loh-thriks); desmids]

Class 3. Chrysophyceae (kry-soh-*fy*-sih-ee): Golden-brown algae [diatoms]

Class 4. Phaeophyceae (fay-oh-*fy*-sih-ee): Brown algae [*Fucus;* kelp; *Sargassum*]

Class 5. Rhodophyceae (roh-doh-*fy*-sih-ee): Red algae [seaweed; *Chondrus*]

SUBPHYLUM 2. FUNGI (*fun*-jy): Nongreen parasitic or saprophytic thallophyte plants.

Class 1. Schizomycetes (skiz-oh-my-*see*-teez): Fission fungi [bacteria; spirochetes (*spy*-roh-keets); *actinomycetes* (ak-tih-noh-*my*-seets); *Rickettsiae* (rih-*ket*-see-ee)]

Class 2. Myxomycetes (mik-soh-my-*see*-teez): Amorphous slimy growths resembling animals in form but reproducing by spore formation in plant manner [slime molds]

Class 3. Phycomycetes (fy-koh-my-*see*-teez): Algalike fungi [*Rhizopus* (*ry*-zuh-pus); white " rust "; downy mildews; black mold; *Saprolegnia* (sap-roh-*leg*-nee-uh)]

Class 4. Ascomycetes (as-koh-my-*see*-teez): Sac fungi, producing, usually, eight ascospores in an ascus; many forms producing conidiospores [*Penicillium; Aspergillus;* morel; yeast; cup fungi; blue and green molds; powdery mildews]

Class 5. Basidiomycetes (bas-id-ee-oh-my-*see*-teez): Basidium fungi [smuts; rusts; mushrooms; puffballs; bracket fungi]

Class 6. Deuteromycetes (doo-ter-oh-my-*see*-teez): Imperfect fungi [ringworm fungi]

Class 7. Lichenes (ly-*kee*-neez): Plant body consisting of an alga and a fungus in combination [lichens]

PHYLUM II. BRYOPHYTA (bry-*ah*-fih-tuh) [23,000 species]

Multicellular green plants living on land, in most cases; alternation of generations with the gametophyte the conspicuous generation; vascular tissues lacking; reproduction by spores and gametes.

Class 1. Hepaticae (heh-*pat*-ih-see): Liverworts [*Riccia* (*rik*-see-uh); *Marchantia* (mar-*kan*-shih-uh)]

Class 2. Musci (*mus*-ky): True mosses [*Polytrichium* (pol-ee-*trik*-ee-um), or pigeon-wheat moss; Sphagnum (*sfag*-num) moss]

713

PHYLUM III.   PTERIDOPHYTA (ter-id-*ah*-fih-tuh) [10,000 species]

Mostly terrestrial plants with alternation of generations; both generations green; conspicuous generation the sporophyte leafy frond; vascular tissues and roots, stem, and leaves present; reproduction by spores and gametes.

Class 1.   Filicineae (fil-ih-*sih*-nee-ee): Ferns [wood fern; Boston fern; bracken fern]

Class 2.   Equisetineae (ek-weh-seh-*tih*-nee-ee): Horsetails [*Equisetum* (ek-weh-*see*-tum)]

Class 3.   Lycopodiaceae (ly-koh-poh-dee-*ay*-seh-ee): Club mosses [*Selaginella* (sel-uh-jih-*nel*-uh); *Lycopodium* (ly-koh-*poh*-dee-um)]

PHYLUM IV.   SPERMATOPHYTA (sper-mat-*ah*-fih-tuh) [250,700 species]

Seed plants in which the plant body is the sporophyte generation; highly specialized tissues; roots, stems, leaves, and reproductive organs.

Class 1.   Gymnospermae (*jim*-noh-sperm-ee): Seeds not enclosed in an ovary; mostly large, woody plants; mostly evergreen

Order 1.   Cycadales (sy-kuh-*day*-leez): Primitive fernlike gymnosperms [cycads or sago palms, including *Cycas, Dioön, Zamia*]

Order 2.   Ginkgoales (ging-koh-*ay*-leez): Large trees with two kinds of branches, one bearing most of the wedge-shaped leaves in clusters [*Ginkgo*]

Order 3.   Coniferales (koh-nih-fer-*ay*-leez): Cone-bearing gymnosperms, mostly evergreen; leaves in the form of needles or scales [pine; spruce; fir; cedar; larch]

Order 4.   Gnetales (nee-*tay*-leez): Possible forerunners of the flowering plants; two seed leaves on the embryo; vessels in the wood; only three remaining genera [*Ephedra* (eh-*fee*-druh); *Welwitschia* (wel-*witch*-ee-uh); *Gnetum* (*nee*-tum)]

Class 2.   Angiospermae (*an*-jee-oh-sperm-ee): Flowering plants; seeds enclosed in an ovary which ripens into the fruit

Subclass A.   Monocotyledonae (mon-oh-kot-ih-*lee*-duh-nee): Embryo with one cotyledon; fibrovascular bundles scattered through stem tissues; flower parts in 3's and 6's; leaves parallel-veined [grass; lily; iris; orchid; sedge; palm; including about 9 orders]

Subclass B.   Dicotyledonae (dy-kot-ih-*lee*-duh-nee): Embryo with two cotyledons; fibrovascular bundles forming a cylinder around the pith in the stem; flower parts in 4's or 5's; leaves with netted veins [buttercup; rose; apple; elm; including about 35 orders]

PLANT KINGDOM (Modern Classification)

SUBKINGDOM THALLOPHYTA

PHYLUM Euglenophyta: euglenoids
PHYLUM Cyanophyta: blue-green algae
PHYLUM Chlorophyta: green algae
PHYLUM Chrysophyta: golden-brown algae
PHYLUM Pyrrophyta: cryptomonads and dinoflagellates
PHYLUM Phaeophyta: brown algae
PHYLUM Rhodophyta: red algae

} Algae of traditional system

PHYLUM Schizomycophyta: bacteria
PHYLUM Myxomycophyta: slime molds
PHYLUM Eumycophyta: true fungi

} Fungi of traditional system

SUBKINGDOM EMBRYOPHYTA

PHYLUM Bryophyta
     Class Hepaticae: liverworts
     Class Musci: mosses

} Bryophyta of traditional system

PHYLUM Tracheophyta: vascular plants
  Subphylum Lycopsida: club mosses
    Class Lycopodineae
  Subphylum Sphenopsida: horsetails
    Class Equisetineae
  Subphylum Pteropsida
    Class Filicineae: ferns

        Pteridophyta
          of
       traditional system

    Class Gymnospermae: conifers and their allies
    Class Angiospermae: flowering plants
      Subclass Monocotyledonae
      Subclass Dicotyledonae

        Spermatophyta
          of
       traditional system

ANIMAL KINGDOM

PHYLUM I. PROTOZOA [30,000 species]

Unicellular animals or simple colonies of cells lacking specialization into tissues; reproduction by fission or spores. *AMEBA*
    Class 1. Sarcodina (sar-koh-*dy*-nuh): Protozoa which form pseudopodia; pellicle at cell surface lacking; reproduction principally by fission; many forms marine [*Ameba* (uh-*mee*-buh); *Arcella* (ar-*sel*-uh); *Endameba;* foraminifers; radiolarians]
    Class 2. Mastigophora (mas-tig-*ah*-fer-uh): Protozoa which propel themselves with one or more flagella; pellicle usually present; fission longitudinal; many forms parasitic [*Euglena* (you-*glee*-nuh); *Trypanosoma* (try-pan-oh-*soh*-muh); *Volvox; Leishmania* (leesh-*may*-nee-uh)]
    Class 3. Sporozoa (spor-oh-*zoh*-uh): No structures for locomotion; form spores [*Plasmodium* (plaz-*moh*-dee-um)]
    Class 4. Ciliata (sil-ee-*ay*-tuh): Locomotion by means of cilia; both free-living aquatic and marine forms, and parasitic forms; macronucleus and micronucleus present in many forms [*Paramecium* (pair-uh-*mee*-see-um); *Stylonychia* (sty-loh-*nih*-kee-uh); *Vorticella* (vor-tih-*sel*-uh); *Stentor*]

PHYLUM II. PORIFERA (pore-*if*-er-uh) [2,500 species]

Including marine and fresh-water sponges; body in two cell layers, penetrated by numerous pores; " skeleton " formed by silicious or calcareous spicules or horny spongin.
    Class 1. Calcispongiae (kal-sih-*sponge*-ih-ee): Simple sponges of shallow waters; calcareous spicules forming " skeleton " [ascon and sycon types including *Grantia*]
    Class 2. Hylospongiae (hy-loh-*sponge*-ih-ee): Deep-water sponges; " skeleton " composed of silicious spicules in open framework [Venus's flower basket]
    Class 3. Demospongiae (dem-oh-*sponge*-ih-ee): Large sponges, often brightly colored; " skeleton " of spongin or a combination of spongin and silicious material; fresh-water and marine [finger sponge, crumb-of-bread sponge; bath sponge] *SPON*

PHYLUM III. COELENTERATA (seh-len-ter-*ay*-tuh) [10,000 species]

Usually free-swimming metazoans with a baglike body of two layers of cells with a noncellular substance between them; gastrovascular cavity with one opening leading to the outside; solitary or colonial forms; many have tentacles and all have stinging capsules.
    Class 1. Hydrozoa (hy-droh-*zoh*-uh): Solitary or colonial; fresh-water and marine; reproduction by asexual buds and gametes; alternation of generations in many forms [*Hydra; Obelia* (oh-*bee*-lee-uh); *Gonionemus* (gon-ee-oh-*nee*-mus); *Physalia* (fy-*say*-lee-uh)]
    Class 2. Scyphozoa (sy-foh-*zoh*-uh): Exclusively marine forms; most have mesenteries; polyp stage usually absent [*Cyanea* (sy-*ay*-nee-uh); *Aurelia* (or-*ee*-lee-uh)]
    Class 3. Anthozoa (an-thoh-*zoh*-uh): Marine forms; solitary or colonial; without alternation of generations; body cavity with mesenteries; many tentacles [sea anemone; coral; sea fan]

PHYLUM IV. PLATYHELMINTHES (plat-ee-hel-*min*-theez) [6,500 species]

Flatworms with a ribbonlike body; no true segments; no body cavity; no skeletal, circulatory, or respiratory systems; head provided with sense organs; nervous system composed of two longitudinal nerve cords.

Class 1. Turbellaria (tur-beh-*lair*-ee-uh): Mostly free-living aquatic or terrestrial forms; many with cilia on the epidermis [*Planaria*]

Class 2. Trematoda (trem-uh-*toh*-duh): Parasitic forms with mouth at anterior end; intestine present; no cilia on adults [sheep liver fluke; human liver fluke]

Class 3. Cestoda (ses-*toh*-duh): Parasitic forms; body a series of detachable proglottids; intestine lacking; hooked scolex adapted for attachment to intestine of host [tapeworm]

PHYLUM V. NEMATHELMINTHES (nem-uh-thel-*min*-theez) [3,500 species]

Roundworms with unsegmented bodies; body wall in three layers; body cavity present.

Class 1. Nematoda (nem-uh-*toh*-duh): With intestine but without a proboscis; some forms free-living, others parasitic [vinegar eel, *Ascaris* (*as*-kuh-ris); hookworm; pinworm; *Trichinella* (trih-kih-*nel*-uh)]

PHYLUM VI. ROTIFERA (roh-*tif*-er-uh) [1,500 species]

" Wheel animals " with rows of cilia around the mouth which beat with a motion suggesting the rotation of a wheel; chitinlike jaws and a well-developed digestive system; body usually cylindrical, ending in a forked grasping foot; smallest of the metazoans [rotifers]

PHYLUM VII. ANNELIDA (an-*nel*-ih-duh) [5,000 species]

Segmented worms with the body cavity separated from the digestive tube; brain dorsal and nerve cord ventral; body wall containing circular and longitudinal muscles.

Class 1. Polychaeta (pol-ee-*kee*-tuh): Marine forms; fleshy outgrowths, or parapodia, extending from segments [sandworm, or *Nereis*]

Class 2. Archiannelida (ar-kee-an-*nel*-ih-duh): Similar to Polychaetae but without parapodia and with two rows of cilia [*Polygordius* (pol-ee-*gor*-dee-us)]

Class 3. Oligochaeta (oh-lih-goh-*kee*-tuh): Fresh-water or terrestrial forms; setae on side of body; head not well developed [earthworm; *Tubifex; Chaetogaster* (kee-toh-*gas*-ter)]

Class 4. Hirudinea (hir-oo-*dih*-nee-uh): Body flattened from top to bottom; mostly fresh-water forms, but may also occur as marine or terrestrial organisms; parasites and predators; no setae on body; suckers at both ends [leeches]

PHYLUM VIII. MOLLUSCA (mol-*us*-kuh) [90,000 species]

Soft-bodied invertebrates without segments or jointed appendages; most forms secrete a valve, or calcareous shell, from a mantle; muscular foot usually present; terrestrial, fresh-water, and marine organisms. C L A M

Class 1. Amphineura (am-fee-*new*-ruh): Elongated body and reduced head, without tentacles; many forms with a shell composed of eight plates [chiton]

Class 2. Pelecypoda (peh-leh-*sip*-oh-duh): Axe-footed with bivalve shell; gills in mantle cavity; head, eyes, and tentacles lacking [clam; mussel; oyster; scallop]

Class 3. Gastropoda (gas-*trop*-oh-duh): Flat-footed; with or without coiled shell; head and distinct eyes and tentacles [snail; slug; whelk]

Class 4. Scaphopoda (skuh-*fop*-oh-duh): Marine forms; body elongated and enclosed in a tubular shell, open at both ends; gills lacking [tooth shell]

Class 5. Cephalopoda (sef-uh-*lop*-oh-duh): Head large; foot modified into grasping tentacles; marine forms [squid; octopus; chambered nautilus; cuttlefish]

PHYLUM IX. ECHINODERMATA (eh-ky-noh-der-*may*-tuh) [5,000 species]

Marine forms, radially symmetrical when adult; spiny exoskeleton composed, in some types, of calcareous plates; most forms with tube feet for locomotion.

Class 1. Crinoidea (kry-*noy*-dee-uh): Five branched rays and pinnules; tube feet without suckers; most species with stalk for attachment [sea lily; many fossil forms]

Class 2. Asteroidea (as-ter-*oy*-dee-uh): Body usually with five rays and double rows of tube feet in each ray; eyespot [starfish]

Class 3. Ophiuroidea (off-ee-you-*roy*-dee-uh): Usually with five slender arms or rays [brittle stars]

Class 4. Echinoidea (ek-ih-*noy*-dee-uh): Body spherical, oval, or disk-shaped; no rays; tube feet with suckers [sea urchin; sand dollar]

Class 5. Holothurioidea (hol-oh-thur-ee-*oy*-dee-uh): Elongated, thickened body with tentacles around the mouth; no rays or spines [sea cucumber]

PHYLUM X. ARTHROPODA (ar-*throp*-oh-duh) [674,000 species]

Animals with segmented bodies, the segments bearing jointed appendages; chitinous exoskeleton; terrestrial, aerial, and aquatic forms.

Class 1. Crustacea (kruh-*stay*-shuh): Mostly aquatic; breathe by means of gills; head and thorax usually joined in a cephalothorax; two pairs of antennae; many members have calcareous deposits in the exoskeleton [crayfish; lobster; crab; shrimp; water flea; sow bug; barnacle]

Class 2. Chilopoda (ky-*lop*-oh-duh): Body flattened and consisting of from 15 to 170 or more segments; one pair of legs attached to each segment; maxillipeds developed into poison claws [centipedes]

Class 3. Diplopoda (dip-*lop*-oh-duh): Body more or less cylindrical and composed of 25 to 100 or more segments; most segments bearing two pairs of legs [millepedes]

Class 4. Arachnida (uh-*rak*-nih-duh): Head and thorax usually fused into a cephalothorax; no antennae; four pairs of legs; breathe by means of book lungs or tracheae [spider; scorpion; mite; tick]

Class 5. Insecta (in-*sek*-tuh): Head, thorax, and abdomen separate; three pairs of legs; one pair of antennae; usually two pairs of wings; breathe by means of tracheae.

Order 1. Thysanura (thy-suh-*new*-ruh): Wingless; chewing mouth parts; no metamorphosis; primitive insects [silverfish]

Order 2. Orthoptera (or-*thop*-ter-uh): Two pairs of wings, the outer pair straight and leathery; chewing mouth parts; incomplete metamorphosis [grasshopper; cockroach; walking stick; mantis; cricket]

Order 3. Isoptera (eye-*sop*-ter-uh): Some forms wingless, others with two pairs of long, narrow wings lying flat on back; chewing mouth parts; incomplete metamorphosis; social insects [termites]

Order 4. Neuroptera (new-*rop*-ter-uh): Four membranous wings of equal size, netted with many veins; chewing mouth parts; complete metamorphosis; larvae of some forms aquatic [dobson fly, or hellgrammite; ant lion]

Order 5. Ephemerida (ef-eh-*mair*-ih-duh): Two pairs of membranous wings, the front pair larger than the hind pair; mouth parts nonfunctioning in adults; metamorphosis incomplete; adults short-lived [May fly]

Order 6. Lepidoptera (leh-pih-*dop*-ter-uh): Four wings covered with colored scales; mouth parts modified into a coiled sucking proboscis; complete metamorphosis [butterfly; moth; skipper]

Order 7. Hymenoptera (hy-men-*op*-ter-uh): Wingless or with two pairs of membranous wings, the forewings larger; forewings and hindwings hooked together; chewing and sucking mouth parts; complete metamorphosis; many members living in social colonies [bee; ant; wasp; hornet; ichneumon fly]

Order 8. Odonata (oh-doh-*nay*-tuh): Two pairs of strong, membranous wings, the hind pair as large or larger than the fore pair; chewing mouth parts; incomplete metamorphosis; compound eyes very large; larvae aquatic [dragonfly; damsel fly]

Order 9. Mallophaga (muh-*lah*-fuh-guh): Wings absent; chewing mouth parts; incomplete metamorphosis [chicken lice]

Order 10. Anoplura (an-oh-*plur*-uh): Wingless; piercing and sucking mouth parts; no metamorphosis; external parasites on mammals [human body louse]

Order 11. Coleoptera (koh-lee-*op*-ter-uh): Four wings, the front pair hard and shell-like, the second pair folded and membranous; chewing mouth parts; complete metamorphosis [beetles; lady " bug "; firefly; boll weevil]

Order 12. Hemiptera (heh-*mip*-ter-uh): Wingless, or with forewings leathery at the base and folded over the hindwings; piercing and sucking mouth parts; incomplete metamorphosis [true bugs; water bug; water spider; water boatman; back swimmer; bedbug; squash bug; stink bug]

Order 13. Homoptera (hoh-*mop*-ter-uh): Wingless, or with two pairs of wings held in a sloping position like the sides of a roof; piercing and sucking mouth parts; incomplete metamorphosis [cicada; aphid; leaf hopper; tree hopper; scale insect]

Order 14. Diptera (*dip*-ter-uh): Forewings membranous, hindwings reduced to knobbed threads; mouth parts for piercing, rasping, and sucking; metamorphosis complete [housefly; bot fly; blowfly; midge; mosquito; crane fly; gall gnat]

Order 15. Siphonaptera (sy-fuh-*nop*-ter-uh): Wingless; piercing and sucking mouth parts; complete metamorphosis; legs adapted for leaping; external parasites on mammals [flea]

PHYLUM XI. CHORDATA (kor-*day*-tuh) [400,000 species]

Notochord present at some time, disappearing early in many forms; paired gill slits temporary or permanent; dorsal nerve cord.

SUBPHYLUM 1. HEMICHORDATA (heh-mee-kor-*day*-tuh): Wormlike chordates; body in three regions with a proboscis, collar, and trunk [acorn worm, or tongue worm]

SUBPHYLUM 2. UROCHORDATA (you-roh-kor-*day*-tuh), **also called Tunicata** (too-nih-*kay*-tuh): Marine animals with saclike body in adult; free-swimming or attached [sea squirts and other tunicates]

SUBPHYLUM 3. CEPHALOCHORDATA (seh-fuh-loh-kor-*day*-tuh): Fishlike animals with a permanent notochord [*Amphioxus* (am-fee-*oks*-us), or lancelet]

SUBPHYLUM 4. VERTEBRATA (ver-tuh-*bray*-tuh): Chordates in which most of the notochord is replaced by a spinal column composed of vertebrae and protecting the dorsal nerve cord.

Class 1. Cyclostomata (sy-kloh-stoh-*may*-tuh), **also called Agnatha** (ag-*nay*-thuh): Fresh-water or marine eel-like forms without true jaws, scales, or fins and with a skeleton of cartilage [lamprey; hagfish] *LAMPRey*

Class 2. Chondrichthyes (kon-*drik*-thih-eez), **also called Elasmobranchii** (ee-laz-moh-*brank*-ee-eye): Fishlike forms with true jaws and fins; gills present but not free and opening through gill slits; no swim bladder; cartilaginous skeleton [shark; ray; skate] *ShARK*

Class 3. Osteichthyes (os-tee-*ik*-thih-eez), **also called Pisces:** Fresh-water and marine fishes with gills free and attached to gill arches; one gill opening on each side of body; true jaws and fins; bony skeleton. *Pisces*

Subclass 1. **Ganoidei** (gan-*oy*-dee-eye): Mostly extinct forms with armored body, heterocercal tail and air bladder with duct [sturgeon; garpike; amia; fossil armored fish]

Subclass 2. **Teleostomi** (tel-ee-*os*-toh-mye): Common bony fish; tail rarely heterocercal; air bladder (with or without duct) present or absent [perch; trout; salmon; eel; bass; catfish; sucker; shiner; flounder; cod; haddock]

Subclass 3. **Dipnoi** (*dip*-noy): Air bladder connected with throat and used as a rudimentary lung [lungfish]

Class 4. Amphibia (am-*fib*-ee-uh): Fresh-water or terrestrial forms; gills present at some stage; skin slimy and lacking protective outgrowths; limbs without claws; numerous eggs, usually laid in water; metamorphosis. *FRO 4G*

Order 1. **Apoda** (*ap*-oh-duh): Wormlike amphibians with tail short or lacking; without limbs or limb girdles; small scales embedded in the skin in some forms [caecilians (see-*sil*-ee-uns)]

Order 2. **Caudata** (kaw-*day*-tuh): Body elongated and with a tail throughout life; scales lacking; most forms have two pairs of limbs [salamander; newt; siren]

Order 3. **Salientia** (sal-ee-*en*-tee-uh): Body short and tailless in adult stage; two pairs of limbs, the hind limbs adapted for leaping; gills in larva stage but replaced by lungs in adult stage [frog; toad; tree frog]

Class 5. **Reptilia** (rep-*til*-ee-uh): Terrestrial or semiaquatic vertebrates; breathe by lungs at all stages; body scale-covered; feet, if present, provided with claws; eggs relatively few, large, and leathery; oviparous or ovoviviparous. *S ∩ A K C*

Order 1. **Testudinata** (tes-too-dih-*nay*-tuh): Body enclosed between two bony shields or shells, usually covered with large scales or plates; toothless [turtles; terrapins; tortoises]

Order 2. **Rhynchocephalia** (ring-koh-seh-*fay*-lee-uh): Skeletal characteristics of the oldest fossil reptiles; lizardlike in form; parietal eye in roof of cranium [*Sphenodon* (*sfee*-noh-don) sole surviving species]

Order 3. **Squamata** (squah-*may*-tuh): Body elongated; with or without limbs (vestigial in snakes); body covered with scales which are molted with outer skin at regular intervals [iguana (ih-*gwah*-nuh); Gila (*hee*-luh) monster; horned toad; swift; skink and other lizards; snakes]

Order 4. **Crocodilia** (krok-oh-*dil*-ee-uh): Large, heavily-scaled body with strong, muscular tail; heart approaching four-chambered condition [alligator; crocodile; cayman; gavial]

Class 6. **Aves** (*ay*-veez): Body covered with feathers; front limbs modified into wings; four-chambered heart and double circulation; hollow bones; lung breathing throughout life. *B I R D*

Order 1. **Gaviiformes** (gay-vih-ih-*for*-meez): Loons [common loon]

Order 2. **Colymbiformes** (koh-lim-bih-*for*-meez): Grebes [pied-billed grebe]

Order 3. **Pelecaniformes** (peh-leh-kan-ih-*for*-meez): Tropic birds [white pelican; brown pelican; cormorant]

Order 4. **Ciconiiformes** (sih-koh-nih-ih-*for*-meez): Wading birds with long legs [heron; ibis; spoonbill; flamingo]

Order 5. **Anseriformes** (an-ser-ih-*for*-meez): Short-legged gooselike birds [duck; goose; swan]

Order 6. **Falconiformes** (fal-kon-ih-*for*-meez): Large birds of prey [hawk; falcon; eagle; kite; vulture; buzzard; condor]

Order 7. **Galliformes** (gal-ih-*for*-meez): Fowl-like birds [pheasant; turkey; quail; partridge; grouse; ptarmigan]

Order 8. **Gruiformes** (groo-ih-*for*-meez): Cranelike birds [crane; rail; coot]

Order 9. **Charadriiformes** (kuh-rad-rih-ih-*for*-meez): Shore birds [snipe; plover; sandpiper; gull; tern; auk; puffin]

Order 10. **Columbiformes** (koh-lum-bih-*for*-meez): Pigeons and doves [mourning dove]

Order 11. **Psittaciformes** (sit-uh-sih-*for*-meez): Parrots and parrotlike birds [Carolina paroquet; parrot; parakeet]

Order 12. **Cuculiformes** (koo-kyou-lih-*for*-meez): Cuckoos [cuckoo; road runner]

Order 13. **Strigiformes** (strih-jih-*for*-meez): Nocturnal birds of prey [owl]

Order 14. **Caprimulgiformes** (kap-rih-mul-jih-*for*-meez): Goatsuckers [whippoorwill; chuck-will's-widow; nighthawk]

Order 15. **Apodiformes** (ap-oh-dih-*for*-meez), or **Micropodiformes** (my-kroh-poh-dih-ih-*for*-meez): Swifts [hummingbird, chimney swift]

Order 16. **Coraciiformes** (kor-as-ih-ih-*for*-meez): Fishing birds [kingfisher]

Order 17. **Piciformes** (pih-sih-*for*-meez): Woodpeckers [woodpecker; sapsucker; flicker]

Order 18.   Passeriformes (pas-er-ih-*for*-meez): Perching birds [robin; bluebird; sparrow; warbler; thrush]

Class 7.   Mammalia (mam-*ay*-lee-uh): Body more or less covered with hair; warm-blooded with four-chambered heart; mammary glands; diaphragm; central nervous system highly developed; viviparous except in one order.   *Dog*

Order 1.   Monotremata (mon-oh-tree-*may*-tuh): Egg-laying mammals [duckbill; spiny anteater]

Order 2.   Marsupialia (mar-soo-pee-*ay*-lee-uh): Mammals with young born immature and carried in a pouch [opossum; kangaroo; Koala " bear "]

Order 3.   Edentata (ee-den-*tay*-tuh): Toothless mammals or nearly so [armadillo; sloth]

Order 4.   Insectivora (in-sek-*tih*-vor-uh): Insect-eating mammals mostly [mole; shrew]

Order 5.   Chiroptera (ky-*rop*-ter-uh): Flying, or hand-winged, mammals [bat; vampire]

Order 6.   Cetacea (see-*tay*-shuh): Marine mammals; forelimbs finlike; hindlimbs absent [whale; porpoise; dolphin]

Order 7.   Sirenia (sy-*ree*-nee-uh): Aquatic mammals; forelimbs finlike; hindlimbs absent; tail with horizontal fin; body whalelike but with definite neck [sea cow]

Order 8.   Carnivora (kar-*nih*-vor-uh): Mammals with sharp teeth with cuspids for eating flesh; claws usually present [bear; raccoon; ring-tailed cat; weasel; mink; skunk; otter; lion; tiger; cat; dog; fox; wolf]

Order 9.   Rodentia (roh-*den*-shuh): Mammals equipped with incisor teeth adapted for gnawing [squirrel; woodchuck; prairie dog; chipmunk; mouse; rat; muskrat]

Order 10.   Lagomorpha (lag-oh-*mor*-fuh): Rodentlike mammals with highly developed hindlimbs adapted for jumping [rabbit; hare; pica]

Order 11.   Ungulata (ung-gyou-*lay*-tuh): Hoofed mammals; vegetarians with large, grinding molars [odd-toed: horse; tapir; rhinoceros; even-toed: bison; goat; sheep; deer; antelope; camel; llama; pig; hippopotamus]

Order 12.   Proboscidea (proh-boh-*sih*-dee-uh): Upper lip and nose lengthened to form a long, prehensile trunk; incisor teeth forming long tusks; molars very broad [elephant; fossil mammoth and fossil mastodon]

Order 13.   Primates (pry-*may*-teez): More or less erect mammals with forelimbs adapted for grasping and holding [monkey; gorilla; chimpanzee; orangutan; gibbon] [man is classified structurally by biologists as a primate]

Glossary

abdomen, the body region posterior to the thorax.

abscission (ab-*sih*-shun) **layer,** the two rows of cells near the base of a leaf petiole that are involved in the natural falling of the leaf.

absorption, the process by which water and dissolved substances pass into cells.

acceleration, the rate of change of speed.

acquired immunity, resistance to a disease established during the lifetime of an individual.

acromegaly (ak-roh-*meg*-uh-lee), abnormal growth, especially of the bones of the face and extremities, associated with malfunctioning of the anterior lobe of the pituitary gland.

ACTH, a hormone secretion of the anterior lobe of the pituitary gland which stimulates the cortex of the adrenal glands.

active immunity, an immunity to a disease that results from having had the disease or from injections of vaccine.

adaptation, an adjustment to conditions in an environment.

adductor muscles, those in bivalves which control the opening and closing of the valves.

adenoid, a mass of lymph tissue which grows from the back wall of the nasopharynx, behind the internal nares.

adrenal (ad-*ree*-nul) **gland,** a ductless gland located above the kidney, often referred to as the " gland of emergency."

adventitious (ad-ven-*tih*-shus) **root,** one which develops from the node of a stem or from a leaf.

aeciospore (*ee*-see-oh-spore), a spore produced in an aecium cup on a leaf of common barberry in the life cycle of wheat rust.

aerial roots and stems, those which do not enter the ground.

aerobic (air-*oh*-bik), requiring free atmospheric oxygen for normal activity.

agglutinin (uh-*gloo*-tih-nin), an immune substance in the blood which causes specific substances, including bacteria, to clump.

air bladder, a thin-walled, elliptical sac found in fish which allows the animal to maintain a level in the water.

air sacs, in insects, the enlarged spaces in which the tracheae terminate; in birds, cavities extending from the lungs.

albino, an organism lacking in genes for normal pigmentation.

albumen, a protein substance that surrounds the yolk in a bird's egg.

alga (*al*-guh), a thallophyte plant possessing chlorophyll.

alimentary canal, those organs composing the food tube in animals and man.

allergy, an abnormal reaction in some people to certain foods, drugs, and pollens.

alpha particles, charged nuclei of helium atoms that travel at extremely high speed.

alternation of generations, a type of life cycle in which the asexual reproductive stage alternates with the sexual reproductive stage.

alveoli (al-*vee*-oh-lye), microscopic air sacs in the lungs in which the exchange of gases takes place.

amebocytes, amebalike cells in sponges which function in circulation and excretion.

amino (uh-*mee*-noh) **acids,** substances from which organisms build protein; the end-products of protein digestion.

ammonification, the release of ammonia from decaying protein by means of bacterial action.

amylase (*am*-ih-lase), an enzyme of the pancreatic fluid which changes starch to maltose.

anabolism (uh-*nab*-oh-lizm), the constructive phase of metabolism.

anaerobic (*an*-air-oh-bik), deriving oxygen for life activity from chemical changes and, in some cases, being unable to live actively in free oxygen.

anal (*ay*-nul) **pore,** an opening in the pellicle of the paramecium by which wastes leave the animal.

analogous (an-*al*-uh-gus) **organs,** those which are similar in function.

anaphase, a stage of mitosis during which chromosomes migrate from the equator to opposite poles.

anatomy, the study of the structure of living things.

androgen (*an*-droh-jen), the male sex hormone, secreted by the testes.

anemia (uh-*nee*-mee-uh), a deficiency of red corpuscles, hemoglobin, or both.

angstrom unit, a unit used to measure wave lengths; one ten-millionth of a millimeter.

annual, a plant which lives for only one season.

annual ring, a circle in the stem of a plant marking a season's growth of wood.

annulus (*an*-you-lus), the ring on the stipe of a mushroom marking the point where the rim of the cap and stipe were joined.

anoxia (an-*ok*-see-uh), the condition of oxygen starvation in the tissues.

antenna, a large " feeler " in insects and certain other animals.

antennule, a small " feeler " in the crayfish and certain other animals.

anterior, head, or front, end.

anther, that part of the stamen which bears pollen grains.

antheridium (an-ther-*ih*-dee-um), a sperm-producing structure.

anthocyanin (an-thoh-*sy*-uh-nin), a red, blue, or purple pigment dissolved in cell sap.

anthropology, the study of man and the societies in which he groups himself.

antibiotic (an-tee-by-*ot*-ik), a germ-killing substance produced by a bacterium, mold, or other fungus plant.

antibody, an immune substance in the blood and body fluids.

antigen (*an*-tih-jen), a substance, usually a protein, which when introduced into the body stimulates the formation of antibodies.

antipodals, three nuclei found in the embryo sac at the end farthest from the micropyle.

antiseptic, a substance used locally in contact with body tissue to destroy bacteria.

antitoxin, a substance in the blood which counteracts a specific toxin.

antivenin, a serum used against snakebite.

anus (*ay*-nus), the opening at the posterior end of the intestine.

aorta (ay-*or*-tuh), the great artery leading from the heart to the body (arising from the left ventricle in the bird and mammal).

aortic arch, an arching curve in the aorta, near the heart.

appendage, an outgrowth of the body of an animal, such as a leg, fin, or antenna.

aquatic, living in fresh water.

aqueous (*ay*-kwee-us) **humor,** the watery fluid filling the cavity between the cornea and lens of the eye.

arachnoid mater, the middle of the three membranes of the brain and spinal cord.

arteriole, a tiny artery which eventually branches to become capillaries.

arteriosclerosis, hardening of the arteries resulting from internal deposits.

artery, a large, muscular vessel that carries blood away from the heart.

artificial pollination, controlled pollination to produce a hybrid plant from selected parents.

artificial respiration, a method of artificially forcing the lungs to inspire and expire rhythmically.

ascus (*as*-kus), in Ascomycetes, the saclike structure which contains the spores.

aseptic, free of pathogenic bacteria and other harmful organisms.

asexual reproduction, reproduction without eggs and sperm.

assimilation (uh-sim-ih-*lay*-shun), the process by which protoplasm is organized from food substances.

association fibers, nerve processes connecting different parts of the cerebral cortex.

asymmetrical, having no definite shape.

atom, the smallest unit into which an element can be broken without losing its identity.

auditory nerve, the nerve leading from the inner ear to the brain.

auricle (*or*-ih-kul), a thin-walled, upper chamber of the heart; also called an atrium.

auricular-ventricular node, the structure in the heart which relays the beat to the muscles of the lower heart chambers.

auricular-ventricular valves, the heart valves located between the auricles and ventricles.

autonomic nervous system, a division of the nervous system which regulates the vital internal organs in an involuntary manner.

axil, the angle between a leaf stalk and a stem.

axillary bud, a lateral bud produced in a leaf axil.

axon (*aks*-on), a nerve process which carries an impulse away from the nerve cell body.

bacteria, a group of microscopic, one-celled fungus plants.

bactericide, a substance which kills bacteria.

bacteriology, the study of bacteria.

bacteriolysin (bak-tear-ee-oh-*ly*-sin), a blood antibody which causes a specific kind of bacteria to dissolve.

bacteriophage (bak-*tear*-ee-oh-fahj), one of several kinds of viruses which can destroy bacteria.

balance of nature, an equilibrium which regulates the plant and animal population in a given area.

balanced diet, one in which foods in proper proportion conform to the body needs.

barb, a tiny ray in the vane of a feather.

barbule, one of the divisions of the barb of a feather.

bark, the outer region of a woody stem, composed of several kinds of tissue.

basal disc, the structure that secretes a slimy material by which certain coelenterates are attached to the substrate.

basal metabolism, the activities required to maintain the body and to supply the energy necessary to support the basic life processes.

basidiospore, a reproductive structure found in the basidiomycetes, or club fungi.

basidium (bas-*id*-ee-um), a club-shaped structure found in the club fungi that bears spores.

bast fiber, a tough, thick-walled plant fiber that serves as a supporting structure in the phloem region.

belly (muscle), the body of a striated muscle.

bends, the condition in which nitrogen bubbles form in the blood and tissues following a rapid reduction of air pressure.

beta particles, high-speed electrons emitted by radioactive materials.

biennial, a plant which lives two seasons.

bilateral symmetry, the type exhibited by an organism which may be divided into two equal parts by only one plane.

bile, a brownish-green emulsifying fluid secreted by the liver and stored in the gall bladder.

binomial nomenclature, the system of giving an organism a name composed of two parts.

biology, the science of life.

biotic factors, the living surroundings of an organism.

bivalve, a mollusk possessing two valves, or shells.

blade, the thin, green portion of a leaf, usually strengthened by veins.

blastula (blas-*tyoo*-luh), an early stage in the development of an embryo, in which cells have divided to produce a hollow sphere.

bleeding (plants), the loss of water through a cut plant stem.

block cutting, the clearing of a block of timber, leaving stands around it for natural reseeding and protection.

blood, the fluid tissue of the body.

bony layer, the hard region of a bone between the periosteum and the marrow.

book lungs, the breathing organs of spiders.

botulism (*bot*-you-lizm), a severe type of food poisoning caused by a bacillus.

Bowman's capsule, the tuft-shaped structure forming one end of the tubules in the nephron of the kidney.

brain stem, an enlargement at the base of the brain where it connects with the spinal cord.

branchial arteries, those which lead to and from the gills of the fish.

breathing, the mechanical process of getting air into and out of the body.

bronchial (*bronk*-ee-ul) **tube,** a subdivision of a bronchus within a lung.

bronchiole, one of numerous subdivisions of the bronchial tubes within a lung.

bronchus (*bronk*-us), a division of the lower end of the trachea, leading to a lung.

bud, an undeveloped shoot of a plant, often covered by scales.

budding, the uniting of a bud with a stock; a form of asexual reproduction in yeasts and hydra.

bud-mutant, the offspring of a plant in which a mutation has occurred.

bud-scale scar, a mark at intervals along a twig which shows where the bud scales of a terminal bud were fastened during a previous season.

bulb, a large underground bud protected by scales.

bulbus arteriosus, a muscular bulblike structure attached to the ventricle in the fish heart.

bundle scars, minute dots on the leaf scars of a twig, indicating the previous location of the conducting vessels.

bursa, a fluid-filled sac in a joint which serves as a cushion between bones.

caecum (*see*-kum), a blind pouch extending from the alimentary canal in some animals and man.

Calorie (large), the amount of heat required to raise the temperature of 1,000 grams of water one degree centigrade.

calorimeter (kal-or-*im*-ih-ter), a device for measuring heat production.

calyx (*kay*-liks), the sepals of a flower, collectively.

cambium (*kam*-bee-um), the tissue in roots and stems which is responsible for growth in diameter.

camouflage, the blending of an organism with its surroundings.

canine, an enlarged tooth for tearing.

cap, the spore-bearing part of a mushroom.

capillarity, a force causing the rise of a liquid along the surface of a tube or vessel.

capillary, a tiny blood vessel through which exchange of gases, foods, and wastes takes place between the blood and tissue fluid.

capsule (moss), a spore-producing structure at the top of the stalk.

carapace (*kair*-uh-pace), the shell covering the cephalothorax of a crustacean; the upper shell of a turtle.

carbhemoglobin, hemoglobin when it is carrying carbon dioxide away from the tissues.

carbohydrate, the class of foods including sugars, starches, and cellulose.

cardiac muscle, heart muscle.

cardinal vein, one of the two large collecting veins in the fish.

cardiovascular-renal disease, involvement of the heart, blood vessels, and kidneys during high blood pressure.

carotene (*kair*-oh-teen), an orange pigment found in certain chromoplasts.

carotid (kuh-*rot*-id) **artery,** the great artery leading to the head region.

carrier, an organism which carries the agent of a disease without having the disease.

cartilage, a connective tissue, often called gristle, composing part of the body framework.

catabolism (kuh-*tab*-oh-lizm), the destructive phase of metabolism.

catalyst (*kat*-uh-list), a substance that aids a chemical reaction without being used up or changed.

caudal (*kaw*-dul), pertaining to the tail, as the caudal fin.

cell, the unit of structure and function of all living things.

cell plate, a structure which forms across the middle of the spindle in the late anaphase stage of a plant cell and which marks the point where the cell will split into two halves.

cell sap, the nonliving watery fluid in vacuoles that occur in the general cytoplasm.

cell wall, the outer, nonliving, cellulose wall secreted around plant cells.

cellulose (*sel*-you-lohs), a carbohydrate substance present in the walls of plant cells.

cementum, the covering of the root of a tooth.

central cylinder, the central core of a root, where conduction occurs.

central nervous system, the brain and spinal cord.

central neurons, those in the brain and spinal cord which connect motor nerves to sensory nerves.

cephalothorax (seh-fuh-loh-*thor*-aks), a body region in crustaceans and certain other animals consisting of the head and thorax.

cerebellum (sair-eh-*bel*-um), the brain region between the cerebrum and medulla, concerned with equilibrium and muscular coordination.

cerebrospinal (sair-uh-broh-*spy*-nul) **fluid,** a clear fluid in the brain ventricles and surrounding the spinal cord.

cerebrum (*sair*-eh-brum), the largest region of the human brain, containing the centers of both sensory and motor activity and numerous association fibers.

chain reaction, an atomic disintegration in which the particles produced cause other atoms to disintegrate.

chelicera (keh-*lis*-er-uh), the first pair of appendages of a spider, enlarged and serving as poison fangs.

chemical change, matter changing from one substance to another as a result of a chemical reaction.

chemotherapy, the use of specific chemicals in treating infectious diseases.

chitin (*ky*-tin), a material present in the exoskeleton of insects and other arthropods.

chlorophyll (*kloh*-roh-fil), a green pigment essential to food manufacture in plants.

chloroplast (*kloh*-roh-plast), a plastid containing chlorophyll.

chondriosome (*kon*-dree-oh-sohm), a structure in the cell whose exact function is unknown.

choroid (*kor*-oid) **layer,** the second and innermost layer of the eyeball.

chromatin (*kroh*-muh-tin), the substance forming chromosomes and containing genes.

chromatophores (kroh-*mat*-oh-fores), structures containing pigments in the skin of fish and other animals.

chromoplasts (*kroh*-moh-plasts), plastids containing pigments other than chlorophyll.

chromosome (*kroh*-moh-sohm), a rod-shaped, gene-bearing body formed in the cell nucleus during division.

chrysalis (*krih*-suh-lis), a hard case containing the pupal stage of a butterfly.

chyme (*kyme*), partly digested, acidic food as it leaves the stomach.

cilia (*sil*-ee-uh), tiny hairlike projections of cytoplasm.

ciliary muscles, those which control the shape of the lens.

circulation, the movement or flow of nutritive fluids, such as sap or blood, in living organisms.

climax plant, a species which assumes final prominence in a region.

clitellum (klih-*tel*-um), a swelling on the earthworm involved in reproduction.

cloaca (kloh-*ay*-kuh), a chamber below the large intestine in certain vertebrates into which the alimentary canal, ureters, bladder, and reproductive organs empty.

cochlea (*kok*-lee-uh), the hearing apparatus of the inner ear.

cocoon (kuh-*koon*), a silken case containing the pupal stage of a moth.

cohesion, the clinging together of molecules, as in a column of liquid.

collar cells, flagellated cells in sponges which set up water currents.

colloid (*kol*-loyd), a gelatinous substance such as protoplasm or egg albumen in which one or more solids are dispersed through a liquid.

colon (*koh*-lon), the large intestine.

colonial, living in a group, with each individual living independently but in close association with the others.

comb, the structure in the bee hive composed of six-sided cells made of wax.

commensalism (kuh-*men*-suh-lizm), one organism living in or on another, with only one of the two benefiting.

complete flower, one containing all parts — calyx, corolla, stamens, and pistil.

complete metamorphosis, four stages of development of certain insects — egg, larva, pupa, and adult.

complex sugar, one requiring chemical simplification and conversion before it can be absorbed by the blood and body tissues; disaccharides and polysaccharides.

compound (chemical), two or more elements combined chemically.

compound eye, an eye composed of numerous lenses and containing separate nerve endings, as in insects and crustaceans.

compound leaf, a leaf in which the blade is divided into leaflets.

conditioned reaction, a behavior pattern in which a particular response continually follows a specific stimulus.

cone, a reproductive part of a conifer; also a color-sensitive nerve ending in the retina of the eye.

conifer, a cone-bearing gymnosperm.

conjugation (kon-joo-*gay*-shun), a primitive form of sexual reproduction in *Spirogyra* and certain other algae and fungi in which the content of two cells unite; also an exchange of nuclear substance in the paramecium, resulting in rejuvenation of the cells.

connective tissue, a type of tissue which lies between groups of nerve, gland, and muscle cells and beneath epithelial cells; also includes bone, cartilage, blood, and lymph.

conservation, the preservation and wise use of natural resources.

contact infection, a disease spread through direct contact with an infected person.

contact poison, an insecticide which kills on coming in contact with the body of an insect.

contour farming, the practice of following the contour around a slope in plowing.

contour feathers, those which cover a bird's body to give it a smooth outline.

contractile vacuole, a large cavity in protozoans associated with the discharge of water from the cell and the regulating of osmotic pressure.

contraction (muscle), the shortening of a striated muscle.

conus arteriosus, a large vessel lying against the front side of the frog's heart and leading from the ventricle.

convolution (kon-voh-*loo*-shun), one of many irregular, rounded ridges on the surface of the brain.

cork, a tissue formed by the cork cambium which replaces the epidermis in woody stems and roots.

cork cambium, a layer of cells in the outer bark which produces new cork.

corm, a shortened underground stem in which the leaves are reduced to thin scales.

cornea (*kor*-nee-uh), a transparent bulge of the sclerotic layer of the eye in front of the iris, through which light rays pass.

corolla (kor-*oh*-luh), the petals of a flower, collectively.

coronary, pertaining to the heart.

coronary occlusion, a block in a coronary vessel due to a blood clot formed in the vessel (*thrombosis*) or a migrating clot which lodges there (*embolism*).

cortex, in roots and stems, a storage tissue; in organs such as the kidney and brain, the outer region.

cortin, a hormone complex secreted by the cortex of the adrenal glands.

cosmic rays, high-speed protons that bombard the atmosphere from outer space.

cotyledon, a seed leaf present in the embryo plant that serves as a food reservoir.

countershading, a form of protective coloration in which darker colors on the upper side of the animal fade into lighter colors on the lower side.

cover crop, a crop such as wheat and oats in which the plants grow close together and bind the soil with their closely mingled roots.

coverts, the small feathers which cover the lower portions of the quill feathers in birds.

coxa, a joint of the leg of the grasshopper

which, with the trochanter, acts like a ball and socket.

cranial cavity, the cavity in the skull containing the brain.

cranial nerves, the twelve pairs of nerves connected to the human brain.

cretinism (*kree*-tin-izm), a stunted condition resulting from lack of thyroid secretion.

crop, an organ of the alimentary canal of the earthworm, bird, and certain other animals which serves for food storage.

crop rotation, alternation in the planting of crops which use nitrates with those which replace nitrates.

cross-pollination, the transfer of pollen from the anther of one plant to the stigma of another.

crossing-over, the exchange of segments of two chromosomes, and the genes in the segments, when the two chromosomes lie side by side during reduction division.

crown, the exposed portion of a tooth above the gum line.

cud, food stored in the first stomach by ruminants and later chewed.

culture medium, a nutrient mixture used for growing bacteria, molds, and other fungi.

cuticle, a waxy, transparent layer covering the upper epidermis of certain leaves; the outer covering of an earthworm.

cyst (*sist*), in lower animals and plants, a spore with a capsule covering constituting a resting stage.

cytoplasm (*sy*-toh-plazm), the protoplasm lying outside the nucleus of a cell.

daughter cell, a newly formed cell resulting from the division of a previously existing cell.

decay, the reduction of the substances of a plant or animal body to simple compounds by the action, usually, of bacteria.

deciduous, woody plants which shed their leaves seasonally.

deficiency disease, a condition resulting from the lack of one or more vitamins.

degeneration, the loss of a system or structure by an animal which is a parasite.

dehiscent (dee-*hih*-sunt), a class of fruits which open and discharge seeds.

dehydration, loss of water from body tissues.

deliquescent (del-ih-*queh*-sunt), a type of branching in which the trunk divides into several main branches, resulting in a wide, spreading crown.

dendrite (*den*-dryte), a branching nerve process which carries an impulse toward the nerve cell body.

denitrification, the process that is carried on by denitrifying bacteria of breaking down ammonia, nitrites, and nitrates and liberating free nitrogen.

dentine, a substance that is relatively softer than enamel, forming the bulk of the tooth.

deoxygenation, the process during which oxygen is removed from the blood or tissues.

depletion, mineral exhaustion of the soil through continued planting of agricultural crops without proper fertilizing.

dermis, the skin layer beneath the epidermis.

diabetes mellitus (dy-uh-*bee*-teez meh-*lye*-tus), a condition resulting from the lack of insulin so that the body cannot store or oxidize sugar efficiently.

diaphragm (*dy*-uh-fram), a muscular partition separating the thoracic cavity from the abdominal cavity.

diastase (*dy*-uh-stase), an enzyme in green plants that changes starch to sugar.

diastolic blood pressure, arterial blood pressure maintained between heart beats.

dicotyledon, a seed plant with two seed leaves, or cotyledons.

diffuse root system, one composed of spreading roots of similar size.

diffusion, the spreading out of molecules in a given space.

digestion, the process during which foods are chemically simplified and made soluble so that they can be used by the cells.

dihybrid (dy-*hy*-brid), an offspring having genes for two contrasting characters.

dioecious (dy-*ee*-shus), bearing only staminate or pistillate flowers.

diploid number, the full set of chromosomes in a nucleus, with both members of each pair present.

disease, any condition which interferes with the normal functioning of the body of an organism.

disinfectant, a substance used in the chemical destruction of microbes.

disk flower, one of a cluster of flowers that fills the center of the head of a composite flower.

division of labor, specialization of cell functions resulting in interdependence.

dominant, in genetics, refers to a trait which appears in a hybrid.

dormancy, a period of inactivity.

dorsal, pertaining to the upper surface of an animal.

double-cross, one in which four pure-line parents are mixed in two crosses.

down feathers, those which form the plumage of newly hatched birds.

drone, the male bee.

droplet infection, a disease spread through cough or sneeze droplets bearing microbes from the respiratory tract or mouth.

drupe, a stone fruit.

ductless gland, one which secretes one or more hormones directly into the blood stream.

duodenum (doo-oh-*dee*-num), the region of the small intestine immediately following the stomach; in man, about 10 inches long.

dura mater, the outer of the three membranes of the brain and spinal cord.

ecology (ee-*kol*-uh-jee), the study of the relationships of living things to their surroundings.

ectoderm, the outer layer of cells of a simple animal body; in vertebrates, the layer of cells from which the skin and nervous system develop.

ectoplasm (*ek*-toh-plazm), the outer layer of thin, clear cytoplasm, as in the ameba.

egg, a female gamete, or germ cell.

electron, a subatomic particle with a negative electrical charge.

electromagnetic radiation, energy which travels in waves.

element, a substance which cannot be broken down into a simpler substance.

elongation region, the area behind the embryonic region of a root or stem in which cells grow in length.

embryo, a developing organism.

embryo sac, the tissue in a plant ovule which contains the egg, the antipodals, the polar nuclei, and the synergids.

embryonic region, the area near the tip of a root or stem in which cells are formed by division.

enamel, the hard covering of the crown of a tooth.

endocrine (*en*-doh-krin) **gland,** a ductless gland that secretes hormones directly into the blood.

endoderm, the inner layer of cells of a simple animal body; in vertebrates, the layer of cells from which the lining of the digestive system, the liver, the lungs, etc. develop.

endodermis, a single layer of cells located at the inner edge of the cortex of a root.

endoplasm (*en*-doh-plazm), the inner layer of cytoplasm, as in the ameba.

endoskeleton, the internal skeleton of vertebrates.

endosperm, the tissue in some seeds containing stored food.

endosperm nucleus, that formed by the union of two polar nuclei in the embryo sac just before fertilization.

endotoxin, an insoluble toxin which remains in a bacterial cell until the cell disintegrates.

entomologist (en-toh-*mol*-uh-jist), a person who studies insects.

environment, all those factors, both living and nonliving, which make up the surroundings of an organism.

enzyme (*en*-zym), a catalyst present in a digestive fluid which brings about a chemical change in food.

epidermis (ep-ih-*der*-mis), the outer tissue of a young root or stem, a leaf, and other plant parts; the outer layer of the skin.

epiglottis (ep-ih-*glot*-tis), a leaflike lid which partially covers the opening of the trachea during swallowing.

epinephrine (eh-pih-*nef*-reen), the hormone secreted by the medulla of the adrenal glands.

epithelial tissue, that composing the coverings of various organs of the body.

equator, the imaginary center of the cell.

equilibrium, a state of balance between forces or substances.

erepsin (ee-*rep*-sin), a digestive enzyme of the intestinal fluid which changes peptids to amino acids.

ergosterol, a compound present in the human skin from which vitamin D is produced on exposure to the sun's rays.

erosion (uh-*roh*-zhun), the loss of soil by the action of water or wind.

esophagus (ee-*sof*-uh-gus), the food tube, or gullet, which connects the mouth and the stomach.

estivation (es-tih-*vay*-shun), a period of summer inactivity in certain animals.

estrogen (*es*-troh-jen), a female hormone secreted by the ovaries.

eugenics (you-*jeh*-niks), the science of human heredity.

Eustachian (you-*stay*-kee-un) **tube,** a tube connecting the pharynx with the middle ear.

excited atom, one which is unstable and gives off particles.

excretion (eks-*kree*-shun), the process by which waste materials are removed from living cells or from the body.

excurrent, a form of branching in which a single stem extends through a plant as a shaft.

excurrent pore, in sponges, the osculum.

excurrent siphon, the structure in the clam through which water passes out of the body.

exoskeleton, the hard, outer covering or skeleton of certain animals, especially arthropods.

exotoxin, a soluble toxin excreted by certain bacteria and absorbed by the tissues of the host.

expiration, the discharge of air from the lungs.

explosive decompression, a sudden loss of pressure.

extensor, a muscle which straightens a joint.

extinct, no longer in existence.

eyespot, the sensory structure in the euglena and planaria which is believed to perceive light and dark.

fang, a hollow tooth of a poisonous snake through which venom is ejected.

fat bodies, structures in the frog which store fat.

fats, a class of foods which supplies energy to the body.

fatty acids, one of the end-products of fat digestion.

feces (*fee*-seez), solid intestinal waste material.

femur (*fee*-mer), the long bone of the upper leg.

fertilization, the union of sperm and egg.

fetus (*fee*-tus), the later stages of embryonic development in vertebrates.

fever, elevation of the normal body temperature, associated with infection.

fibrin (*fy*-brin), a substance formed during blood clotting by the union of thrombin and fibrinogen.

fibrinogen (fy-*brin*-oh-jen), a blood protein present in the plasma, involved in clotting.

fibrous root, a small, slender, secondary root that is generally very much branched.

fibrovascular (fy-broh-*vas*-kyoo-ler) **bundle,** a strand containing xylem and phloem tissues in higher plants.

filament, a stalk of a stamen, bearing the anther at its tip; in algae, a threadlike group of cells.

filoplume, the slender, hairlike feathers in birds, having a tuft at the end.

filtrable virus, an organism, small enough to pass through the pores of a bacteriological filter, which invades living tissue.

fin, a membranous appendage of a fish and certain other aquatic animals.

fire line, a lane cut through a forest to prevent a possible fire from spreading.

fission, cell reproduction by division into two parts.

flagellate, an organism bearing one or more whiplike appendages, or flagella.

flagellum (fluh-*jel*-um), a whiplike projection of cytoplasm used in locomotion by certain simple organisms.

fleshy root, an enlarged root which serves as a reservoir of food for the plant.

flexor, a muscle which bends a joint.

flower, an organ of a flowering plant specialized for reproduction.

follicle, an indentation in the skin from which hair grows.

food, any substance absorbed into the body which yields material for energy, growth, and repair of tissue and regulation of the life processes without harming the organism.

food-borne infection, any infection caused by contaminated food.

food infection, the introduction of infectious organisms into the body by means of food.

food poisoning, a condition resulting from the action of preformed toxins present in food.

forebrain, that part of the brain composed of the cerebrum.

fossils, preserved remains or mineral replacements of living things of previous ages.

fovea (*foh*-vee-uh), a small, sensitive spot on the retina of the eye where cones are especially abundant.

fraternal twins, those which are produced from two separately fertilized eggs.

fruit, a ripened ovary, with or without associated parts.

fumigant, a gaseous insecticide or chemical used in destroying animal pests.

functional disorder, a condition resulting from impaired activity of a body organ.

fungus (*fung*-gus), a thallophyte plant lacking chlorophyll and, therefore, deriving nourishment from an organic source.

g, the unit used to measure the increase in weight due to an accelerating force.

gall bladder, a sac in which bile from the liver is stored and concentrated.

gamete (gam-*eet*), a male or female reproductive cell, or germ cell.

gametophyte, the stage which produces gametes in an organism having alternation of generations.

gamma globulin, a blood protein sometimes used to give temporary immunity to polio.

gamma rays, extremely short electromagnetic waves, similar to X rays, given off by radioactive materials.

ganglion (*gang*-glee-un), a mass of nerve cells lying outside of the central nervous system.

gastric, referring to the stomach.

gastric caeca (*see*-kuh), structures in the digestive system of the grasshopper.

gastrovascular cavity, the central cavity of Coelenterata.

gastrula (*gas*-troo-luh), a stage in embryonic development during which the primary germ layers are formed.

gemmule (*jem*-yoole), a coated cell mass produced by the parent sponge and capable of growing into an adult sponge.

gene (*jeen*), a determiner of heredity, located in a chromosome.

generative nucleus, the nucleus in a pollen grain which divides to form two sperm.

genetics (jeh-*neh*-tiks), the science of heredity.

genus (*jee*-nus), a group of closely related species.

geologist, a scientist who studies the earth.

geotropism (jee-*ot*-roh-pizm), the response of plants to gravity.

germination, growth of the seed when favorable conditions occur.

gestation (jes-*tay*-shun) **period,** the period between fertilization and birth of a mammal.

gill, an organ modified for absorbing dissolved oxygen from water; in mushrooms, a platelike structure bearing the reproductive organs.

gill arch, a cartilaginous structure in fish to which the gill filaments are attached.

gill filament, one of many threadlike projections forming the gills in fish.

gill raker, fingerlike projections of the gill arches in fish.

girdling, destruction of the entire bark region around a tree.

gizzard, an organ in the digestive system of the earthworm and birds modified for grinding food.

glomerulus (gloh-*mair*-you-lus), the knob of capillaries in a Bowman's capsule.

glottis, the upper opening of the trachea in land vertebrates.

glucose (*gloo*-kohs), a simple sugar, or monosaccharide, which is a product of photosynthesis and which is also an end-product of digestion.

glycerin, one of the end-products of fat digestion.

glycogen (*gly*-koh-jen), animal starch, formed in the liver and muscles.

goiter (simple), an enlarged condition of the thyroid gland, resulting from iodine deficiency.

gonadotropic hormone, a hormone of the anterior lobe of the pituitary gland which influences activity of the reproductive organs.

gonads (*goh*-nadz), the male and female reproductive organs.

grafting, the union of the cambium layers of two woody stems, one the stock and the other the scion.

gray matter, those nerve cells in the cerebral cortex and spinal cord which lack a fatty sheath.

green gland, an excretory organ of crustaceans.

ground water, that which enters the soil following precipitation.

guard cell, one of the two epidermal cells surrounding a stoma.

gullet, the passageway to a food vacuole in paramecia; the food tube or esophagus.

gully erosion, an advanced stage of water erosion following rill erosion.

guttation (guh-*tay*-shun), the loss of excess water through veins at the margin of a leaf.

haploid number, half the number of chromosomes that are ordinarily present in the nucleus; occurs during reduction division.

haustoria (haws-*tor*-ee-uh), short, branching hyphae that absorb nourishment in certain fungi.

Haversian (hav-*er*-zhun) **canals,** numerous channels penetrating the bony layer of a bone.

heartwood, inner, inactive wood usually darker in color than sapwood.

hemoglobin (hee-moh-*gloh*-bin), an iron-containing protein compound giving red corpuscles their color; combines easily with oxygen.

hemophilia (hee-moh-*fee*-lee-uh), an inherited disease in which the blood does not clot properly.

herbaceous (her-*bay*-shus), an annual stem with little woody tissue.

heredity, the transmission of traits from parent to offspring.

hermaphroditic (her-maf-roh-*dih*-tik), having the organs of both sexes.

heterocysts (*heh*-ter-oh-sists), in *Nostoc,* empty cells with thick walls which enable the filaments to break into shorter pieces.

heterogametes, male and female gametes which are unlike in appearance and structure.

hexose, the saccharide, or sugar unit, of which all sugars are composed.

hibernate, to spend the winter months in an inactive condition.

hilum (*hy*-lum), the scar on a seed where it was attached to the ovary wall.

hindbrain, that part of the brain which is composed of the cerebellum, the pons, and the medulla.

holdfast, the special cell at the base of certain algae which anchors them to the substrate.

homologous (huh-*mol*-uh-gus) **organs,** those similar in origin and structure but not necessarily in function.

hormone (*hor*-mohn), the chemical secretion of a ductless gland producing a definite physiological effect.

horns, in mammals, permanent bony structures which grow from the base throughout life; also the tips of the wings of the gray matter of the spinal cord.

horny layer, the outer layer of the epidermis; in bivalves, the outermost layer of the shell.

host, in a parasitic relationship, the organism from which the parasite derives its food supply.

humus (*hyoo*-mus), black organic matter in the soil formed by the decomposition of plant and animal remains.

hybrid, an offspring from a cross between parents differing in one or more traits.

hybrid vigor, having desirable characteristics lacking in both parents.

hybridization, the crossing of two different varieties to produce a new one.

hydrophytes (*hy*-droh-fytes), plants which grow in water or partially submerged in water in very wet surroundings.

hydrotropism (hy-*drot*-roh-pizm), the response of roots to water.

hyperthyroidism, overactivity of the thyroid gland and its attendant symptoms.

hypha (*hy*-fuh), a threadlike filament of the vegetative body of a fungus.

hypocotyl (hy-poh-*kot*-ul), that part of a plant embryo from whose lower end the root develops.

hypothesis, a scientific idea or working theory.

hypothyroidism, underactivity of the thyroid gland and its attendant symptoms.

identical twins, those which develop from the fertilization of one egg which later splits into two organisms.

ileum (*il*-ee-um), the third and longest region of the small intestine.

imbibition (im-bih-*bih*-shun), the absorption of liquids by a solid with the result that the solid swells.

immune therapy, the assistance and stimulation of the natural body defenses in preventing infectious disease.

immunity, the power of the body to resist a disease by natural or artificial means.

imperfect flower, one in which either the stamens or the pistils are missing.

improvement cutting, the removal of diseased or injured trees from a managed forest.

inbreeding, line breeding.

incisor, a tooth in the front of the jaw; highly developed for gnawing in rodents.

inclusion, a nonliving substance in a cell.

incomplete dominance, the equal appearance or blending of two unlike characteristics in the offspring, resulting from a cross of these characteristics.

incomplete flower, one in which one or more of the parts is missing.

incomplete metamorphosis, the life stages of certain insects consisting of the egg, several nymph stages, and the adult.

incubation, the providing of ideal conditions for growth and development, as in the incubation of eggs or the growth of bacteria.

incurrent pore, one of many holes in the sponge through which water passes into the animal.

incurrent siphon, the structure in a clam through which water passes into the body.

indehiscent (in-dee-*hih*-sunt), a class of fruits which do not open to discharge seeds.

inoculation, voluntary addition of germs or viruses to a culture medium or to a living organism.

inorganic, not containing a hydrocarbon or derivative.

insect vector, an insect which carries the agent of a disease.

insecticide, a chemical used to destroy insects.

insertion, the attachment of a muscle at its movable end.

inspiration, the intake of air into the lungs.

instinct, a natural urge, or drive, not depending on experience or intelligence.

insulin, a hormone secretion of the islet cells of the pancreas which regulates the oxidation of sugar in the tissues.

integument, one of the two layers of the walls of an ovule.

interdependence, the dependence of cells on other cells for complete functioning, or of organisms on the activities of other organisms.

internode, the space between two nodes.

interphase, the period of growth of a cell which occurs before and after mitosis.

intestine, the portion or portions of the alimentary canal extending beyond the stomach.

invertebrate, an animal lacking a backbone.

involuntary muscle, one which cannot be controlled at will.

ionization, the formation of ions from molecules present in cells due to bombardment by radioactive particles.

iris, the muscular, colored portion of the eye, behind the cornea and surrounding the pupil.

irrigation (of soil), diversion of water into an area during dry periods.

irritability, the ability to respond to a stimulus.

islets of Langerhans, the special cells in the pancreas which secrete insulin.

isogametes, male and female gametes which look alike.

isotope, atoms of an element that have different numbers of neutrons than the most frequently occurring variety.

jejunum (jeh-*june*-um), a section of the small intestine lying between the duodenum and the ileum.

joint, the point at which two separate bones are joined by ligaments.

kidney, a glandular organ which excretes urine.

kinesthetic sense, the awareness of the whereabouts of the body parts when moved.

Koch postulates, the steps in Robert Koch's procedure in the investigation of anthrax.

labium (*lay*-bee-um), the lower portion or " lip " of an insect's mouth.

labrum (*lay*-brum), the two-lobed upper portion of an insect's mouth.

lactase, a digestive enzyme of the intestinal fluid which changes lactose to glucose.

lacteal (*lak*-tee-ul), a lymph vessel which absorbs digested fat from the intestinal wall.

lactic acid, the chemical produced when food is oxidized in the cells for energy.

larva (*lar*-vuh), the stage which follows the egg in the development of certain animals.

larynx, the voice box; also called the " Adam's apple."

lateral bud, a bud which develops at a point other than at the end of a stem.

lateral line, a row of pitted scales along each side of the fish, functioning as a sensory organ.

Law of Conservation of Energy, in ordinary chemical changes, energy is neither created nor destroyed.

Law of Conservation of Matter, in ordinary chemical changes, matter is neither created nor destroyed.

Law of Dominance, in a cross involving two characters, one character may dominate the other.

Law of Independent Assortment, the separation of pairs of genes and distribution of the genes to gametes (spores in lower plants) during reduction division is entirely independent of the distribution of other genes.

Law of Segregation, a pair of factors (genes) is segregated, or separated, during the formation of gametes (spores in lower plants) in reduction division.

Law of Unit Characters, the various hereditary characteristics are controlled by factors (genes), and these factors occur in pairs.

leaching, the loss of soluble soil minerals as a result of the movement of ground water.

leaf scar, a mark on a twig left at the point of attachment of a leaf stalk of a previous growing season.

leaflet, a division of a compound leaf.

legume (leg-*yoom*), a dry, dehiscent pod fruit with many seeds attached in a row along the side of the fruit.

lens, the transparent disk by means of which light rays are directed to the retina of the eye.

lenticel (*len*-tih-sul), a small pore in the epidermis or bark of a young stem through which gases are exchanged.

lethal gene, one which bears a characteristic which is usually fatal to the organism.

leucoplast (*lew*-koh-plast), a colorless plastid serving as a food reservoir in certain plant cells.

life function, a vital activity of a plant or animal.

life span, the period of existence of an organism.

ligament, a tough strand of connective tissue which holds bones together at a joint.

line breeding, the process of plants being self-pollinated over several generations, removing offspring with undesirable traits in each generation; inbreeding in plants and animals.

lipase (*ly*-pase), a digestive enzyme of the pancreatic fluid that changes fats to glycerin and fatty acids.

liver, the largest organ in the human body, associated with several vital activities including digestion and sugar metabolism.

locomotion, the spontaneous movement of an organism from one place to another.

lung, an organ for aerial breathing.

lymph (*limf*), the clear, liquid part of blood which enters the tissue spaces and lymph vessels.

macronucleus, the large nucleus of the paramecium and certain other protozoans.

maggot, the larval stage of a fly.

Malpighian (mal-*pig*-ee-un) **tubules,** the structures in the digestive system of the grasshopper which collect wastes from the blood.

maltase, a digestive enzyme of the intestinal fluid which changes maltose to glucose.

mammary glands, those found in female mammals which secrete milk and give the class its name.

mandible (*man*-dih-bul), a strong, cutting mouth part of arthropods; a jaw, as in the beak of a bird or the bony structure of a mammal.

mantle, the tissue covering the soft parts of a mollusk.

marine, living in salt water.

marrow, the soft tissue in the central cavity of a larger bone.

mass selection, the picking of ideal plants or animals from a large number to serve as parents for further breeding.

matrix, a gelatinous secretion of cells of *Nostoc* and certain other blue-green algae.

maturation region, the area of a root or stem where embryonic cells mature into tissues.

maxilla (max-*il*-uh), a mouth part of an arthropod; the upper jaw of vertebrates.

maxilliped (max-*il*-ih-ped), a "jaw foot," or first thoracic appendage, of the crayfish and other arthropods.

medulla (meh-*dul*-uh), in the kidney, the inner portion containing pyramids which, in turn, contain numerous tubules; in the adrenal gland, the inner portion which secretes epinephrine.

medulla oblongata, the enlargement at the upper end of the spinal cord, at the base of the brain.

meiosis (my-*oh*-sis), the type of cell division in which there is reduction of chromosomes to the haploid number during oögenesis and spermatogenesis.

membrane, a thin material through which substances may pass.

meninges (meh-*nin*-jeez), the three membranes covering the brain and spinal cord.

mesentery (*mes*-en-tair-ee), a folded membrane which connects to the intestines and the dorsal body wall of vertebrates.

mesoderm, the middle layer of cells in an embryo.

mesophytes (*mez*-oh-fytes), plants which occupy neither extremely wet nor extremely dry surroundings.

mesothorax (mes-oh-*thor*-aks), the middle portion of the thorax of an insect, bearing the second pair of legs and, usually, a pair of wings.

metabolism (meh-*tab*-oh-lizm), the sum of the chemical processes of the body.

metamorphosis (meh-tuh-*mor*-foh-sis), a marked change in structure of an animal during its growth, as the change from larve to pupa and adult in insects.

metaphase, the stage of mitosis in which the chromosomes line up at the equator.

metathorax, the posterior portion of the thorax of an insect, bearing the third pair of legs and the second pair of wings.

Metazoa, many-celled animals.

micronucleus, a small nucleus found in the paramecium and certain other protozoans.

micropyle (*my*-kroh-pile), the opening in the ovule wall through which the pollen tube enters.

midbrain, that part of the brain which is composed of nerve fibers connecting the forebrain to the hindbrain.

middle lamella (luh-*mel*-uh), a portion of the plant cell wall that forms a common boundary between two touching cells.

midrib, the large, central vein of a pinnately veined leaf.

migration, seasonal movement of animals from one place to another.

milt, the spermatic fluid of a male fish.

mimicry, a form of protective coloration in which an animal closely resembles another kind of animal or an object in its environment.

mitochondria (my-toh-*kon*-dree-uh), chondriosomes.

mitosis (my-*toh*-sis), the division of chromosomes preceding the division of cytoplasm.

mixed nerve, one which consists of both sensory and motor nerve fibers.

mixture, two or more substances which intermingle without chemical combination.

molar, a large tooth for grinding, highly developed in herbivores.

molecule, a unit mass of a compound, formed by the chemical combination of two or more atoms.

molting, shedding of the outer layer of exoskeleton of arthropods, or of a scale layer of reptiles, or of plumage of birds.

monocotyledon, a flowering plant which develops a single seed leaf or cotyledon.

monoecious (mon-*ee*-shus), bearing staminate and pistillate flowers on different parts of the same plant.

motor end plate, the terminus of the axon of a motor nerve in a muscle.

motor nerve, any nerve which consists only of axons.

motor neuron, one which carries impulses from the brain or spinal cord to a muscle or gland.

mucous membrane, a form of epithelial tissue which lines the body openings and digestive tract and secretes mucus.

mucus (*myou*-kus), a slimy secretion of mucous glands.

mulch, a substance placed on or in the soil to retard water loss or to improve soil texture.

multicellular, having many cells.

muscle tissue, one found in all animals, except the lowest, which produces movement by contraction.

mutant, an offspring possessing a characteristic which was not inherited.

mutation, a change in genetic make-up resulting in a new characteristic which may be passed on to offspring.

mycelium (my-*see*-lee-um), the vegetative body of molds and other fungi, composed of hyphae.

mycologist, a scientist who studies fungi.

mycorhiza (my-koh-*ry*-zuh), a fungus which lives in a symbiotic relationship with the roots of trees and other higher plants.

natural immunity, one which is present in the individual at birth and is not artificially acquired.

natural selection, the result of survival in the struggle for existence among organisms possessing those characteristics which give them an advantage.

nematocyst (*nem*-uh-toh-sist), a stinging cell in coelenterates.

nephridia (neh-*frih*-dee-uh), the excretory structures in worms, mollusks, and certain arthropods.

nephron, one of the numerous excretory structures in the kidney, including the Bowman's capsule, glomerulus, and tubules.

nerve, a cordlike structure containing bundles of nerve fibers, or processes.

nerve cell body, the body of a neuron containing cytoplasm and a nucleus.

nerve net, the network of sensory cells in the hydra.

neuron (*new*-ron), a nerve cell body and its processes.

neutron, a particle in the nucleus of an atom which carries no electrical charge.

nictitating (*nik*-tih-tay-ting) **membrane,** a thin, transparent covering, or lid, associated with the eyes of certain vertebrates; a third eyelid.

nitrification, the action of a group of soil bacteria on ammonia, producing nitrates.

nitrogen fixation, the process by which certain bacteria in soil or on the roots of leguminous plants convert free nitrogen into nitrogen compounds which the plants can use.

node, a growing region of a stem from which leaves, branches, or flowers develop.

nonprotein nitrogen, nitrogen-containing waste products of cell activity which are taken up by the blood.

notochord (*noh*-toh-kord), a rod of cartilage running longitudinally along the dorsal side of lower chordates and always present in the early embryological stages of vertebrates.

nuclear membrane, a living membrane surrounding the nucleus.

nuclear sap, the liquid present in a living nucleus.

nucleolus (new-*klee*-oh-lus), a small, spherical body within the nucleus.

nucleoplasm (*new*-klee-oh-plazm), the dense, gelatinous living content of the nucleus.

nucleus, a division of the protoplast of a cell, important in cell division; the central mass of an atom, containing protons and neutrons.

nymph, a stage between egg and adult in an insect having incomplete metamorphosis.

olfactory lobe, the region of the brain registering smell.

olfactory nerve, the nerve leading from the olfactory receptor endings to the olfactory lobe of the brain.

oögonium (oh-oh-*goh*-nee-um), an egg-producing cell in certain thallophytes.

oötid (oh-*oh*-tid), a cell which matures into an egg.

open system, a circulatory system in which the blood is not confined in a continuous system of vessels.

operculum (oh-*per*-kyoo-lum), the gill cover in fish.

opsonin (*op*-soh-nin), a blood antibody which prepares bacteria for ingestion by white corpuscles.

optic lobe, the region of the brain registering sight.

optic nerve, the nerve leading from the retina of the eye to the optic lobe of the brain.

oral groove, a deep cavity along one side of the paramecium and similar Protozoa.

organ, different tissues grouped together to perform a function or functions.

organic, containing a hydrocarbon or derivative.

organic diseases, those originating in an organ and not due to pathogenic organisms; noninfectious.

organic nutrients, the three classes of foods: carbohydrates, fats, and proteins.

organism, a complete and entire living thing.

origin, the attachment of a muscle at its immovable end.

ornithology, the study of birds.

osculum (*os*-kyoo-lum), an opening in the central cavity of sponges through which water leaves the animal; the excurrent pore.

osmosis (os-*moh*-sis), the diffusion of water through a semipermeable membrane from a region of greater concentration of water to a region of lesser concentration.

osmotic pressure, that built up inside a cell as water diffuses into it by means of osmosis.

ossification (os-ih-fih-*kay*-shun), the process by which cartilage cells of childhood are replaced by bone cells, resulting in a hardening of the body framework as the organism grows.

ostia (*os*-tee-uh), pairs of openings through which blood enters the crayfish heart.

outbreeding, hybridization.

ovary, the basal part of the pistil containing the ovules which become seeds; a female reproductive organ.

oviduct, a tube in a female through which eggs travel from an ovary.

oviparous (oh-*vip*-uh-rus), egg-laying animals.

ovipositor (oh-vih-*poz*-ih-tor), an egg-laying organ in insects.

ovoviviparous (oh-voh-vy-*vip*-uh-rus), bringing forth the young alive after they have developed without placental connection in the mother.

ovule, a structure in the ovary of a flower which, when fertilized, can become a seed.

oxidation, the union of any substance with oxygen and the resulting release of energy.

oxygenation, the process whereby the blood is supplied with oxygen from the lungs.

oxyhemoglobin, hemoglobin with which oxygen has combined.

palisade layer, a dense tissue in green leaves and twigs consisting of elongated cells.

palmate venation, leaf veining in which the main veins radiate from a central point.

palpus (*pal*-pus), an appendage of a mouth part of an arthropod.

pancreas, a gland located between the stomach and intestine which is both endocrine and digestive.

parallel venation, a vein pattern characteristic of the leaves of a monocot.

parasite, an organism which obtains its food entirely from another living thing.

parasympathetic nervous system, a division of the autonomic nervous system.

parathormone, the hormone secreted by the parathyroid glands.

parathyroid, one of the four small ductless glands embedded in the thyroid.

parenchyma (puh-*ren*-kih-muh), the thin-walled, soft tissue in plants forming petals, blades, cortex, and pith.

parotid (puh-*rot*-id), one of the pair of salivary glands near the ear.

particulate radiation, streams of particles emitted by radioactive substances.

passive immunity, immunity acquired artificially by the injection of antibodies.

pasteurization, the process of killing and/or retarding the growth of bacteria in milk by heating.

pathogenic, disease-causing.

pearly layer, the inner layer of the shell of bivalves.

peat, a substance formed by the decomposition of plants in the presence of water.

pectin substances, jellylike material in the middle lamella of plant cells.

pedicel (*ped*-ih-sel), the stalk that supports a single flower.

pedipalps, the second pair of head appendages in spiders.

pellicle (*pel*-ih-kul), a thickened membrane surrounding the cell of a paramecium.

pelvis, the hip girdle, in man consisting of the ilium, ischium, and pubis bones; the central portion of a kidney.

pepsin, a digestive enzyme of the gastric juice which changes proteins to peptones and proteoses.

peptone, a stage in protein digestion prior to the formation of amino acids.

perennials, plants which grow more than two growing seasons.

perfect flower, one which has both stamens and pistils.

pericardial cavity, the area in which the heart lies.

pericardial sinus, a cavity surrounding the crayfish heart.

pericardium, the membrane around the heart.

pericycle, the tissue in roots from which secondary roots arise.

periderm, the corky layer forming the outer edge of a root after secondary thickening.

periodontal (pair-ee-oh-*don*-tul) **membrane,** the fibrous structure that anchors the root of the tooth in the jaw socket.

periosteum (pair-ee-*os*-tee-um), the tough membrane covering the outside of a bone.

peripheral nervous system, the nerves communicating the central nervous system and other parts of the body.

permeable (*per*-mee-uh-bul) **membrane,** one which allows substances to pass through it.

petal, one of the colored parts of the flower. (In some flowers the sepals are also colored.)

petiole (*pet*-ee-ohl), the stalk of a leaf.

petrifaction, the replacement of skeletal remains by mineral matter.

pharynx (*fair*-inks), the muscular throat cavity, extending up over the soft palate and to the nasal cavity.

phloem (*flow*-em), the tissue in roots and stems which conducts dissolved food substances downward.

photoperiodism, the dependence of some plants on the relation between the length of light and the length of darkness in a given day.

photoreceptor, an organ which is sensitive to light.

photosynthesis (foh-toh-*sin*-theh-sis), the process by which certain living plant cells combine carbon dioxide and water, in the presence of chlorophyll and light energy, to form glucose and release oxygen as a waste product.

phototropism (foh-*tot*-troh-pizm), the response of plants to light.

phycocyanin (fy-koh-*sy*-uh-nin), the blue pigment found in certain algae.

phylum, one of the large divisions in the classification of plants and animals.

physical change, one in which no change occurs in the chemical composition.

physical factors, the nonbiological elements in the environment.

physiology, the study of the functions, or life activities, of living things.

pia mater, the inner of the three membranes of the brain and spinal cord.

pineal (*pin*-ee-ul) **body,** a gland of undetermined function that lies between the cerebral hemispheres and near the pituitary gland.

pinnate venation, a vein pattern in which the leaves have a single large vein extending through the center of the blade.

pistil, the part of the flower bearing the ovary at its base.

pistillate flower, one containing only pistils.

pith, a tissue of roots and stems consisting of thin-walled cells and used for food storage.

pith rays, thin cellular layers leading from the pith to the bark in stems of dicotyledons.

pitocin (pih-*toh*-sin), a hormone secreted by the posterior lobe of the pituitary gland which stimulates smooth muscles.

pitressin (pih-*tres*-in), a hormone secreted by the posterior lobe of the pituitary gland which regulates the amount of water in the blood and the blood pressure.

pituitary (pih-*tew*-ih-tair-ee) **gland,** a ductless gland composed of two lobes, located beneath the cerebrum.

placenta (pluh-*sen*-tuh), a vascular structure that is present during the development of the embryo in the uterus.

plasma, the liquid portion of blood tissue.

plasma membrane, in plants, a thin living membrane located where cytoplasm lies against the cell wall; in animals, the outer surface of the cell.

plasmolysis (plaz-*mol*-ih-sis), the collapse of cell protoplasm due to loss of water.

plastids, living bodies in the cytoplasm of plant cells.

plastron, the lower shell of the turtle.

platelet, the smallest of the solid components in the blood, releasing thromboplastin in clotting.

pleural membrane, one of two membranes surrounding each lung.

plexus, a mass of nerve cell bodies.

plumule (*ploom*-yool), that part of a plant embryo from which the shoot develops.

polar nuclei, the two structures in the embryo sac in flowers which fuse to form the endosperm nucleus.

pollen grain, the male reproductive structure of flowering plants.

pollen sacs, structures in the anther containing pollen grains.

pollen tube, the tube formed by a pollen grain when it grows down the style.

pollination, the transfer of pollen from anther to stigma.

polyp, one of the stages in the life cycle of coelenterates.

polyploidy, the condition of a plant having some multiple of the diploid number of chromosomes.

pome, an applelike fruit consisting of a ripened receptacle surrounding the ovary.

pons, a part of the hindbrain located in the brain stem.

portal circulation, an extensive system of veins which lead from the stomach, pancreas, small intestine, and colon, unite and enter the liver.

posterior, tail, or rear end, of an animal.

precipitin (pree-*sih*-pih-tin), a blood antibody which causes bacteria to settle out.

predator (*pred*-uh-ter), any animal which preys on other animals.

premolars, large teeth for grinding.

primaries, in birds, those quill feathers which grow from the end section of the wing.

primary oöcyte (*oh*-oh-syte), the structure in the female gonads which divides to form the secondary oöcyte and first polar body.

primary root, the first root of the plant coming from the seed.

prismatic layer, the middle of the shell of bivalves.

proboscis (proh-*bos*-is), a tubular mouth part in certain insects; the trunk of an elephant.

proglottid, a segment of a tapeworm's body.

prolegs, the extra pairs of fleshy legs at the end of the abdomen in caterpillars.

propagation, the multiplication of plants by vegetative parts.

prophase, the stage of mitosis in which chromosomes form and split longitudinally.

propolis, a brown substance gathered by bees from the sticky leaf buds of some plants.

prostomium (proh-*stoh*-mee-um), a kind of upper lip in the earthworm.

protective coloration, the blending of an organism with the color of its surroundings.

protective resemblance, similarity in shape to something in the environment.

proteins (*proh*-tee-ins), a complex tissue-building class of foods containing not only C, H, and O, but also N, S, and usually P.

proteoses (proh-tee-*oh*-seez), a stage in protein digestion prior to the formation of amino acids.

prothallus (proh-*thal*-us), the tiny heart-shaped structure which develops from the spore of the fern.

prothorax, the first segment of an insect's thorax to which the head and first pair of legs are attached.

prothrombin (proh-*throm*-bin), an enzyme produced in the liver; it is an inactive part of blood plasma except during clotting.

proton, a particle in the nucleus of an atom which bears a positive electrical charge.

protonema (proh-toh-*nee*-muh), a filamentous structure produced by a spore in mosses.

protoplasm (*proh*-toh-plazm), the living substance which is the physical basis of all life.

protoplast, all the living content of a cell.

Protozoa (proh-toh-*zoh*-uh), one-celled animals.

pruning, the cutting off of surplus branches of trees and shrubs.

pseudopodium (soo-doh-*poh*-dee-um), a "false foot" of the ameba or amebalike cells.

psychiatrist (sy-*ky*-uh-trist), a doctor who specializes in treating mental disturbances.

ptyalin (*ty*-uh-lin), a digestive enzyme of saliva which changes starch to maltose.

pulmocutaneous (pul-moh-kyoo-*tay*-nee-us) **arteries,** those in the frog that branch to the lungs, skin, and mouth membrane.

pulmonary, pertaining to the lungs.

pulp cavity, the area within the dentine of a tooth containing nerves and blood vessels.

pulse, regular expansion of the artery walls caused by the beating of the heart.

pupa (*pyoo*-puh), the stage in an insect having complete metamorphosis following the larva stage.

pupil, the opening in the front of the eyeball, the size of which is controlled by the iris.

pus, collection of dead bacteria and white corpuscles at the site of an infection.

pyloric caeca, pouches extending from the intestine in fish.

pylorus, a muscular valve situated at the junction of the stomach and intestine in vertebrates.

pyramids, conical projections of the medulla of the kidney.

pyrenoid (*py*-reh-noid), a small protein body surrounded by starch on a chloroplast of *Spirogyra* and certain other algae.

quadrate bone, a bone in the snake's skull to which the lower jaw is attached.

quarantine, isolation of plants or animals to prevent the spread of suspected infection.

queen, the egg-laying female bee in a hive.

quill feathers, the large stiff feathers in the wing or tail of a bird.

rachis (*ray*-kis), the axis of quill feathers of a bird.

radial symmetry, the type exhibited by an organism which may be divided into two equal parts by any plane which passes through the diameter of the disk and the central axis.

radiation, a movement of energy from one place to another.

radioactive, a state in which a substance is unstable and gives off particles as it disintegrates.

radula (*rad*-yoo-luh), a tonguelike structure in snails which acts as a scraper.

ray flowers, those around the outside of a composite flower, not seed-producing.

reaction time, the elapsed time between the moment a stimulus is received and a response occurs.

receptacle, the end of the flower stalk bearing the reproductive structures.

receptor, a cell or group of cells which receive a stimulus.

recessive, refers to a gene or character which is masked when a dominant gene in a pair is present.

rectum, the posterior portion of the large intestine, above the anus.

red corpuscles, the cells in blood containing hemoglobin.

reduction division, the reduction of chromosomes during meiosis from the diploid number to the haploid number.

reflex action, a stimulus causes the passage of a sensory nerve impulse to the spinal cord or brain, from which, involuntarily, a motor impulse is transmitted to a muscle or gland.

reforestation, the planting of forest trees in an open area from which previous trees have been removed.

regeneration, the ability of organisms to form new parts.

renal, relating to the kidneys.

rennin, an enzyme in the gastric fluid of some mammals which coagulates casein.

repellent, a chemical which arouses aversion in insects.

reproduction, the process during which plants and animals produce new organisms of their kind.

respiration, the exchange of gases between cells and their surroundings and accompanying oxidation and energy release.

response, the reaction to a stimulus.

retina, the inner layer of the eyeball, formed from the expanded end of the optic nerve.

Rh factor, any one of six or more protein substances in the blood of certain people.

rhizoid (*ry*-zoid), a rootlike growth which carries on absorption.

rhizome (*ry*-zome), a rootlike horizontal underground stem often enlarged for storage.

Rickettsiae (rih-*ket*-see-eye), a group of organisms midway between the viruses and bacteria in size, which cause disease.

rill erosion, the formation of tiny channels as a result of rain water carrying particles of soil down a hill.

rind, the outer covering of a monocot stem, composed of thick-walled, hard cells.

ring canals, those which lead through each ray in the starfish to a circular canal in the central disk.

rod, a cell of the retina of the eye that receives impulses from light rays and which is sensitive to shades but not to colors.

root cap, a tissue at the tip of a root protecting the tissues behind it.

root hair, a projection of an epidermal cell of a young root.

root pressure, that which is built up in roots due to water intake and resulting turgor.

rostrum (*ros*-trum), a protective area which is an extension of the carapace in crustaceans.

row crop, that grown in rows with soil exposed between them.

rumen, the first of the four stomach divisions in the ruminant mammals.

ruminant (*roo*-mih-nunt), a cud-chewing ungulate.

runoff water, rain water which runs off the surface of the ground and enters the drainage system.

saliva, a digestive fluid secreted into the mouth by the salivary glands.

saprophyte (*sap*-roh-fyt), a plant which lives on nonliving organic matter.

sapwood, active tissue in the outer area of wood in a stem.

scales, the epidermal plates forming the outer covering in fish and reptiles.

science, the branch of knowledge which deals with facts from which conclusions are drawn.

scion (*sy*-un), the portion of a twig grafted on to a rooted stock.

sclerotic (sklair-*ot*-ik) **layer,** the outer layer of the wall of the eyeball.

scutes, the broad scales on the lower side of the snake's body.

secondaries, in birds, those quill feathers which grow from the modified forearm section of the wing.

secondary oöcyte, the cell that results from reduction division and develops into the oötid.

secondary root, a branch root developing from the pericycle of another root.

secretion (see-*kree*-shun), formation of essential chemical substances by cells.

sedimentary rock, that formed of sediment, usually deposited in water.

seed, a complete embryo plant protected by one or more seed coats.

selective absorption, the phenomenon in a root by which certain dissolved minerals enter a root hair independently of water intake while others are rejected.

selective cutting, cutting timber trees from a managed forest only when they are mature.

self-pollination, the transfer of pollen from anther to stigma in the same flower or another flower of the same plant.

self-preservation, a basic instinct possessed by all animals to stay alive.

semicircular canals, the three curved passages in the inner ear that are associated with the sense of balance.

semilunar valves, the heart valves located at the base of the arteries where they join the auricles.

seminal receptacles, structures that receive sperm cells in certain animals.

seminal vesicles (*ves*-ih-kuls), structures that store sperm cells in certain animals.

semipermeable membrane, one which is permeable to different substances to different degrees.

sensory nerve, any nerve which consists only of dendrites.

sensory neurons, those that carry impulses from a receptor to the spinal cord or brain.

sepal (*see*-pul), the outermost part of a flower, usually green and not involved in the reproductive process.

septum, a wall separating two cavities or masses of tissues, as the nasal or heart septum.

serum (*sear*-um), a substance, usually an extract of blood containing antibodies, used in treating a disease after it has struck and to produce immediate passive immunity.

serum albumin (al-*byou*-min), a blood protein necessary for absorption.

serum globulin (*glob*-you-lin), a blood protein which contains antibodies.

setae (*see*-tee), bristles on the earthworm used in locomotion.

sex-influenced character, a characteristic which is dominant in one sex but recessive in the other, as baldness.

sex-limited character, a characteristic which develops only in the presence of sex hormones, as the beard.

sex-linked character, a recessive character carried on the X, or sex, chromosomes, as color blindness.

sexual reproduction, that involving the union of a female gamete, or egg, and a male gamete, or sperm.

sheet erosion, the loss of a thin layer of soil due to standing water.

shelterbelts, rows of trees planted at intervals to break the force of the wind.

shock, the sudden lowering of vital activities due to loss of blood or depressed rate of circulation.

shoot, the first part of the plant visible above ground, formed from the plumule.

sieve plate, in the starfish, the opening of the water-vascular system to the outside.

sieve tube, a conducting tube of the phloem.

simple leaf, one in which the blade is in one piece.

simple sugar, a monosaccharide, one which can be absorbed by the body without further simplification, as glucose.

sinoauricular node, a small mass of tissue on top of the heart in which the automatic beat originates.

sinus venosus, a thin-walled sac which is an enlargement of the cardinal vein of the fish and frog, and which lies at the entrance to the heart.

slime layer, that which surrounds a bacterium.

smooth muscle, that which is involuntary and found lining the walls of the intestine, stomach, and arteries.

soil, a mass of rock particles and humus from which plants obtain essential materials.

solar plexus, the large nerve ganglion of the sympathetic nervous system located in the abdomen.

sori (*sor*-eye), small clusters of sporangia which appear on fern leaves when they are mature.

spawn, the eggs of aquatic animals, especially when laid in masses.

species, a group of plants or animals exhibiting the same characteristics and freely interbreeding.

species characteristic, one possessed by all members of a species.

species immunity, a natural immunity to a particular disease possessed by all members of a species.

sperm, a male reproductive cell.

sperm nuclei, the two structures formed from the generative nucleus in the pollen grain which function in double fertilization.

spermatid, a structure formed from secondary spermatocytes, which mature into sperm.

spermatocyte, a structure formed by reduction division from a spermatogonial cell.

spherical symmetry, the type exhibited by an organism which may be divided into two equal parts at any point passing through the diameter of the body.

spicule (*spik*-yool), the material forming the skeleton of certain sponges.

spinal cord, the main dorsal nerve of the central nervous system in vertebrates, extending down the back from the medulla.

spinal nerve, one leading directly to or from the spinal cord.

spindle, the numerous fine threads formed between the poles of the nucleus during mitosis.

spinnerets, organs in spiders through which silk passes from the silk glands.

spiracles (*spy*-ruh-kuls), external openings of the insect's trachea tubes on the thorax and abdomen.

spirochete (*spy*-roh-keet), a group of spiral-shaped, one-celled organisms resembling both Protozoa and bacteria and producing disease in animals and man.

spongin, fibers comprising the skeleton of certain sponges.

spongocoel (*sponge*-oh-seel), the central cavity in sponges.

spongy layer, a term applied to loosely constructed tissue with many spaces.

sporangiophore, in molds, an ascending hypha bearing sporangia.

sporangium (spor-*an*-jee-um), a structure which produces spores.

spore, an asexual reproductive cell.

sporophyte, the stage which produces spores in an organism having alternation of generations.

sport, a mutant.

spring wood, wood containing many large vessels mingled with tracheids and fibers.

stamen, a part of the flower bearing an anther at its tip.

staminate flower, one containing stamens and no pistils.

sterilization, the destruction of all life in an area, in a substance, or on an object.

stigma, the part of the pistil which receives pollen grains.

stimulus, a factor or environmental change capable of producing activity in protoplasm.

stipe, the stalk of a mushroom.

stock, the plant on which a scion has been grafted; a line of descent; to supply with seed, plants, eggs, or animals.

stolon (*stoh*-lon), a transverse hypha of a mold.

stomach poison, an insecticide which acts in the alimentary canal.

stomata (stoh-*mah*-tuh), pores regulating the passage of air and water vapor to and from the leaf.

streaming, the movement of cytoplasm in a cell.

striated muscle, skeletal, voluntary muscle.

strip cropping, the alternation of strips of row crops and cover crops.

style, the stalk of the pistil.

subclavian vessels, large arteries and veins in the arm area in vertebrates.

sublingual (sub-*ling*-wul), one of the pair of salivary glands lying under the tongue.

submaxillary, one of the pair of salivary glands lying in the angle of the lower jaw.

subsoil, soil which lies below topsoil and which is usually poor in plant nutrients.

succession, the changing plant and animal population of a given area.

successive osmosis, the cell-to-cell diffusion of water.

sucrase, a digestive enzyme of the intestinal fluid which changes sucrose to glucose.

summer wood, wood containing few vessels and a large number of fibers.

sustained yield, a forest so managed as to give regular crops for cutting.

swimmerets, appendages on the abdomen of a crustacean.

symbiosis (sim-bee-*oh*-sis), the relationship in which two organisms live together for the mutual advantage of each.

symmetrical, having a definite shape.

sympathetic nervous system, a division of the autonomic nervous system.

synapse (*sih*-naps), the space between nerve endings.

synergid (*sih*-ner-jid), one of two structures formed on either side of the egg in the embryo sac of flowers.

synovial (sih-*noh*-vee-ul) **fluid,** a secretion of cartilage that lubricates a joint.

systematic circulation, the body circulation as distinct from the pulmonary circulation.

systems, groups of organs performing similar functions.

systolic blood pressure, arterial pressure produced when the heart beats.

tadpole, the larval stage of a frog or toad.

taproot, the main root of a plant, often serving as a food reservoir.

tarsus, the foot of the grasshopper; a bone of the human foot.

taste buds, flask-shaped structures in the tongue containing nerve endings that are stimulated by taste.

taxonomy, the branch of biology which groups and names living things.

teliospore (*tee*-lee-oh-spore), a two-celled, black, winter spore of wheat rust.

telophase, the last stage of mitosis, during which two daughter cells are formed.

telson, the posterior segment of the abdomen of certain Crustacea.

tendon, a strong band of connective tissue in which the fleshy portion of a muscle terminates.

tendril, a part of a plant modified for climbing.

tentacle, a long appendage or " feeler " of certain invertebrates.

terminal bud, the terminal growing point of the stem.

terracing, the checking of water on sloping land by building level areas to prevent soil erosion.

terrestrial (ter-*es*-tree-ul), land-living.

testa, the outer seed coat.

testes, male reproductive organs of higher animals.

testosterone (tes-*tos*-ter-ohn), a male hormone produced in the testes and in the cortex of the adrenal glands in both males and females.

thoracic (thor-*as*-ik), pertaining to the chest cavity.

thorax, the middle region of the body of an insect between the head and abdomen; the chest region of mammals.

thrombin, a substance formed in blood clotting as a result of the reaction of prothrombin, thromboplastin, and calcium.

thromboplastin, a substance essential to blood clotting formed by the disintegration of blood platelets.

thymus, one of the ductless glands, situated near the breastbone, which begins to atrophy at puberty, and whose function is undetermined.

thyroid, a ductless gland, located in the neck on either side of the larynx, which regulates metabolism.

thyroid hormone, the secretion of the thyroid gland.

tibia, one of the long bones of the lower leg.

tissue, a group of cells similar in structure and function.

tissue destruction, the destruction of cells b pathogenic organisms.

tissue fluid, that which bathes the cells of th body and is called lymph when contained i vessels.

tone (muscle), the condition in which flexc and extensor muscles oppose each other, resul ing in a continuous state of slight contractior

topography, the physical features of the eartl

topsoil, that top part of the soil consisting c mineral matter combined with organic mattei

toxin-antitoxin, a mixture of diphtheria ant toxin and toxin, formerly used to develop im munity.

toxoid, toxin weakened by mixing with for maldehyde or salt solution, used extensively t develop immunity to diphtheria, scarlet fever and tetanus.

tracer element, a radioactive isotope whicl can be followed by means of a counter in a par ticular substance.

trachea (*tray*-kee-uh), an air tube in insect and spiders; the windpipe in air-breathing verte brates.

tracheids, thick-walled conducting tubes tha strengthen woody tissue.

translocation, the movement of dissolvec foods in plants.

transpiration, the loss of water from plants

trichinosis (trih-kih-*noh*-sis), the infestation of muscle by encysted trichina worms.

trichocysts (*trih*-koh-sists), sensitive proto plasmic threads in the paramecium, concerned with protection.

trochanter (troh-*kan*-ter), a joint in the ap pendages of the grasshopper which with the coxa forms a ball and socket.

tropism (*troh*-pizm), the involuntary response of an organism to a stimulus.

trypsin (*trip*-sin), an enzyme of the pancreatic juice which converts protein to peptones and proteoses.

tube nucleus, one of the two nuclei present in a pollen grain.

tuber, an enlarged tip of a rhizome swollen with stored food.

tuberculin, a substance containing dead tuberculosis organisms, used in testing for tuberculosis.

turbinate, one of three layers of bones in the nasal passages.

turgor, the stiffness of plant cells due to the presence of water.

tympanic (tim-*pan*-ik) **membrane,** the eardrum.

tympanum (*tim*-puh-num), a membrane in certain arthropods serving a vibratory function.

umbilical cord, that in female mammals leading from the placenta to the embryo.

urea, a nitrogenous waste substance found chiefly in the urine of mammals but formed in the liver from broken-down proteins.

uredospore (you-*ree*-doh-spore), a one-celled, red, summer spore of wheat rust.

ureter (you-*ree*-ter), a tube leading from a kidney to the bladder or cloaca.

urethra (you-*ree*-thruh), the tube leading from the urinary bladder to an external opening in the body.

urinary bladder, the sac at the base of the ureters which stores urine.

urine, the liquid waste filtered from the blood in the kidney and excreted by the bladder.

uropod, a flipper, or developed swimmeret, at the posterior end of the crayfish.

uterus (*yoo*-ter-us), the organ in which young mammals are nourished until they are born.

uvula (*you*-vyoo-luh), the extension of the soft palate.

vaccination, producing active immunity by inoculating with a vaccine.

vaccine (*vak*-seen), a substance used to produce active immunity.

vacuolar (vak-you-*oh*-ler) **membrane,** a membrane surrounding a vacuole in a cell and regulating the movement of materials in and out of the vacuole.

vacuole (*vak*-you-ohl), one of the spaces scattered through the cytoplasm of a cell and containing fluid.

vagus (*vay*-gus) **nerve,** the principal nerve of the parasympathetic nervous system.

valve, a structure regulating the flow of blood in the heart and in veins.

vane, part of a quill feather of a bird.

variations, the differences that occur within the offspring of a given species.

vasa efferentia, tiny tubes in the reproductive system of the frog through which sperm pass into the kidneys.

veins, strengthening and conducting structures in leaves; vessels carrying blood to the heart.

venation, the arrangement of veins through the leaf blade.

vena cava (*vee*-nuh *kay*-vuh), a large collecting vein found in many vertebrates.

venom, the poison secreted by glands of poisonous snakes or other animals.

ventral, front, or lower (abdominal), surface of animals.

ventricle (*ven*-trih-kul), a muscular chamber of the heart; a space in the brain.

venules (*ven*-yooles), small branches of veins.

vermiform appendix, a fingerlike outgrowth of the intestinal caecum.

vertebra (*ver*-tuh-bruh), a bone of the spinal column of vertebrates.

vestigial (ves-*tij*-ih-ul) **organs,** those which are poorly developed and not functioning.

viability (vy-uh-*bil*-ih-tee), the ability of seeds to germinate after dormancy.

villi (*vil*-eye), microscopic projections of the wall of the small intestine which increase the absorbing surface.

virus, the simplest form of living matter.

visceral hump, the area in bivalves containing the principal digestive organs.

visual purple, the chemical in the rods of the eye necessary for their proper functioning in reduced light.

vitamin, an organic substance, though not a food, that is essential for normal body activity.

vitreous (*vih*-tree-us) **humor,** a transparent substance that fills the interior of the eyeball.

viviparous (vy-*vip*-uh-rus), bearing the young alive, and nourishing them before birth by means of the placenta.

vocal cords, those structures within the larynx which vibrate to produce speech.

vocal sacs, membranous sacs between the ear and shoulder of certain male frogs which serve as resonators and increase the volume of sound.

voluntary muscle, that controlled by the will of the organism.

vomerine teeth, those in the roof of the mouth of the frog which aid in holding prey.

water-borne infections, those produced by certain pathogenic organisms present in water.

water cycle, the continuous movement of water from the atmosphere to the earth and from the earth to the atmosphere.

watershed, a hilly region, usually extending over a large area, which conducts surface water to streams.

water table, the level at which water is standing in the ground.

water-vascular system, the circulatory system of certain echinoderms.

web membrane, the flexible structure lying between the toes of frogs.

weightlessness, a condition in which objects have no weight because of the lack of gravity.

white corpuscles, colorless cells of the blood.

white matter, the fibers of nerve cells in the brain and spinal cord.

whorled, in stems, having three or more leaves at each node.

wigglers, the larvae of the mosquito.

wildlife, all native animals.

woody stem, one containing conducting and supporting tissue that forms layers which are added to year after year.

worker bee, an infertile female bee.

X chromosome, a sex-determining chromosome present singly in males and as a pair in females.

X rays, a form of radiation having a short wave length and high energy value.

xanthophyll (*zan*-thoh-fil), a yellow pigment found in certain chromoplasts.

xerophyte (*zer*-oh-fyte), a plant which requires very little water to live.

xylem (*zy*-lem), the woody tissue of a root or stem which conducts water and dissolved minerals upward.

Y chromosome, a sex chromosome found only in males.

yolk, the part of the bird's egg from which the egg cell obtains its nourishment.

zoospores (*zoh*-oh-spores), in *Ulothrix*, the flagellated cells which leave the mother cell and later develop into new organisms.

zygote (*zy*-goht), the fertilized egg cell in plants and animals.

zymase, the enzyme system in yeast cell which acts on sugar to produce carbon dioxide and alcohol.

Index

Page references for illustrations are printed in **boldface type.**

Abalones, 267
Abdomen, of crayfish, 274; of grasshopper, 289; of honeybee, 301; of insect, 285–286; of Lepidoptera, 296
Abdominal cavity, 425
Abdominal muscles of man, 460
Aberdeen-Angus cattle, 643
Abscission layer, 197
Absorption, 34–35; the cell membrane and, 158–159; through imbibition, 164; of minerals, 164–165; by roots, 158–165; selective, 164; in small intestine, 456–458
Acceleration, 547; effects of upon leaving earth's atmosphere, 547–548
Accidents and alcohol, 526–527
Acetylcholine, 500
Acid, soil, 67; of stomach, 572
Acne, 475
Acquired immunity, 574
Acquired skills, 649–650
Acridiidae, 84
Acromegaly, 518
ACTH, 518
Active immunity, 574
"Adam's apple," 461
Adaptation, 18–19; of cells, 241–242; of frogs' legs, 347–348
Addiction, to alcohol, 525–526; to narcotics, 529
Adductor muscles, 266
Adenoids, 449
Adrenal cortex, 518–519
Adrenal glands, 518–**519**
Adrenaline, 519
Adreno-cortico-tropic-hormone, 518
Adult stage, of Lepidoptera, 297; in metamorphosis, 287
Adventitious roots, 155–**156**
Aeciospores, 119
Aedes mosquito, 307, **567**
Aerobic organisms, 35, 108
African sleeping sickness, 239
Agar-agar, 102, 109
Agglutinins, 573
Agnatha, 326
Air, bacteria in relation to, 108–109; capacity of lungs, 462; complemental, 462; gases in, 7; residual, 462; supplemental, 462; tidal, 462
Air bladder, of fish, 334

Air-conditioning, 469
Air sacs, of bird, 385; of grasshopper, 290
Air spaces, in leaf, 185
Albinos, 399, 632
Albumen, 386
Albumin, serum, 478
Alcohol, 524–527; addiction to, 525–526; in the body, 524; effects of on driving, 526–527; effects of on nervous system, 525; food value of, 524; and length of life, 526; and society, 526
Alcoholism, 526
Algae, 91–102; blue-green, 93–95; brown, 101; classes of (Table), 92; description of, 91–92; economic importance of, 101–102; green, 95–100; harm done by, 102; red, 101; use of in space travel, 102, 549; structure of and reproduction in, 92–93; use in foods, 101–102
Alimentary canal, in frog, 350; in human, 447, 448, 454
Alkaline soil, 67
Allergy, pollen, 206–207
Alligator, 370–**371**
Alpha, particles, 539; satellite, 539
Alpine region, 70
Alternate leaves, 168
Alternation of generations, 127, 248
Alveoli, of human, 461
Ambergris, 410
Ameba, 230–232; food digestion in, 231–232; and paramecium compared (Table), 237; reproduction in, 232; sensitivity in, 232; structure of, 230–**231**
Amebic dysentery, 239
Amebocytes, 244
Ameboid movement, 231
American chestnut tree, disease of, 696
American hellbender, 344
Amino acids, 34, 50–51, 441, 454, 456; in plasma, 478
Ammonia, in nitrogen cycle, 58
Ammonification, 58
Amphibia, 342–356; characteristics of, 342; orders of, 342–344

Amylase, 455
Anabaena, 94
Anabolism, 31, 467
Anaerobic, bacteria, 108–109; respiration, 35
Anal fin, 331
Anal opening, of fish, 332; of human, 454
Anal pore, of paramecium, 235
Analogous organs, 275
Anaphase stage, 611–612
Anatomy, 10, 423
Ancient man, 418–421; compared with modern, 422–423
Androgen, 520
Anemia, 484
Angiosperms, 139, 141–143
Angstrom unit, 534
Angular joints, 431
Animal kingdom, phyla (Table), 81, 83
Animals, as agents in seed dispersal, 215; camouflage, 74–76; characteristics compared with plants, 85–87, 229; classification of, 77–87; dependence on light, 534–536; destruction of, 63–64; destruction of fur-bearing, 707; destruction of trees by, 697; forests as shelter for, 692; origin of domestic (Table), 667; in past geological ages, 656–664; photoreceptors of, **535**; phyla (Table), 83; problems of temperature changes for, 68–69; respiration in, 193; true hybrid, 643–645
Annelids, 258–260
Annual rings, 172
Annuals, 144
Annulus, 121
Anopheles mosquito, 238, 306–307, **569**
Anoxia, 467
Antennae, of crayfish, **274**, 275; of grasshopper, **288**, **289**, 290; of honeybee, 301
Antennules, 275
Anther, 200, 203
Antheridium, **98**, 100
Anthocyanin, 196
Anthrax, 562–563, 573–574; vaccine, 583
Anthropoid apes, 413
Anthropology, 418–419
Antibiotics, 577

Antibodies, 573
Antigen, 482, 651
Antihistamines, 207, 588
Antipodals, 207
Antiseptic surgery, 594, **595**
Antiseptics, 594–595
Antitoxin, discovery of, 585; preparation of diphtheria, 573, **575**
Antivenin, 368
Antlers, 399–400
Ants, 303
Anus, of earthworm, 259; of nematodes, 256
Anvil bone, 507
Aorta, of grasshopper, **289,** 290; of humans, 485
Aortic arch, of earthworm, 261; of frog, 351
Aortic sinus, 485–486
Apes, 413
Apical cell, 94
Apoda, 342
Appendages, of crayfish, 275; jointed, 273
Apple worm, 298–299
Aquarist, amateur, 340
Aquarium, balance in an, 61–62
Aqueous humor, 509
Arachnida, 281–286
Arachnoid mater, 492
Archaeopteryx, 374
Arctic region, 70
Aristotle, **1;** and classification of plants and animals, 79
Armadillo, **399,** 408–409
Arteries, of fish, 333; of frog, 351; hardening of, 601; of human, 487, **488;** pulmonary, 461, **462,** 485; renal, 473
Arterioles, of blood, 487; of kidney, 473
Arteriosclerosis, 601
Arthropods, 272–292; characteristics of, 273; classes of (Table), 273
Artificial propagation, 703
Artificial radiations, 540–541
Artificial respiration, 464, **465**
Ascaris, 256–**257**
Ascending colon, 454
Ascomycetes, (Table), 114, 115, 117, 118
Ascorbic acid, 442
Ascus, 115, 118
Aseptic surgery, 594
Asexual reproduction, 39; in *Ulothrix,* **97–98;** of yeast cells (budding), 118
Aspergillus, 116
Assimilation, 35–36, 58, 467
Association fibers, 494–495
Association neurons, 498

Astronauts, 553
Athlete's foot, 124
Atmosphere, as a factor in environment, 72–73; layers of earth's, **545;** in nitrogen cycle, 58–60
Atmospheric pressure, in space ship, 551
Atoll, 250
Atomic radiation, 538–539
Atomic reactors, 541
Atoms, 42–46, 538
Attitudes, and science, 2–3
Auditory nerve, 508
Audubon, John James, 387–388, 705
Audubon Law, 707
Aurelia, 248–**249**
Aureomycin, 579; for pneumonia, 589
Auricle, of bird, 386; of fish, 333; of frog, 350–**351;** of human, 484, **486**
Auricular-ventricular node, 432
Auricular-ventricular valves, 484
Australoid type man, 422
Autoclave, 109
Automatic beat, of heart muscle, 432
Automatic behavior, of mammals, 404–405
Autonomic nervous system, 492, 501–502
Avoiding reaction, 235
Axil, 168
Axillary buds, 168
Axolotl stage, 345
Axons, 497

Bacillus anthracis, **563**
Bacillus forms of bacteria, 105, **106**
Back pressure-arm lift method, of artificial respiration, 464
Bacteria, 104–112; aerobic, 108; anaerobic, 108–109; beneficial activities of, 110–111; chemotrophic, 108; conditions for growth of, 107–108; dentrifying, 60; description of, 104; in food industry, 110–111; forms of, 105–106; harmful, 111–112; importance of, 104–105; in industries, 111; laboratory culture of, 109; microscopic examination of, 110; nitrifying, 58; pathogenic, 105, 565; in relation to air, 108–109; in relation to food supply, 108; reproduction of, 106; in soil, 111; spores in, 106–107

Bactericides, 110
Bacteriology, 10, 109
Bacteriolysins, 573
Bacteriophage, 579
" Bad air," 561
" Bad humor," 560
Balance, in an aquarium, 61–62; biological, 62; function of cerebellum and, 496; in nature, 56–65; sense of, 50
Ball-and-socket joint, **430,** 43
Ballooning, 282
Balloonometer, 525
Banding, of birds, 391
Barberry plant, and wheat rus 119–121, **120**
Barber's itch, 124
Barbs, 377
Barbules, 377
Bark, 171, 172–173
Barley, 224
Barnacles, 280
Barrier, 663
Basal disks, 246
Basal metabolism, 468–46 rate of, 468
Basic Four foods, (Table), 44 445
Basidiomycetes, 114, 119
Basidiospores, 119; of mus room, 121, **122**
Basidium, 119, 121
Bast fibers, 173
Bat, **401,** 404, 409
Bay lynx, 411
Beak, of bird, 381, (Table), 3
Bean, germination of, **221**–22 structure of, 217, **218**
Bears, hibernation of, 406; typ of, 410–411
Beaver, 412; home of, 405
Becquerel, Antoine Henri, 5
Bedbugs, 311
" Beebread," 302
Beehive, products of, 302
Bees, honeybee, 300–303; pollination, 204, **205**
Beetles, 304
Behavior, of vertebrates, 32 324
Belly, of muscle, 431
Bends, 550
Berger, Hans, 495
Berlandier's tortoise, 373
Beta particles, 539
Biceps muscle, 433
Bicuspid teeth, 450
Bicuspid valve, 599
Biennials, 144–145
" Big Tree," 15
Bilateral symmetry, 252
Bile, 453; in excretion, 4 functions of, 455

le duct, of frog, 349
nominal nomenclature, 80
ology, cellular, 21; definition of, 1; Father of, 1; goals and objectives of, 8–10; history of, 1–2; specialized branches of, 10–11
otic factors, 67, 74–76
rd Banding Association, 391
rds, 375–395; adaptations for flight, 375–376; banding, 391; barbules of, 377; beaks of, 381, (Table), 382; characteristics of, 375; circulatory system of, 385–386; conservation of, 705–707; destruction of insects by, 393; destruction of weed seeds by, 393; digestive system of, 384–385; excretory system of, 385–386; external view of, 379; feathers of, 376–378; food of, 381–384, (Table), 383; forests as shelter for, 692; habitats of, 389; harm done by, 394–395; head and neck of, 381; incubation and development of, 387; internal organs of, 384; laws to protect, 707; legs and feet of, 379–381, Table), 380; migration of, 389–391; molting of, 377–378; as natural enemies of insects, 313; need for light, 535–536; nervous system of, 386; nests of, 392–393, (Table), 394; rare species of, 705–706; reproduction of, 386–387; respiratory system of, 385–386; seasonal study of, 391–392; sense organs of, 381; useless destruction of, 704–705; wings of, 378–379
on, American, 708
alve mollusks, 266–267
lack 'Death," 560
ck snake, 365
ck widow spider, 282, 283
ckout, 548
de, of leaf, 183
stula, 615, 616
leeder's disease," 651–652
ding, through a stem, 163
id spot, 510
ck cutting, 698
od, cells, red, 478–479; cells, hite, 479–480; characteristics controlled by, 608; and irculation, 477–490; circulation through heart, 484–86; clotting of (Table), 481; omposition of, 478–480, Table), 480; definition of,

478; in earthworms, 261; of frog, 350–351; function of (Table), 480; plasma, 438, 478, 482, 483–484; platelets, 480; pressure in arteries, 487; Rh factor in, 483–484; smear, 481; sugar, 478; supply to lungs, 461–462; transfusions, 481–482, 483; as transportation medium (Table), 480; type, inheritance of, 651; vessels, 487, 488
Blood banks, 483–484
Bloodletting, 560–561
" Bloodsucker," see Leech
Blue crab, 280
Blue heron, 392
Blue molds, 116–117
Blue racer snake, 365
Blue whale, 409–410
Blue-winged teal duck, 375
Boa constrictor, 361
Board of Health, 596
Bobcat, 411
Body (human), defenses and aids against disease, 571–580; elements in, 42; regions in man, 425
Body oxidation, 467–468
Boll weevil, 312
Bones, of humans, 428–430; mineral deposit in, 429; structure of, 429–430; tissue of, 428–429
Bony fish, 316
Bony layer, 430
Book lungs, 282
Boreal forest, 685
Botany, 11
Botulism, 566–567
Bowman's capsule, 473
Box turtle, 372, 373
Brace roots, 155
Brachiopods, 658
Bracket fungi, 32, 122–123
Brahman cattle, 643
Brain, of earthworm, 261; of fish, 335; of frog, 352; of humans, 418, 492–496, 493; internal deposit in blood vessels of, 600; of mammals, 403; stem, 496; waves, 495
Branches, of roots, 146
Branchial artery, 334
Branching, due to bud arrangement, 169–170; types of, 168
Brangus cattle, 644
Bread mold, 115–116
Breathing, 460; air changes in, 464; control of, 464; external influences upon, 469; of frog, 350; mechanics of, 462–463; movements of, 463–464

Breeding, animal, 642–645; plant, 635–641; results of, 664
Bridge, of turtle, 372
Bronchi, of birds, 385; of man, 460, 461
Bronchial pneumonia, 589
Bronchial tubes, 461
Bronchioles, 461
Brontosaurus, 358
Brood comb, 302
Bryophytes, 127
Bubonic plague, 560
Bud-mutant, 640
Bud-scale scars, 169
Bud scales, 167
Budding, 118, 176, 177
Buds, 167–170; of hydra, 248; of sponges, 245; of yeast cells, 118
Bufo, 345
Bugs, insects compared with, 285–286
Bulb, 180
Bulbar polio, 591
Bulbus arteriosus, 333
Bull snake, 365
Bullfrog, 346, 347
Bundle scars, 168
Bundles (muscle), 431
Burbank, Luther, 635; crossing of species by, 640; mass selection used by, 636; propagation used by, 637–638
Burbank potatoes, 635
Bureau of Animal Industries, 596
Bureau of Entomology and Plant Quarantine, 311–312
Bursa, 430
Butterflies, 75–76, 294–300; comparison of with moth (Table), 298
Buttons, of mushroom, 121

Caecilians, 342
Caecum, 454
Caimans, 371
Calcium, control of in body, 517; use in body, 438; in Protozoa, 237
Calcium carbonate, in bone, 428, 429
Calcium phosphate, in bone, 428, 429
California condor, 705, 706
Callus, 474
Calorie, 439, (Table), 440
Calorimeter, 467–468
Calosoma beetle, 304
Calyx, 200
Cambium, 172; activities of, 173–174; of herbaceous stem,

177; of root, 151; of woody stem, 172
Camels, 663, 666
Camouflage, 74–76
Canada lynx, 411
Canals, of paramecium, 235
Cancer, 601–602; diagnosis and treatment of, 602; treatment of by radioactive materials, 541; smoking and, 530; symptoms of, 601
Canine teeth, of humans, 450; of mammals, 400–401, 410
Cap, of mushroom, 121
Cape Canaveral, Florida, 539
Capillaries, of fish, 333; of human, 487, 488
Capillarity, 175
Capsule, Bowman's, 473; of mosses, 127–128
Carapace, 274–275, 372
Carbhemoglobin, 479
Carbohydrates, 48–50; digestion of, 456; use of in body, 439–440
Carbon, radioactive and photosynthesis, 188–189
Carbon atom, 43
Carbon dioxide, 46; in green plants, 32; in lungs, 462; -oxygen cycle, use of in space travel, 549; in photosynthesis, 187, 191
Carbon-14, 187, 540
Carbon monoxide, 47; poisoning, 469
Carbonic acid, in root cap, 149
Carboniferous Period, 130, 139, 342
Carcinogenic agents, 530
Cardiac muscle, 432; cells of, 431
Cardinal vein, 333
Cardiovascular-renal disease, 600
Carnivora, 410–411
Carotene, 25, 95; in leaf, 196
Carotid artery, 351
Carpenter ants, 303
Carriers, of disease, 568–569
Carrion beetle, 304
Carrot, sectional view of, 151
Cartilage, 428, 430; of vertebrates, 321
Case histories, use of, 647–648
Casein, 455
Catabolism, 31, 467
Catalysts, 32, 186, 444
Caterpillar, 296, 297
Caterpillar movement, of snakes, 364
Cattle, improvement in breeding of, 643

Caucasoid type man, 423
Caudal fin, 331
Caudata, 342
"Cave man," 421
Cecropia moth, 296
Cedar-apple rust, 121
Cell, 6, 21–29; adaptations of, 241–242; apical, 94; body, 497; concave, 94–95; daughter, 236; division, 38–39; division of labor, 241–242; of Elodea, 26; interdependence of, 242; membrane of and absorption, 158–159; of onion skin, 26; plant and animal, 23–25, 24, 27; plate, 612; red blood, 478–479; sap, 26; specialization, 28; structure of, 23–26, 28; theory, 22; tissue and, 28–29; as unit of heredity, 608–616; use of oxygen by, 464–466; wall, 23, 27; wall, of human tongue, 29; white blood, 479–480; of wood, 173
Cellular biology, 21
Cellulose, 23, 49, 188; use of in body, 440
Cementum, of teeth, 450
Cenozoic Era, 396–397
Centipede, 280, 281
Central cylinder, 150
Central hardwood forest, 686–687
Central nervous system, 492–497
Central neurons, 498
Cephalopods, 268–269
Cephalothorax, of Arachnida, 281; of crayfish, 274
Cereal grains, 222–224
Cerebellum, of bird, 386; of fish, 335; of frog, 352; of humans, 492, 496; of mammals, 403
Cerebrospinal fluid, 492
Cerebrum, of bird, 386; of fish, 335; of frog, 352; of human, 494–495; of vertebrates, 322, 403
Cetacea, 409–410
Chain reaction, 540, 541
Chameleon, 369
Chance distribution, 616–617
Characteristics, inherited, 608; of phylum, 242
Check dams, 677
Chelicera, 281–282
Chemical change, in digestion, 447; of matter, 41; in photosynthesis, 187
Chemical control, of insects, 313–315

Chemical cycles, 58
Chemical formula, 46
Chemical processes, 31
Chemotherapy, 575–576
Chemotrophic bacteria, 108
Chemotropism (Table), 153
Chest, X ray of, 464
Chickenpox, 590
Chiggers, 283
Childbirth, and Rh factor, 4[
Childhood diseases, 589–590[
Chilopoda, 281
Chimpanzee, 413
Chiroptera, 409
Chitin, 273; of grasshopp[287
Chlorella, 95; use of in spa[travel, 549
Chloromycetin, 579
Chlorophyll, 25; of eugle[233; in leaf, 184–185, 1[necessary for photosynthe[189–190; in plants, 32
Chloroplasts, 25, 26–28; [euglena, 233; in green plar[32; in leaf, 184
Cholinesterase, 500
Chondrichthyes, 328–329
Chondriosomes, 25
Chordates, 320–321
Choroid layer, of eyeball, 50[
Chromatin, 26, 609; net, 609[reproduction, 39
Chromatophores, 330
Chromoplasts, 25, 27
Chromosomes, 609–6[changes in during reduct[division, 614, 615; content 612–613; human, 647; nu[bers of, 614; plants with creased numbers of, 640
Chronological age, 652
Chrysalis, 297
Chyme, 452
Cicada, 304
Cilia, 37; of paramecium, 2[of trachea, 461
Ciliary muscles, of eye, 509
Ciliated epithelium, 27, 493
Circular muscles, 259, 452
Circulation, 477–490; in bo[489–490; through heart, 4[486
Circulatory system, of b[385–386; of crayfish, 276[earthworm, 260–261; of f[332–334, 333; of frog, 3.[352; of grasshopper, 290[human, 489–490; of ve[brates, 321
Cirrhosis, 524
Civilization, and balance of [ture, 63

Cladonia, 125
Clam, **266–267**
Classes, of plants and animals, 81
Classification, of grasshopper, 83–85, (Table), 84; of plants and animals, 77–87; scientific, 81–87
Cleft grafting, **177**
Climate, effects of forests on, 692
Climatic zones, of North America, 70–71
Climax plants, 74
Clitellum, 259
Cloaca, of bird, 385; of frog, 349, **352**
Clostridium tetani, **566**
Clover, 677
Club fungi, 119
Club mosses, 18, 133
Coal, formation of, 130, 658
Cocaine, 528–529
Coccus forms of bacteria, 105, **106**
Cochlea, of ear, 507–508
Cocoon, 297
Cod liver oil, 338
Codein, 528
Coelenterates, 246–250; classes of (Table), 246
Cohesion, 176
Colchicine, 640, 664
Cold, sensation of, 505
Colds, immunization, 588
Coleoptera, 304
Collar cells, 244
Collarbone, of bird, 378
Collecting tubule, 473
Colloid, 22
Colon, of frog, 349; of grasshopper, **289**, 290; of human, 454; water absorbed by, 458
Colonial organism, 28
Colonies, of algae, 92–93
Color blindness, **630**–631
Coloration, of leaf, 196
Comb, 302
Commensalism, 33
Commercial fish, 338
Common bile duct, 453
Common names, of organisms, 78
Communal life, of bee, 303
Communication, lumber for, 690–691
Compatible blood, 482
Complemental air, 462
Complete flower, 200
Complete metamorphosis, 287; stages of (Table), 298
Complex organisms, 29
Complex sugars, 440

Composite flowers, 202–203
Compound eyes, of crayfish, 275; of grasshopper, 290, **291**
Compound leaf, 184
Compound microscope, **6–8**
Compounds, chemical, 46–47; different from mixtures, 47; inorganic and organic, 47–48; mineral, 48
Concave cell, 94–95
Concussion, 493
Condor, California, **705, 706**
Conditioned reaction, 324; of mammals, 405
Cone, of eye, 510
Cone-bearing gymnosperms, 140–141
Conifers, 140–141, 686; of today (Table), 140
Conjugation, in paramecium, 236; in *Spirogyra,* 96
Connective tissue, 423, (Table), 424, **425**
Conservation, balance by, 64; of fish, 340, 700–701; of forests, 684–698; of matter, 41–42; of natural enemies of insects, 312–313; of plants, 710; problems of in soil and water, 679–680; of soil, 671–682; of water, 682–683; of wildlife, 700–710
Constructive processes, 56, 58
Consumer scientist, 2
Contact infection, 568
Contact poisons, 314
Contour farming, 676–677
Contour feathers, 377
Contractile vacuole, 26; in ameba, 232; in paramecium, 235
Contraction, of muscle cells, 37
Conus arteriosus, of frog, 351
Convolutions, 492, 494; of mammals, 403
Cooper's hawk, 394
Copperhead snake, **367,** 368
Coracoid bone, of bird, 378
Coral, 249; reefs, **250**
Coral snake, **367,** 368
Cork, cambium, 173; cell wells in, **21;** of plants, 143; in woody stem, 173
Corm, 180
Corn, as crop, 223–224; germination of, **222;** hybrid, 638–640, **639;** kernel, structure of, **218**–219; pollination of, 638; refining, **223**
Corn smut, **120**–121
Cornea, 509
Corolla, 200

Coronary, arteries, 485; circulation, 489; embolism, 601; heart disease, 600–601; occlusion, 601; thrombosis, 601
Corpuscles, 478; red and white, **29**
Corridor, 663
Cortex, 143; of adrenal gland, 518–519; of cerebrum, 494–495, 501; of kidney, 472; of root, 150; in woody stem, 173
Cortin, 518
Cosmic rays, 538–539; in space, 551–552
Cotton-mouth moccasin snake, **367,** 368
Cotyledon, **138,** 142, 217; of bean, 217–**218, 221;** of corn, **218,** 219, 222
Cougar, 411
Countershading, 75; of fish, 330–331
Cover crops, 672
Cowpox, 582
Coxa, 288–289
Coyote, 411
Crabs, **278,** 280
Cranial cavity, of fish, 335; of human, 425
Cranial nerves, 496; of frog, 352; of mammals, 403
Crayfish, **274–279;** circulatory system of, 276; life history of, 277; locomotion of, 277; molting of, 277–278; nervous system of, 276–277; respiration of, 277
Cretaceous Period, 359
Cretin, 516, 653
Cretinism, 516
Cricket, **292**
Crimson-spotted newt, 345
Crocodiles, 371
Crocodilians, 370–371
Cro-Magnon man, **420,** 421, **422**
Crop, of bird, 385; of earthworm, 26; of grasshopper, **289,** 290
Crop rotation, 673
Cross fox, 399
Cross-pollination, 204
Crossing-over, of genes, 628
Crown, of tooth, 450
Crustacea, 273–280; economic importance of, 279–280
Cud, 412
Culex mosquito, **306**–307, 569
Culture, inoculation of a, 110; medium, 109
Cumberland terrapin, 373
Cup fungus, 118
Curd, 455

Curie, Pierre and Marie, 532
Cuspid teeth, 450, **451**
Cuticle, of earthworm, 261; of leaf, 184
Cyanophyceae, 92, 93
Cycads, **139**
Cycle, chemical, 58; man's interference with natural, 64; nitrogen, 58–60, **59;** oxygen-carbon dioxide, 60–62, **61**
Cyclops, **278,** 280
Cyclostomata, 326–328
Cypress " knees," 155
Cyst, 255
Cytology, 10
Cytoplasm, 23–25, **27;** of cell body, 497; motion of, 37; types of, 231

Daddy longlegs, 283
Dam (female animal), 643
Dams, and reservoirs, 682–683
Daphnia, **278,** 280
Darters, 334
Darwin, Charles, 664, 665
Data, scientific, 4
Daughter cells, 236
DDT, 311, 315
De Vries, Hugo, 664, 667
" Death angel " mushroom, **123**
Decay, 57; in nitrogen cycle, 58
Deciduous trees, 687
Deer, antlers of, 399–400; whitetail, **19,** 708
Deficiency diseases, 441
Degeneration, 256
Dehiscent fruits, 214, (Table), 215
Dehydration, 438
Deliquescent branching, 170
Delirium tremens, 526
Demonic theory, 559
Dendrites, 497, 505
Dentine, 450
Deoxygenated blood, 350
Depressant, 524
Dermis, of human skin, 474; of mammals, 398
Descending colon, 454
Desert tortoise, 373
Desmids, 100
Desoxyribonucleic acid, 579
Deuterium atom, 43, **46**
Deuteromycetes (Table), 114
Diabetes mellitus, 519
Diamondback terrapin, 373
Diaphragm, 350; of humans, 425; of mammals, 398, 401
Diarrhea, 239
Diastase, 220
Diastole, 486
Diastolic pressure, 487
Diatomaceous earth, 101

Diatoms, 101
Dicots (Table), 141–142; flowers of, 202–203, **205;** herbaceous stem of, 177
Dicotyledonae, 142
Diet, balanced, 445
Diffusion, 35, 159–162
Digestion, 447–458; of carbohydrates, fats, and proteins, **456;** chemical changes in, 447; definition of, 34; extracellular, 454; intracellular, 454; organs of, 448; phases of, 447; summary of (Table), 457
Digestive enzymes, 447
Digestive glands, 447
Digestive system, of birds, 384–385; of crayfish, 275–276; of earthworm, 260; of fish, 332; of frog, 349–350; of grasshopper, 289–290; of humans, **448**–449, 452–458; of vertebrates, 321
Dihybrids, 624
Dinosaurs, 358–359
Dioecious plants, 202
Diphtheria, antitoxin, discovery of, 585–586; antitoxin, production of, 574, **575;** conquest of, 585–586; Schick test for, 586
Diplococcus, 105, **106**
Diplococcus pneumoniae, **566**
Diploid number, 614
Diplopoda, 281
Diptera, 304–305
Direct fertilization, 353
Disaccharides, 188, 440, 455
Diseases, bacterial, 565; body defenses against, 571–580; childhood, 589–590; conquest of, 581–592; defenses against, 572–574; forms of, 563–564; of heart, 599–601; human carriers of, 568; immunity against, 573–574; inheritance of, 651; insects as vectors of (Table), 310–311; mental, 602–603; microbes as cause of, 569–570; in Middle Ages, 560; in 19th century, 560–561; noninfectious, 563–564; organic and functional, 598–599; organisms causing, 564–565; prevention of, 594–604; primitive, man's fear of, 558–559; resistant crops against, 636–637; spread of by contact, 568; spread of by insects, 568–569; *see also* Infectious disease
Disinfectants, 594–595

Disk flowers, 202
Disposition theory, 561
Distillation products, 691
Division of labor, 23; of Hmenoptera, 300–303; of Mazoa, 241–242; nerve cells 28–29
DNA, 579
Dodo bird, **18**
Dolphins, 410
Domagk, Dr. Gerald, 576
Domestic animals, origin (Table), 667
Dominance, Law of, 620–621
Dominant genes, 620; in guinpigs, 623–624
Dominant trait, **629**
Dormancy, of animals, 68– of seeds, 219
Dorsal aorta, of fish, 333; frog, 351
Dorsal blood vessel, in earworm, 261
Dorsal fin, 331
Dorsal surface, 252
Double-cross method, 638–(
Double sugar, 188
Down feathers, 376
Downy mildews, 117
Driven wells, 680
Drivers and alcohol, 526–52'
Drone bee, 302
Droplet infection, 567–568
Drosophila, chromosomes **609;** research with, 633; chromosomes of, **629**
Drupe, 214
Dry fruits, 214, (Table), 21
Duckbill, 406–408
Ductless glands, 515–522; their secretions (Table), .
Ducts, 448, **449**
Dug wells, 680
Dujardin, 21–22
Duodenum, 452
Dura mater, 492–493
Durum (hard wheat), 223
" Dust Bowl," 678
Dutch elm disease, **313,** 696
Dynamic balance, 515

Eagle, northern bald, **705**
Eardrum, 507
Ears, care of, 508–509; of f 331; of frog, 348; hum **507**–509
Earth, age of, 656
Earthworm, 258–262, **260, 2** circulatory system of, 2 digestive system of, 260; n ous system of, 261; repro tion in, 261–**262;** respira system of, 261

hinodermata, 269
cology, 10, 66
ctoderm, of flatworms, 253;
of gastrula stage, 615; of hydra, 246
ctoplasm, 231
czema, 475
dentata, 408–409
el, spawning habits of, 337
gg, 39, 93, 207; of bird, 387;
of crayfish, 277; fertilized, 39,
388; formation of, 614, **615;**
of frog, 353; of housefly, 305;
of human female, 613; of
mammals, 401–402; in metamorphosis, 287
gg cell, of bird, 386–387
rlich, Paul, 576
asmobranchii, 328–329
astic ligament, 363
ectrocardiograph, 601
ectromagnetic radiation, 533;
wave lengths of (Table), 534
ectron microscope, 8
ectrons, 43
ements, 42–47; in compounds,
46–47; essential to all living
things (Table), 45; essential
to life (Tables), **42;** free, 46;
more common (Table), 44
ephants, 412–413; reproduction of, 665–666
k, **68;** migration of, 406
m tree, **170;** disease of Dutch,
313, 696
odea cells, 26
ongation region, of root, 149
mbryo, 216; of corn, 219;
vertebrate, development of,
663
mbryo plant, **138**
mbryo sac, 207, **208**
mbryology, 10, 662
mbryonic region, of root, 149;
of stem, 171
mbryonic tissues, 143
motional responses, of mammals, 404–405
mulsification, 455
namel, of teeth, 450
ndocrine glands, 515–522; lo-
ation of in body, **516**
ndocrine system, of humans,
15–522; of vertebrates, 321
ndoderm, of flatworms, 253;
of gastrula stage, 615; of hy-
ra, 246
ndodermis, 150
ndoplasm, 231
ndoskeleton, of man, 425; of
ertebrates, 321
ndosperm, of corn, 219; nu-
leus, 208; in seeds, 217

Endotoxins, 570
Energy, 51; factor in photosynthesis, 186; from fuels, 191;
Law of Conservation of, 52
Energy change, in photosyn-
thesis, 187
Energy waves, **533**
Engelmann spruce trees, **687**
Ensilage, 111
Entire-edged leaf, 184
Entomologist, 294
Entomology, 10; Bureau of,
311–312
Environment, 16; and heredity,
608; influence on human de-
velopment, 653; as means of
insect control, 312; protec-
tion by, 74; vital factors of,
66–76
Enzymes, 32, 51, 108; in gastric
juice, 454–455; importance
of to photosynthesis, 186;
functional similarities of, 662
Eohippus, 397
Ephyra, 249
Epidermal plates, 372
Epidermis, of flowering plants,
143; of human skin, 474;
lower of leaf, 185; of mam-
mals, 398; of root, 148–149,
150; of sponge, 244; upper
of leaf, 184
Epiglottis, 461
Epinephrine, 519
Epithelial tissue, **423,** (Table),
424
Epithelium, **27**
Equator, in mitosis, 611
Equilibrium, 160, 508
Equisetum, 132–**133**
Erect mammals, 413
Erepsin, 456
Ergosterol, 536
Ermine, 411
Erosion, 64, 672, **675;** acceler-
ated, 674; geologic, 674;
gully, 676, **677;** prevention
of by forests, 692; by water,
676; by wind, 678–679
Erythrocytes, 478
Erythromycin, 579
Esophagus, of bird, 385; of
earthworm, 260; of fish, 332;
fluoroscope screen of, **536;** of
grasshopper, **289,** 290; of
humans, 452
Essential parts, of a flower, 200
Estivation, 69
Estrogen, 520
Eugenics, 10, 646–654
Eugenist, 648
Euglena, 232–234; eyespots of,
535

Euglenoid movement, 233
Eustachian tube, of frog, 348;
of human, **506,** 507
Euthenics, 653–654
Evaporation, 438, 680, **681**
Evergreen trees, uses of, 689
Evidence of change in living
things, embryological, 662;
fossil, 657–658; geographical,
662–664
Evolution, and faith, 667
Excretion, in cells, 36; in earth-
worm, 261; produced by me-
tabolism, 469, 472
Excretory system, of bird, 385–
386; of frog, 352; of grass-
hopper, 290; of human, 469,
472–475; of vertebrates, 321
Excurrent branching, 169–170
Excurrent pore, 244
Exercise, 433, 436; heart action
and, 486–487
Exoskeleton, 272
Exosphere, **545**
Exotoxins, 569–570
Expiration, 463–**464**
Explosive decompression, 550
Extensor muscle, 277, 432–433
External respiration, 460, **461**
Extinct organisms, 17–18
" Eye " teeth, of humans, 451;
of mammals, 401
Eyes, camera compared with
(Table), 511–512; defects of,
511, (Table), 513; of fish,
331; of frog, 348; of grass-
hopper, 290, **291;** of humans,
509; of snake, 362
Eyespot, of euglena, 233, 535;
of planaria, 253, 535

F_1 generation, 619–620
F_2 generation, 619–620
Factor(s), variable, 5; of envi-
ronment, 66–76; in heredity,
620
" Fairy ring " mushrooms, 122,
123
Fall-out, 540
False feet, 231
Family, of plants and animals,
81
Fangs, of snake, 362–363, 367–
368
Farm ponds, 703–704
Farsightedness, **512**
Fat bodies, 353
Father of bacteriological tech-
nique, 652
Father of Biology, 1
Father of Medicine, 559
Fatigue, mechanism of, 466
Fats, 50; in body, 440–441; di-

gestion of, **456;** formation of during photosynthesis, 191; in plasma, 478; in protoplasm, 22; sources of, 441

Fatty acids, 34, 455

Feather, of birds, 376–378

Feces, in humans, 458; in tapeworms, 256

Federal Food, Drug, and Cosmetic Act, 598

Federal Tariff Bill, 707

Feeble-mindedness, 652–653

Feet, of bird, 379–**380** (also Table)

Femur of grasshopper, 288; fracture of, **428;** of humans, **429,** 431

Fermentation, of yeast, 118

Fermenting, 111

Ferns, 130–134; gametophyte stage of, **131**–132; life cycle of, 130–132, **131;** relatives of, 130, 132–133; sporophyte stage of, **131**

Fertilization, 39, 97, 127; of ferns, 132; of frog, 353; of mammals, 402; of moss, 127–128; of plants, 208; see also Reproduction

Fertilized egg, 39, **388**

Fetus, 402

Fever, 572

Fibers, of woody stem, 173; xylem, 143

Fibrin, 481

Fibrinogen, 478, 481

Fibrous roots, 147

Fibrovascular bundles, 177

Filament, of algae, 92; of flower, 200

Filoplumes, 376

Filtrable virus, 564

Finely-divided leaf, 184

Fingernails, of mammals, 399

Fins, 329, 331

Fire lines, 695

Fire towers, **695**

Fires, causes and prevention of forest, 693–696

First filial generation, 619–620

First line of defense, against disease, 571–572

First polar body, 614, **615**

Fish, 329–340; amateur aquarist and, 340; circulatory system of, 332–334; conservation of, 340, 700–701; digestive system of, 332; economic importance of, 338; external structure of, 329–**330;** hatcheries for, 703; laws protecting, 704; nervous system of, 335; reproductive system of, 336–

337; respiratory system, 334; sensory system of, 336; water for, 701–703

Fish ladder, 702

Fish meal, 338

Fish oil, 338

Fish and Wildlife Service, 707

Fishing, commercial, 338; importance of, 704; for sport, 338–340

Fission, of algae, 92; of paramecium, 236

Fission fungi, 104, (Table), 114

Flagellates, 100

Flagellum, 37; in algae, 98, 100; in bacteria, 105; in euglena, 233

Flamingos, 376

Flatworms, 252–256; classes of, 253–256

Fleming, Dr. Alexander, 4, 117, 577

Flesh-eating mammals, 410–411

Fleshy fruits, 214, (Table), 215

Fleshy taproots, 147

Flexor muscle, 277, 432

Flies, housefly, 304–306; reproduction of (Table), 305–306; tsetse fly, 305

Flight, of birds, 379

Flipper, 275

Floods, 682

Florey, Dr. Howard, 577

Florida terrapin, 373

Flowering plants, 141–143; tissues of, 143

Flowers, composite, 202–203; of monocots and dicots, 202–203; reproduction and, 200–210; of seed plants, 143; structure of, 200

Flukes, 254–**255**

Fluorine, 452

Flying mammals, 409

Folic acid, 442

Foliose lichens, 124

Follicles, of mammals, 398

Food(s), 437–445; bacteria in industry of, 110–111; Basic Four Groups of, **443,** 445; of birds, 381–384, (Table), 383; classes of, 437–438; definition of, 437; for independent organisms, 33–34; inspection of, 596; and life processes, 56–57; movement of in plants, 176; relation of bacteria to, 108; spoilage of by bacteria, 111–112; sterilization of by radiation, 541; supplying of for life functions, 31–34

Food-borne infections, 566

Food chain, 57, 74

Food-getting, as life-functi◖ 33–34

Food infection, 566

Food poisoning, 566–567

Food substances (Table), 44◖

Food vacuole, 26, 231–232; paramecium, 235

Forage fish, 701

Foraminifers, 237

Forebrain, 494–495

Forests, animal destruction 697; areas of, 685–689, 6◖ benefit to soil of, 692; cons◖ vation of, 684–698; in cont◖ of water supply, 692; ef◖ on climate of, 692; fa◖ about, 684–685; fires in, 6◖ 696; as homes for birds ◖ animals, 692; insect dam◖ to, 696–697; management 697; products of, 689–6◖ use and misuse of, 692–69◖

Formations, land, 73; plant ◖ animal, 70–72

Formula, chemical, 46

Fossils, 139–140, 657–659

Fovea, 510

Fracture, of bone, **428**

Fragmentation, 93

Frog, 346–357; circulatory ◖ tem of, 350–352; digest◖ system of, 349–350; econo◖ importance of, 346–347; cretory system of, 352; ternal structure of, 347; h◖ of, 348; hibernation and ◖ vation of, 355; legs of, 3◖ **348;** mouth of, 348–3◖ nervous system of, 352; gans of, **343;** reproduc◖ system of, 352–353; resp◖ tory system of, 350

Frond, 132

Frontal lobes, 494

Fruit fly, see *Drosophila*

Fruits, 211–225; classifica◖ of, 214, (Table), 215; de◖ cent, 214, 215; dry, 214, 2 fleshy, 214, 215; of flowe◖ plant, 143; indehiscent, ◖ 215; relation of seeds ◖ 211–213; structure of, 2◖ 214, 215

Fruticose lichen, 124

Fry (small fish), 337, 701

Fucus, 101

Fuels, energy from, 191

Fumigants, 314

Functional basis, of life, 31◖

Fungus, 33, 113–125; brac◖ **32,** 122–123; classes of ◖ ble), 114; description of, ◖

growth characteristics of, 122; imperfect, 123–124; mycorhiza, 74; reproduction of, 115; true, 114–121

unk, Dr. Casimir, 441

ur-bearing animals, destruction of, 707

ur farms, 709

ur seal, migration of, 406

urniture, lumber for, 689–690

's, **547**, 548

alen, Claudius, 561

all bladder, of human, 453; of bird, 385; in excretion, 475; of fish, 332; of frog, 349

Galloping caries," 451

alton, Sir Francis, 646–647

ame, destruction of on highways, 709–710

ame birds, 706

ame fish, 338, 701

ame preserves, 709

ametes, 39, 98, 127; in algae, 93

ametophyte stage, of ferns, **131**–132; of mosses, 127–**128**

amma globulin, 591–592

amma rays, 537

anglia, of earthworm, 261; of grasshopper, 291; of humans, 501

anglion, 497

rbage disposal, 313, 597

rter snakes, 364, **366**

ses, 41

stric caeca, **289**, 290

stric fluid, of bird, 385; of frog, 350; of human, 452

stric glands, of frog, 350; of humans, 452; secretion in, **36**

stric juice, enzymes in, 454–455

stritis, 524

stropods, 267–268, 658

strovascular cavity, of hydra, 47, 249

strula, 615, **616**

vials, 371

zelles, **400**

mmules, 245

ie linkage, 628

eral resistance, against disase, 172

erative nucleus, 203, 207

es, 565, 610, 620; chance istribution of, **616**–617; ominant, 620; incomplete ominance of, 627; lethal, 33; recessive, 620–621

etic mutation, 654

Genetic radiation, 654

Genetics, 10, 607; applied to human inheritance, 646–654; experiments in, 664; *see also* Heredity

Genus, 80, 81

Geographical distribution, evidence from, 662–664

Geological eras, 656, (Table), 661

Geological timetable, **660**

Geologists, 656

Geotropism, **152**–153

German measles, 590

Germicides, 110

Germination, 219–222; conditions for, 220; food changes during, 220; stages in, 220–222

Germinative layer, 474

Gestation period, 402, (Table), 403

GG, 591

Giant redwood, 141, 688

Giantism, 518

Gibberellic acid, 640

Gibbon, 413

Gila monster, 370

Gill arch, 334

Gill filaments, 334

Gill rakers, 334

Gills, of crayfish, 273, 277; of fish, 329, 334; of mollusks, 266; of mushroom, 121

Ginkgo tree, **139**–140

Ginkgoales, 139

Girdling, 174

Gizzard, of bird, 385; of earthworm, 260; of grasshopper, **289**, 290

Glacial Age, 397

Glacial Epoch, 420

Glands, of emergency, 519; of human, 515–522

Gliding joints, **430**, 431

Gloeocapsa, 94

Glomerulus, 473

Glottis, of frog, 349; of snake, 363

Glucose, 34; in digestion, 49; in photosynthesis, 187–188; in plasma, 478

Glue, 338

Gluten, 222

Glyceric acid, 188

Glycerin, 34, 455

Glycogen, 49; use in body, 440

Gnawing mammals, 411–412

Goiter, 516–517

Golden plover, 375; route of, **390**

Goldfish, 340

Goldfish bird, **392**

Gonadotropic hormone, 517–518

Gonads, of fish, 249, 336

Gopher tortoise, 373

Gorilla, 413

Grafting, 167, **177**

Grasshopper, **287**–292; abdomen of, 289; circulatory system of, 290; classification of, 83–85, (Table), 84; digestive system of, 289–290; excretory system of, 290; internal view of, **289**; legs of, 288–289; life history of, **286**; mouth parts of, **287**–288; relatives of, 291–292; reproductive system of, 291; respiratory system of, 290; sense organs of, 290–291; skeletal and muscular system of, 289; thorax of, 287; wings of, 289

Gray matter, 494, 497; of mammals, 403

Gray wolf, 411

Green glands, 276

Green molds, 116–117

Green turtle, 373

Grey fox, **709**

Ground water, 680–681

Growing regions, of plants, 171

Guard cells, in leaf, 185

Guard hair, of mammals, 398

Guernsey cow, 643, **644**

Guinea pig, crossing of, 623, **624**

Gullet, of euglena, 233; of paramecia, 235

Gullet opening, of frog, 349

Gully erosion, 676, **677**; control of, 678

Guttation, 163

Gymnosperms, 139–141

Habit, compared with addiction, 525

Hair, of mammals, 398

Hair cell, 508

Hair coloration, in mammals, 399

Half-life, 540

Hammer bone, 507

Haploid number, 614

Hard palate, 448

Hardwood trees, 687

Hares, 412

Harvestman, 283

Harvey, William, 2

Hatchery, 703

Haustoria, 117

Haversian canals, 430

Hawksbill turtle, 373

Hay fever, 206–207

Head appendages, 275

Hearing, 507–508
Heart, of bird, 386; diseases of, 599–601; of fish, 332–333; of frog, **351;** of grasshopper, **289,** 290; of human, 484–490, **485;** of mammals, 401; of vertebrates, 322
Heart muscle, 432
Heartwood, 172
Heat, loss from body, 438
Heat, sensation of, 505
Heat sterilization, 109
Heat waves, 533–534
Heidelberg man, 419
Helium, use of in space travel, 550
Helium atom, **43,** 539
Hemiptera, 304
Hemoglobin, 464, 479
Hemophilia, 651–652
Hemorrhage, 481, 569
Henle's loop, 473
Herb, 143
Herbaceous stems, 167; structure of, 177
Herbaceous and woody plants, 143–144
Herbs, 79
Hereditary traits, 610
Heredity, basis of, 608–617; cell as unit of, 608–616; definition of, 608; environment and, 608; laws of, 620–621; of man, 647–653; principles of, 618–634; *see also* Genetics
Hereford steer, 643, **644**
Hermaphroditic, 254
Hermit crab, **33**
Heroin, 528
Herpetology, 10
Heterocysts, 94
Heterogametes, 100
Hexose, 187, 439
Hibernation, 69; in frog, 355; in mammals, 406
Highland moccasin snake, 368
Hilum, 217, **218**
Hindbrain, **492,** 496
Hinge joint, **430**
Hippocrates, 559
Hippocratic Oath, 559
Histamines, 488
Histology, 10
Hobbies, biological, 10
Hog-nosed snake, 365, **366**
Holdfast, 97
Homes, of mammals, 405–406
Hominidae, 413
Homo sapiens, 413, 421
Homologous organs, 275
Homologous structures, 659
Homoptera, 304
Honey, 302

Honeybee, 300–303; life history of, 301; structure of, 300–301
Hoofed mammals, 412
Hooke, Robert, 21
Hooks, in tapeworms, 255
Hookworm, 256, 257
Hormone, 418, 515; adreno-cortico-tropic, 518; androgen, 520; epinephrine, 519; estrogen, 520; gonadotropic, 517–518; influence in cell activity, 37; lactogenic, 518; parathyrotropic, 518; sex, 520; somatropic, 517; thyroid, 516, 517; thyrotropic, 518
Horned toad, 369, **370**
Horns, 400; of gray matter, 497
Horny layer, of human skin, 474
Horny outer layer, of clam shell, 266
Horsetail rushes, 132–133
Host, 33; of infectious organisms, 569
Housefly, 304–306
Human body, regions in, 425; bones of, 428–430; circulatory system of, 489–490; compared with mammals, 418; digestive system of, **448**–449, 452–458; joints of, **430**–431; muscles of, 431–436; organs of, 425; respiratory system of, 459–469, **460;** skeleton of, 425–426; structure of, 418–436; systems of, 423–425; tissues of, 423–425, (Table), 424
Human carriers of disease, 568
Hummingbirds, in pollination, 204
Humus, 671
Hybrid, 621; true, 643
Hybrid corn, production of, 638–640, **641**
Hybrid vigor, 637
Hybridization, 637
Hydra, 246–248
Hydrochloric acid, 452; in stomach, 455
Hydrogen atom, **43**
Hydrogen isotope, **43**
Hydrophobia, 583–585
Hydrophyte plants, 69–**70**
Hydrotropism, 153
Hyla, 345–346
Hymenoptera, 300–303
Hypertension, 599–600
Hyperthyroidism, 516
Hypha, 114, 115–116; in mildew, 117
Hypocotyl, of bean, 217–**218, 221;** of corn, **218,** 219, 222

Hypothesis, 4
Hypothyroidism, 516

Ichneumon fly, 289, 303
Ichthyology, 10
Idiocy, 652
Iguana, 369–370
Ileum, 452
Imbibition, 164
Immovable joints, **430, 431**
Immune therapy, 574
Immunity, to disease, 573–⁙
Immunization, against co⁙ 588; against diphtheria, 5⁙ 586; against smallpox, 5⁙ 583; against tetanus, 5⁙ against tuberculosis, 5⁙ 588; against typhoid fe⁙ 586–587
Imperfect flower, 201, **204**
Imperfect fungi, 123–124
Improvement cutting, 697
Inbreeding, 638
Incisors, of humans, 450; mammals, 400–401
Inclusions, 23, 26
Incompatible bloods, 481
Incomplete dominance, **626,** ⁙
Incomplete flower, 200
Incomplete metamorphosis, ⁙
Incubation, bacteria dur⁙ 110; of bird, 387
Incurrent pores, 242, 244
Incurrent siphon, 266
Indehiscent fruits, 214, (Tab⁙ 215
Individual characteristics, 60⁙
Infantile paralysis, *see* Polio⁙
Infection, body defenses aga⁙ 517–580; carriers of, 5⁙ 569; contact, 568; dro⁙ 567–568; food-borne, ⁙ water-borne, 567; white ⁙ puscles as defense aga⁙ 479–480; wound, 568
Infectious diseases, control ⁙ 581–592; early beliefs ab⁙ 560–561; spread of, 565
Influenza, 588–589; virus c⁙ ing, **564**
Infrared waves, 533–534
Inheritance, and acquired sk⁙ 649–650; of blood type, ⁙ of desirable and undesir⁙ traits, 650–651; of me⁙ ability, 652; of mental di⁙ ders, 652–653; of Rh fa⁙ 651; study of human, ⁙ 647
Inoculation, 110, 581
Inorganic minerals, 478
Insect-eating mammals, 409
Insect pollinators, 204

ct vectors, 311
cta, 84, 273
cticides, 313–315
ctivora, 409
ctivorous plants, 198
cts, 285–292; bugs com-
ared with, 285–286; com-
on orders of, 294, **295,** (Ta-
e), 307; control of, 311–
15; destruction of by birds,
93; disease spread by, 568–
69; economic importance of,
07–308; as enemies of trees,
96–697; habits of, 294–308;
ason for dominance, 310–
1; specialization of, 286;
ecies of, 285; structure of,
85–286; as vectors of dis-
se (Table), 310–311
rtion, of muscle, 432
iration, 463, **464**
ncts, 324; of mammals,
04–405
lin, 519, 662
gumentary system, of ver-
brates, 321
guments, 207
ligence quotient, 652
ligence tests, 652
ligent behavior, 324
cellular spaces, 23
dependence, of cells, 242
nal respiration, 460
rnode, 168
phase, 610
tinal fluid, 456
tinal glands, 455–456
tine, of earthworm, 260; of
h, 332; of flatworm, 253–
4; of frog, 349; of grass-
pper, **289,** 290; of humans,
2, 454, 456–458
rtebrates, definition of,
1–242; development of,
9–320
luntary muscles, 431
luntary response, 324
e, in algae, 101; in thyroid
nd, 516
e salts, 438
ation, 537–538
ing radiations, 538
sphere, **545**
652
of eye, 509
compounds, 438
ation, 679
bility, 37
of Langerhans, 519
metes, 98
pes, 43, 538; use of, 542
us, 331; of thyroid,
5

Jacobson's organs, 361
Japanese beetle, 304
Java man, 419, **420**
" Jaw teeth," 401
Jejunum, 452
Jellyfish, **248**–249
Jenner, Edward, 2, 581–582
Joints, of body, **430**–431
Jupiter rocket, **546, 547**

Kangaroo, 408, **409**
Kelp, **100,** 101
Kidneys, of bird, 386; of frog,
352; of man, **472**–474, **473**
Kinesthetic sense, 548
Kinetic energy, 51
King snake, 365
Kingdoms, plant and animal, 81
Koch, Robert, 562–563
Koch postulates, 563
Komodo dragon lizard, **369**

Labium, of grasshopper, 288; of
honeybee, 301; of Lepidop-
tera, 296
Labrum, of grasshopper, 288; of
honeybee, 301
Lactase, 456
Lacteals, 457
Lactic acid, 111, 466
Lactogenic hormone, 518
Lactose, 49
Lady bugs, 304
Lagomorpha, 412
Lake forest, 685–686
Lakes, 703–704; productive, 701
Lamarck, Jean Baptiste, 664–
665
Lamprey trap, 328
" Land bridge," 663
Land formations, 73
Landsteiner, 483
Large intestine, in excretion,
475; of frog, 349; of human,
454; water absorbed by, 458
Larva, of *Ascaris,* 256; of flukes,
254–255; of Lepidoptera,
297; in metamorphosis (Ta-
ble), 287
Larynx, of man, 461
Lateral buds, 168; line, 332;
undulatory movement, 363–
364; ventricle, of brain, 493
Law of, Conservation of En-
ergy, 52; Conservation of
Matter, 41–42; Dominance,
620–621; Independent Assortment, 626–627; Segregation,
621, **622;** Unit characters,
620
Laws, to protect birds, 707; to
protect fish, 704
Leaching, 672; problems of, 674

Leaf, 182–199; activities of
(Table), 195; arrangement of,
195–196; chlorophyll in, 184–
185, 186; coloration, 196; effects of moisture on, 196; external features of, 183–184;
as factory (Table), 192; falling of, 197; of flowering
plant, 142–143; forms, 184;
internal structure of, 184; in
relation to light, 195–196;
scars, 168; special modifications of, 197–198; transpiration in, 193–194; venation of,
183, 184
Leaflet, 184
Leather turtle, 373
Leech, **259,** 262
Legs, of bird, 379, 381; of
frog, 347–**348;** of grasshopper, 288–289
Legume, 214; in crop rotation,
673; as food, 224
Leguminoseae, 214
Lemurs, 413
Lens, of eye, 509
Lenses, grinding of, 6
Lenticels, 168
Leopard frog, 346, **347;** fertilization of eggs of, 353
Lepidoptera, 294–300; abdomen
of, 296; economic importance
of, 298; head of, 294–296;
life history of, 296–298; mi-
grations of, 299–300; thorax
of, 296
Leprosy, bacteria causing, **566**
Lespedeza, 673
Leucocytes, 478
Leucoplast, 25, **27**
Leukemia, 484
Lichens, 124–125
Life, condition of protoplasm,
14; functional basis of, 31–
40; functions, 15–16; funda-
mental properties of, 12–19;
physical basis of, 21–30; requirements of, 16
Life cycle, of corn smut, **120;**
of the fern, 130–132, **131;** of
mosses, 127–128; of wheat
rust, 120
Life span, 14–15; of seed plants,
144–145
Ligaments, 431
Light, a factor in environment,
72; leaf in relation to, 195–
196; in photosynthesis, 191;
as variable factor, 5
Limbs, of mammals, 400
Lime, in soil, 673
Lime-producing glands, 386–
387

Line breeding, 637–638
Linkage, of genes, 628
Linnaeus, Carolus, 79–80, 85
Lipase, 455
Liquids, 41
Lister, Sir Joseph, 2, 594, **595**
Liver, of bird, 385; cirrhosis of the, 524; in excretion, 475; of fish, 332; of frog, 349; human, 452–453, 455
Liverworts, 127, 129–**130**
Livestock, improvement in, 643
Living things, characteristics of, 12–17
Lizards, 368–370
Loam, 67; soils, 155, 671
Lobar pneumonia, 589
Lobed leaf, 184
Loblolly pines, **686,** 687
Lobsters, 279
Lockjaw, 107, 586
Locomotion, 37; in snakes, 363–364
Longitudinal, muscles, 259, 452; nerve cords, 254
Louse, 310
Lumber, 689–690; timber trees supplying (Table), 690; for transportation and communication, 690–691
Lungs, air capacity of, 462; in excretion, 475; of frog, 350; of mammals, 401; of man, 461
Lymph, 489–**490**
Lymph nodes, 489
Lymphatics, **490**

Macronucleus, 236
Maggots, 305
Magnification, 5
Maidenhair fern, 139
Malaria, **238**–239, 569
Malpighian tubules, 290
Maltase, 456
Maltose, 456
Mammals, 396–414; antlers and horns of, 399–400; body covering of, 398–399; characteristics of, 398; conditioned reactions of, 405; destruction of harmful, 394; destruction of larger, 707–708; hair coloration in, 399; hibernation of, 406; homes of, 405–406; instincts of, 404–405; internal organs of, 401; limbs of, 400; migration of, 406; nervous system of, 403; orders of, 406–413; parental care, 403; prehistoric, 396–397; reproduction of, 401–**402**; sense organs of, 403–404; structure

compared with man, 418; teeth of, 400–401
Mammary glands, 398, 518
Man, as supreme form of life, 19
Mandibles, of crayfish, 275; of grasshopper, 288
Manganese, in algae, 101
Manic-depressive psychosis, 653
Mantle, 265; cavity, 265–266
Maple sugar, 691–692
Marchantia, 130
Marginal sense organ, 248
Marijuana, 529
Marine, Hospital Service, 598; mammals, 409–410; plants and animals, 69
Market hunting, 705
Marmosets, 413
Marrow, red and yellow, 430
Marsupialia, 408, **409**
Mass selection, in animal breeding, 642–643; in plant breeding, 636–637
Mathematical calculations, 3
Matrix, 93–**94**
Matter, 41–43; Law of Conservation of, 41–42
Maturation region, of root, 149
Maxillae, of crayfish, 275; of grasshopper, 288; of Lepidoptera, 296
Maxillipeds, 275
Measles, 590
Mechanical, change in digestion, 447; dispersal of seeds, 214–215
Medicine, in ancient Greece, 559–560; curative, 594; in Middle Ages, 560; in 19th century, 560–561; patent, 598; preventive, 594, 595–597; uses of radiation in, 542
Medulla, of adrenal gland, 518–519; of bird, 386; of frog, 352; of kidney, 472; of mammals, 403
Medulla oblongata, of fish, 335; of human, 496
Medusa, 248
Meiosis, 614; crossing-over in, **628**
Membrane, of cytoplasm, 24; diffusion through, 160–161; of nucleus, 25
Mendel, Gregor, 618–628; experiments with peas, 618; laws of, 620–628
Meninges, 492
Mental, ability, inheritance of, 652; age, 652; disease, 602–604; disorders, inheritance of, 652–653; fatigue, 502

Mesentery, 349
Mesoderm, of flatworms, 2.; of gastrula stage, 615
Mesophyte plants, **70**
Mesothorax, 288
Mesozoic Era, 357, 359, 39 397
Metabolism, 31, 467; assimi tion and, 35; basal, 468–4(excretion produced by, 4 472; thyroid hormone a 516
Metamorphosis, complete, 2: of frog, 342, 353–355, **3** incomplete, 287; in inse 286–287
Metaphase, 611
Metathorax, 288
Metazoa, 241; groups of (ble), 243
Microbes, 558–570; cause disease, 569–570
" Micrographia," 21
Micronucleus, 236
Micropyle, 207; of bean, 2 **218;** of corn, 218
Microscope, 5–8, **6, 7, 8;** amination of bacteria by, 1
Midbrain, **492,** 495, 496
Middle lamella, 23, **27**
Midget, 518
Mid-latitude zone, 70
Midrib veins, 184
Migration, of animals, 68; birds, 389–391, 535; of f 337; of mammals, 406
Migratory Bird Treaty Act, '
Mildew, 117
Milk, snake, 365, **366;** sou of infection, 596; teeth, 1
Millepede, **280,** 281
Milt, 336
Mimicry, 75–76, 298
Mineral compounds, 48; use body, 438
Mineral deposit, in bone, 429
Mineral salts, for body fu tions, 438, **439;** in pr plasm, 22
Minerals, absorption of, 1 165; depletion in soil, 6 674
Mink, 411, **709**
Mites, 283
Mitochondria, 25
Mitosis, 39; stages of, 610–(**611**
Mitral valve, 599
Mixed nerves, 498
Mixture, 47
Mobile terrapin, 373
Modern man, 421–423; c pared with ancient, 422–

›isture, for bacteria, 107; effect on leaves, 196; for germination, 220
›lar teeth, of humans, 450; of mammals, 400–401
›ld, 115–117
›le, 404, 409
›lecules, 35, 46–47
›llusks, 265–269; bivalve, 266–267; univalve, 267–268; ›alveless, 268–269
›lting, in birds, 377–378, 536; ›f crayfish, 277–278; of grasshopper, 291; of snakes, 361 ›lts, 277
›narch butterfly, 75–76, 299–300
›ngoloid type man, 421–422
›nkeys, Able and Baker in ›ocket, 546, 547; New World, 413; Old World, 413
›nocots (Table), 141–142; ›lowers of, 202, 205; herbaceous stem of, 177, 178–179
›nocotyledonae, 141–142
›noecious plants, 202
›nosaccharides, 439–440
›notremata, 406–408
›rel, 118–119
›rgan, Thomas Hunt, 633
›rphine, 528
›rphology, 10
›squito, 306–307; control of, 13
›sses, 126–130; economic importance of, 128–129; gametophyte stage in, 127–128; ›fe cycle of, 127–128; reproduction of, 127–128; *Sphagum,* 129; sporophyte stage ›, 127–128, 129
›th, 294–300; comparison of butterfly and (Table), 298
›tion, of hydra, 247; types f in a cell, 37
›tion sickness, 508
›tor, areas, of cerebrum, 494; ›nd plates, 500; nerve, 498; ›eurons, 498
›unt Vesuvius, 658
›untain lion, 411
›uth, of earthworm, 259; of ›og, 348–349; of human, ›48, 449; parts of honeybee, ›01; of roundworms, 256; of ›nake, 361
›th cavity, 234–235
›uth-to-mouth method, of arficial respiration, 464, 465
›vement, of crayfish, 277
›cous, glands of frog, 350; ›embranes, 571–572
›cus, feeders, 267; in frog

glands, 347, 350; of human, 448; as lubricating substance, 37
Mud puppy, 344
Mulch, 129, 155
Mule, 643–645
Muller, Dr. H. J., 633
Multicellular organism, 28, 241
Mumps, 448, 590
Muscle, action, 432–433; of bird wing, 378; cells, 37; cells, kinds of, 431–**432**; function of cerebellum and, 496; human, 431–436; movement of, 431; tissue, 423, (Table), 424
Muscular, coordination, 433; exercise, 433, 436
Muscular system, of grasshopper, 289; of vertebrates, 321
Mushrooms, 121–**122**, **123**; "fairy ring," 122, **123**; poisonous and edible, 122; reproductive structure of, 121; sponge, 118
Muskrat, 412; house of, 406
Mutant, 632, 667
Mutation, 632, 664; causes of, 633; plant varieties from, 640; theory, 667
Mycelium, 114–115; mushroom, 121
Mycobacterium, leprae, **566;** *tuberculosis,* **563**
Mycology, 10, 113
Mycorhiza, 74, 125
Myriapoda, 281
Myths, examples of, 1
Myxomycetes, 114

Naked seeds, 139
Names, reason for scientific, 81
Naphthalene, 314–315
Narcotics, 527–529
Nasal, cavity of fish, 331; opening of sea lamprey, 316; passages, of man, 460–461
National, Aeronautics and Space Administration, 553; Audubon Society, 705, 707; Foundation, 591; Institutes of Health, 592; Tuberculosis Association, 588
National parks and forests, 698
Natural enemies, of insects, 312–313; as nature's check, 62–63
Natural immunity, 573–574
Natural selection, 666–667; Darwin's theory of, 665
Nature, environments in, 66–67
Nautilus, 535
Naval stores, 687
Neanderthal man, 419–421

Nearsightedness, **512**
Neck, of teeth, 450
Necturus, 344
Negroid type man, 422
Nelmes, Sarah, 581
Nemathelminthes, 256
Nematocysts, 247
Nematoda, 256
Nephridia, 261
Nephritis, chronic, 600
Nephron, 473
Nereis, **259**
Nerve, canal, 451; cell body, 497; endings, of skin, 505–506; fiber, 498; impulse, 500; net, 247; tissue, 423, (Table), 424
Nerves, of human body, 497–498, **499**
Nervous, fatigue, 502; reactions, 500–501
Nervous system, of bird, 386; of crayfish, 276–277; of earthworm, 261; effects of alcohol on, 525; of fish, 335; of frog, 352; of human, 492–503; of mammals, 403; of vertebrates, 321
Nests, of birds, 392–393, (Table), 394
Neuron, 497, 498, **500**
Neutrons, 43
Newts, 345
Niacin, 442
Nicotine, 530
Nicitating membrane, 348; of bird, 381; of turtle, 372–373
Night blindness, 511
Nitrates, 34; in nitrogen cycle, 58
Nitrification, 58
Nitrifying organisms, 58
Nitrites, 58
Nitrogen, cycle, 58–60, **59;** fixation, 58; use of in space travel, 550
Nitrogen-containing wastes, 478
Nitrogenous wastes, 469
Nobel Prize, 564; in genetics, 633
Node, 168
Nodules, **34**
Nonliving substances, in protoplasm, 23
Nonprotein nitrogen, 478
Northern bald eagle, **705**
Northern forest, 685–686
Nose, of man, 460–461, **506**
Nostoc, 93–**94**
Nostrils, of man, 461
Notochord, 320–321
Nuclear, Age, 533; membrane, 25, 609; net, 609; sap, 26

Nucleolus, 25, 609
Nucleoplasm, 25, 609
Nucleus, 43; in ameba, 231; of cell, 23; of nerve cell body, 497; center of cell heredity, 609; division of, **38**, 39; of euglena, 233; of paramecium, 236; structure of, 25–26
Nutritional, processes, 31; relationships, 33–34
Nuts, 224
Nymph, in metamorphosis, 287, 291

Oak wilt, 696–697
Oats, 224
Oblique muscle, 452
Occipital lobes, 494
Octopus, **269**
Oculist, 513
Odonata, 303–304
Oedogonium, 98–100
Oil, formation of during photosynthesis, 191; in onion cells, 187; in photosynthesis, 188
Olfactory lobes, of bird, 386; of fish, 335; of frog, 352; of mammals, 403
Olfactory nerve, 506
Onion skin, cells of, **26**; stages of mitosis in cells of, **612**
Oöcyte, 614
Oögonial cells, 614, **615**
Oögonium, **98**, 100
Oötid, 614, **615**
Open system, 276
Operculum, 331, 334
Opium, 528
Opossum, 408
Opposite leaves, 168
Opsonins, 573
Opthalmologist, 513
Optic lobes, of bird, 386; of fish, 335; of frog, 352; of grasshopper, 291; of mammals, 403
Optic nerves, 496, 509
Optician, 513
Optometrist, 513
Oral groove, of paramecium, 234
Orangutan, 413
Orb weavers, 281
Orders, of mammals, 406–413, **407**; of plants and animals, 81; of reptiles (Table), 359
Organic, compounds, 47–48; disease, 598–599; matter, in soil, 155, 674; needs, 16; nutrients, 48, 438–439
Organisms, 13, 29, 423; causing disease, 564–565; characteristics of (Table), 629; common names of, 78; nitrifying, 58
Organs, definition of, 29, 423; systems of, 29
Origin, of muscle, 432
Origin of Species by Natural Selection, 665
Ornithological Union, 707
Ornithologist, 388
Ornithology, 10
Orthoptera, 84, 287
Oscillatoria, 94–95
Osculum, 244
Osmosis, 35; as physical process, 164; "reverse," 163; as a type of diffusion, **160**, 161–164
Osmotic pressure, 162
Ossification, 428, 429
Osteichthyes, 329
Ostia, 276
Outbreeding, 637
Ovary, of bird, 386, **387**; of fish, 336; of flower, 200, **202**; of frog, 353; of grasshopper, 291; of humans, 520; of hydra, 248; of mammals, 401–**402**
Overproduction, 665–**666**
Oviduct, of bird, 386, **387**; of frog, 353; of mammals, 401–**402**
Oviparous snakes, 364, **366**
Ovipositors, 289, 291
Ovoviviparous snakes, 364
Ovules, of flower, 200, **202**; structure of, in flower, 207
Oxidation, 35, 192–193
Oxidized, 479
Oxygen, atom, **43**; debt, 466; in germination, 220; during photosynthesis, 188–189; produced by green plants, 190; use of by cells, 464–466; as waste product, 188–189, 190
Oxygen-carbon dioxide cycle, 60–62, **61**
Oxygenated blood, 350–351, 479, 489
Oxyhemoglobin, 479
Oyster, eggs of, 665

P generation, 619
Pacific Coastal forest, 688–689
Pain, sensation of, 505
Painted turtle, **372**
Paleontology, 10
Palisade layer, of leaf, 184
Palmate, 400; venation, 184
Palmately compound leaf, 184
Palpus, 288
Pancreas, of bird, 385; of frog, 349; human, **453**–454, 45?, 519
Pancreatic, duct, 454; fluid, 454, 455
Paper, manufacture of, 689, 691; pulp mill, **689**
Papillae, 449
Paradichlorobenzene, 314–315
Parallel venation, 184
Paramecium, 234–236; and ameba compared (Table), 237; reproduction in, 236; sensitivity in, 235
Parasites, 33, 108; mildew, 111; spore-forming Protozoa, 238, 239
Parasitic, fungi, 115; plants, 3?
Parasitology, 10
Parasympathetic nervous system, 501–502
Parathormone, 517
Parathyroid glands, 517
Parathyrotropic hormone, 518
Parenchyma, 143
Parental care, in mammals, 40?
Parietal, eye, 360; lobes, 494
Park, Dr. William H., 585
Parotid glands, 448
Partially movable joints, 43?, 431
Particulate radiation, 538–539
Passenger pigeons, 705
Passive immunity, 574
Pasteur, Louis, 2, 562; conquest of rabies, 583–585; discovery of anthrax vaccine, 583
Pasteurization, 112
Patch test, 587
Patent medicines, 598
Pathogenic bacteria, 105
Pathogenic organisms, 564
Pathology, 10
Peach, 214
Peanuts, 224
Pearly layer, of clam shell, 2?
Peas, crossing of, 624–626, **62?**; Mendel's experiments with, 618
Peat, 128, 155, 671
Pectin substances, 23
Pectoral fins, 331
Pedicel, 200, **201**
Pedipalps, 282
Peking man, 419
Pellicle, 234
Pelvic fins, 331
Pelvis, 431; of kidney, 472
Penicillin, 117, 577–578; and pneumonia, 589
Penicillium, 116–117
Penicillium notatum, **577**, 57?
Pepsin, 454–455, 662

ptids, 455
ptones, 454
rcheron, 665
rennials, 145
rfect flower, 200–201
ricardial, cavity, 333; sinus, 276
ricardium, 484
ricycle, 150
riderm, of root, 151
riodontal membrane, 450
riosteum, 429
ripheral nervous system, 492
rmanent, cartilage, 430; residents (birds), 391; teeth, 451
rmeable membrane, 160
rnicious anemia, 484
rspiration, 474
tals, of flower, 200
tiole, 183–184
tri dishes, 109
trification, 657
aeophyceae, 101
arynx, of earthworm, 260; of fish, 332; of flatworm, 253; of human, 448, 461
easant, 706
ipps, James, 581–582
loem, of flowering plants, 143; of root, 150–151; of woody stem, 173
osphorus, use in body, 438
otoperiodism, 535
otoreceptor, 510, 535
otosynthesis, 32–33, 60–61, 86–191; by algae, 91–92, 6; chemical equation, 189; hlorophyll in, 186; conditions for, 190–191; definition of, 189; energy factor n, 187; importance of, 191; xygen released by, 188, 190; roduct of, 187–188; radioctive carbon and, 188–189; espiration and (Table), 191–93; waste product of, 188–89
ototropism (Table), 153, 196
cocyanin, 93
cology, 10
comycetes (Table), 114, 15, 116, 117
la, 81; of animal kingdom, 1, (Table), 83; of plant ingdom (Table), 82
sical change, of matter, 41
sical factors in environment, 7–74
siological similarities, of ertebrates, 662
siology, 10, 423
mater, 492
s, 412

Pike fish, 340
Pill bug, 278, 279
Pine tar, 691
Pine trees, products of, 691; species of, 687
Pineal body, 520, 522
Pinnate venation, 184
Pinnately compound leaf, 184
Pinus, 80
Pistil, 200
Pistillate flowers, 201, 202, 204
Pit vipers, 366, 367, 368
Pitcher plants, 197–198
Pith, 143, 172, 174; rays, 172; cells of, 173
Pitocin, 518
Pitressin, 518
Pituitary gland, 517–518
Pivot joint, 431
Placenta, of mammals, 402
Planaria, 253–254; eyespots of, 535; reproduction in, 254
Plant breeding, 635–641; objectives in, 635–636
Plants, Aristotle's grouping of, 79; cells of, 23–25, 24, 27; characteristics compared with animal, 85–87, 229; classification of, 77–87; conservation of, 710; flowering, 141–143; food movement in, 176; formations, of United States, 71–72; green and nongreen, 32–33; herbaceous and woody, 143–144; increased chromosome numbers of, 640; need for light, 535; in past geological ages, 656–664; phyla, 81, 82, (Table), 83; propagation, 176; respiration in, 193; transpiration in, 193–194; varieties from mutations, 640
Planula, 249
Plasma, 438, 478, 482; membrane, 24, 34–35; powdered, 483–484
Plasmodium, 238–239; life cycle of, 238
Plasmolysis, 163–164
Plastids, 25
Plastron, 372
Platelets, 478, 480
Platyhelminthes, 253, 254, 255
Pleisotocene, fossils of, 658
Pleural membrane, 461
Plexus, 497
Plumule, of bean, 218, 221; of corn, 218, 219, 222
Pneumococcus, 589
Pneumonia, 589; bacteria causing, 566
Point of attachment, 218

Poland China hog, 643
Polar, bear, 410; nuclei, 207; zone, 70
Polio, 590–592; vaccine, 5, 590, 591, 592; virus, 564, 569
Pollen, 200; allergy, 206–207; formation of, 203; grains, 203, 207–208; sacs, 202; tube, 207–208
Pollination, 203–208; adaptations for, 204; agents for, 204; artificial, 206; cross-, 204; self-, 204–206
Pollution, 64
Polyp, 249–250
Polyploidy, 640
Polysaccharides, 440
Pome, 213
Ponds, 703–704
Pons, 492, 496
Porcupine, 398–399
Pores, of sponge, 242, 244
Porifera, 242
Porpoises, 410
Portal, circulation, 489; vein, 351
Portuguese man-of-war, 249
Posture, 436
Potassium, 438
Potato, beetle, 304; cells of, 27, 28
Potential energy, 51
Pouched mammals, 408
Poultry, breeds of, 642
Powdery mildews, 117
Prairie, chicken, 705–706; wolf, 411
Praying mantis, 292
Precipitation, 680
Precipitins, 573
Predator, 62–64
Prehistoric mammals, 397
Premolar teeth, of humans, 450; of mammals, 400–401
Prenatal influence, 650
Pressure, problems in space, 549–551; sensation of, 505; suit used in space travel, 550
Preventive medicine, 594; in the community, 595–597
Primaries, of bird feathers, 379
Primary, oöcyte, 614, 615; root, 146–147; sex determiners, 629
Primates, 413
Prismatic layer, of clam shell, 266
Proboscidea, 413
Proboscis, 296
Processes, of life, 56; of nerve body, 497
Producer scientist, 2
Productive lake and stream, 701

Proglottids, 255
Prolegs, 297
Prontosil, 576
Propagation, 176; roots for, 156
Prophase, 610–611
Propolis, 302
Prostomium, 259
Protective coloration, 75; of insects, 298
Protective resemblance, 75, 291
Proteins, 50; in body, 441; digestion of, **456;** formation of, 192; in nitrogen cycle, 58; in protoplasm, 22
Proteoses, 454
Prothallus, 131–132
Prothorax, 288
Prothrombin, 478, 481
Protococcus, 95
Protonema, 128
Protons, 43
Protoplasm, 14, 15; in body, 441; characteristics of, 22–23; discovery of, 21–22; division of labor of, 23; life activities of, 31; specialization of in Protozoa, 237
Protoplast, 23–26
Protozoa, 229–239; ciliated, **230;** classes of (Table), 230; economic importance of, 237–238; specialization of protoplasm in, 237; spore-forming, 238–239; types of, 239
Protozoology, 10
Pruning, 177
Pseudopodia, 231
Psittacosis, 574
Psychiatrist, 603, **604**
Pteridophytes, 130–134
Ptyalin, 454
Puberty, 520
Public health organizations, 595–596
Puff adder snake, 365, **366**
Puffballs, 123
Pulmocutaneous artery, 351
Pulmonary, artery, 461, **462,** 485; circulation, 489; veins, **462,** 485
Pulp cavity, 450–451
Pulpwood, 691
Pulse, 487
Puma, 411
Punnett squares, 623, **625**
Pupa, of Lepidoptera, 297; in metamorphosis, 287
Pupil, of eye, 509
Pure characteristic, 618
Pus, 480, 572
Pyloric, caeca, 332; valve, 349, 452

Pylorus, of fish, 332; of frog, 349
Pyramids, of kidney, 472
Pyrenoids, 96
Python, 361, **362**

Quadrate bone, 363
Quarantine, 311–312
Queen bee, 301
Quill feathers, 377, 379

Rabbits, 412
Rabies, 583–585
Raccoon, 411
Rachis, of bird, 377
Racial development, theories of, 664–665, 668
" Radar " system, of mammals, 404, 409
Radial symmetry, 252
Radiation, biology and, 532–543; definition of, 533; in determining age of living things, 540; effects of, on body, 537–538; medical uses of, 542; natural, 539–540; special precautions against, 542–543; sterilization of food by, 541
Radio waves, 533
Radioactive carbon and photosynthesis, 188–189
Radioactive particles, 540
Radioactive substances, 43; influence on genes, 633
Radiolarians, 237
Radium, naturally excited atom, 538; in treating cancer, 602
Radula, 268
Rain, 680
Rainfall, and plants, 71–72
Rancho La Brea, tar pits at, 658
Ratios, in breeding experiments, 627–628
Rattles, of snakes, 367
Rattlesnakes, 366–368, **367**
Ray flowers, 202
Rays, sting, 328–329; form of radiation, 533; of starfish, 269
Reaction time, 525
Receptacle, 200, 213
Receptors, 505
Recessive genes, 620–621; in guinea pigs, 623–624
Recessive trait, **629**
Rectum, of bird, 385; of grasshopper, **289,** 290; of human, 454
Red-bellied terrapin, 373
Red elf, 345
Red foxes, 399, 411
Red-tailed hawk, 394
Redi, Francesco, 13–14
Reduced hemoglobin, 479

Reduction division, 614
Reefs, coral, **250**
Reflex action, 500–**501**
Reforestation, 697
Regeneration, of Amphib 355; of Crustacea, 278; planaria, **254;** of sponges, :
Reindeer moss, 125
Relapsing fever, 311
Remora, and shark, 33
Renal artery, 473
Renal circulation, 489
Renal pelvis, **472,** 473
Renal veins, 474
Rennin, 455
Repellents, 314–315
Reproduction, 16–17, 38–39; algae, 92–93, 95, 96, **97,** of ameba, 232; asexual, of bacteria, 106; conjugati 96–97; of earthworm, 2 **262**
Reproduction, of flower plants, 142–143; of **l** (Table), 305–306; flow and, 200–210; of fungi, 1 of hydra, 248; of mos 127–128; of *Oedogonium,* ' 100; of paramecium, 236; planaria, 254; sexual, 96; spiders, 282; in *Spirog* 96; of sponges, 244–245; spore-forming Protozoa, 2 of *Ulothrix,* **97;** of yeast c (budding), 118
Reproductive organs, of flow ing plant, 143; of mosses,
Reproductive system, of b 386–387; of fish, 336–337 frog, 352–353; of grassh per, 291; of mammals, 4 **402;** of snakes, 364; of ve brates, 321
Reptiles, 357–373; characte tics of, 359; classification 359; orders of (Table),
Research method, 3–4
Reservoir, of euglena, 233
Reservoirs, 682–683
Residual air, 462
Resin, 691
Respiration, 35, 60–**61;** chem equation for, 192; of cray 277; definition of, 459; ternal influences upon, 4 of flowering plant, 143; high altitudes, 466–467; living tissues, 192–**l** phases of, 460; photosynth and (Table), 192–193; plants and animals, 193; space, 549
Respiratory system, of b

85–386; of earthworm, 261;
 f fish, 334; of frog, 350; of
rasshopper, 290; of man,
59–469, 460; of vertebrates,
21
ponse, 16; of animals, 322–
24; in plant cell, 38
ina, 509–510
ting, 111
everse osmosis," 163
 factor, 418, 482–483; in-
eritance of, 651
sus monkey, 418, 482
umatic fever, 599
zobium, 34
zoids, 115, 116
zomes, 130, 180
zopus, 115
dophyceae, 101
nchocephalia, 359
oflavin, 118, 442
s, of human, 350; of snake,
64
e, 224
ketts, Dr. Howard T., 565
kettsiae, 565
 erosion, 676
d, 178
g canal, 269
g-necked snake, 366
gworm fungi, 123–124
k, study of, 656
kefeller Foundation, 598
kets, Jupiter, 546, 547
ky Mountain forest, 687–
88
ky Mountain spotted fever,
65
ky Mountain tick, 283
l, of eye, 510
lentia, 411–412
lentlike mammals, 412
sevelt, Theodore, and forest
onservation, 693
 t, 146–165; adventitious,
55–156; aquatic, 155; brace,
55; climbing, 156; direct
ses of, 156–157; elongation
egion of, 149; embryonic re-
ion of, 149; environments
f, 154–155; of flowering
lant, 142; maturation region
f, 149; osmosis in, 160–162;
rop, 155; for propagation,
56; regions and tissues of,
49–151, (Table), 152; re-
ponses of to surroundings,
51–152; secondary, 146–
47; systems of, 146–148; tip
ayering process of, 156; of
ooth, 450; turgor in, 162–
63
t cap, 149

Root crops, 157
Root hairs, 148–149
Root pressure, 162–163, 175
Root tip, structure of, 149
Rose fever, 206–207
Rosin, 691
Rostrum, 275
Roundworms, 256–258
Row crops, 672
Ruddy turnstone, 375
Rumen, 412
Ruminants, 412
Runoff water, 680, 681–682
Rust fungi, 119–121
Rye, 224

Sac fungi, 115
Saccharide, 439
Sacroiliac joint, 430
Salamanders, 342, 344–345
Salientia, 342–344
Saliva, 448–449, 454
Salivary glands, of grasshopper,
 289, 290; of human, 448–449
Salk, Dr. Jonas, 5, 592
Salk vaccine, 592
Salmon, life history of, 337,
 338
Salvarsan, 576
Sandworm, 259
Saprolegnia, 116
Saprophytes, 33, 108
Saprophytic fungi, 115
Sapwood, 172
Sarcode, 22
Satellite, 539, 547
Scales, of fish, 329, 330–331
Scarlet tanager, 393
Schick test, 586
Schistocerca, 84
Schizomycetes, 104, 114
Schleiden, Matthias, 22
Schwann, Theodor, 22
Science, meaning of, 2
Scientific attitudes, 2
Scientific classification, 81–87
Scientific experiment, 4–5
Scientific methods, 3–4
Scientific names, of organisms,
 80–81, (Tables), 82–83; need
 for, 85
Scion, 176
Sclerotic layer, of eyeball, 509
Scorpions, 282–283
Scurvy, 441
Scutes, 361
Scyphistoma, 249
Sea anemone, 33, 252
Sea cows, 400, 410
Sea cucumber, 269
Sea lamprey, 326–328
Sea urchin, 269
Seals, 400, 406, 410

Seaweeds, 101
Second filial generation, 619–
 620
Second line of defense, against
 disease, 572
Second polar body, 614
Secondaries, of bird feathers,
 379
Secondary oöcyte, 614, 615
Secondary roots, 146–147
Secretion, 36–37
Sedimentary rock, 656; fossil
 evidence in, 657–658
Seed, 138; definition of, 211,
 216–217; relation of fruit to,
 211–213
Seed coats, 216
Seed dispersal, 214–216
Seed plants, 138–225; classes of,
 139; life span of, 144–145
Seedling, 221
Seeds, comparison of bean and
 corn (Table), 219; dormancy
 in, 219–220; of flowering
 plant, 143; as foods, 222;
 germination of, 219–222
" Seeds of vermin," 560
Segregation, 621
Selective absorption, 164
Selective cutting, 697
Self-pollination, 204–206, 638
Self-preservation, 324; instinct,
 404
Semiaquatic plants, 69–70
Semicircular canals, 508
Semilunar valves, 484
Seminal receptacle, of earth-
 worm, 261–262; of grasshop-
 per, 291; of spiders, 282
Seminal vesicles, 261; of earth-
 worm, 261–262; of frog, 352
Semipermeable membrane, 160,
 161
Semitropical region, 70
Sense organs, of bird, 381; of
 grasshopper, 290–291; of hu-
 mans, 504–514; of mammals,
 403–404
Sensory system, of fish, 335–336
Sensitivity, 37–38
Sensory areas, of cerebrum, 494
Sensory nerve, 498
Sensory neurons, 498, 500
Sepals, 200
Septum, of heart, 484; of nose,
 461; of snake, 364
Sequoia trees, 141, 688
Serum, 574; production of diph-
 theria, 574
Serum albumin, 478
Serum globulin, 478
Sessile, 184
Setae, 259

Sewage disposal, 313, 597
Sex, determination of, 628–**629**
Sex chromosomes, of fruit fly,
  629
Sex hormones, 520
Sex-influenced character, 631–
  632
Sex-limited characters 631; in
  human inheritance, 651–652
Sex-linked characters, in human
  inheritance, 651–652
Sexual reproduction, 96; hered-
  itary characteristics and, 612–
  613; in *Oedogonium,* 98–100;
  in *Spirogyra,* 96; in *Ulothrix,*
  97
Shark(s), 328–329; and remora,
  33
Shasta daisy, 640
Sheep liver fluke, **255**
Sheet erosion, 676
Shellac, 304
Shellfish, 265
Shelterbelts, 678
Shields, of turtle, 372
Shock, 482
Shoot, of bean, 221
Shorthorn cattle, **627,** 643
Shoulder blade, of bird, 378
Shrew, 409
Shrimp, **278,** 280
Shrubs, 79
Side winding, of snakes, 364
Sieve plate, 269, **270**
Sieve tubes, 143, 173
Sigmoid colon, 454
Silicon, in algae, 101; in Pro-
  tozoa, 237
Silk scar, 218
Silkworm, 298
Silver fox, 399
Simple eyes of grasshopper, 290,
  291
Simple goiter, 516–517
Simple leaf, 184
Simple sugars, 440
Sinoauricular node, 432
Sinus venosus, 333, 351
Sinuses, of crayfish, 276
Siphons, of mollusks, 266
Sire, 643
Sirenia, 410
Skeletal muscle, 431
Skeletal system, of grasshopper,
  289; of vertebrates, 321, 322
Skeleton, functions of, 428
Skin, of humans, 474–475; care
  of, 474–475; as defense
  against disease, 571; functions
  of, 474; sensations of the,
  505
Skin respiration, of amphibian,
  350

Skinks, 370
Sleep, need for, 502
Sleet, 680
Slime fungi (Table), 114
Slime layer, 105
Sloth, 408–409
Slug, 268
Small intestine, of frog, 349;
  human, 452, 455–458
Smallpox, vaccination against,
  2, 582–583
Smear, of bacteria, 110
Smell, 506–507
Smoking, damage to body by,
  530–531
Smooth muscle, 431, **432;** in
  stomach wall, 452
Smuts, 121
Snails, **268**
Snakebites, treatment of, 368
Snakes, 360–368; body structure
  of, 361; feeding habits of,
  362–363; history of, 361; in-
  ternal organs of, 364; loco-
  motion in, 363–364; myths
  and superstitions about, 360–
  361; nonpoisonous, 364–365;
  poisonous, 366–368; repro-
  duction in, 364; skull of, **363**
Snapping turtle, 373
Snow-blindness, 536
Social insects, 300
Sodium chloride, in foods, 438
Sodium citrate, 483
Soft palate, 448
Soft-shelled turtles, 373
Soil, 154, 671–672; bacteria in,
  111; as basic factor of envi-
  ronment, 67; benefits of for-
  est to, 692; conservation of,
  671–682; loss of, 672; loss of
  organic matter in, 674; min-
  eral depletion in, 672–674
Soil flora, 672
Soil roots, 154
Solar plexus, 501
Solid components (blood), 478–
  479
Solids, 41
Somatotropic hormone, 517,
  518
Song box, 386
Sonora coral snake, 368
Sorus, 131–**132**
Southern forest, 687
Sow bug, **278,** 279
Soy beans, 224
Space, cosmic rays in, 551–552;
  definition of, 544, 546; facts
  about, 546–547
Space Age, 544
Space biology, 10, 544–554
Space capsule, 554

Space travel, plans in, 547; pr
  sure problems in, 549–5:
  psychological effects of, 55
  553; respiration in, 549; sel
  tion of man for, 553–554; ▮
  of algae in, 102; weightle
  ness in, 548–549
Spawning habits, of fish, 337
Species, 80, 81
Species characteristics, 608
Species immunity, 573
Species preservation, 324; as
  stinct, 404
Specific antibodies, 573
Sperm, 39, 93; of crayfish, 2
  formation of, 614, **615;**
  mammals, 402
Sperm nuclei, **207**–208
Sperm whale, 410
Spermatids, 614
Spermatocytes, 614, **615**
Spermatophytes, 138
Sphagnum, 128–**129**
Sphenodon punctatus, 359–**3**
Spherical symmetry, 252
Sphincter muscle, 454
Spicules, 244
Spiders, 281–**282**
Spinal cord, of fish, 335; of ▮
  man, 497; of mammals, 4
Spinal nerves, of frog, 352;
  human, 497; of mamm▮
  403
Spindle, 611
Spinnerets, of spiders, 282
Spiny anteater, 406, 408
Spiny lobster, 279
Spiracles, 289, 290
Spirillum forms of bacte▮
  105, **106**
Spirochetes, 565
Spirogyra, 95–96
Sponge mushroom, 118
Sponges, 242–245; food dig
  tion by, 244; reproduction
  244–245
Spongin, 244
Spongocoel, 244
Spongy layer, of leaf, 184–▮
Spontaneous generation, 13–
  562
Sporangiophore, 116
Sporangium, 131–**132,** 116
Spore case, 116
Spore-forming Protozoa, 2.
  239
Spore leaves, 140
Spores, of algae, 93; of bacte
  106–107; of ferns, 131;
  fungi, 115, 119; of moss, 1
  of mushrooms, 121; in re▮
  duction, 39, 128; reprod
  tion by, 238

orophyte, 127–**128, 129**
ort, 640
otted salamander, 345
reading viper snake, 365, **366**
ring wheat, 223
ring wood, 173–174
rings, 680
utum test, 587
uid, **268,** 269
lagmites, **36**
men, 200
minate flowers, 201, **204**
nley, Dr. Wendell, 564
phylococcus, 105, **106**
rch, for the body, 439–440; in carbohydrates, 48–49; in photosynthesis, 188; in protoplasm, 22
rfish, 269–**270, 271**
am sterilizer, 109
gosaurus, 358
ms, 166–181; aerial, 179; climbing, 179; corm, 180; creeping, 179; dicot, 177–178; external structure of woody, 167–169; of flowering plant, 142; growth of, 170–171; herbaceous, 167; internal structure of woody, 171–174, **172;** monocot, 177, 178–179; movement of materials in, 174–176; structure of herbaceous, 177; woody, 167–177
ntor, **230**
rilization, 109–110; of food by radiation, 541
kleback, nest of, **336**
gma, of flower, 200, **202**
nulus, 16, 38, 322
g ray, 329
e, 121
rup bone, 507
ck, 176
ons, 115
mach, of bird, 385; cancer of, **601;** of fish, 332; of frog, 349; of grasshopper, **289,** 290; of humans, 452, **453**
mach poisons, 313–314
mata, of leaf, 185–**186**
red food, 216
tosphere, **545**
eam, productive, 701
eaming, 37
eptobacillus, 106
eptococcus, 105–106; bacteria causing, **566**
ptococcus pyogenes, 566
ptomyces griseus, 578–579
ptomycin, 578–579
ated muscle, 431, **432**
ations, **27**
p cropping, 677

Strobilus, 249
Strontium-90, 540–541
Structural similarity, 81
Struggle for existence, 17, 666
Style, of flower, 200, **202**
Stylonychia, **230**
Subarachnoid space, 493
Subclavian veins, 490
Sublingual glands, of humans, 449
Submaxillary glands, of humans, 449
Subsoil, 671
Succession, 73–74
Successive osmosis, 162
Suckers, in leeches, 255
Sucrase, 456
Sucrose, 49, 188
Sugar, for the body, 439–440; in carbohydrates, 48–49; in green plants, 32; in protoplasm, 22
Sulfa drugs, 577
Sulfanilamide, 577
Summer residents (birds), 392
Summer wood, 174
Sun, as source of radiation, 539; radiations of, and space travel, 551
Sunburn, 536
Sunfish, nest of, **336**
Superphosphate, 673
Superstitions, examples of, 1
Supplemental air, 462
Suprarenals, 518
Surgery, 594; cancer treatment by, 602
Survival, of the fittest, 666; of living things, 17; of predatory animals, 63–64
Suspended animation, 15
Sustained yield, 697
Sweat, 474
Sweepstakes dispersal, 664
Swift (lizard), 369, 370
Swimmerets, 275
Swine raising, 643
Symbiosis, 33–34, 124–125
Symbols, to denote separate sexes, 291; of elements, 44
Symmetry, types of, 252
Sympathetic nervous system, 501
Synapse, 498
Synergid, 207
Synovial fluid, 430
Synthetic insecticides, 315
Synthetic vitamins, 444–445
Systematic circulation, 489
Systems, 29, 423; of human body, 425
Systole, 486–487
Systolic pressure, 487

Tadpoles, 346, 353–355, **354**
Tamworth hogs, 643
Tannic acid, 692; in leaf, 196
Tanning materials, 692
Tapeworm, 255–256
Tar pits, 656
Tarantula, 282
Tarsus, 288
Taste, 505–506
Taste buds, **29,** 449–450, 505–506
Taxonomists, 86–87
Taxonomy, 10, 86–87
Tears, antiseptic qualities of, 572
Technical method, 3
Teeth, functions of, 450; hygiene of, 451–452; of mammals, 400–401; number and kinds of, 450; structure of, 450–451; vomerine, 349
Teliospores, 119
Telophase, 612
Telson, 275
Temperate region, 70
Temperature, as factor of environment, 67–69; in germination, 220; in photosynthesis, 191; ranges in North America, 70–71; requirements for bacteria growth, 107; in space, 551
Temporal lobes, 494
Temporary cartilage, 430
Temporary teeth, 451
Tendons, 431–432
Tendrils, of climbing stem, 179; of leaf, 197
Tension fatigue, 433, 502
Tentacles, 246, 248
Terminal bud, 168
Terracing, 677–**678**
Terramycin, 579
Terrapins, 372
Testa, 217
Testes, of bird, 386; of fish, 336; of frog, 352; of grasshopper, 291; of human, 520; of hydra, 248
Testosterone, 520
Tetanus, 107; antitoxin for, 574; bacteria causing, **566;** immunization against, 586
Tetracycline, 579
Tetrads, 614
Tetraploid number, 640
Texas-fever tick, 283
Thallophytes, 91, 113–125
Thermotropism (Table), 153
Thiamin, 442
Thigmotropism (Table), 153
Third line of defense, against disease, 572–573

Thoracic cavity, of human, 425
Thoracic duct, 490
Thorax, appendages of crayfish on, 275; of crayfish, 274; of grasshoppers, 288; of honeybee, 301; of insect, 285–286; of Lepidoptera, 296
Thrombin, 481
Thrombocytes, 478
Thromboplastin, 481
Thrush, 124
Thymus, 522
Thyroid extract, 517
Thyroid gland, 515–**517;** deficiency in, 653
Thyroid hormone, 516, 662; preparation of, 517
Thyrotropic hormone, 518
Tibia, of grasshopper, 288
Ticks, 283
Tidal air, 462
Tiger salamander, **344**–345
Timber trees (Table), 690
Timber wolf, 411
Timetable, geological, **660**
Tip layering, of roots, 156
Tissue, 28–29, 423; of bones, 428–429; destruction of, 569; of earthworm, 259; of flowering plants, 143; of human body, 423–425, (Table), 424; of mature root, 149–151, (Table), 152
Tissue fluid, 477, 488, 489–490
Tissue suffocation, 469
Toads, 342, 345, **346**
"Toadstool," 122
Tobacco, habitual use of, 529–531
Tocopherol, 442
Toenails, of mammals, 399
Tomato, cells of, 28
Tone, of muscles, 433
Tongue, of frog, **348**–349; of human, **29,** 450; of snake, 361
Toothed leaf, 184
Toothless mammals, 408–409
Topography, 73
Topsoil, 154–155, 671–672
Tortoises, 372
Touch, sensation of, 505
Toxin, 112
Toxin-antitoxin, 575, 585–586
Toxoid, 575
Tracer element, 542
Trachea, of bird, 385; of man, 461; of snake, 363
Tracheae of Crustacea, 273; of grasshopper, 290; of insects, 286
Tracheids, 143, 173
Training, of mammals, 405
Traits, dominant, **629;** inherit-

ance of, 650–651; recessive, **629**
Transfusions, of blood, 481–482, 483
Translocation, 176, 191
Transpiration, of flowering plant, 143; in plants, 193–194
Transpiration pull, 176
Transportation, lumber for, 690–691
Transverse colon, 454
Transverse nerves, 254
Trap-door spider, 282
Tree Farm Program, 697
Tree frog, 345–**346**
Trees, Aristotle's grouping of, 79; branching of, 169–170; determining age of, 170; diseases of, 696–697; girdling of, 174; insect damage to, 696–697; stem growth in, 170–171; structure of woody stem of, 167–169
Triceps muscle, **433**
Trichina worm, 257
Trichinella, 257–**258**
Trichinosis, 258
Trichocysts, 235–236
Trilobites, 656
Triple fusion, 208
Tritium atom, 43, **46**
Trochanter, 288–289
Tropical fish, 340
Tropical forest, 687
Tropical zone, 70
Tropics, 70
Tropism, 38, 152, (Table), 153
Troposphere, **545**
Trout fish, 340
True bugs, 304
True fungi, 114–121
True hybrid, 643
Trunk, of fish, 331–332
Trunk-nosed mammals, 412–413
Trypanosoma, 239
Trypsin, 455
Tsetse fly, 239, 305
Tuatara, 359–360
Tube feet, 269, **270**
Tube nucleus, 203
Tuberculin, 587
Tuberculosis, 573; discovery of, 563; immunization against, 587–588
Tubers, 180
Tubule, 473
Tularemia, 574
Turbinates, 506
Turgor, 162–164
Turpentine, 691
Turtles, 371–373
Twins, **647, 648**–649

Tympanic membrane, of f 348; of human, 507; of tu 373
Tympanum, 289
Typhoid fever, immuniza against, 586–587
Typhoid fly, see Housefly
Typhus fever, 311, 565
Tyrannosaurus, 358

Ulothrix, 97–98
Ultraviolet waves, 536
Umbilical cord, 402
Unconscious mind, 495
Under hair, of mammals, 3
Underground stems, 179
Undulant fever, 573
Ungulata, 412
Unicellular organism, 28, 2
United States, Army Mec Corps of, 311; Departmer Agriculture of, 311–312, forest regions of, **688;** Fc Service of, 692–693, Public Health Service of, 549; Soil Conservation S ice of, 679
Univalve mollusks, 267–26ξ
Unstriated muscle, 431
Upland game birds, 706–7(
Urea, 441, 469, 478
Uredospores, 119
Ureters, of frog, 352; of hur 472
Urethra, 474
Uric acid, 469; of bird, 38(
Urinary bladder, 472
Urine, 474
Urogenital organs, of frog,
Uropod, 275
Uterus, of frog, 353; of m mals, 401–**402**
Uvula, 448

Vaccination, original ex| ment of, 581–582
Vaccine, 574; influenza, polio, **590, 591,** 592; pro tion of, 574–575
Vaccinia, 582
Vacuolar membrane, 24
Vacuoles, 26
Vagus nerve, 496, 502
Valveless mollusks, 268–26
Valves, 488
Vampires, 409
Van Allen Radiation Belts,
Van Leeuwenhoek, Anton,
Vane, of bird feather, 377
Variable factor, 5
Variations, 18–19, 666
Varieties, 81
Vasa efferentia, 352

:tors, of infection, 568
ȝetative organs, 142–143
ns, of fish, 333; of frog, 351;
f human, 487, **488;** of leaf,
83–184, 185; subclavian, 490
ıa cava, of frog, 351; in-
ȝrior, of humans, 474, 484–
85; superior, of humans,
84–485
ıation, **183,** 184
ıeer, 690
ıom, 362–363
ıtila⁺ion, 469
ıtral aorta, 333
ıtral blood vessel, 261
ıtral nerve cord, 261
ıtral nervous system, of ar-
ıropod, 273
ıtral siphon, 266, 267
ıtral surface, 252
ıtricle(s), of bird, 386; of
ȝsh, 333; of frog, 350–**351;**
f human, 484, **486,** in hu-
ıan brain, 493
ıules, 487
ıus's-flytrap, 198
ımiform appendix, 454
ıebrae, definition of, 321;
ıuman, 431
ıebrates, 319–325; charac-
ȝristics of, 320, 321; classes
f, 321, (Table), 322, **323;**
ȝfinition of, 241; develop-
ıent of, 322–324; develop-
ıent of embryos of, **663;**
ȝshlike, 326–329; importance
f, 320; systems of, 321–322
ȝsels, 143; of wood, 173
ȝtigial organs, **659,** 662
ȝility, 220
ȝrations, of ear, 542
ȝroy butterfly, **75–76**
ȝ, 456–457
ȝlogy, 10
ıs pneumonia, 589
ıses, 564–565
ȝeral hump, 265
ȝble light, 534
ıal purple, 511
ȝl capacity, 462
ȝmins, 51, 441–444; func-
ȝns and important sources
f (Table), 442; synthetic,
ȝ4–445
ȝeous humor, 509
ȝparous mammals, 398
ȝparous snakes, 364
ȝal cords, 461
ȝal sacs, 349
ȝuntary muscles, 431
ȝuntary response, 324

Vomerine teeth, 349
Von Behring, Emil, 585–586
Von Roentgen, Wilhelm Kon-
rad, 532
Vorticella, **230**

Waksman, Dr. Selman, 578–579
Walking stick, 298
Walruses, 400
Wasps, 303
Waste products, in man, 469,
472
Water, absorbed by colon, 458;
as agent in seed dispersal,
216; conservation of, 682–
683; contaminated, 239; erosion by, 676; an essential to
life, 69–70; forests to control supply of, 692; in green
plants, 32; necessary to hu-
man body, 438; in photo-
synthesis, 190–191; pressure
in cells of, 162–164; in proto-
plasm, 22; supply, safety of,
596–597; unfit for fish, 702–
703
Water-borne infections, 567
Water cycle, 680, **681;** space
travel and, 551
Water dog, 344
Water table, 680
Water vapor, 194, 680
Water moccasin snake, 368
Water-vascular system, 269, **270**
Watersheds, 682
Wave lengths, of electromag-
netic radiation (Table), 534
Waves, as form of radiation,
533
Wax, of worker bees, 302
Weasel, 399, 411
Web membrane, 348
Weed seeds, destruction of by
birds, 393
Weevils, 304
Weightlessness, in space, 548–
549
Whales, 400, 409–410
Wheat, 223; plant, and wheat
rust, 119–121, **120;** winter,
223
Whelk crab, **33**
Whip grafting, **176**
White corpuscles, **27, 29,** 478–
479; against disease, 572; and
leukemia, 484
White matter, 494, 497; of
mammals, 403
White pine blister rust, 121,
696
White shark, **329**

Whole blood, 481
Whooping cough, 589–590
Whooping crane, 705
Whorled leaves, 168
Widal test, **586**–587
Wiener, 482
Wigglers, 306
Wildlife, conservation of, 700–
710; divisions of, 700; resto-
ration of, 708
Wilson Society, 707
Wind, as agent in seed dispersal,
216; erosion by, 678–679
Wind-pollinated plants, 204
Windbreaks, 678
Wings, of bird, **378**–379; of
grasshopper, 289
Winter residents (birds), 391
Winter sleep, 68–69, 406
Winter wheat, 223
Wireless waves, 533
Withdrawal symptoms, 525–
526, **529**
Wolverine, 411
"Wonder drug," 577
Wood tissues, 173
Wood-boring beetle, 304
Woodchuck, 405, 406
Woody plants, 143–144
Woody stems, 167–177; external
structure of, 167–169; inter-
nal structure of, 171–174,
172
Worker bees, 302–303
Worms, 252–263; characteris-
tics of (Table), 263
Wound infections, 568

X chromosome, 628–629
X ray, 537; discovery of, 532–
533; precautions against, 543;
in treating cancer, 602, **603**
Xanthophyll, 25, 95; in leaf,
196
Xerophyte plants, 70
Xylem, 143; of root, 150, **151;**
of woody stem, 173

Y chromosome, 628–629
Yeasts, 111, 117–118
Yellow-bellied sea snake, 368
Yolk sac, 336
Yolks, 386
Yorkshire hog, **643**

Zero gravity, 549
Zoology, 11
Zoospores, 98
Zygote, 39, 97, 127, 208; in al-
gae, 93, 97, 98, 100
Zymase, 118